The Basics of General, Organic, and Biological Chemistry Version 1.0

By

David W. Ball, John W. Hill and Rhonda J. Scott

S-134872-CO-3

9 781453 311103

Contents

About the Authors		**1**
Acknowledgements		**3**
Preface		**5**
Chapter 1	**Chemistry, Matter, and Measurement**	**7**
	What Is Chemistry?	7
	The Classification of Matter	12
	Measurements	17
	Expressing Numbers: Scientific Notation	19
	Expressing Numbers: Significant Figures	23
	The International System of Units	27
	Converting Units	32
	End-of-Chapter Material	39
Chapter 2	**Elements, Atoms, and the Periodic Table**	**43**
	The Elements	43
	Atomic Theory	49
	The Structure of Atoms	51
	Nuclei of Atoms	55
	Atomic Masses	59
	Arrangements of Electrons	61
	The Periodic Table	64
	End-of-Chapter Material	71
Chapter 3	**Ionic Bonding and Simple Ionic Compounds**	**73**
	Two Types of Bonding	73
	Ions	75
	Formulas for Ionic Compounds	81
	Ionic Nomenclature	88
	Formula Mass	93
	End-of-Chapter Material	97
Chapter 4	**Covalent Bonding and Simple Molecular Compounds**	**101**
	Covalent Bonds	102
	Covalent Compounds: Formulas and Names	106
	Multiple Covalent Bonds	111
	Characteristics of Covalent Bonds	113
	Characteristics of Molecules	119

Introduction to Organic Chemistry 123
End-of-Chapter Material 133

Chapter 5 Introduction to Chemical Reactions 137

The Law of Conservation of Matter 138
Chemical Equations 139
Quantitative Relationships Based on Chemical Equations 143
Some Types of Chemical Reactions 147
Oxidation-Reduction (Redox) Reactions 150
Redox Reactions in Organic Chemistry and Biochemistry 154
End-of-Chapter Material 157

Chapter 6 Quantities in Chemical Reactions 159

The Mole 159
Atomic and Molar Masses 163
Mole-Mass Conversions 166
Mole-Mole Relationships in Chemical Reactions 169
Mole-Mass and Mass-Mass Problems 172
End-of-Chapter Material 177

Chapter 7 Energy and Chemical Processes 179

Energy and Its Units 179
Heat 182
Phase Changes 185
Bond Energies and Chemical Reactions 188
The Energy of Biochemical Reactions 191
End-of-Chapter Material 194

Chapter 8 Solids, Liquids, and Gases 197

Intermolecular Interactions 198
Solids and Liquids 203
Gases and Pressure 206
Gas Laws 208
End-of-Chapter Material 218

Chapter 9 Solutions 221

Solutions 221
Concentration 224
The Dissolution Process 236
Properties of Solutions 240
End-of-Chapter Material 246

Chapter 10 Acids and Bases 249

Arrhenius Definition of Acids and Bases 250
Brønsted-Lowry Definition of Acids and Bases 255

Water: Both an Acid and a Base 259
The Strengths of Acids and Bases 261
Buffers 266
End-of-Chapter Material 269

Chapter 11 Nuclear Chemistry 273

Radioactivity 274
Half-Life 278
Units of Radioactivity 281
Uses of Radioactive Isotopes 285
Nuclear Energy 288
End-of-Chapter Material 292

Chapter 12 Organic Chemistry: Alkanes and Halogenated Hydrocarbons 295

Organic Chemistry 295
Structures and Names of Alkanes 298
Branched-Chain Alkanes 301
Condensed Structural and Line-Angle Formulas 305
IUPAC Nomenclature 307
Physical Properties of Alkanes 313
Chemical Properties of Alkanes 315
Halogenated Hydrocarbons 317
Cycloalkanes 321
End-of-Chapter Material 324

Chapter 13 Unsaturated and Aromatic Hydrocarbons 329

Alkenes: Structures and Names 329
Cis-Trans Isomers (Geometric Isomers) 334
Physical Properties of Alkenes 340
Chemical Properties of Alkenes 342
Polymers 345
Alkynes 348
Aromatic Compounds: Benzene 349
Structure and Nomenclature of Aromatic Compounds 351
End-of-Chapter Material 361

Chapter 14 Organic Compounds of Oxygen 365

Organic Compounds with Functional Groups 365
Alcohols: Nomenclature and Classification 367
Physical Properties of Alcohols 373
Reactions That Form Alcohols 376
Reactions of Alcohols 379
Glycols and Glycerol 386
Phenols 388

Ethers 390
Aldehydes and Ketones: Structure and Names 394
Properties of Aldehydes and Ketones 400
Organic Sulfur Compounds 405
End-of-Chapter Material 407

Chapter 15 Organic Acids and Bases and Some of Their Derivatives 413

Functional Groups of the Carboxylic Acids and Their Derivatives 413
Carboxylic Acids: Structures and Names 416
The Formation of Carboxylic Acids 421
Physical Properties of Carboxylic Acids 422
Chemical Properties of Carboxylic Acids: Ionization and Neutralization 424
Esters: Structures and Names 427
Physical Properties of Esters 431
Preparation of Esters 433
Hydrolysis of Esters 435
Esters of Phosphoric Acid 437
Amines: Structures and Names 440
Physical Properties of Amines 446
Amines as Bases 449
Amides: Structures and Names 453
Physical Properties of Amides 456
Formation of Amides 458
Chemical Properties of Amides: Hydrolysis 459
End-of-Chapter Material 461

Chapter 16 Carbohydrates 467

Carbohydrates 468
Classes of Monosaccharides 471
Important Hexoses 477
Cyclic Structures of Monosaccharides 481
Properties of Monosaccharides 485
Disaccharides 487
Polysaccharides 496
End-of-Chapter Material 501

Chapter 17 Lipids 507

Fatty Acids 509
Fats and Oils 513
Membranes and Membrane Lipids 520
Steroids 530
End-of-Chapter Material 535

Chapter 18 **Amino Acids, Proteins, and Enzymes** 539

Properties of Amino Acids 540
Reactions of Amino Acids 547
Peptides 550
Proteins 553
Enzymes 561
Enzyme Action 563
Enzyme Activity 567
Enzyme Inhibition 570
Enzyme Cofactors and Vitamins 575
End-of-Chapter Material 577

Chapter 19 **Nucleic Acids** 583

Nucleotides 584
Nucleic Acid Structure 593
Replication and Expression of Genetic Information 599
Protein Synthesis and the Genetic Code 605
Mutations and Genetic Diseases 610
Viruses 617
End-of-Chapter Material 621

Chapter 20 **Energy Metabolism** 625

ATP—the Universal Energy Currency 627
Stage I of Catabolism 630
Overview of Stage II of Catabolism 637
Stage III of Catabolism 638
Stage II of Carbohydrate Catabolism 647
Stage II of Lipid Catabolism 654
Stage II of Protein Catabolism 660
End-of-Chapter Material 664

Chapter 21 **Appendix: Periodic Table of the Elements** 669

Index 677

About the Authors

DAVID W. BALL

Dr. Ball is a professor of chemistry at Cleveland State University in Ohio. He earned his PhD from Rice University in Houston, Texas. His specialty is physical chemistry, which he teaches at the undergraduate and graduate levels. About 50% of his teaching is in general chemistry: chemistry for nonscience majors, GOB, and general chemistry for science and engineering majors. In addition to this text, he is the author of a math review book for general chemistry students, a physical chemistry textbook with accompanying student and instructor solutions manuals, and two books on spectroscopy (published by SPIE Press). He is coauthor of a general chemistry textbook (with Dan Reger and Scott Goode), whose third edition was published in January 2009. His publication list has over 180 items, roughly evenly distributed between research papers and articles of educational interest.

JOHN W. HILL

Dr. Hill is professor emeritus from the University of Wisconsin–River Falls. He earned his PhD from the University of Arkansas. As an organic chemist, he has more than 50 publications in refereed journals, most of which have an educational bent. He has authored or coauthored several introductory level chemistry textbooks, all of which have gone into multiple editions. He has also presented over 60 papers at national conferences, many relating to science education. He has received several awards for outstanding teaching and has long been active in the American Chemical Society—both locally and nationally.

RHONDA J. SCOTT

Dr. Scott is a professor of chemistry at Southern Adventist University in Collegedale, Tennessee. She earned her PhD from the University of California at Riverside and has a background in enzyme and peptide chemistry. Previous to Southern Adventist, she taught at Loma Linda University and the University of Wisconsin–River Falls. In the past 10 years, she has made several presentations at national American Chemical Society meetings and other workshops and conferences. She has also been very active in the development of teaching materials, having reviewed or contributed to other textbooks and test banks.

Acknowledgements

How this book found its publisher is an unusual story. One of the authors was meeting with a sales representative of another publishing company. In the course of that conversation, it was discovered that these two people had a mutual friend—a person who had encouraged the author to publish his first academic book about a dozen years back when this friend was working for another publisher. The sales representative passed along to the mutual friend that they (the author and the sales rep) had met. That resulted in an e-mail reunion between the author and his old friend, who let it be known that she now works for a textbook publishing company called Flat World Knowledge. "Gee, would the company be interested in a one-semester general, organic, and biochemistry text?" was the flippant response. Wrong—or right, depending on your perspective—comment to make! Within an hour (no joke), the editorial director of the company was on the phone with the author, discussing the project and its possibilities. That talk lead to a discussion between all the authors on the team, a visit by the editorial director to the first author's hometown, and the subsequent signing of a contract for the book to be published by Flat World Knowledge. So the initial thanks must go to Jen Welchans of Flat World Knowledge for being the right person at the right place and the right time. You never know when old friends will meet again and make good things happen. Thanks, Jen.

Thanks to Michael Boezi, the editorial director of Flat World Knowledge, who always gave enthusiastic support to this project (and still does). Thanks also to Jenn Yee, project manager, who deftly dealt with 3 authors, 20 chapters, multiple reviews, production issues, illustrations, and photos—and seemed to keep it all straight. Kudos to the technology team at Flat World Knowledge, who had the ultimate job of getting this book out: Brian Brennan, David Link, Christopher Loncar, Jessica Carey, Jon Gottfried, Jon Williams, Katie Damo, Keith Avery, Mike Shnaydman, Po Ki Chui, and Ryan Lowe. We would also like to thank the production team at Scribe, Inc., including Stacy Claxton, Chrissy Chimi, Melissa Tarrao, and Kevin McDermott. This book would not exist without these people.

This project has benefited tremendously from the feedback of reviewers at several stages in its development. We thank the following people for their input:

- David Bailey, Emporia State University
- Michael Bissell, Ohio State University
- Stephen Milczanowski, Florida State College at Jacksonville
- Pamela Strong, Quincy College
- Susan Cordova, Central New Mexico Community College
- Ilene Diamond, Central New Mexico Community College
- Margaret Kimble, Indiana University–Purdue University at Fort Wayne
- Chris Massone, Molloy College
- P. J. Ball, Northern Kentucky University
- Booker Juma, Fayetteville State University
- Elizabeth Ferguson, University of Kentucky
- Brad Sieve, Northern Kentucky University
- Deborah Heyl-Clegg, Eastern Michigan University
- Karen Ericson, Indiana University–Purdue University at Fort Wayne
- Maria Vogt, Bloomfield College
- Ellafe Cockroft, Miami Dade College
- Rebecca Barlag, Ohio University
- Bidisha Bose-Basu, Fayetteville State University
- Ken Johnson, Husson University
- E. J. Behrman, Ohio State University
- Julie Larson, Bemidji State University
- Kenneth French, Blinn College
- Grace Lasker, Lake Washington Technical College

Thanks especially to ANSR Source, who performed accuracy checks on various parts of the text. Should any inaccuracies remain, they are the responsibility of the authors. We hope that readers will let us know if they find any; one of the beauties of the Flat World process is the ability to update the textbook quickly, so that it will be an even better book tomorrow.

On a more personal level: RJS would like to thank her colleagues at Southern Adventist University and her family and friends for their help and encouragement during her work on this book. She is especially indebted to her sons, Michael and Chris, for their patience and encouragement. JWH owes a special thanks to his wonderful spouse, Ina, for doing so many things that allow him time to concentrate on writing. Most of all, he is grateful for her boundless patience, unflagging support, understanding, and enduring love. He is also grateful to his beloved daughter, Cindy, for her help with the house and the yard and so many other things. DWB thanks his wife, Gail, for things too numerous to mention but in particular the constant support of and appreciation for the vagaries of an academic life and for being the single parent on those nights when professional obligations keep him out later than normal. Thanks also to his sons, Stuart and Casey—the proverbial causes of gray hair—for being two of the (many) things worth living and writing for.

DWB

JWH

RJS

February 2011

Preface

When a new entry-level textbook in chemistry comes out, the obvious first question is "Why?" Why write another book when there are other texts available?

Actually, we had two main reasons. First, of all the textbooks that are available for a one-semester general chemistry, organic chemistry, and biochemistry (GOB) course, virtually all are single-author textbooks. Why this one stands out—and, we would argue, why this textbook might be preferable—is that the author team is composed of chemistry faculty who specialize in the G part, the O part, and the B part. One of us (DWB) is a physical chemist who spends a lot of time in the general chemistry sequence, whether for nonscience majors, health profession majors, or science and engineering majors. Another author (JWH) is an organic chemist by training and an experienced textbook author, while the third author (RJS) is a biochemistry professor and also a successful textbook author. All three authors are experienced, successful teachers. Thus, right from the start, this author team brings the appropriate experience and expertise that can combine to write a superior textbook for this market.

The second reason was the opportunity presented by the unique publishing strategy of Flat World Knowledge. The entire author team is excited about the potential for online presentation of content in this Internet age. In addition to having the content online, print copies of the textbook are readily available, as are individual chapters, vocabulary cards, exercise solutions, and other products. The easy availability of these items maximizes the ability of students to customize their personal tools, increasing their chances for success in a one-semester chemistry course.

This textbook is intended for the one-semester GOB course. Although a two-semester GOB sequence is available at many colleges and universities, one-semester GOB offerings are increasing in popularity. The need to cover so many topics in one semester or quarter places additional pressure on the tools used to teach the course, and the authors feel that a textbook developed explicitly for the one-semester course will provide students with a superior educational experience. Many one-semester GOB courses employ either a rewritten, watered-down two-semester textbook or a bona fide two-semester textbook with cherry-picked topics. In the opinion of this author team, neither choice provides students with the best learning experience. This textbook does not have a two-semester counterpart. It was developed specifically for the one-semester GOB course. As such, the chapters are short and succinct, covering the fundamental material and leaving out the extraneous. We recognize that students taking this particular course are likely interested in health professions, such as nursing, occupational therapy, physical therapy, physician assistance, and the like. As such, we have focused certain examples and textbook features on these areas so students realize from the beginning how these basic chemistry topics apply to their career choice.

This textbook is divided into approximately one-half general chemistry topics, one-fourth organic chemistry topics, and one-fourth biochemistry topics. We feel that these fractions provide the appropriate mix of chemistry topics for most students' needs. The presentation is standard: there is no attempt to integrate organic and biological chemistry throughout a general chemistry textbook, although there is an early introduction to organic chemistry so that carbon-containing compounds can be included as soon as possible. The first chapter stands out a bit for covering a relatively large amount of material, but that is necessary. There is a certain skill set that students *must* have to be successful in any GOB course, and rather than relegate these skills to an appendix that is too often overlooked, the first chapter covers them explicitly. Some of these topics can be omitted at the instructor's discretion.

The G part of the textbook then continues into atoms and molecules, chemical reactions, simple stoichiometry, energy, the phases of matter, solutions, and acids and bases (including a short treatment of equilibrium) and then ends with nuclear chemistry. The O part of the textbook starts with hydrocarbons and quickly covers aromatic compounds and the basic functional groups, focusing on those functional groups that have specific applications in biochemistry. The B part starts by immediately applying the organic knowledge to carbohydrates and other biologically important compounds. This section ends with a chapter on metabolism, which is, after all, the ultimate goal for a textbook like this—a discussion of the chemistry of life.

Each chapter is filled with example problems that illustrate the concepts at hand. In the mathematical exercises, a consistent style of problem solving has been used. We understand that there may be more than one way to solve a mathematical problem, but having a consistent problem-solving style increases the chance for student comprehension. Particular emphasis is placed on the units of quantities and how they have to work out appropriately in algebraic treatments. For each example problem, there is a Skill-Building Exercise immediately following that will help students practice the very same concept but without an elaborate answer worked out.

Every section of each chapter starts with one or more Learning Objectives that preview the section. These Learning Objectives are echoed at the end of each section with Key Takeaways as well as Concept Review Exercises that ask about the main ideas of the section. Sections then end with a set of exercises that students can use to immediately put the knowledge of that section into practice. Most of the exercises are paired, so that students can work two similar exercises for additional practice. Finally, Additional Exercises at the end of each chapter ask more challenging questions, bring multiple concepts together into a single exercise, or extend the chapter concepts to broader perspectives. The complete exercise portfolio of the textbook—Skill-Building Exercises, Concept Review Exercises, end-of-section exercises, and Additional Exercises—provides multiple opportunities for students to practice the content.

Other features in the textbook include Looking Closer, a chance to expand on a topic more than a typical textbook would. We have selected topics that are relevant and should appeal to students at this level. There are essays titled To Your Health that focus on how some of the topics relate directly to health issues—the focus of most of the students in this course. Do students realize that the simple act of breathing, something most of us do without thinking, is a gas law in action? Most chapters also have a Career Focus that presents an occupation related to the health professions. Students at this level may not know exactly what they want to do in the health professions, so having these essays gives some information about the career possibilities awaiting them.

These features are kept to a minimum, however; this is a one-semester textbook covering general chemistry, organic chemistry, and biochemistry. We recognize that users appreciate features like this, but we also recognize the need to focus on the core chemistry content. We hope we have reached an appropriate balance with the amount of additional features.

We hope that this textbook meets your and your students' goals.

David W. Ball

John W. Hill

Rhonda J. Scott

February 2011

CHAPTER 1
Chemistry, Matter, and Measurement

Opening Essay

In April 2003, the US Pharmacopeia, a national organization that establishes quality standards for medications, reported a case in which a physician ordered "morphine [a powerful painkiller] 2–3 mg IV [intravenously] every 2–3 hours for pain." A nurse misread the dose as "23 mg" and thus administered approximately 10 times the proper amount to an 8-year-old boy with a broken leg. The boy stopped breathing but was successfully resuscitated and left the hospital three days later.

Quantities and measurements are as important in our everyday lives as they are in medicine. The posted speed limits on roads and highways, such as 55 miles per hour (mph), are quantities we might encounter all the time. Both parts of a quantity, the amount (55) and the unit (mph), must be properly communicated to prevent potential problems. In chemistry, as in any technical endeavor, the proper expression of quantities is a necessary fundamental skill. As we begin our journey into chemistry, we will learn this skill so that errors—from homework mistakes to traffic tickets to more serious consequences—can be avoided.

The study of chemistry will open your eyes to a fascinating world. Chemical processes are continuously at work all around us. They happen as you cook and eat food, strike a match, shampoo your hair, and even read this page. Chemistry is called the central science because a knowledge of chemical principles is essential for other sciences. You might be surprised at the extent to which chemistry pervades your life.

1. WHAT IS CHEMISTRY?

LEARNING OBJECTIVES

1. **Define chemistry in relation to other sciences.**
2. **Identify the general steps in the scientific method.**

Chemistry is the study of matter—what it consists of, what its properties are, and how it changes. Being able to describe the ingredients in a cake and how they change when the cake is baked is called chemistry. **Matter** is anything that has mass and takes up space—that is, anything that is physically real. Some things are easily identified as matter—this book, for example. Others are not so obvious. Because we move so easily through air, we sometimes forget that it, too, is matter.

Chemistry is one branch of science. **Science** is the process by which we learn about the natural universe by observing, testing, and then generating models that explain our observations. Because the physical universe is so vast, there are many different branches of science (Figure 1.1). Thus, chemistry is the study of matter, biology is the study of living things, and geology is the study of rocks and the earth. Mathematics is the language of science, and we will use it to communicate some of the ideas of chemistry.

Although we divide science into different fields, there is much overlap among them. For example, some biologists and chemists work in both fields so much that their work is called biochemistry. Similarly, geology and chemistry overlap in the field called geochemistry. Figure 1.1 shows how many of the individual fields of science are related.

chemistry

The study of matter.

matter

Anything that has mass and takes up space.

science

The process by which we learn about the natural universe by observing, testing, and then generating models that explain our observations.

FIGURE 1.1 The Relationships between Some of the Major Branches of Science

Chemistry lies more or less in the middle, which emphasizes its importance to many branches of science.

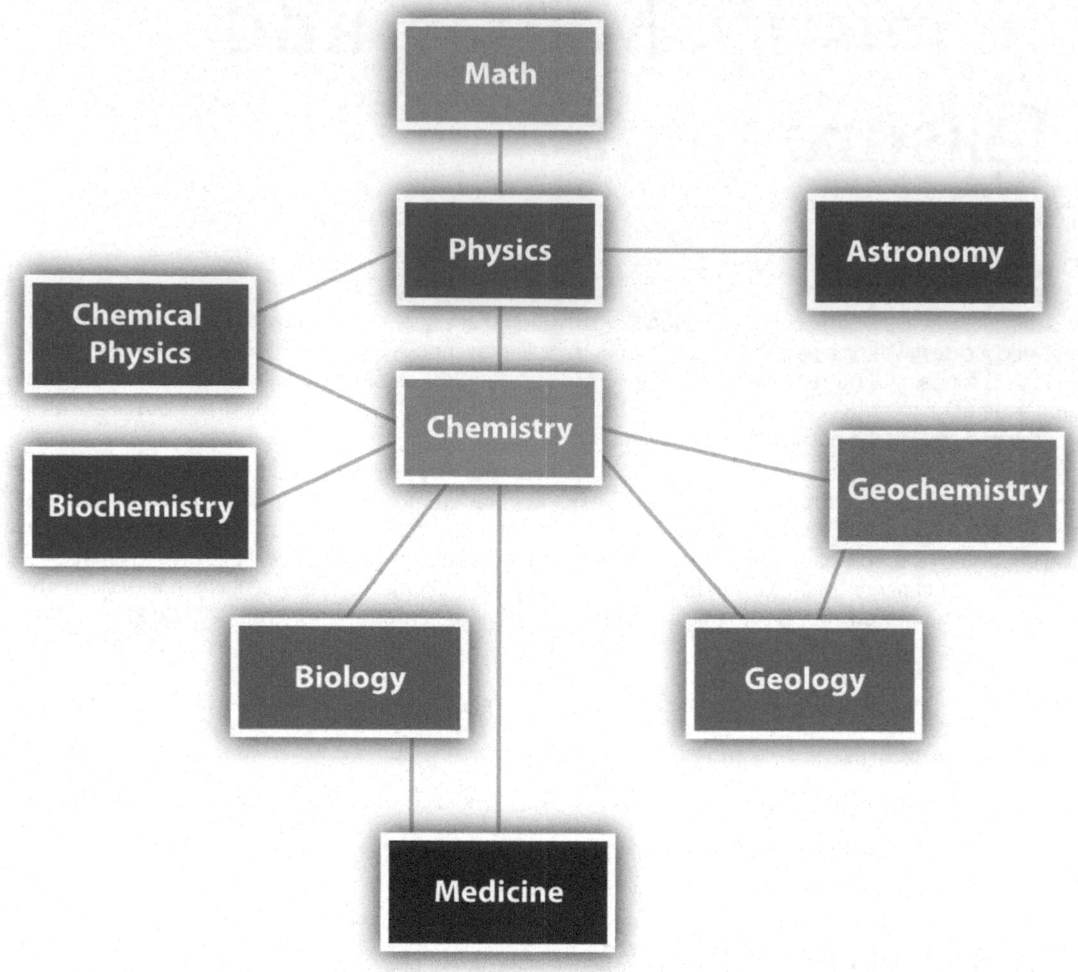

Note

There are many other fields of science, in addition to the ones (biology, medicine, etc.) listed here.

Looking Closer: Alchemy

As our understanding of the universe has changed over time, so has the practice of science. Chemistry in its modern form, based on principles that we consider valid today, was developed in the 1600s and 1700s. Before that, the study of matter was known as *alchemy* and was practiced mainly in China, Arabia, Egypt, and Europe.

Alchemy was a somewhat mystical and secretive approach to learning how to manipulate matter. Practitioners, called alchemists, thought that all matter was composed of different proportions of the four basic elements—fire, water, earth, and air—and believed that if you changed the relative proportions of these elements in a substance, you could change the substance. The long-standing attempts to "transmute" common metals into gold represented one goal of alchemy. Alchemy's other major goal was to synthesize the philosopher's stone, a material that could impart long life—even immortality. Alchemists used symbols to represent substances, some of which are shown in the accompanying figure. This was not done to better communicate ideas, as chemists do today, but to maintain the secrecy of alchemical knowledge, keeping others from sharing in it.

Alchemists used symbols like these to represent substances.

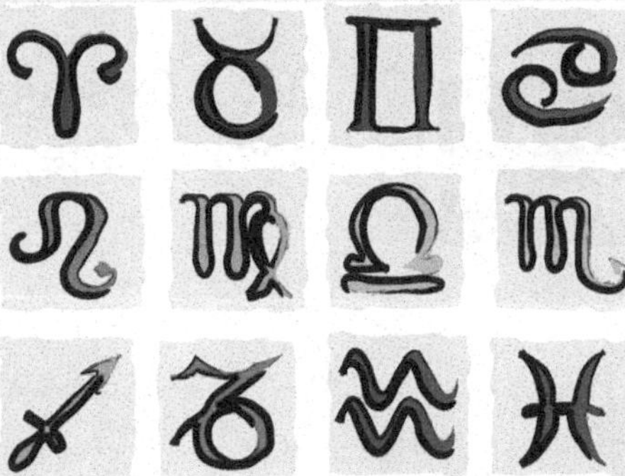

In spite of this secrecy, in its time alchemy was respected as a serious, scholarly endeavor. Isaac Newton, the great mathematician and physicist, was also an alchemist.

EXAMPLE 1

Which fields of study are branches of science? Explain.

1. sculpture
2. astronomy

Solution

1. Sculpture is not considered a science because it is not a study of some aspect of the natural universe.
2. Astronomy is the study of stars and planets, which are part of the natural universe. Astronomy is therefore a field of science.

SKILL-BUILDING EXERCISE

Which fields of study are branches of science?

1. politics
2. physiology (the study of the function of an animal's or a plant's body)
3. geophysics
4. agriculture

How do scientists work? Generally, they follow a process called the scientific method. The **scientific method** is an organized procedure for learning answers to questions. To find the answer to a question (for example, "Why do birds fly toward Earth's equator during the cold months?"), a scientist goes through the following steps, which are also illustrated in Figure 1.2:

scientific method

An organized procedure for learning answers to questions.

FIGURE 1.2 The General Steps of the Scientific Method

The steps may not be as clear-cut in real life as described here, but most scientific work follows this general outline.

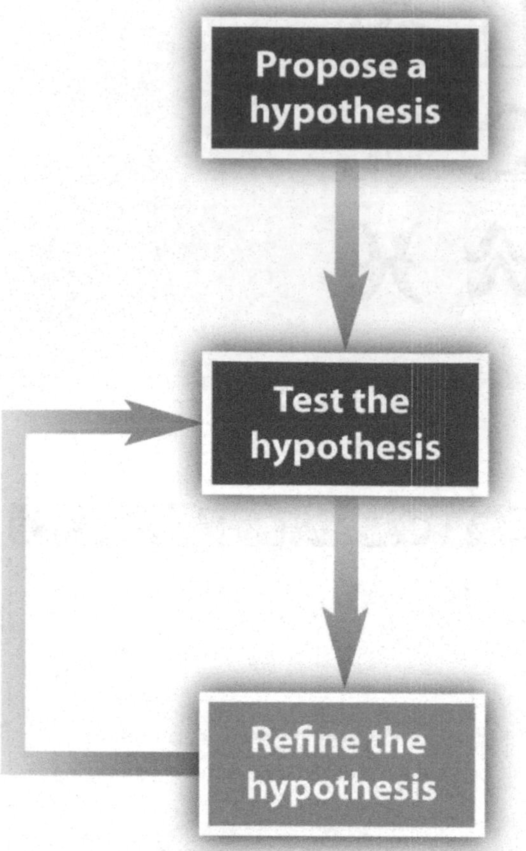

hypothesis

A testable idea.

theory

A general statement that describes a large set of observations and data.

1. **Propose a hypothesis.** A scientist generates a testable idea, or **hypothesis**, to try to answer a question or explain how the natural universe works. Some people use the word theory in place of hypothesis, but the word hypothesis is the proper word in science. For scientific applications, the word **theory** is a general statement that describes a large set of observations and data. A theory represents the highest level of scientific understanding.
2. **Test the hypothesis.** A scientist evaluates the hypothesis by devising and carrying out experiments to test it. If the hypothesis passes the test, it may be a proper answer to the question. If the hypothesis does not pass the test, it may not be a good answer.
3. **Refine the hypothesis if necessary.** Depending on the results of experiments, a scientist may want to modify the hypothesis and then test it again. Sometimes the results show the original hypothesis to be completely wrong, in which case a scientist will have to devise a new hypothesis.

Not all scientific investigations are simple enough to be separated into these three discrete steps. But these steps represent the general method by which scientists learn about our natural universe.

CONCEPT REVIEW EXERCISES

1. Define *science* and *chemistry*.
2. Name the steps of the scientific method.

ANSWERS

1. Science is a process by which we learn about the natural universe by observing, testing, and then generating models that explain our observations. Chemistry is the study of matter.

2. propose a hypothesis, test the hypothesis, and refine the hypothesis if necessary

KEY TAKEAWAYS

- Chemistry is the study of matter and how it behaves.
- The scientific method is the general process by which we learn about the natural universe.

EXERCISES

1. Based on what you know, which fields are branches of science?
   a. meteorology (the study of weather)
   b. astrophysics (the physics of planets and stars)
   c. economics (the study of money and monetary systems)
   d. astrology (the prediction of human events based on planetary and star positions)
   e. political science (the study of politics)
2. Based on what you know, which fields are a branches of science?
   a. history (the study of past events)
   b. ornithology (the study of birds)
   c. paleontology (the study of fossils)
   d. zoology (the study of animals)
   e. phrenology (using the shape of the head to determine personal characteristics)
3. Which of the following are examples of matter?
   a. a baby
   b. an idea
   c. the Empire State Building
   d. an emotion
   e. the air
   f. Alpha Centauri, the closest known star (excluding the sun) to our solar system
4. Which of the following are examples of matter?
   a. your textbook
   b. brain cells
   c. love
   d. a can of soda
   e. breakfast cereal
5. Suggest a name for the science that studies the physics of rocks and the earth.
6. Suggest a name for the study of the physics of living organisms.
7. Engineering is the practical application of scientific principles and discoveries to develop things that make our lives easier. Is medicine science or engineering? Justify your answer.
8. Based on the definition of engineering in Exercise 7, would building a bridge over a river or road be considered science or engineering? Justify your answer.
9. When someone says, "I have a theory that excess salt causes high blood pressure," does that person really have a theory? If it is not a theory, what is it?
10. When a person says, "My hypothesis is that excess calcium in the diet causes kidney stones," what does the person need to do to determine if the hypothesis is correct?
11. Some people argue that many scientists accept many scientific principles on faith. Using what you know about the scientific method, how might you argue against that assertion?
12. Most students take multiple English classes in school. Does the study of English use the scientific method?

ANSWERS

1. a. science
   b. science
   c. not science
   d. not science
   e. not science
3. a. matter
   b. not matter
   c. matter
   d. not matter
   e. matter
   f. matter
5. geophysics

7. Medicine is probably closer to a field of engineering than a field of science, but this may be arguable. Ask your doctor.
9. In scientific terms, this person has a hypothesis.
11. Science is based on reproducible facts, not blind belief.

2. THE CLASSIFICATION OF MATTER

LEARNING OBJECTIVES

1. **Use physical and chemical properties, including phase, to describe matter.**
2. **Identify a sample of matter as an element, a compound, or a mixture.**

Part of understanding matter is being able to describe it. One way chemists describe matter is to assign different kinds of properties to different categories.

2.1 Physical and Chemical Properties

The properties that chemists use to describe matter fall into two general categories. **Physical properties** are characteristics that describe matter. They include characteristics such as size, shape, color, and mass. **Chemical properties** are characteristics that describe how matter changes its chemical structure or composition. An example of a chemical property is flammability—a material's ability to burn—because burning (also known as combustion) changes the chemical composition of a material.

physical property

A charactristic that describes matter, such as size, shape, and color.

chemical property

A characteristic that describes how matter changes its chemical structure or composition.

2.2 Elements and Compounds

Any sample of matter that has the same physical and chemical properties throughout the sample is called a **substance**. There are two types of substances. A substance that cannot be broken down into chemically simpler components is an **element**. Aluminum, which is used in soda cans, is an element. A substance that can be broken down into chemically simpler components (because it has more than one element) is a **compound** (Figure 1.2). Water is a compound composed of the elements hydrogen and oxygen. Today, there are about 118 elements in the known universe. In contrast, scientists have identified tens of millions of different compounds to date.

substance

Any sample of matter that has the same physical and chemical properties throughout the sample.

element

A substance that cannot be broken down into chemically simpler components.

compound

A substance that can be broken down into chemically simpler components.

Note

Sometimes the word *pure* is added to substance, but this is not absolutely necessary. By definition, any single substance is pure.

The smallest part of an element that maintains the identity of that element is called an **atom**. Atoms are extremely tiny; to make a line 1 inch long, you would need 217 million iron atoms. The smallest part of a compound that maintains the identity of that compound is called a **molecule**. Molecules are composed of atoms that are attached together and behave as a unit. Scientists usually work with millions and millions of atoms and molecules at a time. When a scientist is working with large numbers of atoms or molecules at a time, the scientist is studying the **macroscopic** view of the universe. However, scientists can also describe chemical events on the level of individual atoms or molecules, which is referred to as the **microscopic** viewpoint. We will see examples of both macroscopic and microscopic viewpoints throughout this book (Figure 1.3).

atom

The smallest part of an element that maintains the identity of that element.

molecule

The smallest part of a compound that maintains the identity of that compound.

macroscopic

A view of the universe in which one is working with large numbers of atoms or molecules at a time.

microscopic

A view of the universe in which one is working with a few atoms or molecules at a time.

FIGURE 1.3 How Many Particles Are Needed for a Period in a Sentence?

Although we do not notice it from a macroscopic perspective, matter is composed of microscopic particles so tiny that billions of them are needed to make a speck we can see with the naked eye. The ×25 and ×400,000,000 indicate the number of times the image is magnified.

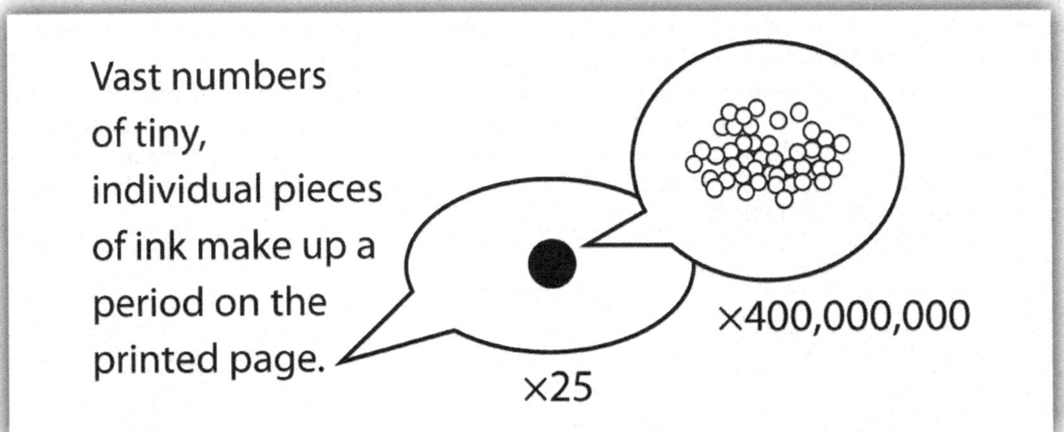

2.3 Mixtures

A material composed of two or more substances is a **mixture**. In a mixture, the individual substances maintain their chemical identities. Many mixtures are obvious combinations of two or more substances, such as a mixture of sand and water. Such mixtures are called **heterogeneous mixtures**. In some mixtures, the components are so intimately combined that they act like a single substance (even though they are not). Mixtures with a consistent composition throughout are called **homogeneous mixtures (or solutions)**. Sugar dissolved in water is an example of a solution. A metal alloy, such as steel, is an example of a solid solution. Air, a mixture of mainly nitrogen and oxygen, is a gaseous solution.

mixture

A sample composed of two or more substances.

heterogeneous mixture

A mixture that is a combination of two or more substances.

homogeneous mixture (solution)

A mixture that acts as a single substance so that it is not obvious that two or more substances are present.

EXAMPLE 2

How would a chemist categorize each example of matter?

1. saltwater
2. soil
3. water
4. oxygen

Solution

1. Saltwater acts as if it were a single substance even though it contains two substances—salt and water. Saltwater is a homogeneous mixture, or a solution.
2. Soil is composed of small pieces of a variety of materials, so it is a heterogeneous mixture.
3. Water is a substance; more specifically, because water is composed of hydrogen and oxygen, it is a compound.
4. Oxygen, a substance, is an element.

SKILL-BUILDING EXERCISE

How would a chemist categorize each example of matter?

1. coffee
2. hydrogen
3. an egg

2.4 Phases

phase

A certain form of matter that includes a specific set of physical properties.

phase change

A physical process in which a substance goes from one phase to another.

Another way to classify matter is to describe it as a solid, a liquid, or a gas, which was done in the examples of solutions. These three descriptions, each implying that the matter has certain physical properties, represent the three **phases** of matter. A solid has a definite shape and a definite volume. Liquids ordinarily have a definite volume but not a definite shape; they take the shape of their containers. Gases have neither a definite shape nor a definite volume, and they expand to fill their containers. We encounter matter in each phase every day; in fact, we regularly encounter water in all three phases: ice (solid), water (liquid), and steam (gas).

We know from our experience with water that substances can change from one phase to another if the conditions are right. Typically, varying the temperature of a substance (and, less commonly, the pressure exerted on it) can cause a **phase change**, a physical process in which a substance goes from one phase to another (Figure 1.4). Phase changes have particular names depending on what phases are involved, as summarized in Table 1.1.

TABLE 1.1 Phase Changes

Change	Name
solid to liquid	melting, fusion
solid to gas	sublimation
liquid to gas	boiling, evaporation
liquid to solid	solidification, freezing
gas to liquid	condensation
gas to solid	deposition

Figure 1.5 illustrates the relationships between the different ways matter can be classified.

FIGURE 1.4
Boiling Water

When liquid water boils to make gaseous water, it undergoes a phase change.

FIGURE 1.5 The Classification of Matter

Matter can be classified in a variety of ways, depending on its properties.

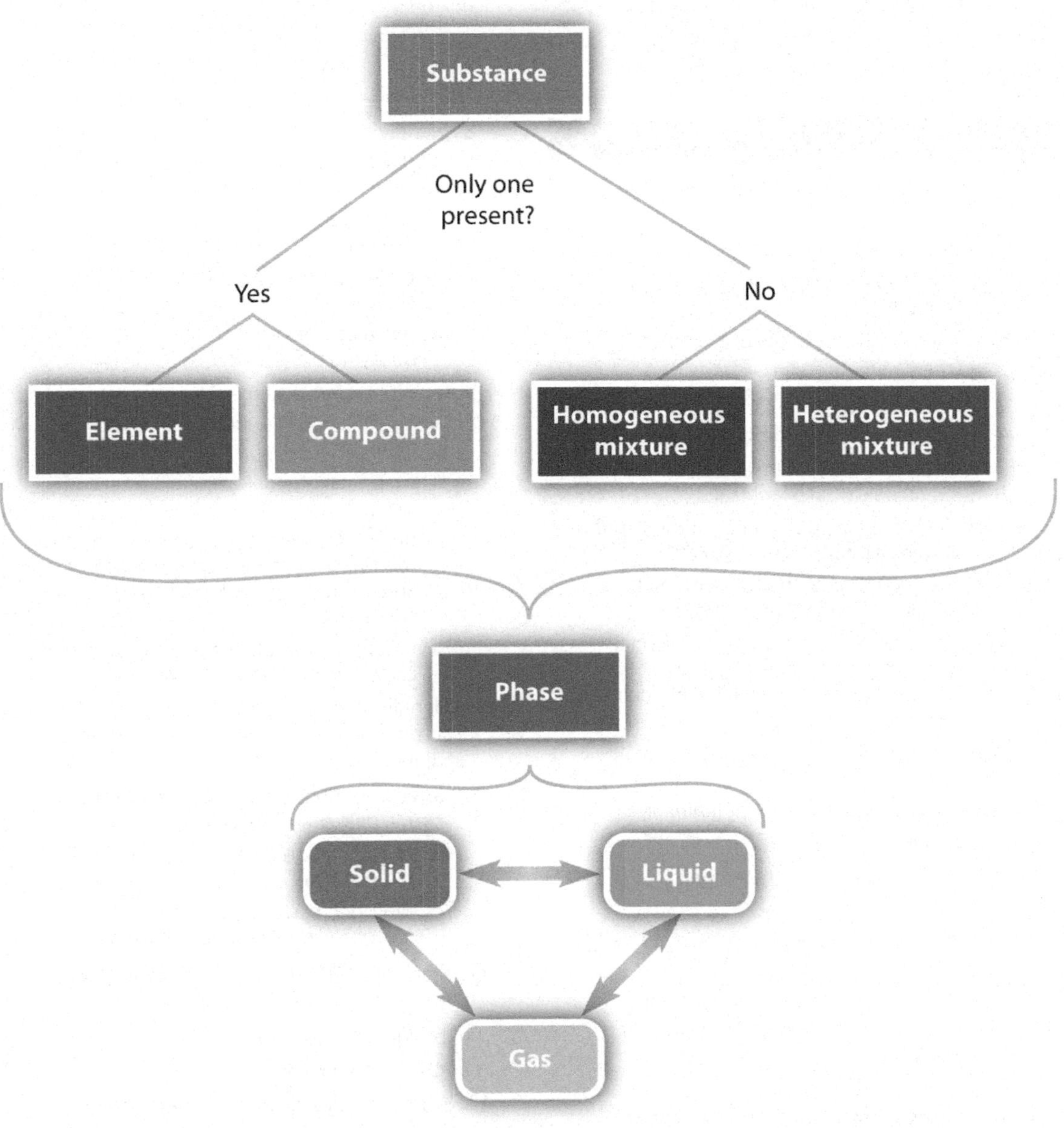

CONCEPT REVIEW EXERCISES

1. Explain the differences between the physical properties of matter and the chemical properties of matter.
2. What is the difference between a heterogeneous mixture and a homogeneous mixture? Give an example of each.
3. Give at least two examples of a phase change and state the phases involved in each.

ANSWERS

1. Physical properties describe the existence of matter, and chemical properties describe how substances change into other substances.
2. A heterogeneous mixture is obviously a mixture, such as dirt; a homogeneous mixture behaves like a single substance, such as saltwater.
3. solid to liquid (melting) and liquid to gas (boiling) (answers will vary)

KEY TAKEAWAYS

- Matter can be described with both physical properties and chemical properties.
- Matter can be identified as an element, a compound, or a mixture.

EXERCISES

1. Does each statement refer to a chemical property or a physical property?
   a. Balsa is a very light wood.
   b. If held in a flame, magnesium metal burns in air.
   c. Mercury has a density of 13.6 g/mL.
   d. Human blood is red.
2. Does each statement refer to a chemical property or a physical property?
   a. The elements sodium and chlorine can combine to make table salt.
   b. The metal tungsten does not melt until its temperature exceeds 3,000°C.
   c. The ingestion of ethyl alcohol can lead to disorientation and confusion.
   d. The boiling point of isopropyl alcohol, which is used to sterilize cuts and scrapes, is lower than the boiling point of water.
3. Define *element*. How does it differ from a compound?
4. Define *compound*. How does it differ from an element?
5. Give two examples of a heterogeneous mixture.
6. Give two examples of a homogeneous mixture.
7. Identify each substance as an element, a compound, a heterogeneous mixture, or a solution.
   a. xenon, a substance that cannot be broken down into chemically simpler components
   b. blood, a substance composed of several types of cells suspended in a salty solution called plasma
   c. water, a substance composed of hydrogen and oxygen
8. Identify each substance as an element, a compound, a heterogeneous mixture, or a solution.
   a. sugar, a substance composed of carbon, hydrogen, and oxygen
   b. hydrogen, the simplest chemical substance
   c. dirt, a combination of rocks and decaying plant matter
9. Identify each substance as an element, a compound, a heterogeneous mixture, or a solution.
   a. air, primarily a mixture of nitrogen and oxygen
   b. ringer's lactate, a standard fluid used in medicine that contains salt, potassium, and lactate compounds all dissolved in sterile water
   c. tartaric acid, a substance composed of carbon, hydrogen, and oxygen
10. Identify each material as an element, a compound, a heterogeneous mixture, or a solution.
   a. equal portions of salt and sand placed in a beaker and shaken up
   b. a combination of beeswax dissolved in liquid hexane
   c. hydrogen peroxide, a substance composed of hydrogen and oxygen
11. What word describes each phase change?
   a. solid to liquid
   b. liquid to gas
   c. solid to gas
12. What word describes each phase change?
   a. liquid to solid
   b. gas to liquid
   c. gas to solid

ANSWERS

1. a. physical property
   b. chemical property
   c. physical property
   d. physical property
3. An element is a substance that cannot be broken down into chemically simpler components. Compounds can be broken down into simpler substances.
5. a salt and pepper mix and a bowl of cereal (answers will vary)
7. a. element
   b. heterogeneous mixture
   c. compound

9. a. solution
   b. solution
   c. compound

11. a. melting or fusion
    b. boiling or evaporation
    c. sublimation

3. MEASUREMENTS

LEARNING OBJECTIVE

1. **Express quantities properly, using a number and a unit.**

A coffee maker's instructions tell you to fill the coffeepot with 4 cups of water and use 3 scoops of coffee. When you follow these instructions, you are measuring. When you visit a doctor's office, a nurse checks your temperature, height, weight, and perhaps blood pressure (Figure 1.6). The nurse is also measuring.

Chemists measure the properties of matter and express these measurements as quantities. A **quantity** is an amount of something and consists of a **number** and a **unit**. The number tells us how many (or how much), and the unit tells us what the scale of measurement is. For example, when a distance is reported as "5 kilometers," we know that the quantity has been expressed in units of kilometers and that the number of kilometers is 5. If you ask a friend how far he or she walks from home to school, and the friend answers "12" without specifying a unit, you do not know whether your friend walks—for example, 12 miles, 12 kilometers, 12 furlongs, or 12 yards. *Both a number and a unit must be included to express a quantity properly.*

To understand chemistry, we need a clear understanding of the units chemists work with and the rules they follow for expressing numbers. The next two sections examine the rules for expressing numbers.

FIGURE 1.6
Measuring Blood Pressure

A nurse or a doctor measuring a patient's blood pressure is taking a measurement.

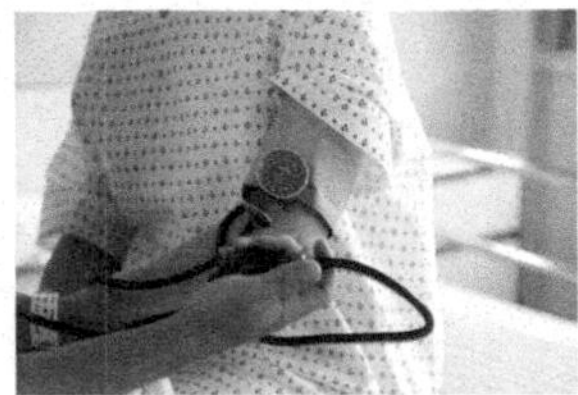

quantity

An amount of something.

number

How many (or how much) of something in a quantity.

unit

The scale of measurement for a quantity.

EXAMPLE 3

Identify the number and the unit in each quantity.

1. one dozen eggs
2. 2.54 centimeters
3. a box of pencils
4. 88 meters per second

Solution

1. The number is one, and the unit is dozen eggs.
2. The number is 2.54, and the unit is centimeter.
3. The number 1 is implied because the quantity is only *a* box. The unit is box of pencils.
4. The number is 88, and the unit is meters per second. Note that in this case the unit is actually a combination of two units: meters and seconds.

SKILL-BUILDING EXERCISE

Identify the number and the unit in each quantity.

1. 99 bottles of soda
2. 60 miles per hour
3. 32 fluid ounces
4. 98.6 degrees Fahrenheit

CONCEPT REVIEW EXERCISE

1. What are the two necessary parts of a quantity?

ANSWER

1. The two necessary parts are the number and the unit.

To Your Health: Dosages

As we saw in the chapter-opening essay, a medicine can be more harmful than helpful if it is not taken in the proper dosage. A dosage (or dose) is the specific amount of a medicine that is known to be therapeutic for an ailment in a patient of a certain size. Dosages of the active ingredient in medications are usually described by units of mass, typically grams or milligrams, and generally are equated with a number of capsules or teaspoonfuls to be swallowed or injected. (For more information about mass, see Section 6.) The amount of the active ingredient in a medicine is carefully controlled so that the proper number of pills or spoonfuls contains the proper dose.

Most drugs must be taken in just the right amount. If too little is taken, the desired effects will not occur (or will not occur fast enough for comfort); if too much is taken, there may be potential side effects that are worse than the original ailment. Some drugs are available in multiple dosages. For example, tablets of the medication levothyroxine sodium, a synthetic thyroid hormone for those suffering from decreased thyroid gland function, are available in 11 different doses, ranging from 25 micrograms (µg) to 300 µg. It is a doctor's responsibility to prescribe the correct dosage for a patient, and it is a pharmacist's responsibility to provide the patient with the correct medicine at the dosage prescribed. Thus, proper quantities—which are expressed using numbers and their associated units—are crucial for keeping us healthy.

KEY TAKEAWAY

- Identify a quantity properly with a number and a unit.

EXERCISES

1. Why are both parts of a quantity important when describing it?
2. Why are measurements an important part of any branch of science, such as chemistry?
3. You ask a classmate how much homework your chemistry professor assigned. Your classmate answers, "twenty." Is that a proper answer? Why or why not?
4. Identify the number and the unit in each quantity.
   a. five grandchildren
   b. 16 candles
   c. four score and seven years
   d. 40 days and 40 nights
   e. 12.01 grams
   f. 9.8 meters per second squared
   g. 55 miles per hour
   h. 98.6 degrees Fahrenheit

ANSWERS

1. The number states how much, and the unit states of what. Without the number and the unit, a quantity cannot be properly communicated.
3. No, it is not a proper answer; you do not know whether the professor meant homework problem number 20 or 20 homework problems.

4. EXPRESSING NUMBERS: SCIENTIFIC NOTATION

LEARNING OBJECTIVE

1. **Express a large number or a small number in scientific notation.**

The instructions for making a pot of coffee specified 3 scoops (rather than 12,000 grounds) because any measurement is expressed more efficiently with units that are appropriate in size. In science, however, we often must deal with quantities that are extremely small or incredibly large. For example, you may have 5,000,000,000,000 red blood cells in a liter of blood, and the diameter of an iron atom is 0.000000014 inches. Numbers with many zeros can be cumbersome to work with, so scientists use scientific notation.

Scientific notation is a system for expressing very large or very small numbers in a compact manner. It uses the idea that such numbers can be rewritten as a simple number multiplied by 10 raised to a certain exponent, or **power**.

scientific notation

A system for expressing very large or very small numbers in a compact manner.

power

The exponent in a number expressed in scientific notation.

Let us look first at large numbers. Suppose a spacecraft is 1,500,000 miles from Mars. The number 1,500,000 can be thought of as follows:

$$1.5 \times \underbrace{\underbrace{1{,}000{,}000}_{10 \times 10 \times 10 \times 10 \times 10 \times 10}}_{10^6} = 1.5 \times 10^6$$

That is, 1,500,000 is the same as 1.5 times 1 million, and 1 million is 10 × 10 × 10 × 10 × 10 × 10, or 10^6 (which is read as "ten to the sixth power"). Therefore, 1,500,000 can be rewritten as 1.5 times 10^6, or 1.5×10^6. The distance of the spacecraft from Mars can therefore be expressed as 1.5×10^6 miles.

$10^0 = 1$

$10^1 = 10$

$10^2 = 100$

$10^3 = 1{,}000$

$10^4 = 10{,}000$

and so forth

The convention for expressing numbers in scientific notation is to write a single nonzero first digit, a decimal point, and the rest of the digits, excluding any trailing zeros. This figure is followed by a multiplication sign and then by 10 raised to the power necessary to reproduce the original number. For example, although 1,500,000 can also be written as $15. \times 10^5$ (which would be 15. × 100,000), the convention is to have only one digit before the decimal point. How do we know to what power 10 is raised? The power is the number of places you have to move the decimal point to the left to make it follow the first digit, so that the number being multiplied is between 1 and 10:

$$1{,}500{,}000 = 1.5 \times 10^6$$

EXAMPLE 4

Express each number in scientific notation.

1. 67,000,000,000
2. 1,689
3. 12.6

Solution

1. Moving the decimal point 10 places to the left gives 6.7×10^{10}.
2. The decimal point is assumed to be at the end of the number, so moving it three places to the left gives 1.689×10^3.
3. In this case, we need to move the decimal point only one place to the left, which yields 1.26×10^1.

SKILL-BUILDING EXERCISE

Express each number in scientific notation.

1. 1,492
2. 102,000,000
3. 101,325

To change scientific notation to standard notation, we reverse the process, moving the decimal point to the right. Add zeros to the end of the number being converted, if necessary, to produce a number of the proper magnitude.

EXAMPLE 5

Express each number in standard, or nonscientific, notation.

1. 5.27×10^4
2. 1.0008×10^6

Solution

1. Rather than moving the decimal to the left, we move it four places to the right and add zeros to give 52,700.
2. Moving the decimal six places to the right gives 1,000,800.

SKILL-BUILDING EXERCISE

Express each number in standard, or nonscientific, notation.

1. 6.98×10^8
2. 1.005×10^2

We can also use scientific notation to express numbers whose magnitudes are less than 1. For example, the number 0.006 can be expressed as follows:

$$6 \times \underbrace{\frac{1}{1,000}}_{\underbrace{\frac{1}{10} \times \frac{1}{10} \times \frac{1}{10}}_{10^{-3}}} = 6 \times 10^{-3}$$

$10^{-1} = 1/10$

$10^{-2} = 1/100$

$10^{-3} = 1/1{,}000$

$10^{-4} = 1/10{,}000$

$10^{-5} = 1/100{,}000$

and so forth

We use a negative number as the power to indicate the number of places we have to move the decimal point to the right to follow the first nonzero digit. This is illustrated as follows:

$$0.006 = 6 \times 10^{-3}$$

In scientific notation, numbers with a magnitude greater than one have a positive power, while numbers with a magnitude less than one have a negative power.

EXAMPLE 6

Express each number in scientific notation.

1. 0.000006567
2. −0.0004004
3. 0.000000000000123

Solution

1. Move the decimal point six places to the right to get 6.567×10^{-6}.
2. Move the decimal point four places to the right to get -4.004×10^{-4}. The negative sign on the number itself does not affect how we apply the rules of scientific notation.
3. Move the decimal point 13 places to the right to get 1.23×10^{-13}.

SKILL-BUILDING EXERCISE

Express each number in scientific notation.

1. 0.000355
2. 0.314159

As with numbers with positive powers of 10, when changing from scientific notation to standard notation, we reverse the process.

EXAMPLE 7

Express each number in standard notation.

1. 6.22×10^{-2}
2. 9.9×10^{-9}

Solution

1. 0.0622
2. 0.0000000099

SKILL-BUILDING EXERCISE

Express each number in standard notation.

1. 9.98×10^{-5}
2. 5.109×10^{-8}

Although calculators can show 8 to 10 digits in their display windows, that is not always enough when working with very large or very small numbers. For this reason, many calculators are designed to handle scientific notation. The method for entering scientific notation differs for each calculator model, so take the time to learn how to do it properly on your calculator, *asking your instructor for assistance if necessary*. If you do not learn to enter scientific notation into your calculator properly, you will not get the correct final answer when performing a calculation.

CONCEPT REVIEW EXERCISES

1. Why it is easier to use scientific notation to express very large or very small numbers?
2. What is the relationship between how many places a decimal point moves and the power of 10 used in changing a conventional number into scientific notation?

ANSWERS

1. Scientific notation is more convenient than listing a large number of zeros.
2. The number of places the decimal point moves equals the power of 10—positive if the decimal point moves to the left and negative if the decimal point moves to the right.

KEY TAKEAWAY

- Large or small numbers are expressed in scientific notation, which use powers of 10.

EXERCISES

1. Why is scientific notation useful in expressing numbers?
2. What is the relationship between the power and the number of places a decimal point is moved when going from standard to scientific notation?
3. Express each number in scientific notation.
   a. 0.00064
   b. 5,230,000
   c. −56,200
   d. 0.000000000220
   e. 1.0
4. Express each number in scientific notation.
   a. 678
   b. −1,061
   c. 0.000560
   d. 0.0000003003
   e. 100,000,000
5. Express each number in standard form.
   a. 6.72×10^{4}
   b. 2.088×10^{-4}
   c. -3×10^{6}
   d. 9.98×10^{-7}
6. Express each number in standard form.
   a. 9.05×10^{5}
   b. 1.0×10^{-3}
   c. 6.022×10^{23}
   d. 8.834×10^{-12}
7. Complete the following table:

Incorrect Scientific Notation	Correct Scientific Notation
54.7×10^{4}	
0.0066×10^{3}	
$3,078 \times 10^{0}$	

8. Complete the following table:

Incorrect Scientific Notation	Correct Scientific Notation
234.0×10^1	
36×10^{-4}	
0.993×10^5	

ANSWERS

1. Scientific notation is more convenient than listing a large number of zeros.
3. a. 6.4×10^{-4}
   b. 5.23×10^6
   c. -5.62×10^4
   d. 2.20×10^{-10}
   e. 1.0×10^0
5. a. 67,200
   b. 0.0002088
   c. −3,000,000
   d. 0.000000998
7.

Incorrect Scientific Notation	Correct Scientific Notation
54.7×10^4	5.47×10^5
0.0066×10^3	6.6×10^0
$3{,}078 \times 10^0$	3.078×10^3

5. EXPRESSING NUMBERS: SIGNIFICANT FIGURES

LEARNING OBJECTIVES

1. **Identify the number of significant figures in a reported value.**
2. **Use significant figures correctly in arithmetical operations.**

Scientists have established certain conventions for communicating the degree of precision of a measurement. Imagine, for example, that you are using a meterstick to measure the width of a table. The centimeters (cm) are marked off, telling you how many centimeters wide the table is. Many metersticks also have millimeters (mm) marked off, so we can measure the table to the nearest millimeter. But most metersticks do not have any finer measurements indicated, so you cannot report the table's width any more exactly than to the nearest millimeter. All you can do is estimate the next decimal place in the measurement (Figure 1.7).

FIGURE 1.7 Measuring an Object to the Correct Number of Digits

How many digits should be reported for the length of this object?

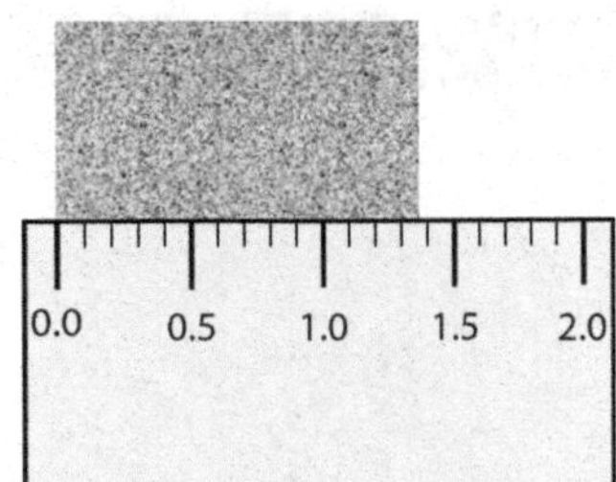

The concept of significant figures takes this limitation into account. The **significant figures** of a measured quantity are defined as all the digits known with certainty and the first uncertain, or estimated, digit. It makes no sense to report any digits after the first uncertain one, so it is the last digit reported in a measurement. Zeros are used when needed to place the significant figures in their correct positions. Thus, zeros may not be significant figures.

significant figures

All the digits of a measured quantity known with certainty and the first uncertain, or estimated, digit.

Note

"Sig figs" is a common abbreviation for significant figures.

For example, if a table is measured and reported as being 1,357 mm wide, the number 1,357 has four significant figures. The 1 (thousands), the 3 (hundreds), and the 5 (tens) are certain; the 7 (units) is assumed to have been estimated. It would make no sense to report such a measurement as 1,357.0 or 1,357.00 because that would suggest the measuring instrument was able to determine the width to the nearest tenth or hundredth of a millimeter, when in fact it shows only tens of millimeters and the units have to be estimated.

On the other hand, if a measurement is reported as 150 mm, the 1 (hundreds) and the 5 (tens) are known to be significant, but how do we know whether the zero is or is not significant? The measuring instrument could have had marks indicating every 10 mm or marks indicating every 1 mm. Is the zero an estimate, or is the 5 an estimate and the zero a placeholder?

The rules for deciding which digits in a measurement are significant are as follows:

1. All nonzero digits are significant. In 1,357, all the digits are significant.
2. *Captive (or embedded) zeros*, which are zeros between significant digits, are significant. In 405, all the digits are significant.
3. *Leading zeros*, which are zeros at the beginning of a decimal number less than 1, are not significant. In 0.000458, the first four digits are leading zeros and are not significant. The zeros serve only to put the digits 4, 5, and 8 in the correct positions. This number has three significant figures.
4. *Trailing zeros*, which are zeros at the end of a number, are significant only if the number has a decimal point. Thus, in 1,500, the two trailing zeros are not significant because the number is written without a decimal point; the number has two significant figures. However, in 1,500.00, all six digits are significant because the number has a decimal point.

EXAMPLE 8

How many significant digits does each number have?

1. 6,798,000
2. 6,000,798
3. 6,000,798.00
4. 0.0006798

Solution

1. four (by rules 1 and 4)
2. seven (by rules 1 and 2)
3. nine (by rules 1, 2, and 4)
4. four (by rules 1 and 3)

SKILL-BUILDING EXERCISE

How many significant digits does each number have?

1. 2.1828
2. 0.005505
3. 55,050
4. 5
5. 500

5.1 Combining Numbers

It is important to be aware of significant figures when you are mathematically manipulating numbers. For example, dividing 125 by 307 on a calculator gives 0.4071661238… to an infinite number of digits.

But do the digits in this answer have any practical meaning, especially when you are starting with numbers that have only three significant figures each? When performing mathematical operations, there are two rules for limiting the number of significant figures in an answer—one rule is for addition and subtraction, and one rule is for multiplication and division.

For addition or subtraction, the rule is to stack all the numbers with their decimal points aligned and then limit the answer's significant figures to the rightmost column for which all the numbers have significant figures. Consider the following:

```
     56.789
+   102.2
+ 1,300.099
= 1,459.088
         ↑ Limit to this column
```

The arrow points to the rightmost column in which all the numbers have significant figures—in this case, the tenths place. Therefore, we will limit our final answer to the tenths place. Is our final answer therefore 1,459.0? No, because when we drop digits from the end of a number, we also have to **round** the number. Notice that the second dropped digit, in the hundredths place, is 8. This suggests that the answer is actually closer to 1,459.1 than it is to 1,459.0, so we need to round up to 1,459.1. The rules in rounding are simple: If the first dropped digit is 5 or higher, round up. If the first dropped digit is lower than 5, do not round up.

rounding

The process of assessing the final significant figure of a quantity to determine if it should be kept or moved higher.

For multiplication or division, the rule is to count the number of significant figures in each number being multiplied or divided and then limit the significant figures in the answer to the lowest count. An example is as follows:

$$\underbrace{38.65}_{\text{4 sig figs}} \times \underbrace{105.93}_{\text{5 sig figs}} = \underbrace{4{,}094.1945}_{\text{reduce to 4 sig figs}}$$

The final answer, limited to four significant figures, is 4,094. The first digit dropped is 1, so we do not round up.

Scientific notation provides a way of communicating significant figures without ambiguity. You simply include all the significant figures in the leading number. For example, the number 450 has two significant figures and would be written in scientific notation as 4.5×10^2, whereas 450.0 has four significant figures and would be written as 4.500×10^2. In scientific notation, all significant figures are listed explicitly.

EXAMPLE 9

Write the answer for each expression using scientific notation with the appropriate number of significant figures.

1. 23.096×90.300
2. 125×9.000
3. $1{,}027 + 610 + 363.06$

Solution

1. The calculator answer is 2,085.5688, but we need to round it to five significant figures. Because the first digit to be dropped (in the hundredths place) is greater than 5, we round up to 2,085.6, which in scientific notation is 2.0856×10^3.
2. The calculator gives 1,125 as the answer, but we limit it to three significant figures and convert into scientific notation: 1.13×10^3.
3. The calculator gives 2,000.06 as the answer, but because 610 has its farthest-right significant figure in the tens column, our answer must be limited to the tens position: 2.0×10^3.

SKILL-BUILDING EXERCISE

Write the answer for each expression using scientific notation with the appropriate number of significant figures.

1. $217 \div 903$
2. $13.77 + 908.226 + 515$

3. 255.0 – 99
4. 0.00666 × 321

Remember that calculators do not understand significant figures. *You* are the one who must apply the rules of significant figures to a result from your calculator.

CONCEPT REVIEW EXERCISES

1. Explain why the concept of significant figures is important in numerical calculations.
2. State the rules for determining the significant figures in a measurement.
3. When do you round a number up, and when do you *not* round a number up?

ANSWERS

1. Significant figures represent all the known digits of a measurement plus the first estimated one.
2. All nonzero digits are significant; zeros between nonzero digits are significant; zeros at the end of a nondecimal number or the beginning of a decimal number are not significant; zeros at the end of a decimal number are significant.
3. Round up only if the first digit dropped is 5 or higher.

KEY TAKEAWAYS

- Significant figures properly report the number of measured and estimated digits in a measurement.
- There are rules for applying significant figures in calculations.

EXERCISES

1. Define *significant figures*. Why are they important?
2. Define the different types of zeros found in a number and explain whether or not they are significant.
3. How many significant figures are in each number?
   a. 140
   b. 0.009830
   c. 15,050
   d. 221,560,000
   e. 5.67×10^3
   f. 2.9600×10^{-5}
4. How many significant figures are in each number?
   a. 1.05
   b. 9,500
   c. 0.0004505
   d. 0.00045050
   e. 7.210×10^6
   f. 5.00×10^{-6}
5. Round each number to three significant figures.
   a. 34,705
   b. 34,750
   c. 34,570
6. Round each number to four significant figures.
   a. 34,705
   b. 0.0054109
   c. 8.90443×10^8
7. Perform each operation and express the answer to the correct number of significant figures.
   a. 467.88 + 23.0 + 1,306 = ?
   b. 10,075 + 5,822.09 – 34.0 = ?
   c. 0.00565 + 0.002333 + 0.0991 = ?
8. Perform each operation and express the answer to the correct number of significant figures.
   a. 0.9812 + 1.660 + 8.6502 = ?
   b. 189 + 3,201.8 – 1,100 = ?
   c. 675.0 – 24 + 1,190 = ?

9. Perform each operation and express the answer to the correct number of significant figures.
   a. $439 \times 8{,}767 = ?$
   b. $23.09 \div 13.009 = ?$
   c. $1.009 \times 876 = ?$
10. Perform each operation and express the answer to the correct number of significant figures.
   a. $3.00 \div 1.9979 = ?$
   b. $2{,}300 \times 185 = ?$
   c. $16.00 \times 4.0 = ?$
11. Use your calculator to solve each equation. Express each answer in proper scientific notation and with the proper number of significant figures. If you do not get the correct answers, you may not be entering scientific notation into your calculator properly, so ask your instructor for assistance.
   a. $(5.6 \times 10^3) \times (9.04 \times 10^{-7}) = ?$
   b. $(8.331 \times 10^{-2}) \times (2.45 \times 10^5) = ?$
   c. $983.09 \div (5.390 \times 10^5) = ?$
   d. $0.00432 \div (3.9001 \times 10^3) = ?$
12. Use your calculator to solve each equation. Express each answer in proper scientific notation and with the proper number of significant figures. If you do not get the correct answers, you may not be entering scientific notation into your calculator properly, so ask your instructor for assistance.
   a. $(5.2 \times 10^6) \times (3.33 \times 10^{-2}) = ?$
   b. $(7.108 \times 10^3) \times (9.994 \times 10^{-5}) = ?$
   c. $(6.022 \times 10^7) \div (1.381 \times 10^{-8}) = ?$
   d. $(2.997 \times 10^8) \div (1.58 \times 10^{34}) = ?$

ANSWERS

1. Significant figures represent all the known digits plus the first estimated digit of a measurement; they are the only values worth reporting in a measurement.
3. a. two
   b. four
   c. four
   d. five
   e. three
   f. five
5. a. 34,700
   b. 34,800
   c. 34,600
7. a. 1,797
   b. 15,863
   c. 0.1071
9. a. 3,850,000
   b. 1.775
   c. 884
11. a. 5.1×10^{-3}
   b. 2.04×10^4
   c. 1.824×10^{-3}
   d. 1.11×10^{-6}

6. THE INTERNATIONAL SYSTEM OF UNITS

LEARNING OBJECTIVE

1. **Recognize the SI base units and explain the system of prefixes used with them.**

Now that we have discussed some of the conventions for expressing numbers, let us focus on the other component of a quantity—the units.

People who live in the United States measure weight in pounds, height in feet and inches, and a car's speed in miles per hour. In contrast, chemistry and other branches of science use the International System of Units (also known as **SI** after *Système Internationale d'Unités*), which was established so that scientists around the world could communicate efficiently with each other. Many countries have also adopted SI units for everyday use as well. The United States is one of the few countries that has not.

6.1 Base SI Units

base (basic) unit

A fundamental unit of SI.

Base (or basic) units, are the fundamental units of SI. There are seven base units, which are listed in Table 1.2. Chemistry uses five of the base units: the mole for amount, the kilogram for mass, the meter for length, the second for time, and the kelvin for temperature. The degree Celsius (°C) is also commonly used for temperature. The numerical relationship between kelvins and degrees Celsius is as follows:

$$K = °C + 273$$

TABLE 1.2 The Seven Base SI Units

Property	Unit	Abbreviation
length	meter	m
mass	kilogram	kg
time	second	s
amount	mole	mol
temperature	kelvin	K
electrical current	ampere	amp
luminous intensity	candela	cd

Note

The United States uses the English system of units for many quantities. Inches, feet, miles, gallons, pounds, and so forth, are all units connected with the English system of units.

The size of each base unit is defined by international convention. For example, the kilogram is defined as the quantity of mass of a special metal cylinder kept in a vault in France (Figure 1.8). The other base units have similar definitions. The sizes of the base units are not always convenient for all measurements. For example, a meter is a rather large unit for describing the width of something as narrow as human hair. Instead of reporting the diameter of hair as 0.00012 m or even 1.2×10^{-4} m, SI also provides a series of prefixes that can be attached to the units, creating units that are larger or smaller by powers of 10.

Common prefixes and their multiplicative factors are listed in Table 1.3. (Perhaps you have already noticed that the base unit *kilogram* is a combination of a prefix, kilo- meaning 1,000 ×, and a unit of mass, the gram.) Some prefixes create a multiple of the original unit: 1 kilogram equals 1,000 grams, and 1 megameter equals 1,000,000 meters. Other prefixes create a fraction of the original unit. Thus, 1 centimeter equals 1/100 of a meter, 1 millimeter equals 1/1,000 of a meter, 1 microgram equals 1/1,000,000 of a gram, and so forth.

FIGURE 1.8 The Kilogram

The standard for the kilogram is a platinum-iridium cylinder kept in a special vault in France.

Source: Photo reproduced by permission of the Bureau International des Poids et Mesures, who retain full internationally protected copyright.

TABLE 1.3 Prefixes Used with SI Units

Prefix	Abbreviation	Multiplicative Factor	Multiplicative Factor in Scientific Notation
giga-	G	1,000,000,000 ×	10^9 ×
mega-	M	1,000,000 ×	10^6 ×
kilo-	k	1,000 ×	10^3 ×
deca-	D	10 ×	10^1 ×
deci-	d	1/10 ×	10^{-1} ×
centi-	c	1/100 ×	10^{-2} ×
milli-	m	1/1,000 ×	10^{-3} ×
micro-	µ*	1/1,000,000 ×	10^{-6} ×
nano-	n	1/1,000,000,000 ×	10^{-9} ×

***The letter µ is the Greek lowercase letter for *m* and is called "mu," which is pronounced "myoo."**

Both SI units and prefixes have abbreviations, and the combination of a prefix abbreviation with a base unit abbreviation gives the abbreviation for the modified unit. For example, kg is the abbreviation for kilogram. We will be using these abbreviations throughout this book.

6.2 Derived SI Units

Derived units are combinations of SI base units. Units can be multiplied and divided, just as numbers can be multiplied and divided. For example, the area of a square having a side of 2 cm is 2 cm × 2 cm, or 4 cm^2 (read as "four centimeters squared" or "four square centimeters"). Notice that we have squared a length unit, the centimeter, to get a derived unit for area, the square centimeter.

derived unit

A combinations of the SI base units.

volume

The amount of space that a given substance occupies.

Volume is an important quantity that uses a derived unit. **Volume** is the amount of space that a given substance occupies and is defined geometrically as length × width × height. Each distance can be expressed using the meter unit, so volume has the derived unit m × m × m, or m^3 (read as "meters cubed" or "cubic meters"). A cubic meter is a rather large volume, so scientists typically express volumes in terms of 1/1,000 of a cubic meter. This unit has its own name—the liter (L). A liter is a little larger than 1 US quart in volume. (Table 1.4 gives approximate equivalents for some of the units used in chemistry.) As shown in Figure 1.9, a liter is also 1,000 cm^3. By definition, there are 1,000 mL in 1 L, so 1 milliliter and 1 cubic centimeter represent the same volume.

$$1\ \text{mL} = 1\ \text{cm}^3$$

FIGURE 1.9 The Liter

A liter is defined as a cube 10 cm (1/10th of a meter) on a side. A milliliter, 1/1,000th of a liter, is equal to 1 cubic centimeter.

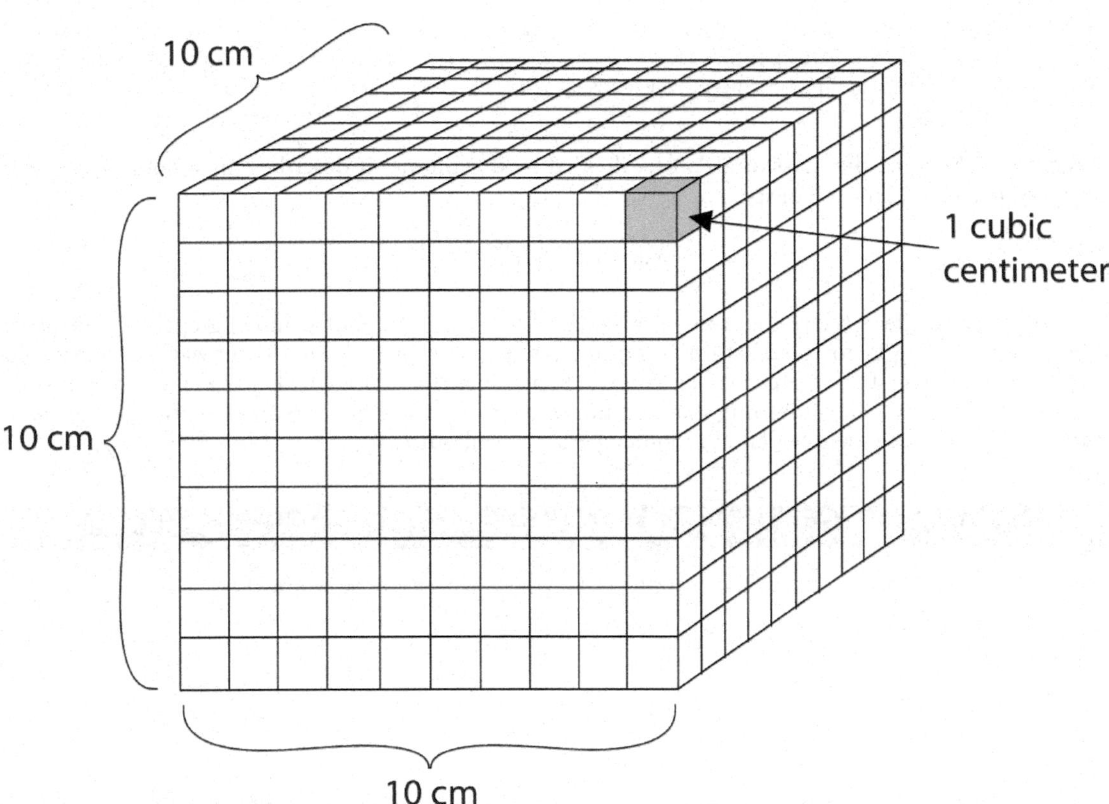

TABLE 1.4 Approximate Equivalents to Some SI Units

1 m ≈ 39.36 in. ≈ 3.28 ft ≈ 1.09 yd
1 cm ≈ 2.54 in.
1 km ≈ 0.62 mi
1 kg ≈ 2.20 lb
1 lb ≈ 454 g
1 L ≈ 1.06 qt
1 qt ≈ 0.946 L

energy

The ability to perform work.

joule

The SI unit of energy.

Energy, another important quantity in chemistry, is the ability to perform work, such as moving a box of books from one side of a room to the other side. It has a derived unit of $kg{\cdot}m^2/s^2$. (The dot between the kg and m units implies the units are multiplied together.) Because this combination is cumbersome, this collection of units is redefined as a **joule** (J). An older unit of energy, the calorie (cal), is also widely used. There are 4.184 J in 1 cal. All chemical processes occur with a simultaneous change in energy. (For more information on energy changes, see Chapter 7.)

To Your Health: Energy and Food

The food in our diet provides the energy our bodies need to function properly. The energy contained in food could be expressed in joules or calories, which are the conventional units for energy, but the food industry prefers to use the kilocalorie and refers to it as the Calorie (with a capital C). The average daily energy requirement of an adult is about 2,000–2,500 Calories, which is 2,000,000–2,500,000 calories (with a lowercase c).

If we expend the same amount of energy that our food provides, our body weight remains stable. If we ingest more Calories from food than we expend, however, our bodies store the extra energy in high-energy-density compounds, such as fat, and we gain weight. On the other hand, if we expend more energy than we ingest, we lose weight. Other factors affect our weight as well—genetic, metabolic, behavioral, environmental, cultural factors—but dietary habits are among the most important.

In 2008 the US Centers for Disease Control and Prevention issued a report stating that 73% of Americans were either overweight or obese. More alarmingly, the report also noted that 19% of children aged 6–11 and 18% of adolescents aged 12–19 were overweight—numbers that had tripled over the preceding two decades. Two major reasons for this increase are excessive calorie consumption (especially in the form of high-fat foods) and reduced physical activity. Partly because of that report, many restaurants and food companies are working to reduce the amounts of fat in foods and provide consumers with more healthy food options.

density

The mass of an object divided by its volume.

Density is defined as the mass of an object divided by its volume; it describes the amount of matter contained in a given amount of space.

$$\text{density} = \frac{\text{mass}}{\text{volume}}$$

Thus, the units of density are the units of mass divided by the units of volume: g/cm^3 or g/mL (for solids and liquids), g/L (for gases), kg/m^3, and so forth. For example, the density of water is about 1.00 g/cm^3, while the density of mercury is 13.6 g/mL. (Remember that 1 mL equals 1 cm^3.) Mercury is over 13 times as dense as water, meaning that it contains over 13 times the amount of matter in the same amount of space. The density of air at room temperature is about 1.3 g/L.

EXAMPLE 10

Give the abbreviation for each unit and define the abbreviation in terms of the base unit.

1. kiloliter
2. microsecond
3. decimeter
4. nanogram

Solution

1. The abbreviation for a kiloliter is kL. Because kilo means "1,000 ×," 1 kL equals 1,000 L.
2. The abbreviation for microsecond is µs. Micro implies 1/1,000,000th of a unit, so 1 µs equals 0.000001 s.
3. The abbreviation for decimeter is dm. Deci means 1/10th, so 1 dm equals 0.1 m.
4. The abbreviation for nanogram is ng and equals 0.000000001 g.

SKILL-BUILDING EXERCISE

Give the abbreviation for each unit and define the abbreviation in terms of the base unit.

1. kilometer
2. milligram
3. nanosecond

4. centiliter

EXAMPLE 11

What is the density of a section of bone if a 25.3 cm^3 sample has a mass of 27.8 g?

Solution

Because density is defined as the mass of an object divided by its volume, we can set up the following relationship:

$$\text{density} = \frac{\text{mass}}{\text{volume}} = \frac{27.8\ \text{g}}{25.3\ \text{cm}^3} = 1.10\ \text{g/cm}^3$$

Note that we have limited our final answer to three significant figures.

SKILL-BUILDING EXERCISE

1. What is the density of oxygen gas if a 15.0 L sample has a mass of 21.7 g?

CONCEPT REVIEW EXERCISES

1. What is the difference between a base unit and a derived unit? Give two examples of each type of unit.
2. Do units follow the same mathematical rules as numbers do? Give an example to support your answer.

ANSWERS

1. Base units are the seven fundamental units of SI; derived units are constructed by making combinations of the base units; base units: kilograms and meters (answers will vary); derived units: grams per milliliter and joules (answers will vary).
2. yes; $\text{mL} \times \frac{\text{g}}{\text{mL}} = \text{g}$ (answers will vary)

KEY TAKEAWAYS

- Recognize the SI base units.
- Combining prefixes with base units creates new units of larger or smaller sizes.

EXERCISES

1. List four base units.
2. List four derived units.
3. How many meters are in 1 km? How many centimeters are in 1 m?
4. How many grams are in 1 Mg? How many microliters are in 1 L?
5. Complete the following table:

Unit	Abbreviation
centiliter	
	ms
	cm
	kL
micrometer	

6. Complete the following table:

Unit	Abbreviation
microliter	
kilosecond	
	dL
	ns
millimeter	

7. What are some appropriate units for density?
8. A derived unit for velocity, which is the change of position with respect to time, is meters per second (m/s). Give three other derived units for velocity.

ANSWERS

1. second, meter, kilogram, and kelvin (answers will vary)
3. 1,000; 100
5.

Unit	Abbreviation
centiliter	cL
millisecond	ms
centimeter	cm
kiloliter	kL
micrometer	μm

7. grams per liter, grams per milliliter, and kilograms per liter (answers will vary)

7. CONVERTING UNITS

LEARNING OBJECTIVE

1. **Convert a value reported in one unit to a corresponding value in a different unit.**

The ability to convert from one unit to another is an important skill. For example, a nurse with 50 mg aspirin tablets who must administer 0.2 g of aspirin to a patient needs to know that 0.2 g equals 200 mg, so 4 tablets are needed. Fortunately, there is a simple way to convert from one unit to another.

7.1 Conversion Factors

If you learned the SI units and prefixes described in Section 6, then you know that 1 cm is 1/100th of a meter.

$$1\text{ cm} = \frac{1}{100}\text{ m}$$

or

$$100\text{ cm} = 1\text{ m}$$

Suppose we divide both sides of the equation by 1 m (both the number *and* the unit):

$$\frac{100\text{ cm}}{1\text{ m}} = \frac{1\text{ m}}{1\text{ m}}$$

As long as we perform the same operation on both sides of the equals sign, the expression remains an equality. Look at the right side of the equation; it now has the same quantity in the numerator (the top) as it has in the denominator (the bottom). Any fraction that has the same quantity in the numerator and the denominator has a value of 1:

$$\text{same quantity} \quad \frac{100\ \text{cm}}{1\ \text{m}} = 1$$

We know that 100 cm *is* 1 m, so we have the same quantity on the top and the bottom of our fraction, although it is expressed in different units. A fraction that has equivalent quantities in the numerator and the denominator but expressed in different units is called a **conversion factor.**

conversion factor
A fraction that has equivalent quantities in the numerator and the denominator but expressed in different units.

Here is a simple example. How many centimeters are there in 3.55 m? Perhaps you can determine the answer in your head. If there are 100 cm in every meter, then 3.55 m equals 355 cm. To solve the problem more formally with a conversion factor, we first write the quantity we are given, 3.55 m. Then we multiply this quantity by a conversion factor, which is the same as multiplying it by 1. We can write 1 as $\frac{100\ \text{cm}}{1\ \text{m}}$ and multiply:

$$3.55\ \text{m} \times \frac{100\ \text{cm}}{1\ \text{m}}$$

The 3.55 m can be thought of as a fraction with a 1 in the denominator. Because m, the abbreviation for meters, occurs in both the numerator *and* the denominator of our expression, they cancel out:

$$\frac{3.55\ \cancel{\text{m}}}{1} \times \frac{100\ \text{cm}}{1\ \cancel{\text{m}}}$$

The final step is to perform the calculation that remains once the units have been canceled:

$$\frac{3.55}{1} \times \frac{100\ \text{cm}}{1} = 355\ \text{cm}$$

In the final answer, we omit the 1 in the denominator. Thus, by a more formal procedure, we find that 3.55 m equals 355 cm. A generalized description of this process is as follows:

$$\text{quantity (in old units)} \times \text{conversion factor} = \text{quantity (in new units)}$$

You may be wondering why we use a seemingly complicated procedure for a straightforward conversion. In later studies, the conversion problems you will encounter *will not always be so simple.* If you can master the technique of applying conversion factors, you will be able to solve a large variety of problems.

In the previous example, we used the fraction $\frac{100\ \text{cm}}{1\ \text{m}}$ as a conversion factor. Does the conversion factor $\frac{1\ \text{m}}{100\ \text{cm}}$ also equal 1? Yes, it does; it has the same quantity in the numerator as in the denominator (except that they are expressed in different units). Why did we not use *that* conversion factor? If we had used the second conversion factor, the original unit would not have canceled, and the result would have been meaningless. Here is what we would have gotten:

$$3.55\ \text{m} \times \frac{1\ \text{m}}{100\ \text{cm}} = 0.0355\ \frac{\text{m}^2}{\text{cm}}$$

For the answer to be meaningful, we have to *construct the conversion factor in a form that causes the original unit to cancel out.* Figure 1.10 shows a concept map for constructing a proper conversion. The steps for doing a unit conversion problem are summarized in the margin.

FIGURE 1.10 A Concept Map for Conversions

This is how you construct a conversion factor to convert from one unit to another.

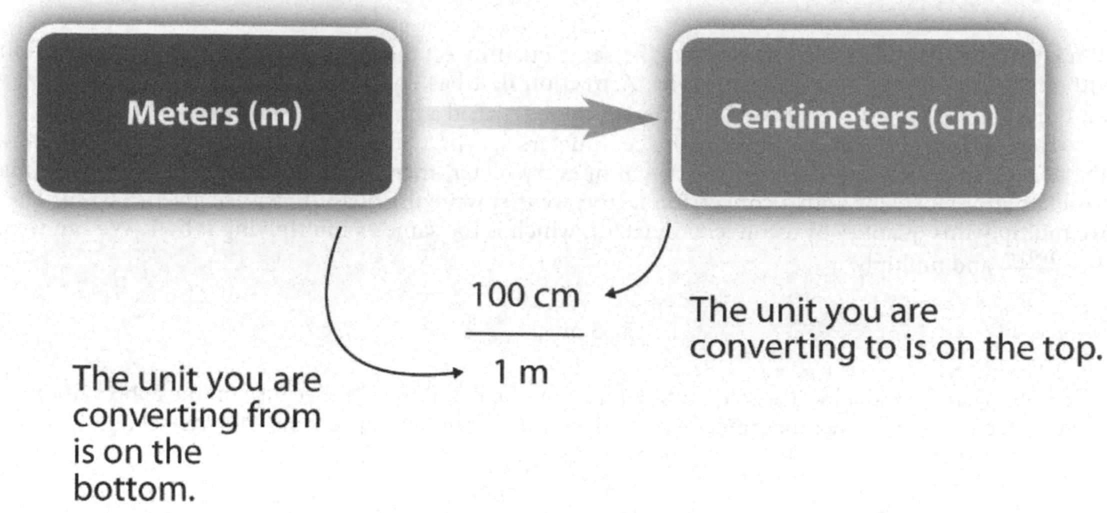

7.2 Significant Figures in Conversions

exact number

A number that is defined or counted.

How do conversion factors affect the determination of significant figures? Numbers in conversion factors based on prefix changes, such as kilograms to grams, are *not* considered in the determination of significant figures in a calculation because the numbers in such conversion factors are exact. **Exact numbers** are defined or counted numbers, not measured numbers, and can be considered as having an infinite number of significant figures. (In other words, 1 kg is exactly 1,000 g, by the definition of kilo-.) Counted numbers are also exact. If there are 16 students in a classroom, the number 16 is exact. In contrast, conversion factors that come from measurements (such as density, as we will see shortly) or are approximations have a limited number of significant figures and should be considered in determining the significant figures of the final answer.

EXAMPLE 12

1. The average volume of blood in an adult male is 4.7 L. What is this volume in milliliters?
2. A hummingbird can flap its wings once in 18 ms. How many seconds are in 18 ms?

Solution

1. We start with what we are given, 4.7 L. We want to change the unit from liters to milliliters. There are 1,000 mL in 1 L. From this relationship, we can construct two conversion factors:

$$\frac{1\ \text{L}}{1{,}000\ \text{mL}} \text{ or } \frac{1{,}000\ \text{mL}}{1\ \text{L}}$$

We use the conversion factor that will cancel out the original unit, liters, and introduce the unit we are converting to, which is milliliters. The conversion factor that does this is the one on the right.

$$4.7\ \cancel{\text{L}} \times \frac{1{,}000\ \text{mL}}{1\ \cancel{\text{L}}} = 4{,}700\ \text{mL}$$

Because the numbers in the conversion factor are exact, we do not consider them when determining the number of significant figures in the final answer. Thus, we report two significant figures in the final answer.

2. We can construct two conversion factors from the relationships between milliseconds and seconds:

$$\frac{1{,}000\ \text{ms}}{1\ \text{s}} \text{ or } \frac{1\ \text{s}}{1{,}000\ \text{ms}}$$

To convert 18 ms to seconds, we choose the conversion factor that will cancel out milliseconds and introduce seconds. The conversion factor on the right is the appropriate one. We set up the conversion as follows:

$$18\ \cancel{\text{ms}} \times \frac{1\ \text{s}}{1{,}000\ \cancel{\text{ms}}} = 0.018\ \text{s}$$

The conversion factor's numerical values do not affect our determination of the number of significant figures in the final answer.

SKILL-BUILDING EXERCISE

Perform each conversion.

1. 101,000 ns to seconds
2. 32.08 kg to grams

Conversion factors can also be constructed for converting between different kinds of units. For example, density can be used to convert between the mass and the volume of a substance. Consider mercury, which is a liquid at room temperature and has a density of 13.6 g/mL. The density tells us that 13.6 g of mercury have a volume of 1 mL. We can write that relationship as follows:

$$13.6\ \text{g mercury} = 1\ \text{mL mercury}$$

This relationship can be used to construct two conversion factors:

$$\frac{13.6\ \text{g}}{1\ \text{mL}} \text{ and } \frac{1\ \text{mL}}{13.6\ \text{g}}$$

Which one do we use? It depends, as usual, on the units we need to cancel and introduce. For example, suppose we want to know the mass of 16 mL of mercury. We would use the conversion factor that has milliliters on the bottom (so that the milliliter unit cancels) and grams on top so that our final answer has a unit of mass:

$$16\ \cancel{\text{mL}} \times \frac{13.6\ \text{g}}{1\ \cancel{\text{mL}}} = 217.6\ \text{g} = 220\ \text{g}$$

In the last step, we limit our final answer to two significant figures because the volume quantity has only two significant figures; the 1 in the volume unit is considered an exact number, so it does not affect the number of significant figures. The other conversion factor would be useful if we were given a mass and asked to find volume, as the following example illustrates.

Note

Density can be used as a conversion factor between mass and volume.

EXAMPLE 13

A mercury thermometer for measuring a patient's temperature contains 0.750 g of mercury. What is the volume of this mass of mercury?

Solution

Because we are starting with grams, we want to use the conversion factor that has grams in the denominator. The gram unit will cancel algebraically, and milliliters will be introduced in the numerator.

$$0.750\,\cancel{g} \times \frac{1\ \text{mL}}{13.6\,\cancel{g}} = 0.055147\ \ldots\ \text{mL} = 0.0551\ \text{mL}$$

We have limited the final answer to three significant figures.

SKILL-BUILDING EXERCISE

1. What is the volume of 100.0 g of air if its density is 1.3 g/L?

Looking Closer: Density and the Body

The densities of many components and products of the body have a bearing on our health.

Bones. Bone density is important because bone tissue of lower-than-normal density is mechanically weaker and susceptible to breaking. The density of bone is, in part, related to the amount of calcium in one's diet; people who have a diet deficient in calcium, which is an important component of bones, tend to have weaker bones. Dietary supplements or adding dairy products to the diet seems to help strengthen bones. As a group, women experience a decrease in bone density as they age. It has been estimated that fully half of women over age 50 suffer from excessive bone loss, a condition known as osteoporosis. Exact bone densities vary within the body, but for a healthy 30-year-old female, it is about 0.95–1.05 g/cm^3. Osteoporosis is diagnosed if the bone density is below 0.6–0.7 g/cm^3.

Urine. The density of urine can be affected by a variety of medical conditions. Sufferers of diabetes insipidus produce an abnormally large volume of urine with a relatively low density. In another form of diabetes, called diabetes mellitus, there is excess glucose dissolved in the urine, so that the density of urine is abnormally high. The density of urine may also be abnormally high because of excess protein in the urine, which can be caused by congestive heart failure or certain renal (kidney) problems. Thus, a urine density test can provide clues to various kinds of health problems. The density of urine is commonly expressed as a specific gravity, which is a unitless quantity defined as $\frac{\text{density of some material}}{\text{density of water}}$. Normal values for the specific gravity of urine range from 1.002 to 1.028.

Body Fat. The overall density of the body is one indicator of a person's total body fat. Fat is less dense than muscle and other tissues, so as it accumulates, the overall density of the body decreases. Measurements of a person's weight and volume provide the overall body density, which can then be correlated to the percentage of body fat. (The body's volume can be measured by immersion in a large tank of water. The amount of water displaced is equal to the volume of the body.)

Sometimes you will have to perform more than one conversion to obtain the desired unit. For example, suppose you want to convert 54.7 km into millimeters. You can either memorize the relationship between kilometers and millimeters, or you can do the conversion in steps. Most people prefer to convert in steps.

To do a stepwise conversion, we first convert the given amount to the base unit. In this example, the base unit is meters. We know that there are 1,000 m in 1 km:

$$54.7\,\cancel{\text{km}} \times \frac{1{,}000\ \text{m}}{1\,\cancel{\text{km}}} = 54{,}700\ \text{m}$$

Then we take the result (54,700 m) and convert it to millimeters, remembering that there are 1,000 mm for every 1 m:

$$54{,}700\,\cancel{m} \times \frac{1{,}000\text{ mm}}{1\,\cancel{m}} = 54{,}700{,}000\text{ mm} = 5.47 \times 10^7\text{ mm}$$

We have expressed the final answer in scientific notation.

As a shortcut, both steps in the conversion can be combined into a single, multistep expression:

$$54.7\,\cancel{km} \times \frac{1{,}000\,\cancel{m}}{1\,\cancel{km}} \times \frac{1{,}000\text{ mm}}{1\,\cancel{m}} = 54{,}700{,}000\text{ mm} = 5.47 \times 10^7\text{ mm}$$

Either method—one step at a time or all the steps together—is acceptable. If you do all the steps together, the restriction for the proper number of significant figures should be done after the last step. As long as the math is performed correctly, you should get the same answer no matter which method you use.

EXAMPLE 14

Convert 58.2 ms to megaseconds in one multistep calculation.

Solution

First, convert the given unit to the base unit—in this case, seconds—and then convert seconds to the final unit, megaseconds:

$$58.2\,\cancel{ms} \times \frac{1\,\cancel{s}}{1{,}000\,\cancel{ms}} \times \frac{1\text{ Ms}}{1{,}000{,}000\,\cancel{s}} = 0.0000000582\text{ Ms} = 5.82 \times 10^{-8}\text{ Ms}$$

Neither conversion factor affects the number of significant figures in the final answer.

SKILL-BUILDING EXERCISE

1. Convert 43.007 ng to kilograms in one multistep calculation.

Career Focus: Pharmacist

A pharmacist dispenses drugs that have been prescribed by a doctor. Although that may sound straightforward, pharmacists in the United States must hold a doctorate in pharmacy and be licensed by the state in which they work. Most pharmacy programs require four years of education in a specialty pharmacy school.

Pharmacists must know a lot of chemistry and biology so they can understand the effects that drugs (which are chemicals, after all) have on the body. Pharmacists can advise physicians on the selection, dosage, interactions, and side effects of drugs. They can also advise patients on the proper use of their medications, including when and how to take specific drugs properly. Pharmacists can be found in drugstores, hospitals, and other medical facilities.

Curiously, an outdated name for pharmacist is *chemist*, which was used when pharmacists formerly did a lot of drug preparation, or *compounding*. In modern times, pharmacists rarely compound their own drugs, but their knowledge of the sciences, including chemistry, helps them provide valuable services in support of everyone's health.

A pharmacist is a person who needs to know a lot of chemistry. Curiously, an old name for pharmacist is *chemist.*

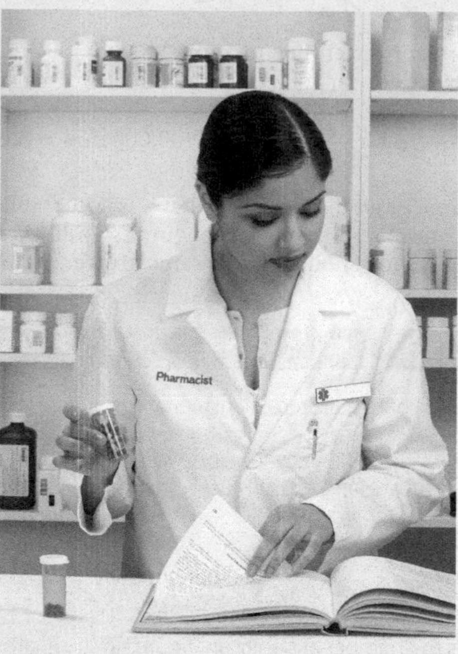

© *Thinkstock*

CONCEPT REVIEW EXERCISES

1. How do you determine which quantity in a conversion factor goes in the denominator of the fraction?
2. State the guidelines for determining significant figures when using a conversion factor.

ANSWERS

1. The unit you want to cancel from the numerator goes in the denominator of the conversion factor.
2. Exact numbers that appear in many conversion factors do not affect the number of significant figures; otherwise, the normal rules of multiplication and division for significant figures apply.

KEY TAKEAWAY

- A unit can be converted to another unit of the same type with a conversion factor.

EXERCISES

1. Give the two conversion factors you can construct using each pair of units.
   a. meters and kilometers
   b. liters and microliters
   c. seconds and milliseconds
2. Give the two conversion factors you can construct using each pair of units.
   a. grams and centigrams
   b. millimeters and meters
   c. liters and megaliters
3. How many meters are in 56.2 km?
4. How many seconds are in 209.7 ms?
5. How many microliters are in 44.1 L?

6. How many megagrams are in 90.532 g?
7. Convert 109.6 kg into micrograms. Express your final answer in scientific notation.
8. Convert 3.8×10^5 mm into kilometers. Express your final answer in scientific notation.
9. Convert 3.009×10^{-5} ML into centiliters. Express your final answer in scientific notation.
10. Convert 99.04 dm into micrometers. Express your final answer in scientific notation.
11. The density of ethyl alcohol is 0.79 g/mL. What is the mass of 340 mL of ethyl alcohol?
12. The density of a certain fraction of crude oil is 1.209 g/mL. What is the mass of 13,500 mL of this fraction?
13. The density of ethyl alcohol is 0.79 g/mL. What is the volume of 340 g of ethyl alcohol?
14. The density of a certain component of crude oil is 1.209 g/mL. What is the volume of 13,500 g of this component?
15. Vitamin C tablets can come in 500 mg tablets. How many of these tablets are needed to obtain 10 g of vitamin C?
16. A tablet of penicillin contains 250 mg of the antibacterial drug. A prescription contains 44 tablets. What is the total mass of penicillin in the prescription?

ANSWERS

1. a. $\frac{1{,}000\text{ m}}{1\text{ km}}; \frac{1\text{ km}}{1{,}000\text{ m}}$

   b. $\frac{1{,}000{,}000\ \mu\text{L}}{1\text{ L}}; \frac{1\text{ L}}{1{,}000{,}000\ \mu\text{L}}$

   c. $\frac{1{,}000\text{ ms}}{1\text{ s}}; \frac{1\text{ s}}{1{,}000\text{ ms}}$

3. 5.62×10^4 m
5. 4.41×10^7 µL
7. 1.096×10^8 µg
9. 3.009×10^3 cL
11. 270 g
13. 430 mL
15. 20 tablets

8. END-OF-CHAPTER MATERIAL

Chapter Summary

To ensure that you understand the material in this chapter, you should review the meanings of the bold terms in the following summary and ask yourself how they relate to the topics in the chapter.

Chemistry is the study of **matter**, which is anything that has mass and takes up space. Chemistry is one branch of **science**, which is the study of the natural universe. Like all branches of science, chemistry relies on the **scientific method**, which is a process of learning about the world around us. In the scientific method, a guess or **hypothesis** is tested through experiment and measurement.

Matter can be described in a number of ways. **Physical properties** describe characteristics of a sample that do not change the chemical identity of the material (size, shape, color, and so on), while **chemical properties** describe how a sample of matter changes its chemical composition. A **substance** is any material that has the same physical and chemical properties throughout. An **element** is a substance that cannot be broken down into chemically simpler components. The smallest chemically identifiable piece of an element is an **atom**. A substance that can be broken down into simpler chemical components is a **compound**. The smallest chemically identifiable piece of a compound is a **molecule**. Two or more substances combine physically to make a **mixture**. If the mixture is composed of discrete regions that maintain their own identity, the mixture is a **heterogeneous mixture**. If the mixture is so thoroughly mixed that the different components are evenly distributed throughout, it is a **homogeneous mixture**. Another name for a homogeneous mixture is a **solution**. Substances can also be described by their **phase**: solid, liquid, or gas.

Scientists learn about the universe by making measurements of **quantities**, which consist of **numbers** (how many) and **units** (of what). The numerical portion of a quantity can be expressed using **scientific notation**, which is based on **powers**, or exponents, of 10. Large numbers have positive powers of 10, while numbers less than 1 have negative powers of 10. The proper reporting of a measurement requires proper use of **significant figures**, which are all the known digits of a measurement plus the first estimated digit. The number of figures to report in the result of a calculation based on measured quantities depends on the numbers of significant figures in those quantities. For addition and subtraction, the number of significant figures is determined by position; for multiplication and division, it is decided by the number of significant figures in the original measured values. Nonsignificant digits are dropped from a final answer in accordance with the rules of **rounding**.

Chemistry uses SI, a system of units based on seven **basic units**. The most important ones for chemistry are the units for length, mass, amount, time, and temperature. Basic units can be combined with numerical prefixes to change the size of the units. They can also be combined with other units to make **derived units**, which are used to express other quantities such as **volume**, **density**, or **energy**. A formal conversion from one unit to another uses a **conversion factor**, which is constructed from the relationship between the two units. Numbers in conversion factors may affect the number of significant figures in a calculated quantity, depending on whether the conversion factor is **exact**. Conversion factors can be applied in separate computations, or several can be used at once in a single, longer computation.

ADDITIONAL EXERCISES

1. A sample of urine has a density of 1.105 g/cm^3. What is the mass of 0.255 L of this urine?
2. The hardest bone in the body is tooth enamel, which has a density of 2.91 g/cm^3. What is the volume, in liters, of 75.9 g of tooth enamel?
3. Some brands of aspirin have 81 mg of aspirin in each tablet. If a person takes 8 tablets per day, how many grams of aspirin is that person consuming every day?
4. The US government has a recommended daily intake (RDI) of 5 µg of vitamin D per day. (The name *recommended daily allowance* was changed to RDI in 1997.) If milk contains 1.2 µg per 8 oz glass, how many ounces of milk are needed to supply the RDI of vitamin D?
5. The population of the United States, according to the 2000 census, was 281.4 million people.
   a. How many significant figures does this number have?
   b. What is the unit in this quantity?
   c. Express this quantity in proper scientific notation.
6. The United States produces 34,800,000,000 lb of sugar each year, and much of it is exported to other countries.
   a. How many significant figures does this number have?
   b. What is the unit in this quantity?
   c. Express this quantity in proper scientific notation.
7. Construct a conversion factor that can convert from one unit to the other in each pair of units.
   a. from millimeters to kilometers
   b. from kilograms to micrograms
   c. from centimeters to micrometers
8. Construct a conversion factor that can convert from one unit to the other in each pair of units.
   a. from kilometers to micrometers
   b. from decaliters to milliliters
   c. from megagrams to milligrams
9. What is the density of a dextrose solution if 355 mL of the solution has a mass of 406.9 g?
10. What is the density of a dental amalgam (an alloy used to fill cavities) if 1.005 kg of the material has a volume of 433 mL? Express your final answer in grams per milliliter.

For Exercises 11–16, see the accompanying table for the relationships between English and SI units.

1 m ≈ 39.36 in. ≈ 3.28 ft ≈ 1.09 yd
1 cm ≈ 2.54 in.
1 km ≈ 0.62 mi
1 kg ≈ 2.20 lb
1 lb ≈ 454 g
1 L ≈ 1.06 qt
1 qt ≈ 0.946 L

11. Approximately how many inches are in 4.76 m?
12. Approximately how many liters are in 1 gal, which is exactly 4 qt?
13. Approximately how many kilograms are in a person who weighs 170 lb?
14. The average distance between Earth and the sun is 9.3×10^7 mi. How many kilometers is that?
15. Show mathematically that 1 L equals 1 dm^3.
16. Show mathematically that 1 L equals 1,000 cm^3.

ANSWERS

1. 282 g
3. 650 mg
5. a. four significant figures
   b. people
   c. 2.841×10^8 people
7. a. $\frac{1\ \text{km}}{10^6\ \text{mm}}$
   b. $\frac{10^9\ \mu\text{g}}{1\ \text{kg}}$
   c. $\frac{10^4\ \mu\text{m}}{1\ \text{cm}}$
9. 1.15 g/mL
11. 187 in.
13. 77 kg
15. $1\ \text{L} = 0.001\ \text{m}^3 \times \left(\frac{1\ \text{dm}}{0.1\ \text{m}}\right)^3 = 1\ \text{dm}^3$

CHAPTER 2

Elements, Atoms, and the Periodic Table

Opening Essay

The hardest material in the human body is tooth enamel. It has to be hard so that our teeth can serve us for a lifetime of biting and chewing; however, tough as it is, tooth enamel is susceptible to chemical attack. Acids found in some foods or made by bacteria that feed on food residues on our teeth are capable of dissolving enamel. Unprotected by enamel, a tooth will start to decay, thus developing cavities and other dental problems.

In the early 1900s, a dentist in Colorado Springs, Colorado, noted that many people who lived in the area had brown-stained teeth that, while unsightly, were surprisingly resistant to decay. After years of study, excess fluorine compounds in the drinking water were discovered to be the cause of both these effects. Research continued, and in the 1930s, the US Public Health Service found that low levels of fluorine in water would provide the benefit of resisting decay without discoloring teeth.

The protective effects of fluorine have a simple chemical explanation. Tooth enamel consists mostly of a mineral called hydroxyapatite, which is composed of calcium, phosphorus, oxygen, and hydrogen. We know now that fluorine combines with hydroxyapatite to make *fluorapatite*, which is more resistant to acidic decay than hydroxyapatite is. Currently about 50% of the US population drinks water that has some fluorine added (in the form of sodium fluoride, NaF) to reduce tooth decay. This intentional *fluoridation*, coupled with the use of fluoride-containing toothpastes and improved oral hygiene, has reduced tooth decay by as much as 60% in children. The nationwide reduction of tooth decay has been cited as an important public health advance in history. (Another important advance was the eradication of polio.)

Just as a language has an alphabet from which words are built, chemistry has an alphabet from which matter is described. However, the chemical alphabet is larger than the one we use for spelling. You may have already figured out that the chemical alphabet consists of the chemical elements. Their role is central to chemistry, for they combine to form the millions and millions of known compounds.

1. THE ELEMENTS

LEARNING OBJECTIVES

1. **Define a chemical element and give examples of the abundance of different elements.**
2. **Represent a chemical element with a chemical symbol.**

An element, as defined in Chapter 1, is a substance that cannot be broken down into simpler chemical substances. There are about 90 naturally occurring elements known on Earth. Using technology, scientists have been able to create nearly 30 additional elements that do not occur in nature. Today, chemistry recognizes 118 elements—some of which were created an atom at a time. Figure 2.1 shows some of the chemical elements.

FIGURE 2.1 Samples of Elements

Gold is a yellowish solid, iron is a silvery solid, whle mercury is a silvery liquid at room temperature.

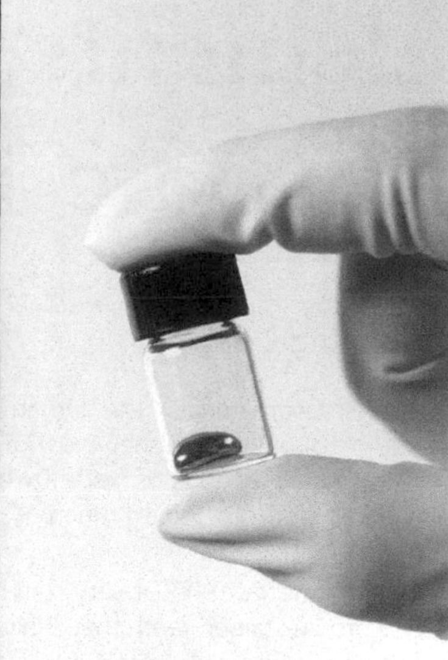

1.1 Abundance

The elements vary widely in abundance. In the universe as a whole, the most common element is hydrogen (about 90% of atoms), followed by helium (most of the remaining 10%). All other elements are present in relatively minuscule amounts, as far as we can detect.

On the planet Earth, however, the situation is rather different. Oxygen makes up 46.1% of the mass of Earth's crust (the relatively thin layer of rock forming Earth's surface), mostly in combination with other elements, while silicon makes up 28.5%. Hydrogen, the most abundant element in the universe, makes up only 0.14% of Earth's crust. Table 2.1 lists the relative abundances of elements on Earth as a whole and in Earth's crust. Table 2.2 lists the relative abundances of elements in the human body. If you compare Table 2.1 and Table 2.2, you will find disparities between the percentage of each element in the human body and on Earth. Oxygen has the highest percentage in both cases, but carbon, the element with the second highest percentage in the body, is relatively rare on Earth and does not even appear as a separate entry in Table 2.1; carbon is part of the 0.174% representing "other" elements. How does the human body concentrate so many apparently rare elements?

TABLE 2.1 Elemental Composition of Earth

Earth's Crust		Earth (overall)	
Element	Percentage	Element	Percentage
oxygen	46.1	iron	34.6
silicon	28.2	oxygen	29.5
aluminum	8.23	silicon	15.2
iron	5.53	magnesium	12.7
calcium	4.15	nickel	2.4
sodium	2.36	sulfur	1.9
magnesium	2.33	all others	3.7
potassium	2.09		
titanium	0.565		
hydrogen	0.14		
phosphorus	0.105		
all others	0.174		

Source: D. R. Lide, ed. CRC Handbook of Chemistry and Physics, 89th ed. (Boca Raton, FL: CRC Press, 2008–9), 14–17.

TABLE 2.2 Elemental Composition of a Human Body

Element	Percentage by Mass
oxygen	61
carbon	23
hydrogen	10
nitrogen	2.6
calcium	1.4
phosphorus	1.1
sulfur	0.20
potassium	0.20
sodium	0.14
chlorine	0.12
magnesium	0.027
silicon	0.026
iron	0.006
fluorine	0.0037
zinc	0.0033
all others	0.174

Source: D. R. Lide, ed. CRC Handbook of Chemistry and Physics, 89th ed. (Boca Raton, FL: CRC Press, 2008–9), 7–24.

The relative amounts of elements in the body have less to do with their abundances on Earth than with their availability in a form we can assimilate. We obtain oxygen from the air we breathe and the water we drink. We also obtain hydrogen from water. On the other hand, although carbon is present in the atmosphere as carbon dioxide, and about 80% of the atmosphere is nitrogen, we obtain those two elements from the food we eat, not the air we breathe.

Looking Closer: Phosphorus, the Chemical Bottleneck

There is an element that we need more of in our bodies than is proportionately present in Earth's crust, and *this* element is not easily accessible. Phosphorus makes up 1.1% of the human body but only 0.105% of Earth's crust. We need phosphorus for our bones and teeth, and it is a crucial component of all living cells. Unlike carbon, which can be obtained from carbon dioxide, there is no phosphorus compound present in our surroundings that can serve as a convenient source. Phosphorus, then, is nature's bottleneck. Its availability limits the amount of life our planet can sustain.

Higher forms of life, such as humans, can obtain phosphorus by selecting a proper diet (plenty of protein); but lower forms of life, such as algae, must absorb it from the environment. When phosphorus-containing detergents were introduced in the 1950s, wastewater from normal household activities greatly increased the amount of phosphorus available to algae and other plant life. Lakes receiving this wastewater experienced sudden increases in growth of algae. When the algae died, concentrations of bacteria that ate the dead algae increased. Because of the large bacterial concentrations, the oxygen content of the water dropped, causing fish to die in large numbers. This process, called *eutrophication*, is considered a negative environmental impact.

Today, many detergents are made without phosphorus so the detrimental effects of eutrophication are minimized. You may even see statements to that effect on detergent boxes. It can be sobering to realize how much impact a single element can have on life—or the ease with which human activity can affect the environment.

1.2 Names and Symbols

Each element has a name. Some of these names date from antiquity, while others are quite new. Today, the names for new elements are proposed by their discoverers but must be approved by the International Union of Pure and Applied Chemistry, an international organization that makes recommendations concerning all kinds of chemical terminology.

Note

Today, new elements are usually named after famous scientists.

chemical symbol

A one- or two-letter abbreviation for an element.

The names of the elements can be cumbersome to write in full, especially when combined to form the names of compounds. Therefore, each element name is abbreviated as a one- or two-letter **chemical symbol**. By convention, the first letter of a chemical symbol is a capital letter, while the second letter (if there is one) is a lowercase letter. The first letter of the symbol is usually the first letter of the element's name, while the second letter is some other letter from the name. Some elements have symbols that derive from earlier, mostly Latin names, so the symbols may not contain any letters from the English name. Table 2.3 lists the names and symbols of some of the most familiar elements.

TABLE 2.3 Element Names and Symbols

aluminum	Al	magnesium	Mg
argon	Ar	manganese	Mn
arsenic	As	mercury	Hg*
barium	Ba	neon	Ne
bismuth	Bi	nickel	Ni
boron	B	nitrogen	N
bromine	Br	oxygen	O
calcium	Ca	phosphorus	P
carbon	C	platinum	Pt
chlorine	Cl	potassium	K*
chromium	Cr	silicon	Si
copper	Cu*	silver	Ag*
fluorine	F	sodium	Na*
gold	Au*	strontium	Sr
helium	He	sulfur	S
hydrogen	H	tin	Sn*
iron	Fe	tungsten	W†
iodine	I	uranium	U
lead	Pb*	zinc	Zn
lithium	Li	zirconium	Zr
***The symbol comes from the Latin name of element.**			
†The symbol for tungsten comes from its German name—*wolfram*.			

Note

Element names in languages other than English are often close to their Latin names. For example, gold is *oro* in Spanish and *or* in French (close to the Latin *aurum*), tin is *estaño* in Spanish (compare to *stannum*), lead is *plomo* in Spanish and *plomb* in French (compare to *plumbum*), silver is *argent* in French (compare to *argentum*), and iron is *fer* in French and *hierro* in Spanish (compare to *ferrum*). The closeness is even more apparent in pronunciation than in spelling.

EXAMPLE 1

Write the chemical symbol for each element without consulting Table 2.3.

1. bromine
2. boron
3. carbon
4. calcium
5. gold

Solution

1. Br
2. B
3. C
4. Ca
5. Au

SKILL-BUILDING EXERCISE

Write the chemical symbol for each element without consulting Table 2.3.

1. manganese
2. magnesium
3. neon
4. nitrogen
5. silver

EXAMPLE 2

What element is represented by each chemical symbol?

1. Na
2. Hg
3. P
4. K
5. I

Solution

1. sodium
2. mercury
3. phosphorus
4. potassium
5. iodine

SKILL-BUILDING EXERCISE

What element is represented by each chemical symbol?

1. Pb
2. Sn
3. U
4. O
5. F

CONCEPT REVIEW EXERCISES

1. What is an element?
2. Give some examples of how the abundance of elements varies.
3. Why are chemical symbols so useful? What is the source of the letter(s) for a chemical symbol?

ANSWERS

1. An element is the basic chemical building block of matter; it is the simplest chemical substance.
2. Elements vary from being a small percentage to more than 30% of the atoms around us.
3. Chemical symbols are useful to concisely represent the elements present in a substance. The letters usually come from the name of the element.

KEY TAKEAWAYS

- All matter is composed of elements.
- Chemical elements are represented by a one- or two-letter symbol.

EXERCISES

1. Which of the following substances are elements?
   a. sodium
   b. milk
   c. gold
   d. water
   e. air
   f. liquefied nitrogen
2. Which of the following substances are elements?
   a. paper
   b. electricity
   c. neon
   d. carbon
   e. wood
   f. concrete
3. Write the chemical symbol for each element.
   a. silver
   b. sulfur
   c. nitrogen
   d. neon
4. Write the chemical symbol for each element.
   a. bromine
   b. oxygen
   c. lithium
   d. boron
5. Explain why it is improper to write CO as the chemical symbol for cobalt.
6. Explain why it is improper to write NO as the chemical symbol for nobelium.
7. Complete the following table.

Element Symbol	Element Name
F	
Fe	
I	
Cr	
C	
P	

8. Complete the following table.

Element Symbol	Element Name
Mg	
Mn	
Ca	
Cl	
K	
Pt	

ANSWERS

1. a. element
   b. not an element
   c. element
   d. not an element
   e. not an element
   f. element
3. a. Ag
   b. S
   c. N
   d. Ne
5. By convention, the second letter in an element's symbol is always lowercase.
7.

Element Symbol	Element Name
F	fluorine
Fe	iron
I	iodine
Cr	chromium
C	carbon
P	phosphorus

2. ATOMIC THEORY

LEARNING OBJECTIVES

1. **Explain how all matter is composed of atoms.**
2. **Describe the modern atomic theory.**

Take some aluminum foil. Cut it in half. Now you have two smaller pieces of aluminum foil. Cut one of the pieces in half again. Cut one of those smaller pieces in half again. Continue cutting, making smaller and smaller pieces of aluminum foil.

It should be obvious that the pieces are still aluminum foil; they are just becoming smaller and smaller. But how far can you take this exercise, at least in theory? Can you continue cutting the aluminum foil into halves forever, making smaller and smaller pieces? Or is there some limit, some absolute smallest piece of aluminum foil? (Thought experiments like this—and the conclusions based on them—were debated as far back as the fifth century BC.)

The **modern atomic theory**, proposed about 1803 by the English chemist John Dalton (Figure 2.2), is a fundamental concept that states that all elements are composed of atoms. In Chapter 1, we defined an atom as the smallest part of an element that maintains the identity of that element. Individual atoms are extremely small; even the largest atom has an approximate diameter of only 5.4×10^{-10} m. With that size, it takes over 18 million of these atoms, lined up side by side, to equal the width of your little finger (about 1 cm).

modern atomic theory

The fundamental concept that all elements are composed of atoms.

Most elements in their pure form exist as individual atoms. For example, a macroscopic chunk of iron metal is composed, microscopically, of individual atoms. Some elements, however, exist as groups of atoms called molecules, as discussed in Chapter 1. Several important elements exist as two-atom combinations and are called **diatomic molecules**. In representing a diatomic molecule, we use the symbol of the element and include the subscript 2 to indicate that two atoms of that element are joined together. The elements that exist as diatomic molecules are hydrogen (H_2), oxygen (O_2), nitrogen (N_2), fluorine (F_2), chlorine (Cl_2), bromine (Br_2), and iodine (I_2).

FIGURE 2.2
John Dalton

John Dalton was an English scientist who enunciated the modern atomic theory.

diatomic molecule

A two-atom grouping that behaves as a single chemical entity.

Looking Closer: Atomic Theory

Dalton's ideas are called the *modern* atomic theory because the concept of atoms is very old. The Greek philosophers Leucippus and Democritus originally introduced atomic concepts in the fifth century BC. (The word *atom* comes from the Greek word *atomos*, which means "indivisible" or "uncuttable.") Dalton had something that the ancient Greek philosophers didn't have, however; he had experimental evidence, such as the formulas of simple chemicals and the behavior of gases. In the 150 years or so before Dalton, natural philosophy had been maturing into modern science, and the scientific method was being used to study nature. So when Dalton announced a modern atomic theory, he was proposing a fundamental theory to describe many previous observations of the natural world; he was not just participating in a philosophical discussion.

CONCEPT REVIEW EXERCISES

1. What is the modern atomic theory?
2. What are atoms?

ANSWERS

1. The modern atomic theory states that all matter is composed of atoms.
2. Atoms are the smallest parts of an element that maintain the identity of that element.

KEY TAKEAWAYS

- Atoms are the ultimate building blocks of all matter.
- The modern atomic theory establishes the concepts of atoms and how they compose matter.

EXERCISES

1. Which of the following elements exist as diatomic molecules?
   a. helium
   b. hydrogen
   c. iodine
   d. gold
2. Which of the following elements exist as diatomic molecules?
   a. chlorine
   b. potassium
   c. silver
   d. oxygen
3. Why is it proper to represent the elemental form of helium as He but improper to represent the elemental form of hydrogen as H?
4. Why is it proper to represent the elemental form of chlorine as Cl_2 but improper to represent the elemental form of calcium as Ca_2?

ANSWERS

1. a. no
   b. yes
   c. yes
   d. no
3. Hydrogen exists as a diatomic molecule in its elemental form; helium does not exist as a diatomic molecule.

3. THE STRUCTURE OF ATOMS

LEARNING OBJECTIVES

1. **Describe the three main subatomic particles.**
2. **State how the subatomic particles are arranged in atoms.**

There have been several minor but important modifications to Dalton's atomic theory. For one thing, Dalton considered atoms to be indivisible. We know now that atoms not only can be divided but also are composed of three different kinds of particles with their own properties that are different from the chemical properties of atoms.

3.1 Subatomic Particles

The first subatomic particle was identified in 1897 and called the **electron**. It is an extremely tiny particle, with a mass of about 9.109×10^{-31} kg. Experiments with magnetic fields showed that the electron has a negative electrical charge.

By 1920, experimental evidence indicated the existence of a second particle. A **proton** has the same amount of charge as an electron, but its charge is positive, not negative. Another major difference between a proton and an electron is mass. Although still incredibly small, the mass of a proton is 1.673×10^{-27} kg, which is almost 2,000 times greater than the mass of an electron. Because opposite charges attract each other (while like charges repel each other), protons attract electrons (and vice versa).

Finally, additional experiments pointed to the existence of a third particle. Evidence produced in 1932 established the existence of the **neutron**, a particle with about the same mass as a proton but with no electrical charge.

We understand now that all atoms can be broken down into subatomic particles: protons, neutrons, and electrons. Table 2.4 lists some of their important characteristics and the symbols used to represent each particle.

electron

A subatomic particle with a negative electric charge.

proton

A subatomic particle with a positive charge.

neutron

A subatomic particle with no electric charge.

TABLE 2.4 Properties of the Subatomic Particles

Particle	Symbol	Mass (kg)	Relative Mass (proton = 1)	Relative Charge
proton	p^+	1.673×10^{-27}	1	+1
neutron	n^0	1.675×10^{-27}	1	0
electron	e^-	9.109×10^{-31}	0.00055	−1

3.2 The Nucleus

How are these subatomic particles arranged? Between 1909 and 1911, Ernest Rutherford, a Cambridge physicist, and his associates Hans Geiger and Ernest Marsden performed experiments that provided strong evidence concerning the internal structure of an atom. They took a very thin metal foil, such as gold or platinum, and aimed a beam of positively charged particles (called alpha particles, which are combinations of two protons and two neutrons) from a radioactive source toward the foil. Surrounding the foil was a detector—either a scintillator (a material that glows when hit by such particles) or some unexposed film (which is exposed where the particles hit it). The detector allowed the scientists to determine the distribution of the alpha particles after they interacted with the foil. Figure 2.3 shows a diagram of the experimental setup.

FIGURE 2.3 The Geiger-Marsden Experimental Setup

Experiments using this setup were used to investigate the structure of atoms.

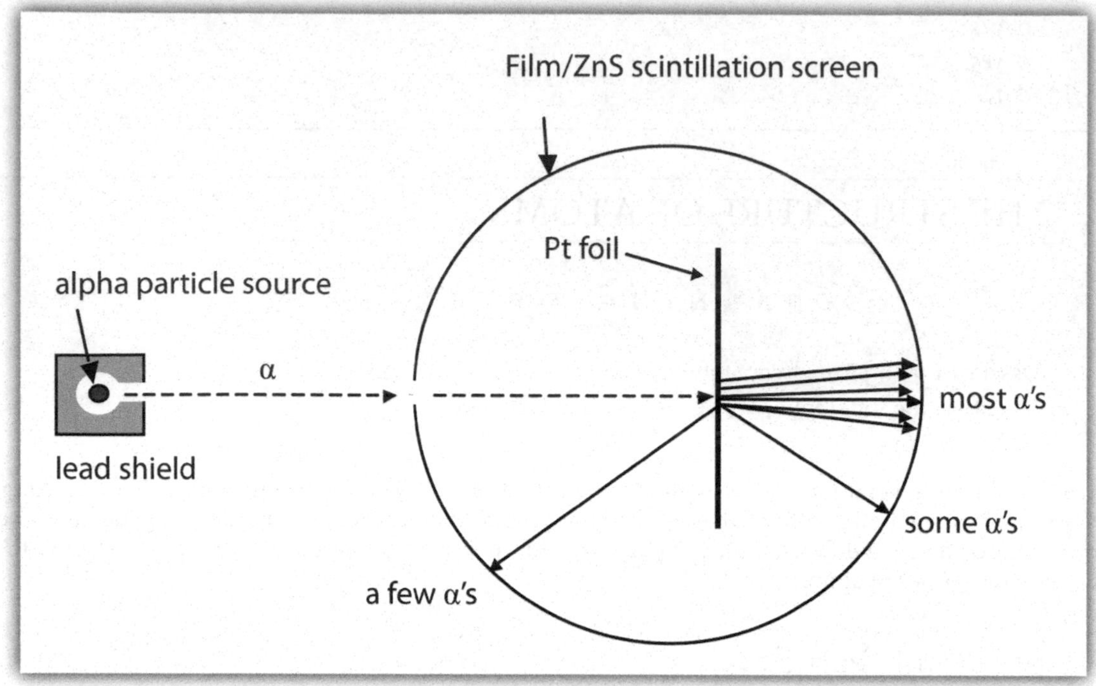

Most of the particles traveled straight through the foil, but some alpha particles were deflected off to one side. Some were even deflected back toward the source. This was unexpected. Rutherford once said, "It was almost as incredible as if you fired a 15-inch shell at a piece of tissue paper and it came back and hit you."

nucleus

The central part of an atom that contains protons and neutrons.

Rutherford proposed the following model to explain these experimental results. Protons and neutrons are concentrated in a central region he called the **nucleus** (plural, *nuclei*) of the atom. Electrons are outside the nucleus and orbit about it because they are attracted to the positive charge in the nucleus. Most of the mass of an atom is in the nucleus, while the orbiting electrons account for an atom's size. As a result, an atom consists largely of empty space. Rutherford called his description the "planetary model" of the atom. Figure 2.4 shows how this model explains the experimental results.

FIGURE 2.4 Rutherford's Metal-Foil Experiments

Rutherford explained the results of the metal-foil experiments by proposing that most of the mass and the positive charge of an atom are located in its nucleus, while the relatively low-mass electrons orbit about the nucleus. Most alpha particles go straight through the empty space, a few particles are deflected, and fewer still ricochet back toward the source. The nucleus is much smaller proportionately than depicted here.

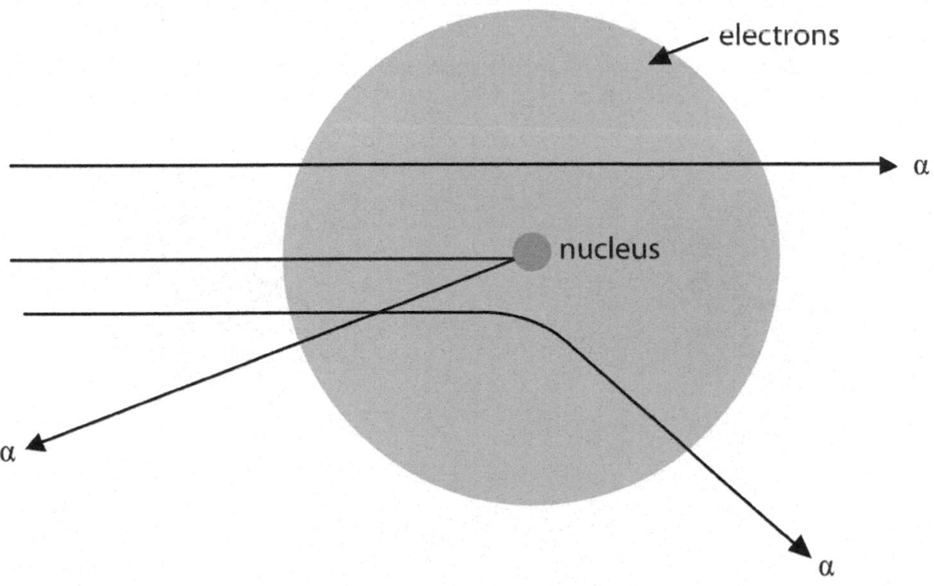

> **Note**
>
> The planetary model of the atom replaced the plum pudding model, which had electrons floating around aimlessly like plums in a "pudding" of positive charge.

Rutherford's model is essentially the same model that we use today to describe atoms but with one important modification. The planetary model suggests that electrons occupy certain specific, circular orbits about the nucleus. We know now that this model is overly simplistic. A better description is that electrons form fuzzy clouds around nuclei. Figure 2.5 shows a more modern version of our understanding of atomic structure.

FIGURE 2.5 A Modern Depiction of Atomic Structure

A more modern understanding of atoms, reflected in these representations of the electron in a hydrogen atom, is that electrons occupy regions of space about the nucleus; they are not in discrete orbits like planets around the sun. (a) The darker the color, the higher the probability that an electron will be at that point. (b) In a two-dimensional cross section of the electron in a hydrogen atom, the more crowded the dots, the higher the probability that an electron will be at that point. In both (a) and (b), the nucleus is in the center of the diagram.

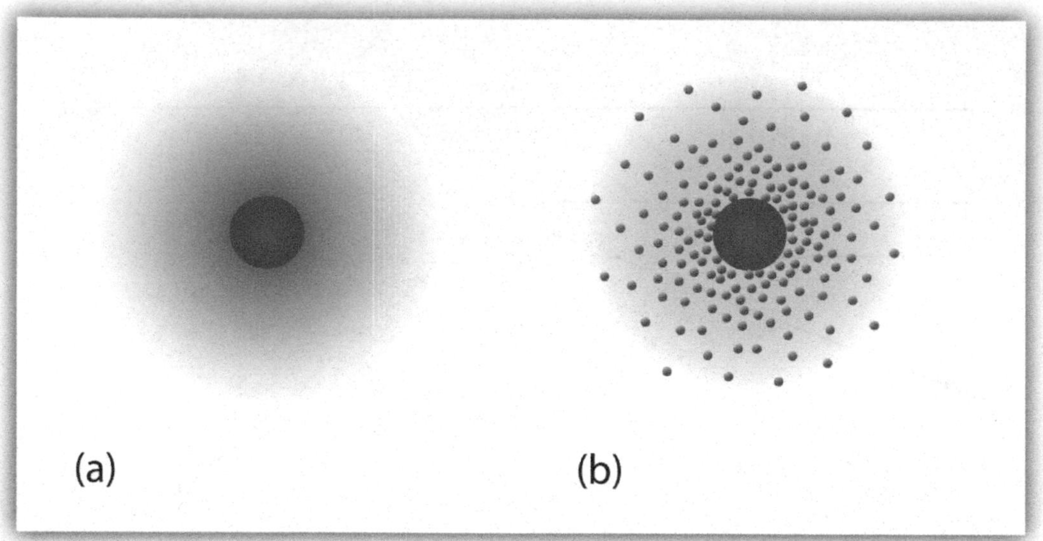

CONCEPT REVIEW EXERCISES

1. What are the charges and the relative masses of the three subatomic particles?
2. Describe the structure of an atom in terms of its protons, neutrons, and electrons.

ANSWERS

1. proton: +1, large; neutron: 0, large; electron: −1, small
2. Protons and neutrons are located in a central nucleus, while electrons orbit about the nucleus.

KEY TAKEAWAYS

- Atoms are composed of three main subatomic particles: protons, neutrons, and electrons.
- Protons and neutrons are grouped together in the nucleus of an atom, while electrons orbit about the nucleus.

EXERCISES

1. Which is smaller—an electron or a helium atom?
2. Which is larger—a proton or an atom of lead?
3. Which subatomic particle has a positive charge? Which subatomic particle has a negative charge?
4. Which subatomic particle is electrically neutral? Does it exist inside or outside the nucleus?
5. Protons are among the (most, least) massive subatomic particles, and they are found (inside, outside) the nucleus.
6. Electrons are among the (most, least) massive subatomic particles, and they are found (inside, outside) the nucleus.

7. Describe why Rutherford used the term *planetary model* to describe his model of atomic structure.
8. Why is the planetary model not an appropriate way to describe the structure of an atom?
9. What happened to most of the alpha particles in Rutherford's experiment? Explain why that happened.
10. Electrons account for the (majority, minority) of the (mass, volume) of an atom.

ANSWERS

1. An electron is smaller.
3. proton; electron
5. most; inside
7. Electrons are in orbit about the nucleus.
9. Most of the alpha particles went through the metal sheet because atoms are mostly empty space.

4. NUCLEI OF ATOMS

LEARNING OBJECTIVES

1. **Define and differentiate between the atomic number and the mass number of an element.**
2. **Explain how isotopes differ from one another.**

Now that we know how atoms are generally constructed, what do atoms of any particular element look like? How many protons, neutrons, and electrons are in a specific kind of atom?

First, if an atom is electrically neutral overall, then the number of protons equals the number of electrons. Because these particles have the same but opposite charges, equal numbers cancel out, producing a neutral atom.

4.1 Atomic Number

In the 1910s, experiments with X rays led to this useful conclusion: the magnitude of the positive charge in the nucleus of every atom of a particular element is the same. In other words, all atoms of the same element have the same number of protons. Furthermore, different elements have a different number of protons in their nuclei, so the number of protons in the nucleus of an atom is characteristic of a particular element. This discovery was so important to our understanding of atoms that the number of protons in the nucleus of an atom is called the **atomic number**.

atomic number

The number of protons in the nucleus of an atom.

For example, hydrogen has the atomic number 1; all hydrogen atoms have 1 proton in their nuclei. Helium has the atomic number 2; all helium atoms have 2 protons in their nuclei. There is no such thing as a hydrogen atom with 2 protons in its nucleus; a nucleus with 2 protons would be a helium atom. The atomic number *defines* an element. Chapter 21 lists the elements and their atomic numbers. From this table, you can determine the number of protons in the nucleus of any element. The largest atoms have over 100 protons in their nuclei.

EXAMPLE 3

What is the number of protons in the nucleus of each element? (Use the table in Chapter 21.)

1. aluminum
2. iron
3. carbon

Solution

1. According to the table, aluminum has an atomic number of 13. Therefore, every aluminum atom has 13 protons in its nucleus.
2. Iron has an atomic number of 26. Therefore, every iron atom has 26 protons in its nucleus.
3. Carbon has an atomic number of 6. Therefore, every carbon atom has 6 protons in its nucleus.

SKILL-BUILDING EXERCISE

What is the number of protons in the nucleus of each element? (Use the table in Chapter 21.)

1. sodium
2. oxygen
3. chlorine

How many electrons are in an atom? Previously we said that for an electrically neutral atom, the number of electrons equals the number of protons, so the total opposite charges cancel. Thus, the atomic number of an element also gives the number of electrons in an atom of that element. (Later we will find that some elements may gain or lose electrons from their atoms, so those atoms will no longer be electrically neutral. Thus we will need a way to differentiate the number of electrons for those elements.)

EXAMPLE 4

How many electrons are present in the atoms of each element?

1. sulfur
2. tungsten
3. argon

Solution

1. The atomic number of sulfur is 16. Therefore, in a neutral atom of sulfur, there are 16 electrons.
2. The atomic number of tungsten is 74. Therefore, in a neutral atom of tungsten, there are 74 electrons.
3. The atomic number of argon is 18. Therefore, in a neutral atom of argon, there are 18 electrons.

SKILL-BUILDING EXERCISE

How many electrons are present in the atoms of each element?

1. magnesium
2. potassium
3. iodine

4.2 Isotopes

isotopes

Atoms of the same element that have different numbers of neutrons.

How many neutrons are in atoms of a particular element? At first it was thought that the number of neutrons in a nucleus was also characteristic of an element. However, it was found that atoms of the same element can have *different* numbers of neutrons. Atoms of the same element that have different numbers of neutrons are called **isotopes**. For example, 99% of the carbon atoms on Earth have 6 neutrons and 6 protons in their nuclei; about 1% of the carbon atoms have 7 neutrons in their nuclei.

Naturally occurring carbon on Earth, therefore, is actually a mixture of isotopes, albeit a mixture that is 99% carbon with 6 neutrons in each nucleus.

An important series of isotopes is found with hydrogen atoms. Most hydrogen atoms have a nucleus with only a single proton. About 1 in 10,000 hydrogen nuclei, however, also has a neutron; this particular isotope is called *deuterium*. An extremely rare hydrogen isotope, *tritium*, has 1 proton and 2 neutrons in its nucleus. Figure 2.6 compares the three isotopes of hydrogen.

FIGURE 2.6 Isotopes of Hydrogen

Most hydrogen atoms have only a proton in the nucleus (a). A small amount of hydrogen exists as the isotope deuterium, which has one proton and one neutron in its nucleus (b). A tiny amount of the hydrogen isotope tritium, with one proton and two neutrons in its nucleus, also exists on Earth (c). The nuclei and electrons are proportionately much smaller than depicted here.

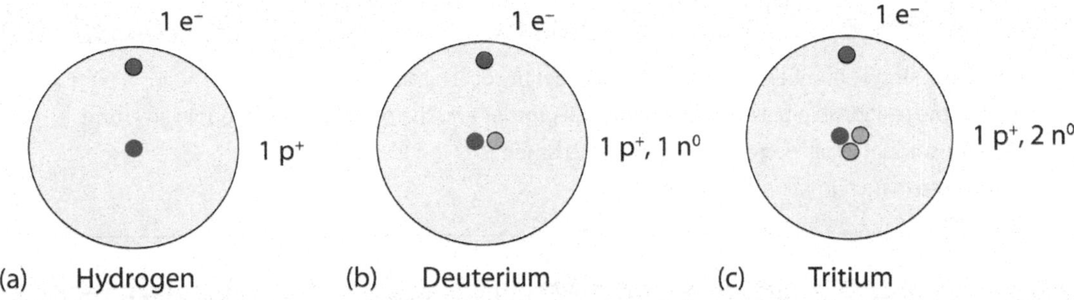

Note

The discovery of isotopes required a minor change in Dalton's atomic theory. Dalton thought that all atoms of the same element were exactly the same.

Most elements exist as mixtures of isotopes. In fact, there are currently over 3,500 isotopes known for all the elements. When scientists discuss individual isotopes, they need an efficient way to specify the number of neutrons in any particular nucleus. The **mass number** of an atom is the sum of the numbers of protons and neutrons in the nucleus. Given the mass number for a nucleus (and knowing the atomic number of that particular atom), you can determine the number of neutrons by subtracting the atomic number from the mass number.

mass number

The sum of the numbers of protons and neutrons in a nucleus of an atom.

A simple way of indicating the mass number of a particular isotope is to list it as a superscript on the left side of an element's symbol. Atomic numbers are often listed as a subscript on the left side of an element's symbol. Thus, we might see

$$\begin{matrix}\text{mass number}\rightarrow \\ \text{atomic number}\rightarrow\end{matrix}\ {}^{56}_{26}\text{Fe}$$

which indicates a particular isotope of iron. The 26 is the atomic number (which is the same for all iron atoms), while the 56 is the mass number of the isotope. To determine the number of neutrons in this isotope, we subtract 26 from 56: 56 − 26 = 30, so there are 30 neutrons in this atom.

EXAMPLE 5

How many protons and neutrons are in each atom?

1. ${}^{35}_{17}\text{Cl}$
2. ${}^{127}_{53}\text{I}$

Solution

1. In ${}^{35}_{17}\text{Cl}$, there are 17 protons, and 35 − 17 = 18 neutrons in each nucleus.
2. In ${}^{127}_{53}\text{I}$, there are 53 protons, and 127 − 53 = 74 neutrons in each nucleus.

SKILL-BUILDING EXERCISE

How many protons and neutrons are in each atom?

1. $^{197}_{79}Au$
2. $^{23}_{11}Na$

It is not absolutely necessary to indicate the atomic number as a subscript because each element has its own unique atomic number. Many isotopes are indicated with a superscript only, such as ^{13}C or ^{235}U. You may also see isotopes represented in print as, for example, carbon-13 or uranium-235.

CONCEPT REVIEW EXERCISES

1. Why is the atomic number so important to the identity of an atom?
2. What is the relationship between the number of protons and the number of electrons in an atom?
3. How do isotopes of an element differ from each other?
4. What is the mass number of an element?

ANSWERS

1. The atomic number defines the identity of an element.
2. In an electrically neutral atom, the number of protons equals the number of electrons.
3. Isotopes have different numbers of neutrons in their nuclei.
4. The mass number is the sum of the numbers of protons and neutrons in the nucleus of an atom.

KEY TAKEAWAYS

- Elements can be identified by their atomic number and mass number.
- Isotopes are atoms of the same element that have different masses.

EXERCISES

1. How many protons are in the nucleus of each element?
   a. radon
   b. tungsten
   c. chromium
   d. beryllium
2. How many protons are in the nucleus of each element?
   a. sulfur
   b. uranium
   c. calcium
   d. lithium
3. What are the atomic numbers of the elements in Exercise 1?
4. What are the atomic numbers of the elements in Exercise 2?
5. How many electrons are in neutral atoms of the elements in Exercise 1?
6. How many electrons are in neutral atoms of the elements in Exercise 2?
7. Complete the following table.

Number of Protons	Number of Neutrons	Element Name	Isotope Symbol
80	120		
			$^{55}_{26}Fe$
	2	hydrogen	

8. Complete the following table.

Number of Protons	Number of Neutrons	Element Name	Isotope Symbol
			${}^{3}_{2}He$
95	153		
	21	potassium	

9. State the number of protons, neutrons, and electrons in neutral atoms of each isotope.
   a. ${}^{131}I$
   b. ${}^{40}K$
   c. ${}^{201}Hg$
   d. ${}^{19}F$

10. State the number of protons, neutrons, and electrons in neutral atoms of each isotope.
    a. ${}^{3}H$
    b. ${}^{133}Cs$
    c. ${}^{56}Fe$
    d. ${}^{207}Pb$

11. What is the mass number of a gallium atom that has 38 neutrons in it?

12. What is the mass number of a uranium atom that has 143 neutrons in it?

13. Complete each sentence.
    a. ${}^{48}Ti$ has _____ neutrons.
    b. ${}^{40}Ar$ has _____ neutrons.
    c. ${}^{3}H$ has _____ neutrons.

14. Complete each sentence.
    a. ${}^{18}O$ has _____ neutrons.
    b. ${}^{60}Ni$ has _____ neutrons.
    c. ${}^{127}I$ has _____ neutrons.

ANSWERS

1. a. 86
   b. 74
   c. 24
   d. 4

3. 86, 74, 24, and 4

5. 86, 74, 24, and 4

7.

Number of Protons	Number of Neutrons	Element Name	Isotope Symbol
80	120	mercury	${}^{200}_{80}Hg$
26	29	iron	${}^{55}_{26}Fe$
1	2	hydrogen	${}^{3}_{1}H$

9. a. protons: 53; neutrons: 78; electrons: 53
   b. protons: 19; neutrons: 21; electrons: 19
   c. protons: 80; neutrons: 121; electrons: 80
   d. protons: 9; neutrons: 10; electrons: 9

11. 69

13. a. 26
    b. 22
    c. 2

5. ATOMIC MASSES

LEARNING OBJECTIVE

1. **Define atomic mass and atomic mass unit.**

Even though atoms are very tiny pieces of matter, they have mass. Their masses are so small, however, that chemists often use a unit other than grams to express them—the atomic mass unit.

The **atomic mass unit** (abbreviated u, although amu is also used) is defined as 1/12 of the mass of a ${}^{12}C$ atom:

atomic mass unit

One-twelfth the mass of a ${}^{12}C$ atom.

$$1\ u = \frac{1}{12}\ \text{the mass of}\ {}^{12}C\ \text{atom}$$

It is equal to 1.661×10^{-24} g.

atomic mass

A weighted average of the masses of all the element's naturally occurring isotopes.

Masses of other atoms are expressed with respect to the atomic mass unit. For example, the mass of an atom of ^{1}H is 1.008 u, the mass of an atom of ^{16}O is 15.995 u, and the mass of an atom of ^{32}S is 31.97 u. Note, however, that these masses are for particular isotopes of each element. Because most elements exist in nature as a mixture of isotopes, any sample of an element will actually be a mixture of atoms having slightly different masses (because neutrons have a significant effect on an atom's mass). How, then, do we describe the mass of a given element? By calculating an average of an element's atomic masses, weighted by the natural abundance of each isotope, we obtain a weighted average mass called the **atomic mass** (also commonly referred to as the *atomic weight*) of an element.

For example, boron exists as a mixture that is 19.9% ^{10}B and 80.1% ^{11}B. The atomic mass of boron would be calculated as (0.199 × 10.0 u) + (0.801 × 11.0 u) = 10.8 u. Similar average atomic masses can be calculated for other elements. Carbon exists on Earth as about 99% ^{12}C and about 1% ^{13}C, so the weighted average mass of carbon atoms is 12.01 u.

The table in Chapter 21 also lists the atomic masses of the elements.

EXAMPLE 6

What is the average mass of a carbon atom in grams?

Solution

This is a simple one-step conversion, similar to conversions we did in Chapter 1. We use the fact that 1 u = 1.661 × 10^{-24} g:

$$12.01\,\cancel{u} \times \frac{1.661 \times 10^{-24}\ \text{g}}{1\,\cancel{u}} = 1.995 \times 10^{-23}\ \text{g}$$

This is an extremely small mass, which illustrates just how small individual atoms are.

SKILL-BUILDING EXERCISE

1. What is the average mass of a tin atom in grams? The atomic mass of tin is 118.71 u.

CONCEPT REVIEW EXERCISES

1. Define atomic mass. Why is it considered a weighted average?
2. What is an atomic mass unit?

ANSWERS

1. The atomic mass is an average of an element's atomic masses, weighted by the natural abundance of each isotope of that element. It is a weighted average because different isotopes have different masses.
2. An atomic mass unit is 1/12th of the mass of a ^{12}C atom.

KEY TAKEAWAY

- Atoms have a mass that is based largely on the number of protons and neutrons in their nucleus.

EXERCISES

1. What is the atomic mass of zinc in atomic mass units?
2. What is the atomic mass of barium in atomic mass units?
3. What is the average mass of a single magnesium atom in grams?

4. What is the average mass of a single calcium atom in grams?
5. What is the mass of 1.00×10^{24} aluminum atoms in grams?
6. What is the mass of 5.00×10^{23} carbon atoms in grams?
7. Which has more mass—1 tungsten atom or 11 oxygen atoms?
8. Which has more mass—1 magnesium atom or 6 helium atoms?

ANSWERS

1. 65.4 u
3. 4.04×10^{-23} g
5. 44.8 g
7. 1 tungsten atom

6. ARRANGEMENTS OF ELECTRONS

LEARNING OBJECTIVE

1. **Describe how electrons are grouped within atoms.**

Although we have discussed the general arrangement of subatomic particles in atoms, we have said little about how electrons occupy the space about the nucleus. Do they move around the nucleus at random, or do they exist in some ordered arrangement?

The modern theory of electron behavior is called **quantum mechanics**. It makes the following statements about electrons in atoms:

- Electrons in atoms can have only certain specific energies. We say that the energies of the electrons are **quantized**.
- Electrons are organized according to their energies into sets called **shells**. Generally the higher the energy of a shell, the farther it is (on average) from the nucleus. Shells do not have specific, fixed distances from the nucleus, but an electron in a higher-energy shell will spend more time farther from the nucleus than does an electron in a lower-energy shell.
- Shells are further divided into subsets of electrons called **subshells**. The first shell has only one subshell, the second shell has two subshells, the third shell has three subshells, and so on. The subshells of each shell are labeled, in order, with the letters *s*, *p*, *d*, and *f*. Thus, the first shell has only an *s* subshell, the second shell has an *s* and a *p* subshell, the third shell has *s*, *p*, and *d* subshells, and so forth.
- Different subshells hold a different maximum number of electrons. Any *s* subshell can hold up to 2 electrons; *p*, 6; *d*, 10; and *f*, 14.

quantum mechanics

The modern theory of electron behavior.

quantized

Having a fixed value.

shell

A grouping of electrons within an atom.

subshell

A grouping of electrons within a shell.

It is the arrangement of electrons into shells and subshells that most concerns us here, so we will focus on that.

We use numbers to indicate which shell an electron is in. The first shell, closest to the nucleus and with the lowest-energy electrons, is shell 1. This first shell has only one subshell, which is labeled *s* and can hold a maximum of 2 electrons. We combine the shell and subshell labels when referring to the organization of electrons about a nucleus and use a superscript to indicate how many electrons are in a subshell. Thus, because a hydrogen atom has its single electron in the *s* subshell of the first shell, we use $1s^1$ to describe the electronic structure of hydrogen. This structure is called an **electron configuration**. Electron configurations are shorthand descriptions of the arrangements of electrons in atoms. The electron configuration of a hydrogen atom is spoken out loud as "one-ess-one."

electron configuration

A shorthand description of the arrangement of electrons in an atom.

Helium atoms have 2 electrons. Both electrons fit into the 1*s* subshell because *s* subshells can hold up to 2 electrons; therefore, the electron configuration for helium atoms is $1s^2$ (spoken as "one-ess-two").

The 1*s* subshell cannot hold 3 electrons (because an *s* subshell can hold a maximum of 2 electrons), so the electron configuration for a lithium atom cannot be $1s^3$. Two of the lithium electrons can fit into the 1*s* subshell, but the third electron must go into the second shell. The second shell has two subshells, *s* and *p*, which fill with electrons in that order. The 2*s* subshell holds a maximum of 2 electrons, and the

2*p* subshell holds a maximum of 6 electrons. Because lithium's final electron goes into the 2*s* subshell, we write the electron configuration of a lithium atom as $1s^22s^1$.

The next largest atom, beryllium, has 4 electrons, so its electron configuration is $1s^22s^2$. Now that the 2*s* subshell is filled, electrons in larger atoms start filling the 2*p* subshell. Thus, the electron configurations for the next six atoms are as follows:

B: $1s^22s^22p^1$
C: $1s^22s^22p^2$
N: $1s^22s^22p^3$
O: $1s^22s^22p^4$
F: $1s^22s^22p^5$
Ne: $1s^22s^22p^6$

With neon, the 2*p* subshell is completely filled. Because the second shell has only two subshells, atoms with more electrons now must begin the third shell. The third shell has three subshells, labeled *s*, *p*, and *d*. The *d* subshell can hold a maximum of 10 electrons. The first two subshells of the third shell are filled in order—for example, the electron configuration of aluminum, with 13 electrons, is $1s^22s^22p^63s^23p^1$. However, a curious thing happens after the 3*p* subshell is filled: the 4*s* subshell begins to fill before the 3*d* subshell does. In fact, the exact ordering of subshells becomes more complicated at this point (after argon, with its 18 electrons), so we will not consider the electron configurations of larger atoms.

A fourth subshell, the *f* subshell, is needed to complete the electron configurations for all elements. An *f* subshell can hold up to 14 electrons.

EXAMPLE 7

What is the electron configuration of a neutral phosphorus atom?

Solution

A neutral phosphorus atom has 15 electrons. Two electrons can go into the 1*s* subshell, 2 can go into the 2*s* subshell, and 6 can go into the 2*p* subshell. That leaves 5 electrons. Of those 5 electrons, 2 can go into the 3*s* subshell, and the remaining 3 electrons can go into the 3*p* subshell. Thus, the electron configuration of neutral phosphorus atoms is $1s^22s^22p^63s^23p^3$.

SKILL-BUILDING EXERCISE

1. What is the electron configuration of a neutral chlorine atom?

Chemistry results from interactions between the outermost shells of electrons on different atoms. Thus, it is convenient to separate electrons into two groups. **Valence shell electrons** (or, more simply, the *valence electrons*) are the electrons in the highest-numbered shell, or **valence shell**, while **core electrons** are the electrons in lower-numbered shells. We can see from the electron configuration of a carbon atom—$1s^22s^22p^2$—that it has 4 valence electrons ($2s^22p^2$) and 2 core electrons ($1s^2$).

valence shell electron

An electron in the highest-numbered shell of an atom.

valence shell

The highest-numbered shell of an atom that contains electrons.

core electron

An electron in a lower-numbered shell of an atom.

EXAMPLE 8

From the electron configuration of neutral phosphorus atoms in Example 7, how many valence electrons and how many core electrons does a neutral phosphorus atom have?

Solution

The highest-numbered shell is the third shell, which has 2 electrons in the 3*s* subshell and 3 electrons in the 3*p* subshell. That gives a total of 5 electrons, so neutral phosphorus atoms have 5 valence electrons. The 10 remaining electrons, from the first and second shells, are core electrons.

SKILL-BUILDING EXERCISE

1. From the electron configuration of neutral chlorine atoms (see the Skill-Building Exercise following Example 7), how many valence electrons and how many core electrons does a neutral chlorine atom have?

CONCEPT REVIEW EXERCISES

1. How are electrons organized in atoms?
2. What information does an electron configuration convey?
3. What is the difference between core electrons and valence electrons?

ANSWERS

1. Electrons are organized into shells and subshells around nuclei.
2. The electron configuration states the arrangement of electrons in shells and subshells.
3. Valence electrons are in the highest-numbered shell; all other electrons are core electrons.

KEY TAKEAWAY

- Electrons are organized into shells and subshells about the nucleus of an atom.

EXERCISES

1. What is the maximum number of electrons that can fit in an *s* subshell? Does it matter what shell the *s* subshell is in?
2. What is the maximum number of electrons that can fit in a *p* subshell? Does it matter what shell the *p* subshell is in?
3. What is the maximum number of electrons that can fit in a *d* subshell? Does it matter what shell the *d* subshell is in?
4. What is the maximum number of electrons that can fit in an *f* subshell? Does it matter what shell the *f* subshell is in?
5. What is the electron configuration of a carbon atom?
6. What is the electron configuration of a sulfur atom?
7. What is the valence shell electron configuration of a calcium atom?
8. What is the valence shell electron configuration of a selenium atom?
9. What atom has the electron configuration $1s^22s^22p^5$?
10. What atom has the electron configuration $1s^22s^22p^63s^23p^3$?
11. Draw a representation of the electronic structure of an oxygen atom.
12. Draw a representation of the electronic structure of a phosphorus atom.
13. A potassium atom has ____ core electrons and ____ valence electrons.
14. A silicon atom has ____ core electrons and ____ valence electrons.

ANSWERS

1. 2; no
3. 10; no
5. $1s^22s^22p^2$
7. $4s^2$
9. fluorine
11.

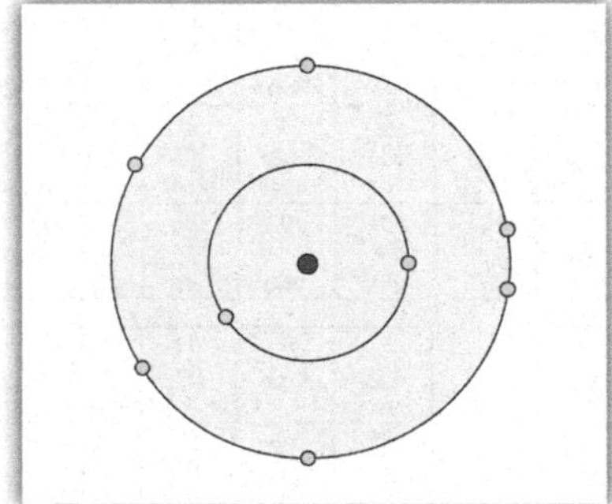

13. 18; 1

7. THE PERIODIC TABLE

LEARNING OBJECTIVES

1. Explain how elements are organized into the periodic table.
2. Describe how some characteristics of elements relate to their positions on the periodic table.

In the 19th century, many previously unknown elements were discovered, and scientists noted that certain sets of elements had similar chemical properties. For example, chlorine, bromine, and iodine react with other elements (such as sodium) to make similar compounds. Likewise, lithium, sodium, and potassium react with other elements (such as oxygen) to make similar compounds. Why is this so?

periodic table

A chart of elements that groups the elements by some of their properties.

In 1864, Julius Lothar Meyer, a German chemist, organized the elements by atomic mass and grouped them according to their chemical properties. Later that decade, Dmitri Mendeleev, a Russian chemist, organized all the known elements according to similar properties. He left gaps in his table for what he thought were undiscovered elements, and he made some bold predictions regarding the properties of those undiscovered elements. When elements were later discovered whose properties closely matched Mendeleev's predictions, his version of the table gained favor in the scientific community. Because certain properties of the elements repeat on a regular basis throughout the table (that is, they are periodic), it became known as the **periodic table**.

Note

Mendeleev had to list some elements out of the order of their atomic masses to group them with other elements that had similar properties.

The periodic table is one of the cornerstones of chemistry because it organizes all the known elements on the basis of their chemical properties. A modern version is shown in Figure 2.7. Most periodic tables provide additional data (such as atomic mass) in a box that contains each element's symbol. The elements are listed in order of atomic number.

FIGURE 2.7 A Modern Periodic Table

A modern periodic table lists elements left to right by atomic number.

B = Solids Hg = Liquids Kr = Gases Pm = Not found in nature

1	2	3	4	5	6	7	8	9	10	11	12	13	14	15	16	17	18
1 H 1.00794																	2 He 4.002602
3 Li 6.941	4 Be 9.012182											5 B 10.811	6 C 12.0107	7 N 14.00674	8 O 15.9994	9 F 18.9984032	10 Ne 20.1797
11 Na 22.989770	12 Mg 24.3050											13 Al 26.581538	14 Si 28.0855	15 P 30.973761	16 S 32.066	17 Cl 35.4527	18 Ar 39.948
19 K 39.0983	20 Ca 40.078	21 Sc 44.955910	22 Ti 47.867	23 V 50.9415	24 Cr 51.9961	25 Mn 54.938049	26 Fe 55.845	27 Co 58.933200	28 Ni 58.6534	29 Cu 63.545	30 Zn 65.39	31 Ga 69.723	32 Ge 72.61	33 As 74.92160	34 Se 78.96	35 Br 79.504	36 Kr 83.80
37 Rb 85.4678	38 Sr 87.62	39 Y 88.90585	40 Zr 91.224	41 Nb 92.90638	42 Mo 95.94	43 Tc (98)	44 Ru 101.07	45 Rh 102.90550	46 Pd 106.42	47 Ag 196.56655	48 Cd 112.411	49 In 114.818	50 Sn 118.710	51 Sb 121.760	52 Te 127.60	53 I 126.90447	54 Xe 131.29
55 Cs 132.90545	56 Ba 137.327	71 Lu 174.967	72 Hf 178.49	73 Ta 180.94.79	74 W 183.84	75 Re 186.207	76 Os 190.23	77 Ir 192.217	78 Pt 195.078	79 Au 196.56655	80 Hg 200.59	81 Tl 204.3833	82 Pb 207.2	83 Bi 208.58038	84 Po (209)	85 At (210)	86 Rn (222)
87 Fr (223)	88 Ra (226)	103 Lr (262)	104 Rf (261)	105 Db (262)	106 Sg (263)	107 Bh (262)	108 Hs (265)	109 Mt (266)	110 Ds (269)	111 Rg (272)	112 Cn (277)	113 Uut (277)	114 Uuq (277)	115 Uup (277)	116 Uuh (277)		118 Uuo (277)
			57 La 138.9055	58 Ce 140.116	59 Pr 140.50765	60 Nd 144.24	61 Pm (145)	62 Sm 150.36	63 Eu 151.964	64 Gd 157.25	65 Tb 158.92534	66 Dy 162.50	67 Ho 164.93032	68 Er 167.26	69 Tm 168.93421	70 Yb 173.04	
			89 Ac 232.0381	90 Th 232.0381	91 Pa 231.035888	92 U 238.0289	93 Np (237)	94 Pu (244)	95 Am (243)	96 Cm (247)	97 Bk (247)	98 Cf (251)	99 Es (252)	100 Fm (257)	101 Md (258)	102 No (259)	

7.1 Features of the Periodic Table

Elements that have similar chemical properties are grouped in columns called **groups (or families)**. As well as being numbered, some of these groups have names—for example, *alkali metals* (the first column of elements), *alkaline earth metals* (the second column of elements), *halogens* (the next-to-last column of elements), and *noble gases* (the last column of elements).

group (or family)

A column of elements on the periodic table.

Note

The word *halogen* comes from the Greek for "salt maker" because these elements combine with other elements to form a group of compounds called salts.

To Your Health: Radon

Radon is an invisible, odorless noble gas that is slowly released from the ground, particularly from rocks and soils whose uranium content is high. Because it is a noble gas, radon is not chemically reactive. Unfortunately, it is radioactive, and increased exposure to it has been correlated with an increased lung cancer risk.

Because radon comes from the ground, we cannot avoid it entirely. Moreover, because it is denser than air, radon tends to accumulate in basements, which if improperly ventilated can be hazardous to a building's inhabitants. Fortunately, specialized ventilation minimizes the amount of radon that might collect. Special fan-and-vent systems are available that draw air from below the basement floor, before it can enter the living space, and vent it above the roof of a house.

After smoking, radon is thought to be the second-biggest *preventable* cause of lung cancer in the United States. The American Cancer Society estimates that 10% of all lung cancers are related to radon exposure. There is uncertainty regarding what levels of exposure cause cancer, as well as what the exact causal agent might be (either radon or one of its breakdown products, many of which are also radioactive and, unlike radon, not gases). The US Environmental Protection Agency recommends testing every floor below the third floor for radon levels to guard against long-term health effects.

Each row of elements on the periodic table is called a **period**. Periods have different lengths; the first period has only 2 elements (hydrogen and helium), while the second and third periods have 8 elements each. The fourth and fifth periods have 18 elements each, and later periods are so long that a segment from each is removed and placed beneath the main body of the table.

period

A row of elements on the periodic table.

Certain elemental properties become apparent in a survey of the periodic table as a whole. Every element can be classified as either a metal, a nonmetal, or a semimetal, as shown in Figure 2.8. A **metal** is a substance that is shiny, typically (but not always) silvery in color, and an excellent conductor of electricity and heat. Metals are also malleable (they can be beaten into thin sheets) and ductile (they can be drawn into thin wires). A **nonmetal** is typically dull and a poor conductor of electricity and heat. Solid nonmetals are also very brittle. As shown in Figure 2.8, metals occupy the left three-fourths of the periodic table, while nonmetals (except for hydrogen) are clustered in the upper right-hand corner of the periodic table. The elements with properties intermediate between those of metals and nonmetals are called **semimetals (or metalloids)**. Elements adjacent to the bold line in the right-hand portion of the periodic table have semimetal properties.

metal

An element that is shiny, typically silvery in color, an excellent conductor of heat and electricity, malleable, and ductile.

nonmetal

An element that is typically dull, not a good conductor of heat and electricity, and brittle.

semimetal (or metalloid)

An element whose properties are intermediate between metals and nonmetals.

FIGURE 2.8 Types of Elements

Elements are either metals, nonmetals, or semimetals. Each group is located in a different part of the periodic table.

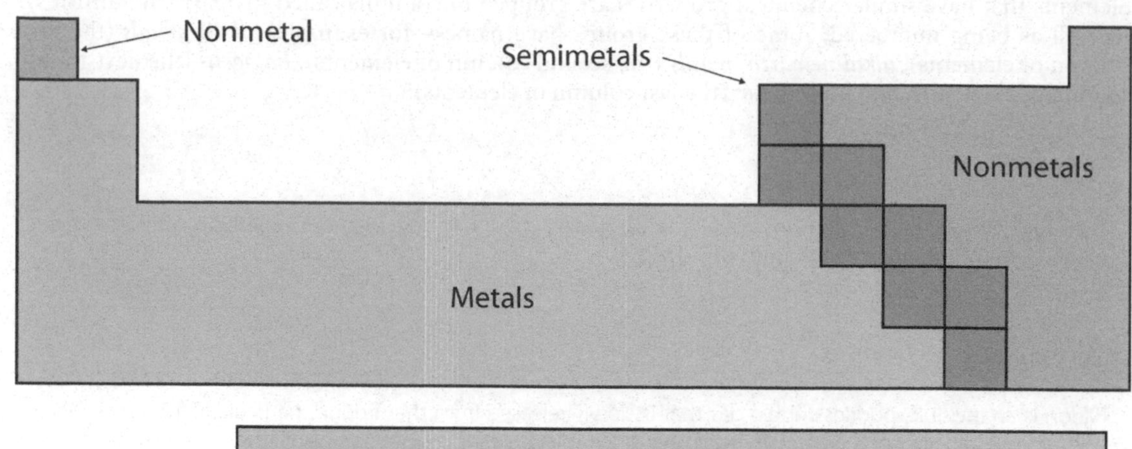

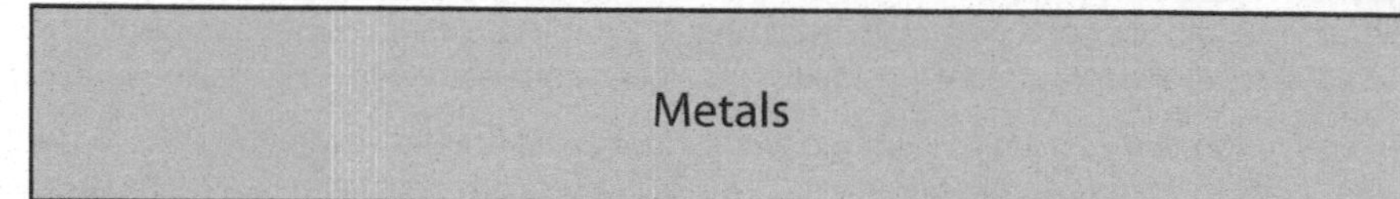

main group element

An element in the first two or the last six columns on the periodic table.

transition metal

An element between the main group elements on the periodic table.

inner transition metal

An element in the two rows beneath the main body on the periodic table. Such metals are also called the lanthanide and actinide elements.

Another way to categorize the elements of the periodic table is shown in Figure 2.9. The first two columns on the left and the last six columns on the right are called the **main group elements**. The ten-column block between these columns contains the **transition metals**. The two rows beneath the main body of the periodic table contain the **inner transition metals**. The elements in these two rows are also referred to as, respectively, the **lanthanide metals** and the **actinide metals**.

FIGURE 2.9 Special Names for Sections of the Periodic Table

Some sections of the periodic table have special names. The elements lithium, sodium, potassium, rubidium, cesium, and francium are collectively known as alkali metals.

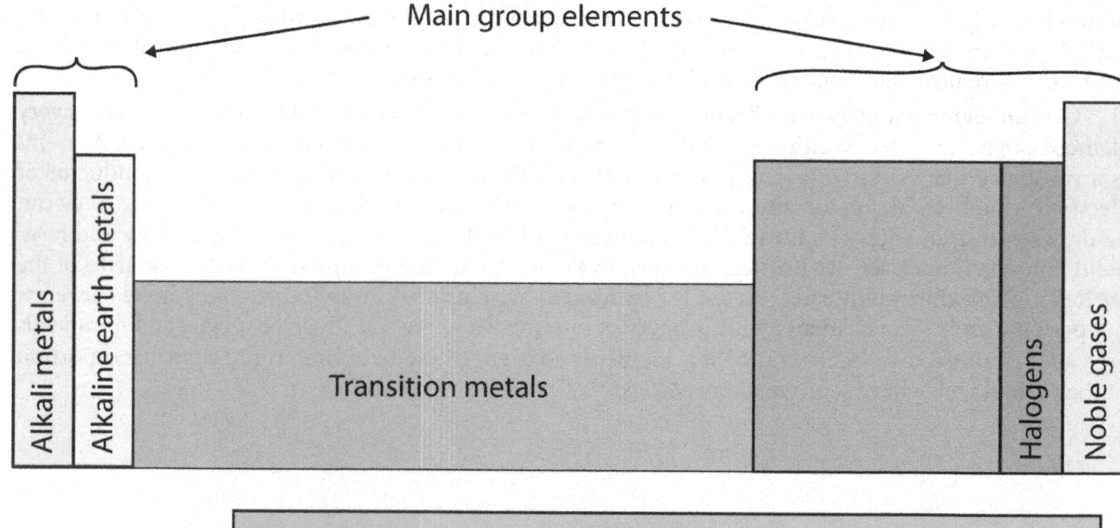

To Your Health: Transition Metals in the Body

According to Table 2.2, most of the elemental composition of the human body consists of main group elements. The first element appearing on the list that is not a main group element is iron, at 0.006 percentage by mass. Because iron has relatively massive atoms, it would appear even lower on a list organized in terms of percent by *atoms* rather than percent by mass.

Iron is a transition metal. Transition metals have interesting chemical properties, partially because some of their electrons are in *d* subshells. (For more information about electron shells, see Section 6.) The chemistry of iron makes it a key component in the proper functioning of red blood cells.

Red blood cells are cells that transport oxygen from the lungs to cells of the body and then transport carbon dioxide from the cells to the lungs. Without red blood cells, animal respiration as we know it would not exist. The critical part of the red blood cell is a protein called *hemoglobin*. Hemoglobin combines with oxygen and carbon dioxide, transporting these gases from one location to another in the body. Hemoglobin is a relatively large molecule, with a mass of about 65,000 u.

The crucial atom in the hemoglobin protein is iron. Each hemoglobin molecule has four iron atoms, which act as binding sites for oxygen. It is the presence of this particular transition metal in your red blood cells that allows you to use the oxygen you inhale.

Other transition metals have important functions in the body, despite being present in low amounts. Zinc is needed for the body's immune system to function properly, as well as for protein synthesis and tissue and cell growth. Copper is also needed for several proteins to function properly in the body. Manganese is needed for the body to metabolize oxygen properly. Cobalt is a necessary component of vitamin B-12, a vital nutrient. (For more information about proteins and vitamins, see Chapter 18.) These last three metals are not listed explicitly in Table 2.2, so they are present in the body in very small quantities. However, even these small quantities are required for the body to function properly.

The periodic table is organized on the basis of similarities in elemental properties, but what explains these similarities? It turns out that the shape of the periodic table reflects the filling of subshells with electrons, as shown in Figure 2.10. Starting with the first period and going from left to right, the table reproduces the order of filling of the electron subshells in atoms. Furthermore, elements in the same column share the same valence shell electron configuration. For example, all elements in the first column have a single *s* electron in their valence shells, so their electron configurations can be described as ns^1 (where *n* represents the shell number). This last observation is crucial. Chemistry is largely the result of interactions between the valence electrons of different atoms. Thus, atoms that have the same valence shell electron configuration will have similar chemistry.

FIGURE 2.10 The Shape of the Periodic Table

The shape of the periodic table reflects the order in which electron shells and subshells fill with electrons.

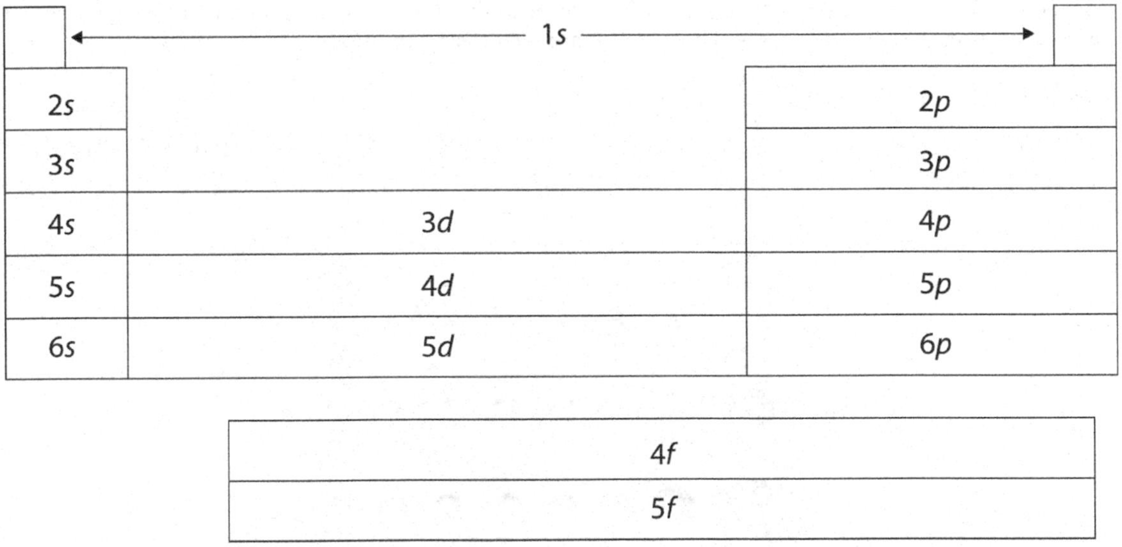

1*s*

2*s*		2*p*
3*s*		3*p*
4*s*	3*d*	4*p*
5*s*	4*d*	5*p*
6*s*	5*d*	6*p*

4*f*
5*f*

EXAMPLE 9

Using the variable *n* to represent the number of the valence electron shell, write the valence shell electron configuration for each group.

1. the alkaline earth metals
2. the column of elements headed by carbon

Solution

1. The alkaline earth metals are in the second column of the periodic table. This column corresponds to the *s* subshell being filled with 2 electrons. Therefore, the valence shell electron configuration is ns^2.
2. The electron configuration of carbon is $1s^22s^22p^2$. Its valence shell electron configuration is $2s^22p^2$. Every element in the same column should have a similar valence shell electron configuration, which we can represent as ns^2np^2.

SKILL-BUILDING EXERCISE

Using the variable *n* to represent the number of the valence electron shell, write the valence shell electron configuration for each group.

1. the halogens
2. the column of elements headed by oxygen

7.2 Atomic Radius

atomic radius

The approximate size of an atom.

The periodic table is useful for understanding atomic properties that show periodic trends. One such property is the **atomic radius** (Figure 2.11). As mentioned earlier, the higher the shell number, the farther from the nucleus the electrons in that shell are likely to be. In other words, the size of an atom is generally determined by the number of the valence electron shell. Therefore, as we go down a column on the periodic table, the atomic radius increases. As we go *across* a period on the periodic table, however, electrons are being added to the *same* valence shell; meanwhile, more protons are being added to the nucleus, so the positive charge of the nucleus is increasing. The increasing positive charge attracts the electrons more strongly, pulling them closer to the nucleus. Consequently, as we go across a period, the atomic radius decreases. These trends are seen clearly in Figure 2.11.

FIGURE 2.11 Trends on the Periodic Table

The relative sizes of the atoms show several trends with regard to the structure of the periodic table. Atoms become larger going down a column and smaller going across a period.

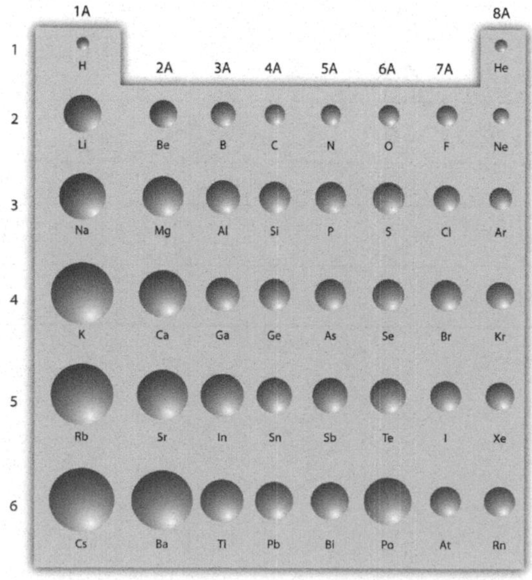

EXAMPLE 10

Using the periodic table (rather than Figure 2.11), which atom is larger?

1. N or Bi
2. Mg or Cl

Solution

1. Because Bi is below N on the periodic table and has electrons in higher-numbered shells, we expect that Bi atoms are larger than N atoms.
2. Both Mg and Cl are in period 3 of the periodic table, but Cl lies farther to the right. Therefore we expect Mg atoms to be larger than Cl atoms.

SKILL-BUILDING EXERCISE

Using the periodic table (rather than Figure 2.11), which atom is larger?

1. Li or F
2. Na or K

Career Focus: Clinical Chemist

Clinical chemistry is the area of chemistry concerned with the analysis of body fluids to determine the health status of the human body. Clinical chemists measure a variety of substances, ranging from simple elements such as sodium and potassium to complex molecules such as proteins and enzymes, in blood, urine, and other body fluids. The absence or presence, or abnormally low or high amounts, of a substance can be a sign of some disease or an indication of health. Many clinical chemists use sophisticated equipment and complex chemical reactions in their work, so they not only need to understand basic chemistry, but also be familiar with special instrumentation and how to interpret test results.

CONCEPT REVIEW EXERCISES

1. How are the elements organized into the periodic table?
2. Looking at the periodic table, where do the following elements appear?
   a. the metals
   b. the nonmetals
   c. the halogens
   d. the transition metals
3. Describe the trends in atomic radii as related to an element's position on the periodic table.

ANSWERS

1. Elements are organized by atomic number.
2. a. the left three-quarters of the periodic table
   b. the right quarter of the periodic table
   c. the next-to-last column of the periodic table
   d. the middle section of the periodic table
3. As you go across the periodic table, atomic radii decrease; as you go down the periodic table, atomic radii increase.

KEY TAKEAWAYS

- The chemical elements are arranged in a chart called the periodic table.
- Some characteristics of the elements are related to their position on the periodic table.

EXERCISES

1. Which elements have chemical properties similar to those of magnesium?
   a. sodium
   b. fluorine
   c. calcium
   d. barium
   e. selenium
2. Which elements have chemical properties similar to those of lithium?
   a. sodium
   b. calcium
   c. beryllium
   d. barium
   e. potassium
3. Which elements have chemical properties similar to those of chlorine?
   a. sodium
   b. fluorine
   c. calcium
   d. iodine
   e. sulfur
4. Which elements have chemical properties similar to those of carbon?
   a. silicon
   b. oxygen
   c. germanium
   d. barium
   e. argon
5. Which elements are alkali metals?
   a. sodium
   b. magnesium
   c. aluminum
   d. potassium
   e. calcium
6. Which elements are alkaline earth metals?
   a. sodium
   b. magnesium
   c. aluminum
   d. potassium
   e. calcium
7. Which elements are halogens?
   a. oxygen
   b. fluorine
   c. chlorine
   d. sulfur
   e. carbon
8. Which elements are noble gases?
   a. helium
   b. hydrogen
   c. oxygen
   d. neon
   e. chlorine
9. Which pairs of elements are located in the same period?
   a. H and Li
   b. H and He
   c. Na and S
   d. Na and Rb
10. Which pairs of elements are located in the same period?
    a. V and Nb
    b. K and Br
    c. Na and P
    d. Li and Mg
11. In each pair of atoms, which atom has the greater atomic radius?
    a. H and Li
    b. N and P
    c. Cl and Ar
    d. Al and Cl
12. In each pair of atoms, which atom has the greater atomic radius?
    a. H and He
    b. N and F
    c. Cl and Br
    d. Al and B
13. Scandium is a (metal, nonmetal, semimetal) and is a member of the (main group elements, transition metals).
14. Silicon is a (metal, nonmetal, semimetal) and is a member of the (main group elements, transition metals).

ANSWERS

1. a. no
   b. no
   c. yes
   d. yes
   e. no
3. a. no
   b. yes
   c. no
   d. yes
   e. no
5. a. yes
   b. no
   c. no
   d. yes
   e. no
7. a. no
   b. yes
   c. yes
   d. no
   e. no
9. a. no
   b. yes
   c. yes
   d. no
11. a. Li
    b. P
    c. Cl
    d. Al
13. metal; transition metals

8. END-OF-CHAPTER MATERIAL

Chapter Summary

To ensure that you understand the material in this chapter, you should review the meanings of the following bold terms and ask yourself how they relate to the topics in the chapter.

An element is a substance that cannot be broken down into simpler chemical substances. Only about 90 naturally occurring elements are known. They have varying abundances on Earth and in the body. Each element has a one- or two-letter **chemical symbol**.

The **modern atomic theory** states that the smallest piece of an element is an **atom**. Individual atoms are extremely small, on the order of 10^{-10} m across. Most elements exist in pure form as individual atoms, but some exist as **diatomic molecules**. Atoms themselves are composed of subatomic particles. The **electron** is a tiny subatomic particle with a negative charge. The **proton** has a positive charge and, while small, is much larger than the electron. The **neutron** is also much larger than an electron but has no electrical charge.

Protons, neutrons, and electrons have a specific arrangement in an atom. The protons and neutrons are found in the center of the atom, grouped together into a **nucleus**. The electrons are found in fuzzy clouds around the nucleus.

Each element has a characteristic number of protons in its nucleus. This number of protons is the **atomic number** of the element. An element may have different numbers of neutrons in the nuclei of its atoms; such atoms are referred to as **isotopes**. Two isotopes of hydrogen are deuterium, with a proton and a neutron in its nucleus, and tritium, with a proton and two neutrons in its nucleus. The sum of the numbers of protons and neutrons in a nucleus is called the **mass number** and is used to distinguish isotopes from each other.

Masses of individual atoms are measured in **atomic mass units**. An atomic mass unit is equal to 1/12th of the mass of a single carbon-12 atom. Because different isotopes of an element have different masses, the **atomic mass** of an element is a weighted average of the masses of all the element's naturally occurring isotopes.

The modern theory of electron behavior is called **quantum mechanics**. According to this theory, electrons in atoms can only have specific, or **quantized**, energies. Electrons are grouped into general regions called **shells**, and within these into more specific regions called **subshells**. There are four types of subshells, and each type can hold up to a maximum number of electrons. The distribution of electrons into shells and subshells is the **electron configuration** of an atom. Chemistry typically occurs because of interactions between the electrons of the outermost shell of different atoms, called the valence shell electrons. Electrons in inner shells are called core electrons.

Elements are grouped together by similar chemical properties into a chart called the **periodic table**. Vertical columns of elements are called **groups** or **families**. Some of the groups of elements have names, like the alkali metals, the alkaline earth metals, the halogens, and the noble gases. A horizontal row of elements is called a **period**. Periods and groups have differing numbers of elements in them. The periodic table separates elements into **metals**, **nonmetals**, and **semimetals**. The periodic table is also separated into **main group elements**, **transition metals**, **lanthanide elements**, and **actinide elements**. The lanthanide and actinide elements are also referred to as **inner transition metal elements**. The shape of the periodic table reflects the sequential filling of shells and subshells in atoms.

The periodic table helps us understand trends in some of the properties of atoms. One such property is the **atomic radius** of atoms. From top to bottom of the periodic table, atoms get bigger because electrons are occupying larger and bigger shells. From left to right across the periodic table, electrons are filling the same shell but are being attracted by an increasing positive charge from the nucleus, and thus the atoms get smaller.

ADDITIONAL EXERCISES

1. If the atomic radius of sodium atoms is 1.86 × 10^{-10} m, how many sodium atoms are needed to make a line that is 1.00 cm in length?
2. If the atomic radius of osmium atoms is 1.34 × 10^{-10} m, how many osmium atoms are needed to make a line that is 5.85 m in length?
3. What might be the electron configuration of K^+, an atom that has lost an electron?
4. What might be the electron configuration of Cl^-, an atom that has gained an additional electron?
5. The electron configuration of the Ti atom is $1s^22s^22p^63s^23p^64s^23d^2$. What is the valence shell electron configuration of Ti?
6. The electron configuration of the Ge atom is $1s^22s^22p^63s^23p^64s^23d^{10}4p^2$. What is the valence shell electron configuration of Ge?
7. What is the mass of an electron in atomic mass units?
8. In a footnote in this chapter, an alpha particle was defined as a particle with 2 protons and 2 neutrons. What is the mass, in grams, of an alpha particle? (Hint: what element does an alpha particle resemble?)
9. A sample of the nonexistent element mythium consists of 25.59% of an isotope with mass number 580, 32.74% of an isotope with mass number 582, and 41.67% of an isotope with mass number 581. What is the atomic mass of mythium?
10. Because the distribution of isotopes is different on different planets in the solar system, the average atomic mass of any element differs from planet to planet. Assume that on Mercury, a rather hot planet, there is more deuterium left in the atmosphere than on Earth, so that 92.55% of the hydrogen on Mercury is ^1H, while the remainder is ^2H. What is the atomic mass of hydrogen on Mercury?
11. The compound that sodium makes with chlorine has sodium and chlorine atoms in a 1:1 ratio. Name two other elements that should make a compound having a 1:1 ratio of atoms with sodium.
12. The compound that magnesium makes with oxygen has magnesium to oxygen atoms in a 1:1 ratio. Name two other elements that should make a compound having a 1:1 ratio of atoms with magnesium.

ANSWERS

1. 5.38 × 10^7 atoms
3. $1s^22s^22p^63s^23p^6$
5. $4s^2$
7. 0.000545 u
9. 581.1 u
11. potassium and bromine (answers will vary)

CHAPTER 3

Ionic Bonding and Simple Ionic Compounds

Opening Essay

We will see that the word *salt* has a specific meaning in chemistry, but to most people, this word refers to table salt. This kind of salt is used as a condiment throughout the world, but it was not always so abundant. Two thousand years ago, Roman soldiers received part of their pay as salt, which explains why the words *salt* and *salary* come from the same Latin root (*salarium*). Today, table salt is either mined or obtained from the evaporation of saltwater.

Table salt is sodium chloride (NaCl), which is a simple compound of two elements that are necessary for the human body to function properly. Sodium, for example, is important for nerve conduction and fluid balance. In fact, human blood is about a 0.9% sodium chloride solution, and a solution called *normal saline* is commonly administered intravenously in hospitals.

Although some salt in our diets is necessary to replenish the sodium and chloride ions that we excrete in urine and sweat, too much is unhealthy, and many people may be ingesting more salt than their bodies need. The RDI of sodium is 2,400 mg—the amount in about 1 teaspoon of salt—but the average intake of sodium in the United States is between 4,000 mg and 5,000 mg, partly because salt is a common additive in many prepared foods. Previously, the high ingestion of salt was thought to be associated with high blood pressure, but current research does not support this link. Even so, some doctors still recommend a low-salt diet (never a "no-salt" diet) for patients with high blood pressure, which may include using a salt substitute. Most salt substitutes use potassium instead of sodium, but some people complain that the potassium imparts a slightly bitter taste.

There are only 118 known chemical elements but tens of millions of known chemical compounds. Compounds can be very complex combinations of atoms, but many important compounds are fairly simple. Table salt, as we have seen, consists of only two elements: sodium and chlorine. Nevertheless, the compound has properties completely different from either elemental sodium (a chemically reactive metal) or elemental chlorine (a poisonous, green gas). We will see additional examples of such differences in this chapter and Chapter 4, as we consider how atoms combine to form compounds.

1. TWO TYPES OF BONDING

LEARNING OBJECTIVES

1. **Define the octet rule.**
2. **Describe how ionic bonds are formed.**

Atoms can join together by forming a **chemical bond**, which is a very strong attraction between two atoms. Chemical bonds are formed when electrons in different atoms interact with each other to make an arrangement that is more stable than when the atoms are apart.

chemical bond

A very strong attraction between two atoms.

octet rule

The idea that atoms tend to have eight electrons in their valence shell.

What causes atoms to make a chemical bond with other atoms, rather than remaining as individual atoms? A clue comes by considering the noble gas elements, the rightmost column of the periodic table. These elements—helium, neon, argon, krypton, xenon, and radon—do not form compounds very easily, which suggests that they are especially stable as lone atoms. What else do the noble gas elements have in common? Except for helium, they all have eight valence electrons. Chemists have concluded that atoms are especially stable if they have eight electrons in their outermost shell. This useful rule of thumb is called the **octet rule**, and it is a key to understanding why compounds form.

Note

Of the noble gases, only krypton, xenon, and radon have been found to make compounds.

ion

A charged atom.

ionic bond

An attraction between oppositely charged ions.

ionic compound

A compound formed with an ionic bond.

There are two ways for an atom that does not have an octet of valence electrons to obtain an octet in its outer shell. One way is the transfer of electrons between two atoms until all atoms have octets. Because some atoms will lose electrons and some atoms will gain electrons, there is no overall change in the number of electrons, but individual atoms acquire a nonzero electric charge. Those that lose electrons become positively charged, and those that gain electrons become negatively charged. Charged atoms are called **ions**. Because opposite charges attract (while like charges repel), these oppositely charged ions attract each other, forming **ionic bonds**. The resulting compounds are called **ionic compounds** and are the primary subject of this chapter.

The second way for an atom to obtain an octet of electrons is by sharing electrons with another atom. These shared electrons simultaneously occupy the outermost shell of more than one atom. The bond made by electron sharing is called a **covalent bond**. Covalent bonding and covalent compounds will be discussed in Chapter 4.

Note

Despite our focus on the octet rule, we must remember that for small atoms, such as hydrogen, helium, and lithium, the first shell is, or becomes, the outermost shell and hold only two electrons. Therefore, these atoms satisfy a "duet rule" rather than the octet rule.

EXAMPLE 1

A sodium atom has one valence electron. Do you think it is more likely for a sodium atom to lose one electron or gain seven electrons to obtain an octet?

Solution

Although either event is possible, a sodium atom is more likely to lose its single valence electron. When that happens, it becomes an ion with a net positive charge. This can be illustrated as follows:

Sodium atom		Sodium ion	
11 protons	11+	11 protons	11+
11 electrons	<u>11–</u>	10 electrons	<u>10–</u>
	0 overall charge		+1 overall charge

SKILL-BUILDING EXERCISE

1. A fluorine atom has seven valence electrons. Do you think it is more likely for a fluorine atom to lose seven electrons or gain one electron to obtain an octet?

CONCEPT REVIEW EXERCISES

1. What is the octet rule?
2. How are ionic bonds formed?

ANSWERS

1. The octet rule is the concept that atoms tend to have eight electrons in their valence electron shell.
2. Ionic bonds are formed by the attraction between oppositely charged ions.

KEY TAKEAWAYS

- Atoms have a tendency to have eight electrons in their valence shell.
- The attraction of oppositely charged ions is what makes ionic bonds.

EXERCISES

1. Why is an ionic compound unlikely to consist of two positively charged ions?
2. Why is an ionic compound unlikely to consist of two negatively charged ions?
3. A calcium atom has two valence electrons. Do you think it will lose two electrons or gain six electrons to obtain an octet in its outermost electron shell?
4. An aluminum atom has three valence electrons. Do you think it will lose three electrons or gain five electrons to obtain an octet in its outermost electron shell?
5. A selenium atom has six valence electrons. Do you think it will lose six electrons or gain two electrons to obtain an octet in its outermost electron shell?
6. An iodine atom has seven valence electrons. Do you think it will lose seven electrons or gain one electron to obtain an octet in its outermost electron shell?

ANSWERS

1. Positive charges repel each other, so an ionic compound is not likely between two positively charged ions.
3. It is more likely to lose two electrons.
5. It is more likely to gain two electrons.

2. IONS

LEARNING OBJECTIVES

1. **Define the two types of ions.**
2. **Use Lewis diagrams to illustrate ion formation.**

Most atoms do not have eight electrons in their valence electron shell. Some atoms have only a few electrons in their outer shell, while some atoms lack only one or two electrons to have an octet. In cases where an atom has three or fewer valence electrons, the atom may lose those valence electrons quite easily until what remains is a lower shell that contains an octet. Atoms that lose electrons acquire a positive charge as a result because they are left with fewer negatively charged electrons to balance the positive charges of the protons in the nucleus. Positively charged ions are called **cations**. Most metals become cations when they make ionic compounds.

cation

A positively charged ion.

Some atoms have nearly eight electrons in their valence shell and can gain additional valence electrons until they have an octet. When these atoms gain electrons, they acquire a negative charge because they now possess more electrons than protons. Negatively charged ions are called **anions**. Most nonmetals become anions when they make ionic compounds.

anion

A negatively charged ion.

Note

The names for positive and negative ions are pronounced CAT-eye-ons and ANN-eye-ons, respectively.

2.1 Electron Transfer

We can use electron configurations to illustrate the electron transfer process between sodium atoms and chlorine atoms. Recall the electron configuration of sodium from Chapter 2:

$$\text{Na: } 1s^2 2s^2 2p^6 3s^1$$

As demonstrated in Example 1 (in Section 1), sodium is likely to achieve an octet in its outermost shell by losing its one valence electron. The remaining species has the following electron configuration:

$$\text{Na} \longrightarrow \underbrace{\text{Na}^+}_{1s^2\,2s^2\,2p^6} + e^-$$

The cation produced in this way, Na^+, is called the sodium ion to distinguish it from the element. The outermost shell of the sodium ion is the second electron shell, which has eight electrons in it. The octet rule has been satisfied. Figure 3.1 is a graphical depiction of this process.

FIGURE 3.1 The Formation of a Sodium Ion

On the left, a sodium atom has 11 electrons. On the right, the sodium ion only has 10 electrons and a 1+ charge.

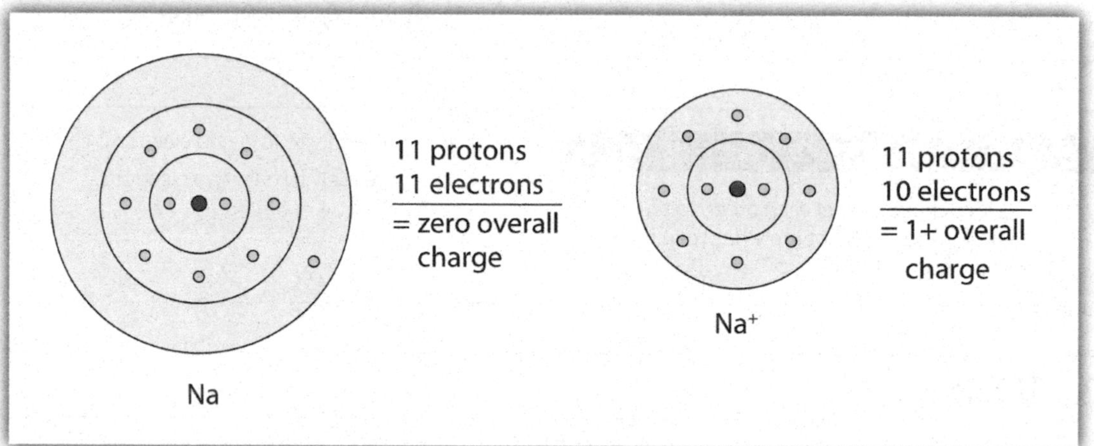

A chlorine atom has the following electron configuration:

$$\text{Cl: } 1s^2 2s^2 2p^6 3s^2 3p^5$$

Only one more electron is needed to achieve an octet in chlorine's valence shell. (In table salt, this electron comes from the sodium atom.) The electron configuration of the new species that results is as follows:

$$e^- + \text{Cl} \longrightarrow \underbrace{\text{Cl}^-}_{1s^2\,2s^2\,2p^6\,3s^2\,3p^6}$$

In this case, the ion has the same outermost shell as the original atom, but now that shell has eight electrons in it. Once again, the octet rule has been satisfied. The resulting anion, Cl^-, is called the chloride ion; note the slight change in the suffix (*-ide* instead of *-ine*) to create the name of this anion. Figure 3.2 is a graphical depiction of this process.

FIGURE 3.2 The Formation of a Chlorine Ion

On the left, the chlorine atom has 17 electrons. On the right, the chloride ion has 18 electrons and has a 1− charge.

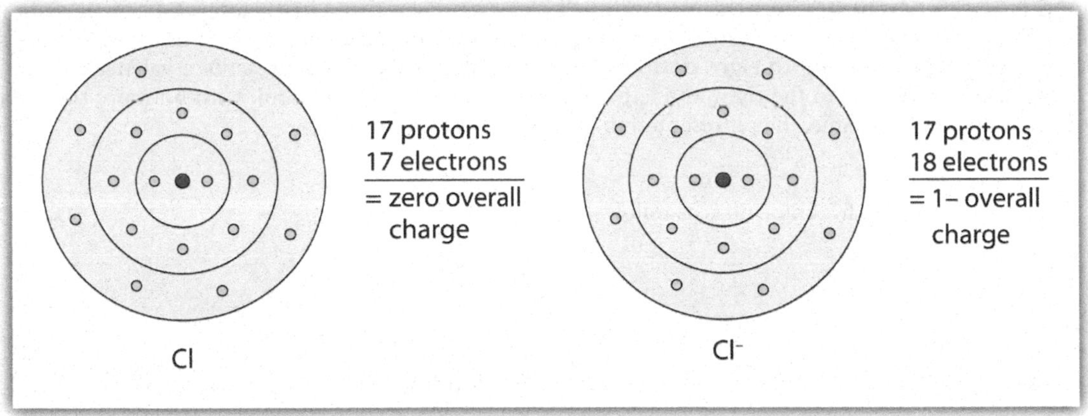

With two oppositely charged ions, there is an electrostatic attraction between them because opposite charges attract. The resulting combination is the compound sodium chloride. Notice that there are no leftover electrons. The number of electrons lost by the sodium atom (one) equals the number of electrons gained by the chlorine atom (one), so the compound is electrically neutral. In macroscopic samples of sodium chloride, there are billions and billions of sodium and chloride ions, although there is always the same number of cations and anions.

In many cases, elements that belong to the same group (vertical column) on the periodic table form ions with the same charge because they have the same number of valence electrons. Thus, the periodic table becomes a tool for remembering the charges on many ions. For example, all ions made from alkali metals, the first column on the periodic table, have a 1+ charge. Ions made from alkaline earth metals, the second group on the periodic table, have a 2+ charge. On the other side of the periodic table, the next-to-last column, the halogens, form ions having a 1− charge. Figure 3.3 shows how the charge on many ions can be predicted by the location of an element on the periodic table. Note the convention of first writing the number and then the sign on a multiply charged ion. The barium cation is written Ba^{2+}, not Ba^{+2}.

FIGURE 3.3 Predicting Ionic Charges

The charge that an atom acquires when it becomes an ion is related to the structure of the periodic table. Within a group (family) of elements, atoms form ions of a certain charge.

1A	2A	3A	4A	5A	6A	7A	8A
H^+							
Li^+				N^{3-}	O^{2-}	F^-	
Na^+	Mg^{2+}	Al^{3+}		P^{3-}	S^{2-}	Cl^-	
K^+	Ca^{2+}				Se^{2-}	Br^-	
Rb^+	Sr^{2+}					I^-	

2.2 Lewis Diagrams

Chemists use simple diagrams to show an atom's valence electrons and how they transfer. These diagrams have two advantages over the electron shell diagrams introduced in Chapter 2. First, they show only valence electrons. Second, instead of having a circle around the chemical symbol to represent the electron shell, they have up to eight dots around the symbol; each dot represents a valence electron. These dots are arranged to the right and left and above and below the symbol, with no more than two dots on a side. For example, the representation for sodium is as follows:

Na•

and the representation for chlorine is as follows:

Note

It does not matter what sides the dots are placed on in Lewis diagrams as long as each side has a maximum of two dots.

Lewis diagram

A representation that shows valence electrons as dots around the chemical symbol of an atom (also called Lewis electron dot diagrams).

These diagrams are called **Lewis electron dot diagrams**, or simply **Lewis diagrams**, after Gilbert N. Lewis, the American chemist who introduced them. Figure 3.4 shows the electron configurations and Lewis diagrams of the elements lithium through neon, which is the entire second period of the periodic table. For the main group elements, the number of valence electrons is the same as the group number listed at the top of the periodic table.

FIGURE 3.4 Lewis Diagrams of the Elements Lithium through Neon

Li• •Be• •B• •C• •N: :O: :F: :Ne:

The transfer of electrons can be illustrated easily with Lewis diagrams:

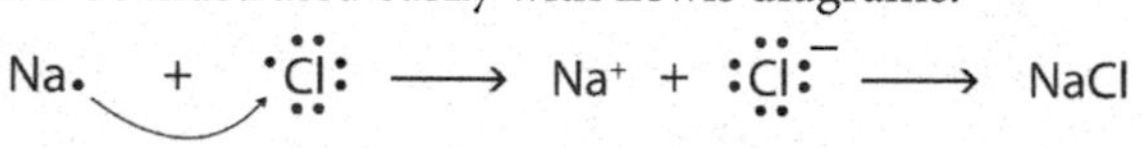

$$\text{Na}\cdot + \cdot\ddot{\text{Cl}}: \longrightarrow \text{Na}^+ + :\ddot{\text{Cl}}:^- \longrightarrow \text{NaCl}$$

In representing the final formula, the dots are omitted.

EXAMPLE 2

Starting with lithium and bromine atoms, use Lewis diagrams to show the formation of the ionic compound LiBr.

Solution

From the periodic table, we see that lithium is in the same column as sodium, so it will have the same valence shell electron configuration. That means that the neutral lithium atom will have the same Lewis diagram that the sodium atom has. Similarly, bromine is in the same column as chlorine, so it will have the same Lewis diagram that chlorine has. Therefore,

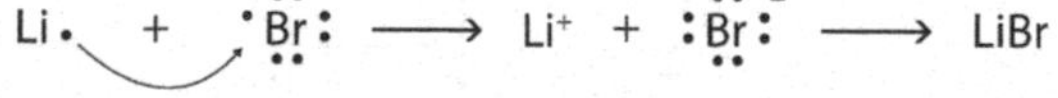

$$\text{Li}\cdot + \cdot\ddot{\text{Br}}: \longrightarrow \text{Li}^+ + :\ddot{\text{Br}}:^- \longrightarrow \text{LiBr}$$

SKILL-BUILDING EXERCISE

1. Starting with magnesium and oxygen atoms, use Lewis diagrams to show the formation of the ionic compound MgO.

Some ionic compounds have different numbers of cations and anions. In those cases, electron transfer occurs between more than one atom. For example, here is the formation of $MgBr_2$:

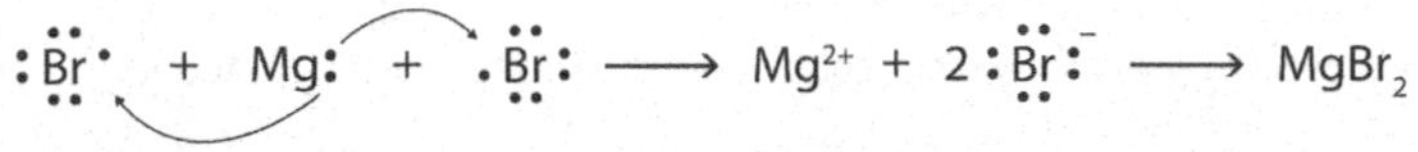

$$:\ddot{Br}\cdot \; + \; Mg: \; + \; \cdot\ddot{Br}: \longrightarrow Mg^{2+} + 2:\ddot{Br}:^{-} \longrightarrow MgBr_2$$

Most of the elements that make ionic compounds form an ion that has a characteristic charge. For example, sodium makes ionic compounds in which the sodium ion always has a 1+ charge. Chlorine makes ionic compounds in which the chloride ion always has a 1− charge. Some elements, especially transition metals, can form ions of multiple charges. Figure 3.5 shows the characteristic charges for some of these ions. As we saw in Figure 3.1, there is a pattern to the charges on many of the main group ions, but there is no simple pattern for transition metal ions (or for the larger main group elements).

FIGURE 3.5 Charges of the Monatomic Ions

Note that some atoms commonly form ions of different charges.

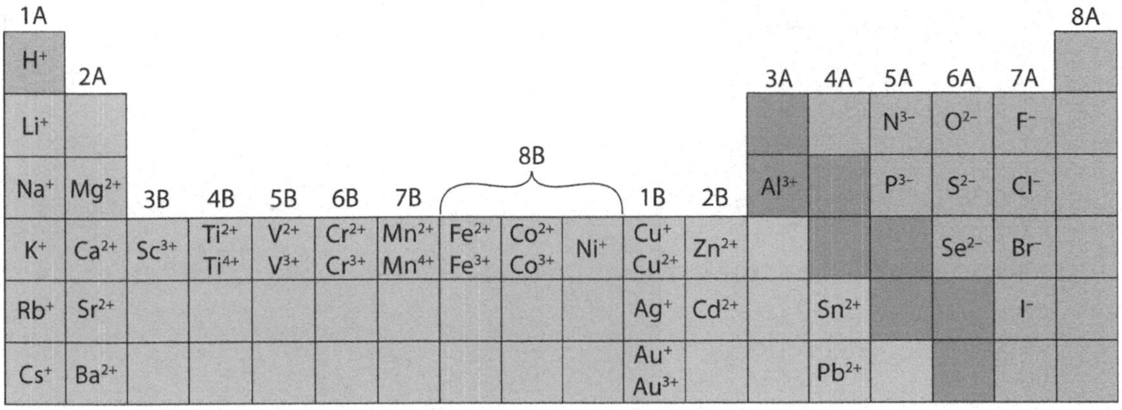

1A	2A	3B	4B	5B	6B	7B	8B	8B	8B	1B	2B	3A	4A	5A	6A	7A	8A
H^+																	
Li^+														N^{3-}	O^{2-}	F^-	
Na^+	Mg^{2+}											Al^{3+}		P^{3-}	S^{2-}	Cl^-	
K^+	Ca^{2+}	Sc^{3+}	Ti^{2+} Ti^{4+}	V^{2+} V^{3+}	Cr^{2+} Cr^{3+}	Mn^{2+} Mn^{4+}	Fe^{2+} Fe^{3+}	Co^{2+} Co^{3+}	Ni^+	Cu^+ Cu^{2+}	Zn^{2+}				Se^{2-}	Br^-	
Rb^+	Sr^{2+}									Ag^+	Cd^{2+}		Sn^{2+}			I^-	
Cs^+	Ba^{2+}									Au^+ Au^{3+}			Pb^{2+}				

CONCEPT REVIEW EXERCISES

1. What are the two types of ions?
2. Use Lewis diagrams to illustrate the formation of an ionic compound from a potassium atom and an iodine atom.
3. When the following atoms become ions, what charges do they acquire?
   a. Li
   b. S
   c. Ca
   d. F

ANSWERS

1. Cations have positive charges, and anions have negative charges.
2.

$$K\cdot \; + \; \cdot\ddot{\underset{..}{I}}: \longrightarrow K^+ + :\ddot{\underset{..}{I}}:^- \longrightarrow KI$$

3. a. 1+
   b. 2−
   c. 2+
   d. 1−

KEY TAKEAWAYS

- Ions can be positively charged or negatively charged.
- A Lewis diagram is used to show how electrons are transferred to make ions and ionic compounds.

EXERCISES

1. Identify each as a cation, an anion, or neither.
   a. H^+
   b. Cl^-
   c. O_2
   d. Ba^{2+}
   e. CH_4
   f. CS_2
2. Identify each as a cation, an anion, or neither.
   a. NH_3
   b. Br^-
   c. H^-
   d. Hg^{2+}
   e. CCl_4
   f. SO_3
3. Write the electron configuration for each ion.
   a. Li^+
   b. Mg^{2+}
   c. F^-
   d. S^{2-}
4. Write the electron configuration for each ion.
   a. Na^+
   b. Be^{2+}
   c. Cl^-
   d. O^{2-}
5. Draw Lewis diagrams for the ions listed in Exercise 3. Also include Lewis diagrams for the respective neutral atoms as a comparison.
6. Draw Lewis diagrams for the ions listed in Exercise 4. Also include Lewis diagrams for the respective neutral atoms as a comparison.
7. Using Lewis diagrams, show the electron transfer for the formation of LiF.
8. Using Lewis diagrams, show the electron transfer for the formation of MgO.
9. Using Lewis diagrams, show the electron transfer for the formation of Li_2O.
10. Using Lewis diagrams, show the electron transfer for the formation of CaF_2.
11. What characteristic charge do atoms in the first column of the periodic table have when they become ions?
12. What characteristic charge do atoms in the second column of the periodic table have when they become ions?
13. What characteristic charge do atoms in the third-to-last column of the periodic table have when they become ions?
14. What characteristic charge do atoms in the next-to-last column of the periodic table have when they become ions?

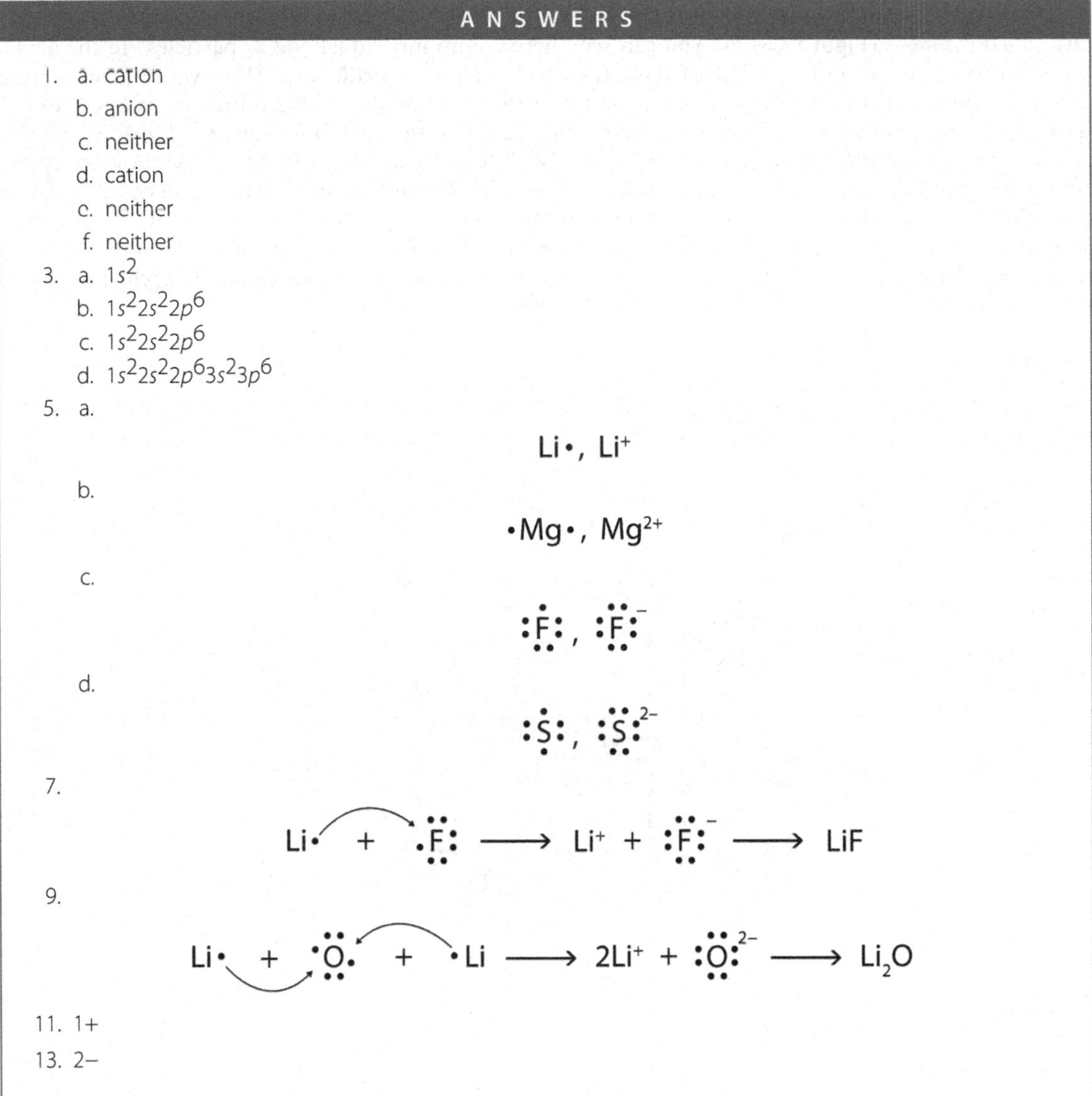

ANSWERS

1. a. cation
   b. anion
   c. neither
   d. cation
   e. neither
   f. neither
3. a. $1s^2$
   b. $1s^22s^22p^6$
   c. $1s^22s^22p^6$
   d. $1s^22s^22p^63s^23p^6$
5. a. Li•, Li^+
   b. •Mg•, Mg^{2+}
   c.
   d.
7. Li^+ + F^- ⟶ LiF
9. ⟶ $2Li^+$ + O^{2-} ⟶ Li_2O
11. 1+
13. 2−

3. FORMULAS FOR IONIC COMPOUNDS

LEARNING OBJECTIVES

1. **Write the chemical formula for a simple ionic compound.**
2. **Recognize polyatomic ions in chemical formulas.**

We have already encountered some chemical formulas for simple ionic compounds. A **chemical formula** is a concise list of the elements in a compound and the ratios of these elements. To better understand what a chemical formula means, we must consider how an ionic compound is constructed from its ions.

chemical formula

A concise list of the elements in a compound and the ratios of these elements.

crystal

A three-dimensional array of alternating positive and negative ions.

formula unit

A set of oppositely charged ions that compose an ionic compound.

Ionic compounds exist as alternating positive and negative ions in regular, three-dimensional arrays called **crystals** (Figure 3.6). As you can see, there are no individual NaCl "particles" in the array; instead, there is a continuous lattice of alternating sodium and chloride ions. However, we can use the ratio of sodium ions to chloride ions, expressed in the lowest possible whole numbers, as a way of describing the compound. In the case of sodium chloride, the ratio of sodium ions to chloride ions, expressed in lowest whole numbers, is 1:1, so we use NaCl (one Na symbol and one Cl symbol) to represent the compound. Thus, NaCl is the chemical formula for sodium chloride, which is a concise way of describing the relative number of different ions in the compound. A macroscopic sample is composed of myriads of NaCl pairs; each pair called a **formula unit**. Although it is convenient to think that NaCl crystals are composed of individual NaCl units, Figure 3.6 shows that no single ion is exclusively associated with any other single ion. Each ion is surrounded by ions of opposite charge.

FIGURE 3.6 A Sodium Chloride Crystal

A crystal contains a three-dimensional array of alternating positive and negative ions. The precise pattern depends on the compound. A crystal of sodium chloride, shown here, is a collection of alternating sodium and chlorine ions.

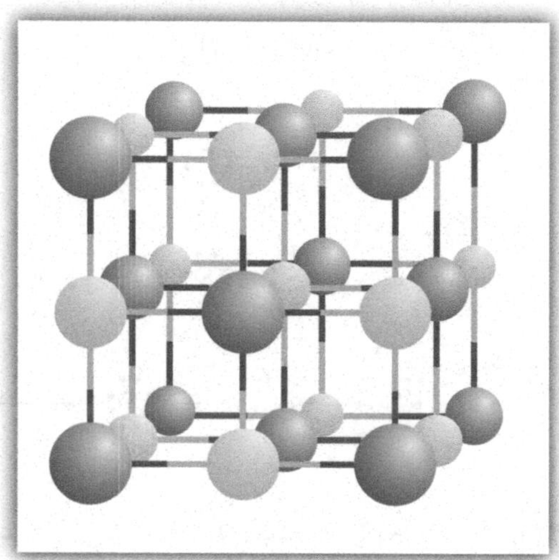

Note

In Section 2, we encountered LiBr and MgO, which are formulas for other ionic compounds.

The formula for an ionic compound follows several conventions. First, the cation is written before the anion. Because most metals form cations and most nonmetals form anions, formulas typically list the metal first and then the nonmetal. Second, charges are not written in a formula. Remember that in an ionic compound, the component species are ions, not neutral atoms, even though the formula does not contain charges. Finally, the proper formula for an ionic compound always obeys the following rule: the total positive charge must equal the total negative charge. To determine the proper formula of any combination of ions, determine how many of each ion is needed to balance the total positive and negative charges in the compound.

Note

This rule is ultimately based on the fact that matter is, overall, electrically neutral.

Note

By convention, assume that there is only one atom if a subscript is not present. We do not use 1 as a subscript.

If we look at the ionic compound consisting of lithium ions and bromide ions, we see that the lithium ion has a 1+ charge and the bromide ion has a 1− charge. Only one ion of each is needed to balance these charges. The formula for lithium bromide is LiBr.

When an ionic compound is formed from magnesium and oxygen, the magnesium ion has a 2+ charge, and the oxygen atom has a 2– charge. Although both of these ions have higher charges than the ions in lithium bromide, they still balance each other in a one-to-one ratio. Therefore, the proper formula for this ionic compound is MgO.

Now consider the ionic compound formed by magnesium and chlorine. A magnesium ion has a 2+ charge, while a chlorine ion has a 1– charge:

$$Mg^{2+}\ Cl^{-}$$

Combining one ion of each does not completely balance the positive and negative charges. The easiest way to balance these charges is to assume the presence of *two* chloride ions for each magnesium ion:

$$Mg^{2+}\ Cl^{-}\ Cl^{-}$$

Now the positive and negative charges are balanced. We could write the chemical formula for this ionic compound as MgClCl, but the convention is to use a numerical subscript when there is more than one ion of a given type—$MgCl_2$. This chemical formula says that there are one magnesium ion and *two* chloride ions in this formula. (Do not read the "Cl_2" part of the formula as a molecule of the diatomic elemental chlorine. Chlorine does not exist as a diatomic element in this compound. Rather, it exists as two individual chloride ions.) By convention, the lowest whole number ratio is used in the formulas of ionic compounds. The formula Mg_2Cl_4 has balanced charges with the ions in a 1:2 ratio, but it is not the lowest whole number ratio.

Note

By convention, the lowest whole-number ratio of the ions is used in ionic formulas. There are exceptions for certain ions, such as Hg_2^{2+}.

EXAMPLE 3

Write the chemical formula for an ionic compound composed of each pair of ions.

1. the sodium ion and the sulfur ion
2. the aluminum ion and the fluoride ion
3. the 3+ iron ion and the oxygen ion

Solution

1. To obtain a valence shell octet, sodium forms an ion with a 1+ charge, while the sulfur ion has a 2– charge. Two sodium 1+ ions are needed to balance the 2– charge on the sulfur ion. Rather than writing the formula as NaNaS, we shorten it by convention to Na_2S.
2. The aluminum ion has a 3+ charge, while the fluoride ion formed by fluorine has a 1– charge. Three fluorine 1– ions are needed to balance the 3+ charge on the aluminum ion. This combination is written as AlF_3.
3. Iron can form two possible ions, but the ion with a 3+ charge is specified here. The oxygen atom has a 2– charge as an ion. To balance the positive and negative charges, we look to the least common multiple—6: two iron 3+ ions will give 6+, while three 2– oxygen ions will give 6–, thereby balancing the overall positive and negative charges. Thus, the formula for this ionic compound is Fe_2O_3.

SKILL-BUILDING EXERCISE

Write the chemical formula for an ionic compound composed of each pair of ions.

1. the calcium ion and the oxygen ion
2. the 2+ copper ion and the sulfur ion
3. the 1+ copper ion and the sulfur ion

3.1 Polyatomic Ions

polyatomic ions

An ion with more than one atom.

Some ions consist of groups of atoms bonded together and have an overall electric charge. Because these ions contain more than one atom, they are called **polyatomic ions**. Polyatomic ions have characteristic formulas, names, and charges that should be memorized. For example, NO_3^- is the nitrate ion; it has one nitrogen atom and three oxygen atoms and an overall 1− charge. Table 3.1 lists the most common polyatomic ions.

TABLE 3.1 Some Polyatomic Ions

Name	Formula
ammonium ion	NH_4^+
acetate ion	$C_2H_3O_2^-$ (also written $CH_3CO_2^-$)
carbonate ion	CO_3^{2-}
chromate ion	CrO_4^{2-}
dichromate ion	$Cr_2O_7^{2-}$
hydrogen carbonate ion (bicarbonate ion)	HCO_3^-
cyanide ion	CN^-
hydroxide ion	OH^-
nitrate ion	NO_3^-
nitrite ion	NO_2^-
permanganate ion	MnO_4^-
phosphate ion	PO_4^{3-}
hydrogen phosphate ion	HPO_4^{2-}
dihydrogen phosphate ion	$H_2PO_4^-$
sulfate ion	SO_4^{2-}
hydrogen sulfate ion (bisulfate ion)	HSO_4^-
sulfite ion	SO_3^{2-}

The rule for constructing formulas for ionic compounds containing polyatomic ions is the same as for formulas containing monatomic (single-atom) ions: the positive and negative charges must balance. If more than one of a particular polyatomic ion is needed to balance the charge, the *entire formula* for the polyatomic ion must be enclosed in parentheses, and the numerical subscript is placed *outside* the parentheses. This is to show that the subscript applies to the entire polyatomic ion. An example is $Ba(NO_3)_2$.

EXAMPLE 4

Write the chemical formula for an ionic compound composed of each pair of ions.

1. the potassium ion and the sulfate ion
2. the calcium ion and the nitrate ion

Solution

1. Potassium ions have a charge of 1+, while sulfate ions have a charge of 2−. We will need two potassium ions to balance the charge on the sulfate ion, so the proper chemical formula is K_2SO_4.
2. Calcium ions have a charge of 2+, while nitrate ions have a charge of 1−. We will need two nitrate ions to balance the charge on each calcium ion. The formula for nitrate must be enclosed in parentheses. Thus, we write $Ca(NO_3)_2$ as the formula for this ionic compound.

SKILL-BUILDING EXERCISE

Write the chemical formula for an ionic compound composed of each pair of ions.

1. the magnesium ion and the carbonate ion
2. the aluminum ion and the acetate ion

3.2 Recognizing Ionic Compounds

There are two ways to recognize ionic compounds. First, compounds between metal and nonmetal elements are usually ionic. For example, $CaBr_2$ contains a metallic element (calcium, a group 2A metal) and a nonmetallic element (bromine, a group 7A nonmetal). Therefore, it is most likely an ionic compound. (In fact, it *is* ionic.) In contrast, the compound NO_2 contains two elements that are both nonmetals (nitrogen, from group 5A, and oxygen, from group 6A). It is not an ionic compound; it belongs to the category of covalent compounds that we will study in Chapter 4. Also note that this combination of nitrogen and oxygen has no electric charge specified, so it is *not* the nitrite ion.

Second, if you recognize the formula of a polyatomic ion in a compound, the compound is ionic. For example, if you see the formula $Ba(NO_3)_2$, you may recognize the "NO_3" part as the nitrate ion, NO_3^-. (Remember that the convention for writing formulas for ionic compounds is not to include the ionic charge.) This is a clue that the other part of the formula, Ba, is actually the Ba^{2+} ion, with the 2+ charge balancing the overall 2− charge from the two nitrate ions. Thus, this compound is also ionic.

EXAMPLE 5

Identify each compound as ionic or not ionic.

1. Na_2O
2. PCl_3
3. NH_4Cl
4. OF_2

Solution

1. Sodium is a metal, and oxygen is a nonmetal; therefore, Na_2O is expected to be ionic.
2. Both phosphorus and chlorine are nonmetals. Therefore, PCl_3 is not ionic.
3. The NH_4 in the formula represents the ammonium ion, NH_4^+, which indicates that this compound is ionic.
4. Both oxygen and fluorine are nonmetals. Therefore, OF_2 is not ionic.

SKILL-BUILDING EXERCISE

Identify each compound as ionic or not ionic.

1. N_2O
2. $FeCl_3$
3. $(NH_4)_3PO_4$
4. $SOCl_2$

Looking Closer: Blood and Seawater

Science has long recognized that blood and seawater have similar compositions. After all, both liquids have ionic compounds dissolved in them. The similarity may be more than mere coincidence; many scientists think that the first forms of life on Earth arose in the oceans.

A closer look, however, shows that blood and seawater are quite different. A 0.9% solution of sodium chloride approximates the salt concentration found in blood. In contrast, seawater is principally a 3% sodium chloride solution, over three times the concentration in blood. Here is a comparison of the amounts of ions in blood and seawater:

Ion	Percent in Seawater	Percent in Blood
Na^+	2.36	0.322
Cl^-	1.94	0.366
Mg^{2+}	0.13	0.002
SO_4^{2-}	0.09	—
K^+	0.04	0.016
Ca^{2+}	0.04	0.0096
HCO_3^-	0.002	0.165
HPO_4^{2-}, $H_2PO_4^-$	—	0.01

Most ions are more abundant in seawater than they are in blood, with some important exceptions. There are far more hydrogen carbonate ions (HCO_3^-) in blood than in seawater. This difference is significant because the hydrogen carbonate ion and some related ions have a crucial role in controlling the acid-base properties of blood. (For more information on the acid-base properties of blood, see Chapter 10, [Unsupported Reference Type: chapter-section].) The amount of hydrogen phosphate ions—HPO_4^{2-} and $H_2PO_4^-$—in seawater is very low, but they are present in higher amounts in blood, where they also affect acid-base properties. Another notable difference is that blood does not have significant amounts of the sulfate ion (SO_4^{2-}), but this ion is present in seawater.

CONCEPT REVIEW EXERCISES

1. What information is contained in the formula of an ionic compound?
2. Why do the chemical formulas for some ionic compounds contain subscripts, while others do not?
3. Write the chemical formula for the ionic compound formed by each pair of ions.
   a. Mg^{2+} and I^-
   b. Na^+ and O^{2-}

ANSWERS

1. the ratio of each kind of ion in the compound
2. Sometimes more than one ion is needed to balance the charge on the other ion in an ionic compound.
3. a. MgI_2
   b. Na_2O

KEY TAKEAWAYS

- Proper chemical formulas for ionic compounds balance the total positive charge with the total negative charge.
- Groups of atoms with an overall charge, called polyatomic ions, also exist.

EXERCISES

1. Write the chemical formula for the ionic compound formed by each pair of ions.
   a. Na^+ and Br^-
   b. Mg^{2+} and Br^-
   c. Mg^{2+} and S^{2-}
2. Write the chemical formula for the ionic compound formed by each pair of ions.
   a. K^+ and Cl^-
   b. Mg^{2+} and Cl^-
   c. Mg^{2+} and Se^{2-}

3. Write the chemical formula for the ionic compound formed by each pair of ions.
   a. Na^+ and N^{3-}
   b. Mg^{2+} and N^{3-}
   c. Al^{3+} and S^{2-}
4. Write the chemical formula for the ionic compound formed by each pair of ions.
   a. Li^+ and N^{3-}
   b. Mg^{2+} and P^{3-}
   c. Li^+ and P^{3-}
5. Write the chemical formula for the ionic compound formed by each pair of ions.
   a. Fe^{3+} and Br^-
   b. Fe^{2+} and Br^-
   c. Au^{3+} and S^{2-}
   d. Au^+ and S^{2-}
6. Write the chemical formula for the ionic compound formed by each pair of ions.
   a. Cr^{3+} and O^{2-}
   b. Cr^{2+} and O^{2-}
   c. Pb^{2+} and Cl^-
   d. Pb^{4+} and Cl^-
7. Write the chemical formula for the ionic compound formed by each pair of ions.
   a. Cr^{3+} and NO_3^-
   b. Fe^{2+} and PO_4^{3-}
   c. Ca^{2+} and CrO_4^{2-}
   d. Al^{3+} and OH^-
8. Write the chemical formula for the ionic compound formed by each pair of ions.
   a. NH_4^+ and NO_3^-
   b. H^+ and $Cr_2O_7^{2-}$
   c. Cu^+ and CO_3^{2-}
   d. Na^+ and HCO_3^-
9. For each pair of elements, determine the charge for their ions and write the proper formula for the resulting ionic compound between them.
   a. Ba and S
   b. Cs and I
10. For each pair of elements, determine the charge for their ions and write the proper formula for the resulting ionic compound between them.
    a. K and S
    b. Sc and Br
11. Which compounds would you predict to be ionic?
    a. Li_2O
    b. $(NH_4)_2O$
    c. CO_2
    d. $FeSO_3$
    e. C_6H_6
    f. C_2H_6O
12. Which compounds would you predict to be ionic?
    a. $Ba(OH)_2$
    b. CH_2O
    c. NH_2CONH_2
    d. $(NH_4)_2CrO_4$
    e. C_8H_{18}
    f. NH_3

ANSWERS

1. a. NaBr
   b. $MgBr_2$
   c. MgS
3. a. Na_3N
   b. Mg_3N_2
   c. Al_2S_3
5. a. $FeBr_3$
   b. $FeBr_2$
   c. Au_2S_3
   d. Au_2S
7. a. $Cr(NO_3)_3$
   b. $Fe_3(PO_4)_2$
   c. $CaCrO_4$
   d. $Al(OH)_3$
9. a. Ba^{2+}, S^{2-}, BaS
   b. Cs^+, I^-, CsI
11. a. ionic
    b. ionic
    c. not ionic
    d. ionic
    e. not ionic
    f. not ionic

4. IONIC NOMENCLATURE

LEARNING OBJECTIVE

1. Use the rules for naming ionic compounds.

nomenclature

The systematic naming of chemical compounds.

After learning a few more details about the names of individual ions, you will be a step away from knowing how to name ionic compounds. This section begins the formal study of **nomenclature**, the systematic naming of chemical compounds.

4.1 Naming Ions

The name of a monatomic cation is simply the name of the element followed by the word *ion*. Thus, Na^+ is the sodium ion, Al^{3+} is the aluminum ion, Ca^{2+} is the calcium ion, and so forth.

We have seen that some elements lose different numbers of electrons, producing ions of different charges (Figure 3.3). Iron, for example, can form two cations, each of which, when combined with the same anion, makes a different compound with unique physical and chemical properties. Thus, we need a different name for each iron ion to distinguish Fe^{2+} from Fe^{3+}. The same issue arises for other ions with more than one possible charge.

Stock system

The system of indicating a cation's charge with roman numerals.

There are two ways to make this distinction. In the simpler, more modern approach, called the **Stock system**, an ion's positive charge is indicated by a roman numeral in parentheses after the element name, followed by the word *ion*. Thus, Fe^{2+} is called the iron(II) ion, while Fe^{3+} is called the iron(III) ion. This system is used only for elements that form more than one common positive ion. We do not call the Na^+ ion the sodium(I) ion because (I) is unnecessary. Sodium forms only a 1+ ion, so there is no ambiguity about the name *sodium ion*.

The second system, called the **common system**, is not conventional but is still prevalent and used in the health sciences. This system recognizes that many metals have two common cations. The common system uses two suffixes (*-ic* and *-ous*) that are appended to the stem of the element name. The *-ic* suffix represents the greater of the two cation charges, and the *-ous* suffix represents the lower one. In many cases, the stem of the element name comes from the Latin name of the element. Table 3.2 lists the elements that use the common system, along with their respective cation names.

TABLE 3.2 The Common System of Cation Names

Element	Stem	Charge	Name
iron	ferr-	2+	ferrous ion
		3+	ferric ion
copper	cupr-	1+	cuprous ion
		2+	cupric ion
tin	stann-	2+	stannous ion
		4+	stannic ion
lead	plumb-	2+	plumbous ion
		4+	plumbic ion
chromium	chrom-	2+	chromous ion
		3+	chromic ion
gold	aur-	1+	aurous ion
		3+	auric ion

The name of a monatomic anion consists of the stem of the element name, the suffix *-ide*, and then the word *ion*. Thus, as we have already seen, Cl^- is "chlor-" + "-ide ion," or the chloride ion. Similarly, O^{2-} is the oxide ion, Se^{2-} is the selenide ion, and so forth. Table 3.3 lists the names of some common monatomic ions.

TABLE 3.3 Some Monatomic Anions

Ion	Name
F^-	fluoride ion
Cl^-	chloride ion
Br^-	bromide ion
I^-	iodide ion
O^{2-}	oxide ion
S^{2-}	sulfide ion
P^{3-}	phosphide ion
N^{3-}	nitride ion

The polyatomic ions have their own characteristic names, as we saw in Table 3.1.

EXAMPLE 6

Name each ion.

1. Ca^{2+}
2. S^{2-}
3. $SO_3{}^{2-}$
4. $NH_4{}^+$
5. Cu^+

Solution

1. the calcium ion
2. the sulfide ion (from Table 3.3)
3. the sulfite ion (from Table 3.1)
4. the ammonium ion (from Table 3.1)
5. the copper(I) ion or the cuprous ion (Figure 3.5 shows that copper can form cations with either a 1+ or 2+ charge, so we have to specify which charge this ion has)

SKILL-BUILDING EXERCISE

Name each ion.

1. Fe^{2+}
2. Fe^{3+}
3. $SO_4{}^{2-}$
4. Ba^{2+}
5. $HCO_3{}^-$

EXAMPLE 7

Write the formula for each ion.

1. the bromide ion
2. the phosphate ion
3. the cupric ion
4. the magnesium ion

Solution

1. Br^-
2. PO_4^{3-}
3. Cu^{2+}
4. Mg^{2+}

SKILL-BUILDING EXERCISE

Write the formula for each ion.

1. the fluoride ion
2. the carbonate ion
3. the stannous ion
4. the potassium ion

4.2 Naming Compounds

Now that we know how to name ions, we are ready to name ionic compounds. We do so by placing the name of the cation first, followed by the name of the anion, and dropping the word *ion* from both parts.

For example, what is the name of the compound whose formula is $Ba(NO_3)_2$?

Ba^{2+} NO_3^-

barium ion nitrate ion

(remove the word "ion")

↓

barium + nitrate

barium nitrate

The compound's name does not indicate that there are two nitrate ions for every barium ion. You must determine the relative numbers of ions by balancing the positive and negative charges.

If you are given a formula for an ionic compound whose cation can have more than one possible charge, you must first determine the charge on the cation before identifying its correct name. For example, consider $FeCl_2$ and $FeCl_3$. In the first compound, the iron ion has a 2+ charge because there are two Cl^- ions in the formula (1− charge on each chloride ion). In the second compound, the iron ion has a 3+ charge, as indicated by the three Cl^- ions in the formula. These are two different compounds that need two different names. By the Stock system, the names are iron(II) chloride and iron(III) chloride. If we were to use the stems and suffixes of the common system, the names would be ferrous chloride and ferric chloride, respectively.

EXAMPLE 8

Name each ionic compound, using both Stock and common systems if necessary.

1. $Ca_3(PO_4)_2$
2. $(NH_4)_2Cr_2O_7$
3. KCl
4. CuCl
5. SnF_2

Solution

1. calcium phosphate
2. ammonium dichromate (the prefix *di-* is part of the name of the anion, as in Table 3.1)
3. potassium chloride
4. copper(I) chloride or cuprous chloride
5. tin(II) fluoride or stannous fluoride

SKILL-BUILDING EXERCISE

Name each ionic compound, using both Stock and common systems if necessary.

1. $ZnBr_2$
2. $Fe(NO_3)_3$
3. Al_2O_3
4. AuF_3
5. AgF

Figure 3.7 is a synopsis of how to name simple ionic compounds.

FIGURE 3.7 A Guide to Naming Simple Ionic Compounds

Follow these steps to name a simple ionic compound.

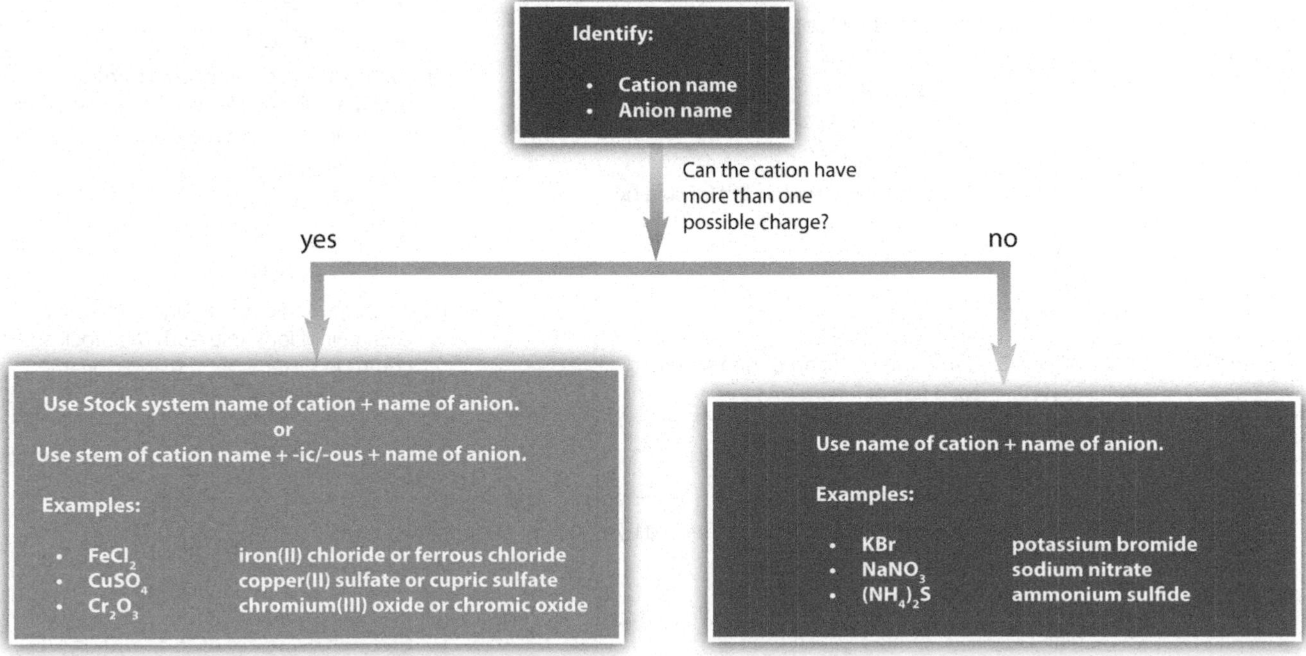

CONCEPT REVIEW EXERCISES

1. Briefly describe the process for naming an ionic compound.
2. In what order do the names of ions appear in the names of ionic compounds?
3. Which ionic compounds can be named using two different systems? Give an example.

ANSWERS

1. Name the cation and then the anion but don't use numerical prefixes.
2. the cation name followed by the anion name
3. Ionic compounds in which the cation can have more than one possible charge have two naming systems. $FeCl_3$ is either iron(III) chloride or ferric chloride (answers will vary).

KEY TAKEAWAY

- Each ionic compound has its own unique name that comes from the names of the ions.

EXERCISES

1. Name each ion.
   a. Ra^{2+}
   b. P^{3-}
   c. $H_2PO_4^-$
   d. Sn^{4+}
2. Name each ion.
   a. Cs^+
   b. As^{3-}
   c. HSO_4^-
   d. Sn^{2+}
3. Name the ionic compound formed by each pair of ions.
   a. Na^+ and Br^-
   b. Mg^{2+} and Br^-
   c. Mg^{2+} and S^{2-}
4. Name the ionic compound formed by each pair of ions.
   a. K^+ and Cl^-
   b. Mg^{2+} and Cl^-
   c. Mg^{2+} and Se^{2-}
5. Name the ionic compound formed by each pair of ions.
   a. Na^+ and N^{3-}
   b. Mg^{2+} and N^{3-}
   c. Al^{3+} and S^{2-}
6. Name the ionic compound formed by each pair of ions.
   a. Li^+ and N^{3-}
   b. Mg^{2+} and P^{3-}
   c. Li^+ and P^{3-}
7. Name the ionic compound formed by each pair of ions. Use both the Stock and common systems, where appropriate.
   a. Fe^{3+} and Br^-
   b. Fe^{2+} and Br^-
   c. Au^{3+} and S^{2-}
   d. Au^+ and S^{2-}
8. Name the ionic compound formed by each pair of ions. Use both the Stock and common systems, where appropriate.
   a. Cr^{3+} and O^{2-}
   b. Cr^{2+} and O^{2-}
   c. Pb^{2+} and Cl^-
   d. Pb^{4+} and Cl^-
9. Name the ionic compound formed by each pair of ions. Use both the Stock and common systems, where appropriate.
   a. Cr^{3+} and NO_3^-
   b. Fe^{2+} and PO_4^{3-}
   c. Ca^{2+} and CrO_4^{2-}
   d. Al^{3+} and OH^-
10. Name the ionic compound formed by each pair of ions. Use both the Stock and common systems, where appropriate.
    a. NH_4^+ and NO_3^-
    b. H^+ and $Cr_2O_7^{2-}$
    c. Cu^+ and CO_3^{2-}
    d. Na^+ and HCO_3^-
11. Give two names for each compound.
    a. $Al(HSO_4)_3$
    b. $Mg(HSO_4)_2$
12. Give two names for each compound.
    a. $Co(HCO_3)_2$
    b. $LiHCO_3$

ANSWERS

1. a. the radium ion
   b. the phosphide ion
   c. the dihydrogen phosphate ion
   d. the tin(IV) ion or the stannic ion
3. a. sodium bromide
   b. magnesium bromide
   c. magnesium sulfide
5. a. sodium nitride
   b. magnesium nitride
   c. aluminum sulfide
7. a. iron(III) bromide or ferric bromide
   b. iron(II) bromide or ferrous bromide
   c. gold(III) sulfide or auric sulfide
   d. gold(I) sulfide or aurous sulfide
9. a. chromium(III) nitrate or chromic nitrate
   b. iron(II) phosphate or ferrous phosphate
   c. calcium chromate
   d. aluminum hydroxide
11. a. aluminum hydrogen sulfate or aluminum bisulfate
    b. magnesium hydrogen sulfate or magnesium bisulfate

5. FORMULA MASS

LEARNING OBJECTIVE

1. **Determine the formula mass of an ionic compound.**

One skill needed in future chapters is the ability to determine the mass of the formula of an ionic compound. This quantity is called the **formula mass**. The formula mass is obtained by adding the masses of each individual atom in the formula of the compound. Because a proper formula is electrically neutral (with no net electrons gained or lost), the ions can be considered atoms for the purpose of calculating the formula mass.

formula mass

The sum of the masses of the elements in the formula of an ionic compound.

Let us start by calculating the formula mass of sodium chloride (NaCl). This formula mass is the sum of the atomic masses of one sodium atom and one chlorine atom, which we find from the periodic table; here, we use the masses to two decimal places:

Na:	22.99 u
Cl:	+ 35.45 u
Total:	58.44 u

To two decimal places, the formula mass of NaCl is 58.44 u.

When an ionic compound has more than one anion or cation, you must remember to use the proper multiple of the atomic mass for the element in question. For the formula mass of calcium fluoride (CaF_2), we must multiply the mass of the fluorine atom by 2 to account for the two fluorine atoms in the chemical formula:

Ca:	1 × 40.08	40.08 u
F:	2 × 19.00 =	+ 38.00 u
Total:		78.08 u

The formula mass of CaF_2 is 78.08 u.

For ionic compounds with polyatomic ions, the sum must include the number and mass of each atom in the formula for the polyatomic ion. For example, potassium nitrate (KNO_3) has one potassium atom, one nitrogen atom, and three oxygen atoms:

K:	1 × 39.10	39.10 u
N:	1 × 14.00	+ 14.00 u
O:	3 × 16.00 =	+ 48.00 u
Total:		101.10 u

The formula mass of KNO_3 is 101.10 u.

Note

Potassium nitrate is a key ingredient in gunpowder and has been used clinically as a diuretic.

When a formula contains more than one polyatomic unit in the chemical formula, as in $Ca(NO_3)_2$, don't forget to multiply the atomic mass of every atom inside the parentheses by the subscript outside the parentheses. This is necessary because the subscript refers to the *entire polyatomic ion*. Thus, for $Ca(NO_3)_2$, the subscript 2 implies two complete nitrate ions, so we must sum the masses of two (1 × 2) nitrogen atoms and six (3 × 2) oxygen atoms, along with the mass of a single calcium atom:

Ca:	1 × 40.08	40.08 u
N:	2 × 14.00 =	+ 28.00 u
O:	6 × 16.00 =	+ 96.00 u
Total:		164.08 u

The key to calculating the formula mass of an ionic compound is to correctly count each atom in the formula and multiply the atomic masses of its atoms accordingly.

EXAMPLE 9

Use the atomic masses (rounded to two decimal places) from the inside cover of this book to determine the formula mass for each ionic compound.

1. $FeCl_3$
2. $(NH_4)_3PO_4$

Solution

1. | | | |
   |---|---|---|
   | Fe: | | 55.85 u |
   | Cl: | 3 × 35.45 = | + 106.35 u |
   | Total: | | 162.20 u |

   The formula mass of $FeCl_3$ is 162.20 u.
2. When we distribute the subscript 3 through the parentheses containing the formula for the ammonium ion, we see that we have 3 nitrogen atoms and 12 hydrogen atoms. Thus, we set up the sum as follows:

N:	3 × 14.00 =	42.00 u
H:	12 × 1.00 =	+ 12.00 u
P:		+ 30.97 u
O:	4 × 16.00 =	+ 64.00 u
Total:		148.97 u

   The formula mass for $(NH_4)_3PO_4$ is 148.97 u.

SKILL-BUILDING EXERCISE

Use the atomic masses (rounded to two decimal places) from the inside cover of this book to determine the formula mass for each ionic compound.

1. TiO_2
2. AgBr
3. $Au(NO_3)_3$
4. $Fe_3(PO_4)_2$

To Your Health: Hydrates

Some ionic compounds have water (H_2O) incorporated within their formula unit. These compounds, called *hydrates*, have a characteristic number of water units associated with each formula unit of the compound. Hydrates are solids, not liquids or solutions, despite the water they contain.

To write the chemical formula of a hydrate, write the number of water units per formula unit of compound after its chemical formula. The two chemical formulas are separated by a vertically centered dot. The hydrate of copper(II) sulfate has five water units associated with each formula unit, so it is written as $CuSO_4{\cdot}5H_2O$. The name of this compound is copper(II) sulfate pentahydrate, with the *penta-* prefix indicating the presence of five water units per formula unit of copper(II) sulfate.

Hydrates have various uses in the health industry. Calcium sulfate hemihydrate ($CaSO_4{\cdot}½H_2O$), known as plaster of Paris, is used to make casts for broken bones. Epsom salt ($MgSO_4{\cdot}7H_2O$) is used as a bathing salt and a laxative. Aluminum chloride hexahydrate is an active ingredient in antiperspirants. The accompanying table lists some useful hydrates.

Calcium sulfate hemihydrate ($CaSO_4{\cdot}½H_2O$), or plaster of Paris, is used to make casts to immobilize broken bones until they heal.

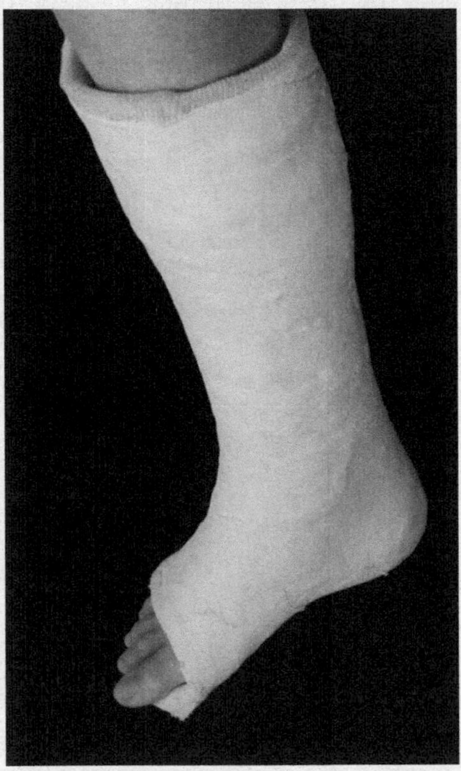

TABLE 3.4 Names and Formulas of Some Widely Used Hydrates

Formula	Name	Uses
$AlCl_3{\cdot}6H_2O$	aluminum chloride hexahydrate	antiperspirant
$CaSO_4{\cdot}½H_2O$	calcium sulfate hemihydrate (plaster of Paris)	casts (for broken bones and castings)
$CaSO_4{\cdot}2H_2O$	calcium sulfate dihydrate (gypsum)	drywall component
$CoCl_2{\cdot}6H_2O$	cobalt(II) chloride hexahydrate	drying agent, humidity indicator
$CuSO_4{\cdot}5H_2O$	copper(II) sulfate pentahydrate	fungicide, algicide, herbicide
$MgSO_4{\cdot}7H_2O$	magnesium sulfate heptahydrate (Epsom salts)	laxative, bathing salt
$Na_2CO_3{\cdot}10H_2O$	sodium carbonate decahydrate (washing soda)	laundry additive/cleaner

CONCEPT REVIEW EXERCISES

1. What is the relationship between atomic mass and formula mass?
2. How are subscripts used to determine a formula mass when more than one polyatomic ion is present in a chemical formula?

ANSWERS

1. The formula mass is the sum of the atomic masses of the atoms in the formula.
2. The subscript is distributed throughout the parentheses to determine the total number of atoms in the formula.

KEY TAKEAWAY

- Formula masses of ionic compounds can be determined from the masses of the atoms in their formulas.

EXERCISES

1. What is the formula mass for the ionic compound formed by each pair of ions?
   a. Na^+ and Br^-
   b. Mg^{2+} and Br^-
   c. Mg^{2+} and S^{2-}
2. What is the formula mass for the ionic compound formed by each pair of ions?
   a. K^+ and Cl^-
   b. Mg^{2+} and Cl^-
   c. Mg^{2+} and Se^{2-}
3. What is the formula mass for the ionic compound formed by each pair of ions?
   a. Na^+ and N^{3-}
   b. Mg^{2+} and N^{3-}
   c. Al^{3+} and S^{2-}
4. What is the formula mass for the ionic compound formed by each pair of ions?
   a. Li^+ and N^{3-}
   b. Mg^{2+} and P^{3-}
   c. Li^+ and P^{3-}
5. What is the formula mass for each compound?
   a. $FeBr_3$
   b. $FeBr_2$
   c. Au_2S_3
   d. Au_2S
6. What is the formula mass for each compound?
   a. Cr_2O_3
   b. CrO
   c. $PbCl_2$
   d. $PbCl_4$
7. What is the formula mass for each compound?
   a. $Cr(NO_3)_3$
   b. $Fe_3(PO_4)_2$
   c. $CaCrO_4$
   d. $Al(OH)_3$
8. What is the formula mass for each compound?
   a. NH_4NO_3
   b. $H_2Cr_2O_7$
   c. Cu_2CO_3
   d. $NaHCO_3$
9. What is the formula mass for each compound?
   a. $Al(HSO_4)_3$
   b. $Mg(HSO_4)_2$
10. What is the formula mass for each compound?
    a. $Co(HCO_3)_2$
    b. $LiHCO_3$

ANSWERS

1. a. 102.90 u
   b. 184.11 u
   c. 56.38 u
3. a. 83.00 u
   b. 100.93 u
   c. 150.17 u

5. a. 295.50 u
   b. 215.60 u
   c. 490.30 u
   d. 426.10 u
7. a. 238.00 u
   b. 357.49 u
   c. 156.08 u
   d. 78.01 u
9. a. 318.22 u
   b. 218.47 u

6. END-OF-CHAPTER MATERIAL

Chapter Summary

To ensure that you understand the material in this chapter, you should review the meanings of the following bold terms and ask yourself how they relate to the topics in the chapter.

Atoms combine into compounds by forming **chemical bonds**. A survey of stable atoms and molecules leads to the **octet rule**, which says that stable atoms tend to have eight electrons in their outermost, or valence, shell. One way atoms obtain eight electrons in the valence shell is for some atoms to lose electrons while other atoms gain them. When this happens, the atoms take on an electrical charge. Charged atoms are called **ions**. Ions having opposite charges attract each other. This attraction is called **ionic bonding**, and the compounds formed are called **ionic compounds**.

Positively charged ions are called **cations**, while negatively charged ions are called **anions**. The formation of both cations and anions can be illustrated using electron configurations. Because elements in a column of the periodic table have the same valence shell electron configuration, atoms in the same column of the periodic table tend to form ions having the same charge. **Electron dot diagrams**, or **Lewis diagrams**, can also be used to illustrate the formation of cations and anions.

Ionic compounds are represented in writing by a **chemical formula**, which gives the lowest ratio of cations and anions present in the compound. In a formula, the symbol of the cation is written first, followed by the symbol of the anion. **Formula unit** is considered the basic unit of an ionic compound because ionic compounds do not exist as discrete units. Instead, they exist as **crystals**, three-dimensional arrays of ions, with cations surrounded by anions and anions surrounded by cations. Chemical formulas for ionic compounds are determined by balancing the positive charge from the cation(s) with the negative charge from the anion(s). A subscript to the right of the ion indicates that more than one of that ion is present in the chemical formula.

Some ions are groups of atoms bonded together and having an overall electrical charge. These are called **polyatomic ions**. Writing formulas with polyatomic ions follows the same rules as with monatomic ions, except that when more than one polyatomic ion is present in a chemical formula, the polyatomic ion is enclosed in parentheses and the subscript is outside the right parenthesis. Ionic compounds typically form between metals and nonmetals or between polyatomic ions.

Names of ionic compounds are derived from the names of the ions, with the name of the cation coming first, followed by the name of the anion. If an element can form cations of different charges, there are two alternate systems for indicating the compound's name. In the **Stock system**, a roman numeral in parentheses indicates the charge on the cation. An example is the name for $FeCl_2$, which is iron(II) chloride. In the common system, the suffixes *-ous* and *-ic* are used to stand for the lower and higher possible charge of the cation, respectively. These suffixes are attached to a stem representing the element (which frequently comes from the Latin form of the element name). An example is the common name for $FeCl_2$, which is ferrous chloride.

The **formula mass** of an ionic compound is the sum of the masses of each individual atom in the formula. Care must be taken when calculating formula masses for formulas containing multiple polyatomic ions because the subscript outside the parentheses refers to all the atoms in the polyatomic ion.

ADDITIONAL EXERCISES

1. What number shell is the valence electron shell of a sodium atom? What number shell is the valence shell of a sodium ion? Explain the difference.
2. What number shell is the valence electron shell of a bromine atom? What number shell is the valence shell of a bromide ion? Explain the difference between these answers and the answers to Exercise 1.

3. What is the electron configuration of each ion?
   a. K^+
   b. Mg^{2+}
   c. F^-
   d. S^{2-}
4. What is the electron configuration of each ion?
   a. Li^+
   b. Ca^{2+}
   c. Cl^-
   d. O^{2-}
5.
   a. If a sodium atom were to lose two electrons, what would be the electron configuration of the resulting cation?
   b. Considering that electron shells are typically separated by large amounts of energy, use your answer to Exercise 5a to suggest why sodium atoms do not form a 2+ cation.
6.
   a. If a chlorine atom were to gain two electrons, what would be the electron configuration of the resulting anion?
   b. Considering that electron shells are typically separated by large amounts of energy, use your answer to Exercise 6a to suggest why chlorine atoms do not form a 2− anion.
7. Use Lewis diagrams and arrows to show the electron transfer that occurs during the formation of an ionic compound among Mg atoms and F atoms. (Hint: how many atoms of each will you need?)
8. Use Lewis diagrams and arrows to show the electron transfer that occurs during the formation of an ionic compound among K atoms and O atoms. (Hint: how many atoms of each will you need?)
9. Mercury forms two possible cations—Hg^{2+} and Hg_2^{2+}, the second of which is actually a two-atom cation with a 2+ charge.
   a. Using common names, give the probable names of these ions.
   b. What are the chemical formulas of the ionic compounds these ions make with the oxide ion, O^{2-}?
10. The uranyl ion (UO_2^{2+}) is a common water-soluble form of uranium. What is the chemical formula of the ionic compound uranyl nitrate? What is the chemical formula of the ionic compound uranyl phosphate?
11. The formal chemical name of the mineral *strengite* is iron(III) phosphate dihydrate. What is the chemical formula of strengite? What is the formula mass of strengite?
12. What is the formula mass of $MgSO_4{\cdot}7H_2O$?
13. What is the formula mass of $CaSO_4{\cdot}½H_2O$?
14. What mass does 20 formula units of NaCl have?
15. What mass does 75 formula units of K_2SO_4 have?
16. If an atomic mass unit equals 1.66×10^{-24} g, what is the mass in grams of one formula unit of NaCl?
17. If an atomic mass unit equals 1.66×10^{-24} g, what is the mass in grams of 5.00×10^{22} formula units of NaOH?
18. If an atomic mass unit equals 1.66×10^{-24} g, what is the mass in grams of 3.96×10^{23} formula units of $(NH_4)_2SO_4$?
19. Both tin and lead acquire 2+ or 4+ charges when they become ions. Use the periodic table to explain why this should not surprise you.
20. Which ion would you expect to be larger in size—In^{3+} or Tl^{3+}? Explain.
21. Which ion would you expect to be smaller in size—I^- or Br^-? Explain.
22. Which ion with a 2+ charge has the following electron configuration? $1s^22s^22p^6$
23. Which ion with a 3− charge has the following electron configuration? $1s^22s^22p^6$

ANSWERS

1. For sodium, the valence shell is the third shell; for the sodium ion, the valence shell is the second shell because it has lost all its third shell electrons.

3. a. $1s^2 2s^2 2p^6 3s^2 3p^6$
   b. $1s^2 2s^2 2p^6$
   c. $1s^2 2s^2 2p^6$
   d. $1s^2 2s^2 2p^6 3s^2 3p^6$
5. a. $1s^2 2s^2 2p^5$
   b. It probably requires too much energy to form.
7.

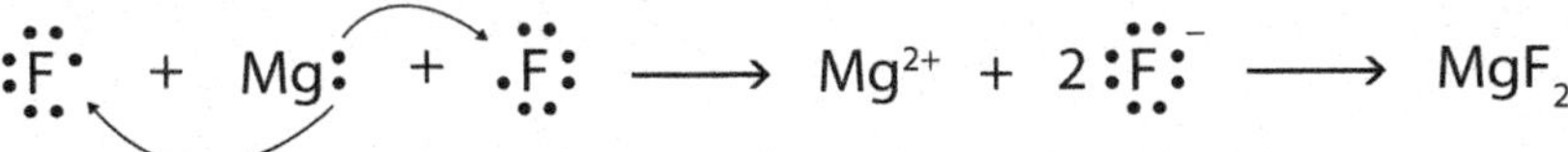

9. a. mercuric and mercurous, respectively
   b. HgO and Hg2O, respectively
11. FePO4·2H2O; 186.86 u
13. 145.16 u
15. 13,070.25 u
17. 3.32 g
19. Both tin and lead have two *p* electrons and two *s* electrons in their valence shells.
21. Br^- because it is higher up on the periodic table
23. N^{3-}

CHAPTER 4

Covalent Bonding and Simple Molecular Compounds

Opening Essay

Cholesterol ($C_{27}H_{46}O$), a compound that is sometimes in the news, is a white, waxy solid produced in the liver of every animal, including humans. It is important for building cell membranes and in producing certain hormones (chemicals that regulate cellular activity in the body). As such, it is necessary for life, but why is cholesterol the object of attention?

Besides producing cholesterol, we also ingest some whenever we eat meat or other animal-based food products. People who eat such products in large quantities, or whose metabolisms are unable to handle excess amounts, may experience an unhealthy buildup of cholesterol in their blood. Deposits of cholesterol, called plaque, may form on blood vessel walls, eventually blocking the arteries and preventing the delivery of oxygen to body tissues. Heart attacks, strokes, and other circulatory problems can result.

Most medical professionals recommend diets that minimize the amount of ingested cholesterol as a way of preventing heart attacks and strokes. Tests are available to measure cholesterol in the blood, and there are several drugs capable of lowering cholesterol levels.

A Molecular Model of Cholesterol

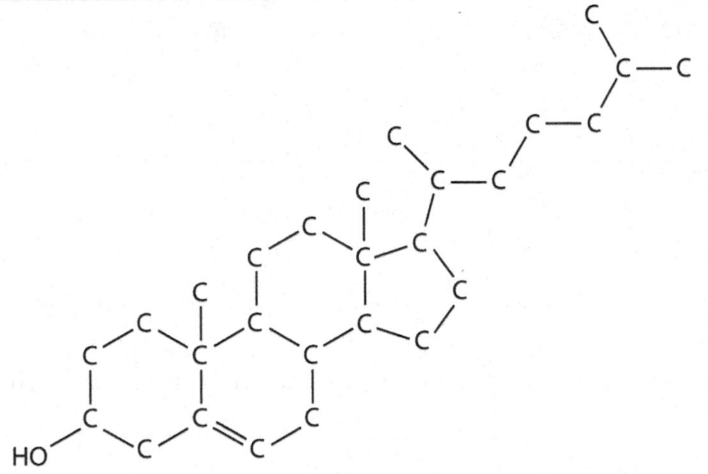

Chapter 3 discussed ionic bonding, which results from the transfer of electrons among atoms or groups of atoms. In this chapter, we will consider another type of bonding—covalent bonding. We will examine how atoms share electrons to form these bonds, and we will begin to explore how the resulting compounds, such as cholesterol, are different from ionic compounds.

1. COVALENT BONDS

LEARNING OBJECTIVE

1. Describe how a covalent bond forms.

You have already seen examples of substances that contain covalent bonds. One substance mentioned in Chapter 3 was water (H_2O). You can tell from its formula that it is not an ionic compound; it is not composed of a metal and a nonmetal. Consequently, its properties are different from those of ionic compounds.

1.1 Electron Sharing

Chapter 3 described how electrons can be transferred from one atom to another so that both atoms have an energy-stable outer electron shell. Because most filled electron shells have eight electrons in them, chemists called this tendency the octet rule. But there is another way an atom can achieve a full valence shell: atoms can *share* electrons.

This concept can be illustrated by using two hydrogen atoms, each of which has a single electron in its valence shell. (For small atoms such as hydrogen atoms, the valence shell will be the first shell, which holds only two electrons.) We can represent the two individual hydrogen atoms as follows:

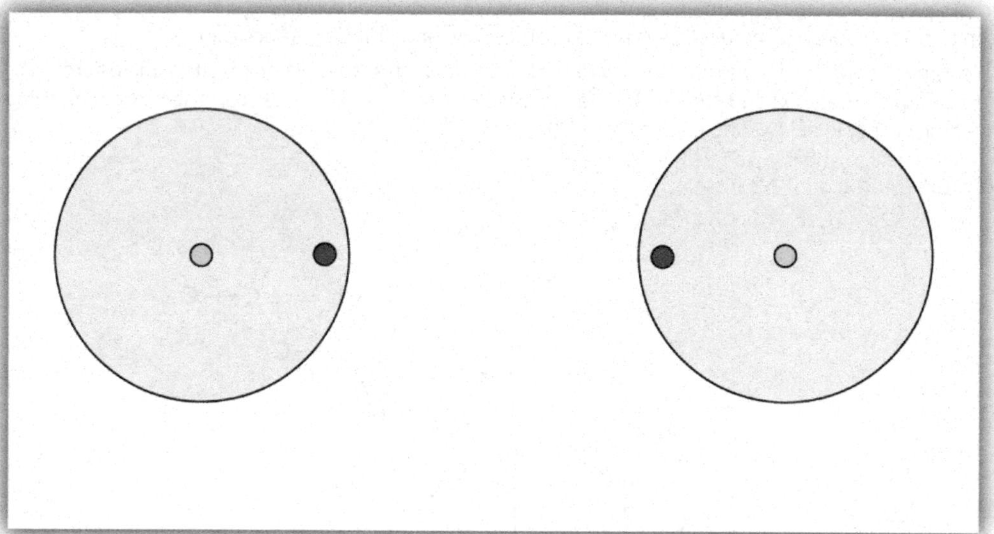

In contrast, when two hydrogen atoms get close enough together to share their electrons, they can be represented as follows:

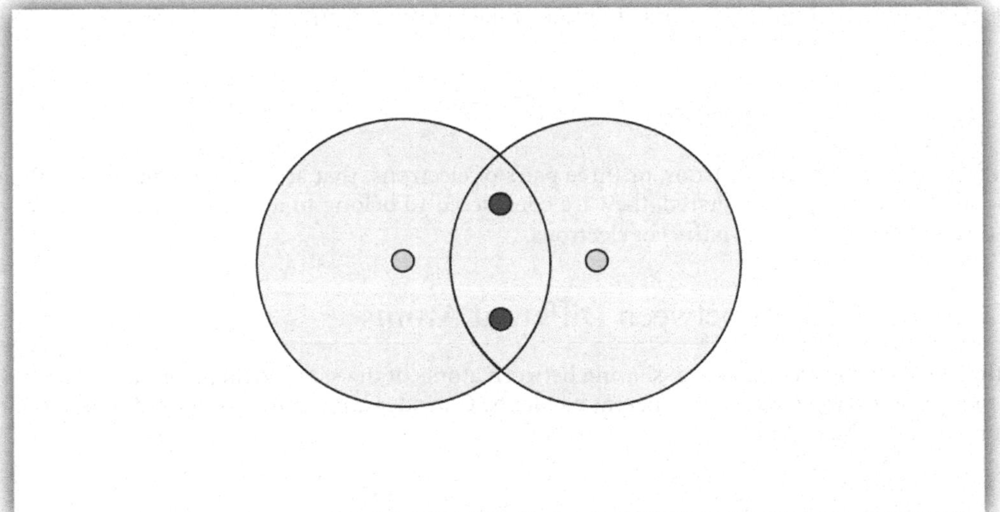

By sharing their valence electrons, both hydrogen atoms now have two electrons in their respective valence shells. Because each valence shell is now filled, this arrangement is more stable than when the two atoms are separate. The sharing of electrons between atoms is called a **covalent bond**, and the two electrons that join atoms in a covalent bond are called a **bonding pair of electrons**. A discrete group of atoms connected by covalent bonds is called a **molecule**—the smallest part of a compound that retains the chemical identity of that compound.

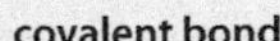

covalent bond

The sharing of electrons between two atoms.

bonding pair of electrons

The two electrons that join atoms in a covalent bond.

molecule

A discrete group of atoms connected by covalent bonds.

Chemists frequently use Lewis diagrams to represent covalent bonding in molecular substances. For example, the Lewis diagrams of two separate hydrogen atoms are as follows:

H•   •H

The Lewis diagram of two hydrogen atoms sharing electrons looks like this:

H:H

This depiction of molecules is simplified further by using a dash to represent a covalent bond. The hydrogen molecule is then represented as follows:

H—H

Remember that the dash, also referred to as a **single bond**, represents a *pair* of electrons.

single bond

A covalent bond formed by a single pair of electrons.

The bond in a hydrogen molecule, measured as the distance between the two nuclei, is about 7.4×10^{-11} m, or 74 picometers (pm; 1 pm = 1×10^{-12} m). This particular **bond length** represents a balance between several forces: the attractions between oppositely charged electrons and nuclei, the repulsion between two negatively charged electrons, and the repulsion between two positively charged nuclei. If the nuclei were closer together, they would repel each other more strongly; if the nuclei were farther apart, there would be less attraction between the positive and negative particles.

bond length

The distance between two nuclei in a covalent bond.

Fluorine is another element whose atoms bond together in pairs to form *diatomic* (two-atom) molecules. Two separate fluorine atoms have the following electron dot diagrams:

Each fluorine atom contributes one valence electron, making a single bond and giving each atom a complete valence shell, which fulfills the octet rule:

The circles show that each fluorine atom has eight electrons around it. As with hydrogen, we can represent the fluorine molecule with a dash in place of the bonding electrons:

F—F

nonbonding pair (or lone pair) of electrons

Electron pair that does not participate in covalent bonds.

Each fluorine atom has six electrons, or three pairs of electrons, that are not participating in the covalent bond. Rather than being shared, they are considered to belong to a single atom. These are called **nonbonding pairs (or lone pairs)** of electrons.

1.2 Covalent Bonds between Different Atoms

Now that we have looked at electron sharing between atoms of the same element, let us look at covalent bond formation between atoms of different elements. Consider a molecule composed of one hydrogen atom and one fluorine atom:

H•   •F:

Each atom needs one additional electron to complete its valence shell. By each contributing one electron, they make the following molecule:

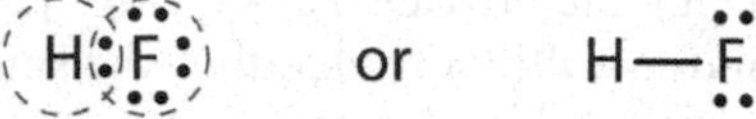

In this molecule, the hydrogen atom does not have nonbonding electrons, while the fluorine atom has six nonbonding electrons (three lone electron pairs). The circles show how the valence electron shells are filled for both atoms.

EXAMPLE 1

Draw the Lewis diagram for each compound.

1. a molecule composed of two chlorine atoms
2. a molecule composed of a hydrogen atom and a bromine atom

Solution

1. Chlorine has the same valence shell electron configuration as fluorine, so the Lewis diagram for a molecule composed of two chlorine atoms is similar to the one for fluorine:

   Cl:Cl

2. Bromine has the same valence shell electron configuration as fluorine, so the Lewis diagram for a molecule composed of a hydrogen atom and a bromine atom is similar to that for hydrogen and fluorine:

   H:Br

SKILL-BUILDING EXERCISE

Draw the Lewis diagram for each compound.

1. a molecule composed of one chlorine atom and one fluorine atom
2. a molecule composed of one hydrogen atom and one iodine atom

Larger molecules are constructed in a similar fashion, with some atoms participating in more than one covalent bond. For example, water, with two hydrogen atoms and one oxygen atom, and methane (CH_4), with one carbon atom and four hydrogen atoms, can be represented as follows:

```
  ••            H
H:O:            ••
  ••          H:C:H
  H             ••
                H
```

Atoms typically form a characteristic number of covalent bonds in compounds. Figure 4.2 shows the number of covalent bonds various atoms typically form.

FIGURE 4.2 How Many Covalent Bonds Are Formed?

In molecules, there is a pattern to the number of covalent bonds that different atoms can form. Each block with a number indicates the number of covalent bonds formed by that atom in neutral compounds.

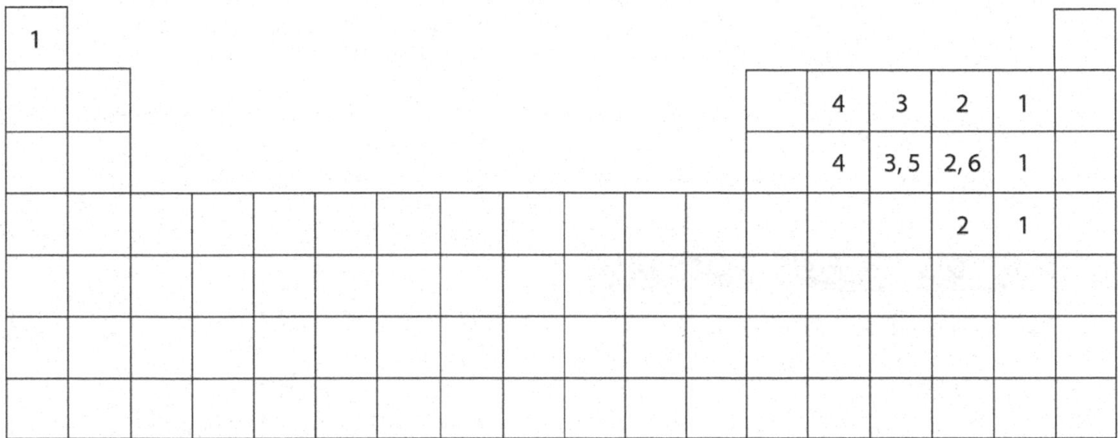

CONCEPT REVIEW EXERCISES

1. How is a covalent bond formed between two atoms?
2. How does covalent bonding allow atoms in group 6A to satisfy the octet rule?

ANSWERS

1. Covalent bonds are formed by two atoms sharing electrons.
2. The atoms in group 6A make two covalent bonds.

KEY TAKEAWAY

- A covalent bond is formed between two atoms by sharing electrons.

EXERCISES

1. Define *covalent bond.*
2. What is electron sharing?
3. Draw the Lewis diagram for the covalent bond in the Br_2 molecule.
4. Draw the Lewis diagram for the covalent bond in the I_2 molecule.
5. Draw the Lewis diagram for the covalent bond in the HCl molecule.
6. Draw the Lewis diagram for the covalent bond in the HI molecule.
7. What is the difference between a molecule and a formula unit?
8. Why do hydrogen atoms not follow the octet rule when they form covalent bonds?

9. Draw the Lewis diagram for the covalent bonding in H_2S. How many bonding electrons and nonbonding electrons are in the molecule?
10. Draw the Lewis diagram for the covalent bonding in NI_3. How many bonding electrons and nonbonding electrons are in the molecule?
11. Draw the Lewis diagram for the covalent bonding in CF_4. How many bonding electrons and nonbonding electrons are in the molecule?
12. Draw the Lewis diagram for the covalent bonding in PCl_3. How many bonding electrons and nonbonding electrons are in the molecule?
13. How many covalent bonds does a hydrogen atom typically form? Why?
14. How many covalent bonds does an oxygen atom typically form? Why?
15. Tellurium atoms make covalent bonds. How many covalent bonds would a tellurium atom make? Predict the formula of a compound between tellurium and hydrogen.
16. Tin atoms make covalent bonds. How many covalent bonds would a tin atom make? Predict the formula of a compound between tin and hydrogen.
17. Astatine is a synthetic element, made one atom at a time in huge "atom-smasher" machines. It is in the halogen group on the periodic table. How many covalent bonds would an atom of this element form?
18. There have been reports that atoms of element 116 were made by smashing smaller atoms together. Using the periodic table, determine what column element 116 would be in and suggest how many covalent bonds an atom of this element would form.

ANSWERS

1. A covalent bond is formed when two atoms share electrons.

3.

:Br:Br:

5.

:I:I:

7. A molecule is a discrete combination of atoms; a formula unit is the lowest ratio of ions in a crystal.

9.

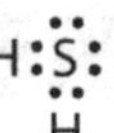

bonding electrons: 4; nonbonding electrons: 4

11.

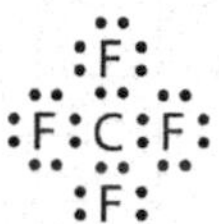

bonding electrons: 8; nonbonding electrons: 24

13. Hydrogen atoms form only one covalent bond because they have only one valence electron to pair.
15. two; H_2Te
17. one

2. COVALENT COMPOUNDS: FORMULAS AND NAMES

LEARNING OBJECTIVES

1. **Determine the chemical formula of a simple covalent compound from its name.**
2. **Determine the name of a simple covalent compound from its chemical formula.**

What elements make covalent bonds? Covalent bonds form when two or more nonmetals combine. For example, both hydrogen and oxygen are nonmetals, and when they combine to make water, they do so by forming covalent bonds. Nonmetal atoms in polyatomic ions are joined by covalent bonds, but the ion as a whole participates in ionic bonding. For example, ammonium chloride has ionic bonds between a polyatomic ion, NH_4^+, and Cl^- ions, but within the ammonium ion, the nitrogen and hydrogen atoms are connected by covalent bonds:

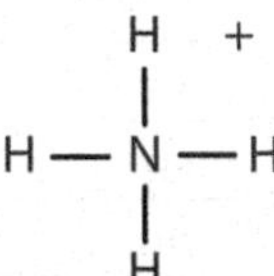

EXAMPLE 2

Is each compound formed from ionic bonds, covalent bonds, or both?

1. Na_2O
2. Na_3PO_4
3. N_2O_4

Solution

1. The elements in Na_2O are a metal and a nonmetal, which form ionic bonds.
2. Because sodium is a metal and we recognize the formula for the phosphate ion (see Table 3.1), we know that this compound is ionic. However, polyatomic ions are held together by covalent bonds, so this compound contains both ionic and covalent bonds.
3. The elements in N_2O_4 are both nonmetals, rather than a metal and a nonmetal. Therefore, the atoms form covalent bonds.

SKILL-BUILDING EXERCISE

Is each compound are formed from ionic bonds, covalent bonds, or both?

1. $Ba(OH)_2$
2. F_2
3. PCl_3

The chemical formulas for covalent compounds are referred to as **molecular formulas** because these compounds exist as separate, discrete molecules. Typically, a molecular formula begins with the nonmetal that is closest to the lower left corner of the periodic table, except that hydrogen is almost never written first (H_2O is the prominent exception). Then the other nonmetal symbols are listed. Numerical subscripts are used if there is more than one of a particular atom. For example, we have already seen CH_4, the molecular formula for methane.

molecular formula

A chemical formula for a covalent compound.

Naming *binary* (two-element) covalent compounds is similar to naming simple ionic compounds. The first element in the formula is simply listed using the name of the element. The second element is named by taking the stem of the element name and adding the suffix *-ide*. A system of numerical prefixes is used to specify the number of atoms in a molecule. Table 4.1 lists these numerical prefixes. Normally, no prefix is added to the first element's name if there is only one atom of the first element in a molecule. If the second element is oxygen, the trailing vowel is usually omitted from the end of a polysyllabic prefix but not a monosyllabic one (that is, we would say "monoxide" rather than "monooxide" and "trioxide" rather than "troxide").

TABLE 4.1 Numerical Prefixes for Naming Binary Covalent Compounds

Number of Atoms in Compound	Prefix on the Name of the Element
1	mono-*
2	di-
3	tri-
4	tetra-
5	penta-
6	hexa-
7	hepta-
8	octa-
9	nona-
10	deca-
***This prefix is not used for the first element's name.**	

Let us practice by naming the compound whose molecular formula is CCl_4. The name begins with the name of the first element—carbon. The second element, chlor*ine*, becomes chlor*ide*, and we attach the correct numerical prefix ("tetra-") to indicate that the molecule contains four chlorine atoms. Putting these pieces together gives the name *carbon tetrachloride* for this compound.

EXAMPLE 3

Write the molecular formula for each compound.

1. chlorine trifluoride
2. phosphorus pentachloride
3. sulfur dioxide
4. dinitrogen pentoxide

Solution

If there is no numerical prefix on the first element's name, we can assume that there is only one atom of that element in a molecule.

1. ClF_3
2. PCl_5
3. SO_2
4. N_2O_5 (The *di-* prefix on nitrogen indicates that two nitrogen atoms are present.)

SKILL-BUILDING EXERCISE

Write the molecular formula for each compound.

1. nitrogen dioxide
2. dioxygen difluoride
3. sulfur hexafluoride
4. selenium monoxide

Note

Because it is so unreactive, sulfur hexafluoride is used as a spark suppressant in electrical devices such as transformers.

EXAMPLE 4

Write the name for each compound.

1. BrF_5
2. S_2F_2
3. CO

Solution

1. bromine pentafluoride
2. disulfur difluoride
3. carbon monoxide

SKILL-BUILDING EXERCISE

Write the name for each compound.

1. CF_4
2. $SeCl_2$
3. SO_3

For some simple covalent compounds, we use common names rather than systematic names. We have already encountered these compounds, but we list them here explicitly:

- H_2O: water
- NH_3: ammonia
- CH_4: methane

Methane is the simplest **organic compound**. Organic compounds are compounds with carbon atoms and are named by a separate nomenclature system that we will introduce in Section 6.

organic compound

A compound containing carbon atoms.

CONCEPT REVIEW EXERCISES

1. How do you recognize a covalent compound?
2. What are the rules for writing the molecular formula of a simple covalent compound?
3. What are the rules for naming a simple covalent compound?

ANSWERS

1. A covalent compound is usually composed of two or more nonmetal elements.
2. It is just like an ionic compound except that the element further down and to the left on the periodic table is listed first and is named with the element name.
3. Name the first element first and then the second element by using the stem of the element name plus the suffix *-ide*. Use numerical prefixes if there is more than one atom of the first element; always use numerical prefixes for the number of atoms of the second element.

KEY TAKEAWAYS

- The chemical formula of a simple covalent compound can be determined from its name.
- The name of a simple covalent compound can be determined from its chemical formula.

EXERCISES

1. Identify whether each compound has covalent bonds.
   a. NaI
   b. Na_2CO_3
   c. N_2O
   d. SiO_2
2. Identify whether each compound has covalent bonds.
   a. C_2H_6
   b. C_6H_5Cl
   c. $KC_2H_3O_2$
   d. $Ca(OH)_2$
3. Identify whether each compound has ionic bonds, covalent bonds, or both.
   a. Na_3PO_4
   b. K_2O
   c. $COCl_2$
   d. $CoCl_2$
4. Identify whether each compound has ionic bonds, covalent bonds, or both.
   a. $FeCl_3$
   b. $Fe(NO_3)_3$
   c. $(NH_2)_2CO$
   d. SO_3
5. Which is the correct molecular formula—H_4Si or SiH_4? Explain.
6. Which is the correct molecular formula—SF_6 or F_6S? Explain.
7. Write the name for each covalent compound.
   a. SiF_4
   b. NO_2
   c. CS_2
   d. P_2O_5
8. Write the name for each covalent compound.
   a. CO
   b. S_2O_3
   c. BF_3
   d. GeS_2
9. Write the formula for each covalent compound.
   a. iodine trichloride
   b. disulfur dibromide
   c. arsenic trioxide
   d. xenon hexafluoride
10. Write the formula for each covalent compound.
    a. boron trichloride
    b. carbon dioxide
    c. tetraphosphorus decoxide
    d. germanium dichloride
11. Write two covalent compounds that have common rather than systematic names.
12. What is the name of the simplest organic compound? What would its name be if it followed the nomenclature for binary covalent compounds?

ANSWERS

1. a. no
   b. yes
   c. yes
   d. yes
3. a. both
   b. ionic
   c. covalent
   d. ionic
5. SiH_4; except for water, hydrogen is almost never listed first in a covalent compound.
7. a. silicon tetrafluoride
   b. nitrogen dioxide
   c. carbon disulfide
   d. diphosphorus pentoxide
9. a. ICl_3
   b. S_2Br_2
   c. AsO_3
   d. XeF_6
11. H_2O and NH_3 (water and ammonia) (answers will vary)

3. MULTIPLE COVALENT BONDS

LEARNING OBJECTIVE

1. **Recognize molecules that are likely to have multiple covalent bonds.**

In many molecules, the octet rule would not be satisfied if each pair of bonded atoms shares two electrons. Consider carbon dioxide (CO_2). If each oxygen atom shares one electron with the carbon atom, we get the following:

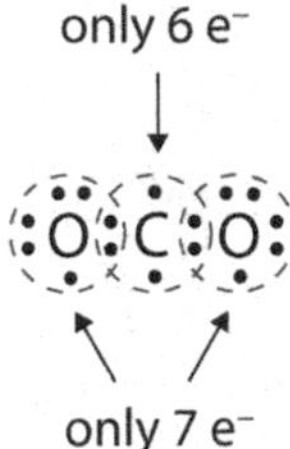

This does not give the carbon atom a complete octet; you will find only six electrons in its valence shell. In addition, each oxygen atom has only seven electrons in its valence shell. Finally, no atom makes the number of bonds it typically forms (Figure 4.2). This arrangement of shared electrons is far from satisfactory.

Sometimes more than one pair of electrons must be shared between two atoms for both atoms to have an octet. In carbon dioxide, a second electron from each oxygen atom is also shared with the central carbon atom, and the carbon atom shares one more electron with each oxygen atom:

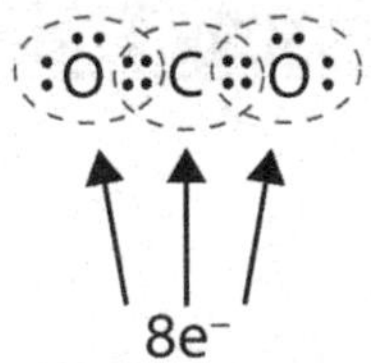

In this arrangement, the carbon atom shares four electrons (two pairs) with the oxygen atom on the left and four electrons with the oxygen atom on the right. There are now eight electrons around each atom. Two pairs of electrons shared between two atoms make a **double bond** between the atoms, which is represented by a double dash:

double bond

Two pairs of electrons being shared by two atoms in a molecule.

$$:\ddot{O}=C=\ddot{O}:$$

Some molecules contain **triple bonds**, covalent bonds in which *three* pairs of electrons are shared by two atoms. A simple compound that has a triple bond is acetylene (C_2H_2), whose Lewis diagram is as follows:

triple bond

Three pairs of electrons being shared by two atoms in a molecule.

$$H:C\vdots\vdots C:H \quad \text{or} \quad H:C\equiv C:H$$

EXAMPLE 5

Draw the Lewis diagram for each molecule.

1. N_2
2. CH_2O (The carbon atom is the central atom.)

Solution

1. The bond between the two nitrogen atoms is a triple bond. The Lewis diagram for N_2 is as follows:

:N:::N: or :N≡N:

2. In CH_2O, the central atom is surrounded by two different types of atoms. The Lewis diagram that fills each atom's valence electron shell is as follows:

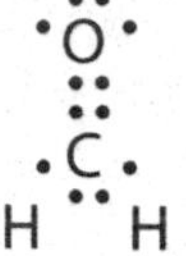

or

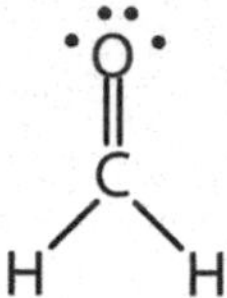

Note

One application of CH_2O, also called formaldehyde, is the preservation of biological specimens. Aqueous solutions of CH_2O are called formalin and have a sharp, characteristic (pungent) odor.

SKILL-BUILDING EXERCISE

Draw the Lewis diagram for each molecule.

1. O_2
2. C_2H_4

CONCEPT REVIEW EXERCISE

1. What is one clue that a molecule has a multiple bond?

ANSWER

1. If single bonds between all atoms do not give all atoms (except hydrogen) an octet, multiple covalent bonds may be present.

KEY TAKEAWAY

- Some molecules must have multiple covalent bonds between atoms to satisfy the octet rule.

EXERCISES

1. Each molecule contains multiple bonds. Draw the Lewis diagram for each. The first element is the central atom.
   a. CS_2
   b. C_2F_4
   c. $COCl_2$
2. Each molecule contains double bonds. Draw the Lewis diagram for each. Assume that the first element is the central atom, unless otherwise noted.
   a. N_2
   b. HCN (The carbon atom is the central atom.)
   c. POCl (The phosphorus atom is the central atom.)
3. Explain why hydrogen atoms do not form double bonds.
4. Why is it incorrect to draw a double bond in the Lewis diagram for MgO?

ANSWERS

1. a.

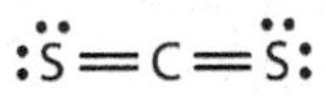

   :S=C=S:

   b.

   :F:C=C:F:
   :F: :F:

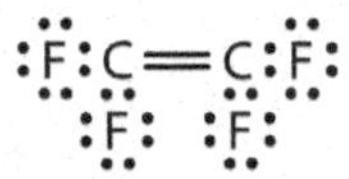

   c.

   O
   C
   :Cl: :Cl:

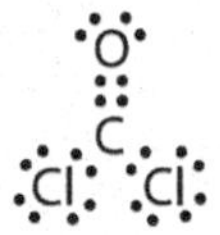

3. Hydrogen can accept only one more electron; multiple bonds require more than one electron pair to be shared.

4. CHARACTERISTICS OF COVALENT BONDS

LEARNING OBJECTIVE

1. **Compare covalent bonds in terms of bond length and bond polarity.**

Covalent bonds have certain characteristics that depend on the identities of the atoms participating in the bond. Two characteristics are bond length and bond polarity.

4.1 Bond Length

In Section 1, we stated that the covalent bond in the hydrogen molecule (H_2) has a certain length (about 7.4×10^{-11} m). Other covalent bonds also have known bond lengths, which are dependent on both the identities of the atoms in the bond and whether the bonds are single, double, or triple bonds. Table 4.2 lists the approximate bond lengths for some single covalent bonds. The exact bond length may vary depending on the identity of the molecule but will be close to the value given in the table.

TABLE 4.2 Approximate Bond Lengths of Some Single Bonds

Bond	Length (× 10^{-12} m)
H–H	74
H–C	110
H–N	100
H–O	97
H–I	161
C–C	154
C–N	147
C–O	143
N–N	145
O–O	145

Table 4.3 compares the lengths of single covalent bonds with those of double and triple bonds between the same atoms. Without exception, as the number of covalent bonds between two atoms increases, the bond length decreases. With more electrons between the two nuclei, the nuclei can get closer together before the internuclear repulsion is strong enough to balance the attraction.

TABLE 4.3 Comparison of Bond Lengths for Single and Multiple Bonds

Bond	Length (× 10^{-12} m)
C–C	154
C=C	134
C≡C	120
C–N	147
C=N	128
C≡N	116
C–O	143
C=O	120
C≡O	113
N–N	145
N=N	123
N≡N	110
O–O	145
O=O	121

4.2 Electronegativity and Bond Polarity

polar covalent bond

A covalent bond with an unbalanced electron distribution across the bond.

nonpolar covalent bond

A covalent bond with a balanced electron distribution across the bond.

Although we defined covalent bonding as electron sharing, the electrons in a covalent bond are not always shared equally by the two bonded atoms. Unless the bond connects two atoms of the same element, there will always be one atom that attracts the electrons in the bond more strongly than the other atom does, as shown in Figure 4.3. When such an imbalance occurs, there is a resulting buildup of some negative charge (called a partial negative charge and designated δ−) on one side of the bond and some positive charge (designated δ+) on the other side of the bond. A covalent bond that has an unequal sharing of electrons, as in part (b) of Figure 4.3, is called a **polar covalent bond**. A covalent bond that has an equal sharing of electrons (part (a) of Figure 4.3) is called a **nonpolar covalent bond**.

FIGURE 4.3 Polar versus Nonpolar Covalent Bonds

(a) The electrons in the covalent bond are equally shared by both hydrogen atoms. This is a nonpolar covalent bond. (b) The fluorine atom attracts the electrons in the bond more than the hydrogen atom does, leading to an imbalance in the electron distribution. This is a polar covalent bond.

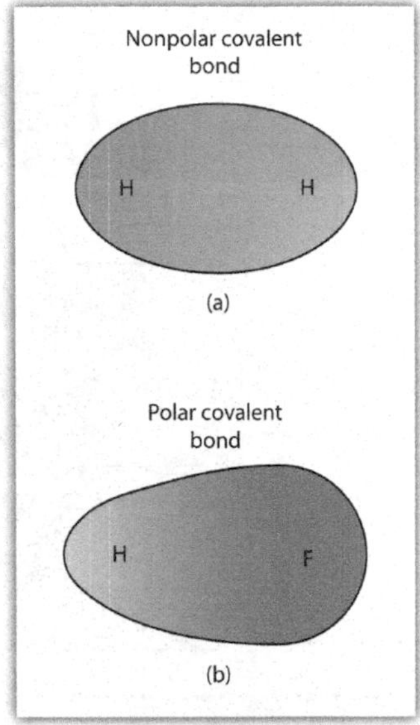

Any covalent bond between atoms of different elements is a polar bond, but the degree of polarity varies widely. Some bonds between different elements are only minimally polar, while others are strongly polar. Ionic bonds can be considered the ultimate in polarity, with electrons being transferred rather than shared. To judge the relative polarity of a covalent bond, chemists use **electronegativity**, which is a relative measure of how strongly an atom attracts electrons when it forms a covalent bond. There are various numerical scales for rating electronegativity. Figure 4.4 shows one of the most popular—the Pauling scale. The polarity of a covalent bond can be judged by determining the difference in the electronegativities of the two atoms making the bond. The greater the difference in electronegativities, the greater the imbalance of electron sharing in the bond. Although there are no hard and fast rules, the general rule is if the difference in electronegativities is less than about 0.4, the bond is considered nonpolar; if the difference is greater than 0.4, the bond is considered polar. If the difference in electronegativities is large enough (generally greater than about 1.8), the resulting compound is considered ionic rather than covalent. An electronegativity difference of zero, of course, indicates a nonpolar covalent bond.

electronegativity

A relative measure of how strongly an atom attracts electrons when it forms a covalent bond.

FIGURE 4.4 Electronegativities of Various Elements

A popular scale for electronegativities has the value for fluorine atoms set at 4.0, the highest value.

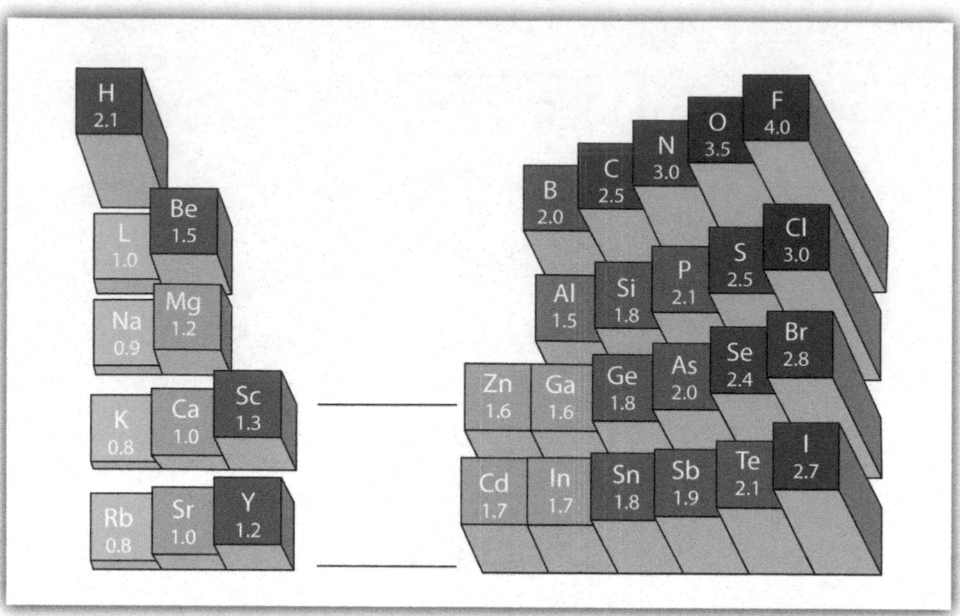

Looking Closer: Linus Pauling

Arguably the most influential chemist of the 20th century, Linus Pauling (1901–94) is the only person to have won two individual (that is, unshared) Nobel Prizes. In the 1930s, Pauling used new mathematical theories to enunciate some fundamental principles of the chemical bond. His 1939 book *The Nature of the Chemical Bond* is one of the most significant books ever published in chemistry.

By 1935, Pauling's interest turned to biological molecules, and he was awarded the 1954 Nobel Prize in Chemistry for his work on protein structure. (He was very close to discovering the double helix structure of DNA when James Watson and James Crick announced their own discovery of its structure in 1953.) He was later awarded the 1962 Nobel Peace Prize for his efforts to ban the testing of nuclear weapons.

In his later years, Pauling became convinced that large doses of vitamin C would prevent disease, including the common cold. Most clinical research failed to show a connection, but Pauling continued to take large doses daily. He died in 1994, having spent a lifetime establishing a scientific legacy that few will ever equal.

Linus Pauling was one of the most influential chemists of the 20th century.

EXAMPLE 6

Describe the electronegativity difference between each pair of atoms and the resulting polarity (or bond type).

1. C and H
2. H and H
3. Na and Cl
4. O and H

Solution

1. Carbon has an electronegativity of 2.5, while the value for hydrogen is 2.1. The difference is 0.3, which is rather small. The C–H bond is therefore considered nonpolar.
2. Both hydrogen atoms have the same electronegativity value—2.1. The difference is zero, so the bond is nonpolar.
3. Sodium's electronegativity is 0.9, while chlorine's is 3.0. The difference is 2.1, which is rather high, and so sodium and chlorine form an ionic compound.
4. With 2.1 for hydrogen and 3.5 for oxygen, the electronegativity difference is 1.4. We would expect a very polar bond, but not so polar that the O–H bond is considered ionic.

SKILL-BUILDING EXERCISE

Describe the electronegativity difference between each pair of atoms and the resulting polarity (or bond type).

1. C and O
2. K and Br
3. N and N
4. Cs and F

When a molecule's bonds are polar, the molecule as a whole can display an uneven distribution of charge, depending on how the individual bonds are oriented. For example, the orientation of the two O–H bonds in a water molecule (Figure 4.5) is bent: one end of the molecule has a partial positive charge, and the other end has a partial negative charge. In short, the molecule itself is polar. The polarity of water has an enormous impact on its physical and chemical properties. (For example, the boiling point of water [100°C] is high for such a small molecule and is due to the fact that polar molecules attract each other strongly.) In contrast, while the two C=O bonds in carbon dioxide are polar, they lie directly opposite each other and so cancel each other's effects. Thus, carbon dioxide molecules are nonpolar overall. This lack of polarity influences some of carbon dioxide's properties. (For example, carbon dioxide becomes a gas at −77°C, almost 200° lower than the temperature at which water boils.)

FIGURE 4.5 Physical Properties and Polarity

The physical properties of water and carbon dioxide are affected by their polarities.

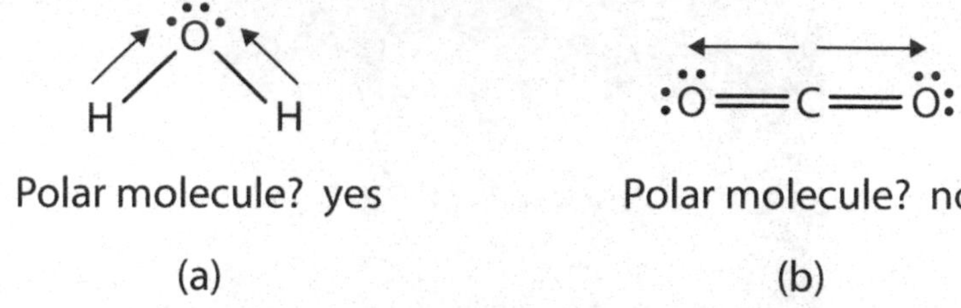

CONCEPT REVIEW EXERCISES

1. What is the name for the distance between two atoms in a covalent bond?
2. What does the electronegativity of an atom indicate?
3. What type of bond is formed between two atoms if the difference in electronegativities is small? Medium? Large?

ANSWERS

1. bond length
2. Electronegativity is a qualitative measure of how much an atom attracts electrons in a covalent bond.
3. nonpolar; polar; ionic

KEY TAKEAWAYS

- Covalent bonds between different atoms have different bond lengths.
- Covalent bonds can be polar or nonpolar, depending on the electronegativity difference between the atoms involved.

EXERCISES

1. Which is longer—a C–H bond or a C–O bond? (Refer to Table 4.2.)
2. Which is shorter—an N–H bond or a C–H bond? (Refer to Table 4.2.)
3. A nanometer is 10^{-9} m. Using the data in Table 4.2 and Table 4.3, determine the length of each bond in nanometers.
   a. a C–O bond
   b. a C=O bond
   c. an H–N bond
   d. a C≡N bond

4. An angstrom (Å) is defined as 10^{-10} m. Using Table 4.2 and Table 4.3, determine the length of each bond in angstroms.
   a. a C–C bond
   b. a C=C bond
   c. an N≡N bond
   d. an H–O bond
5. Refer to Exercise 3. Why is the nanometer unit useful as a unit for expressing bond lengths?
6. Refer to Exercise 4. Why is the angstrom unit useful as a unit for expressing bond lengths?
7. Using Figure 4.4, determine which atom in each pair has the higher electronegativity.
   a. H or C
   b. O or Br
   c. Na or Rb
   d. I or Cl
8. Using Figure 4.4, determine which atom in each pair has the lower electronegativity.
   a. Mg or O
   b. S or F
   c. Al or Ga
   d. O or I
9. Will the electrons be shared equally or unequally across each covalent bond? If unequally, to which atom are the electrons more strongly drawn?
   a. a C–O bond
   b. an F–F bond
   c. an S–N bond
   d. an I–Cl bond
10. Will the electrons be shared equally or unequally across each covalent bond? If unequally, to which atom are the electrons more strongly drawn?
   a. a C–C bond
   b. a S–Cl bond
   c. an O–H bond
   d. an H–H bond

ANSWERS

1. A C–O bond is longer.
3. a. 0.143 nm
   b. 0.120 nm
   c. 0.100 nm
   d. 0.116 nm
5. Actual bond lengths are very small, so the nanometer unit makes the expression of length easier to understand.
7. a. C
   b. O
   c. Na
   d. Cl
9. a. unequally toward the O
   b. equally
   c. unequally toward the N
   d. unequally toward the Cl

5. CHARACTERISTICS OF MOLECULES

LEARNING OBJECTIVES

1. **Determine the molecular mass of a molecule.**
2. **Predict the general shape of a simple covalent molecule.**

Unlike the ions in ionic compounds, which are arranged in lattices called crystals, molecules of covalent compounds exist as discrete units with a characteristic mass and a certain three-dimensional shape.

5.1 Molecular Mass

The mass of a molecule—the **molecular mass** (sometimes called the molecular weight)—is simply the sum of the masses of its atoms. As with formula masses, it is important that you keep track of the number of atoms of each element in the molecular formula to obtain the correct molecular mass. (For more information about formula masses, see Chapter 3, [Unsupported Reference Type: chapter-section].)

molecular mass

The mass of a molecule, which is the sum of the masses of its atoms.

EXAMPLE 7

What is the molecular mass of each covalent compound?

1. H_2O
2. C_6H_6
3. NO_2
4. N_2O_5

Solution

Use the masses of the atoms from the periodic table in Chapter 21.

1. The molecular formula H_2O indicates that there are two hydrogen atoms and one oxygen atom in each molecule. Summing the masses of these atoms,

2 H:	2 × 1.01 =	2.02 u
1 O:		+ 16.00 u
Total:		18.02 u

The molecular mass of H_2O is 18.02 u.

2.

6 C:	6 × 12.01 =	72.06 u
6 H:	6 × 1.01 =	+ 6.06 u
Total:		78.12 u

The molecular mass of C_6H_6 is 78.12 u.

3.

1 N:		14.01 u
2 O:	2 × 16.00 =	+ 32.00 u
Total:		46.01 u

The molecular mass of NO_2 is 46.01 u.

4.

2 N:	2 × 14.01 =	28.02 u
5 O:	5 × 16.00 =	+ 80.00 u
Total:		108.02 u

The molecular mass of N_2O_5 is 108.02 u. (Note that the two different nitrogen and oxygen compounds in these examples have different molecular masses.)

SKILL-BUILDING EXERCISE

What is the molecular mass of each covalent compound?

1. C_2H_2
2. CO
3. CO_2
4. BF_3

5.2 Molecular Shape: VSEPR Theory

valence shell electron pair repulsion (VSEPR)

The general concept that estimates the shape of a simple molecule.

Unlike ionic compounds, with their extended crystal lattices, covalent molecules are discrete units with specific three-dimensional shapes. The shape of a molecule is determined by the fact that covalent bonds, which are composed of negatively charged electrons, tend to repel one another. This concept is called the **valence shell electron pair repulsion (VSEPR)** theory. For example, the two covalent bonds in $BeCl_2$ stay as far from each other as possible, ending up 180° apart from each other. The result is a linear molecule:

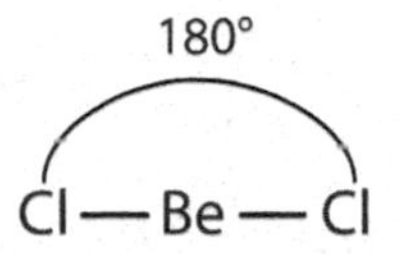

The three covalent bonds in BF_3 repel each other to form 120° angles in a plane, in a shape called *trigonal planar*:

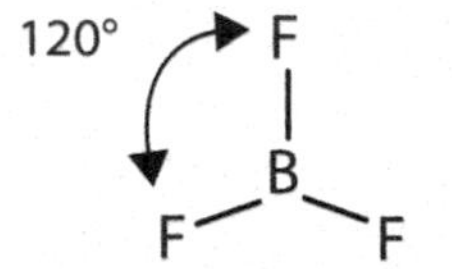

The molecules $BeCl_2$ and BF_3 actually violate the octet rule; however, such exceptions are rare and will not be discussed in this text.

Note

Try sticking three toothpicks into a marshmallow or a gumdrop and see if you can find different positions where your "bonds" are farther apart than the planar 120° orientation.

The four covalent bonds in CCl_4 arrange themselves three dimensionally, pointing toward the corner of a tetrahedron and making bond angles of 109.5°:

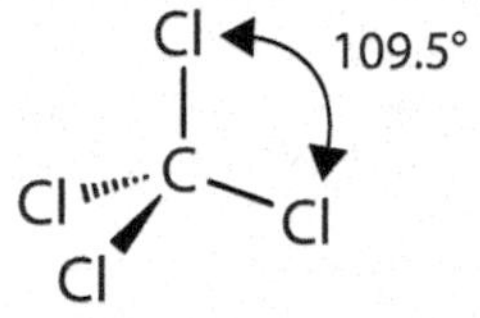

Molecules with lone electron pairs around the central atom have a shape based on the position of the atoms, not the electron pairs. For example, NH_3 has one lone electron pair and three bonded electron pairs. These four electron pairs repel each other and adopt a tetrahedral arrangement:

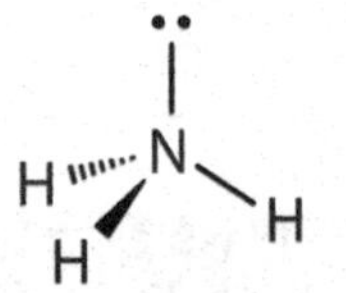

However, the shape of the molecule is described in terms of the positions of the atoms, not the lone electron pairs. Thus, NH_3 is said to have a pyramidal shape, not a tetrahedral one. Similarly, H_2O has two lone pairs of electrons around the central oxygen atom, in addition to the two bonded pairs:

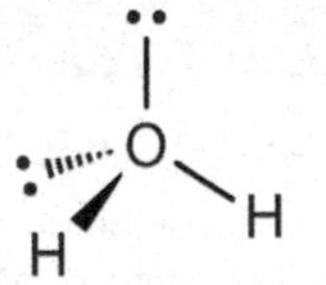

Although the four electron pairs adopt a tetrahedral arrangement due to repulsion, the shape of the molecule is described by the positions of the atoms only. The shape of H_2O is bent.

In determining the shapes of molecules, it is useful to first determine the Lewis diagram for a molecule. The shapes of molecules with multiple bonds are determined by treating the multiple bonds as one bond. Thus, CH_2O has a shape similar to that of BF_3:

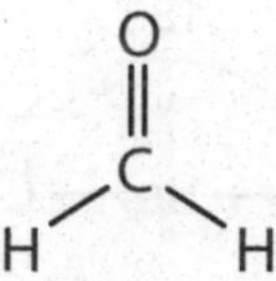

EXAMPLE 8

Describe the shape of each molecule.

1. PCl_3
2. CO_2

Solution

1. The Lewis diagram for PCl_3 is as follows:

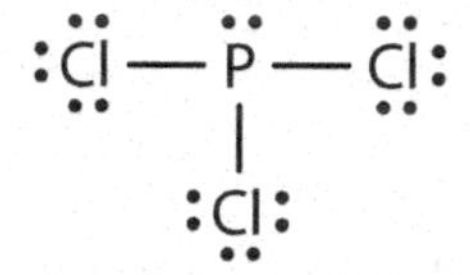

   The four electron pairs arrange themselves tetrahedrally, but the lone electron pair is not considered in describing the molecular shape. Like NH_3, this molecule is pyramidal.
2. The Lewis diagram for CO_2 is as follows:

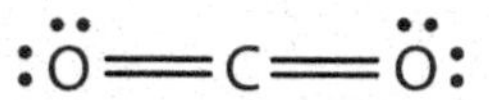

   The multiple bonds are treated as one group. Thus, CO_2 has only two groups of electrons that repel each other. They will direct themselves 180° apart from each other, so CO_2 molecules are linear.

SKILL-BUILDING EXERCISE

Describe the shape of each molecule.

1. CBr_4
2. BCl_3

CONCEPT REVIEW EXERCISES

1. How do you determine the molecular mass of a covalent compound?
2. How do you determine the shape of a molecule?

ANSWERS

1. The molecular mass is the sum of the masses of the atoms in the formula.
2. The shape of a molecule is determined by the position of the atoms, which in turn is determined by the repulsion of the bonded and lone electron pairs around the central atom.

KEY TAKEAWAYS

- A molecule has a certain mass, called the molecular mass.
- Simple molecules have geometries that can be determined from VSEPR theory.

EXERCISES

1. What is the molecular mass of each compound?
   a. H_2S
   b. N_2O_4
   c. ICl_3
   d. HCl
2. What is the molecular mass of each compound?
   a. O_2F_2
   b. CCl_4
   c. C_6H_6
   d. SO_3
3. Aspirin ($C_9H_8O_4$) is a covalent compound. What is its molecular mass?
4. Cholesterol ($C_{27}H_{46}O$) is a biologically important compound. What is its molecular mass?
5. What is the shape of each molecule?
   a. H_2S
   b. $COCl_2$
   c. SO_2
6. What is the shape of each molecule?
   a. NBr_3
   b. SF_2
   c. SiH_4
7. Predict the shape of nitrous oxide (N_2O), which is used as an anesthetic. A nitrogen atom is in the center of this three-atom molecule.
8. Predict the shape of acetylene (C_2H_2), which has the two carbon atoms in the middle of the molecule with a triple bond. What generalization can you make about the shapes of molecules that have more than one central atom?

ANSWERS

1. a. 34.62 u
   b. 92.02 u
   c. 233.25 u
   d. 36.46 u
3. 180.17 u
5. a. bent
   b. trigonal planar
   c. bent
7. bent

6. INTRODUCTION TO ORGANIC CHEMISTRY

LEARNING OBJECTIVES

1. **Define *organic chemistry*.**
2. **Identify organic molecules as alkanes, alkenes, alkynes, alcohols, or carboxylic acids.**

When methane was mentioned at the end of Section 2, we described it as the simplest organic compound. In this section, we introduce organic chemistry more formally.

Organic chemistry is the study of the chemistry of carbon compounds. Carbon is singled out because it has a chemical diversity unrivaled by any other chemical element. Its diversity is based on the following:

organic chemistry

The study of the chemistry of carbon compounds.

- Carbon atoms bond reasonably strongly with other carbon atoms.
- Carbon atoms bond reasonably strongly with atoms of other elements.
- Carbon atoms make a large number of covalent bonds (four).

Curiously, elemental carbon is not particularly abundant. It does not even appear in the list of the most common elements in Earth's crust. (See Table 2.1 in Chapter 2.) Nevertheless, all living things consist of organic compounds.

Most organic chemicals are covalent compounds, which is why we introduce organic chemistry here. By convention, compounds containing carbonate ions and bicarbonate ions, as well as carbon dioxide and carbon monoxide, are not considered part of organic chemistry, even though they contain carbon.

hydrocarbon

The simplest organic compound, composed of carbon and hydrogen atoms only.

alkane (saturated hydrocarbon)

A hydrocarbon with only single covalent bonds and existing as a chain of carbon atoms also bonded to hydrogen atoms.

The simplest organic compounds are the **hydrocarbons**, compounds composed of carbon and hydrogen atoms only. Some hydrocarbons have only single bonds and appear as a chain (which can be a straight chain or can have branches) of carbon atoms also bonded to hydrogen atoms. These hydrocarbons are called **alkanes (saturated hydrocarbons)**. Each alkane has a characteristic, systematic name depending on the number of carbon atoms in the molecule. These names consist of a stem that indicates the number of carbon atoms in the chain plus the ending *-ane*. The stem *meth-* means one carbon atom, so methane is an alkane with one carbon atom. Similarly, the stem *eth-* means two carbon atoms; ethane is an alkane with two carbon atoms. Continuing, the stem *prop-* means three carbon atoms, so propane is an alkane with three carbon atoms. Figure 4.6 gives the formulas and the molecular models of the three simplest alkanes. (For more information about alkanes, see Chapter 12.)

FIGURE 4.6 Formulas and Molecular Models of the Three Simplest Alkanes

The three smallest alkanes are methane, ethane, and propane.

methane, CH_4

```
      H
      |
  H — C — H
      |
      H
```

ethane, C_2H_6

```
      H   H
      |   |
  H — C — C — H
      |   |
      H   H
```

propane, C_3H_8

```
      H   H   H
      |   |   |
  H — C — C — C — H
      |   |   |
      H   H   H
```

alkene

A hydrocarbon with one or more carbon–carbon double bonds.

Some hydrocarbons have one or more carbon–carbon double bonds (denoted C=C). These hydrocarbons are called **alkenes**. Figure 4.7 shows the formulas and the molecular models of the two simplest alkenes. Note that the names of alkenes have the same stem as the alkane with the same number of carbon atoms in its chain but have the ending *-ene*. Thus, ethene is an alkene with two carbon atoms per molecule, and propene is a compound with three carbon atoms and one double bond.

FIGURE 4.7 Formulas and Molecular Models of the Two Simplest Alkenes

Ethene is commonly called ethylene, while propene is commonly called propylene.

ethene, C_2H_4

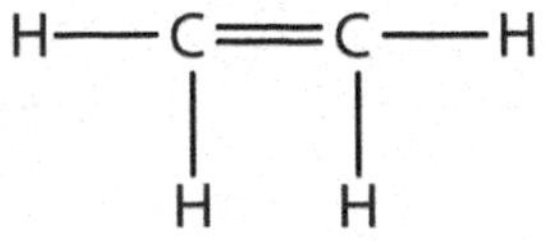

```
H—C═C—H
  |  |
  H  H
```

propene, C_3H_6

```
          H
          |
H—C═C—C—H
  |  |  |
  H  H  H
```

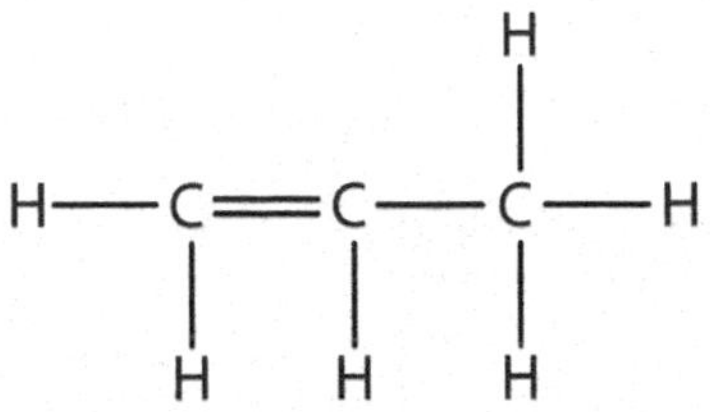

Alkynes are hydrocarbons with a carbon–carbon triple bond (denoted C≡C) as part of their carbon skeleton. Figure 4.8 shows the formulas and the molecular models of the two simplest alkynes and their systematic names. The names for alkynes have the same stems as for alkanes but with the ending *-yne*. (For more information about alkenes and alkynes, see Chapter 13.)

alkyne

A hydrocarbon with a carbon–carbon triple bond.

FIGURE 4.8 Formulas and Molecular Models of the Two Simplest Alkynes

Ethyne is more commonly called acetylene.

ethyne, C_2H_2

```
H—C≡C—H
```

propyne, C_3H_4

```
          H
          |
H—C≡C—C—H
          |
          H
```

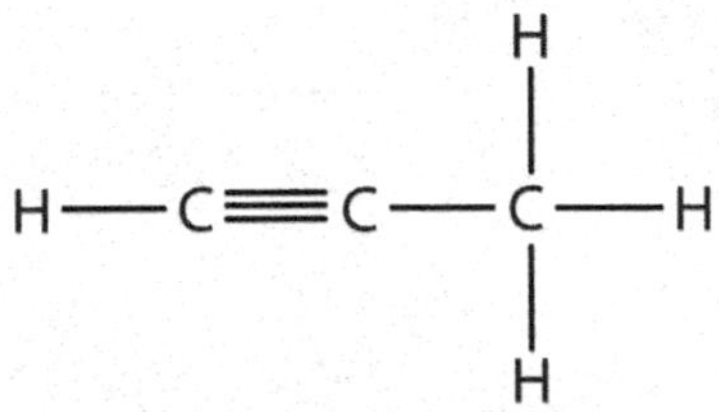

Note

The compound acetylene, with its carbon–carbon triple bond, was introduced in Section 3 and is an alkyne.

To Your Health: Saturated and Unsaturated Fats

Hydrocarbons are not the only compounds that can have carbon–carbon double bonds. A group of compounds called fats can have them as well, and their presence or absence in the human diet is becoming increasingly correlated with health issues.

Fats are combinations of long-chain organic compounds (fatty acids) and glycerol ($C_3H_8O_3$). (For more information on fats, see Chapter 17, [Unsupported Reference Type: chapter-section].) The long carbon chains can have either all single bonds, in which case the fat is classified as *saturated*, or one or more double bonds, in which case it is a *monounsaturated* or a *polyunsaturated* fat, respectively. Saturated fats are typically solids at room temperature; beef fat (tallow) is one example. Mono- or polyunsaturated fats are likely to be liquids at room temperature and are often called oils. Olive oil, flaxseed oil, and many fish oils are mono- or polyunsaturated fats.

Studies have linked higher amounts of saturated fats in people's diets with a greater likelihood of developing heart disease, high cholesterol, and other diet-related diseases. In contrast, increases in unsaturated fats (either mono- or polyunsaturated) have been linked to a lower incidence of certain diseases. Thus, there have been an increasing number of recommendations by government bodies and health associations to decrease the proportion of saturated fat and increase the proportion of unsaturated fat in the diet. Most of these organizations also recommend decreasing the total amount of fat in the diet.

Recently, certain fats called trans fats have been implicated in the presence of heart disease. These are fats from animal sources and are also produced when liquid oils are exposed to partial hydrogenation, an industrial process that increases their saturation. Trans fats are used in many prepared and fried foods. Because they bring with them the health risks that naturally occurring saturated fats do, there has been some effort to better quantify the presence of trans fats in food products. US law now requires that food labels list the amount of trans fat in each serving.

Since 1992, the US Department of Agriculture has been promoting a food pyramid that gives a simple, visual picture of how much of what kind of foods make up a good, balanced diet. It recommends eating as few fats as possible. Although nutritionists recognize that some fat is necessary (and largely unavoidable, even by strict vegetarians), they emphasize that a large proportion of any fat, saturated or unsaturated, in the diet is unhealthy. Even so, a difference as simple as the difference between a single and double carbon–carbon bond can have a significant impact on health.

The food pyramid has suggestions for the number of daily servings of each type of food.

Source: Image courtesy of the USDA, http://www.mypyramid.gov/downloads/MiniPoster.pdf.

functional group

A specific structural arrangement of atoms or bonds that imparts a characteristic chemical reactivity to a molecule.

alcohol

An organic compound with an OH functional group.

The carbon–carbon double and triple bonds are examples of **functional groups** in organic chemistry. A functional group is a specific structural arrangement of atoms or bonds that imparts a characteristic chemical reactivity to a molecule. Alkanes have no functional group. A carbon–carbon double bond is considered a functional group because carbon–carbon double bonds chemically react in specific ways that differ from reactions of alkanes (for example, under certain circumstances, alkenes react with water); a carbon–carbon triple bond also undergoes certain specific chemical reactions. In the remainder of this section, we introduce two other common functional groups.

If an OH group (also called a hydroxyl group) is substituted for a hydrogen atom in a hydrocarbon molecule, the compound is an **alcohol**. Alcohols are named using the parent hydrocarbon name but with the final *-e* dropped and the suffix *-ol* attached. The two simplest alcohols are methanol and ethanol. Figure 4.9 shows their formulas along with a molecular model of each.

FIGURE 4.9 The Two Simplest Organic Alcohol Compounds

Alcohols have an OH functional group in the molecule.

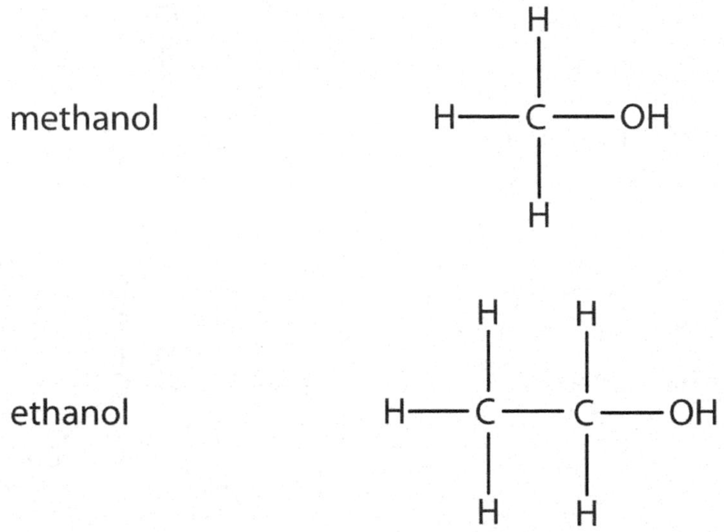

methanol

$$\begin{array}{ccccc} & & H & & \\ & & | & & \\ H & — & C & — & OH \\ & & | & & \\ & & H & & \end{array}$$

ethanol

$$\begin{array}{ccccccc} & & H & & H & & \\ & & | & & | & & \\ H & — & C & — & C & — & OH \\ & & | & & | & & \\ & & H & & H & & \end{array}$$

Note

Cholesterol, described in the chapter-opening essay, has an alcohol functional group, as its name implies.

Note

Ethanol (also called ethyl alcohol) is the alcohol in alcoholic beverages. Other alcohols include methanol (or methyl alcohol), which is used as a solvent and a cleaner, and isopropyl alcohol (or rubbing alcohol), which is used as a medicinal disinfectant. Neither methanol nor isopropyl alcohol should be ingested, as they are toxic even in small quantities.

Another important family of organic compounds has a **carboxyl group**, in which a carbon atom is double-bonded to an oxygen atom and to an OH group. Compounds with a carboxyl functional group are called **carboxylic acids**, and their names end in *-oic acid*. Figure 4.10 shows the formulas and the molecular models of the two simplest carboxylic acids, perhaps best known by the common names formic acid and acetic acid. The carboxyl group is sometimes written in molecules as COOH.

carboxyl group

A functional group that contains a carbon–oxygen double bond and an OH group also attached to the same carbon atom.

carboxylic acid

An organic compound that has a carboxyl functional group.

FIGURE 4.10 The Two Smallest Organic Acids

The two smallest carboxylic acids are formic acid (found in the stingers of ants) and acetic acid (found in vinegar).

methanoic acid

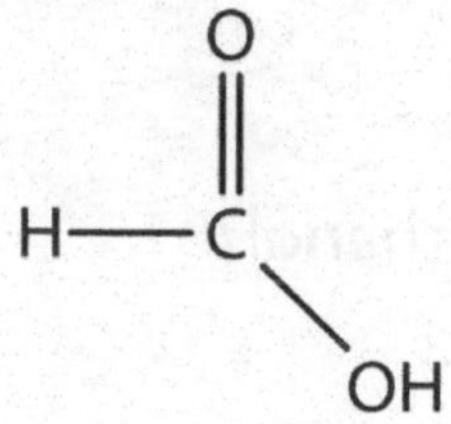

ethanoic acid

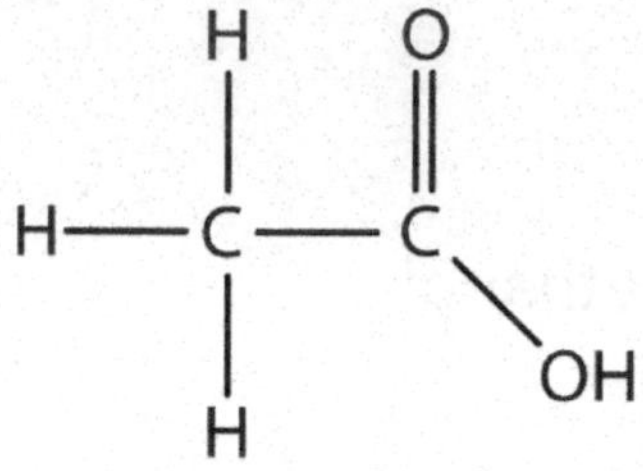

Many organic compounds are considerably more complex than the examples described here. Many compounds, such as cholesterol discussed in the chapter-opening essay, contain more than one functional group. The formal names can also be quite complex. In Chapter 12 through Chapter 15, we will examine the characteristics and chemistry of other important organic compounds and functional groups.

EXAMPLE 9

Identify the functional group(s) in each molecule as a double bond, a triple bond, an alcohol, or a carboxyl.

1. $CH3CH2CH2CH2OH$
2. 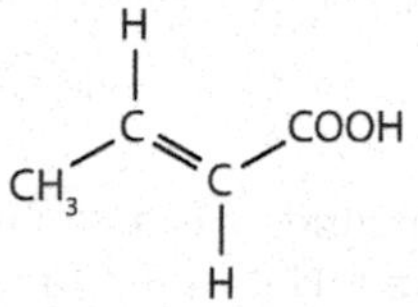
3. 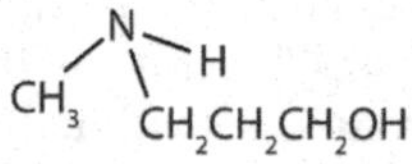
4.

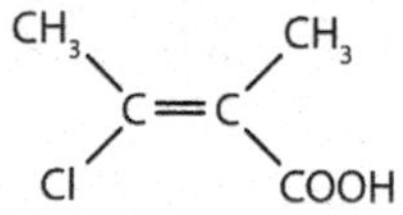

Solution

1. This molecule has an alcohol functional group.
2. This molecule has a double bond and a carboxyl functional group.
3. This molecule has an alcohol functional group.
4. This molecule has a double bond and a carboxyl functional group.

SKILL-BUILDING EXERCISE

Identify the functional group(s) in each molecule as a double bond, a triple bond, an alcohol, or a carboxyl.

1. $CH_3C{\equiv}CCH3$

2.

$$CH_3-CH_2-CH_2-CH(OH)-CH_2-CH_3$$

3.

$$H-C(=O)-OH$$

4.

$$CH_2{=}CH-COOH$$

Career Focus: Forensic Chemist

The main job of a forensic chemist is to identify unknown materials and their origins. Although forensic chemists are most closely associated in the public mind with crime labs, they are employed in pursuits as diverse as tracing evolutionary patterns in living organisms, identifying environmental contaminants, and determining the origin of manufactured chemicals.

In a crime lab, the forensic chemist has the job of identifying the evidence so that a crime can be solved. The unknown samples may consist of almost anything—for example, paint chips, blood, glass, cloth fibers, drugs, or human remains. The forensic chemist subjects them to a variety of chemical and instrumental tests to discover what the samples are. Sometimes these samples are extremely small, but sophisticated forensic labs have state-of-the-art equipment capable of identifying the smallest amount of unknown sample.

Another aspect of a forensic chemist's job is testifying in court. Judges and juries need to be informed about the results of forensic analyses, and it is the forensic chemist's job to explain those results. Good public-speaking skills, along with a broad background in chemistry, are necessary to be a successful forensic chemist.

CONCEPT REVIEW EXERCISES

1. What is organic chemistry?
2. What is a functional group? Give at least two examples of functional groups.

ANSWERS

1. Organic chemistry is the study of the chemistry of carbon compounds.
2. A functional group is a specific structural arrangement of atoms or bonds that imparts a characteristic chemical reactivity to the molecule; alcohol group and carboxylic group (answers will vary).

KEY TAKEAWAYS

- Organic chemistry is the study of the chemistry of carbon compounds.
- Organic molecules can be classified according to the types of elements and bonds in the molecules.

EXERCISES

1. Give three reasons why carbon is the central element in organic chemistry.
2. Are organic compounds based more on ionic bonding or covalent bonding? Explain.
3. Identify the type of hydrocarbon in each structure.

   a.

   $$\begin{matrix} & CH_2 & & CH_2 & \\ CH_3 & & CH_2 & & CH_3 \end{matrix}$$

   b.

   $$\begin{matrix} & CH_2 & & CH & \\ CH_3 & & CH & & CH_3 \end{matrix}$$

   c.

   $$\begin{matrix} & CH & & CH & \\ CH_2 & & CH & & CH_3 \end{matrix}$$

   d.

   $$\begin{matrix} & & CH_2 & \\ CH{\equiv}C{-}CH_2 & & & CH_3 \end{matrix}$$

4. Identify the type of hydrocarbon in each structure.

   a.

   $$\begin{matrix} & CH_2 & CH \\ CH_2 & & \| \\ & CH_2 & CH \end{matrix}$$

   b.

   $$\begin{matrix} & CH_2 & & CH_3 \\ CH_3 & & CH_2 & \end{matrix}$$

   c.

   $$CH{\equiv}C{-}CH_2{-}CH_3$$

   d.

   $$\begin{matrix} & CH_2 & \\ CH & & \\ \| & & CH \\ CH & & \\ & CH & \end{matrix}$$

5. Identify the functional group(s) in each molecule.

a.

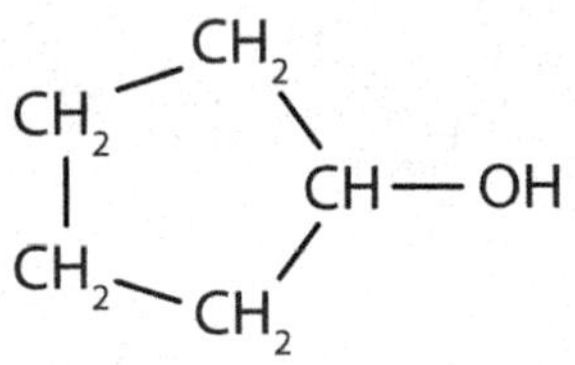

$$\text{cyclo-}(CH_2-CH_2-CH_2-CH_2-CH)-OH$$

b.

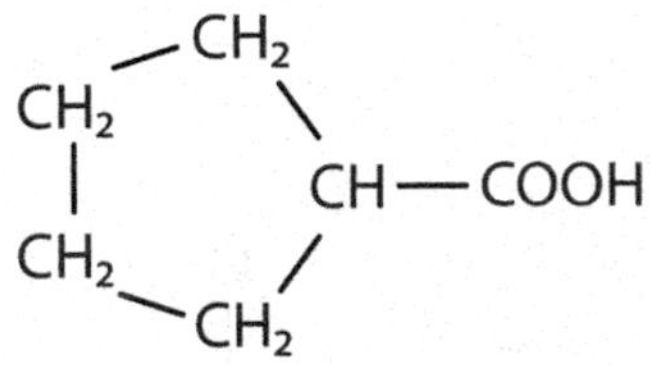

$$\text{cyclo-}(CH_2-CH_2-CH_2-CH_2-CH)-COOH$$

c.

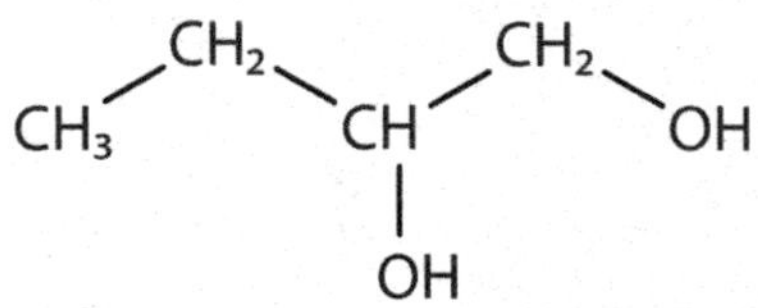

$$CH_3-CH_2-CH(OH)-CH_2-OH$$

d.

$$CH\equiv C-CH_2-CH_2-CH=CH_2$$

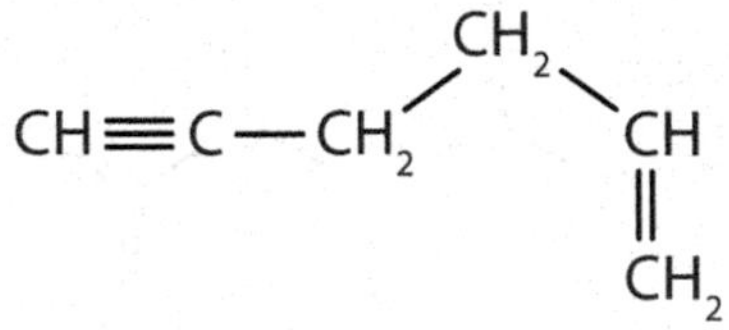

6. Identify the functional group(s) in each molecule.

   a.

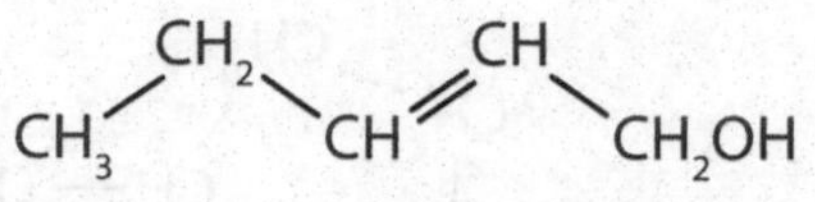

   CH_2 CH
   CH_3 CH CH_2OH

   b.

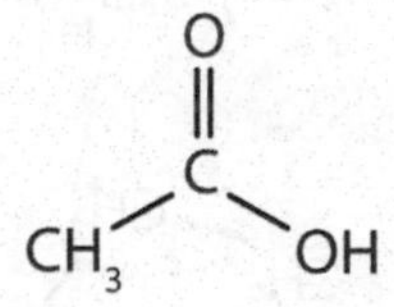

   O
   C
   CH_3 OH

   c.

   OH
   CH CH_2
   CH_3 CH

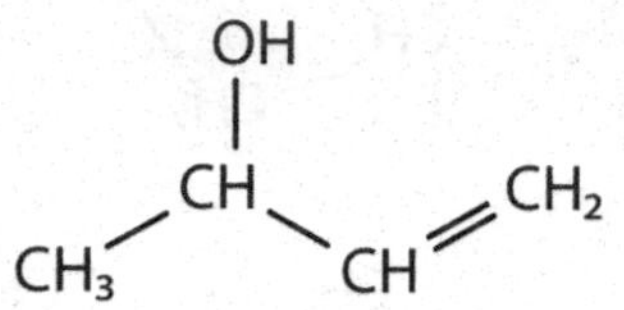

   d.

   H
   H C OH
   C C
   C C OH
   H C C
   H O

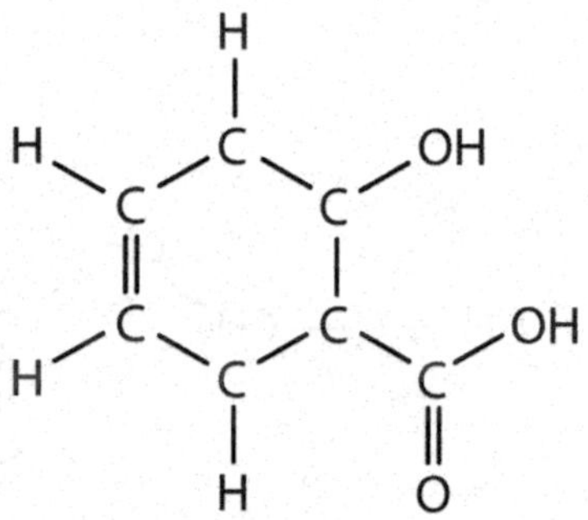

7. How many functional groups described in this section contain carbon and hydrogen atoms only? Name them.
8. What is the difference in the ways the two oxygen atoms in the carboxyl group are bonded to the carbon atom?

ANSWERS

1. Carbon atoms bond reasonably strongly with other carbon atoms. Carbon atoms bond reasonably strongly with atoms of other elements. Carbon atoms make a large number of covalent bonds (four).
3. a. alkane
   b. alkene
   c. alkene
   d. alkyne
5. a. alcohol
   b. carboxyl
   c. alcohol
   d. carbon-carbon double bond and carbon-carbon triple bond
7. two; carbon-carbon double bonds and carbon-carbon triple bonds

7. END-OF-CHAPTER MATERIAL

Chapter Summary

To ensure that you understand the material in this chapter, you should review the meanings of the following bold terms in the following summary and ask yourself how they relate to the topics in the chapter.

Atoms can share pairs of valence electrons to obtain a valence shell octet. This sharing of electrons is a **covalent bond**. A species formed from covalently bonded atoms is a **molecule** and is represented by a **molecular formula**, which gives the number of atoms of each type in the molecule. The two electrons shared in a covalent bond are called a **bonding pair of electrons**. The electrons that do not participate in covalent bonds are called **nonbonding pairs** (or **lone pairs**) **of electrons**. A covalent bond consisting of one pair of shared electrons is called a **single bond**.

Covalent bonds occur between nonmetal atoms. Naming simple covalent compounds follows simple rules similar to those for ionic compounds. However, for covalent compounds, numerical prefixes are used as necessary to specify the number of atoms of each element in the compound.

In some cases, more than one pair of electrons is shared to satisfy the octet rule. Two pairs of electrons are shared by two atoms to make a **double bond**. Three pairs of atoms are shared to make a **triple bond**. Single, double, and triple covalent bonds may be represented by one, two, or three dashes, respectively, between the symbols of the atoms.

The distance between two covalently bonded atoms is the **bond length**. Bond lengths depend on the types of atoms participating in the bond as well as the number of electron pairs being shared. A covalent bond can be a **polar covalent bond** if the electron sharing between the two atoms is unequal. If the sharing is equal, the bond is a **nonpolar covalent bond**. Because the strength of an atom's attraction for electrons in a bond is rated by the atom's **electronegativity**, the difference in the two atoms' electronegativities indicates how polar a covalent bond between those atoms will be.

The mass of a molecule is called its **molecular mass** and is the sum of the masses of the atoms in the molecule. The shape of a molecule can be predicted using **valence shell electron pair repulsion (VSEPR)**, which uses the fact that the negative electrons in covalent bonds repel each other as much as possible.

Organic chemistry is the chemistry of carbon compounds. Carbon forms covalent bonds with other carbon atoms and with the atoms of many other elements. The simplest organic compounds are **hydrocarbons**, which consist solely of carbon and hydrogen. Hydrocarbons containing only single bonds are called **alkanes (saturated hydrocarbons)**. Hydrocarbons containing carbon–carbon double bonds are **alkenes**, while hydrocarbons with carbon–carbon triple bonds are **alkynes**. Carbon-carbon double and triple bonds are examples of **functional groups**, atoms or bonds that impart a characteristic chemical function to the molecule. Other functional groups include the alcohol functional group (OH) and the **carboxyl functional group** (COOH). They are the characteristic functional group in organic compounds called **alcohols** and **carboxylic acids**.

ADDITIONAL EXERCISES

1. An atomic mass unit equals 1.661×10^{-24} g. What is the mass in grams of each molecule of (a) H_2S (b) N_2O_4 (c) ICl_3 (d) NCl_3?
2. An atomic mass unit equals 1.661×10^{-24} g. What is the mass in grams of (a) O_2F_2 (b) CCl_4 (c) C_6H_6 (d) SO_3?
3. An atomic mass unit equals 1.661×10^{-24} g. What is the mass in grams of 5.00×10^{22} molecules of $C_9H_8O_4$?
4. An atomic mass unit equals 1.661×10^{-24} g. What is the mass in grams of 1.885×10^{20} molecules of $C_{27}H_{46}O$?

5. Acetic acid has the following structure:

$$CH_3-C(=O)-OH$$

This molecule can lose a hydrogen ion (H^+) and the resulting anion can combine with other cations, such as Na^+:

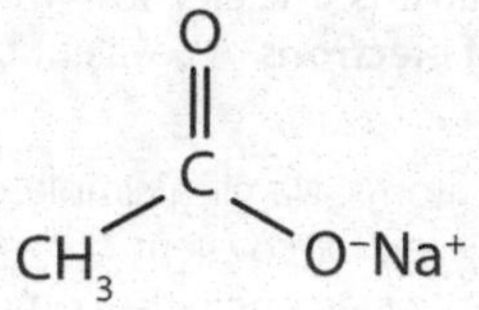

$$CH_3-C(=O)-O^-Na^+$$

Name this ionic compound.

6. Formic acid (HCOOH) loses a hydrogen ion to make the formate ion ($HCOO^-$). Write the formula for each ionic compound: potassium formate, calcium formate, and ferric formate.
7. Cyanogen has the formula C_2N_2. Propose a bonding scheme that gives each atom the correct number of covalent bonds. (Hint: the two carbon atoms are in the center of a linear molecule.)
8. The molecular formula C_3H_6 represents not only propene, a compound with a carbon–carbon double bond, but also a molecule that has all single bonds. Draw the molecule with formula C_3H_6 that has all single bonds.
9. How many carbon–carbon single bonds, linked together, are needed to make a carbon chain that is 1.000 cm long?
10. How many carbon–carbon double bonds, linked together, are needed to make a carbon chain that is 1.000 cm long?
11. In addition to themselves, what other atoms can carbon atoms bond with and make covalent bonds that are nonpolar (or as nonpolar as possible)?
12. What is the greatest possible electronegativity difference between any two atoms? Use Figure 4.4 to find the answer.
13. Acetaminophen, a popular painkiller, has the following structure:

$$CH_3-C(=O)-N(H)-C_6H_4-OH$$

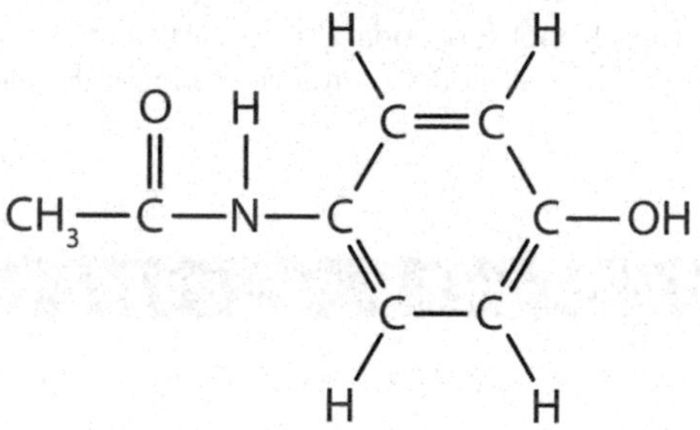

Name the recognizable functional groups in this molecule. Do you think there are other groups of atoms in this molecule that might qualify as functional groups?

14. Glutamic acid is the parent compound of monosodium glutamate (known as MSG), which is used as a flavor enhancer. Glutamic acid has the following structure:

$$OH-C(=O)-CH_2-CH_2-C(H)(NH_2)-C(=O)-OH$$

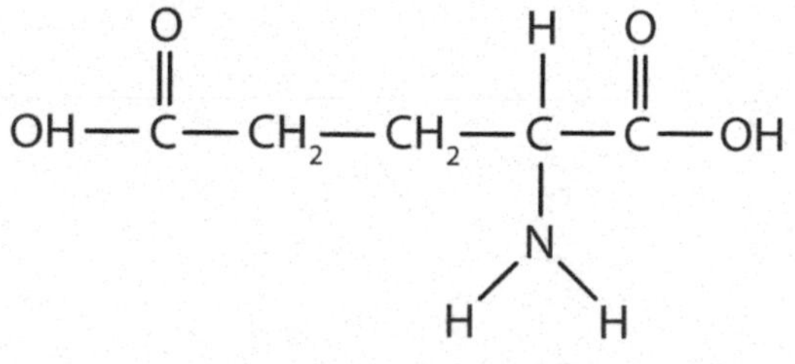

Name the functional groups you recognize in this molecule. Do you think there are other groups of atoms in this molecule that might qualify as functional groups?

ANSWERS

1. 1a: 5.75×10^{-23} g; 1b: 1.53×10^{-22} g; 1c: 3.88×10^{-22} g; 1d: 6.06×10^{-23} g
3. 14.96 g
5. sodium acetate
7. N≡C–C≡N
9. 6.49×10^{7} bonds
11. Hydrogen atoms make relatively nonpolar bonds with carbon atoms.
13. alcohol; the N–H group, the ring with double bonds, and the C=O are also likely functional groups.

CHAPTER 5
Introduction to Chemical Reactions

Opening Essay

Although yeast has been used for thousands of years, its true nature has been known only for the last two centuries. Yeasts are single-celled fungi. About 1,000 species are recognized, but the most common species is *Saccharomyces cerevisiae*, which is used in bread making. Other species are used for the fermentation of alcoholic beverages. Some species can cause infections in humans.

Yeasts live primarily on sugars, such as glucose ($C_6H_{12}O_6$). They convert glucose into carbon dioxide (CO_2) and ethanol (C_2H_5OH) in a chemical transformation that is represented as follows:

$$C_6H_{12}O_6 \rightarrow 2CO_2(g) + 2C_2H_5OH(\ell)$$

Bread making depends on the production of carbon dioxide. The gas, which is produced in tiny pockets in bread dough, acts as a leavening agent: it expands during baking and makes the bread rise. Leavened bread is softer, lighter, and easier to eat and chew than unleavened bread. The other major use of yeast, fermentation, depends on the production of ethanol, which results from the same chemical transformation. Some alcoholic beverages, such as champagne, can also be carbonated using the carbon dioxide produced by the yeast.

Yeast is among the simplest life forms on Earth, yet it is absolutely necessary for at least two major food industries. Without yeast to turn dough into bread and juice into wine, these foods and food industries would not exist today.

The bread-making industry depends on a chemical reaction performed by yeast.

© *Thinkstock*

Chemical change is a central concept in chemistry. The goal of chemists is to know how and why a substance changes in the presence of another substance or even by itself. Because there are tens of millions of known substances, there are a huge number of possible chemical reactions. In this chapter, we will find that many of these reactions can be classified into a small number of categories according to certain shared characteristics.

1. THE LAW OF CONSERVATION OF MATTER

LEARNING OBJECTIVES

1. **Correctly define a law as it pertains to science.**
2. **State the law of conservation of matter.**

law

A general statement that explains a large number of observations.

law of conservation of matter

In any given system that is closed to the transfer of matter (in and out), the amount of matter in the system stays constant.

In science, a **law** is a general statement that explains a large number of observations. Before being accepted, a law must be verified many times under many conditions. Laws are therefore considered the highest form of scientific knowledge and are generally thought to be inviolable. Scientific laws form the core of scientific knowledge.

One scientific law that provides the foundation for understanding in chemistry is the **law of conservation of matter**. It states that in any given system that is closed to the transfer of matter (in and out), the amount of matter in the system stays constant. A concise way of expressing this law is to say that the amount of matter in a system is *conserved*.

What does this mean for chemistry? In any chemical change, one or more initial substances change into a different substance or substances. Both the initial and final substances are composed of atoms because all matter is composed of atoms. According to the law of conservation of matter, matter is neither created nor destroyed, so we must have the same number and type of atoms after the chemical change as were present before the chemical change.

Before looking at explicit examples of the law of conservation of matter, we need to examine the method chemists use to represent chemical changes.

CONCEPT REVIEW EXERCISES

1. What is the law of conservation of matter?
2. How does the law of conservation of matter apply to chemistry?

ANSWERS

1. The law of conservation of matter states that in any given system that is closed to the transfer of matter, the amount of matter in the system stays constant
2. The law of conservation of matter says that in chemical reactions, the total mass of the products must equal the total mass of the reactants.

KEY TAKEAWAY

- The amount of matter in a closed system is conserved.

EXERCISES

1. Express the law of conservation of matter in your own words.
2. Explain why the concept of conservation of matter is considered a scientific law.

ANSWER

1. Matter may not be created or destroyed.

2. CHEMICAL EQUATIONS

LEARNING OBJECTIVES

1. **Define *chemical reaction*.**
2. **Use a balanced chemical equation to represent a chemical reaction.**

Water (H_2O) is composed of hydrogen and oxygen. Suppose we imagine a process in which we take some elemental hydrogen (H_2) and elemental oxygen (O_2) and let them react to make water. The statement

hydrogen and oxygen react to make water

is one way to represent that process, which is called a **chemical reaction**. Figure 5.1 shows a rather dramatic example of this very reaction.

chemical reaction

A representation of a chemical change.

FIGURE 5.1 The Formation of Water

Hydrogen and oxygen combine to form water. Here, the hydrogen gas in the zeppelin *SS Hindenburg* reacts with oxygen in the air to make water.

Source: Photo courtesy of the US Navy, http://commons.wikimedia.org/wiki/File:Hindenburg_burning.jpg.

To simplify the writing of reactions, we use formulas instead of names when we describe a reaction. We can also use symbols to represent other words in the reaction. A plus sign connects the initial substances (and final substances, if there is more than one), and an arrow (→) represents the chemical change:

$$H_2 + O_2 \rightarrow H_2O$$

chemical equation

An abbreviated way of using symbols to represent a chemical change.

reactant

A substance on the left side of the arrow in a chemical equation.

product

A substance on the right side of the arrow in a chemical equation.

This statement is one example of a **chemical equation**, an abbreviated way of using symbols to represent a chemical change. The substances on the left side of the arrow are called **reactants**, and the substances on the right side of the arrow are called **products**. It is not uncommon to include a phase label with each formula—(s) for solid, (ℓ) for liquid, (g) for gas, and (aq) for a substance dissolved in water, also known as an *aqueous solution*. If we included phase labels for the reactants and products, under normal environmental conditions, the reaction would be as follows:

$$H_2(g) + O_2(g) \rightarrow H_2O(\ell)$$

Note

Chemical equations can also be used to describe physical changes. We will see examples of this soon.

This equation is still not complete because *it does not satisfy the law of conservation of matter*. Count the number of atoms of each element on each side of the arrow. On the reactant side, there are two H atoms and two O atoms; on the product side, there are two H atoms and only one oxygen atom. The equation is not balanced because the number of oxygen atoms on each side is not the same (Figure 5.2).

FIGURE 5.2 Balanced—Yes or No?

By counting the atoms of each element, we can see that the reaction is not balanced as written.

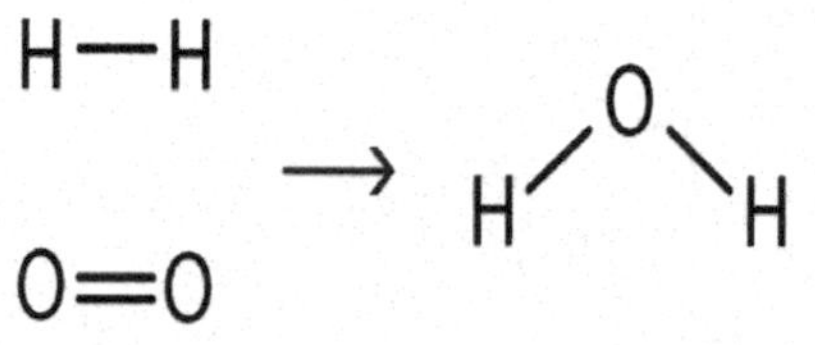

To make this chemical equation conform to the law of conservation of matter, we must revise the amounts of the reactants and the products as necessary to get the same number of atoms of a given element on each side. Because every substance has a characteristic chemical formula, we cannot change the chemical formulas of the individual substances. For example, we cannot change the formula for elemental oxygen to O. However, we can assume that different numbers of reactant molecules or product molecules may be involved. For instance, perhaps two water molecules are produced, not just one:

$$H_2(g) + O_2(g) \rightarrow 2H_2O(\ell)$$

coefficient

A number that gives the number of molecules of a substance in a balanced chemical equation.

The 2 preceding the formula for water is called a **coefficient**. It implies that two water molecules are formed. There are now two oxygen atoms on each side of the equation.

Note

This point is so important that we should repeat it. You **cannot** change the formula of a chemical substance to balance a chemical reaction! You **must** use the proper chemical formula of the substance.

Unfortunately, by inserting the coefficient 2 in front of the formula for water, we have also changed the number of hydrogen atoms on the product side as well. As a result, we no longer have the same number of hydrogen atoms on each side. This can be easily fixed, however, by putting a coefficient of 2 in front of the diatomic hydrogen reactant:

$$2H_2(g) + O_2(g) \rightarrow 2H_2O(\ell)$$

balanced

A property of a chemical equation when there are the same number of atoms of each element in the reactants and products.

Now we have four hydrogen atoms and two oxygen atoms on each side of the equation. The law of conservation of matter is satisfied because we now have the same number of atoms of each element in the reactants and in the products. We say that the reaction is **balanced** (Figure 5.3). The diatomic oxygen has a coefficient of 1, which typically is not written but assumed in balanced chemical equations.

FIGURE 5.3 Balanced—Yes or No?

By counting the atoms of each element, we can see that the reaction is now balanced.

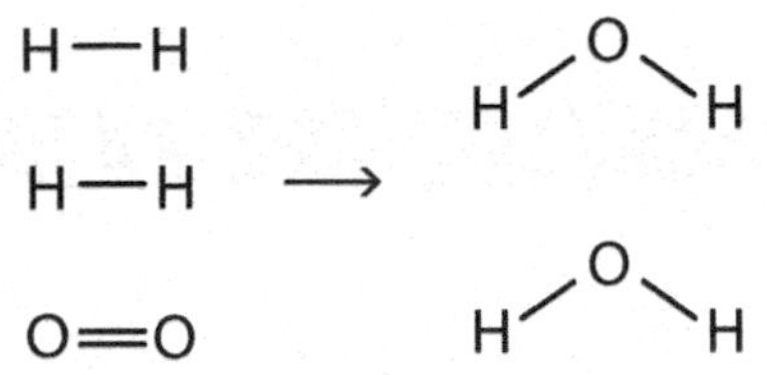

Proper chemical equations should be balanced. Writing balanced reactions is a chemist's way of acknowledging the law of conservation of matter.

EXAMPLE 1

Is each chemical equation balanced?

1. $2Na(s) + O_2(g) \rightarrow 2Na_2O(s)$
2. $CH_4(g) + 2O_2(g) \rightarrow CO_2(g) + 2H_2O(\ell)$
3. $AgNO_3(aq) + 2KCl(aq) \rightarrow AgCl(s) + KNO_3(aq)$

Solution

1. By counting, we find two sodium atoms and two oxygen atoms in the reactants and four sodium atoms and two oxygen atoms in the products. This equation is not balanced.
2. The reactants have one carbon atom, four hydrogen atoms, and four oxygen atoms. The products have one carbon atom, four hydrogen atoms, and four oxygen atoms. This equation is balanced.
3. The reactants have one silver atom, one nitrogen atom, three oxygen atoms, two potassium atoms, and two chlorine atoms. The products have one silver atom, one chlorine atom, one potassium atom, one nitrogen atom, and three oxygen atoms. Because there are different numbers of chlorine and potassium atoms, this equation is not balanced.

SKILL-BUILDING EXERCISE

Is each chemical equation balanced?

1. $2Hg(\ell) + O_2(g) \rightarrow Hg_2O_2(s)$
2. $C_2H_4(g) + 2O_2(g) \rightarrow 2CO_2(g) + 2H_2O(\ell)$
3. $Mg(NO_3)_2(s) + 2Li(s) \rightarrow Mg(s) + 2LiNO_3(s)$

How does one balance a chemical equation, starting with the correct formulas of the reactants and products? Basically, a back-and-forth approach is adopted, counting the number of atoms of one element on one side, checking the number of atoms of that element on the other side, and changing a coefficient if necessary. Then check another element, going back and forth from one side of the equation to another, until each element has the same number of atoms on both sides of the arrow. In many cases, it does not matter which element is balanced first and which is balanced last, as long as all elements have the same number of atoms on each side of the equation.

For example, to balance the equation

$$CH_4 + Cl_2 \rightarrow CCl_4 + HCl$$

we might choose to count the carbon atoms first, finding that both sides are balanced with one carbon atom. The reactant side has four hydrogen atoms, so the product side must also have four hydrogen atoms. We fix this by putting a 4 in front of the HCl:

$$CH_4 + Cl_2 \rightarrow CCl_4 + \mathbf{4}HCl$$

Now each side has four hydrogen atoms. The product side has a total of eight chlorine atoms (four from the CCl_4 and four from the four molecules of HCl), so we need eight chlorine atoms as reactants. Because elemental chlorine is a diatomic molecule, we need four chlorine molecules to get a total of eight chlorine atoms. We add another 4 in front of the Cl_2 reactant:

$$CH_4 + 4Cl_2 \rightarrow CCl_4 + 4HCl$$

Now we check: each side has one carbon atom, four hydrogen atoms, and eight chlorine atoms. The chemical equation is balanced.

CONCEPT REVIEW EXERCISES

1. What are the parts of a chemical equation?
2. Explain why chemical equations need to be balanced.

ANSWERS

1. reactants and products
2. Chemical equations need to be balanced to satisfy the law of conservation of matter.

KEY TAKEAWAYS

- Chemical reactions are represented by chemical equations that list reactants and products.
- Proper chemical equations are balanced; the same number of each element's atoms appears on each side of the equation.

EXERCISES

1. Write a chemical equation to express the fact that hydrogen gas and solid iodine react to make gaseous hydrogen iodide. Make sure the equation satisfies the law of conservation of matter.
2. Write a chemical equation to express the fact that sodium metal and chlorine gas react to make solid sodium chloride. Make sure the equation satisfies the law of conservation of matter.
3. Write an equation expressing the fact that hydrogen gas and fluorine gas react to make gaseous hydrogen fluoride. Make sure the equation satisfies the law of conservation of matter.
4. Write an equation expressing the fact that solid potassium and fluorine gas react to make solid potassium fluoride. Make sure the equation satisfies the law of conservation of matter.
5. Mercury reacts with oxygen to make mercury(II) oxide. Write a balanced chemical equation that summarizes this reaction.
6. Octane (C_8H_{18}) reacts with oxygen to make carbon dioxide and water. Write a balanced chemical equation that summarizes this reaction.
7. Propyl alcohol (C_3H_7OH) reacts with oxygen to make carbon dioxide and water. Write a balanced chemical equation that summarizes this reaction.
8. Sulfuric acid reacts with iron metal to make iron(III) sulfate and hydrogen gas. Write a balanced chemical equation that summarizes this reaction.
9. Balance each equation.
   a. $MgCl_2 + K \rightarrow KCl + Mg$
   b. $C_6H_{12}O_6 + O_2 \rightarrow CO_2 + H_2O$
   c. $NaN_3 \rightarrow Na + N_2$ (This is the reaction used to inflate airbags in cars.)
10. Balance each equation.
    a. $NH_4NO_3 \rightarrow N_2O + H_2O$
    b. $TiBr_4 + H_2O \rightarrow TiO_2 + HBr$
    c. $C_3H_5N_3O_9 \rightarrow CO_2 + N_2 + O_2 + H_2O$ (This reaction represents the decomposition of nitroglycerine.)
11. Balance each equation.
    a. $NH_3 + O_2 \rightarrow NO + H_2O$
    b. $Li + N_2 \rightarrow Li_3N$
    c. $AuCl \rightarrow Au + AuCl_3$
12. Balance each equation.
    a. $NaOH + H_3PO_4 \rightarrow Na_3PO_4 + H_2O$
    b. $N_2H_4 + Cl_2 \rightarrow N_2 + HCl$
    c. $Na_2S + H_2S \rightarrow NaSH$
13. Chromium(III) oxide reacts with carbon tetrachloride to make chromium(III) chloride and phosgene ($COCl_2$). Write the balanced chemical equation for this reaction.

14. The reaction that occurs when an Alka-Seltzer tablet is dropped into a glass of water has sodium bicarbonate reacting with citric acid ($H_3C_6H_5O_7$) to make carbon dioxide, water, and sodium citrate ($Na_3C_6H_5O_7$). Write the balanced chemical equation for this reaction.
15. When sodium hydrogen carbonate is used to extinguish a kitchen fire, it decomposes into sodium carbonate, water, and carbon dioxide. Write a balanced chemical equation for this reaction.
16. Elemental bromine gas can be generated by reacting sodium bromide with elemental chlorine. The other product is sodium chloride. Write a balanced chemical equation for this reaction.

ANSWERS

1. $H_2(g) + I_2(s) \rightarrow 2HI(g)$
3. $H_2(g) + F_2(g) \rightarrow 2HF(g)$
5. $2Hg + O_2 \rightarrow 2HgO$
7. $2C_3H_7OH + 9O_2 \rightarrow 6CO_2 + 8H_2O$
9. a. $MgCl_2 + 2K \rightarrow 2KCl + Mg$
   b. $C_6H_{12}O_6 + 6O_2 \rightarrow 6CO_2 + 6H_2O$
   c. $2NaN_3 \rightarrow 2Na + 3N_2$
11. a. $4NH_3 + 5O_2 \rightarrow 4NO + 6H_2O$
   b. $6Li + N_2 \rightarrow 2Li_3N$
   c. $3AuCl \rightarrow 2Au + AuCl_3$
13. $Cr_2O_3 + 3CCl_4 \rightarrow 2CrCl_3 + 3COCl_2$
15. $2NaHCO_3 \rightarrow Na_2CO_3 + CO_2 + H_2O$

3. QUANTITATIVE RELATIONSHIPS BASED ON CHEMICAL EQUATIONS

LEARNING OBJECTIVE

1. **Calculate the amount of one substance that will react with or be produced from a given amount of another substance.**

A balanced chemical equation not only describes some of the chemical properties of substances—by showing us what substances react with what other substances to make what products—but also shows numerical relationships between the reactants and the products. The study of these numerical relationships is called **stoichiometry**. The stoichiometry of chemical equations revolves around the coefficients in the balanced chemical equation because these coefficients determine the molecular ratio in which reactants react and products are made.

stoichiometry

The study of the numerical relationships between the reactants and the products in a balanced chemical equation.

Note

The word *stoichiometry* is pronounced "stow-eh-key-OM-et-tree." It is of mixed Greek and English origins, meaning roughly "measure of an element."

Looking Closer: Stoichiometry in Cooking

Let us consider a stoichiometry analogy from the kitchen. A recipe that makes 1 dozen biscuits needs 2 cups of flour, 1 egg, 4 tablespoons of shortening, 1 teaspoon of salt, 1 teaspoon of baking soda, and 1 cup of milk. If we were to write this as a chemical equation, we would write

2 c flour + 1 egg + 4 tbsp shortening + 1 tsp salt + 1 tsp baking soda + 1 c milk → 12 biscuits

(Unlike true chemical reactions, this one has all 1 coefficients written explicitly—partly because of the many different units here.) This equation gives us ratios of how much of what reactants are needed to make how much of what product. Two cups of flour, when combined with the proper amounts of the other ingredients, will yield 12 biscuits. One teaspoon of baking soda (when also combined with the right amounts of the other ingredients) will make 12 biscuits. One egg must be combined with 1 cup of milk to yield the product food. Other relationships can also be expressed.

We can use the ratios we derive from the equation for predictive purposes. For instance, if we have 4 cups of flour, how many biscuits can we make if we have enough of the other ingredients? It should be apparent that we can make a double recipe of 24 biscuits.

But how would we find this answer formally, that is, mathematically? We would set up a conversion factor, much like we did in Chapter 1. Because 2 cups of flour make 12 biscuits, we can set up an equivalency ratio:

$$\frac{12 \text{ biscuits}}{2 \text{ c flour}}$$

We then can use this ratio in a formal conversion of flour to biscuits:

$$4\text{c} \cancel{\text{flour}} \times \frac{12 \text{ biscuits}}{2\text{c} \cancel{\text{flour}}} = 24 \text{ biscuits}$$

Similarly, by constructing similar ratios, we can determine how many biscuits we can make from any amount of ingredient.

When you are doubling or halving a recipe, you are doing a type of stoichiometry. Applying these ideas to chemical reactions should not be difficult if you use recipes when you cook.

A recipe shows how much of each ingredient is needed for the proper reaction to take place.

© *Thinkstock*

Consider the following balanced chemical equation:

$$2C_2H_2 + 5O_2 \rightarrow 4CO_2 + 2H_2O$$

The coefficients on the chemical formulas give the ratios in which the reactants combine and the products form. Thus, we can make the following statements and construct the following ratios:

Statement from the Balanced Chemical Reaction	Ratio	Inverse Ratio
two C_2H_2 molecules react with five O_2 molecules	$\frac{2C_2H_2}{5O_2}$	$\frac{5O_2}{2C_2H_2}$
two C_2H_2 molecules react to make four CO_2 molecules	$\frac{2C_2H_2}{4CO_2}$	$\frac{4CO_2}{2C_2H_2}$
five O_2 molecules react to make two H_2O molecules	$\frac{5O_2}{2H_2O}$	$\frac{2H_2O}{5O_2}$
four CO_2 molecules are made at the same time as two H_2O molecules	$\frac{2H_2O}{4CO_2}$	$\frac{4CO_2}{2H_2O}$

Other relationships are possible; in fact, 12 different conversion factors can be constructed from this balanced chemical equation. In each ratio, the unit is assumed to be molecules because that is how we are interpreting the chemical equation.

Any of these fractions can be used as a conversion factor to relate an amount of one substance to an amount of another substance. For example, suppose we want to know how many CO_2 molecules are formed when 26 molecules of C_2H_2 are reacted. As usual with a conversion problem, we start with the amount we are given—$26C_2H_2$—and multiply it by a conversion factor that cancels out our original unit and introduces the unit we are converting to—in this case, CO_2. That conversion factor is $\frac{4CO_2}{2C_2H_2}$, which is composed of terms that come directly from the balanced chemical equation. Thus, we have

$$26C_2H_2 \times \frac{4CO_2}{2C_2H_2}$$

The molecules of C_2H_2 cancel, and we are left with molecules of CO_2. Multiplying through, we get

$$26\cancel{C_2H_2} \times \frac{4CO_2}{2\cancel{C_2H_2}} = 52CO_2$$

Thus, 52 molecules of CO_2 are formed.

This application of stoichiometry is extremely powerful in its predictive ability, as long as we begin with a balanced chemical equation. Without a balanced chemical equation, the predictions made by simple stoichiometric calculations will be incorrect.

EXAMPLE 2

Start with this balanced chemical equation.

$$KMnO_4 + 8HCl + 5FeCl_2 \rightarrow 5\ FeCl_3 + MnCl_2 + 4H_2O + KCl$$

1. Verify that the equation is indeed balanced.
2. Give 2 ratios that give the relationship between HCl and $FeCl_3$.

Solution

1. Each side has 1 K atom and 1 Mn atom. The 8 molecules of HCl yield 8 H atoms, and the 4 molecules of H_2O also yield 8 H atoms, so the H atoms are balanced. The Fe atoms are balanced, as we count 5 Fe atoms from 5 $FeCl_2$ reactants and 5 $FeCl_3$ products. As for Cl, on the reactant side, there are 8 Cl atoms from HCl and 10 Cl atoms from the 5 $FeCl_2$ formula units, for a total of 18 Cl atoms. On the product side, there are 15 Cl atoms from the 5 $FeCl_3$ formula units, 2 from the $MnCl_2$ formula unit, and 1 from the KCl formula unit. This is a total of 18 Cl atoms in the products, so the Cl atoms are balanced. All the elements are balanced, so the entire chemical equation is balanced.
2. Because the balanced chemical equation tells us that 8 HCl molecules react to make 5 $FeCl_3$ formula units, we have the following 2 ratios: $\frac{8HCl}{5FeCl_3}$ and $\frac{5FeCl_3}{8HCl}$. There are a total of 42 possible ratios. Can you find the other 40 relationships?

SKILL-BUILDING EXERCISE

Start with this balanced chemical equation.

$$2KMnO_4 + 3CH_2{=}CH_2 + 4H_2O \rightarrow 2MnO_2 + 3HOCH_2CH_2OH + 2KOH$$

1. Verify that the equation is balanced.
2. Give 2 ratios that give the relationship between $KMnO_4$ and $CH_2{=}CH_2$. (A total of 30 relationships can be constructed from this chemical equation. Can you find the other 28?)

CONCEPT REVIEW EXERCISES

1. Explain how stoichiometric ratios are constructed from a chemical equation.

2. Why is it necessary for a chemical equation to be balanced before it can be used to construct conversion factors?

ANSWERS

1. Stoichiometric ratios are made using the coefficients of the substances in the balanced chemical equation.
2. A balanced chemical equation is necessary so one can construct the proper stoichiometric ratios.

KEY TAKEAWAY

- A balanced chemical equation gives the ratios in which molecules of substances react and are produced in a chemical reaction.

EXERCISES

1. Balance this equation and write every stoichiometric ratio you can from it.

$$NH_4NO_3 \rightarrow N_2O + H_2O$$

2. Balance this equation and write every stoichiometric ratio you can from it.

$$N_2 + H_2 \rightarrow NH_3$$

3. Balance this equation and write every stoichiometric ratio you can from it.

$$Fe_2O_3 + C \rightarrow Fe + CO_2$$

4. Balance this equation and write every stoichiometric ratio you can from it.

$$Fe_2O_3 + CO \rightarrow Fe + CO_2$$

5. Balance this equation and determine how many molecules of CO_2 are formed if 15 molecules of C_6H_6 are reacted.

$$C_6H_6 + O_2 \rightarrow CO_2 + H_2O$$

6. Balance this equation and determine how many molecules of Ag_2CO_3(s) are produced if 20 molecules of Na_2CO_3 are reacted.

$$Na_2CO_3(aq) + AgNO_3(aq) \rightarrow NaNO_3(aq) + Ag_2CO_3(s)$$

7. Copper metal reacts with nitric acid according to this equation:

$$3Cu(s) + 8HNO_3(aq) \rightarrow 3Cu(NO_3)_2(aq) + 2NO(g) + 4H_2O(\ell)$$

   a. Verify that this equation is balanced.
   b. How many Cu atoms will react if 488 molecules of aqueous HNO_3 are reacted?

8. Gold metal reacts with a combination of nitric acid and hydrochloric acid according to this equation:

$$Au(s) + 3HNO_3(aq) + 4HCl(aq) \rightarrow HAuCl_4(aq) + 3NO_2(g) + 3H_2O(\ell)$$

   a. Verify that this equation is balanced.
   b. How many Au atoms react with 639 molecules of aqueous HNO_3?

9. Sulfur can be formed by reacting sulfur dioxide with hydrogen sulfide at high temperatures according to this equation:

$$SO_2(g) + 2H_2S(g) \rightarrow 3S(g) + 2H_2O(g)$$

   a. Verify that this equation is balanced.
   b. How many S atoms will be formed from by reacting 1,078 molecules of H_2S?

10. Nitric acid is made by reacting nitrogen dioxide with water:

$$3NO_2(g) + H_2O(\ell) \rightarrow 2HNO_3(aq) + NO(g)$$

   a. Verify that this equation is balanced.
   b. How many molecules of NO will be formed by reacting 2,268 molecules of NO_2?

ANSWERS

1. $NH_4NO_3 \rightarrow N_2O + 2H_2O$; the stoichiometric ratios are $\frac{1NH_4NO_3}{1N_2O}$, $\frac{1NH_4NO_3}{2H_2O}$, $\frac{1N_2O}{2H_2O}$, and their reciprocals.
3. $2Fe_2O_3 + 3C \rightarrow 4Fe + 3CO_2$; the stoichiometric ratios are $\frac{2Fe_2O_3}{3C}$, $\frac{2Fe_2O_3}{4Fe}$, $\frac{2Fe_2O_3}{3CO_2}$, $\frac{3C}{4Fe}$, $\frac{3C}{3CO_2}$, $\frac{4Fe}{3CO_2}$, and their reciprocals.
5. $2C_6H_6 + 15O_2 \rightarrow 12CO_2 + 6H_2O$; 90 molecules
7. a. It is balanced.
   b. 183 atoms
9. a. It is balanced.
   b. 1,617 atoms

4. SOME TYPES OF CHEMICAL REACTIONS

LEARNING OBJECTIVE

1. **Classify a given chemical reaction into a variety of types.**

Although there are untold millions of possible chemical reactions, most can be classified into a small number of general reaction types. Classifying reactions has two purposes: it helps us to recognize similarities among them, and it enables us to predict the products of certain reactions. A particular reaction may fall into more than one of the categories that we will define in this book.

A **combination (composition) reaction** is a chemical reaction that makes a single substance from two or more reactants. There may be more than one molecule of product in the balanced chemical equation, but there is only one substance produced.

combination (composition) reaction

A chemical reaction that makes a single substance from two or more reactants.

For example, the equation

$$4Fe + 3O_2 \rightarrow 2Fe_2O_3$$

is a combination reaction that produces Fe_2O_3 from its constituent elements—Fe and O_2. Combination reactions do not have to combine elements, however. The chemical equation

$$Fe_2O_3 + 3SO_3 \rightarrow Fe_2(SO_4)_3$$

shows a combination reaction in which Fe_2O_3 combines with three molecules of SO_3 to make $Fe_2(SO_4)_3$.

EXAMPLE 3

Which equations are combination reactions?

1. $Co(s) + Cl_2(g) \rightarrow CoCl_2(s)$
2. $CO(g) + Cl_2(g) \rightarrow COCl_2(g)$
3. $N_2H_4(\ell) + O_2(g) \rightarrow N_2(g) + 2H_2O(\ell)$

Solution

1. This is a combination reaction.
2. This is a combination reaction. (The compound $COCl_2$ is called phosgene and, in the past, was used as a gassing agent in chemical warfare.)
3. This is not a combination reaction.

SKILL-BUILDING EXERCISE

Which equations are combination reactions?

1. $P_4(s) + 6Cl_2(g) \rightarrow 4PCl_3(g)$
2. $SO_3(\ell) + H_2O(\ell) \rightarrow H_2SO_4(\ell)$
3. $NaOH(s) + HCl(g) \rightarrow NaCl(s) + H_2O(\ell)$

decomposition reaction

A chemical reaction in which a single substance is converted into two or more products.

A **decomposition reaction** is the reverse of a combination reaction. In a decomposition reaction, a single substance is converted into two or more products. There may be more than one molecule of the reactant, but there is only one substance initially. For example, the equation

$$2NaHCO_3(s) \rightarrow Na_2CO_3(s) + CO_2(g) + H_2O(\ell)$$

is a decomposition reaction that occurs when $NaHCO_3$ is exposed to heat. Another example is the decomposition of $KClO_3$:

$$2KClO_3(s) \rightarrow 2KCl(s) + 3O_2(g)$$

This reaction was once commonly used to generate small amounts of oxygen in the chemistry lab.

Note

The decomposition reaction of $NaHCO_3$ is the reaction that occurs when baking soda is poured on a small kitchen fire. The intent is that the H_2O and CO_2 produced by the decomposition will smother the flames.

combustion reaction

A chemical reaction accompanied by the production of light and/or heat, typically a vigorous reaction because of combination with oxygen.

A **combustion reaction** occurs when a substance combines with molecular oxygen to make oxygen-containing compounds of other elements in the reaction. One example is the burning of acetylene (C_2H_2) in torches:

$$2C_2H_2 + 5O_2 \rightarrow 4CO_2 + 2H_2O$$

Oxygen (in its elemental form) is a crucial reactant in combustion reactions, and it is also present in the products.

Note

Energy in the form of heat is usually given off as a product in a combustion reaction as well.

EXAMPLE 4

Identify each type of reaction.

1. $2K(s) + S(s) + 2O_2(g) \rightarrow K_2SO_4(s)$
2. $(NH_4)_2Cr_2O_7(s) \rightarrow N_2(g) + Cr_2O_3(s) + 4H_2O(\ell)$
3. $CH_4(g) + 2O_2(g) \rightarrow CO_2(g) + 2H_2O(\ell)$

Solution

1. Multiple reactants are combining to make a single product, so this reaction is a combination reaction.
2. A single substance reacts to make several products, so we have a decomposition reaction.
3. Oxygen reacts with a compound to make carbon dioxide (an oxide of carbon) and water (an oxide of hydrogen). This is a combustion reaction.

SKILL-BUILDING EXERCISE

Identify each type of reaction.

1. $C_2H_5OH + 3O_2 \rightarrow 2CO_2 + 3H_2O$
2. $2Ca(s) + O_2(g) \rightarrow 2CaO(s)$

3. $CaCO_3(s) \rightarrow CaO(s) + CO_2(g)$

CONCEPT REVIEW EXERCISES

1. What is the difference between a combination reaction and a combustion reaction?
2. Give the distinguishing characteristic(s) of a decomposition reaction.
3. How do we recognize a combustion reaction?

ANSWERS

1. A combination reaction produces a certain substance; a combustion reaction is a vigorous reaction, usually a combination with oxygen, that is accompanied by the production of light and/or heat.
2. In a decomposition reaction, a single substance reacts to make multiple substances as products.
3. A combustion reaction is typically a vigorous reaction accompanied by light and/or heat, usually because of reaction with oxygen.

KEY TAKEAWAY

- There are several recognizable types of chemical reactions: combination, decomposition, and combustion reactions are examples.

EXERCISES

1. Identify each type of reaction.
   a. $C_6H_5CH_3 + 9O_2 \rightarrow 7CO_2 + 4H_2O$
   b. $2NaHCO_3 \rightarrow Na_2CO_3 + H_2O + CO_2$
   c. $C + 2H_2 \rightarrow CH_4$
2. Identify each type of reaction.
   a. $P_4O_{10} + 6H_2O \rightarrow 4H_3PO_4$
   b. $FeO + SO_3 \rightarrow FeSO_4$
   c. $CaCO_3(s) \rightarrow CO_2(g) + CaO(s)$
3. Identify each type of reaction.
   a. $2NH_4NO_3(s) \rightarrow 2N_2(g) + 4H_2O(g) + O_2(g)$
   b. $Hg(\ell) + ½O_2\ (g) \rightarrow HgO(s)$
   c. $CH_2CH_2(g) + Br_2(\ell) \rightarrow CH_2BrCH_2Br$
4. Identify each type of reaction.
   a. $Ti(s) + O_2(g) \rightarrow TiO_2(s)$
   b. $H_2SO_3(aq) \rightarrow H_2O(\ell) + SO_2(g)$
   c. $3O_2(g) \rightarrow 2O_3(g)$

ANSWERS

1. a. combustion
   b. decomposition
   c. combination
3. a. decomposition
   b. combustion or combination
   c. combination

5. OXIDATION-REDUCTION (REDOX) REACTIONS

LEARNING OBJECTIVE

1. Identify a chemical reaction as an oxidation-reduction reaction.

FIGURE 5.4
Zinc Metal plus Hydrochloric Acid

It is fairly obvious that zinc metal reacts with aqueous hydrochloric acid! The bubbles are hydrogen gas.

Source: Photo courtesy of Chemicalinterest, http://commons.wikimedia.org/wiki/File:Zn_reaction_with_HCl.JPG.

When zinc metal is submerged into a quantity of aqueous HCl, the following reaction occurs (Figure 5.4):

$$Zn(s) + 2HCl(aq) \rightarrow H_2(g) + ZnCl_2(aq)$$

This is one example of what is sometimes called a *single replacement reaction* because Zn replaces H in combination with Cl.

Because some of the substances in this reaction are aqueous, we can separate them into ions:

$$Zn(s) + 2H^+(aq) + 2Cl^-(aq) \rightarrow H_2(g) + Zn^{2+}(aq) + 2Cl^-(aq)$$

Viewed this way, the net reaction seems to be a charge transfer between zinc and hydrogen atoms. (There is no net change experienced by the chloride ion.) In fact, electrons are being transferred from the zinc atoms to the hydrogen atoms (which ultimately make a molecule of diatomic hydrogen), changing the charges on both elements.

To understand electron-transfer reactions like the one between zinc metal and hydrogen ions, chemists separate them into two parts: one part focuses on the loss of electrons, and one part focuses on the gain of electrons. The loss of electrons is called **oxidation**. The gain of electrons is called **reduction**. Because any loss of electrons by one substance must be accompanied by a gain in electrons by something else, oxidation and reduction always occur together. As such, electron-transfer reactions are also called **oxidation-reduction reactions**, or simply **redox reactions**. The atom that loses electrons is **oxidized**, and the atom that gains electrons is **reduced**. Also, because we can think of the species being oxidized as causing the reduction, the species being oxidized is called the **reducing agent**, and the species being reduced is called the **oxidizing agent**.

oxidation
The loss of electrons by an atom.

reduction
The gain of electrons by an atom.

oxidation-reduction reaction
A chemical reaction in which electrons are transferred from one atom to another. Also called a redox reaction.

reducing agent
A species that causes reduction, which is itself oxidized.

oxidizing agent
A species that causes oxidation, which is itself reduced.

half reaction
A chemical reaction that shows only oxidation or reduction.

Note

Because batteries are used as sources of electricity (that is, of electrons), all batteries are based on redox reactions.

Although the two reactions occur together, it can be helpful to write the oxidation and reduction reactions separately as **half reactions**. In half reactions, we include only the reactant being oxidized or reduced, the corresponding product species, any other species needed to balance the half reaction, and the electrons being transferred. Electrons that are lost are written as products; electrons that are gained are written as reactants. For example, in our earlier equation, now written without the chloride ions,

$$Zn(s) + 2H^+(aq) \rightarrow Zn^{2+}(aq) + H_2(g)$$

zinc atoms are oxidized to Zn^{2+}. The half reaction for the oxidation reaction, omitting phase labels, is as follows:

$$Zn \rightarrow Zn^{2+} + 2e^-$$

This half reaction is balanced in terms of the number of zinc atoms, and it also shows the two electrons that are needed as products to account for the zinc atom losing two negative charges to become a 2+ ion. With half reactions, there is one more item to balance: the overall charge on each side of the reaction. If you check each side of this reaction, you will note that both sides have a zero net charge.

Hydrogen is reduced in the reaction. The balanced reduction half reaction is as follows:

$$2H^+ + 2e^- \rightarrow H_2$$

There are two hydrogen atoms on each side, and the two electrons written as reactants serve to neutralize the 2+ charge on the reactant hydrogen ions. Again, the overall charge on both sides is zero.

The overall reaction is simply the combination of the two half reactions and is shown by adding them together.

$$\begin{array}{r} Zn \rightarrow Zn^{2+} + \cancel{2e^-} \\ 2H^+ + \cancel{2e^-} \rightarrow H_2 \\ \hline Zn + 2H^+ \rightarrow Zn^{2+} + H_2 \end{array}$$

Because we have two electrons on each side of the equation, they can be canceled. This is the key criterion for a balanced redox reaction: the electrons have to cancel exactly. If we check the charge on both sides of the equation, we see they are the same—2+. (In reality, this positive charge is balanced by the negative charges of the chloride ions, which are not included in this reaction because chlorine does not participate in the charge transfer.)

Redox reactions are often balanced by balancing each individual half reaction and then combining the two balanced half reactions. Sometimes a half reaction must have all of its coefficients multiplied by some integer for all the electrons to cancel. The following example demonstrates this process.

EXAMPLE 5

Write and balance the redox reaction that has silver ions and aluminum metal as reactants and silver metal and aluminum ions as products.

Solution

We start by using symbols of the elements and ions to represent the reaction:

$$Ag^+ + Al \rightarrow Ag + Al^{3+}$$

The equation looks balanced as it is written. However, when we compare the overall charges on each side of the equation, we find a charge of +1 on the left but a charge of +3 on the right. This equation is not properly balanced. To balance it, let us write the two half reactions. Silver ions are reduced, and it takes one electron to change Ag^+ to Ag:

$$Ag^+ + e^- \rightarrow Ag$$

Aluminum is oxidized, losing three electrons to change from Al to Al^{3+}:

$$Al \rightarrow Al^{3+} + 3e^-$$

To combine these two half reactions and cancel out all the electrons, we need to multiply the silver reduction reaction by 3:

$$\begin{array}{r} 3(Ag^+ + e^- \rightarrow Ag) \\ Al \rightarrow Al^{3+} + 3e^- \\ \hline 3Ag^+ + Al \rightarrow 3Ag + Al^{3+} \end{array}$$

Now the equation is balanced, not only in terms of elements but also in terms of charge.

SKILL-BUILDING EXERCISE

1. Write and balance the redox reaction that has calcium ions and potassium metal as reactants and calcium metal and potassium ions as products.

Note

Potassium has been used as a reducing agent to obtain various metals in their elemental form.

To Your Health: Redox Reactions and Pacemaker Batteries

All batteries use redox reactions to supply electricity because electricity is basically a stream of electrons being transferred from one substance to another. Pacemakers—surgically implanted devices for regulating a person's heartbeat—are powered by tiny batteries, so the proper operation of a pacemaker depends on a redox reaction.

Pacemakers used to be powered by NiCad batteries, in which nickel and cadmium (hence the name of the battery) react with water according to this redox reaction:

$$Cd(s) + 2NiOOH(s) + 2H_2O(\ell) \rightarrow Cd(OH)_2(s) + 2Ni(OH)_2(s)$$

The cadmium is oxidized, while the nickel atoms in NiOOH are reduced. Except for the water, all the substances in this reaction are solids, allowing NiCad batteries to be recharged hundreds of times before they stop operating. Unfortunately, NiCad batteries are fairly heavy batteries to be carrying around in a pacemaker. Today, the lighter lithium/iodine battery is used instead. The iodine is dissolved in a solid polymer support, and the overall redox reaction is as follows:

$$2Li(s) + I_2(s) \rightarrow 2LiI(s)$$

Lithium is oxidized, and iodine is reduced. Although the lithium/iodine battery cannot be recharged, one of its advantages is that it lasts up to 10 years. Thus, a person with a pacemaker does not have to worry about periodic recharging; about once per decade a person requires minor surgery to replace the pacemaker/battery unit. Lithium/iodine batteries are also used to power calculators and watches.

A small button battery like this is used to power a watch, pacemaker, or calculator.

Oxidation and reduction can also be defined in terms of changes in composition. The original meaning of oxidation was "adding oxygen," so when oxygen is added to a molecule, the molecule is being oxidized. The reverse is true for reduction: if a molecule loses oxygen atoms, the molecule is being reduced. For example, the acetaldehyde (CH_3CHO) molecule takes on an oxygen atom to become acetic acid (CH_3COOH).

$$2CH_3CHO + O_2 \rightarrow 2CH_3COOH$$

Thus, acetaldehyde is being oxidized.

Similarly, oxidation and reduction can be defined in terms of the gain or loss of hydrogen atoms. If a molecule adds hydrogen atoms, it is being reduced. If a molecule loses hydrogen atoms, the molecule is being oxidized. For example, in the conversion of acetaldehyde into ethanol (CH_3CH_2OH), hydrogen atoms are added to acetaldehyde, so the acetaldehyde is being reduced:

$$CH_3CHO + H_2 \rightarrow CH_3CH_2OH$$

EXAMPLE 6

In each conversion, indicate whether oxidation or reduction is occurring.

1. $N_2 \rightarrow NH_3$
2. $CH_3CH_2OHCH_3 \rightarrow CH_3COCH_3$
3. $HCHO \rightarrow HCOOH$

Solution

1. Hydrogen is being added to the original reactant molecule, so reduction is occurring.
2. Hydrogen is being removed from the original reactant molecule, so oxidation is occurring.
3. Oxygen is being added to the original reactant molecule, so oxidation is occurring.

SKILL-BUILDING EXERCISE

In each conversion, indicate whether oxidation or reduction is occurring.

1. $CH_4 \rightarrow CO_2 + H_2O$
2. $NO_2 \rightarrow N_2$
3. $CH_2{=}CH_2 \rightarrow CH_3CH_3$

CONCEPT REVIEW EXERCISES

1. Give two different definitions for oxidation and reduction.
2. Give an example of each definition of oxidation and reduction.

ANSWERS

1. Oxidation is the loss of electrons or the addition of oxygen; reduction is the gain of electrons or the addition of hydrogen.
2. $Zn \rightarrow Zn^{2+} + 2e^-$ (oxidation); $C_2H_4 + H_2 \rightarrow C_2H_6$ (reduction) (answers will vary)

KEY TAKEAWAYS

- Chemical reactions in which electrons are transferred are called oxidation-reduction, or redox, reactions.
- Oxidation is the loss of electrons.
- Reduction is the gain of electrons.
- Oxidation and reduction always occur together, even though they can be written as separate chemical equations.

EXERCISES

1. Which reactions are redox reactions? For those that are redox reactions, identify the oxidizing and reducing agents.
   a. $NaOH + HCl \rightarrow H_2O + NaCl$
   b. $3Mg + 2AlCl_3 \rightarrow 2Al + 3MgCl_2$
   c. $H_2O_2 + H_2 \rightarrow 2H_2O$
   d. $KCl + AgNO_3 \rightarrow AgCl + KNO_3$
2. Which reactions are redox reactions? For those that are redox reactions, identify the oxidizing and reducing agents.
   a. $3Cu + 8HNO_3 \rightarrow 3Cu(NO_3)_2 + 2NO + 4H_2O$
   b. $2C_2H_6 + 7O_2 \rightarrow 4CO_2 + 6H_2O$
   c. $2NaHCO_3 \rightarrow Na_2CO_3 + CO_2 + H_2O$
   d. $2K + 2H_2O \rightarrow 2KOH + H_2$

3. Balance each redox reaction by writing appropriate half reactions and combining them to cancel the electrons.
   a. $Ca(s) + H^+(aq) \rightarrow Ca^{2+}(aq) + H_2(g)$
   b. $I^-(aq) + Br_2(\ell) \rightarrow Br^-(aq) + I_2(s)$

4. Balance each redox reaction by writing appropriate half reactions and combining them to cancel the electrons.
   a. $Fe(s) + Sn^{4+}(aq) \rightarrow Fe^{3+}(aq) + Sn^{2+}(aq)$
   b. $Pb(s) + Pb^{4+}(aq) \rightarrow Pb^{2+}(aq)$ (Hint: both half reactions will start with the same reactant.)

ANSWERS

1. a. no
   b. yes; oxidizing agent: $AlCl_3$; reducing agent: Mg
   c. yes; oxidizing agent: H_2O_2; reducing agent: H_2
   d. no

3. a. $Ca \rightarrow Ca^{2+} + 2e^-$
   $2H^+ + 2e^- \rightarrow H_2$
   Combined: $Ca + 2H^+ \rightarrow Ca^{2+} + H_2$
   b. $Br_2 + 2e^- \rightarrow 2Br^-$
   $2I^- \rightarrow I_2 + 2e^-$
   Combined: $Br_2 + 2I^- \rightarrow 2Br^- + I_2$

6. REDOX REACTIONS IN ORGANIC CHEMISTRY AND BIOCHEMISTRY

LEARNING OBJECTIVE

1. **Identify oxidation-reduction reactions with organic compounds.**

Oxidation-reduction reactions are of central importance in organic chemistry and biochemistry. The burning of fuels that provides the energy to maintain our civilization and the metabolism of foods that furnish the energy that keeps us alive both involve redox reactions.

All combustion reactions are also redox reactions. A typical combustion reaction is the burning of methane, the principal component of natural gas (Figure 5.5).

$$CH_4 + 2O_2 \rightarrow CO_2 + 2H_2O$$

In **respiration**, the biochemical process by which the oxygen we inhale in air oxidizes foodstuffs to carbon dioxide and water, redox reactions provide energy to living cells. A typical respiratory reaction is the oxidation of glucose ($C_6H_{12}O_6$), the simple sugar we encountered in the chapter-opening essay that makes up the diet of yeast:

$$C_6H_{12}O_6 + 6O_2 \rightarrow 6CO_2 + 6H_2O$$

Organic chemists use a variety of redox reactions. For example, potassium dichromate ($K_2Cr_2O_7$) is a common oxidizing agent that can be used to oxidize alcohols (symbolized by the general formula ROH). The product of the reaction depends on the location of the OH functional group in the alcohol molecule, the relative proportions of alcohol and the dichromate ion, and reaction conditions such as temperature. If the OH group is attached to a terminal carbon atom and the product is distilled off as it forms, the product is an aldehyde, which has a terminal *carbonyl group* (C=O) and is often written as RCHO. One example is the reaction used by the Breathalyzer to detect ethyl alcohol (C_2H_5OH) in a person's breath:

$$3C_2H_5OH + Cr_2O_7^{2-} + 8H^+ \rightarrow 3CH_3CHO + 2Cr^{3+} + 7H_2O$$

If the product acetaldehyde (CH_3CHO) is not removed as it forms, it is further oxidized to acetic acid (CH_3COOH). In this case, the overall reaction is as follows:

$$3C_2H_5OH + 2Cr_2O_7^{2-} + 16H^+ \rightarrow 3CH_3COOH + 4Cr^{3+} + 11H_2O$$

In this reaction, the chromium atom is reduced from $Cr_2O_7^{2-}$ to Cr^{3+}, and the ethanol is oxidized to acetic acid.

When the OH group of the alcohol is bonded to an interior carbon atom, the oxidation of an alcohol will produce a ketone. (The formulas of ketones are often written as RCOR, and the carbon–oxygen bond is a double bond.) The simplest ketone is derived from 2-propanol ($CH_3CHOHCH_3$). It is the common solvent acetone [$(CH_3)_2CO$], which is used in varnishes, lacquers, rubber cement, and nail polish remover. Acetone can be formed by the following redox reaction:

$$3CH_3CHOHCH_3 + Cr_2O_7^{2-} + 8H^+ \rightarrow 3(CH_3)_2CO + 2Cr^{3+} + 7H_2O$$

As we have just seen, aldehydes and ketones can be formed by the oxidation of alcohols. Conversely, aldehydes and ketones can be reduced to alcohols. Reduction of the carbonyl group is important in living organisms. For example, in **anaerobic metabolism**, in which biochemical processes take place in the absence of oxygen, pyruvic acid ($CH_3COCOOH$) is reduced to lactic acid ($CH_3CHOHCOOH$) in the muscles.

$$CH_3COCOOH \rightarrow CH_3CHOHCOOH$$

(Pyruvic acid is both a carboxylic acid and a ketone; only the ketone group is reduced.) The buildup of lactic acid during vigorous exercise is responsible in large part for the fatigue that we experience.

In food chemistry, the substances known as **antioxidants** are reducing agents. Ascorbic acid (vitamin C; $C_6H_8O_6$) is thought to retard potentially damaging oxidation of living cells. In the process, it is oxidized to dehydroascorbic acid ($C_6H_6O_6$). In the stomach, ascorbic acid reduces the nitrite ion (NO_2^-) to nitric oxide (NO):

$$C_6H_8O_6 + 2H^+ + 2NO_2^- \rightarrow C_6H_6O_6 + 2H_2O + 2NO$$

If this reaction did not occur, nitrite ions from foods would oxidize the iron in hemoglobin, destroying its ability to carry oxygen.

Tocopherol (vitamin E) is also an antioxidant. In the body, vitamin E is thought to act by scavenging harmful by-products of metabolism, such as the highly reactive molecular fragments called free radicals. In foods, vitamin E acts to prevent fats from being oxidized and thus becoming rancid. Vitamin C is also a good antioxidant (Figure 5.6).

FIGURE 5.5
The Burning of Natural Gas

The burning of natural gas is not only a combustion reaction but also a redox reaction. Similar reactions include the burning of gasoline and coal. These are also redox reactions.

respiration

The biochemical process by which the oxygen we inhale oxidizes foodstuffs to carbon dioxide and water.

anaerobic metabolism

A biochemical process that takes place in the absence of oxygen.

antioxidant

A substance in foods that acts as a reducing agent.

FIGURE 5.6 Citrus Fruits

Citrus fruits, such as oranges, lemons, and limes, are good sources of vitamin C, which is an antioxidant.

© Thinkstock

photosynthesis

The process by which plants use solar energy to convert carbon dioxide and water to glucose.

Finally, and of greatest importance, green plants carry out the redox reaction that makes possible almost all life on Earth. They do this through a process called **photosynthesis**, in which carbon dioxide and water are converted to glucose ($C_6H_{12}O_6$). The synthesis of glucose requires a variety of proteins called enzymes and a green pigment called chlorophyll that converts sunlight into chemical energy (Figure 5.7). The overall change that occurs is as follows:

$$6CO_2 + 6H_2O \rightarrow C_6H_{12}O_6 + 6O_2$$

FIGURE 5.7 Life on Earth

Photosynthesis is the fundamental process by which plants use sunlight to convert carbon dioxide and water into glucose and oxygen. Then plants make more complex carbohydrates. It is the ultimate source of all food on Earth, and it is a redox reaction.

© Thinkstock

In this reaction, carbon dioxide is reduced to glucose, and water is oxidized to oxygen gas. Other reactions convert the glucose to more complex carbohydrates, plant proteins, and oils.

CONCEPT REVIEW EXERCISE

1. Give some biochemical examples of oxidation and reduction reactions.

ANSWER

1. photosynthesis and antioxidants in foods (answers will vary)

KEY TAKEAWAY

- Redox reactions are common in organic and biological chemistry, including the combustion of organic chemicals, respiration, and photosynthesis.

EXERCISES

1. A typical respiratory reaction discussed in the text is the oxidation of glucose ($C_6H_{12}O_6$):

$$C_6H_{12}O_6 + 6O_2 \rightarrow 6CO_2 + 6H_2O$$

Is this a redox reaction? If so, what are the oxidizing and reducing agents?

2. The major net reaction in photosynthesis is as follows:

$$6CO_2 + 6H_2O \rightarrow C_6H_{12}O_6 + 6O_2$$

Is this a redox reaction? If so, what are the oxidizing and reducing agents?

3. What would be the ultimate organic product if $CH_3CH_2CH_2OH$ were to react with a solution of $K_2Cr_2O_7$?
4. What would be the ultimate organic product if $CH_3CH_2CH_2OH$ were to react with a solution of $K_2Cr_2O_7$?
5. What would be the final organic product if $CH_3CH_2CHOHCH_3$ were to react with a solution of $K_2Cr_2O_7$?
6. What would be the major organic product if $CH_3CH_2CHOHCH_2CH_3$ were to react with a solution of $K_2Cr_2O_7$?
7. What alcohol is produced in the reduction of acetone [$(CH_3)_2CO$]?
8. What alcohol is produced in the reduction of propanal (CH_3CH_2CHO)?

ANSWERS

1. yes; oxidizing agent: O_2; reducing agent: $C_6H_{12}O_6$
3. CH_3CH_2COOH
5. $CH_3CH_2C(O)CH_3$, where the carbon is double bonded to the oxygen
7. $CH_3CHOHCH_3$, or isopropyl alcohol

7. END-OF-CHAPTER MATERIAL

Chapter Summary

To ensure that you understand the material in this chapter, you should review the meanings of the following bold terms in the following summary and ask yourself how they relate to the topics in the chapter.

Scientific **laws** are general statements that apply to a wide variety of circumstances. One important law in chemistry is the **law of conservation of matter**, which states that in any closed system, the amount of matter stays constant.

Chemical equations are used to represent **chemical reactions**. **Reactants** change chemically into **products**. The law of conservation of matter requires that a proper chemical equation be **balanced**. **Coefficients** are used to show the relative numbers of reactant and product molecules.

In **stoichiometry**, quantities of reactants and/or products can be related to each other using the balanced chemical equation. The coefficients in a balanced chemical reaction are used to devise the proper ratios that relate the number of molecules of one substance to the number of molecules of another substance.

Chemical reactions can be classified by type. **Combination reactions** (also called **composition reactions**) make a substance from other substances. **Decomposition reactions** break one substance down into multiple substances. **Combustion reactions** combine molecular oxygen with the atoms of another reactant.

Oxidation reactions are reactions in which an atom loses an electron. **Reduction reactions** are reactions in which an atom gains an electron. These two processes always occur together, so they are collectively referred to as **oxidation-reduction** (or **redox**) **reactions**. The species being oxidized it called the **reducing agent**, while the species being reduced is the **oxidizing agent**. Alternate definitions of oxidation and reduction focus on the gain or loss of oxygen atoms, or the loss or gain of hydrogen atoms. Redox reactions are easily balanced if the overall reaction is first separated into **half reactions**, which are individually balanced.

Oxidation-reduction reactions are common in organic and biological chemistry. **Respiration**, the process by which we inhale and metabolize oxygen, is a series of redox reactions. In the absence of oxygen, redox reactions still occur in a process called **anaerobic metabolism**. **Antioxidants** such as ascorbic acid also play a part in the human diet, acting as reducing agents in various biochemical reactions. **Photosynthesis**, the process by which plants convert water and carbon dioxide to glucose, is also based on redox reactions.

ADDITIONAL EXERCISES

1. Isooctane (C_8H_{18}) is used as a standard for comparing gasoline performance. Write a balanced chemical equation for the combustion of isooctane.
2. Heptane (C_7H_{16}), like isooctane (see Exercise 1), is also used as a standard for determining gasoline performance. Write a balanced chemical equation for the combustion of heptane.
3. What is the difference between a combination reaction and a redox reaction? Are all combination reactions also redox reactions? Are all redox reactions also combination reactions?
4. Are combustion reactions always redox reactions as well? Explain.
5. A friend argues that the equation

   $$Fe^{2+} + Na \rightarrow Fe + Na^{+}$$

   is balanced because each side has one iron atom and one sodium atom. Explain why your friend is incorrect.
6. Some antacids contain aluminum hydroxide [$Al(OH)_3$]. This compound reacts with excess hydrochloric acid (HCl) in the stomach to neutralize it. If the products of this reaction are water and aluminum chloride, what is the balanced chemical equation for this reaction?
7. Sulfuric acid is made in a three-step process: (1) the combustion of elemental sulfur to produce sulfur dioxide, (2) the continued reaction of sulfur dioxide with oxygen to produce sulfur trioxide, and (3) the reaction of sulfur trioxide with water to make sulfuric acid (H_2SO_4). Write balanced chemical equations for all three reactions.
8. If the products of glucose metabolism are carbon dioxide and water, what is the balanced chemical equation for the overall process? What is the stoichiometric ratio between the number of CO_2 molecules made to the number of H_2O molecules made?
9. Historically, the first true battery was the Leclanché cell, named after its discoverer, Georges Leclanché. It was based on the following reaction:

   $$Zn(s) + Cu^{2+}(aq) \rightarrow Zn^{2+}(aq) + Cu(s)$$

   Identify what is being oxidized, what is being reduced, and the respective reducing and oxidizing agents.

ANSWERS

1. $2C_8H_{18} + 25O_2 \rightarrow 16CO_2 + 18H_2O$
3. A combination reaction makes a new substance from more than one reactant; a redox reaction rearranges electrons. Not all combination reactions are redox reactions, and not all redox reactions are combination reactions.
5. Your friend is incorrect because the number of electrons transferring is not balanced.
7. (1) $S + O_2 \rightarrow SO_2$; (2) $2SO_2 + O_2 \rightarrow 2SO_3$; (3) $SO_3 + H_2O \rightarrow H_2SO_4$
9. oxidized and reducing agent: Zn; reduced and oxidizing agent: Cu^{2+}

CHAPTER 6

Quantities in Chemical Reactions

Opening Essay

When the disengaged gasses are carefully examined, they are found to weigh **113.7 grs.**; *these are of two kinds, viz.* **144 cubical inches** *of carbonic acid gas, weighing* **100 grs.** *and* **380 cubical inches** *of a very light gas, weighing only* **13.7 grs.**...*and, when the water which has passed over into the bottle [labeled] H is carefully examined, it is found to have lost* **85.7 grs.** *of its weight. Thus, in this experiment,* **85.7 grs.** *of water, joined to* **28 grs.** *of charcoal, have combined in such a way as to form* **100 grs.** *of carbonic acid, and* **13.7 grs.** *of a particular gas capable of being burnt. (Bold emphasis added.)*

In this paragraph from the *Elements of Chemistry*, Antoine Lavoisier (1743–94) is explaining an experiment in which he was trying to demonstrate that water is not an element but instead is composed of hydrogen (the gas "capable of being burnt") and oxygen. This is a historical account of a groundbreaking experiment and illustrates the importance of amounts in chemistry. Lavoisier was pointing out that the initial total mass of water and charcoal, 85.7 g plus 28 g, equals the final total mass of carbonic acid and the particular gas, 100 g plus 13.7 g. In this way, he was illustrating the law of conservation of matter, which was introduced in Chapter 5. It is another way of saying that *amounts matter*.

Amounts do matter and in a variety of circumstances. The chapter-opening essay in Chapter 1 tells the story of a nurse who mistakenly read "2–3 mg" as "23 mg" and administered the higher and potentially fatal dose of morphine to a child. Food scientists who work in test kitchens must keep track of specific amounts of ingredients as they develop new products for us to eat. Quality control technicians measure amounts of substances in manufactured products to ensure that the products meet company or government standards. Supermarkets routinely weigh meat and produce and charge consumers by the ounce or the pound.

So far, we have talked about chemical reactions in terms of individual atoms and molecules. Although this works, most of the reactions occurring around us involve much larger amounts of chemicals. Even a tiny sample of a substance will contain millions, billions, or a hundred billion billions of atoms and molecules. How do we compare amounts of substances to each other in chemical terms when it is so difficult to count to a hundred billion billion?

Actually, there are ways to do this, which we will explore in this chapter. In doing so, we will increase our understanding of stoichiometry, which is the study of the numerical relationships between the reactants and the products in a balanced chemical reaction.

1. THE MOLE

LEARNING OBJECTIVE

1. **Define the mole unit.**

Figure 6.1 shows that we need 2 hydrogen atoms and 1 oxygen atom to make 1 water molecule. If we want to make 2 water molecules, we will need 4 hydrogen atoms and 2 oxygen atoms. If we want to make 5 molecules of water, we need 10 hydrogen atoms and 5 oxygen atoms. The ratio of atoms we will need to make any number of water molecules is the same: 2 hydrogen atoms to 1 oxygen atom.

FIGURE 6.1 Water Molecules

The ratio of hydrogen atoms to oxygen atoms used to make water molecules is always 2:1, no matter how many water molecules are being made.

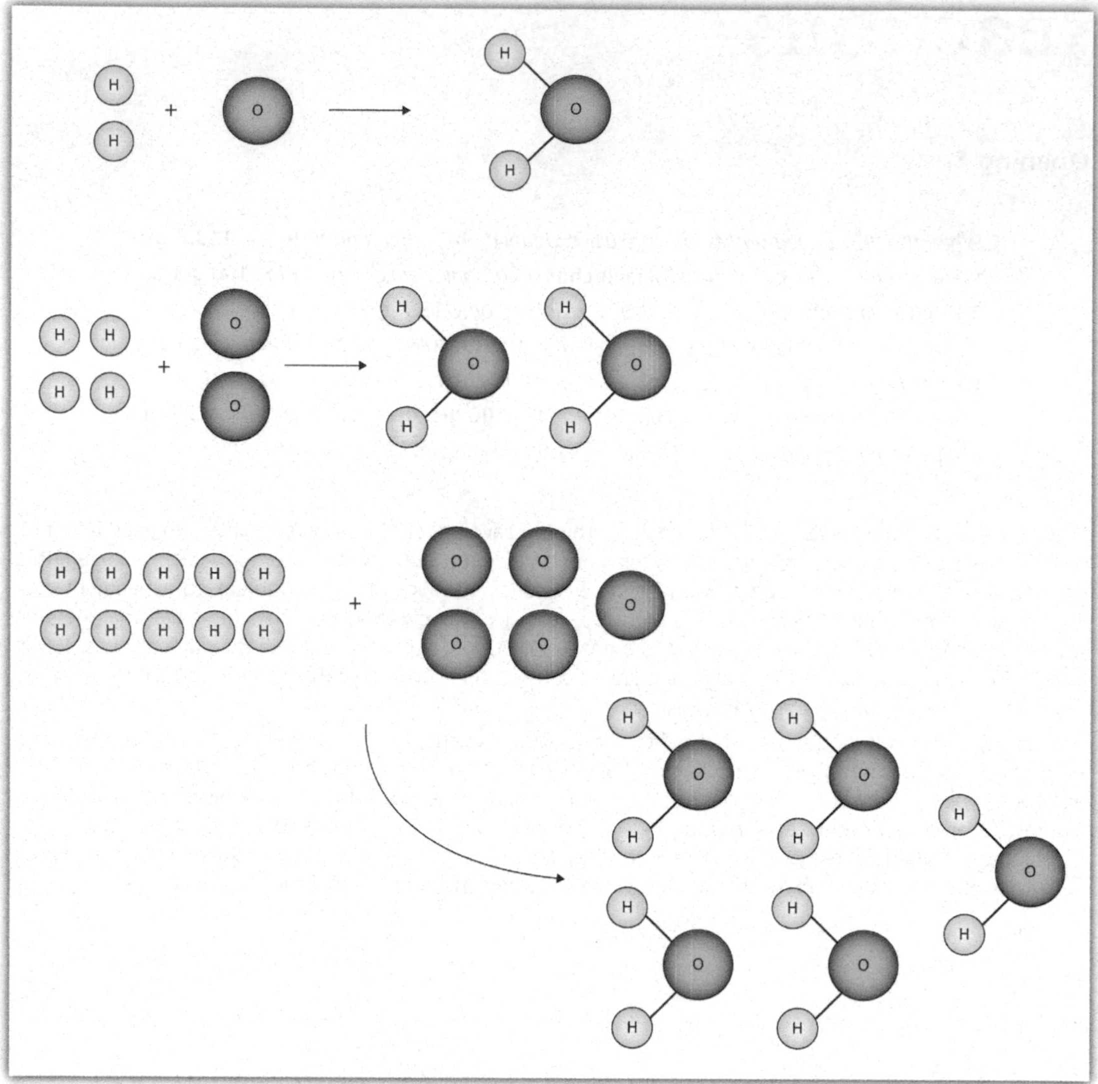

One problem we have, however, is that it is extremely difficult, if not impossible, to organize atoms one at a time. As stated in the introduction, we deal with billions of atoms at a time. How can we keep track of so many atoms (and molecules) at a time? We do it by using mass rather than by counting individual atoms.

A hydrogen atom has a mass of approximately 1 u. An oxygen atom has a mass of approximately 16 u. The ratio of the mass of an oxygen atom to the mass of a hydrogen atom is therefore approximately 16:1.

If we have 2 atoms of each element, the ratio of their masses is approximately 32:2, which reduces to 16:1—the same ratio. If we have 12 atoms of each element, the ratio of their total masses is approximately $(12 \times 16):(12 \times 1)$, or 192:12, which also reduces to 16:1. If we have 100 atoms of each element, the ratio of the masses is approximately 1,600:100, which again reduces to 16:1. As long as we have equal numbers of hydrogen and oxygen atoms, the ratio of the masses will always be 16:1.

The same consistency is seen when ratios of the masses of other elements are compared. For example, the ratio of the masses of silicon atoms to equal numbers of hydrogen atoms is always approximately 28:1, while the ratio of the masses of calcium atoms to equal numbers of lithium atoms is approximately 40:7.

So we have established that the masses of atoms are constant with respect to each other, as long as we have the same number of each type of atom. Consider a more macroscopic example. If a sample contains 40 g of Ca, this sample has the same number of atoms as there are in a sample of 7 g of Li. What we need, then, is a number that represents a convenient quantity of atoms so we can relate macroscopic quantities of substances. Clearly even 12 atoms are too few because atoms themselves are so small. We need a number that represents billions and billions of atoms.

Chemists use the term **mole** to represent a large number of atoms or molecules. Just as a dozen implies 12 things, a mole (mol) represents 6.022×10^{23} things. The number 6.022×10^{23}, called **Avogadro's number** after the 19th-century chemist Amedeo Avogadro, is the number we use in chemistry to represent macroscopic amounts of atoms and molecules. Thus, if we have 6.022×10^{23} O atoms, we say we have 1 mol of O atoms. If we have 2 mol of Na atoms, we have $2 \times (6.022 \times 10^{23})$ Na atoms, or 1.2044×10^{24} Na atoms. Similarly, if we have 0.5 mol of benzene (C_6H_6) molecules, we have $0.5 \times (6.022 \times 10^{23})$ C_6H_6 molecules, or 3.011×10^{23} C_6H_6 molecules.

mole

A number of things equal to 6.022×10^{23} items.

Avogadro's number

The value 6.022×10^{23}.

Note

A mole represents a very large number! If 1 mol of quarters were stacked in a column, it could stretch back and forth between Earth and the sun *6.8 billion* times.

Notice that we are applying the mole unit to different types of chemical entities. In these examples, we cited moles of atoms *and* moles of molecules. The word *mole* represents a number of things—6.022×10^{23} of them—but does not by itself specify what "they" are. They can be atoms, formula units (of ionic compounds), or molecules. That information still needs to be specified.

Because 1 H_2 molecule contains 2 H atoms, 1 mol of H_2 molecules (6.022×10^{23} molecules) has 2 mol of H atoms. Using formulas to indicate how many atoms of each element we have in a substance, we can relate the number of moles of molecules to the number of moles of atoms. For example, in 1 mol of ethanol (C_2H_6O), we can construct the following relationships (Table 6.1):

TABLE 6.1 Molecular Relationships

1 Molecule of C_2H_6O Has	1 Mol of C_2H_6O Has	Molecular Relationships
2 C atoms	2 mol of C atoms	$\frac{2 \text{ mol C atoms}}{1 \text{ mol } C_2H_6O \text{ molecules}}$ or $\frac{1 \text{ mol } C_2H_6O \text{ molecules}}{2 \text{ mol C atoms}}$
6 H atoms	6 mol of H atoms	$\frac{6 \text{ mol H atoms}}{1 \text{ mol } C_2H_6O \text{ molecules}}$ or $\frac{1 \text{ mol } C_2H_6O \text{ molecules}}{6 \text{ mol H atoms}}$
1 O atom	1 mol of O atoms	$\frac{1 \text{ mol O atoms}}{1 \text{ mol } C_2H_6O \text{ molecules}}$ or $\frac{1 \text{ mol } C_2H_6O \text{ molecules}}{1 \text{ mol O atoms}}$

The following example illustrates how we can use these relationships as conversion factors.

EXAMPLE 1

If a sample consists of 2.5 mol of ethanol (C_2H_6O), how many moles of carbon atoms, hydrogen atoms, and oxygen atoms does it have?

Solution

Using the relationships in Table 6.1, we apply the appropriate conversion factor for each element:

$$2.5 \text{ mol } \cancel{C_2H_6O \text{ molecules}} \times \underbrace{\frac{2 \text{ mol C atoms}}{1 \text{ mol } \cancel{C_2H_6O \text{ molecules}}}}_{\text{conversion factor}} = 5.0 \text{ mol C atoms}$$

Note how the unit *mol C_2H_6O molecules* cancels algebraically. Similar equations can be constructed for determining the number of H and O atoms:

$$2.5 \text{ mol } \cancel{C_2H_6O \text{ molecules}} \times \frac{6 \text{ mol H atoms}}{1 \text{ mol } \cancel{C_2H_6O \text{ molecules}}} = 15 \text{ mol H atoms}$$

$$2.5 \text{ mol } \cancel{C_2H_6O \text{ molecules}} \times \frac{1 \text{ mol O atoms}}{1 \text{ mol } \cancel{C_2H_6O \text{ molecules}}} = 2.5 \text{ mol O atoms}$$

SKILL-BUILDING EXERCISE

1. If a sample contains 6.75 mol of Na_2SO_4, how many moles of sodium atoms, sulfur atoms, and oxygen atoms does it have?

The fact that 1 mol equals 6.022×10^{23} items can also be used as a conversion factor.

EXAMPLE 2

How many formula units are present in 2.34 mol of NaCl? How many ions are in 2.34 mol?

Solution

Typically in a problem like this, we start with what we are given and apply the appropriate conversion factor. Here, we are given a quantity of 2.34 mol of NaCl, to which we can apply the definition of a mole as a conversion factor:

$$2.34\ \cancel{\text{mol NaCl}} \times \frac{6.022 \times 10^{23}\ \text{NaCl units}}{1\ \cancel{\text{mol NaCl}}} = 1.41 \times 10^{24}\ \text{NaCl units}$$

Because there are two ions per formula unit, there are

$$1.41 \times 10^{24}\ \cancel{\text{NaCl units}} \times \frac{2\ \text{ions}}{\cancel{\text{NaCl units}}} = 2.82 \times 10^{24}\ \text{ions}$$

in the sample.

SKILL-BUILDING EXERCISE

1. How many molecules are present in 16.02 mol of C_4H_{10}? How many atoms are in 16.02 mol?

CONCEPT REVIEW EXERCISE

1. What is a mole?

ANSWER

1. A mole is 6.022×10^{23} things.

KEY TAKEAWAY

- A mole is 6.022×10^{23} things.

EXERCISES

1. How many dozens are in 1 mol? Express your answer in proper scientific notation.
2. A gross is a dozen dozen, or 144 things. How many gross are in 1 mol? Express your answer in proper scientific notation.
3. How many moles of each type of atom are in 1.0 mol of $C_6H_{12}O_6$?
4. How many moles of each type of atom are in 1.0 mol of $K_2Cr_2O_7$?
5. How many moles of each type of atom are in 2.58 mol of Na_2SO_4?
6. How many moles of each type of atom are in 0.683 mol of $C_{34}H_{32}FeN_4O_4$? (This is the formula of heme, a component of hemoglobin.)
7. How many molecules are in 16.8 mol of H_2O?

8. How many formula units are in 0.778 mol of iron(III) nitrate?
9. A sample of gold contains 7.02×10^{24} atoms. How many moles of gold is this?
10. A flask of mercury contains 3.77×10^{22} atoms. How many moles of mercury are in the flask?
11. An intravenous solution of normal saline may contain 1.72 mol of sodium chloride (NaCl). How many sodium and chlorine atoms are present in the solution?
12. A lethal dose of arsenic is 1.00×10^{21} atoms. How many moles of arsenic is this?

ANSWERS

1. 5.018×10^{22} dozens
3. 6.0 mol of C atoms, 12.0 mol of H atoms, and 6.0 mol of O atoms
5. 5.16 mol of Na atoms, 2.58 mol of S atoms, and 10.32 mol of O atoms
7. 1.012×10^{25} molecules
9. 11.7 mol
11. 1.04×10^{24} Na atoms and 1.04×10^{24} Cl atoms

2. ATOMIC AND MOLAR MASSES

LEARNING OBJECTIVE

1. **Learn how the masses of moles of atoms and molecules are expressed.**

Now that we have introduced the mole and practiced using it as a conversion factor, we ask the obvious question: why is the mole *that particular* number of things? Why is it 6.022×10^{23} and not 1×10^{23} or even 1×10^{20}?

The number in a mole, Avogadro's number, is related to the relative sizes of the atomic mass unit and gram mass units. Whereas one hydrogen atom has a mass of approximately 1 u, 1 mol of H atoms has a mass of approximately 1 *gram*. And whereas one sodium atom has an approximate mass of 23 u, 1 mol of Na atoms has an approximate mass of 23 *grams*.

One mole of a substance has the same mass in grams that one atom or molecule has in atomic mass units. The numbers in the periodic table that we identified as the atomic masses of the atoms not only tell us the mass of one atom in u but also tell us the mass of 1 mol of atoms in grams.

Note

One mole of a substance has the same mass in grams that one atom or molecule has in atomic mass units.

EXAMPLE 3

What is the mass of each quantity?

1. 1 mol of Al atoms
2. 2 mol of U atoms

Solution

1. One mole of Al atoms has a mass in grams that is numerically equivalent to the atomic mass of aluminum. The periodic table shows that the atomic mass (rounded to two decimal points) of Al is 26.98, so 1 mol of Al atoms has a mass of 26.98 g.
2. According to the periodic table, 1 mol of U has a mass of 238.03 g, so the mass of 2 mol is twice that, or 476.06 g.

SKILL-BUILDING EXERCISE

What is the mass of each quantity?

1. 1 mol of Au atoms
2. 5 mol of Br atoms

molar mass

The mass of 1 mol of atoms or molecules.

The mole concept can be extended to masses of formula units and molecules as well. The mass of 1 mol of molecules (or formula units) in grams is numerically equivalent to the mass of one molecule (or formula unit) in atomic mass units. For example, a single molecule of O_2 has a mass of 32.00 u, and 1 mol of O_2 molecules has a mass of 32.00 g. As with atomic mass unit–based masses, to obtain the mass of 1 mol of a substance, we simply sum the masses of the individual atoms in the formula of that substance. The mass of 1 mol of a substance is referred to as its **molar mass**, whether the substance is an element, an ionic compound, or a covalent compound.

EXAMPLE 4

What is the mass of 1 mol of each substance?

1. NaCl
2. bilirubin ($C_{33}H_{36}N_4O_6$), the principal pigment present in bile (a liver secretion)

Solution

1. Summing the molar masses of the atoms in the NaCl formula unit gives

1 Na molar mass:	23.00 g
1 Cl molar mass:	35.45 g
Total:	58.45 g

The mass of 1 mol of NaCl is 58.45 g.

2. Multiplying the molar mass of each atom by the number of atoms of that type in bilirubin's formula and adding the results, we get

33 C molar mass:	33 × 12.01 g	396.33 g
36 H molar mass:	36 × 1.01 =	36.36 g
4 N molar mass:	4 × 14.00 =	56.00 g
6 O molar mass:	6 × 16.00 =	96.00 g
Total:		584.69 g

The mass of 1 mol of bilirubin is 584.69 g.

SKILL-BUILDING EXERCISE

What is the mass of 1 mol of each substance?

1. barium sulfate ($BaSO_4$), used to take X rays of the gastrointestional tract
2. adenosine ($C_{10}H_{13}N_5O_4$), a component of cell nuclei crucial for cell division

Be careful when counting atoms. In formulas with polyatomic ions in parentheses, the subscript outside the parentheses is applied to every atom inside the parentheses. For example, the molar mass of $Ba(OH)_2$ requires the sum of 1 mass of Ba, 2 masses of O, and 2 masses of H:

1 Ba molar mass:	1 × 137.33 g =	137.33 g
2 O molar mass:	2 × 16.00 g =	32.00 g
2 H molar mass:	2 × 1.01 g =	2.02 g
Total:		171.35 g

Because molar mass is defined as the mass for 1 mol of a substance, we can refer to molar mass as grams per mole (g/mol). The division sign (/) implies "per," and "1" is implied in the denominator. Thus, the molar mass of bilirubin can be expressed as 584.05 g/mol, which is read as "five hundred eighty four point zero five grams per mole."

CONCEPT REVIEW EXERCISES

1. How are molar masses of the elements determined?
2. How are molar masses of compounds determined?

ANSWERS

1. Molar masses of the elements are the same numeric value as the masses of a single atom in atomic mass units but in units of grams instead.
2. Molar masses of compounds are calculated by adding the molar masses of their atoms.

KEY TAKEAWAY

- The mass of moles of atoms and molecules is expressed in units of grams.

EXERCISES

1. What is the molar mass of Si? What is the molar mass of U?
2. What is the molar mass of Mn? What is the molar mass of Mg?
3. What is the molar mass of $FeCl_2$? What is the molar mass of $FeCl_3$?
4. What is the molar mass of C_6H_6? What is the molar mass of $C_6H_5CH_3$?
5. What is the molar mass of $(NH_4)_2S$? What is the molar mass of $Ca(OH)_2$?
6. What is the molar mass of $(NH_4)_3PO_4$? What is the molar mass of $Sr(HCO_3)_2$?
7. Aspirin ($C_9H_8O_4$) is an analgesic (painkiller) and antipyretic (fever reducer). What is the molar mass of aspirin?
8. Ibuprofen ($C_{13}H_{18}O_2$) is an analgesic (painkiller). What is the molar mass of ibuprofen?
9. Morphine ($C_{17}H_{19}NO_3$) is a narcotic painkiller. What is the mass of 1 mol of morphine?
10. Heroin ($C_{21}H_{23}NO_5$) is a narcotic drug that is a derivative of morphine. What is the mass of 1 mol of heroin?

ANSWERS

1. 28.09 g/mol; 238.00 g/mol
3. 126.75 g/mol; 162.20 g/mol
5. 68.15 g/mol; 74.10 g/mol
7. 180.17 g/mol
9. 285.36 g

3. MOLE-MASS CONVERSIONS

LEARNING OBJECTIVE

1. Convert quantities between mass units and mole units.

Example 3 in Section 2 stated that the mass of 2 mol of U is twice the molar mass of uranium. Such a straightforward exercise does not require any formal mathematical treatment. Many questions concerning mass are not so straightforward, however, and require some mathematical manipulations.

mole-mass conversion

The conversion from moles of material to the mass of that same material.

The simplest type of manipulation using molar mass as a conversion factor is a **mole-mass conversion** (or its reverse, a mass-mole conversion). In such a conversion, we use the molar mass of a substance as a conversion factor to convert mole units into mass units (or, conversely, mass units into mole units).

We established that 1 mol of Al has a mass of 26.98 g (Example 3 in Section 2). Stated mathematically,

$$1 \text{ mol Al} = 26.98 \text{ g Al}$$

We can divide both sides of this expression by either side to get one of two possible conversion factors:

$$\frac{1 \text{ mol Al}}{26.98 \text{ g Al}} \text{ and } \frac{26.98 \text{ g Al}}{1 \text{ mol Al}}$$

The first conversion factor can be used to convert from mass to moles, and the second converts from moles to mass. Both can be used to solve problems that would be hard to do "by eye."

Note

The algebra skills we are using here are the same skills that we used in Chapter 1 to perform unit conversions.

EXAMPLE 5

What is the mass of 3.987 mol of Al?

Solution

The first step in a conversion problem is to decide what conversion factor to use. Because we are starting with mole units, we want a conversion factor that will cancel the mole unit and introduce the unit for mass in the numerator. Therefore, we should use the $\frac{26.98 \text{ g Al}}{1 \text{ mol Al}}$ conversion factor. We start with the given quantity and multiply by the conversion factor:

$$3.987 \text{ mol Al} \times \frac{26.98 \text{ g Al}}{1 \text{ mol Al}}$$

Note that the mol units cancel algebraically. (The quantity 3.987 mol is understood to be in the numerator of a fraction that has 1 in the unwritten denominator.) Canceling and solving gives

$$3.987 \cancel{\text{mol Al}} \times \frac{26.98 \text{ g Al}}{1 \cancel{\text{mol Al}}} = 107.6 \text{ g Al}$$

Our final answer is expressed to four significant figures.

SKILL-BUILDING EXERCISE

1. How many moles are present in 100.0 g of Al? (Hint: you will have to use the other conversion factor we obtained for aluminum.)

Conversions like this are possible for any substance, as long as the proper atomic mass, formula mass, or molar mass is known (or can be determined) and expressed in grams per mole. Figure 6.2 is a chart for determining what conversion factor is needed, and Figure 6.3 is a flow diagram for the steps needed to perform a conversion.

FIGURE 6.2 A Simple Flowchart for Converting between Mass and Moles of a Substance

It takes one mathematical step to convert from moles to mass or from mass to moles.

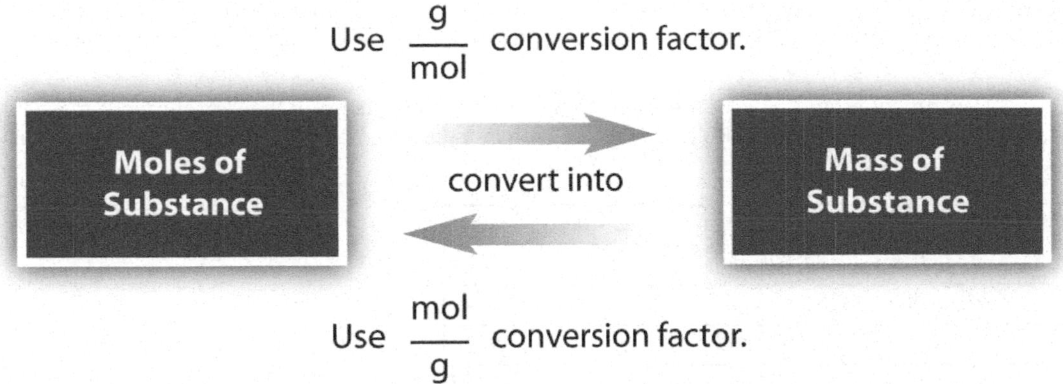

FIGURE 6.3 A Flowchart Illustrating the Steps in Performing a Unit Conversion

When performing many unit conversions, the same logical steps can be taken.

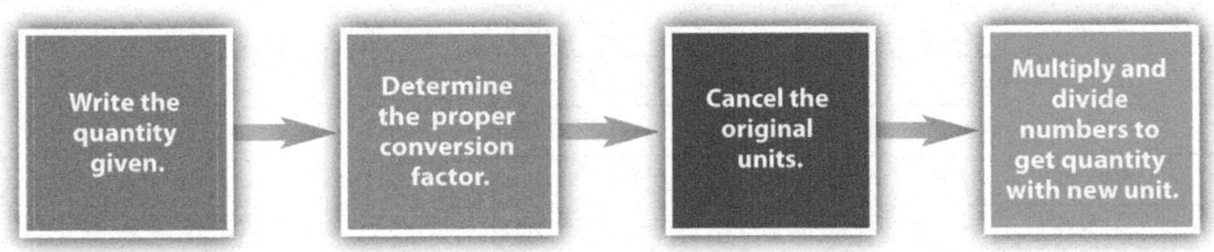

EXAMPLE 6

A biochemist needs 0.00655 mol of bilirubin ($C_{33}H_{36}N_4O_6$) for an experiment. How many grams of bilirubin will that be?

Solution

To convert from moles to mass, we need the molar mass of bilirubin, which we can determine from its chemical formula:

33 C molar mass:	33 × 12.01 g =	396.33 g
36 H molar mass:	36 × 1.01 g =	36.36 g
4 N molar mass:	4 × 14.00 g =	56.00 g
6 O molar mass:	6 × 16.00 g =	96.00 g
Total:		584.69 g

The molar mass of bilirubin is 584.69 g. (We did this calculation in Example 4 in Section 2.) Using the relationship

$$1 \text{ mol bilirubin} = 584.69 \text{ g bilirubin}$$

we can construct the appropriate conversion factor for determining how many grams there are in 0.00655 mol. Following the steps from Figure 6.3:

$$0.00655 \cancel{\text{mol bilirubin}} \times \frac{584.69 \text{ g bilirubin}}{\cancel{\text{mol bilirubin}}} = 3.83 \text{ g bilirubin}$$

The mol bilirubin unit cancels. The biochemist needs 3.83 g of bilirubin.

SKILL-BUILDING EXERCISE

1. A chemist needs 457.8 g of KMnO4 to make a solution. How many moles of KMnO4 is that?

To Your Health: Minerals

For our bodies to function properly, we need to ingest certain substances from our diets. Among our dietary needs are minerals, the noncarbon elements our body uses for a variety of functions, such developing bone or ensuring proper nerve transmission.

The US Department of Agriculture has established some recommendations for the RDIs of various minerals. The accompanying table lists the RDIs for minerals, both in mass and moles, assuming a 2,000-calorie daily diet.

Mineral	Male (age 19–30 y)		Female (age 19–30 y)	
Ca	1,000 mg	0.025 mol	1,000 mg	0.025 mol
Cr	35 µg	6.7×10^{-7} mol	25 µg	4.8×10^{-7} mol
Cu	900 µg	1.4×10^{-5} mol	900 µg	1.4×10^{-5} mol
F	4 mg	2.1×10^{-4} mol	3 mg	1.5×10^{-4} mol
I	150 µg	1.2×10^{-6} mol	150 µg	1.2×10^{-6} mol
Fe	8 mg	1.4×10^{-4} mol	18 mg	3.2×10^{-4} mol
K	3,500 mg	9.0×10^{-2} mol	3,500 mg	9.0×10^{-2} mol
Mg	400 mg	1.6×10^{-2} mol	310 mg	1.3×10^{-2} mol
Mn	2.3 mg	4.2×10^{-5} mol	1.8 mg	3.3×10^{-5} mol
Mo	45 mg	4.7×10^{-7} mol	45 mg	4.7×10^{-7} mol
Na	2,400 mg	1.0×10^{-1} mol	2,400 mg	1.0×10^{-1} mol
P	700 mg	2.3×10^{-2} mol	700 mg	2.3×10^{-2} mol
Se	55 µg	7.0×10^{-7} mol	55 µg	7.0×10^{-7} mol
Zn	11 mg	1.7×10^{-4} mol	8 mg	1.2×10^{-4} mol

This table illustrates several things. First, the needs of men and women for some minerals are different. The extreme case is for iron; women need over twice as much as men do. In all other cases where there is a different RDI, men need more than women.

Second, the amounts of the various minerals needed on a daily basis vary widely—both on a mass scale and a molar scale. The average person needs 0.1 mol of Na a day, which is about 2.5 g. On the other hand, a person needs only about 25–35 µg of Cr per day, which is under one millionth of a mole. As small as this amount is, a deficiency of chromium in the diet can lead to diabetes-like symptoms or neurological problems, especially in the extremities (hands and feet). For some minerals, the body does not require much to keep itself operating properly.

Although a properly balanced diet will provide all the necessary minerals, some people take dietary supplements. However, too much of a good thing, even minerals, is not good. Exposure to too much chromium, for example, causes a skin irritation, and certain forms of chromium are known to cause cancer (as presented in the movie *Erin Brockovich*).

CONCEPT REVIEW EXERCISES

1. What relationship is needed to perform mole-mass conversions?
2. What information determines which conversion factor is used in a mole-mass conversion?

ANSWERS

1. The atomic or molar mass is needed for a mole-mass conversion.

2. The unit of the initial quantity determines which conversion factor is used.

KEY TAKEAWAY

- It is possible to convert between moles of material and mass of material.

EXERCISES

1. What is the mass of 8.603 mol of Fe metal?
2. What is the mass of 0.552 mol of Ag metal?
3. What is the mass of 6.24×10^4 mol of Cl_2 gas?
4. What is the mass of 0.661 mol of O_2 gas?
5. What is the mass of 20.77 mol of $CaCO_3$?
6. What is the mass of 9.02×10^{-3} mol of the hormone epinephrine ($C_9H_{13}NO_3$)?
7. How many moles are present in 977.4 g of $NaHCO_3$?
8. How many moles of erythromycin ($C_{37}H_{67}NO_{13}$), a widely used antibiotic, are in 1.00×10^3 g of the substance?
9. Cortisone ($C_{21}H_{28}O_5$) is a synthetic steroid that is used as an anti-inflammatory drug. How many moles of cortisone are present in one 10.0 mg tablet?
10. Recent research suggests that the daily ingestion of 85 mg of aspirin (also known as acetylsalicylic acid, $C_9H_8O_4$) will reduce a person's risk of heart disease. How many moles of aspirin is that?

ANSWERS

1. 480.5 g
3. 4.42×10^6 g
5. 2,079 g
7. 11.63 mol
9. 2.77×10^{-5} mol

4. MOLE-MOLE RELATIONSHIPS IN CHEMICAL REACTIONS

LEARNING OBJECTIVE

1. **Use a balanced chemical reaction to determine molar relationships between the substances.**

In Chapter 5, you learned to balance chemical equations by comparing the numbers of each type of atom in the reactants and products. The coefficients in front of the chemical formulas represent the numbers of molecules or formula units (depending on the type of substance). Here, we will extend the meaning of the coefficients in a chemical equation.

Consider the simple chemical equation

$$2H_2 + O_2 \rightarrow 2H_2O$$

The convention for writing balanced chemical equations is to use the lowest whole-number ratio for the coefficients. However, the equation is balanced as long as the coefficients are in a 2:1:2 ratio. For example, this equation is also balanced if we write it as

$$4H_2 + 2O_2 \rightarrow 4H_2O$$

The ratio of the coefficients is 4:2:4, which reduces to 2:1:2. The equation is also balanced if we were to write it as

$$22H_2 + 11O_2 \rightarrow 22H_2O$$

because 22:11:22 also reduces to 2:1:2.

Suppose we want to use larger numbers. Consider the following coefficients:

$$12.044 \times 10^{23}\ H_2 + 6.022 \times 10^{23}\ O_2 \rightarrow 12.044 \times 10^{23}\ H_2O$$

These coefficients also have the ratio 2:1:2 (check it and see), so this equation is balanced. But 6.022×10^{23} is 1 mol, while 12.044×10^{23} is 2 mol (and the number is written that way to make this more obvious), so we can simplify this version of the equation by writing it as

$$2\ \text{mol}\ H_2 + 1\ \text{mol}\ O_2 \rightarrow 2\ \text{mol}\ H_2O$$

We can leave out the word *mol* and not write the 1 coefficient (as is our habit), so the final form of the equation, still balanced, is

$$2H_2 + O_2 \rightarrow 2H_2O$$

Now we interpret the coefficients as referring to molar amounts, not individual molecules. The lesson? *Balanced chemical equations are balanced not only at the molecular level but also in terms of molar amounts of reactants and products.* Thus, we can read this reaction as "two moles of hydrogen react with one mole of oxygen to produce two moles of water."

By the same token, the ratios we constructed in Chapter 5 can also be constructed in terms of moles rather than molecules. For the reaction in which hydrogen and oxygen combine to make water, for example, we can construct the following ratios:

$$\frac{2\ \text{mol}\ H_2}{1\ \text{mol}\ O_2}\ \text{or}\ \frac{1\ \text{mol}\ O_2}{2\ \text{mol}\ H_2}$$

$$\frac{2\ \text{mol}\ H_2O}{1\ \text{mol}\ O_2}\ \text{or}\ \frac{1\ \text{mol}\ O_2}{2\ \text{mol}\ H_2O}$$

$$\frac{2\ \text{mol}\ H_2}{2\ \text{mol}\ H_2O}\ \text{or}\ \frac{2\ \text{mol}\ H_2O}{2\ \text{mol}\ H_2}$$

We can use these ratios to determine what amount of a substance, in moles, will react with or produce a given number of moles of a different substance. The study of the numerical relationships between the reactants and the products in balanced chemical reactions is called *stoichiometry*.

EXAMPLE 7

How many moles of oxygen react with hydrogen to produce 27.6 mol of H_2O? The balanced equation is as follows:

$$2H_2 + O_2 \rightarrow 2H_2O$$

Solution

Because we are dealing with quantities of H_2O and O_2, we will use a ratio that relates those two substances. Because we are given an amount of H_2O and want to determine an amount of O_2, we will use the ratio that has H_2O in the denominator (so it cancels) and O_2 in the numerator (so it is introduced in the answer). Thus,

$$27.6\ \cancel{\text{mol}\ H_2O} \times \frac{1\ \text{mol}\ O_2}{2\ \cancel{\text{mol}\ H_2O}} = 13.8\ \text{mol}\ O_2$$

To produce 27.6 mol of H_2O, 13.8 mol of O_2 react.

SKILL-BUILDING EXERCISE

1. Using $2H_2 + O_2 \rightarrow 2H_2O$, how many moles of hydrogen react with 3.07 mol of oxygen to produce H_2O?

CONCEPT REVIEW EXERCISE

1. How do we relate molar amounts of substances in chemical reactions?

ANSWER

1. Amounts of substances in chemical reactions are related by their coefficients in the balanced chemical equation.

KEY TAKEAWAY

- The balanced chemical reaction can be used to determine molar relationships between substances.

EXERCISES

1. List the molar ratios you can derive from this balanced chemical equation:

$$NH_3 + 2O_2 \rightarrow HNO_3 + H_2O$$

2. List the molar ratios you can derive from this balanced chemical equation

$$2C_2H_2 + 5O_2 \rightarrow 4CO_2 + 2H_2O$$

3. Given the following balanced chemical equation,

$$6NaOH + 3Cl_2 \rightarrow NaClO_3 + 5NaCl + 3H_2O$$

how many moles of NaCl can be formed if 3.77 mol of NaOH were to react?

4. Given the following balanced chemical equation,

$$C_5H_{12} + 8O_2 \rightarrow 5CO_2 + 6H_2O$$

how many moles of H_2O can be formed if 0.0652 mol of C_5H_{12} were to react?

5. Balance the following unbalanced equation and determine how many moles of H_2O are produced when 1.65 mol of NH_3 react.

$$NH_3 + O_2 \rightarrow N_2 + H_2O$$

6. Trinitrotoluene [$C_6H_2(NO_2)_2CH_3$], also known as TNT, is formed by reacting nitric acid (HNO_3) with toluene ($C_6H_5CH_3$):

$$HNO_3 + C_6H_5CH_3 \rightarrow C_6H_2(NO_2)_2CH_3 + H_2O$$

Balance the equation and determine how many moles of TNT are produced when 4.903 mol of HNO_3 react.

7. Chemical reactions are balanced in terms of molecules and in terms of moles. Are they balanced in terms of dozens? Defend your answer.
8. Explain how a chemical reaction balanced in terms of moles satisfies the law of conservation of matter.

ANSWERS

1. 1 mol NH_3:2 mol O_2:1 mol HNO_3:1 mol H_2O

3. 3.14 mol

5. $4NH_3 + 3O_2 \rightarrow 2N_2 + 6H_2O$; 2.48 mol

7. Yes, they are still balanced.

5. MOLE-MASS AND MASS-MASS PROBLEMS

LEARNING OBJECTIVE

1. **Convert from mass or moles of one substance to mass or moles of another substance in a chemical reaction.**

We have established that a balanced chemical equation is balanced in terms of moles as well as atoms or molecules. We have used balanced equations to set up ratios, now in terms of moles of materials, that we can use as conversion factors to answer stoichiometric questions, such as how many moles of substance A react with so many moles of reactant B. We can extend this technique even further. Recall that we can relate a molar amount to a mass amount using molar mass. We can use that ability to answer stoichiometry questions in terms of the masses of a particular substance, in addition to moles. We do this using the following sequence:

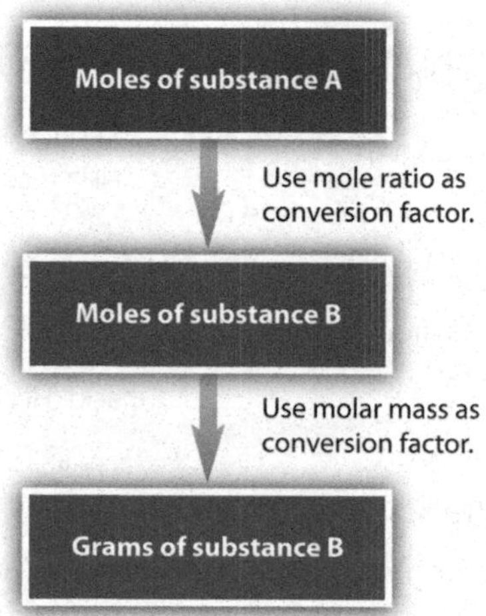

mole-mass calculation

A stoichiometry calculation converting between masses and moles of different substances in a chemical reaction.

Collectively, these conversions are called **mole-mass calculations**.

As an example, consider the balanced chemical equation

$$Fe_2O_3 + 3SO_3 \rightarrow Fe_2(SO_4)_3$$

If we have 3.59 mol of Fe_2O_3, how many grams of SO_3 can react with it? Using the mole-mass calculation sequence, we can determine the required mass of SO_3 in two steps. First, we construct the appropriate molar ratio, determined from the balanced chemical equation, to calculate the number of moles of SO_3 needed. Then using the molar mass of SO_3 as a conversion factor, we determine the mass that this number of moles of SO_3 has.

The first step resembles the exercises we did in Section 4. As usual, we start with the quantity we were given:

$$3.59\ \cancel{\text{mol Fe}_2\text{O}_3} \times \frac{3\ \text{mol SO}_3}{1\ \cancel{\text{mol Fe}_2\text{O}_3}} = 10.77\ \text{mol SO}_3$$

The mol Fe_2O_3 units cancel, leaving mol SO_3 unit. Now, we take this answer and convert it to grams of SO_3, using the molar mass of SO_3 as the conversion factor:

$$10.77\ \cancel{\text{mol SO}_3} \times \frac{80.06\ \text{g SO}_3}{1\ \cancel{\text{mol SO}_3}} = 862\ \text{g SO}_3$$

Our final answer is expressed to three significant figures. Thus, in a two-step process, we find that 862 g of SO_3 will react with 3.59 mol of Fe_2O_3. Many problems of this type can be answered in this manner.

The same two-step problem can also be worked out in a single line, rather than as two separate steps, as follows:

$$3.59 \text{ mol } Fe_2O_3 \times \underbrace{\frac{3 \text{ mol } SO_3}{1 \text{ mol } Fe_2O_3}}_{\text{converts to moles of } SO_3} \times \underbrace{\frac{80.06 \text{ g } SO_3}{1 \text{ mol } SO_3}}_{\text{converts to grams of } SO_3} = 862 \text{ g } SO_3$$

We get exactly the same answer when combining all the math steps together as we do when we calculate one step at a time.

EXAMPLE 8

How many grams of CO_2 are produced if 2.09 mol of HCl are reacted according to this balanced chemical equation?

$$CaCO_3 + 2HCl \rightarrow CaCl_2 + CO_2 + H_2O$$

Solution

Our strategy will be to convert from moles of HCl to moles of CO_2 and then from moles of CO_2 to grams of CO_2. We will need the molar mass of CO_2, which is 44.01 g/mol. Performing these two conversions in a single-line gives 46.0 g of CO_2:

$$2.09 \text{ mol HCl} \times \underbrace{\frac{1 \text{ mol } CO_2}{2 \text{ mol HCl}}}_{\text{from the coefficients of the balanced equation}} \times \frac{44.01 \text{ g } CO_2}{1 \text{ mol } CO_2} = 46.0 \text{ g } CO_2$$

The molar ratio between CO_2 and HCl comes from the balanced chemical equation.

SKILL-BUILDING EXERCISE

1. How many grams of glucose ($C_6H_{12}O_6$) are produced if 17.3 mol of H_2O are reacted according to this balanced chemical equation?

$$6CO_2 + 6H_2O \rightarrow C_6H_{12}O_6 + 6O_2$$

It is a small step from mole-mass calculations to **mass-mass calculations**. If we start with a known mass of one substance in a chemical reaction (instead of a known number of moles), we can calculate the corresponding masses of other substances in the reaction. The first step in this case is to convert the known mass into moles, using the substance's molar mass as the conversion factor. Then—and only then—we use the balanced chemical equation to construct a conversion factor to convert that quantity to moles of another substance, which in turn can be converted to a corresponding mass. Sequentially, the process is as follows:

mass-mass calculation

A stoichiometry calculation converting between the mass of one substance and the mass of a different substance in a chemical reaction.

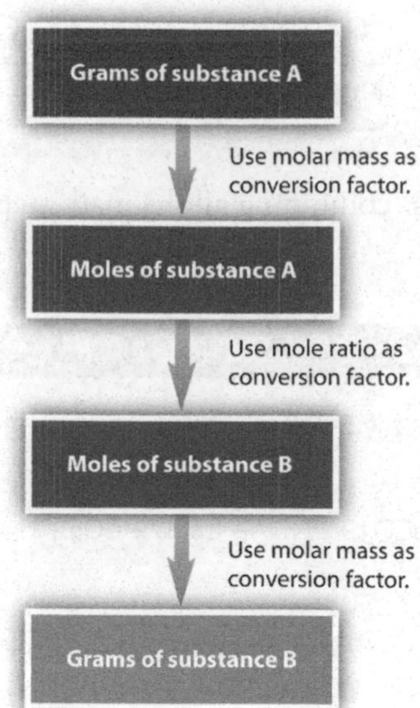

This three-part process can be carried out in three discrete steps or combined into a single calculation that contains three conversion factors. The following example illustrates both techniques.

EXAMPLE 9

Methane can react with elemental chlorine to make carbon tetrachloride (CCl_4). The balanced chemical equation is as follows:

$$CH_4 + 4Cl_2 \rightarrow CCl_4 + 4HCl$$

How many grams of HCl are produced by the reaction of 100.0 g of CH_4?

Solution

First, let us work the problem in stepwise fashion. We begin by converting the mass of CH_4 to moles of CH_4, using the molar mass of CH_4 (16.05 g/mol) as the conversion factor:

$$100.0\ \cancel{\text{g CH}_4} \times \frac{1\ \text{mol CH}_4}{16.05\ \cancel{\text{g CH}_4}} = 6.231\ \text{mol CH}_4$$

Note that we inverted the molar mass so that the gram units cancel, giving us an answer in moles. Next, we use the balanced chemical equation to determine the ratio of moles CH_4 and moles HCl and convert our first result into moles of HCl:

$$6.231\ \cancel{\text{mol CH}_4} \times \frac{4\ \text{mol HCl}}{1\ \cancel{\text{mol CH}_4}} = 24.92\ \text{mol HCl}$$

Finally, we use the molar mass of HCl (36.46 g/mol) as a conversion factor to calculate the mass of 24.92 mol of HCl:

$$24.92\ \cancel{\text{mol HCl}} \times \frac{36.46\ \text{g HCl}}{1\ \cancel{\text{mol HCl}}} = 908.5\ \text{g HCl}$$

In each step, we have limited the answer to the proper number of significant figures. If desired, we can do all three conversions on a single line:

$$100.0\ \cancel{\text{g CH}_4} \times \frac{1\ \cancel{\text{mol CH}_4}}{16.05\ \cancel{\text{g CH}_4}} \times \frac{4\ \cancel{\text{mol HCl}}}{1\ \cancel{\text{mol CH}_4}} \times \frac{36.46\ \text{g HCl}}{1\ \cancel{\text{mol HCl}}} = 908.7\ \text{g HCl}$$

This final answer is slightly different from our first answer because only the final answer is restricted to the proper number of significant figures. In the first answer, we limited each intermediate quantity to the proper number of significant figures. As you can see, both answers are essentially the same.

SKILL-BUILDING EXERCISE

1. The oxidation of propanal (CH_3CH_2CHO) to propionic acid (CH_3CH_2COOH) has the following chemical equation:

$$CH_3CH_2CHO + 2K_2Cr_2O_7 \rightarrow CH_3CH_2COOH + \text{other products}$$

How many grams of propionic acid are produced by the reaction of 135.8 g of $K_2Cr_2O_7$?

CONCEPT REVIEW EXERCISES

1. What is the general sequence of conversions for a mole-mass calculation?
2. What is the general sequence of conversions for a mass-mass calculation?

ANSWERS

1. mol first substance → mol second substance → mass second substance
2. mass first substance → mol first substance → mol second substance → mass second substance

To Your Health: The Synthesis of Taxol

Taxol is a powerful anticancer drug that was originally extracted from the Pacific yew tree (*Taxus brevifolia*). As you can see from the accompanying figure, taxol is a very complicated molecule, with a molecular formula of $C_{47}H_{51}NO_{14}$. Isolating taxol from its natural source presents certain challenges, mainly that the Pacific yew is a slow-growing tree, and the equivalent of six trees must be harvested to provide enough taxol to treat a single patient. Although related species of yew trees also produce taxol in small amounts, there is significant interest in synthesizing this complex molecule in the laboratory.

After a 20-year effort, two research groups announced the complete laboratory synthesis of taxol in 1994. However, each synthesis required over 30 separate chemical reactions, with an overall efficiency of less than 0.05%. To put this in perspective, to obtain a single 300 mg dose of taxol, you would have to begin with 600 g of starting material. To treat the 26,000 women who are diagnosed with ovarian cancer each year with one dose, almost 16,000 kg (over 17 tons) of starting material must be converted to taxol. Taxol is also used to treat breast cancer, with which 200,000 women in the United States are diagnosed every year. This only increases the amount of starting material needed.

Clearly, there is intense interest in increasing the overall efficiency of the taxol synthesis. An improved synthesis is not only will be easier but also will produce less waste materials, which will allow more people to take advantage of this potentially life-saving drug.

The Structure of the Cancer Drug Taxol

Because of the complexity of the molecule, hydrogen atoms are not shown, but they are present on every atom to give the atom the correct number of covalent bonds (four bonds for each carbon atom).

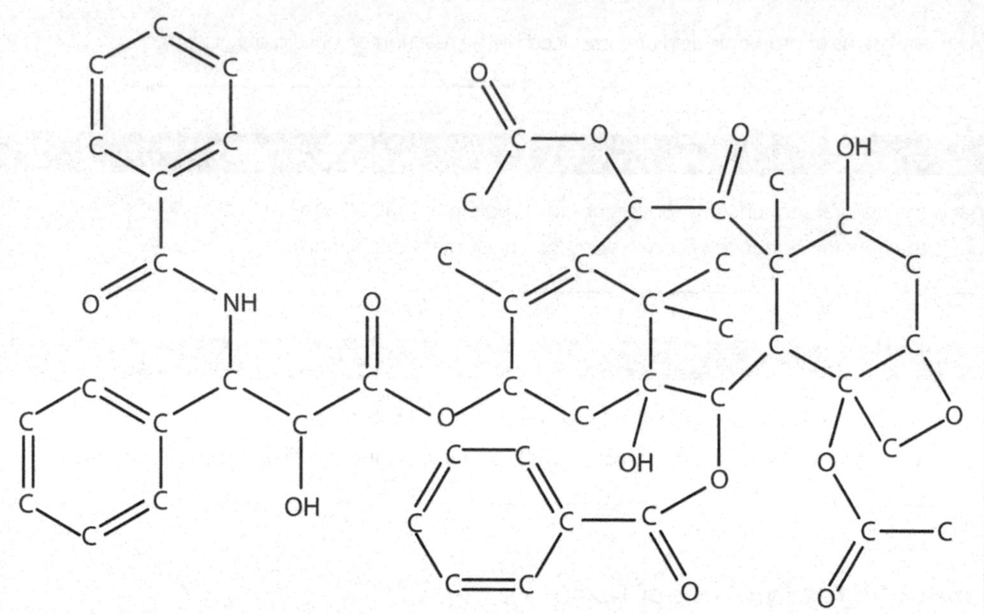

KEY TAKEAWAY

- A balanced chemical equation can be used to relate masses or moles of different substances in a reaction.

EXERCISES

1. Given the following unbalanced chemical equation,

$$H_3PO_4 + NaOH \rightarrow H_2O + Na_3PO_4$$

what mass of H_2O is produced by the reaction of 2.35 mol of H_3PO_4?

2. Given the following unbalanced chemical equation,

$$C_2H_6 + Br_2 \rightarrow C_2H_4Br_2 + HBr$$

what mass of HBr is produced if 0.884 mol of C_2H_6 is reacted?

3. Certain fats are used to make soap, the first step being to react the fat with water to make glycerol (also known as glycerin) and compounds called fatty acids. One example is as follows:

$$\underset{\text{a fat}}{C_3H_5(OOC(CH_2)_{14}CH_3)_3} + 3H_2O \rightarrow \underset{\text{glycerol}}{C_3H_5(OH)_3} + \underset{\text{fatty acid}}{3CH_3(CH_2)_{14}COOH}$$

How many moles of glycerol can be made from the reaction of 1,000.0 g of $C_3H_5(OOC(CH_2)_{14}CH_3)_3$?

4. Photosynthesis in plants leads to the general overall reaction for producing glucose ($C_6H_{12}O_6$):

$$6CO_2 + 6H_2O \rightarrow C_6H_{12}O_6 + 6O_2$$

How many moles of glucose can be made from the reaction of 544 g of CO_2?

5. Precipitation reactions, in which a solid (called a precipitate) is a product, are commonly used to remove certain ions from solution. One such reaction is as follows:

$$Ba(NO_3)_2(aq) + Na_2SO_4(aq) \rightarrow BaSO_4(s) + 2NaNO_3(aq)$$

How many grams of Na_2SO_4 are needed to precipitate all the barium ions produced by 43.9 g of $Ba(NO_3)_2$?

6. Nitroglycerin [$C_3H_5(ONO_2)_3$] is made by reacting nitric acid (HNO_3) with glycerol [$C_3H_5(OH)_3$] according to this reaction:

$$C_3H_5(OH)_3 + 3HNO_3 \rightarrow C_3H_5(ONO_2)_3 + 3H_2O$$

If 87.4 g of HNO_3 are reacted with excess glycerol, what mass of nitroglycerin can be made?

7. Antacids are bases that neutralize acids in the digestive tract. Magnesium hydroxide [$Mg(OH)_2$] is one such antacid. It reacts with hydrochloric acid in the stomach according to the following reaction:

$$Mg(OH)_2 + 2HCl \rightarrow MgCl_2 + 2H_2O$$

How many grams of HCl can a 200 mg dose of $Mg(OH)_2$ neutralize?

8. Acid rain is caused by the reaction of nonmetal oxides with water in the atmosphere. One such reaction involves nitrogen dioxide (NO_2) and produces nitric acid (HNO_3):

$$3NO_2 + H_2O \rightarrow 2HNO_3 + NO$$

If 1.82×10^{13} g of NO_2 enter the atmosphere every year due to human activities, potentially how many grams of HNO_3 can be produced annually?

9. A simplified version of the processing of iron ore into iron metal is as follows:

$$2Fe_2O_3 + 3C \rightarrow 4Fe + 3CO_2$$

How many grams of C are needed to produce 1.00×10^9 g of Fe?

10. The *SS Hindenburg* contained about 5.33×10^5 g of H_2 gas when it burned at Lakehurst, New Jersey, in 1937. The chemical reaction is as follows:

$$2H_2 + O_2 \rightarrow 2H_2O$$

How many grams of H_2O were produced?

ANSWERS

1. 127 g
3. 1.236 mol
5. 23.9 g
7. 0.251 g
9. 1.61×10^8 g

6. END-OF-CHAPTER MATERIAL

Chapter Summary

To ensure that you understand the material in this chapter, you should review the meanings of the following bold terms in the following summary and ask yourself how they relate to the topics in the chapter.

Chemical reactions relate quantities of reactants and products. Chemists use the **mole** unit to represent 6.022×10^{23} things, whether the things are atoms of elements or molecules of compounds. This number, called **Avogadro's number**, is important because this number of atoms or molecules has the same mass in grams as one atom or molecule has in atomic mass units. **Molar masses** of substances can be determined by summing the appropriate masses from the periodic table; the final molar mass will have units of grams.

Because one mole of a substance will have a certain mass, we can use that relationship to construct conversion factors that will convert a mole amount into a mass amount, or vice versa. Such **mole-mass conversions** typically take one algebraic step.

Chemical reactions list reactants and products in molar amounts, not just molecular amounts. We can use the coefficients of a balanced chemical equation to relate moles of one substance in the reaction to moles of other substances (stoichiometry). In a **mole-mass calculation**, we relate the number of moles of one substance to the mass of another substance. In a **mass-mass calculation**, we relate the mass of one substance to the mass of another substance.

ADDITIONAL EXERCISES

1. If the average male has a body mass of 70 kg, of which 60% is water, how many moles of water are in an average male?
2. If the average female is 60.0 kg and contains 0.00174% iron, how many moles of iron are in an average female?
3. How many moles of each element are present in 2.67 mol of each compound?
   a. HCl
   b. H_2SO_4
   c. $Al(NO_3)_3$
   d. $Ga_2(SO_4)_3$
4. How many moles of each element are present in 0.00445 mol of each compound?
   a. HCl
   b. H_2SO_4
   c. $Al_2(CO_3)_3$
   d. $Ga_2(SO_4)_3$
5. What is the mass of one hydrogen atom in grams? What is the mass of one oxygen atom in grams? Do these masses have a 1:16 ratio, as expected?
6. What is the mass of one sodium atom in grams?
7. If 6.63×10^{-6} mol of a compound has a mass of 2.151 mg, what is the molar mass of the compound?
8. Hemoglobin (molar mass is approximately 64,000 g/mol) is the major component of red blood cells that transports oxygen and carbon dioxide in the body. How many moles are in 0.034 g of hemoglobin?

ANSWERS

1. 2,330 mol
3. a. 2.67 mol of H and 2.67 mol of Cl
   b. 5.34 mol of H, 2.67 mol of S, and 10.68 mol of O
   c. 2.67 mol of Al, 8.01 mol of N, and 24.03 mol of O
   d. 5.34 mol of Ga, 8.01 mol of S, and 32.04 mol of O
5. H = 1.66×10^{-24} g and O = 2.66×10^{-23} g; yes, they are in a 1:16 ratio.
7. 324 g/mol

CHAPTER 7

Energy and Chemical Processes

Opening Essay

Metabolism, which we will study in Chapter 20, is the collective term for the chemical reactions that occur in cells and provide energy to keep cells alive. Some of the energy from metabolism is in the form of heat, and some animals use this heat to regulate their body temperatures. Such *warm-blooded* animals are called *endotherms*. In endotherms, problems with metabolism can lead to fluctuations in body temperature. When humans get sick, for instance, our body temperatures can rise higher than normal; we develop a fever. When food is scarce (especially in winter), some endotherms go into a state of controlled decreased metabolism called *hibernation*. During hibernation, the body temperatures of these endotherms actually decrease. In hot weather or when feverish, endotherms will pant or sweat to rid their bodies of excess heat.

Average Body Temperatures of Selected Endotherms

Endotherm	Body Temperature (°F)	Body Temperature (°C)
bird	up to 110	up to 43.5
cat	101.5	38.6
dog	102	38.9
horse	100.0	37.8
human	98.6	37.0
pig	102.5	39.2

Ectotherms, sometimes called *cold-blooded* animals, do not use the energy of metabolism to regulate body temperature. Instead, they depend on external energy sources, such as sunlight. Fish, for example, will seek out water of different temperatures to regulate body temperature. The amount of energy available is directly related to the metabolic rate of the animal. When energy is scarce, ectotherms may also hibernate.

The connection between metabolism and body temperature is a reminder that energy and chemical reactions are intimately related. A basic understanding of this relationship is especially important when those chemical reactions occur within our own bodies.

Energy is a vital component of the world around us. Nearly every physical and chemical process, including all the chemical reactions discussed in previous chapters, occurs with a simultaneous energy change. In this chapter, we will explore the nature of energy and how energy and chemistry are related.

1. ENERGY AND ITS UNITS

LEARNING OBJECTIVE

1. **Define *energy* and *heat*.**

Energy is the ability to do work. You can understand what this means by thinking about yourself when you feel "energetic." You feel ready to go—to jump up and get something done. When you have a lot of energy, you can perform a lot of work. By contrast, if you do not feel energetic, you have very little desire to do much of anything. This description is not only applicable to you but also to all physical and

energy
The ability to do work.

chemical processes. The quantity of work that can be done is related to the quantity of energy available to do it.

heat

The transfer of energy from one part of the universe to another due to temperature differences.

joule

The SI unit of energy, work, and heat.

calorie

A unit of energy widely used in the health professions and everyday life.

Energy can be transferred from one object to another if the objects have different temperatures. The transfer of energy due to temperature differences is called **heat**. For example, if you hold an ice cube in your hand, the ice cube slowly melts as energy in the form of heat is transferred from your hand to the ice. As your hand loses energy, it starts to feel cold.

Because of their interrelationships, energy, work, and heat have the same units. The SI unit of energy, work, and heat is the **joule** (J). A joule is a tiny amount of energy. For example, it takes about 4 J to warm 1 mL of H_2O by 1°C. Many processes occur with energy changes in thousands of joules, so the kilojoule (kJ) is also common.

Another unit of energy, used widely in the health professions and everyday life, is the **calorie** (cal). The calorie was initially defined as the amount of energy needed to warm 1 g of H_2O by 1°C, but in modern times, the calorie is related directly to the joule, as follows:

$$1 \text{ cal} = 4.184 \text{ J}$$

We can use this relationship to convert quantities of energy, work, or heat from one unit to another.

The calorie is used in nutrition to express the energy content of foods. However, because a calorie is a rather small quantity, nutritional energies are usually expressed in kilocalories (kcal), also called Calories (capitalized; Cal). For example, a candy bar may provide 120 Cal (nutritional calories) of energy, which is equal to 120,000 cal. Figure 7.1 shows an example. Proteins and carbohydrates supply 4 kcal/g, while fat supplies 9 kcal/g.

FIGURE 7.1
Nutritional Energy

The energy values of foods are reported in kilocalories, also called Calories.

© Thinkstock

Note

Although the joule is the proper SI unit for energy, we will use the calorie or the kilocalorie (or Calorie) in this chapter because they are widely used by health professionals.

EXAMPLE 1

The energy content of a single serving of bread is 70.0 Cal. What is the energy content in calories? In joules?

Solution

This is a simple conversion-factor problem. Using the relationship 1 Cal = 1,000 cal, we can answer the first question with a one-step conversion:

$$70.0 \not{\text{Cal}} \times \frac{1{,}000 \text{ cal}}{1 \not{\text{Cal}}} = 70{,}000 \text{ cal}$$

Then we convert calories into joules

$$70{,}000 \not{\text{cal}} \times \frac{4.184 \text{ J}}{1 \not{\text{cal}}} = 293{,}000 \text{ J}$$

and then kilojoules

$$293{,}000 \not{\text{J}} \times \frac{1 \text{ kJ}}{1{,}000 \not{\text{J}}} = 293 \text{ kJ}$$

The energy content of bread comes mostly from carbohydrates.

SKILL-BUILDING EXERCISE

1. The energy content of one cup of honey is 1,030 Cal. What is its energy content in calories and joules?

To Your Health: Energy Expenditures

Most health professionals agree that exercise is a valuable component of a healthy lifestyle. Exercise not only strengthens the body and develops muscle tone but also expends energy. After obtaining energy from the foods we eat, we need to expend that energy somehow, or our bodies will store it in unhealthy ways.

Like the energy content in food, the energy expenditures of exercise are also reported in kilocalories, usually kilocalories per hour of exercise. These expenditures vary widely, from about 440 kcal/h for walking at a speed of 4 mph to 1,870 kcal/h for mountain biking at 20 mph. Table 7.2 lists the energy expenditure for a variety of exercises.

Energy Expenditure of a 180-Pound Person during Selected Exercises

Exercise	Energy Expended (kcal/h)
aerobics, low-level	325
basketball	940
bike riding, 20 mph	830
golfing, with cart	220
golfing, carrying clubs	425
jogging, 7.5 mph	950
racquetball	740
skiing, downhill	520
soccer	680
walking upstairs	1,200
yoga	280

Because some forms of exercise use more energy than others, anyone considering a specific exercise regimen should consult with his or her physician first.

CONCEPT REVIEW EXERCISES

1. What is the relationship between energy and heat?
2. What units are used to express energy and heat?

ANSWERS

1. Heat is the exchange of energy from one part of the universe to another. Heat and energy have the same units.
2. Joules and calories are the units of energy and heat.

KEY TAKEAWAYS

- Energy is the ability to do work.
- Heat is the transfer of energy due to temperature differences.
- Energy and heat are expressed in units of joules.

EXERCISES

1. Define *energy*.
2. What is heat?
3. What is the relationship between a calorie and a joule? Which unit is larger?
4. What is the relationship between a calorie and a kilocalorie? Which unit is larger?

5. Express 1,265 cal in kilocalories and in joules.
6. Express 9,043.3 J in calories and in kilocalories.
7. One kilocalorie equals how many kilojoules?
8. One kilojoule equals how many kilocalories?
9. Many nutrition experts say that an average person needs 2,000 Cal per day from his or her diet. How many joules is this?
10. Baby formula typically has 20.0 Cal per ounce. How many ounces of formula should a baby drink per day if the RDI is 850 Cal?

ANSWERS

1. Energy is the ability to do work.
3. 1 cal = 4.184 J; the calorie is larger.
5. 1.265 kcal; 5,293 J
7. 1 kcal = 4.184 kJ
9. 8.4×10^6 J

2. HEAT

LEARNING OBJECTIVE

1. **Relate heat transfer to temperature change.**

Heat is a familiar manifestation of energy. When we touch a hot object, energy flows from the hot object into our fingers, and we perceive that incoming energy as the object being "hot." Conversely, when we hold an ice cube in our palms, energy flows from our hand into the ice cube, and we perceive that loss of energy as "cold." In both cases, the temperature of the object is different from the temperature of our hand, so we can conclude that differences in temperatures are the ultimate cause of heat transfer.

Suppose we consider the transfer of heat from the opposite perspective—namely, what happens to a system that gains or loses heat? Generally, the system's temperature changes. (We will address a few exceptions later.) The greater the original temperature difference, the greater the transfer of heat, and the greater the ultimate temperature change. The relationship between the amount of heat transferred and the temperature change can be written as

$$\text{heat} \propto \Delta T$$

where $\propto$ means "is proportional to" and ΔT is the change in temperature of the system. Any change in a variable is always defined as "the final value minus the initial value" of the variable, so ΔT is $T_{\text{final}} - T_{\text{initial}}$. In addition, the greater the mass of an object, the more heat is needed to change its temperature. We can include a variable representing mass (m) to the proportionality as follows:

$$\text{heat} \propto m\Delta T$$

To change this proportionality into an equality, we include a proportionality constant. The proportionality constant is called the **specific heat**, symbolized by c:

specific heat

A proportionality constant that relates heat to a temperature change.

$$\text{heat} = mc\Delta T$$

Every substance has a characteristic specific heat, which is reported in units of cal/g·°C or cal/g·K, depending on the units used to express ΔT. The specific heat of a substance is the amount of energy that must be transferred to or from 1 g of that substance to change its temperature by 1°. Table 7.3 lists the specific heats for various materials.

TABLE 7.3 Specific Heats of Selected Substances

Substance	c (cal/g·°C)
aluminum (Al)	0.215
aluminum oxide (Al_2O_3)	0.305
benzene (C_6H_6)	0.251
copper (Cu)	0.092
ethanol (C_2H_6O)	0.578
hexane (C_6H_{14})	0.394
hydrogen (H_2)	3.419
ice [$H_2O(s)$]	0.492
iron (Fe)	0.108
iron(III) oxide (Fe_2O_3)	0.156
mercury (Hg)	0.033
oxygen (O_2)	0.219
sodium chloride (NaCl)	0.207
steam [$H_2O(g)$]	0.488
water [$H_2O(\ell)$]	1.00

Note

The proportionality constant *c* is sometimes referred to as the *specific heat capacity* or (incorrectly) the *heat capacity.*

The *direction* of heat flow is not shown in heat = $mc\Delta T$. If energy goes into an object, the total energy of the object increases, and the values of heat ΔT are positive. If energy is coming out of an object, the total energy of the object decreases, and the values of heat and ΔT are negative.

EXAMPLE 2

What quantity of heat is transferred when a 150.0 g block of iron metal is heated from 25.0°C to 73.3°C? What is the direction of heat flow?

Solution

We can use heat = $mc\Delta T$ to determine the amount of heat, but first we need to determine ΔT. Because the final temperature of the iron is 73.3°C and the initial temperature is 25.0°C, ΔT is as follows:

$$\Delta T = T_{\text{final}} - T_{\text{initial}} = 73.3°\text{C} - 25.0°\text{C} = 48.3°\text{C}$$

The mass is given as 150.0 g, and Table 7.3 gives the specific heat of iron as 0.108 cal/g·°C. Substitute the known values into heat = $mc\Delta T$ and solve for amount of heat:

$$\text{heat} = (150.0\,\cancel{\text{g}})\left(0.108\,\frac{\text{cal}}{\cancel{\text{g}}\cdot\cancel{°\text{C}}}\right)(48.3\,\cancel{°\text{C}}) = 782\text{ cal}$$

Note how the gram and °C units cancel algebraically, leaving only the calorie unit, which is a unit of heat. Because the temperature of the iron increases, energy (as heat) must be flowing *into* the metal.

SKILL-BUILDING EXERCISE

1. What quantity of heat is transferred when a 295.5 g block of aluminum metal is cooled from 128.0°C to 22.5°C? What is the direction of heat flow?

EXAMPLE 3

A 10.3 g sample of a reddish-brown metal gave off 71.7 cal of heat as its temperature decreased from 97.5°C to 22.0°C. What is the specific heat of the metal? Can you identify the metal from the data in Table 7.3?

Solution

The question gives us the heat, the final and initial temperatures, and the mass of the sample. The value of ΔT is as follows:

$$\Delta T = T_{\text{final}} - T_{\text{initial}} = 22.0°\text{C} - 97.5°\text{C} = -75.5°\text{C}$$

If the sample gives off 71.7 cal, it loses energy (as heat), so the value of heat is written as a negative number, −71.7 cal. Substitute the known values into heat = $mc\Delta T$ and solve for c:

$$-71.7\ \text{cal} = (10.3\ \text{g})(c)(-75.5°\text{C})$$

$$c = \frac{-71.7\ \text{cal}}{(10.3\ \text{g})(-75.5°\text{C})}$$

$$c = 0.0923\ \text{cal/g·°C}$$

This value for specific heat is very close to that given for copper in Table 7.3.

SKILL-BUILDING EXERCISE

1. A 10.7 g crystal of sodium chloride (NaCl) had an initial temperature of 37.0°C. What is the final temperature of the crystal if 147 cal of heat were supplied to it?

CONCEPT REVIEW EXERCISE

1. Describe the relationship between heat transfer and the temperature change of an object.

ANSWER

1. Heat is equal to the product of the mass, the change in temperature, and a proportionality constant called the specific heat.

KEY TAKEAWAY

- Heat transfer is related to temperature change.

EXERCISES

1. A pot of water is set on a hot burner of a stove. What is the direction of heat flow?
2. Some uncooked macaroni is added to a pot of boiling water. What is the direction of heat flow?
3. How much energy in calories is required to heat 150 g of H_2O from 0°C to 100°C?
4. How much energy in calories is required to heat 125 g of Fe from 25°C to 150°C?
5. If 250 cal of heat were added to 43.8 g of Al at 22.5°C, what is the final temperature of the aluminum?
6. If 195 cal of heat were added to 33.2 g of Hg at 56.2°C, what is the final temperature of the mercury?
7. A sample of copper absorbs 145 cal of energy, and its temperature rises from 37.8°C to 41.7°C. What is the mass of the copper?
8. A large, single crystal of sodium chloride absorbs 98.0 cal of heat. If its temperature rises from 22.0°C to 29.7°C, what is the mass of the NaCl crystal?

9. If 1.00 g of each substance in Table 7.3 were to absorb 100 cal of heat, which substance would experience the largest temperature change?
10. If 1.00 g of each substance in Table 7.3 were to absorb 100 cal of heat, which substance would experience the smallest temperature change?
11. Determine the heat capacity of a substance if 23.6 g of the substance gives off 199 cal of heat when its temperature changes from 37.9°C to 20.9°C.
12. What is the heat capacity of gold if a 250 g sample needs 133 cal of energy to increase its temperature from 23.0°C to 40.1°C?

ANSWERS

1. Heat flows into the pot of water.
3. 15,000 cal
5. 49.0°C
7. 404 g
9. Mercury would experience the largest temperature change.
11. 0.496 cal/g·°C

3. PHASE CHANGES

LEARNING OBJECTIVE

1. **Determine the heat associated with a phase change.**

Depending on the surrounding conditions, normal matter usually exists as one of three *phases*: solid, liquid, or gas.

A **phase change** is a physical process in which a substance goes from one phase to another. Usually the change occurs when adding or removing heat at a particular temperature, known as the melting point or the boiling point of the substance. The **melting point** is the temperature at which the substance goes from a solid to a liquid (or from a liquid to a solid). The **boiling point** is the temperature at which a substance goes from a liquid to a gas (or from a gas to a liquid). The nature of the phase change depends on the direction of the heat transfer. Heat going *into* a substance changes it from a solid to a liquid or a liquid to a gas. Removing heat *from* a substance changes a gas to a liquid or a liquid to a solid.

Two key points are worth emphasizing. First, at a substance's melting point or boiling point, two phases can exist simultaneously. Take water (H_2O) as an example. On the Celsius scale, H_2O has a melting point of 0°C and a boiling point of 100°C. At 0°C, both the solid and liquid phases of H_2O can coexist. However, if heat is added, some of the solid H_2O will melt and turn into liquid H_2O. If heat is removed, the opposite happens: some of the liquid H_2O turns into solid H_2O. A similar process can occur at 100°C: adding heat increases the amount of gaseous H_2O, while removing heat increases the amount of liquid H_2O (Figure 7.2).

phase change

A physical process in which a substance goes from one phase to another.

melting point

The temperature at which a substance goes from a solid to a liquid (or from a liquid to a solid).

boiling point

The temperature at which a substance goes from a liquid to a gas (or from a gas to a liquid).

Note

Water is a good substance to use as an example because many people are already familiar with it. Other substances have melting points and boiling points as well.

FIGURE 7.2
The Boiling Point of Water

At the boiling point of H_2O, liquid water and gaseous steam have the same temperature of 100°C.

isothermal

A process that occurs at constant temperature.

heat of fusion

The amount of heat per gram or per mole required for a phase change that occurs at the melting point.

heat of vaporization

The amount of heat per gram or per mole required for a phase change that occurs at the boiling point.

Second, the temperature of a substance does not change as the substance goes from one phase to another. In other words, phase changes are **isothermal** (isothermal means "constant temperature"). Again, consider H_2O as an example. Solid water (ice) can exist at 0°C. If heat is added to ice at 0°C, some of the solid changes phase to make liquid, which is also at 0°C. Remember, the solid and liquid phases of H_2O can coexist at 0°C. Only after all of the solid has melted into liquid does the addition of heat change the temperature of the substance.

For each phase change of a substance, there is a characteristic quantity of heat needed to perform the phase change per gram (or per mole) of material. The **heat of fusion** (ΔH_{fus}) is the amount of heat per gram (or per mole) required for a phase change that occurs at the melting point. The **heat of vaporization** (ΔH_{vap}) is the amount of heat per gram (or per mole) required for a phase change that occurs at the boiling point. If you know the total number of grams or moles of material, you can use the ΔH_{fus} or the ΔH_{vap} to determine the total heat being transferred for melting or solidification using these expressions:

$$\text{heat} = n \times \Delta H_{fus} \text{ (where } n \text{ is the number of moles)}$$

or

$$\text{heat} = m \times \Delta H_{fus} \text{ (where } m \text{ is the mass in grams)}$$

For the boiling or condensation, use these expressions:

$$\text{heat} = n \times \Delta H_{vap} \text{ (where } n \text{ is the number of moles)}$$

or

$$\text{heat} = m \times \Delta H_{vap} \text{ (where } m \text{ is the mass in grams)}$$

Remember that a phase change depends on the direction of the heat transfer. If heat transfers in, solids become liquids, and liquids become solids at the melting and boiling points, respectively. If heat transfers out, liquids solidify, and gases condense into liquids.

EXAMPLE 4

How much heat is necessary to melt 55.8 g of ice (solid H_2O) at 0°C? The heat of fusion of H_2O is 79.9 cal/g.

Solution

We can use the relationship between heat and the heat of fusion to determine how many joules of heat are needed to melt this ice:

$$\text{heat} = m \times \Delta H_{fus}$$

$$\text{heat} = (55.8\,\cancel{g})\left(\frac{79.9\text{ cal}}{\cancel{g}}\right) = 4{,}460\text{ cal}$$

SKILL-BUILDING EXERCISE

1. How much heat is necessary to vaporize 685 g of H_2O at 100°C? The heat of vaporization of H_2O is 540 cal/g.

Table 7.4 lists the heats of fusion and vaporization for some common substances. Note the units on these quantities; when you use these values in problem solving, make sure that the other variables in your calculation are expressed in units consistent with the units in the specific heats or the heats of fusion and vaporization.

TABLE 7.4 Heats of Fusion and Vaporization for Selected Substances

Substance	ΔH_{fus} (cal/g)	ΔH_{vap} (cal/g)
aluminum (Al)	94.0	2,602
gold (Au)	15.3	409
iron (Fe)	63.2	1,504
water (H_2O)	79.9	540
sodium chloride (NaCl)	123.5	691
ethanol (C_2H_5OH)	45.2	200.3
benzene (C_6H_6)	30.4	94.1

Looking Closer: Sublimation

There is also a phase change where a solid goes directly to a gas:

solid → gas

This phase change is called sublimation. Each substance has a characteristic heat of sublimation associated with this process. For example, the heat of sublimation (ΔH_{sub}) of H_2O is 620 cal/g.

We encounter sublimation in several ways. You may already be familiar with dry ice, which is simply solid carbon dioxide (CO_2). At −78.5°C (−109°F), solid carbon dioxide sublimes, changing directly from the solid phase to the gas phase:

$$CO_2(s) \xrightarrow{-78.5°C} CO_2(g)$$

Solid carbon dioxide is called dry ice because it does not pass through the liquid phase. Instead, it does directly to the gas phase. (Carbon dioxide *can* exist as liquid but only under high pressure.) Dry ice has many practical uses, including the long-term preservation of medical samples.

Even at temperatures below 0°C, solid H_2O will slowly sublime. For example, a thin layer of snow or frost on the ground may slowly disappear as the solid H_2O sublimes, even though the outside temperature may be below the freezing point of water. Similarly, ice cubes in a freezer may get smaller over time. Although frozen, the solid water slowly sublimes, redepositing on the colder cooling elements of the freezer, which necessitates periodic defrosting. (Frost-free freezers minimize this redeposition.) Lowering the temperature in a freezer will reduce the need to defrost as often.

Under similar circumstances, water will also sublime from frozen foods (e.g., meats or vegetables), giving them an unattractive, mottled appearance called freezer burn. It is not really a "burn," and the food has not necessarily gone bad, although it looks unappetizing. Freezer burn can be minimized by lowering a freezer's temperature and by wrapping foods tightly so water does not have any space to sublime into.

CONCEPT REVIEW EXERCISES

1. Explain what happens when heat flows into or out of a substance at its melting point or boiling point.
2. How does the amount of heat required for a phase change relate to the mass of the substance?

ANSWERS

1. The energy goes into changing the phase, not the temperature.
2. The amount of heat is a constant per gram of substance.

KEY TAKEAWAY

- There is an energy change associated with any phase change.

EXERCISES

1. How much energy is needed to melt 43.8 g of Au at its melting point of 1,064°C?
2. How much energy is given off when 563.8 g of NaCl solidifies at its freezing point of 801°C?
3. What mass of ice can be melted by 558 cal of energy?
4. How much ethanol (C_2H_5OH) in grams can freeze at its freezing point if 1,225 cal of heat are removed?
5. What is the heat of vaporization of a substance if 10,776 cal are required to vaporize 5.05 g? Express your final answer in joules per gram.
6. If 1,650 cal of heat are required to vaporize a sample that has a heat of vaporization of 137 cal/g, what is the mass of the sample?
7. What is the heat of fusion of water in calories per mole?
8. What is the heat of vaporization of benzene (C_6H_6) in calories per mole?
9. What is the heat of vaporization of gold in calories per mole?
10. What is the heat of fusion of iron in calories per mole?

ANSWERS

1. 670 cal
3. 6.98 g
5. 8,930 J/g
7. 1,440 cal/mol
9. 80,600 cal/mol

4. BOND ENERGIES AND CHEMICAL REACTIONS

LEARNING OBJECTIVES

1. **Define *bond energy*.**
2. **Determine if a chemical process is exothermic or endothermic.**

What happens when you take a basketball, place it halfway up a playground slide, and then let it go? The basketball rolls down the slide. What happens if you do it again? Does the basketball roll down the slide? It should.

If you were to perform this experiment over and over again, do you think the basketball would ever roll *up* the slide? Probably not. Why not? Well, for starters, in all of our experience, the basketball has always moved to a lower position when given the opportunity. The gravitational attraction of Earth exerts a force on the basketball, and given the chance, the basketball will move down. We say that the basketball is going to a lower *gravitational potential energy*. The basketball can move up the slide, but only if someone exerts some effort (that is, work) on the basketball. A general statement, based on countless observations over centuries of study, is that all objects tend to move spontaneously to a position of minimum energy unless acted on by some other force or object.

A similar statement can be made about atoms in compounds. Atoms bond together to form compounds because in doing so they attain lower energies than they possess as individual atoms. A quantity of energy, equal to the difference between the energies of the bonded atoms and the energies of the separated atoms, is released, usually as heat. That is, the bonded atoms have a lower energy than the individual atoms do. *When atoms combine to make a compound, energy is always given off, and the compound has a lower overall energy.* In making compounds, atoms act like a basketball on a playground slide; they move in the direction of decreasing energy.

We can reverse the process, just as with the basketball. If we put energy into a molecule, we can cause its bonds to break, separating a molecule into individual atoms. Bonds between certain specific elements usually have a characteristic energy, called the **bond energy**, that is needed to break the bond. The same amount of energy was liberated when the atoms made the chemical bond in the first place. The term *bond energy* is usually used to describe the strength of interactions between atoms that make covalent bonds. For atoms in ionic compounds attracted by opposite charges, the term **lattice energy** is used. For now, we will deal with covalent bonds in molecules.

bond energy

The strength of interactions between atoms that make covalent bonds.

lattice energy

The strength of interactions between atoms that make ionic bonds.

Although each molecule has its own characteristic bond energy, some generalizations are possible. For example, although the exact value of a C–H bond energy depends on the particular molecule, all C–H bonds have a bond energy of roughly the same value because they are all C–H bonds. It takes roughly 100 kcal of energy to break 1 mol of C–H bonds, so we speak of the bond energy of a C–H bond as being about 100 kcal/mol. A C–C bond has an approximate bond energy of 80 kcal/mol, while a C=C has a bond energy of about 145 kcal/mol. Table 7.5 lists the approximate bond energies of various covalent bonds.

TABLE 7.5 Approximate Bond Energies

Bond	Bond Energy (kcal/mol)
C–H	100
C–O	86
C=O	190
C–N	70
C–C	85
C=C	145
C≡C	200
N–H	93
H–H	105

When a chemical reaction occurs, the atoms in the reactants rearrange their chemical bonds to make products. The new arrangement of bonds does not have the same total energy as the bonds in the reactants. Therefore, when chemical reactions occur, *there will always be an accompanying energy change.*

In some reactions, the energy of the products is lower than the energy of the reactants. Thus, in the course of the reaction, the substances lose energy to the surrounding environment. Such reactions are **exothermic** and can be represented by an *energy-level diagram* like the one in Figure 7.3. In most cases, the energy is given off as heat (although a few reactions give off energy as light).

exothermic

A process that gives off energy.

FIGURE 7.3 Exothermic Reactions

For an exothermic chemical reaction, energy is given off as reactants are converted to products.

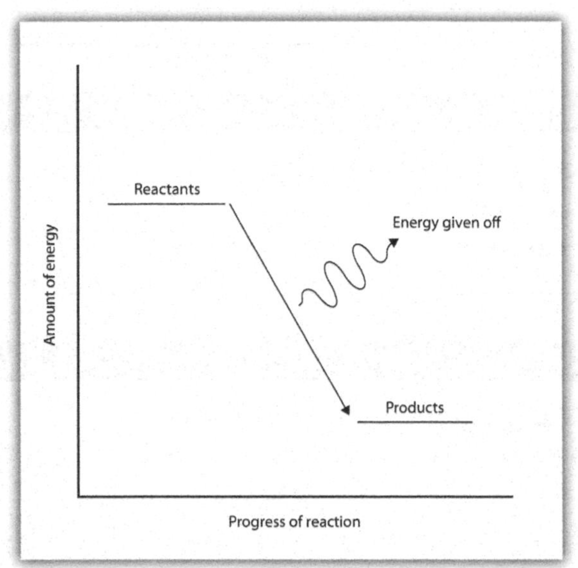

endothermic

A process that absorbs energy.

In chemical reactions where the products have a higher energy than the reactants, the reactants must absorb energy from their environment to react. These reactions are **endothermic** and can be represented by an energy-level diagram like the one shown in Figure 7.4.

FIGURE 7.4 Endothermic Reactions

For an endothermic chemical reaction, energy is absorbed as reactants are converted to products.

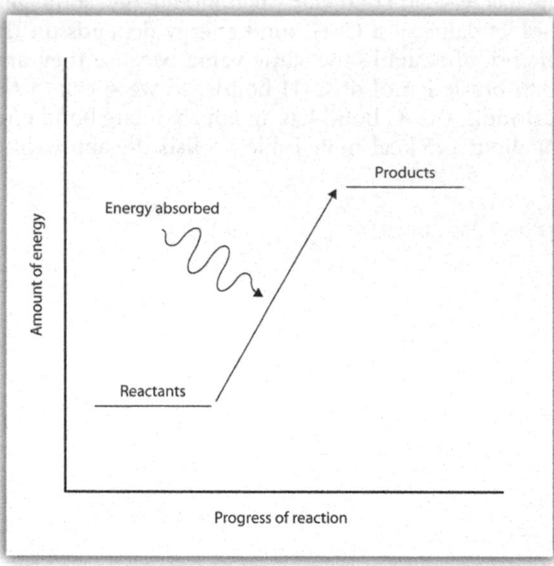

Exothermic and endothermic reactions can be thought of as having energy as either a product of the reaction or a reactant. Exothermic reactions give off energy, so energy is a product. Endothermic reactions require energy, so energy is a reactant.

EXAMPLE 5

Is each chemical reaction exothermic or endothermic?

1. $2H_2(g) + O_2(g) \rightarrow 2H_2O(\ell) + 135$ kcal
2. $N_2(g) + O_2(g) + 45$ kcal $\rightarrow 2NO(g)$

Solution

1. Because energy is a product, energy is given off by the reaction. Therefore, this reaction is exothermic.
2. Because energy is a reactant, energy is absorbed by the reaction. Therefore, this reaction is endothermic.

SKILL-BUILDING EXERCISE

Is each chemical reaction exothermic or endothermic?

1. $H_2(g) + F_2(g) \rightarrow 2HF(g) + 130$ kcal
2. $2C(s) + H_2(g) + 5.3$ kcal $\rightarrow C_2H_2(g)$

CONCEPT REVIEW EXERCISES

1. What is the connection between energy and chemical bonds?
2. Why does energy change during the course of a chemical reaction?

ANSWERS

1. Chemical bonds have a certain energy that is dependent on the elements in the bond and the number of bonds between the atoms.
2. Energy changes because bonds rearrange to make new bonds with different energies.

KEY TAKEAWAYS

- Atoms are held together by a certain amount of energy called bond energy.
- Chemical processes are labeled as exothermic or endothermic based on whether they give off or absorb energy, respectively.

EXERCISES

1. Using the data in Table 7.5, calculate the energy of one C–H bond (as opposed to 1 mol of C–H bonds).
2. Using the data in Table 7.5, calculate the energy of one C=C bond (as opposed to 1 mol of C=C bonds).
3. Is a bond-breaking process exothermic or endothermic?
4. Is a bond-making process exothermic or endothermic?
5. Is each chemical reaction exothermic or endothermic?
   a. $2SnCl_2(s) + 33\ kcal \rightarrow Sn(s) + SnCl_4(s)$
   b. $CH_4(g) + 2O_2(g) \rightarrow CO_2(g) + 2H_2O(\ell) + 213\ kcal$
6. Is each chemical reaction exothermic or endothermic?
   a. $C_2H_4(g) + H_2(g) \rightarrow C_2H_6(g) + 137\ kJ$
   b. $C(s, graphite) + 1.9\ kJ \rightarrow C(s, diamond)$

ANSWERS

1. 1.661×10^{-19} cal
3. endothermic
5. a. endothermic
   b. exothermic

5. THE ENERGY OF BIOCHEMICAL REACTIONS

LEARNING OBJECTIVE

1. **Relate the concept of energy change to chemical reactions that occur in the body.**

The chemistry of the human body, or any living organism, is very complex. Even so, the chemical reactions found in the human body follow the same principles of energy that other chemical reactions follow.

Where does the energy that powers our bodies come from? The details are complex, but we can look at some simple processes at the heart of cellular activity.

An important reaction that provides energy for our bodies is the oxidation of glucose ($C_6H_{12}O_6$):

$$C_6H_{12}O_6(s) + 6O_2(g) \rightarrow 6CO_2(g) + 6H_2O(\ell) + 670\ kcal$$

Considering that 1 mol of $C_6H_{12}O_6(s)$ has a volume of about 115 mL, we can see that glucose is a compact source of energy.

carbohydrate

One of the main dietary components, like glucose and other sugars, that supplies energy for the body.

proteins

Building blocks of structural tissues, like muscle and skin.

fat

A compound, composed largely of hydrocarbon chains, that supplies energy for the body.

Glucose and other sugars are examples of **carbohydrates**, which are one of the three main dietary components of a human diet. All carbohydrates supply approximately 4 kcal/g. You can verify that by taking the heat of reaction for glucose oxidation and dividing it by its molar mass. **Proteins**, the building blocks of structural tissues like muscle and skin, also supply about 4 kcal/g. Other important energy sources for the body are **fats**, which are largely hydrocarbon chains. Fats provide even more energy per gram, about 9 kcal/g. A detailed discussion of carbohydrates and fats and their chemistry in the body is found in Chapter 16 and Chapter 17.

Another important reaction is the conversion of adenosine triphosphate (ATP) to adenosine diphosphate (ADP), which is shown in Figure 7.5. Under physiological conditions, the breaking of an O–P bond and the formation of an O–P and two O–H bonds gives off about 7.5 kcal/mol of ATP. This may not seem like much energy, especially compared to the amount of energy given off when glucose reacts. It is enough energy, however, to fuel other biochemically important chemical reactions in our cells.

FIGURE 7.5 ATP to ADP

The conversion of ATP (top) to ADP (bottom) provides energy for the cells of the body.

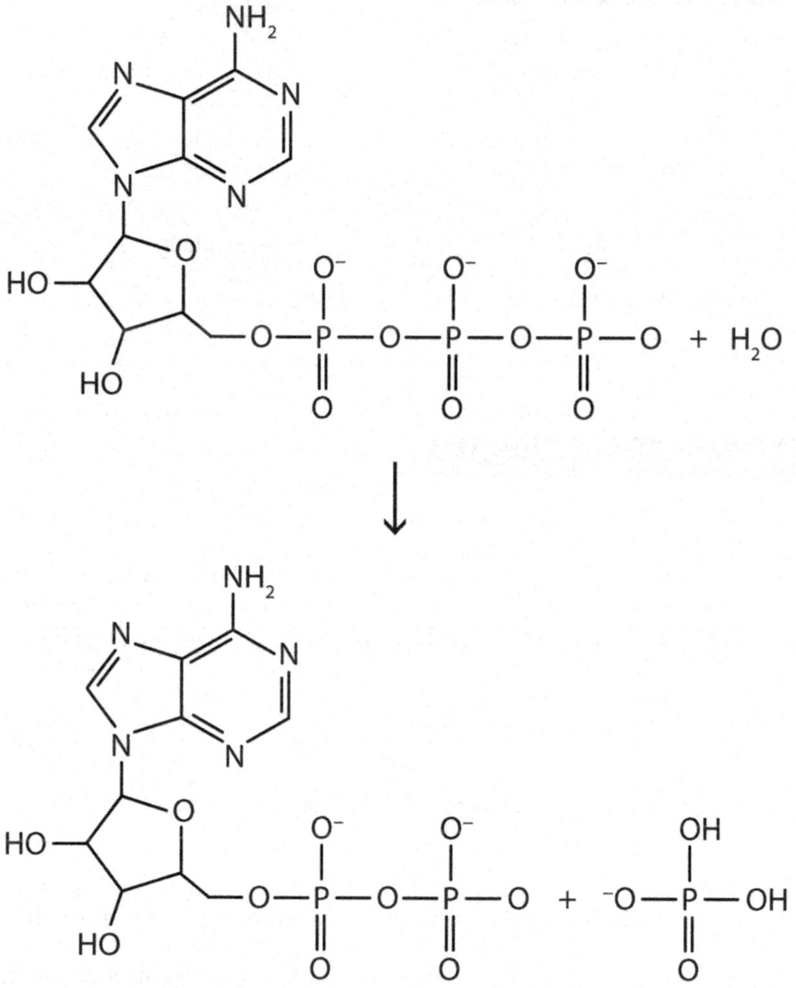

Note

Even complex biological reactions must obey the basic rules of chemistry.

Career Focus: Dietitian

A dietitian is a nutrition expert who communicates food-related information to the general public. In doing so, dietitians promote the general well-being among the population and help individuals recover from nutritionally related illnesses.

Our diet does not just supply us with energy. We also get vitamins, minerals, and even water from what we eat. Eating too much, too little, or not enough of the right foods can lead to a variety of problems. Dietitians are trained to make specific dietary recommendations to address particular issues relating to health. For example, a dietitian might work with a person to develop an overall diet that would help that person lose weight or control diabetes. Hospitals employ dietitians in planning menus for patients, and many dietitians work with community organizations to improve the eating habits of large groups of people.

CONCEPT REVIEW EXERCISE

1. What is the energy content per gram of proteins, carbohydrates, and fats?

ANSWER

1. proteins and carbohydrates: 4 kcal/g; fats: 9 kcal/g

KEY TAKEAWAY

- Energy to power the human body comes from chemical reactions.

EXERCISES

1. An 8 oz serving of whole milk has 8.0 g of fat, 8.0 g of protein, and 13 g of carbohydrates. Approximately how many kilocalories does it contain?
2. A serving of potato chips has 160 kcal. If the chips have 15 g of carbohydrates and 2.0 g of protein, about how many grams of fat are in a serving of potato chips?
3. The average body temperature of a person is 37°C, while the average surrounding temperature is 22°C. Is overall human metabolism exothermic or endothermic?
4. Cold-blooded animals absorb heat from the environment for part of the energy they need to survive. Is this an exothermic or an endothermic process?
5. If the reaction ATP $\rightarrow$ ADP gives off 7.5 kcal/mol, then the reverse process, ADP $\rightarrow$ ATP requires 7.5 kcal/mol to proceed. How many moles of ADP can be converted to ATP using the energy from 1 serving of potato chips (see Exercise 2)?
6. If the oxidation of glucose yields 670 kcal of energy per mole of glucose oxidized, how many servings of potato chips (see Exercise 2) are needed to provide the same amount of energy?

ANSWERS

1. 156 kcal
3. exothermic
5. 21.3 mol

6. END-OF-CHAPTER MATERIAL

Chapter Summary

To ensure that you understand the material in this chapter, you should review the meanings of the following bold terms in the following summary and ask yourself how they relate to the topics in the chapter.

Energy is the ability to do work. The transfer of energy from one place to another is **heat**. Heat and energy are measured in units of **joules**, **calories**, or kilocalories (equal to 1,000 calories). The amount of heat gained or lost when the temperature of an object changes can be related to its mass and a constant called the **specific heat** of the substance.

The transfer of energy can also cause a substance to change from one phase to another. During the transition, called a **phase change**, heat is either added or lost. Despite the fact that heat is going into or coming out of a substance during a phase change, the temperature of the substance does not change until the phase change is complete; that is, phase changes are **isothermal**. Analogous to specific heat, a constant called the **heat of fusion** of a substance describes how much heat must be transferred for a substance to melt or solidify (that is, to change between solid and liquid phases), while the **heat of vaporization** describes the amount of heat transferred in a boiling or condensation process (that is, to change between liquid and gas phases).

Every chemical change is accompanied by an energy change. This is because the interaction between atoms bonding to each other has a certain **bond energy**, the energy required to break the bond (called **lattice energy** for ionic compounds), and the bond energies of the reactants will not be the same as the bond energies of the products. Reactions that give off energy are called **exothermic**, while reactions that absorb energy are called **endothermic**. Energy-level diagrams can be used to illustrate the energy changes that accompany chemical reactions.

Even complex biochemical reactions have to follow the rules of simple chemistry, including rules involving energy change. Reactions of **carbohydrates** and **proteins** provide our bodies with about 4 kcal of energy per gram, while **fats** provide about 9 kcal per gram.

ADDITIONAL EXERCISES

1. Sulfur dioxide (SO_2) is a pollutant gas that is one cause of acid rain. It is oxidized in the atmosphere to sulfur trioxide (SO_3), which then combines with water to make sulfuric acid (H_2SO_4).
   a. Write the balanced reaction for the oxidation of SO_2 to make SO_3. (The other reactant is diatomic oxygen.)
   b. When 1 mol of SO_2 reacts to make SO_3, 23.6 kcal of energy are given off. If 100 lb (1 lb = 454 g) of SO_2 were converted to SO_3, what would be the total energy change?
2. Ammonia (NH_3) is made by the direct combination of H_2 and N_2 gases according to this reaction:

   $$N_2(g) + 3H_2(g) \rightarrow 2NH_3(g) + 22.0 \text{ kcal}$$

   a. Is this reaction endothermic or exothermic?
   b. What is the overall energy change if 1,500 g of N_2 are reacted to make ammonia?
3. A 5.69 g sample of iron metal was heated in boiling water to 99.8°C. Then it was dropped into a beaker containing 100.0 g of H_2O at 22.6°C. Assuming that the water gained all the heat lost by the iron, what is the final temperature of the H_2O and Fe?
4. A 5.69 g sample of copper metal was heated in boiling water to 99.8°C. Then it was dropped into a beaker containing 100.0 g of H_2O at 22.6°C. Assuming that the water gained all the heat lost by the copper, what is the final temperature of the H_2O and Cu?
5. When 1 g of steam condenses, 540 cal of energy is released. How many grams of ice can be melted with 540 cal?
6. When 1 g of water freezes, 79.9 cal of energy is released. How many grams of water can be boiled with 79.9 cal?
7. The change in energy is +65.3 kJ for each mole of calcium hydroxide [$Ca(OH)_2$] according to the following reaction:

   $$Ca(OH)_2(s) \rightarrow CaO(s) + H_2O(g)$$

   How many grams of $Ca(OH)_2$ could be reacted if 575 kJ of energy were available?

8. The thermite reaction gives off so much energy that the elemental iron formed as a product is typically produced in the liquid state:

   $$2Al(s) + Fe_2O_3(s) \rightarrow Al_2O_3(s) + 2Fe(\ell) + 204\ \text{kcal}$$

   How much heat will be given off if 250 g of Fe are to be produced?
9. A normal adult male requires 2,500 kcal per day to maintain his metabolism.
   a. Nutritionists recommend that no more than 30% of the calories in a person's diet come from fat. At 9 kcal/g, what is the maximum mass of fat an adult male should consume daily?
   b. At 4 kcal/g each, how many grams of protein and carbohydrates should an adult male consume daily?
10. A normal adult male requires 2,500 kcal per day to maintain his metabolism.
    a. At 9 kcal/g, what mass of fat would provide that many kilocalories if the diet was composed of nothing but fats?
    b. At 4 kcal/g each, what mass of protein and/or carbohydrates is needed to provide that many kilocalories?
11. The volume of the world's oceans is approximately 1.34×10^{24} cm^3.
    a. How much energy would be needed to increase the temperature of the world's oceans by 1°C? Assume that the heat capacity of the oceans is the same as pure water.
    b. If Earth receives 6.0×10^{22} J of energy per day from the sun, how many days would it take to warm the oceans by 1°C, assuming all the energy went into warming the water?
12. Does a substance that has a small specific heat require a small or large amount of energy to change temperature? Explain.
13. Some biology textbooks represent the conversion of adenosine triphosphate (ATP) to adenosine diphosphate (ADP) and phosphate ions as follows:

    $$\text{ATP} \rightarrow \text{ADP} + \text{phosphate} + \text{energy}$$

    What is wrong with this reaction?
14. Assuming that energy changes are additive, how much energy is required to change 15.0 g of ice at −15°C to 15.0 g of steam at 115°C? (Hint: you will have five processes to consider.)

ANSWERS

1. a. $2SO_2 + O_2 \rightarrow 2SO_3$
   b. 16,700 kcal
3. about 23.1°C
5. 6.76 g
7. 652 g
9. a. 83.3 g
   b. 438 g
11. a. 1.34×10^{24} cal
    b. 93 days
13. A reactant is missing: H_2O is missing.

CHAPTER 8
Solids, Liquids, and Gases

Opening Essay

We normally experience carbon dioxide (CO_2) as a gas, but if it were cooled down to about −78°C, it would become a solid. The everyday term for solid carbon dioxide is *dry ice*.

Why "dry" ice? Solid carbon dioxide is called dry ice because it converts from a solid to a gas directly, without going through the liquid phase, in a process called *sublimation*. Thus, there is no messy liquid phase to worry about. Although it is a novelty, dry ice has some potential dangers. Because it is so cold, it can freeze living tissues very quickly, so people handling dry ice should wear special protective gloves. The cold carbon dioxide gas is also heavier than air (because it is cold *and* more dense), so people in the presence of dry ice should be in a well-ventilated area.

Dry ice has several common uses. Because it is so cold, it is used as a refrigerant to keep other things cold or frozen (e.g., meats or ice cream). In the medical field, dry ice is used to preserve medical specimens, blood products, and drugs. It also has dermatological applications (e.g., freezing off warts). Organs for transplant are kept cool with dry ice until the recipient of the new organ is ready for surgery. In this respect, carbon dioxide is much like water—more than one phase of the same substance has significant uses in the real world.

Most of us are familiar with the three phases of matter: solid, liquid, and gas. Indeed, we addressed the energy changes involved in phase changes in Chapter 7. The picture on this page shows the substance we are probably most familiar with as having those three phases: water. In everyday life, we commonly come in contact with water as a solid (ice), as a liquid, and as a gas (steam). All we have to do is change the conditions of the substance—typically temperature—and we can change the phase from solid to liquid to gas and back again.

Under the proper conditions of temperature and pressure, many substances—not only water—can experience the three different phases (Figure 8.1). An understanding of the phases of matter is important for our understanding of all matter. In this chapter, we will explore the three phases of matter.

FIGURE 8.1 Water

Water is probably the most familiar substance that commonly exhibits in all three phases. However, many substances will exhibit the solid, liquid, and gas phases under certain conditions. For example, in clouds, liquid water exists as tiny droplets condensed from water vapor in the air.

© *Thinkstock*

1. INTERMOLECULAR INTERACTIONS

LEARNING OBJECTIVES

1. **Define *phase*.**
2. **Identify the types of interactions between molecules.**

phase

A form of matter that has the same physical properties throughout.

A **phase** is a certain form of matter that includes a specific set of physical properties. That is, the atoms, the molecules, or the ions that make up the phase do so in a consistent manner throughout the phase. As mentioned in Chapter 1, science recognizes three stable phases: the *solid phase*, in which individual particles can be thought of as in contact and held in place; the *liquid phase*, in which individual particles are in contact but moving with respect to each other; and the *gas phase*, in which individual particles are separated from each other by relatively large distances. Not all substances will readily exhibit all phases. For example, carbon dioxide does not exhibit a liquid phase unless the pressure is greater than about six times normal atmospheric pressure. Other substances, especially complex organic molecules, may decompose at higher temperatures, rather than becoming a liquid or a gas.

Note

For many substances, there are different arrangements the particles can take in the solid phase, depending on temperature and pressure.

Which phase a substance adopts depends on the pressure and the temperature it experiences. Of these two conditions, temperature variations are more obviously related to the phase of a substance. When it is very cold, H_2O exists in the solid form as ice. When it is warmer, the liquid phase of H_2O is present. At even higher temperatures, H_2O boils and becomes steam.

Pressure changes can also affect the presence of a particular phase (as we indicated for carbon dioxide), but its effects are less obvious most of the time. We will mostly focus on the temperature effects on phases, mentioning pressure effects only when they are important. Most chemical substances follow the same pattern of phases when going from a low temperature to a high temperature: the solid phase, then the liquid phase, and then the gas phase. However, the temperatures at which these phases are present differ for all substances and can be rather extreme. Table 8.1 shows the temperature ranges for solid, liquid, and gas phases for three substances. As you can see, there is extreme variability in the temperature ranges.

TABLE 8.1 Temperature Ranges for the Three Phases of Various Substances

Substance	Solid Phase Below	Liquid Phase Above	Gas Phase Above
hydrogen (H_2)	−259°C	−259°C	−253°C
water (H_2O)	0°C	0°C	100°C
sodium chloride (NaCl)	801°C	801°C	1413°C

The *melting point* of a substance is the temperature that separates a solid and a liquid. The *boiling point* of a substance is the temperature that separates a liquid and a gas.

What accounts for this variability? Why do some substances become liquids at very low temperatures, while others require very high temperatures before they become liquids? It all depends on the strength of the **intermolecular interactions** between the particles of substances. (Although ionic compounds are not composed of discrete molecules, we will still use the term *intermolecular* to include interactions between the ions in such compounds.) Substances that experience strong intermolecular interactions require higher temperatures to become liquids and, finally, gases. Substances that experience weak intermolecular interactions do not need much energy (as measured by temperature) to become liquids and gases and will exhibit these phases at lower temperatures.

intermolecular interaction

A force of attraction between different molecules.

Substances with the highest melting and boiling points have **covalent network bonding**. This type of intermolecular interaction is actually a covalent bond. (For more information about covalent bonding, see Chapter 4.) In these substances, all the atoms in a sample are covalently bonded to other atoms; in effect, the entire sample is essentially one large molecule. Many of these substances are solid over a large temperature range because it takes a lot of energy to disrupt all the covalent bonds at once. One example of a substance that shows covalent network bonding is diamond (Figure 8.2), which is a form of pure carbon. At temperatures over 3,500°C, diamond finally vaporizes into gas-phase atoms.

covalent network bonding

A type of interaction in which all the atoms in a sample are covalently bonded to other atoms.

FIGURE 8.2 Diamond

Diamond, a form of pure carbon, has covalent network bonding. It takes a very high temperature—over 3,500°C—for diamond to leave the solid state.

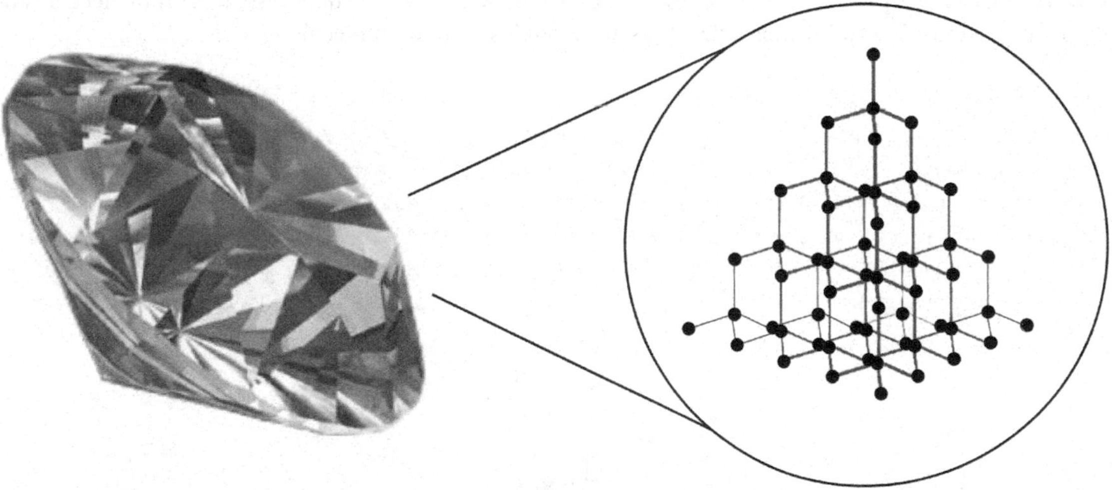

Source: Photo © Thinkstock

The strongest force between any two particles is the ionic bond, in which two ions of opposing charge are attracted to each other. (For more information about ionic bonding, see Chapter 3.) Thus, **ionic interactions** between particles are another type of intermolecular interaction. Substances that contain ionic interactions are relatively strongly held together, so these substances typically have high melting and boiling points. Sodium chloride (Figure 8.3) is an example of a substance whose particles experience ionic interactions (Table 8.1).

ionic interaction

An attraction due to ions of opposite charges.

FIGURE 8.3 Sodium Chloride

Solid NaCl is held together by ionic interactions.

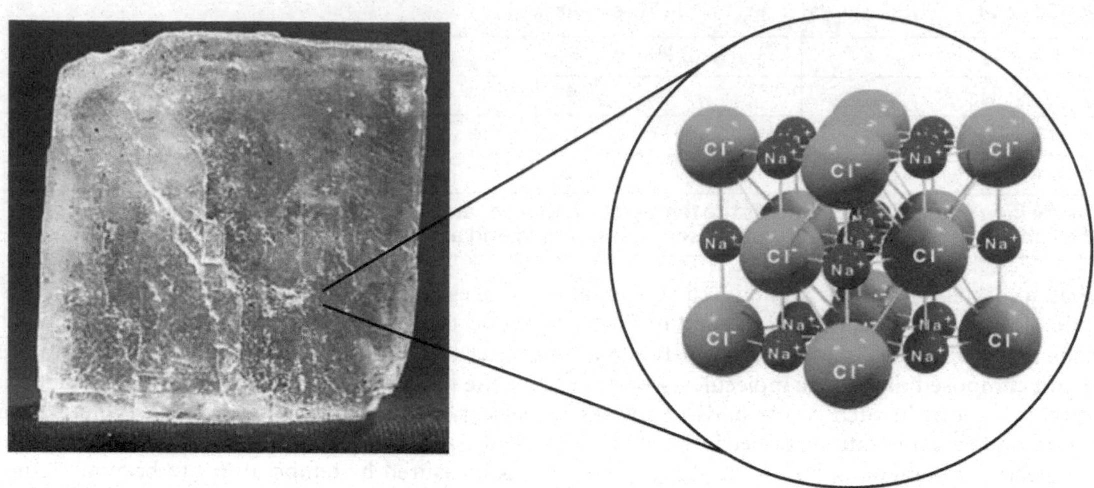

Source: Photo © Thinkstock

polar covalent bond

A covalent bond that has an unequal sharing of electrons.

nonpolar covalent bond

A covalent bond that has an equal sharing of electrons.

polar

A molecule with a net unequal distribution of electrons in its covalent bonds.

Many substances that experience covalent bonding exist as discrete molecules. In many molecules, the electrons that are shared in a covalent bond are not shared equally between the two atoms in the bond. Typically, one of the atoms attracts the electrons more strongly than the other, leading to an unequal sharing of electrons in the bond. This idea is illustrated in Figure 8.4, which shows a diagram of the covalent bond in hydrogen fluoride (HF). The fluorine atom attracts the electrons in the bond more than the hydrogen atom does. The result is an unequal distribution of electrons in the bond, favoring the fluorine side of the covalent bond. Because of this unequal distribution, the fluorine side of the covalent bond actually takes on a partial negative charge (indicated by the δ− in Figure 8.4), while the hydrogen side of the bond, being electron deficient, takes on a partial positive charge (indicated by the δ+ in Figure 8.4). A covalent bond that has an unequal sharing of electrons is called a **polar covalent bond**. (A covalent bond that has an equal sharing of electrons, as in a covalent bond with the same atom on each side, is called a **nonpolar covalent bond**.) A molecule with a net unequal distribution of electrons in its covalent bonds is a **polar** molecule. HF is an example of a polar molecule.

FIGURE 8.4 Polar Covalent Bonds

The electrons in the HF molecule are not equally shared by the two atoms in the bond. Because the fluorine atom has nine protons in its nucleus, it attracts the negatively charged electrons in the bond more than the hydrogen atom does with its one proton in its nucleus. Thus, electrons are more strongly attracted to the fluorine atom, leading to an imbalance in the electron distribution between the atoms. The fluorine side of the bond picks up a partial overall negative charge (represented by the δ− in the diagram), while the hydrogen side of the bond has an overall partial positive charge (represented by the δ+ in the diagram). Such a bond is called a *polar covalent bond*.

δ+ δ-

H◄F

dipole-dipole interaction

An attraction between polar molecules.

The charge separation in a polar covalent bond is not as extreme as is found in ionic compounds, but there is a related result: oppositely charged ends of different molecules will attract each other. This type of intermolecular interaction is called a **dipole-dipole interaction**. Many molecules with polar covalent bonds experience dipole-dipole interactions. The covalent bonds in some molecules are oriented in space in such a way that the bonds in the molecules cancel each other out. The individual bonds are polar, but the overall molecule is not polar; rather, the molecule is *nonpolar*. Such molecules experience little or no dipole-dipole interactions. Carbon dioxide (CO_2) and carbon tetrachloride (CCl_4) are examples of such molecules (Figure 8.5).

FIGURE 8.5 Nonpolar Molecules

Although the individual bonds in both CO_2 and CCl_4 are polar, their effects cancel out because of the spatial orientation of the bonds in each molecule. As a result, such molecules experience little or no dipole-dipole interaction.

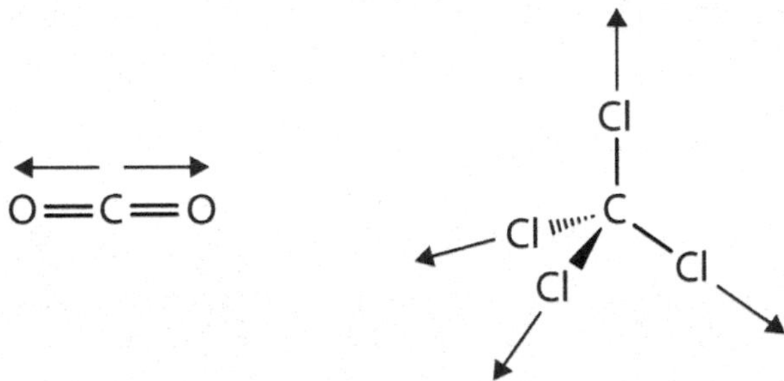

The H–F, O–H, and N–H bonds are strongly polar; in molecules that have these bonds, particularly strong dipole-dipole interactions (as strong as 10% of a true covalent bond) can occur. Because of this strong interaction, **hydrogen bonding** is used to describe this dipole-dipole interaction. The physical properties of water, which has two O–H bonds, are strongly affected by the presence of hydrogen bonding between water molecules. Figure 8.6 shows how molecules experiencing hydrogen bonding can interact.

hydrogen bonding

A particularly strong type of dipole-dipole interaction caused by a hydrogen atom being bonded to a very electronegative element.

FIGURE 8.6 Hydrogen Bonding between Water Molecules

The presence of hydrogen bonding in molecules like water can have a large impact on the physical properties of a substance.

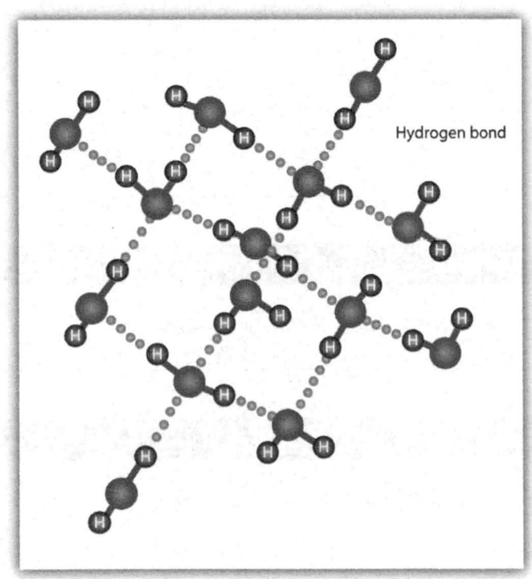

Finally, there are forces between all molecules that are caused by electrons being in different places in a molecule at any one time, which sets up a temporary separation of charge that disappears almost as soon as it appears. These are very weak intermolecular interactions and are called **dispersion forces (or London forces)**. (An alternate name is London dispersion forces.) Molecules that experience no other type of intermolecular interaction will at least experience dispersion forces. Substances that experience only dispersion forces are typically soft in the solid phase and have relatively low melting points. Because dispersion forces are caused by the instantaneous distribution of electrons in a molecule, larger molecules with a large number of electrons can experience substantial dispersion forces. Examples include *waxes*, which are long hydrocarbon chains that are solids at room temperature because the molecules have so many electrons. The resulting dispersion forces between these molecules make them assume the solid phase at normal temperatures.

dispersion force (London force)

A force caused by the instantaneous imbalance of electrons about a molecule.

The phase that a substance adopts depends on the type and magnitude of the intermolecular interactions the particles of a substance experience. If the intermolecular interactions are relatively strong, then a large amount of energy—in terms of temperature—is necessary for a substance to change phases. If the intermolecular interactions are weak, a low temperature is all that is necessary to move a substance out of the solid phase.

EXAMPLE 1

What intermolecular forces besides dispersion forces, if any, exist in each substance? Are any of these substances solids at room temperature?

1. potassium chloride (KCl)
2. ethanol (C_2H_5OH)
3. bromine (Br_2)

Solution

1. Potassium chloride is composed of ions, so the intermolecular interaction in potassium chloride is ionic forces. Because ionic interactions are strong, it might be expected that potassium chloride is a solid at room temperature.
2. Ethanol has a hydrogen atom attached to an oxygen atom, so it would experience hydrogen bonding. If the hydrogen bonding is strong enough, ethanol might be a solid at room temperature, but it is difficult to know for certain. (Ethanol is actually a liquid at room temperature.)
3. Elemental bromine has two bromine atoms covalently bonded to each other. Because the atoms on either side of the covalent bond are the same, the electrons in the covalent bond are shared equally, and the bond is a nonpolar covalent bond. Thus, diatomic bromine does not have any intermolecular forces other than dispersion forces. It is unlikely to be a solid at room temperature unless the dispersion forces are strong enough. Bromine is a liquid at room temperature.

SKILL-BUILDING EXERCISE

What intermolecular forces besides dispersion forces, if any, exist in each substance? Are any of these substances solids at room temperature?

1. methylamine (CH_3NH_2)
2. calcium sulfate ($CaSO_4$)
3. carbon monoxide (CO)

CONCEPT REVIEW EXERCISE

1. What types of intermolecular interactions can exist in compounds?

ANSWER

1. polar and nonpolar covalent bonding, ionic bonding, dispersion forces, dipole-dipole interactions, and hydrogen bonding

KEY TAKEAWAYS

- A phase is a form of matter that has the same physical properties throughout.
- Molecules interact with each other through various forces: ionic and covalent bonds, dipole-dipole interactions, hydrogen bonding, and dispersion forces.

EXERCISES

1. List the three common phases in the order you are likely to find them—from lowest temperature to highest temperature.
2. List the three common phases in the order they exist from lowest energy to highest energy.

3. List these intermolecular interactions from weakest to strongest: London forces, hydrogen bonding, and ionic interactions.
4. List these intermolecular interactions from weakest to strongest: covalent network bonding, dipole-dipole interactions, and dispersion forces.
5. What type of intermolecular interaction is predominate in each substance?
   a. water (H_2O)
   b. sodium sulfate (Na_2SO_4)
   c. decane ($C_{10}H_{22}$)
6. What type of intermolecular interaction is predominate in each substance?
   a. diamond (C, crystal)
   b. helium (He)
   c. ammonia (NH_3)
7. Explain how a molecule like carbon dioxide (CO_2) can have polar covalent bonds but be nonpolar overall.
8. Sulfur dioxide (SO_2) has a formula similar to that of carbon dioxide (see Exercise 7) but is a polar molecule overall. What can you conclude about the shape of the SO_2 molecule?
9. What are some of the physical properties of substances that experience covalent network bonding?
10. What are some of the physical properties of substances that experience only dispersion forces?

ANSWERS

1. solid, liquid, and gas
3. London forces, hydrogen bonding, and ionic interactions
5. a. hydrogen bonding
   b. ionic interactions
   c. dispersion forces
7. The two covalent bonds are oriented in such a way that their dipoles cancel out.
9. very hard, high melting point

2. SOLIDS AND LIQUIDS

LEARNING OBJECTIVE

1. **Describe the solid and liquid phases.**

Solids and liquids are collectively called *condensed phases* because their particles are in virtual contact. The two states share little else, however.

2.1 Solids

In the solid state, the individual particles of a substance are in fixed positions with respect to each other because there is not enough thermal energy to overcome the intermolecular interactions between the particles. As a result, solids have a definite shape and volume. Most solids are hard, but some (like waxes) are relatively soft. Many solids composed of ions can also be quite brittle.

Solids usually have their constituent particles arranged in a regular, three-dimensional array of alternating positive and negative ions called a **crystal**. The effect of this regular arrangement of particles is sometimes visible macroscopically, as shown in Figure 8.7. Some solids, especially those composed of large molecules, cannot easily organize their particles in such regular crystals and exist as **amorphous** (literally, "without form") solids. Glass is one example of an amorphous solid.

FIGURE 8.7 Crystalline Arrangement

Some large crystals look the way they do because of the regular arrangement of atoms (ions) in their crystal structure.

crystal

A regular, three-dimensional array of alternating positive and negative ions.

amorphous

A solid with no regular structure.

2.2 Liquids

If the particles of a substance have enough energy to partially overcome intermolecular interactions, then the particles can move about each other while remaining in contact. This describes the liquid state. In a liquid, the particles are still in close contact, so liquids have a definite volume. However, because the particles can move about each other rather freely, a liquid has no definite shape and takes a shape dictated by its container.

2.3 Gases

If the particles of a substance have enough energy to completely overcome intermolecular interactions, then the particles can separate from each other and move about randomly in space. This describes the gas state, which we will consider further in Section 3. Like liquids, gases have no definite shape, but unlike solids and liquids, gases have no definite volume either. The change from solid to liquid usually does not significantly change the volume of a substance. However, the change from a liquid to a gas significantly increases the volume of a substance, by a factor of 1,000 or more. Figure 8.8 shows the differences among solids, liquids, and gases at the molecular level, while Table 8.2 lists the different characteristics of these states.

FIGURE 8.8 A Representation of the Solid, Liquid, and Gas States

A solid has definite volume and shape, a liquid has a definite volume but no definite shape, and a gas has neither a definite volume nor shape.

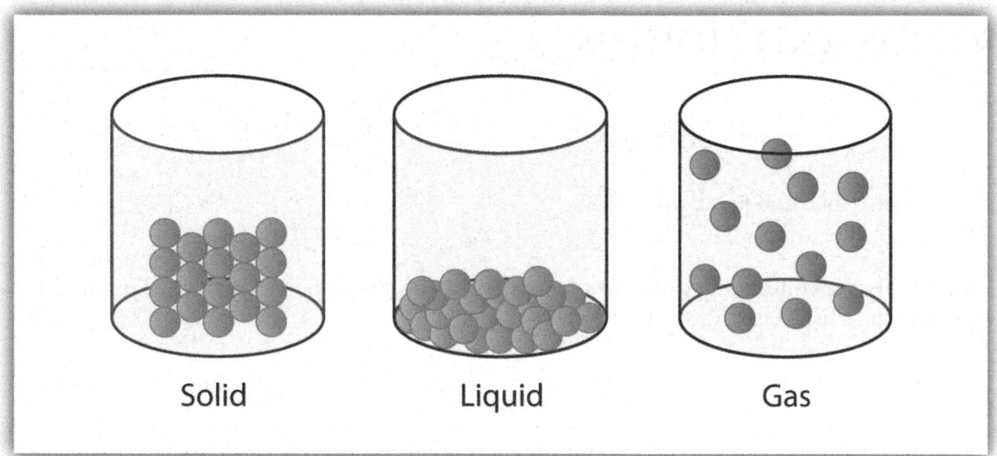

TABLE 8.2 Characteristics of the Three States of Matter

Characteristic	Solid	Liquid	Gas
shape	definite	indefinite	indefinite
volume	definite	definite	indefinite
relative intermolecular interaction strength	strong	moderate	weak
relative particle positions	in contact and fixed in place	in contact but not fixed	not in contact, random positions

EXAMPLE 2

What state or states of matter does each statement, describe?

1. This state has a definite volume.
2. This state has no definite shape.
3. This state allows the individual particles to move about while remaining in contact.

Solution

1. This statement describes either the liquid state or the solid state.
2. This statement describes either the liquid state or the gas state.
3. This statement describes the liquid state.

SKILL-BUILDING EXERCISE

What state or states of matter does each statement describe?

1. This state has individual particles in a fixed position with regard to each other.
2. This state has individual particles far apart from each other in space.
3. This state has a definite shape.

CONCEPT REVIEW EXERCISE

1. How do the strengths of intermolecular interactions in solids and liquids differ?

ANSWER

1. Solids have stronger intermolecular interactions than liquids do.

Looking Closer: Water, the Most Important Liquid

Earth is the only known body in our solar system that has liquid water existing freely on its surface. That is a good thing because life on Earth would not be possible without the presence of liquid water.

Water has several properties that make it a unique substance among substances. It is an excellent solvent; it dissolves many other substances and allows those substances to react when in solution. In fact, water is sometimes called the *universal solvent* because of this ability. Water has unusually high melting and boiling points (0°C and 100°C, respectively) for such a small molecule. The boiling points for similar-sized molecules, such as methane (BP = −162°C) and ammonia (BP = −33°C), are more than 100° lower. Though a liquid at normal temperatures, water molecules experience a relatively strong intermolecular interaction that allows them to maintain the liquid phase at higher temperatures than expected.

Unlike most substances, the solid form of water is less dense than its liquid form, which allows ice to float on water. In colder weather, lakes and rivers freeze from the top, allowing animals and plants to continue to live underneath. Water also requires an unusually large amount of energy to change temperature. While 100 J of energy will change the temperature of 1 g of Fe by 230°C, this same amount of energy will change the temperature of 1 g of H_2O by only 100°C. Thus, water changes its temperature slowly as heat is added or removed. This has a major impact on weather, as storm systems like hurricanes can be impacted by the amount of heat that ocean water can store.

Water's influence on the world around us is affected by these properties. Isn't it fascinating that such a small molecule can have such a big impact?

KEY TAKEAWAY

- Solids and liquids are phases that have their own unique properties.

EXERCISES

1. What are the general properties of solids?
2. What are the general properties of liquids
3. What are the general properties of gases?
4. What phase or phases have a definite volume? What phase or phases do not have a definite volume?
5. Name a common substance that forms a crystal in its solid state.
6. Name a common substance that forms an amorphous solid in its solid state.
7. Are substances with strong intermolecular interactions likely to be solids at higher or lower temperatures? Explain.
8. Are substances with weak intermolecular interactions likely to be liquids at higher or lower temperatures? Explain.
9. State two similarities between the solid and liquid states.
10. State two differences between the solid and liquid states.
11. If individual particles are moving around with respect to each other, a substance may be in either the ________ or ________ state but probably not in the ________ state.
12. If individual particles are in contact with each other, a substance may be in either the _______ or _______ state but probably not in the _______ state.

ANSWERS

1. hard, specific volume and shape, high density, cannot be compressed
3. variable volume and shape, low density, compressible
5. sodium chloride (answers will vary)
7. At higher temperatures, their intermolecular interactions are strong enough to hold the particles in place.
9. high density; definite volume
11. liquid; gas; solid

3. GASES AND PRESSURE

LEARNING OBJECTIVE

1. **Describe the gas phase.**

The gas phase is unique among the three states of matter in that there are some simple models we can use to predict the physical behavior of all gases—independent of their identities. We cannot do this for the solid and liquid states. In fact, the development of this understanding of the behavior of gases represents the historical dividing point between alchemy and modern chemistry. Initial advances in the understanding of gas behavior were made in the mid 1600s by Robert Boyle, an English scientist who founded the Royal Society (one of the world's oldest scientific organizations).

kinetic theory of gases

The fundamental theory of the behavior of gases.

How is it that we can model all gases independent of their chemical identity? The answer is in a group of statements called the **kinetic theory of gases**:

- Gases are composed of tiny particles that are separated by large distances.
- Gas particles are constantly moving, experiencing collisions with other gas particles and the walls of their container.
- The velocity of gas particles is related to the temperature of a gas.
- Gas particles do not experience any force of attraction or repulsion with each other.

Did you notice that none of these statements relates to the identity of the gas? This means that all gases should behave similarly. A gas that follows these statements perfectly is called an *ideal gas*. Most gases show slight deviations from these statements and are called *real gases*. However, the existence of real gases does not diminish the importance of the kinetic theory of gases.

pressure

Force divided by area.

One of the statements of the kinetic theory mentions collisions. As gas particles are constantly moving, they are also constantly colliding with each other and with the walls of their container. There are forces involved as gas particles bounce off the container walls (Figure 8.9). The force generated by gas particles divided by the area of the container walls yields **pressure**. Pressure is a property we can measure for a gas, but we typically do not consider pressure for solids or liquids.

FIGURE 8.9 Gas Pressure

Pressure is what results when gas particles rebound off the walls of their container

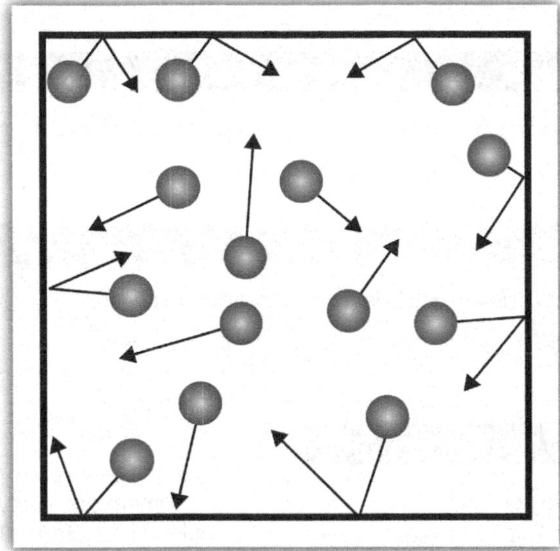

The basic unit of pressure is the newton per square meter (N/m^2). This combined unit is redefined as a **pascal** (Pa). One pascal is not a very large amount of pressure. A more useful unit of pressure is the **bar**, which is 100,000 Pa (1 bar = 100,000 Pa). Other common units of pressure are the **atmosphere** (atm), which was originally defined as the average pressure of Earth's atmosphere at sea level; and **mmHg (millimeters of mercury)**, which is the pressure generated by a column of mercury 1 mm high. The unit millimeters of mercury is also called a **torr**, named after the Italian scientist Evangelista Torricelli, who invented the barometer in the mid-1600s. A more precise definition of atmosphere, in terms of torr, is that there are exactly 760 torr in 1 atm. A bar equals 1.01325 atm. Given all the relationships between these pressure units, the ability to convert from one pressure unit to another is a useful skill.

pascal

A unit of pressure equal to 1 newton of force per square meter of area.

bar

A unit of pressure equal to 100,000 Pa.

atmosphere

A unit of pressure equal to the average atmospheric pressure at sea level.

mmHg (millimeters of mercury)

A unit of pressure equal to the pressure generated by a column of mercury 1 mm high.

torr

Another name for millimeters of mercury.

EXAMPLE 3

Write a conversion factor to determine how many atmospheres are in 1,547 mmHg.

Solution

Because 1 mmHg equals 1 torr, the given pressure is also equal to 1,547 torr. Because there are 760 torr in 1 atm, we can use this conversion factor to do the mathematical conversion:

$$1{,}547\ \cancel{\text{torr}} \times \frac{1\ \text{atm}}{760\ \cancel{\text{torr}}} = 2.04\ \text{atm}$$

Note how the torr units cancel algebraically.

SKILL-BUILDING EXERCISE

1. Write a conversion factor to determine how many millimeters of mercury are in 9.65 atm.

The kinetic theory also states that there is no interaction between individual gas particles. Although we know that there are, in fact, intermolecular interactions in real gases, the kinetic theory assumes that gas particles are so far apart that the individual particles don't "feel" each other. Thus, we can treat gas particles as tiny bits of matter whose identity isn't important to certain physical properties.

CONCEPT REVIEW EXERCISE

1. What is pressure, and what units do we use to express it?

ANSWER

1. Pressure is the force per unit area; its units can be pascals, torr, millimeters of mercury, or atmospheres.

KEY TAKEAWAY

- The gas phase has certain general properties characteristic of that phase.

EXERCISES

1. What is the kinetic theory of gases?
2. According to the kinetic theory of gases, the individual gas particles are (always, frequently, never) moving.
3. Why does a gas exert pressure?
4. Why does the kinetic theory of gases allow us to presume that all gases will show similar behavior?
5. Arrange the following pressure quantities in order from smallest to largest: 1 mmHg, 1 Pa, and 1 atm.
6. Which unit of pressure is larger—the torr or the atmosphere?
7. How many torr are there in 1.56 atm?
8. Convert 760 torr into pascals.
9. Blood pressures are expressed in millimeters of mercury. What would be the blood pressure in atmospheres if a patient's systolic blood pressure is 120 mmHg and the diastolic blood pressure is 82 mmHg? (In medicine, such a blood pressure would be reported as "120/82," spoken as "one hundred twenty over eighty-two.")
10. In weather forecasting, barometric pressure is expressed in inches of mercury (in. Hg), where there are exactly 25.4 mmHg in every 1 in. Hg. What is the barometric pressure in millimeters of mercury if the barometric pressure is reported as 30.21 in. Hg?

ANSWERS

1. Gases are composed of tiny particles that are separated by large distances. Gas particles are constantly moving, experiencing collisions with other gas particles and the walls of their container. The velocity of gas particles is related to the temperature of a gas. Gas particles do not experience any force of attraction or repulsion with each other.
3. A gas exerts pressure as its particles rebound off the walls of its container.
5. 1 Pa, 1 mmHg, and 1 atm
7. 1,190 torr
9. 0.158 atm; 0.108 atm

4. GAS LAWS

LEARNING OBJECTIVE

1. **Predict the properties of gases using the gas laws.**

Experience has shown that several properties of a gas can be related to each other under certain conditions. The properties are pressure (*P*), volume (*V*), temperature (*T*, in kelvins), and amount of material expressed in moles (n). What we find is that a sample of gas cannot have any random values for these properties. Instead, only certain values, dictated by some simple mathematical relationships, will occur.

4.1 Boyle's Law

The first simple relationship, referred to as a **gas law**, is between the pressure of a gas and its volume. If the amount of gas in a sample and its temperature are kept constant, then as the pressure of a gas is increased, the volume of the gas decreases proportionately. Mathematically, this is written as

$$P \propto \frac{1}{V}$$

where the "$\propto$" symbol means "is proportional to." This is one form of **Boyle's law**, which relates the pressure of a gas to its volume.

A more useful form of Boyle's law involves a change in conditions of a gas. For a given amount of gas at a constant temperature, if we know the initial pressure and volume of a gas sample and the pressure or volume changes, we can calculate what the new volume or pressure will be. That form of Boyle's law is written

$$P_i V_i = P_f V_f$$

where the subscript i refers to initial conditions and the subscript f refers to final conditions.

To use $P_i V_i = P_f V_f$, you need to know any three of the variables so that you can algebraically calculate the fourth variable. Also, the pressure quantities must have the same units, as must the two volume quantities. If the two similar variables don't have the same variables, one value must be converted to the other value's unit.

gas law

A simple mathematical formula that relates two or more properties of a gas.

Boyle's law

The gas law that relates pressure and volume.

EXAMPLE 4

What happens to the volume of a gas if its pressure is increased? Assume all other conditions remain the same.

Solution

If the pressure of a gas is increased, the volume decreases in response.

SKILL-BUILDING EXERCISE

1. What happens to the pressure of a gas if its volume is increased? Assume all other conditions remain the same.

EXAMPLE 5

If a sample of gas has an initial pressure of 1.56 atm and an initial volume of 7.02 L, what is the final volume if the pressure is reduced to 0.987 atm? Assume that the amount and the temperature of the gas remain constant.

Solution

The key in problems like this is to be able to identify which quantities represent which variables from the relevant equation. The way the question is worded, you should be able to tell that 1.56 atm is P_i, 7.02 L is V_i, and 0.987 atm is P_f. What we are looking for is the final volume—V_f. Therefore, substituting these values into $P_iV_i = P_fV_f$:

$$(1.56\ \text{atm})(7.02\ \text{L}) = (0.987\ \text{atm}) \times V_f$$

The expression has atmospheres on both sides of the equation, so they cancel algebraically:

$$(1.56)(7.02\ \text{L}) = (0.987) \times V_f$$

Now we divide both sides of the expression by 0.987 to isolate V_f, the quantity we are seeking:

$$\frac{(1.56)(7.02\ \text{L})}{0.987} = V_f$$

Performing the multiplication and division, we get the value of V_f, which is 11.1 L. The volume increases. This should make sense because the pressure decreases, so pressure and volume are inversely related.

SKILL-BUILDING EXERCISE

1. If a sample of gas has an initial pressure of 3.66 atm and an initial volume of 11.8 L, what is the final pressure if the volume is reduced to 5.09 L? Assume that the amount and the temperature of the gas remain constant.

If the units of similar quantities are not the same, one of them must be converted to the other quantity's units for the calculation to work out properly. It does not matter which quantity is converted to a different unit; the only thing that matters is that the conversion and subsequent algebra are performed properly. The following example illustrates this process.

EXAMPLE 6

If a sample of gas has an initial pressure of 1.56 atm and an initial volume of 7.02 L, what is the final volume if the pressure is changed to 1,775 torr? Does the answer make sense? Assume that the amount and the temperature of the gas remain constant.

Solution

This example is similar to Example 5, except now the final pressure is expressed in torr. For the math to work out properly, one of the pressure values must be converted to the other unit. Let us change the initial pressure to torr:

$$1.56\ \cancel{\text{atm}} \times \frac{760\ \text{torr}}{1\ \cancel{\text{atm}}} = 1{,}190\ \text{torr}$$

Now we can use Boyle's law:

$$(1{,}190\ \text{torr})(7.02\ \text{L}) = (1{,}775\ \text{torr}) \times V_f$$

Torr cancels algebraically from both sides of the equation, leaving

$$(1{,}190)(7.02\ \text{L}) = (1{,}775) \times V_f$$

Now we divide both sides of the equation by 1,775 to isolate V_f on one side. Solving for the final volume,

$$V_f = \frac{(1{,}190)(7.02\ \text{L})}{1{,}775} = 4.71\ \text{L}$$

Because the pressure increases, it makes sense that the volume decreases.

Note

The answer for the final volume is essentially the same if we converted the 1,775 torr to atmospheres: $1{,}775\ \text{torr} \times \frac{1\ \text{atm}}{760\ \text{torr}} = 2.336\ \text{atm}$. Using Boyle's law: $(1.56\ \text{atm})(7.02\ \text{L}) = (2.335\ \text{atm}) \times V_f$; $V_f = \frac{(1.56\ \text{atm})(7.02\ \text{L})}{2.336\ \text{atm}} = 4.69\ \text{L}$.

SKILL-BUILDING EXERCISE

1. If a sample of gas has an initial pressure of 375 torr and an initial volume of 7.02 L, what is the final pressure if the volume is changed to 4,577 mL? Does the answer make sense? Assume that amount and the temperature of the gas remain constant.

To Your Health: Breathing

Breathing certainly is a major contribution to your health! Without breathing, we could not survive. Curiously, the act of breathing itself is little more than an application of Boyle's law.

The lungs are a series of ever-narrowing tubes that end in a myriad of tiny sacs called alveoli. It is in the alveoli that oxygen from the air transfers to the bloodstream and carbon dioxide from the bloodstream transfers to the lungs for exhalation. For air to move in and out of the lungs, the pressure inside the lungs must change, forcing the lungs to change volume—just as predicted by Boyle's law.

The pressure change is caused by the diaphragm, a muscle that covers the bottom of the lungs. When the diaphragm moves down, it expands the size of our lungs. When this happens, the air pressure inside our lungs decreases slightly. This causes new air to rush in, and we inhale. The pressure decrease is slight—only 3 torr, or about 0.4% of an atmosphere. We inhale only 0.5–1.0 L of air per normal breath.

Exhaling air requires that we relax the diaphragm, which pushes against the lungs and slightly decreases the volume of the lungs. This slightly increases the pressure of the air in the lungs, and air is forced out; we exhale. Only 1–2 torr of extra pressure is needed to exhale. So with every breath, our own bodies are performing an experimental test of Boyle's law.

4.2 Charles's Law

Another simple gas law relates the volume of a gas to its temperature. Experiments indicate that as the temperature of a gas sample is increased, its volume increases as long as the pressure and the amount of gas remain constant. The way to write this mathematically is

$$V \propto T$$

At this point, the concept of temperature must be clarified. Although the Kelvin scale is the preferred temperature scale, the Celsius scale is also a common temperature scale used in science. The Celsius scale is based on the melting and boiling points of water and is actually the common temperature scale used by most countries around the world (except for the United States, which still uses the Fahrenheit scale). The value of a Celsius temperature is directly related to its Kelvin value by a simple expression:

$$\text{Kelvin temperature} = \text{Celsius temperature} + 273$$

Thus, it is easy to convert from one temperature scale to another.

Note

The Kelvin scale is sometimes referred to as the absolute scale because the zero point on the Kelvin scale is at absolute zero, the coldest possible temperature. On the other temperature scales, absolute zero is −260°C or −459°F.

The expression relating a gas volume to its temperature begs the following question: to which temperature scale is the volume of a gas related? The answer is that gas volumes are directly related to the *Kelvin temperature*. Therefore, the temperature of a gas sample should always be expressed in (or converted to) a Kelvin temperature.

EXAMPLE 7

What happens to the volume of a gas if its temperature is decreased? Assume that all other conditions remain constant.

Solution

If the temperature of a gas sample is decreased, the volume decreases as well.

SKILL-BUILDING EXERCISE

1. What happens to the temperature of a gas if its volume is increased? Assume that all other conditions remain constant.

As with Boyle's law, the relationship between volume and temperature can be expressed in terms of initial and final values of volume and temperature, as follows:

$$\frac{V_i}{T_i} = \frac{V_f}{T_f}$$

where V_i and T_i are the initial volume and temperature, and V_f and T_f are the final volume and temperature. This is **Charles's law**. The restriction on its use is that the pressure of the gas and the amount of gas must remain constant. (Charles's law is sometimes referred to as Gay-Lussac's law, after the scientist who promoted Charles's work.)

Charles's law

The gas law that relates volume and absolute temperature.

EXAMPLE 8

A gas sample at 20°C has an initial volume of 20.0 L. What is its volume if the temperature is changed to 60°C? Does the answer make sense? Assume that the pressure and the amount of the gas remain constant.

Solution

Although the temperatures are given in degrees Celsius, we must convert them to the kelvins before we can use Charles's law. Thus,

$$20°\text{C} + 273 = 293\ \text{K} = T_i$$

$$60°\text{C} + 273 = 333\ \text{K} = T_f$$

Now we can substitute these values into Charles's law, along with the initial volume of 20.0 L:

$$\frac{20.0\ \text{L}}{293\ \text{K}} = \frac{V_f}{333\ \text{K}}$$

Multiplying the 333 K to the other side of the equation, we see that our temperature units will cancel:

$$\frac{(333\ \cancel{\text{K}})(20.0\ \text{L})}{293\ \cancel{\text{K}}} = V_f$$

Solving for the final volume, $V_f = 22.7$ L. So, as the temperature is increased, the volume increases. This makes sense because volume is directly proportional to the absolute temperature (as long as the pressure and the amount of the remain constant).

SKILL-BUILDING EXERCISE

1. A gas sample at 35°C has an initial volume of 5.06 L. What is its volume if the temperature is changed to −35°C? Does the answer make sense? Assume that the pressure and the amount of the gas remain constant.

4.3 Combined Gas Law

Other gas laws can be constructed, but we will focus on only two more. The **combined gas law** brings Boyle's and Charles's laws together to relate pressure, volume, and temperature changes of a gas sample:

$$\frac{P_iV_i}{T_i} = \frac{P_fV_f}{T_f}$$

To apply this gas law, the amount of gas should remain constant. As with the other gas laws, the temperature must be expressed in kelvins, and the units on the similar quantities should be the same. Because of the dependence on three quantities at the same time, it is difficult to tell in advance what will happen to one property of a gas sample as two other properties change. The best way to know is to work it out mathematically.

combined gas law

The gas law that relates pressure, volume, and absolute temperature.

EXAMPLE 9

A sample of gas has P_i = 1.50 atm, V_i = 10.5 L, and T_i = 300 K. What is the final volume if P_f = 0.750 atm and T_f = 350 K?

Solution

Using the combined gas law, substitute for five of the quantities:

$$\frac{(1.50\text{ atm})(10.5\text{ L})}{300\text{ K}} = \frac{(0.750\text{ atm})(V_f)}{350\text{ K}}$$

We algebraically rearrange this expression to isolate V_f on one side of the equation:

$$V_f = \frac{(1.50\cancel{\text{ atm}})(10.5\text{ L})(350\cancel{\text{ K}})}{(300\cancel{\text{ K}})(0.750\cancel{\text{ atm}})} = 24.5\text{ L}$$

Note how all the units cancel except the unit for volume.

SKILL-BUILDING EXERCISE

1. A sample of gas has P_i = 0.768 atm, V_i = 10.5 L, and T_i = 300 K. What is the final pressure if V_f = 7.85 L and T_f = 250 K?

EXAMPLE 10

A balloon containing a sample of gas has a temperature of 22°C and a pressure of 1.09 atm in an airport in Cleveland. The balloon has a volume of 1,070 mL. The balloon is transported by plane to Denver, where the temperature is 11°C and the pressure is 655 torr. What is the new volume of the balloon?

Solution

The first task is to convert all quantities to the proper and consistent units. The temperatures must be expressed in kelvins, and the pressure units are different so one of the quantities must be converted. Let us convert the atmospheres to torr:

$$22°\text{C} + 273 = 295\text{ K} = T_i$$

$$11°\text{C} + 273 = 284\text{ K} = T_f$$

$$1.09\cancel{\text{ atm}} \times \frac{760\text{ torr}}{1\cancel{\text{ atm}}} = 828\text{ torr} = P_i$$

Now we can substitute the quantities into the combined has law:

$$\frac{(828\text{ torr})(1{,}070\text{ mL})}{295\text{ K}} = \frac{(655\text{ torr}) \times V_f}{284\text{ K}}$$

To solve for V_f, we multiply the 284 K in the denominator of the right side into the numerator on the left, and we divide 655 torr in the numerator of the right side into the denominator on the left:

$$\frac{(828\cancel{\text{ torr}})(1{,}070\text{ mL})(284\cancel{\text{ K}})}{(295\cancel{\text{ K}})(655\cancel{\text{ torr}})} = V_f$$

Notice that torr and kelvins cancel, as they are found in both the numerator and denominator. The only unit that remains is milliliters, which is a unit of volume. So V_f = 1,300 mL. The overall change is that the volume of the balloon has increased by 230 mL.

SKILL-BUILDING EXERCISE

1. A balloon used to lift weather instruments into the atmosphere contains gas having a volume of 1,150 L on the ground, where the pressure is 0.977 atm and the temperature is 18°C. Aloft, this gas has a pressure of 6.88 torr and a temperature of −15°C. What is the new volume of the gas?

4.4 The Ideal Gas Law

So far, the gas laws we have used have focused on changing one or more properties of the gas, such as its volume, pressure, or temperature. There is one gas law that relates all the independent properties of a gas under any particular condition, rather than a change in conditions. This gas law is called the **ideal gas law**. The formula of this law is as follows:

ideal gas law

The gas law that relates volume, pressure, temperature, and amount of a gas.

$$PV = nRT$$

In this equation, P is pressure, V is volume, n is amount of moles, and T is temperature. R is called the **ideal gas law constant** and is a proportionality constant that relates the values of pressure, volume, amount, and temperature of a gas sample. The variables in this equation do not have the subscripts i and f to indicate an initial condition and a final condition. The ideal gas law relates the four independent properties of a gas under *any* conditions.

ideal gas law constant

The constant the appears in the ideal gas law.

The value of R depends on what units are used to express the other quantities. If volume is expressed in liters and pressure in atmospheres, then the proper value of R is as follows:

$$R = 0.08205 \frac{\text{L} \cdot \text{atm}}{\text{mol} \cdot \text{K}}$$

This may seem like a strange unit, but that is what is required for the units to work out algebraically.

EXAMPLE 11

What is the volume in liters of 1.45 mol of N_2 gas at 298 K and 3.995 atm?

Solution

Using the ideal gas law where $P = 3.995$ atm, $n = 1.45$, and $T = 298$,

$$(3.995 \text{ atm}) \times V = (1.45 \text{ mol})(\ 0.08205 \frac{\text{L} \cdot \text{atm}}{\text{mol} \cdot \text{K}}\ )(298 \text{ K})$$

On the right side, the moles and kelvins cancel. Also, because atmospheres appear in the numerator on both sides of the equation, they also cancel. The only remaining unit is liters, a unit of volume. So

$$3.995 \times V = (1.45)(0.08205)(298) \text{ L}$$

Dividing both sides of the equation by 3.995 and evaluating, we get $V = 8.87$ L. Note that the conditions of the gas are not changing. Rather, the ideal gas law allows us to determine what the fourth property of a gas (here, volume) *must* be if three other properties (here, amount, pressure, and temperature) are known.

SKILL-BUILDING EXERCISE

1. What is the pressure of a sample of CO_2 gas if 0.557 mol is held in a 20.0 L container at 451 K?

For convenience, scientists have selected 273 K (0°C) and 1.00 atm pressure as a set of standard conditions for gases. This combination of conditions is called **standard temperature and pressure (STP)**. Under these conditions, 1 mol of any gas has about the same volume. We can use the ideal gas law to determine the volume of 1 mol of gas at STP:

standard temperature and pressure (STP)

273 K (0°C) and 1.00 atm pressure.

$$(1.00 \text{ atm}) \times V = (1.00 \text{ mol})(\ 0.08205 \frac{\text{L} \cdot \text{atm}}{\text{mol} \cdot \text{K}}\ )(273 \text{ K})$$

This volume is 22.4 L. Because this volume is independent of the identity of a gas, the idea that 1 mol of gas has a volume of 22.4 L at STP makes a convenient conversion factor:

$$1 \text{ mol gas} = 22.4 \text{ L (at STP)}$$

EXAMPLE 12

Cyclopropane (C_3H_6) is a gas that formerly was used as an anesthetic. How many moles of gas are there in a 100.0 L sample if the gas is at STP?

Solution

We can set up a simple, one-step conversion that relates moles and liters:

$$100.0 \not{L}\ C_3H_6 \times \frac{1\ \text{mol}}{22.4 \not{L}} = 4.46\ \text{mol}\ C_3H_6$$

There are almost 4.5 mol of gas in 100.0 L.

Note

Because of its flammability, cyclopropane is no longer used as an anesthetic gas.

SKILL-BUILDING EXERCISE

1. Freon is a trade name for a series of fluorine- and chlorine-containing gases that formerly were used in refrigeration systems. What volume does 8.75 mol of Freon have at STP?

Note

Many gases known as Freon are no longer used because their presence in the atmosphere destroys the ozone layer, which protects us from ultraviolet light from the sun.

Career Focus: Respiratory Therapist

Certain diseases—such as emphysema, lung cancer, and severe asthma—primarily affect the lungs. Respiratory therapists help patients with breathing-related problems. They can evaluate, help diagnose, and treat breathing disorders and even help provide emergency assistance in acute illness where breathing is compromised.

Most respiratory therapists must complete at least two years of college and earn an associate's degree, although therapists can assume more responsibility if they have a college degree. Therapists must also pass state or national certification exams. Once certified, respiratory therapists can work in hospitals, doctor's offices, nursing homes, or patient's homes. Therapists work with equipment such as oxygen tanks and respirators, may sometimes dispense medication to aid in breathing, perform tests, and educate patients in breathing exercises and other therapy.

Because respiratory therapists work directly with patients, the ability to work well with others is a must for this career. It is an important job because it deals with one of the most crucial functions of the body.

CONCEPT REVIEW EXERCISES

1. What properties do the gas laws help us predict?
2. What makes the ideal gas law different from the other gas laws?

ANSWERS

1. Gas laws relate four properties: pressure, volume, temperature, and number of moles.
2. The ideal gas law does not require that the properties of a gas change.

KEY TAKEAWAY

- The physical properties of gases are predictable using mathematical formulas known as gas laws.

EXERCISES

1. What conditions of a gas sample should remain constant for Boyle's law to be used?
2. What conditions of a gas sample should remain constant for Charles's law to be used?
3. Does the identity of a gas matter when using Boyle's law? Why or why not?
4. Does the identity of a gas matter when using Charles's law? Why or why not?
5. A sample of nitrogen gas is confined to a balloon that has a volume of 1.88 L and a pressure of 1.334 atm. What will be the volume of the balloon if the pressure is changed to 0.662 atm? Assume that the temperature and the amount of the gas remain constant.
6. A sample of helium gas in a piston has a volume of 86.4 mL under a pressure of 447 torr. What will be the volume of the helium if the pressure on the piston is increased to 1,240 torr? Assume that the temperature and the amount of the gas remain constant.
7. If a gas has an initial pressure of 24,650 Pa and an initial volume of 376 mL, what is the final volume if the pressure of the gas is changed to 775 torr? Assume that the amount and the temperature of the gas remain constant.
8. A gas sample has an initial volume of 0.9550 L and an initial pressure of 564.5 torr. What would the final pressure of the gas be if the volume is changed to 587.0 mL? Assume that the amount and the temperature of the gas remain constant.
9. A person draws a normal breath of about 1.00 L. If the initial temperature of the air is 18°C and the air warms to 37°C, what is the new volume of the air? Assume that the pressure and amount of the gas remain constant.
10. A person draws a normal breath of about 1.00 L. If the initial temperature of the air is −10°C and the air warms to 37°C, what is the new volume of the air? Assume that the pressure and the amount of the gas remain constant.
11. An air/gas vapor mix in an automobile cylinder has an initial temperature of 450 K and a volume of 12.7 cm^3. The gas mix is heated to 565°C. If pressure and amount are held constant, what is the final volume of the gas in cubic centimeters?
12. Given the following conditions for a gas: V_i = 0.665 L, T_i = 23.6°C, V_f = 1.034 L. What is T_f in degrees Celsius and kelvins?
13. Assuming the amount remains the same, what must be the final volume of a gas that has an initial volume of 387 mL, an initial pressure of 456 torr, an initial temperature of 65.0°C, a final pressure of 1.00 atm, and a final temperature of 300 K?
14. When the nozzle of a spray can is depressed, 0.15 mL of gas expands to 0.44 mL, and its pressure drops from 788 torr to 1.00 atm. If the initial temperature of the gas is 22.0°C, what is the final temperature of the gas?
15. Use the ideal gas law to show that 1 mol of a gas at STP has a volume of about 22.4 L.
16. Use a standard conversion factor to determine a value of the ideal gas law constant R that has units of L·torr/mol·K.
17. How many moles of gas are there in a 27.6 L sample at 298 K and a pressure of 1.44 atm?
18. How many moles of gas are there in a 0.066 L sample at 298 K and a pressure of 0.154 atm?
19. A 0.334 mol sample of carbon dioxide gas is confined to a volume of 20.0 L and has a pressure of 0.555 atm. What is the temperature of the carbon dioxide in kelvins and degrees Celsius?
20. What must V be for a gas sample if n = 4.55 mol, P = 7.32 atm, and T = 285 K?
21. What is the pressure of 0.0456 mol of Ne gas contained in a 7.50 L volume at 29°C?
22. What is the pressure of 1.00 mol of Ar gas that has a volume of 843.0 mL and a temperature of −86.0°C?

ANSWERS

1. temperature and amount of the gas
3. The identity does not matter because the variables of Boyle's law do not identify the gas.
5. 3.89 L
7. 92.1 mL
9. 1.07 L
11. 23.7 cm^3
13. 206 mL
15. The ideal gas law confirms that 22.4 L equals 1 mol.
17. 1.63 mol
19. 405 K; 132°C
21. 0.151 atm

5. END-OF-CHAPTER MATERIAL

Chapter Summary

To ensure that you understand the material in this chapter, you should review the meanings of the following bold terms in the following summary and ask yourself how they relate to the topics in the chapter.

A **phase** is a certain form of matter that has the same physical properties throughout. Three phases are common: the solid, the liquid, and the gas phase. What determines the phase of a substance? Generally, the strength of the **intermolecular interactions** determines whether a substance is a solid, liquid, or gas under any particular conditions. **Covalent network bonding** is a very strong form of intermolecular interaction. Diamond is one example of a substance that has this intermolecular interaction. **Ionic interactions**, the forces of attraction due to oppositely charged ions, are also relatively strong. Covalent bonds are another type of interaction within molecules, but if the bonds are **polar covalent bonds**, then the unequal sharing of electrons can cause charge imbalances within molecules that cause interactions between molecules. These molecules are described as **polar**, and these interactions are called **dipole-dipole interactions**. A certain rather strong type of dipole-dipole interaction, involving a hydrogen atom, is called **hydrogen bonding**. On the other hand, equal sharing of electrons forms **nonpolar covalent bonds**, and the interactions between different molecules is less because the molecules are nonpolar. All substances have very weak **dispersion forces** (also called **London forces**) caused by the movement of electrons within the bonds themselves.

In the solid phase, intermolecular interactions are so strong that they hold the individual atoms or molecules in place. In many solids, the regular three-dimensional arrangement of particles makes a **crystal**. In other solids, the irregular arrangement of particles makes an **amorphous** solid. In liquids, the intermolecular interactions are strong enough to keep the particles of substance together but not in place. Thus, the particles are free to move over each other but still remain in contact.

In gases, the intermolecular interactions are weak enough that the individual particles are separated from each other in space. The **kinetic theory of gases** is a collection of statements that describe the fundamental behavior of all gases. Among other properties, gases exert a **pressure** on their container. Pressure is measured using units like **pascal**, **bar**, **atmosphere**, or **mmHg** (also called a **torr**).

There are several simple relationships between the variables used to describe a quantity of gas. These relationships are called **gas laws**. **Boyle's law** relates the pressure and volume of a gas, while **Charles's law** relates the volume and absolute temperature of a gas. The **combined gas law** relates the volume, pressure, and absolute temperature of a gas sample. All of these gas laws allow us to understand the changing conditions of a gas. The **ideal gas law** relates the pressure, volume, amount, and absolute temperature of a gas under any conditions. These four variables are related to the **ideal gas law constant**, which is the proportionality constant used to calculate the conditions of a gas. Because the conditions of a gas can change, a set of benchmark conditions called **standard temperature and pressure (STP)** is defined. Standard temperature is 0°C, and standard pressure is 1.00 atm.

ADDITIONAL EXERCISES

1. How many grams of oxygen gas are needed to fill a 25.0 L container at 0.966 atm and 22°C?
2. A breath of air is about 1.00 L in volume. If the pressure is 1.00 atm and the temperature is 37°C, what mass of air is contained in each breath? Use an average molar mass of 28.8 g/mol for air.

3. The balanced chemical equation for the combustion of propane is as follows:

$$C_3H_8(g) + 5O_2(g) \rightarrow 3CO_2(g) + 4H_2O(\ell)$$

   a. If 100.0 g of propane are combusted, how many moles of oxygen gas are necessary for the reaction to occur?
   b. At STP, how many liters of oxygen gas would that be?

4. The equation for the formation of ammonia gas (NH_3) is as follows:

$$N_2(g) + 3H_2(g) \rightarrow 2NH_3(g)$$

   At 500°C and 1.00 atm, 10.0 L of N_2 gas are reacted to make ammonia.

   a. If the pressures and temperatures of H_2 and NH_3 were the same as those of N_2, what volume of H_2 would be needed to react with N_2, and what volume of NH_3 gas would be produced?
   b. Compare your answers to the balanced chemical equation. Can you devise a "shortcut" method to answer Exercise 4a?

5. At 20°C, 1 g of liquid H_2O has a volume of 1.002 mL. What volume will 1 g of water vapor occupy at 20°C if its pressure is 17.54 mmHg? By what factor has the water expanded in going from the liquid phase to the gas phase?
6. At 100°C, 1 g of liquid H_2O has a volume of 1.043 mL. What volume will 1 g of steam occupy at 100°C if its pressure is 760.0 mmHg? By what factor has the water expanded in going from the liquid phase to the gas phase?
7. Predict whether NaCl or NaI will have the higher melting point. Explain. (Hint: consider the relative strengths of the intermolecular interactions of the two compounds.)
8. Predict whether CH_4 or CH_3OH will have the lower boiling point. Explain. (Hint: consider the relative strengths of the intermolecular interactions of the two compounds.)
9. A standard automobile tire has a volume of about 3.2 ft^3 (where 1 ft^3 equals 28.32 L). Tires are typically inflated to an absolute pressure of 45.0 pounds per square inch (psi), where 1 atm equals 14.7 psi. Using this information with the ideal gas law, determine the number of moles of air needed to fill a tire if the air temperature is 18.0°C.
10. Another gas law, Amontons's law, relates pressure and temperature under conditions of constant amount and volume:

$$\frac{P_i}{T_i} = \frac{P_f}{T_f}$$

   If an automobile tire (see Exercise 9) is inflated to 45.0 psi at 18.0°C, what will be its pressure if the operating temperature (i.e., the temperature the tire reaches when the automobile is on the road) is 45.0°C? Assume that the volume and the amount of the gas remain constant.

ANSWERS

1. 31.9 g
3. a. 11.4 mol
   b. 255 L
5. 57.81 L; an expansion of 57,700 times
7. NaCl; with smaller anions, NaCl likely experiences stronger ionic bonding.
9. 11.6 mol

CHAPTER 9
Solutions

Opening Essay

If you watch any of the medical dramas on television, you may have heard a doctor (actually an actor) call for an intravenous solution of "Ringer's lactate" (or "lactated Ringer's"). So what is Ringer's lactate?

Intravenous (IV) solutions are administered for two main reasons: (1) to introduce necessary substances into the bloodstream, such as ions for proper body function, sugar and other food substances for energy, or drugs to treat a medical condition, and (2) to increase the volume of the bloodstream. Many people with acute or long-term medical conditions have received some type of an IV solution.

One basic IV solution, called a *normal saline solution*, is simply a dilute solution of NaCl dissolved in water. Normal saline is 9.0 g of NaCl dissolved in each liter of solution. (The reason for this particular concentration is explained in Section 4.)

Ringer's lactate is a normal saline solution that also has small amounts of potassium and calcium ions mixed in. In addition, it contains about 2.5 g of lactate ions ($C_3H_5O_3^-$) per liter of solution. The liver metabolizes lactate ions into bicarbonate (HCO_3^-) ions, which help maintain the acid-base balance of blood. (Acids and bases are discussed in Chapter 10.) Many medical problems, such as heart attacks and shock, affect the acid-base balance of blood, and the presence of lactate in the IV solution eases problems caused by this imbalance.

Physicians can select from a range of premade IV solutions, in accordance with a patient's particular needs. Ringer's lactate is commonly used when a patient's blood volume must be increased quickly. Another frequently used IV solution, called D5W, is a 5% solution of dextrose (a form of sugar) in water.

Solutions are all around us. Air, for example, is a solution. If you live near a lake, a river, or an ocean, that body of water is not pure H_2O but most probably a solution. Much of what we drink—for example, soda, coffee, tea, and milk—is at least in part a solution. Solutions are a large part of everyday life.

A lot of the chemistry occurring around us happens in solution. In fact, much of the chemistry that occurs in our own bodies takes place in solution, and many solutions—such as the Ringer's lactate IV solution—are important for our health. In our understanding of chemistry, we need to understand a little bit about solutions. In this chapter, you will learn about the special characteristics of solutions, how solutions are characterized, and some of their properties.

1. SOLUTIONS

LEARNING OBJECTIVE

1. **Understand what causes solutions to form.**

A **solution** is another name for a homogeneous mixture. Chapter 1 defined a *mixture* as a material composed of two or more substances. In a solution, the combination is so intimate that the different substances cannot be differentiated by sight, even with a microscope. Compare, for example, a mixture of salt and pepper and another mixture consisting of salt and water. In the first mixture, we can readily see individual grains of salt and the flecks of pepper. A mixture of salt and pepper is not a solution. However, in the second mixture, no matter how carefully we look, we cannot see two different substances. Salt dissolved in water is a solution.

solution

Another name for a homogeneous mixture.

solvent

The major component of a solution.

solute

The minor component of a solution.

alloy

A solid solution of a metal with other substances dissolved in it.

The major component of a solution, called the **solvent**, is typically the same phase as the solution itself. Each minor component of a solution (and there may be more than one) is called the **solute**. In most of the solutions we will describe in this textbook, there will be no ambiguity about whether a component is the solvent or the solute.) For example, in a solution of salt in water, the solute is salt, and solvent is water.

Solutions come in all phases, and the solvent and the solute do not have to be in the same phase to form a solution (such as salt and water). For example, air is a gaseous solution of about 80% nitrogen and about 20% oxygen, with some other gases present in much smaller amounts. An **alloy** is a solid solution consisting of a metal (like iron) with some other metals or nonmetals dissolved in it. Steel, an alloy of iron and carbon and small amounts of other metals, is an example of a solid solution. Table 9.1 lists some common types of solutions, with examples of each.

TABLE 9.1 Types of Solutions

Solvent Phase	Solute Phase	Example
gas	gas	air
liquid	gas	carbonated beverages
liquid	liquid	ethanol (C_2H_5OH) in H_2O (alcoholic beverages)
liquid	solid	saltwater
solid	gas	H_2 gas absorbed by Pd metal
solid	liquid	Hg(ℓ) in dental fillings
solid	solid	steel alloys

What causes a solution to form? The simple answer is that the solvent and the solute must have similar intermolecular interactions. When this is the case, the individual particles of solvent and solute can easily mix so intimately that each particle of solute is surrounded by particles of solute, forming a solution. However, if two substances have very different intermolecular interactions, large amounts of energy are required to force their individual particles to mix intimately, so a solution does not form.

This process leads to a simple rule of thumb: *like dissolves like*. Solvents that are very polar will dissolve solutes that are very polar or even ionic. Solvents that are nonpolar will dissolve nonpolar solutes. Thus water, being polar, is a good solvent for ionic compounds and polar solutes like ethanol (C_2H_5OH). However, water does not dissolve nonpolar solutes, such as many oils and greases (Figure 9.1).

FIGURE 9.1 Solubility

Because of different intermolecular interactions, oil (on top) and water (bottom, colored red) do not dissolve in each other.

We use the word **soluble** to describe a solute that dissolves in a particular solvent, and the word **insoluble** for a solute that does not dissolve in a solvent. Thus, we say that sodium chloride is soluble in water but insoluble in hexane (C_6H_{14}). If the solute and the solvent are both liquids and soluble in any proportion, we use the word **miscible**, and the word **immiscible** if they are not.

soluble

A solute that dissolves in a particular solvent.

insoluble

A solute that does not dissolve in a particular solvent.

miscible

Liquids that dissolve in each other.

immiscible

Liquids that do not dissolve in each other.

EXAMPLE 1

Water is considered a polar solvent. Which substances should dissolve in water?

1. methanol (CH_3OH)
2. sodium sulfate (Na_2SO_4)
3. octane (C_8H_{18})

Solution

Because water is polar, substances that are polar or ionic will dissolve in it.

1. Because of the OH group in methanol, we expect its molecules to be polar. Thus, we expect it to be soluble in water. As both water and methanol are liquids, the word *miscible* can be used in place of *soluble*.
2. Sodium sulfate is an ionic compound, so we expect it to be soluble in water.
3. Like other hydrocarbons, octane is nonpolar, so we expect that it would not be soluble in water.

SKILL-BUILDING EXERCISE

Toluene ($C_6H_5CH_3$) is widely used in industry as a nonpolar solvent. Which substances should dissolve in toluene?

1. water (H_2O)
2. sodium sulfate (Na_2SO_4)
3. octane (C_8H_{18})

CONCEPT REVIEW EXERCISES

1. What causes a solution to form?
2. How does the phrase *like dissolves like* relate to solutions?

ANSWERS

1. Solutions form because a solute and a solvent have similar intermolecular interactions.
2. It means that substances with similar intermolecular interactions will dissolve in each other.

KEY TAKEAWAY

- Solutions form because a solute and a solvent experience similar intermolecular interactions.

EXERCISES

1. Define *solution*.
2. Give several examples of solutions.
3. What is the difference between a solvent and a solute?
4. Can a solution have more than one solute in it? Can you give an example?
5. Does a solution have to be a liquid? Give several examples to support your answer.
6. Give at least two examples of solutions found in the human body.

7. Which substances will probably be soluble in water, a very polar solvent?
   a. sodium nitrate ($NaNO_3$)
   b. hexane (C_6H_{14})
   c. isopropyl alcohol [$(CH_3)_2CHOH$]
   d. benzene (C_6H_6)
8. Which substances will probably be soluble in toluene ($C_6H_5CH_3$), a nonpolar solvent?
   a. sodium nitrate ($NaNO_3$)
   b. hexane (C_6H_{14})
   c. isopropyl alcohol [$(CH_3)_2CHOH$]
   d. benzene (C_6H_6)
9. The solubility of alcohols in water varies with the length of carbon chain. For example, ethanol (CH_3CH_2OH) is soluble in water in any ratio, while only 0.0008 mL of heptanol ($CH_3CH_2CH_2CH_2CH_2CH_2CH_2OH$) will dissolve in 100 mL of water. Propose an explanation for this behavior.
10. Dimethyl sulfoxide [$(CH_3)_2SO$] is a polar liquid. Based on the information in Exercise 9, which do you think will be more soluble in it—ethanol or heptanol?

ANSWERS

1. a homogeneous mixture
3. A solvent is the majority component of a solution; a solute is the minority component of a solution.
5. A solution does not have to be liquid; air is a gaseous solution, while some alloys are solid solutions (answers will vary).
7. a. probably soluble
   b. probably not soluble
   c. probably soluble
   d. probably not soluble
9. Small alcohol molecules have strong polar intermolecular interactions, so they dissolve in water. In large alcohol molecules, the nonpolar end overwhelms the polar end, so they do not dissolve very well in water.

2. CONCENTRATION

LEARNING OBJECTIVES

1. **Express the amount of solute in a solution in various concentration units.**
2. **Use molarity to determine quantities in chemical reactions.**
3. **Determine the resulting concentration of a diluted solution.**

concentration

How much solute is dissolved in a certain amount of solvent.

To define a solution precisely, we need to state its **concentration**: how much solute is dissolved in a certain amount of solvent. Words such as *dilute* or *concentrated* are used to describe solutions that have a little or a lot of dissolved solute, respectively, but these are relative terms whose meanings depend on various factors.

2.1 Solubility

solubility

The limit of how much solute can be dissolved in a given amount of solvent.

There is usually a limit to how much solute will dissolve in a given amount of solvent. This limit is called the **solubility** of the solute. Some solutes have a very small solubility, while other solutes are soluble in all proportions. Table 9.2 lists the solubilities of various solutes in water. Solubilities vary with temperature, so Table 9.2 includes the temperature at which the solubility was determined.

TABLE 9.2 Solubilities of Various Solutes in Water at 25°C (Except as Noted)

Substance	Solubility (g in 100 mL of H_2O)
$AgCl(s)$	0.019
$C_6H_6(\ell)$ (benzene)	0.178
$CH_4(g)$	0.0023
$CO_2(g)$	0.150
$CaCO_3(s)$	0.058
$CaF_2(s)$	0.0016
$Ca(NO_3)_2(s)$	143.9
$C_6H_{12}O_6$ (glucose)	120.3 (at 30°C)
$KBr(s)$	67.8
$MgCO_3(s)$	2.20
$NaCl(s)$	36.0
$NaHCO_3(s)$	8.41
$C_{12}H_{22}O_{11}$ (sucrose)	204.0 (at 20°C)

If a solution contains so much solute that its solubility limit is reached, the solution is said to be **saturated**, and its concentration is known from information contained in Table 9.2. If a solution contains less solute than the solubility limit, it is **unsaturated**. Under special circumstances, more solute can be dissolved even after the normal solubility limit is reached; such solutions are called *supersaturated* and are not stable. If the solute is solid, excess solute can easily recrystallize. If the solute is a gas, it can bubble out of solution uncontrollably, like what happens when you shake a soda can and then immediately open it.

saturated

A solution whose solute is at its solubility limit.

unsaturated

A solution whose solute is less than its solubility limit.

Note

Recrystallization of excess solute from a supersaturated solution usually gives off energy as heat. Commercial heat packs containing supersaturated sodium acetate ($NaC_2H_3O_2$) take advantage of this phenomenon. You can probably find them at your local drugstore.

Most solutions we encounter are unsaturated, so knowing the solubility of the solute does not accurately express the amount of solute in these solutions. There are several common ways of specifying the concentration of a solution.

2.2 Percent Composition

There are several ways of expressing the concentration of a solution by using a percentage. The **mass/mass percent** (% m/m) is defined as the mass of a solute divided by the mass of a solution times 100:

$$\%\ m/m = \frac{\text{mass of solute}}{\text{mass of solution}} \times 100\%$$

mass/mass percent

A concentration unit that relates the mass of the solute to the mass of the solution.

If you can measure the masses of the solute and the solution, determining the mass/mass percent is easy. Each mass must be expressed in the same units to determine the proper concentration.

EXAMPLE 2

A saline solution with a mass of 355 g has 36.5 g of NaCl dissolved in it. What is the mass/mass percent concentration of the solution?

Solution

We can substitute the quantities given in the equation for mass/mass percent:

$$\%\ m/m = \frac{36.5\ g}{355\ g} \times 100\% = 10.3\%$$

SKILL-BUILDING EXERCISE

1. A dextrose (also called D-glucose, $C_6H_{12}O_6$) solution with a mass of 2.00×10^2 g has 15.8 g of dextrose dissolved in it. What is the mass/mass percent concentration of the solution?

volume/volume percent

A concentration unit that relates the volume of the solute to the volume of the solution.

mass/volume percent

A concentration unit that relates the mass of the solute to the volume of the solution.

For gases and liquids, volumes are relatively easy to measure, so the concentration of a liquid or a gas solution can be expressed as a **volume/volume percent** (% v/v): the volume of a solute divided by the volume of a solution times 100:

$$\% \text{ v/v} = \frac{\text{volume of solute}}{\text{volume of solution}} \times 100\%$$

Again, the units of the solute and the solution must be the same. A hybrid concentration unit, **mass/volume percent** (% m/v), is commonly used for intravenous (IV) fluids (Figure 9.2). It is defined as the mass in grams of a solute, divided by volume in milliliters of solution times 100:

$$\% \text{ m/v} = \frac{\text{mass of solute (g)}}{\text{volume of solution (mL)}} \times 100\%$$

FIGURE 9.2
Mass/Volume Percent

The 0.9% concentration on this IV bag is mass/volume percent.

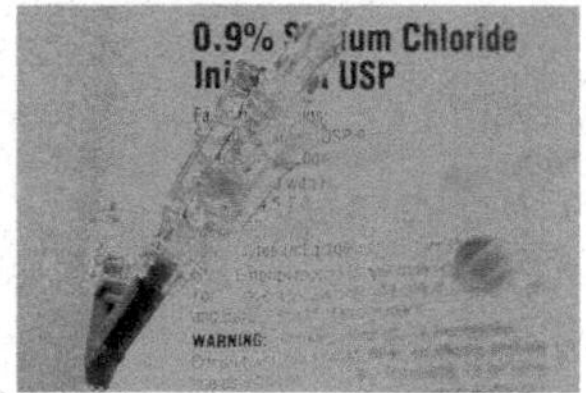

© *Thinkstock*

Each percent concentration can be used to produce a conversion factor between the amount of solute, the amount of solution, and the percent. Furthermore, given any two quantities in any percent composition, the third quantity can be calculated, as the following example illustrates.

EXAMPLE 3

A sample of 45.0% v/v solution of ethanol (C_2H_5OH) in water has a volume of 115 mL. What volume of ethanol solute does the sample contain?

Solution

A percentage concentration is simply the number of parts of solute per 100 parts of solution. Thus, the percent concentration of 45.0% v/v implies the following:

$$45.0\% \text{ v/v} \rightarrow \frac{45 \text{ mL } C_2H_5OH}{100 \text{ mL solution}}$$

That is, there are 45 mL of C_2H_5OH for every 100 mL of solution. We can use this fraction as a conversion factor to determine the amount of C_2H_5OH in 115 mL of solution:

$$115 \cancel{\text{mL solution}} \times \frac{45 \text{ mL } C_2H_5OH}{100 \cancel{\text{mL solution}}} = 51.8 \text{ mL } C_2H_5OH$$

Note

The highest concentration of ethanol that can be obtained normally is 95% ethanol, which is actually 95% v/v.

SKILL-BUILDING EXERCISE

1. What volume of a 12.75% m/v solution of glucose ($C_6H_{12}O_6$) in water is needed to obtain 50.0 g of $C_6H_{12}O_6$?

EXAMPLE 4

A normal saline IV solution contains 9.0 g of NaCl in every liter of solution. What is the mass/volume percent of normal saline?

Solution

We can use the definition of mass/volume percent, but first we have to express the volume in milliliter units:

$$1\text{ L} = 1{,}000\text{ mL}$$

Because this is an exact relationship, it does not affect the significant figures of our result.

$$\%\text{ m/v} = \frac{9.0\text{ g NaCl}}{1{,}000\text{ mL solution}} \times 100\% = 0.90\%\text{ m/v}$$

SKILL-BUILDING EXERCISE

1. The chlorine bleach that you might find in your laundry room is typically composed of 27.0 g of sodium hypochlorite (NaOCl), dissolved to make 500.0 mL of solution. What is the mass/volume percent of the bleach?

In addition to percentage units, the units for expressing the concentration of extremely dilute solutions are **parts per million (ppm)** and **parts per billion (ppb)**. Both of these units are mass based and are defined as follows:

parts per million (ppm)

The mass of a solute compared to the mass of a solution times 1,000,000.

parts per billion (ppb)

The mass of a solute compared to the mass of a solution times 1,000,000,000.

$$\text{ppm} = \frac{\text{mass of solute}}{\text{mass of solution}} \times 1{,}000{,}000$$

$$\text{ppb} = \frac{\text{mass of solute}}{\text{mass of solution}} \times 1{,}000{,}000{,}000$$

Note

Similar to parts per million and parts per billion, related units include parts per thousand (ppth) and parts per trillion (ppt).

Concentrations of *trace elements* in the body—elements that are present in extremely low concentrations but are nonetheless necessary for life—are commonly expressed in parts per million or parts per billion. Concentrations of poisons and pollutants are also described in these units. For example, cobalt is present in the body at a concentration of 21 ppb, while the State of Oregon's Department of Agriculture limits the concentration of arsenic in fertilizers to 9 ppm.

Note

In aqueous solutions, 1 ppm is essentially equal to 1 mg/L, and 1 ppb is equivalent to 1 µg/L.

EXAMPLE 5

If the concentration of cobalt in a human body is 21 ppb, what mass in grams of Co is present in a body having a mass of 70.0 kg?

Solution

A concentration of 21 ppb means "21 g of solute per 1,000,000,000 g of solution." Written as a conversion factor, this concentration of Co is as follows:

$$21 \text{ ppb Co} \rightarrow \frac{21 \text{ g Co}}{1{,}000{,}000{,}000 \text{ g solution}}$$

We can use this as a conversion factor, but first we must convert 70.0 kg to gram units:

$$70.0 \text{ kg} \times \frac{1{,}000 \text{ g}}{1 \text{ kg}} = 7.00 \times 10^4 \text{ g}$$

Now we determine the amount of Co:

$$7.00 \times 10^4 \cancel{\text{g solution}} \times \frac{21 \text{ g Co}}{1{,}000{,}000{,}000 \cancel{\text{g solution}}} = 0.0015 \text{ g Co}$$

This is only 1.5 mg.

SKILL-BUILDING EXERCISE

1. An 85 kg body contains 0.012 g of Ni. What is the concentration of Ni in parts per million?

2.3 Molarity

Another way of expressing concentration is to give the number of moles of solute per unit volume of solution. Such concentration units are useful for discussing chemical reactions in which a solute is a product or a reactant. Molar mass can then be used as a conversion factor to convert amounts in moles to amounts in grams.

molarity

Number of moles of solute per liter of solution.

Molarity is defined as the number of moles of a solute dissolved per liter of solution:

$$\text{molarity} = \frac{\text{number of moles of solute}}{\text{number of liters of solution}}$$

Molarity is abbreviated M (often referred to as "molar"), and the units are often abbreviated as mol/L. It is important to remember that "mol" in this expression refers to moles of solute and that "L" refers to liters of solution. For example, if you have 1.5 mol of NaCl dissolved in 0.500 L of solution, its molarity is therefore

$$\frac{1.5 \text{ mol NaCl}}{0.500 \text{ L solution}} = 3.0 \text{ M NaCl}$$

which is read as "three point oh molar sodium chloride." Sometimes (aq) is added when the solvent is water, as in "3.0 M NaCl(aq)."

Before a molarity concentration can be calculated, the amount of the solute must be expressed in moles, and the volume of the solution must be expressed in liters, as demonstrated in the following example.

EXAMPLE 6

What is the molarity of an aqueous solution of 25.0 g of NaOH in 750 mL?

Solution

Before we substitute these quantities into the definition of molarity, we must convert them to the proper units. The mass of NaOH must be converted to moles of NaOH. The molar mass of NaOH is 40.00 g/mol:

$$25.0\ \cancel{\text{g NaOH}} \times \frac{1\ \text{mol NaOH}}{40.00\ \cancel{\text{g NaOH}}} = 0.625\ \text{mol NaOH}$$

Next, we convert the volume units from milliliters to liters:

$$750\ \cancel{\text{mL}} \times \frac{1\ \text{L}}{1{,}000\ \cancel{\text{mL}}} = 0.750\ \text{L}$$

Now that the quantities are expressed in the proper units, we can substitute them into the definition of molarity:

$$\text{M} = \frac{0.625\ \text{mol NaOH}}{0.750\ \text{L}} = 0.833\ \text{M NaOH}$$

SKILL-BUILDING EXERCISE

1. If a 350 mL cup of coffee contains 0.150 g of caffeine ($C_8H_{10}N_4O_2$), what is the molarity of this caffeine solution?

The definition of molarity can also be used to calculate a needed volume of solution, given its concentration and the number of moles desired, or the number of moles of solute (and subsequently, the mass of the solute), given its concentration and volume. The following example illustrates this.

EXAMPLE 7

1. What volume of a 0.0753 M solution of dimethylamine [$(CH_3)_2NH$] is needed to obtain 0.450 mol of the compound?
2. Ethylene glycol ($C_2H_6O_2$) is mixed with water to make auto engine coolants. How many grams of $C_2H_6O_2$ are in 5.00 L of a 6.00 M aqueous solution?

Solution

In both parts, we will use the definition of molarity to solve for the desired quantity.

1. $$0.0753\ \text{M} = \frac{0.450\ \text{mol}\ (CH_3)_2NH}{\text{volume of solution}}$$

   To solve for the volume of solution, we multiply both sides by volume of solution and divide both sides by the molarity value to isolate the volume of solution on one side of the equation:

   $$\text{volume of solution} = \frac{0.450\ \text{mol}\ (CH_3)_2NH}{0.0753\ \text{M}} = 5.98\ \text{L}$$

   Note that because the definition of molarity is mol/L, the division of mol by M yields L, a unit of volume.
2. The molar mass of $C_2H_6O_2$ is 62.08 g/mol., so

   $$6.00\ \text{M} = \frac{\text{moles of solute}}{5.00\ \text{L}}$$

   To solve for the number of moles of solute, we multiply both sides by the volume:

   $$\text{moles of solute} = (6.00\ \text{M})(5.00\ \text{L}) = 30.0\ \text{mol}$$

   Note that because the definition of molarity is mol/L, the product M × L gives mol, a unit of amount. Now, using the molar mass of $C_3H_8O_3$, we convert mol to g:

   $$30.0\ \cancel{\text{mol}} \times \frac{62.08\ \text{g}}{\cancel{\text{mol}}} = 1{,}860\ \text{g}$$

   Thus, there are 1,860 g of $C_2H_6O_2$ in the specified amount of engine coolant.

Note

Dimethylamine has a "fishy" odor. In fact, organic compounds called amines cause the odor of decaying fish. (For more information about amines, see Chapter 15, [Unsupported Reference Type: chapter-section] and [Unsupported Reference Type: chapter-section] through [Unsupported Reference Type: chapter-section].)

SKILL-BUILDING EXERCISE

1. What volume of a 0.0902 M solution of formic acid (HCOOH) is needed to obtain 0.888 mol of HCOOH?
2. Acetic acid ($HC_2H_3O_2$) is the acid in vinegar. How many grams of $HC_2H_3O_2$ are in 0.565 L of a 0.955 M solution?

2.4 Using Molarity in Stoichiometry Problems

Of all the ways of expressing concentration, molarity is the one most commonly used in stoichiometry problems because it is directly related to the mole unit. Consider the following chemical equation:

$$HCl(aq) + NaOH(s) \rightarrow H_2O(\ell) + NaCl(aq)$$

Suppose we want to know how many liters of aqueous HCl solution will react with a given mass of NaOH. A typical approach to answering this question is as follows:

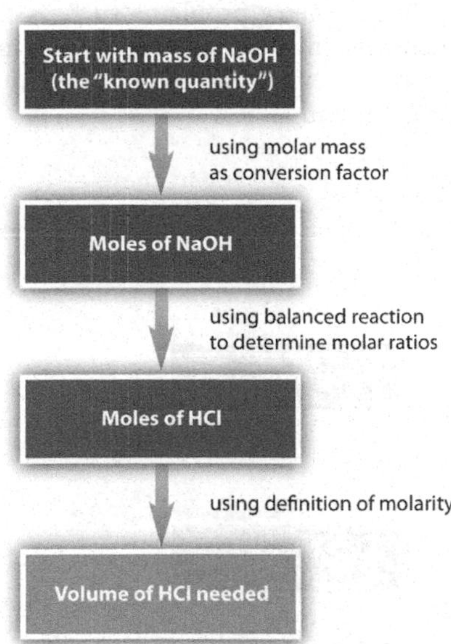

In itself, each step is a straightforward conversion. It is the combination of the steps that is a powerful quantitative tool for problem solving.

EXAMPLE 8

How many milliliters of a 2.75 M HCl solution are needed to react with 185 g of NaOH? The balanced chemical equation for this reaction is as follows:

$$HCl(aq) + NaOH(s) \rightarrow H_2O(\ell) + NaCl(aq)$$

Solution

We will follow the flowchart to answer this question. First, we convert the mass of NaOH to moles of NaOH using its molar mass, 40.00 g/mol:

$$185\ \cancel{\text{g NaOH}} \times \frac{1\ \text{mol NaOH}}{40.00\ \cancel{\text{g NaOH}}} = 4.63\ \text{mol NaOH}$$

Using the balanced chemical equation, we see that there is a one-to-one ratio of moles of HCl to moles of NaOH. We use this to determine the number of moles of HCl needed to react with the given amount of NaOH:

$$4.63\ \cancel{\text{mol NaOH}} \times \frac{1\ \text{mol HCl}}{1\ \cancel{\text{mol NaOH}}} = 4.63\ \text{mol HCl}$$

Finally, we use the definition of molarity to determine the volume of 2.75 M HCl needed:

$$2.75\ \text{M HCl} = \frac{4.63\ \text{mol HCl}}{\text{volume of HCl solution}}$$

$$\text{volume of HCl} = \frac{4.63\ \text{mol HCl}}{2.75\ \text{M HCl}} = 1.68\ \cancel{\text{L}} \times \frac{1{,}000\ \text{mL}}{1\ \cancel{\text{L}}} = 1{,}680\ \text{mL}$$

We need 1,680 mL of 2.75 M HCl to react with the NaOH.

SKILL-BUILDING EXERCISE

1. How many milliliters of a 1.04 M H_2SO_4 solution are needed to react with 98.5 g of $Ca(OH)_2$? The balanced chemical equation for the reaction is as follows:

$$H_2SO_4(aq) + Ca(OH)_2(s) \rightarrow 2H_2O(\ell) + CaSO_4(aq)$$

The general steps for performing stoichiometry problems such as this are shown in Figure 9.3. You may want to consult this figure when working with solutions in chemical reactions. The double arrows in Figure 9.3 indicate that you can start at either end of the chart and, after a series of simple conversions, determine the quantity at the other end.

FIGURE 9.3 Diagram of Steps for Using Molarity in Stoichiometry Calculations

When using molarity in stoichiometry calculations, a specific sequence of steps usually leads you to the correct answer.

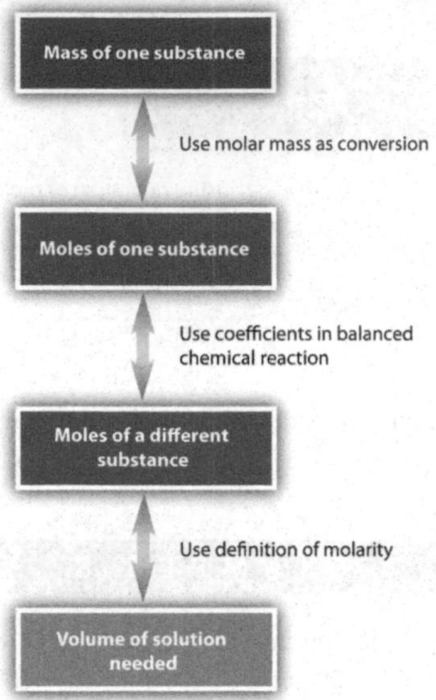

Many of the fluids found in our bodies are solutions. The solutes range from simple ionic compounds to complex proteins. Table 9.3 lists the typical concentrations of some of these solutes.

TABLE 9.3 Approximate Concentrations of Various Solutes in Some Solutions in the Body*

Solution	Solute	Concentration (M)
blood plasma	Na^+	0.138
	K^+	0.005
	Ca^{2+}	0.004
	Mg^{2+}	0.003
	Cl^-	0.110
	HCO_3^-	0.030
stomach acid	HCl	0.10
urine	NaCl	0.15
	PO_4^{3-}	0.05
	NH_2CONH_2 (urea)	0.30
***Note: Concentrations are approximate and can vary widely.**		

Looking Closer: The Dose Makes the Poison

Why is it that we can drink 1 qt of water when we are thirsty and not be harmed, but if we ingest 0.5 g of arsenic, we might die? There is an old saying: *the dose makes the poison*. This means that what may be dangerous in some amounts may not be dangerous in other amounts.

Take arsenic, for example. Some studies show that arsenic deprivation limits the growth of animals such as chickens, goats, and pigs, suggesting that arsenic is actually an essential trace element in the diet. Humans are constantly exposed to tiny amounts of arsenic from the environment, so studies of completely arsenic-free humans are not available; if arsenic is an essential trace mineral in human diets, it is probably required on the order of 50 ppb or less. A toxic dose of arsenic corresponds to about 7,000 ppb and higher, which is over 140 times the trace amount that may be required by the body. Thus, arsenic is not poisonous in and of itself. Rather, it is the amount that is dangerous: the dose makes the poison.

Similarly, as much as water is needed to keep us alive, too much of it is also risky to our health. Drinking too much water too fast can lead to a condition called water intoxication, which may be fatal. The danger in water intoxication is not that water itself becomes toxic. It is that the ingestion of too much water too fast dilutes sodium ions, potassium ions, and other salts in the bloodstream to concentrations that are not high enough to support brain, muscle, and heart functions. Military personnel, endurance athletes, and even desert hikers are susceptible to water intoxication if they drink water but do not replenish the salts lost in sweat. As this example shows, even the right substances in the wrong amounts can be dangerous!

Is this athlete poisoning himself? Drinking too much water too fast can actually be dangerous—even fatal.

2.5 Equivalents

Concentrations of ionic solutes are occasionally expressed in units called **equivalents (Eq)**. One equivalent equals 1 mol of positive or negative charge. Thus, 1 mol/L of Na^+(aq) is also 1 Eq/L because sodium has a 1+ charge. A 1 mol/L solution of Ca^{2+}(aq) ions has a concentration of 2 Eq/L because calcium has a 2+ charge. Dilute solutions may be expressed in milliequivalents (mEq)—for example, human blood plasma has a total concentration of about 150 mEq/L. (For more information about the ions present in blood plasma, see Chapter 3, [Unsupported Reference Type: chapter-section].)

equivalent (Eq)

One mole of charge (either positive or negative).

2.6 Dilution

When solvent is added to dilute a solution, the volume of the solution changes, but the amount of solute does not change. Before dilution, the amount of solute was equal to its original concentration times its original volume:

$$\text{amount in moles} = (\text{concentration} \times \text{volume})_{\text{initial}}$$

After dilution, the same amount of solute is equal to the final concentration times the final volume:

$$\text{amount in moles} = (\text{concentration} \times \text{volume})_{\text{final}}$$

To determine a concentration or amount after a dilution, we can use the following equation:

$$(\text{concentration} \times \text{volume})_{\text{initial}} = (\text{concentration} \times \text{volume})_{\text{final}}$$

Any units of concentration and volume can be used, as long as both concentrations and both volumes have the same unit.

EXAMPLE 9

A 125 mL sample of 0.900 M NaCl is diluted to 1,125 mL. What is the final concentration of the diluted solution?

Solution

Because the volume units are the same, and we are looking for the molarity of the final solution, we can use $(\text{concentration} \times \text{volume})_{\text{initial}} = (\text{concentration} \times \text{volume})_{\text{final}}$:

$$(0.900 \text{ M} \times 125 \text{ mL}) = (\text{concentration} \times 1{,}125 \text{ mL})$$

We solve by isolating the unknown concentration by itself on one side of the equation. Dividing by 1,125 mL gives

$$\text{concentration} = \frac{0.900 \text{ M} \times 125 \cancel{\text{mL}}}{1{,}125 \cancel{\text{mL}}} = 0.100 \text{ M}$$

as the final concentration.

SKILL-BUILDING EXERCISE

1. A nurse uses a syringe to inject 5.00 mL of 0.550 M heparin solution (heparin is an anticoagulant drug) into a 250 mL IV bag, for a final volume of 255 mL. What is the concentration of the resulting heparin solution?

CONCEPT REVIEW EXERCISES

1. What are some of the units used to express concentration?
2. Distinguish between the terms *solubility* and *concentration*.

ANSWERS

1. % m/m, % m/v, ppm, ppb, molarity, and Eq/L (answers will vary)
2. Solubility is typically a limit to how much solute can dissolve in a given amount of solvent. Concentration is the quantitative amount of solute dissolved at any concentration in a solvent.

KEY TAKEAWAYS

- Various concentration units are used to express the amounts of solute in a solution.
- Concentration units can be used as conversion factors in stoichiometry problems.
- New concentrations can be easily calculated if a solution is diluted.

EXERCISES

1. Define *solubility*. Do all solutes have the same solubility?
2. Explain why the terms *dilute* or *concentrated* are of limited usefulness in describing the concentration of solutions.

3. If the solubility of sodium chloride (NaCl) is 30.6 g/100 mL of H_2O at a given temperature, how many grams of NaCl can be dissolved in 250.0 mL of H_2O?
4. If the solubility of glucose ($C_6H_{12}O_6$) is 120.3 g/100 mL of H_2O at a given temperature, how many grams of $C_6H_{12}O_6$ can be dissolved in 75.0 mL of H_2O?
5. How many grams of sodium bicarbonate ($NaHCO_3$) can a 25.0°C saturated solution have if 150.0 mL of H_2O is used as the solvent?
6. If 75.0 g of potassium bromide (KBr) are dissolved in 125 mL of H_2O, is the solution saturated, unsaturated, or supersaturated?
7. Calculate the mass/mass percent of a saturated solution of NaCl. Use the data from Table 9.2, assume that masses of the solute and the solvent are additive, and use the density of H_2O (1.00 g/mL) as a conversion factor.
8. Calculate the mass/mass percent of a saturated solution of $MgCO_3$ Use the data from Table 9.2, assume that masses of the solute and the solvent are additive, and use the density of H_2O (1.00 g/mL) as a conversion factor.
9. Only 0.203 mL of C_6H_6 will dissolve in 100.000 mL of H_2O. Assuming that the volumes are additive, find the volume/volume percent of a saturated solution of benzene in water.
10. Only 35 mL of aniline ($C_6H_5NH_2$) will dissolve in 1,000 mL of H_2O. Assuming that the volumes are additive, find the volume/volume percent of a saturated solution of aniline in water.
11. A solution of ethyl alcohol (C_2H_5OH) in water has a concentration of 20.56% v/v. What volume of C_2H_5OH is present in 255 mL of solution?
12. What mass of KCl is present in 475 mL of a 1.09% m/v aqueous solution?
13. The average human body contains 5,830 g of blood. What mass of arsenic is present in the body if the amount in blood is 0.55 ppm?
14. The Occupational Safety and Health Administration has set a limit of 200 ppm as the maximum safe exposure level for carbon monoxide (CO). If an average breath has a mass of 1.286 g, what is the maximum mass of CO that can be inhaled at that maximum safe exposure level?
15. Which concentration is greater—15 ppm or 1,500 ppb?
16. Express the concentration 7,580 ppm in parts per billion.
17. What is the molarity of 0.500 L of a potassium chromate solution containing 0.0650 mol of K_2CrO_4?
18. What is the molarity of 4.50 L of a solution containing 0.206 mol of urea [$(NH_2)_2CO$]?
19. What is the molarity of a 2.66 L aqueous solution containing 56.9 g of NaBr?
20. If 3.08 g of $Ca(OH)_2$ is dissolved in enough water to make 0.875 L of solution, what is the molarity of the $Ca(OH)_2$?
21. What mass of HCl is present in 825 mL of a 1.25 M solution?
22. What mass of isopropyl alcohol (C_3H_8O) is dissolved in 2.050 L of a 4.45 M aqueous C_3H_8O solution?
23. What volume of 0.345 M NaCl solution is needed to obtain 10.0 g of NaCl?
24. How many milliliters of a 0.0015 M cocaine hydrochloride ($C_{17}H_{22}ClNO_4$) solution is needed to obtain 0.010 g of the solute?
25. Aqueous calcium chloride reacts with aqueous silver nitrate according to the following balanced chemical equation:

$$CaCl_2(aq) + 2AgNO_3(aq) \rightarrow 2AgCl(s) + Ca(NO_3)_2(aq)$$

How many moles of AgCl(s) are made if 0.557 L of 0.235 M $CaCl_2$ react with excess $AgNO_3$? How many grams of AgCl are made?

26. Sodium bicarbonate ($NaHCO_3$) is used to react with acid spills. The reaction with sulfuric acid (H_2SO_4) is as follows:

$$2NaHCO_3(s) + H_2SO_4(aq) \rightarrow Na_2SO_4(aq) + 2H_2O(\ell) + 2CO_2(g)$$

If 27.6 mL of a 6.25 M H_2SO_4 solution were spilled, how many moles of $NaHCO_3$ would be needed to react with the acid? How many grams of $NaHCO_3$ is this?

27. The fermentation of glucose to make ethanol and carbon dioxide has the following overall chemical equation:

$$C_6H_{12}O_6(aq) \rightarrow 2C_2H_5OH(aq) + 2CO_2(g)$$

If 1.00 L of a 0.567 M solution of $C_6H_{12}O_6$ were completely fermented, what would be the resulting concentration of the C_2H_5OH solution? How many moles of CO_2 would be formed? How many grams is this? If each mole of CO_2 had a volume of 24.5 L, what volume of CO_2 is produced?

28. Aqueous sodium bisulfite gives off sulfur dioxide gas when heated:

    $$2NaHSO_3(aq) \rightarrow Na_2SO_3(aq) + H_2O(\ell) + SO_2(g)$$

    If 567 mL of a 1.005 M $NaHSO_3$ solution were heated until all the $NaHSO_3$ had reacted, what would be the resulting concentration of the Na_2SO_3 solution? How many moles of SO_2 would be formed? How many grams of SO_2 would be formed? If each mole of SO_2 had a volume of 25.78 L, what volume of SO_2 would be produced?

29. What is the concentration of a 1.0 M solution of $K^+(aq)$ ions in equivalents/liter?
30. What is the concentration of a 1.0 M solution of $SO_4^{2-}(aq)$ ions in equivalents/liter?
31. A solution having initial concentration of 0.445 M and initial volume of 45.0 mL is diluted to 100.0 mL. What is its final concentration?
32. A 50.0 mL sample of saltwater that is 3.0% m/v is diluted to 950 mL. What is its final mass/volume percent?

ANSWERS

1. Solubility is the amount of a solute that can dissolve in a given amount of solute, typically 100 mL. The solubility of solutes varies widely.
3. 76.5 g
5. 12.6 g
7. 26.5%
9. 0.203%
11. 52.4 mL
13. 0.00321 g
15. 15 ppm
17. 0.130 M
19. 0.208 M
21. 37.6 g
23. 0.496 L
25. 0.262 mol; 37.5 g
27. 1.13 M C_2H_5OH; 1.13 mol of CO_2; 49.7 g of CO_2; 27.7 L of CO_2
29. 1.0 Eq/L
31. 0.200 M

3. THE DISSOLUTION PROCESS

LEARNING OBJECTIVE

1. **Describe the dissolution process at the molecular level.**

What occurs at the molecular level to cause a solute to dissolve in a solvent? The answer depends in part on the solute, but there are some similarities common to all solutes.

solvation

The process by which solute particles are surrounded by solvent particles.

hydration

Solvation by water molecules.

Recall the rule that *like dissolves like*. As we saw in Section 1, this means that substances must have similar intermolecular forces to form solutions. When a soluble solute is introduced into a solvent, the particles of solute can interact with the particles of solvent. In the case of a solid or liquid solute, the interactions between the solute particles and the solvent particles are so strong that the individual solute particles separate from each other and, surrounded by solvent molecules, enter the solution. (Gaseous solutes already have their constituent particles separated, but the concept of being surrounded by solvent particles still applies.) This process is called **solvation** and is illustrated in Figure 9.4. When the solvent is water, the word **hydration**, rather than solvation, is used.

FIGURE 9.4 Solvation

When a solute dissolves, the individual particles of solute become surrounded by solvent particles. Eventually the particle detaches from the remaining solute, surrounded by solvent molecules in solution.

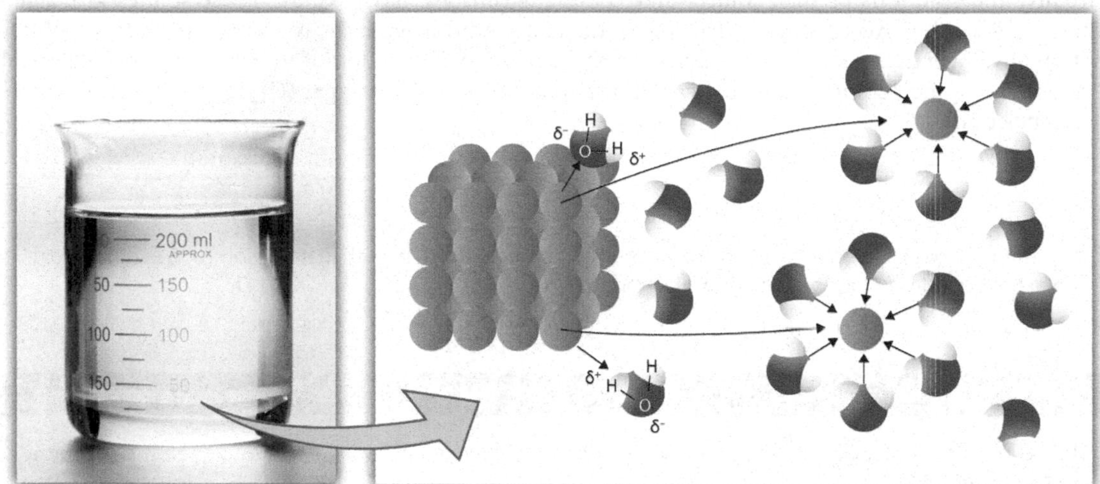

Source: Photo © Thinkstock

In the case of molecular solutes like glucose, the solute particles are individual molecules. However, if the solute is ionic, the individual ions separate from each other and become surrounded by solvent particles. That is, the cations and anions of an ionic solute separate when the solute dissolves. This process is referred to as **dissociation**. Compare the dissociation of a simple ionic solute as shown in Figure 9.5 to the process illustrated in Figure 9.4.

dissociation

The process of cations and anions of an ionic solute separating when the solute dissolves.

FIGURE 9.5 Ionic Dissociation

When an ionic solute dissolves, the individual ions separate from each other as they go into solution.

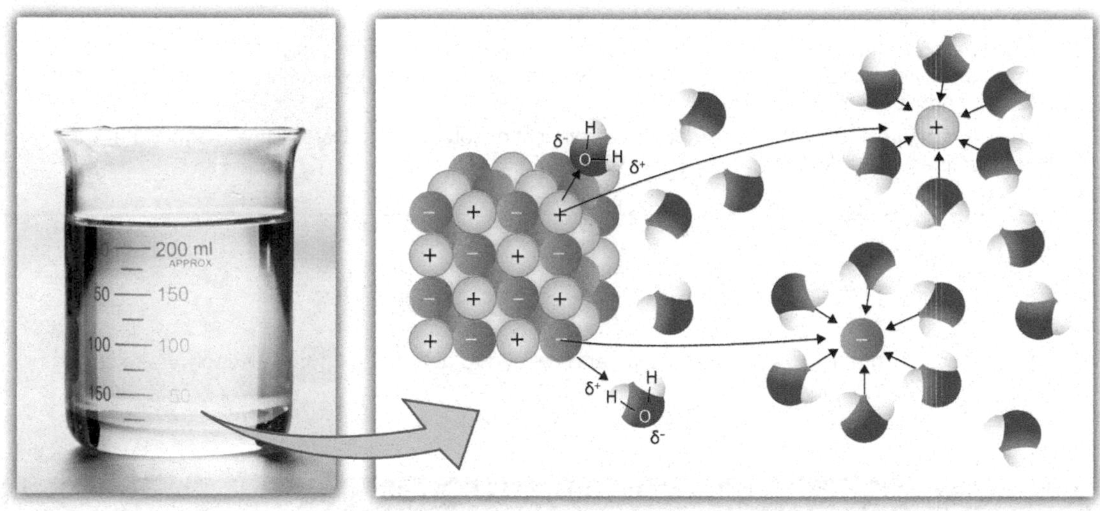

Source: Photo © Thinkstock

electrolyte

An ionic compound that dissolves in water.

strong electrolyte

An ionic compound that ionizes completely when it dissolves.

weak electrolyte

An ionic compound that does not ionize completely when it dissolves.

nonelectrolyte

A compound that does not ionize at all when it dissolves.

The dissociation of soluble ionic compounds gives solutions of these compounds an interesting property: they conduct electricity. Because of this property, soluble ionic compounds are referred to as **electrolytes**. Many ionic compounds dissociate completely and are therefore called **strong electrolytes**. Sodium chloride is an example of a strong electrolyte. Some compounds dissolve but dissociate only partially, and solutions of such solutes may conduct electricity only weakly. These solutes are called **weak electrolytes**. Acetic acid (CH_3COOH), the compound in vinegar, is a weak electrolyte. Solutes that dissolve into individual neutral molecules without dissociation do not impart additional electrical conductivity to their solutions and are called **nonelectrolytes**. Table sugar ($C_{12}H_{22}O_{11}$) is an example of a nonelectrolyte.

Note

The term *electrolyte* is used in medicine to mean any of the important ions that are dissolved in aqueous solution in the body. Important physiological electrolytes include Na^+, K^+, Ca^{2+}, Mg^{2+}, and Cl^-.

EXAMPLE 10

The following substances all dissolve to some extent in water. Classify each as an electrolyte or a nonelectrolyte.

1. potassium chloride (KCl)
2. fructose ($C_6H_{12}O_6$)
3. isopropyl alcohol [$CH_3CH(OH)CH_3$]
4. magnesium hydroxide [$Mg(OH)_2$]

Solution

Each substance can be classified as an ionic solute or a nonionic solute. Ionic solutes are electrolytes, and nonionic solutes are nonelectrolytes.

1. Potassium chloride is an ionic compound; therefore, when it dissolves, its ions separate, making it an electrolyte.
2. Fructose is a sugar similar to glucose. (In fact, it has the same molecular formula as glucose.) Because it is a molecular compound, we expect it to be a nonelectrolyte.
3. Isopropyl alcohol is an organic molecule containing the alcohol functional group. The bonding in the compound is all covalent, so when isopropyl alcohol dissolves, it separates into individual molecules but not ions. Thus, it is a nonelectrolyte.
4. Magnesium hydroxide is an ionic compound, so when it dissolves it dissociates. Thus, magnesium hydroxide is an electrolyte.

Note

More information than that provided in this chapter is needed to determine if some electrolytes are strong or weak. We will consider this in Chapter 10.

SKILL-BUILDING EXERCISE

The following substances all dissolve to some extent in water. Classify each as an electrolyte or a nonelectrolyte.

1. acetone (CH_3COCH_3)
2. iron(III) nitrate [$Fe(NO_3)_3$]
3. elemental bromine (Br_2)
4. sodium hydroxide (NaOH)

CONCEPT REVIEW EXERCISE

1. Explain how the solvation process describes the dissolution of a solute in a solvent.

ANSWER

1. Each particle of the solute is surrounded by particles of the solvent, carrying the solute from its original phase.

KEY TAKEAWAY

- When a solute dissolves, its individual particles are surrounded by solvent molecules and are separated from each other.

EXERCISES

1. Describe what happens when an ionic solute like Na_2SO_4 dissolves in a polar solvent.
2. Describe what happens when a molecular solute like sucrose ($C_{12}H_{22}O_{11}$) dissolves in a polar solvent.
3. Classify each substance as an electrolyte or a nonelectrolyte. Each substance dissolves in H_2O to some extent.
    a. NH_4NO_3
    b. CO_2
    c. NH_2CONH_2
    d. HCl
4. Classify each substance as an electrolyte or a nonelectrolyte. Each substance dissolves in H_2O to some extent.
    a. $CH_3CH_2CH_2OH$
    b. $Ca(CH_3CO_2)_2$
    c. I_2
    d. KOH
5. Will solutions of each solute conduct electricity when dissolved?
    a. $AgNO_3$
    b. $CHCl_3$
    c. $BaCl_2$
    d. Li_2O
6. Will solutions of each solute conduct electricity when dissolved?
    a. CH_3COCH_3
    b. $N(CH_3)_3$
    c. $CH_3CO_2C_2H_5$
    d. $FeCl_2$

ANSWERS

1. Each ion of the ionic solute is surrounded by particles of solvent, carrying the ion from its associated crystal.

3. a. electrolyte
    b. nonelectrolyte
    c. nonelectrolyte
    d. electrolyte

5. a. yes
    b. no
    c. yes
    d. yes

4. PROPERTIES OF SOLUTIONS

LEARNING OBJECTIVE

1. Describe how the properties of solutions differ from those of pure solvents.

Solutions are likely to have properties similar to those of their major component—usually the solvent. However, some solution properties differ significantly from those of the solvent. Here, we will focus on liquid solutions that have a solid solute, but many of the effects we will discuss in this section are applicable to all solutions.

4.1 Colligative Properties

colligative property

A characteristic of solutions that depends only on the number of dissolved particles.

Solutes affect some properties of solutions that depend only on the concentration of the dissolved particles. These properties are called **colligative properties**. Four important colligative properties that we will examine here are vapor pressure depression, boiling point elevation, freezing point depression, and osmotic pressure.

Molecular compounds separate into individual molecules when they are dissolved, so for every 1 mol of molecules dissolved, we get 1 mol of particles. In contrast, ionic compounds separate into their constituent ions when they dissolve, so 1 mol of an ionic compound will produce more than 1 mol of dissolved particles. For example, every mole of NaCl that dissolves yields 1 mol of Na^+ ions and 1 mol of Cl^- ions, for a total of 2 mol of particles in solution. Thus, the effect on a solution's properties by dissolving NaCl may be twice as large as the effect of dissolving the same amount of moles of glucose ($C_6H_{12}O_6$).

4.2 Vapor Pressure Depression

vapor pressure

The pressure of a vapor that is in equilibrium with its liquid phase.

vapor pressure depression

The lowering of the vapor pressure of a solution versus the pure solvent.

All liquids evaporate. In fact, given enough volume, a liquid will turn completely into a vapor. If enough volume is not present, a liquid will evaporate only to the point where the rate of evaporation equals the rate of vapor condensing back into a liquid. The pressure of the vapor at this point is called the **vapor pressure** of the liquid.

The presence of a dissolved solid lowers the characteristic vapor pressure of a liquid so that it evaporates more slowly. (The exceptions to this statement are if the solute itself is a liquid or a gas, in which case the solute will also contribute something to the evaporation process. We will not discuss such solutions here.) This property is called **vapor pressure depression** and is depicted in Figure 9.6.

FIGURE 9.6 Vapor Pressure Depression

The presence of solute particles blocks some of the ability for liquid particles to evaporate. Thus, solutions of solid solutes typically have a lower vapor pressure than the pure solvent.

4.3 Boiling Point and Freezing Point Effects

A related property of solutions is that their boiling points are higher than the boiling point of the pure solvent. Because the presence of solute particles decreases the vapor pressure of the liquid solvent, a higher temperature is needed to reach the boiling point. This phenomenon is called **boiling point elevation**. For every mole of particles dissolved in a liter of water, the boiling point of water increases by about 0.5°C.

boiling point elevation

The raising of the boiling point of a solution versus the pure solvent.

Note

Some people argue that putting a pinch or two of salt in water used to cook spaghetti or other pasta makes a solution that has a higher boiling point, so the pasta cooks faster. In actuality, the amount of solute is so small that the boiling point of the water is practically unchanged.

The presence of solute particles has the opposite effect on the freezing point of a solution. When a solution freezes, only the solvent particles come together to form a solid phase, and the presence of solute particles interferes with that process. Therefore, for the liquid solvent to freeze, more energy must be removed from the solution, which lowers the temperature. Thus, solutions have lower freezing points than pure solvents do. This phenomenon is called **freezing point depression**. For every mole of particles in a liter of water, the freezing point decreases by about 1.9°C.

freezing point depression

The lowering of the freezing point of a solution versus the pure solvent.

Both boiling point elevation and freezing point depression have practical uses. For example, solutions of water and ethylene glycol ($C_2H_6O_2$) are used as coolants in automobile engines because the boiling point of such a solution is greater than 100°C, the normal boiling point of water. In winter, salts like NaCl and $CaCl_2$ are sprinkled on the ground to melt ice or keep ice from forming on roads and sidewalks (Figure 9.7). This is because the solution made by dissolving sodium chloride or calcium chloride in water has a lower freezing point than pure water, so the formation of ice is inhibited.

FIGURE 9.7 Effect of Freezing Point Depression

The salt sprinkled on this sidewalk makes the water on the sidewalk have a lower freezing point than pure water, so it does not freeze as easily. This makes walking on the sidewalk less hazardous in winter.

EXAMPLE 11

Which solution's freezing point deviates more from that of pure water—a 1 M solution of NaCl or a 1 M solution of $CaCl_2$?

Solution

Colligative properties depend on the number of dissolved particles, so the solution with the greater number of particles in solution will show the greatest deviation. When NaCl dissolves, it separates into two ions, Na^+ and Cl^-. But when $CaCl_2$ dissolves, it separates into three ions—one Ca^{2+} ion and two Cl^- ions. Thus, mole for mole, $CaCl_2$ will have 50% more impact on freezing point depression than NaCl.

SKILL-BUILDING EXERCISE

1. Which solution's boiling point deviates more from that of pure water—a 1 M solution of $CaCl_2$ or a 1 M solution of $MgSO_4$?

4.4 Osmotic Pressure

The last colligative property of solutions we will consider is a very important one for biological systems. It involves **osmosis**, the process by which solvent molecules can pass through certain membranes but solute particles cannot. When two solutions of different concentration are present on either side of these membranes (called *semipermeable membranes*), there is a tendency for solvent molecules to move from the more dilute solution to the more concentrated solution until the concentrations of the two solutions are equal. This tendency is called **osmotic pressure**. External pressure can be exerted on a solution to counter the flow of solvent; the pressure required to halt the osmosis of a solvent is equal to the osmotic pressure of the solution.

osmosis

The process by which solvent molecules can pass through certain membranes but solute particles cannot.

osmotic pressure

The tendency for solvent molecules to move from the more dilute solution to the more concentrated solution until the concentrations of the two solutions are equal.

Osmolarity (osmol) is a way of reporting the total number of particles in a solution to determine osmotic pressure. It is defined as the molarity of a solute times the number of particles a formula unit of the solute makes when it dissolves (represented by *i*):

osmolarity

A way of reporting the total number of particles in a solution to determine the osmotic pressure.

$$\text{osmol} = \text{M} \times i$$

If more than one solute is present in a solution, the individual osmolarities are additive to get the total osmolarity of the solution. Solutions that have the same osmolarity have the same osmotic pressure. If solutions of differing osmolarities are present on opposite sides of a semipermeable membrane, solvent will transfer from the lower-osmolarity solution to the higher-osmolarity solution. Counterpressure exerted on the high-osmolarity solution will reduce or halt the solvent transfer. An even higher pressure can be exerted to force solvent from the high-osmolarity solution to the low-osmolarity solution, a process called *reverse osmosis*. Reverse osmosis is used to make potable water from saltwater where sources of fresh water are scarce.

EXAMPLE 12

A 0.50 M NaCl aqueous solution and a 0.30 M $Ca(NO_3)_2$ aqueous solution are placed on opposite sides of a semipermeable membrane. Determine the osmolarity of each solution and predict the direction of solvent flow.

Solution

The solvent will flow into the solution of higher osmolarity. The NaCl solute separates into two ions—Na^+ and Cl^-—when it dissolves, so its osmolarity is as follows:

$$\text{osmol (NaCl)} = 0.50 \text{ M} \times 2 = 1.0 \text{ osmol}$$

The $Ca(NO_3)_2$ solute separates into three ions—one Ca^{2+} and two NO_3^-—when it dissolves, so its osmolarity is as follows:

$$\text{osmol } [Ca(NO_3)_2] = 0.30 \text{ M} \times 3 = 0.90 \text{ osmol}$$

The osmolarity of the $Ca(NO_3)_2$ solution is lower than that of the NaCl solution, so water will transfer through the membrane from the $Ca(NO_3)_2$ solution to the NaCl solution.

SKILL-BUILDING EXERCISE

1. A 1.5 M $C_6H_{12}O_6$ aqueous solution and a 0.40 M $Al(NO_3)_3$ aqueous solution are placed on opposite sides of a semipermeable membrane. Determine the osmolarity of each solution and predict the direction of solvent flow.

To Your Health: Dialysis

The main function of the kidneys is to filter the blood to remove wastes and extra water, which are then expelled from the body as urine. Some diseases rob the kidneys of their ability to perform this function, causing a buildup of waste materials in the bloodstream. If a kidney transplant is not available or desirable, a procedure called dialysis can be used to remove waste materials and excess water from the blood.

In one form of dialysis, called *hemodialysis*, a patient's blood is passed though a length of tubing that travels through an *artificial kidney machine* (also called a *dialysis machine*). A section of tubing composed of a semipermeable membrane is immersed in a solution of sterile water, glucose, amino acids, and certain electrolytes. The osmotic pressure of the blood forces waste molecules and excess water through the membrane into the sterile solution. Red and white blood cells are too large to pass through the membrane, so they remain in the blood. After being cleansed in this way, the blood is returned to the body.

A patient undergoing hemodialysis depends on osmosis to cleanse the blood of waste products that the kidneys are incapable of removing due to disease.

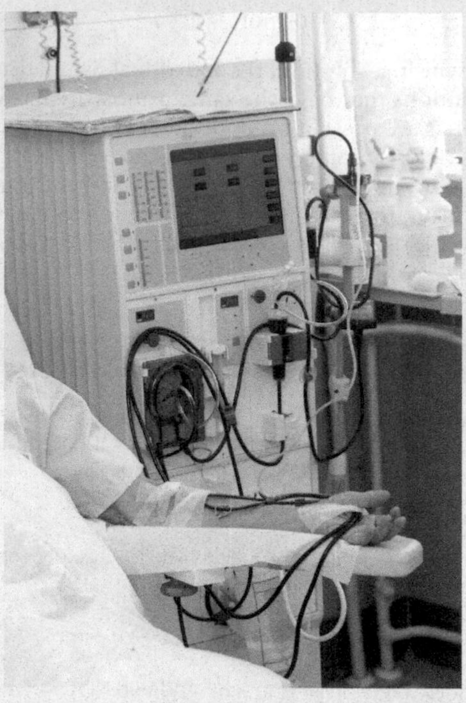

© Thinkstock

Dialysis is a continuous process, as the osmosis of waste materials and excess water takes time. Typically, 5–10 lb of waste-containing fluid is removed in each dialysis session, which can last 2–8 hours and must be performed several times a week. Although some patients have been on dialysis for 30 or more years, dialysis is always a temporary solution because waste materials are constantly building up in the bloodstream. A more permanent solution is a kidney transplant.

Cell walls are semipermeable membranes, so the osmotic pressures of the body's fluids have important biological consequences. If solutions of different osmolarity exist on either side of the cells, solvent (water) may pass into or out of the cells, sometimes with disastrous results. Consider what happens if red blood cells are placed in a *hypotonic* solution, meaning a solution of lower osmolarity than the liquid inside the cells. The cells swell up as water enters them, disrupting cellular activity and eventually causing the cells to burst. This process is called *hemolysis*. If red blood cells are placed in a *hypertonic* solution, meaning one having a higher osmolarity than exists inside the cells, water leaves the cells to dilute the external solution, and the red blood cells shrivel and die. This process is called *crenation*. Only if red blood cells are placed in *isotonic* solutions that have the same osmolarity as exists inside the cells are they unaffected by negative effects of osmotic pressure. Glucose solutions of about 0.31 M, or sodium chloride solutions of about 0.16 M, are isotonic with blood plasma.

Note

The concentration of an isotonic sodium chloride (NaCl) solution is only half that of an isotonic glucose ($C_6H_{12}O_6$) solution because NaCl produces two ions when a formula unit dissolves, while molecular $C_6H_{12}O_6$ produces only one particle when a formula unit dissolves. The osmolarities are therefore the same even though the concentrations of the two solutions are different.

Osmotic pressure explains why you should not drink seawater if you are abandoned in a life raft in the middle of the ocean. Its osmolarity is about three times higher than most bodily fluids. You would actually become thirstier as water from your cells was drawn out to dilute the salty ocean water you ingested. Our bodies do a better job coping with hypotonic solutions than with hypertonic ones. The excess water is collected by our kidneys and excreted.

Osmotic pressure effects are used in the food industry to make pickles from cucumbers and other vegetables and in brining meat to make corned beef. It is also a factor in the mechanism of getting water from the roots to the tops of trees!

Career Focus: Perfusionist

A perfusionist is a medical technician trained to assist during any medical procedure in which a patient's circulatory or breathing functions require support. The use of perfusionists has grown rapidly since the advent of open-heart surgery in 1953.

Most perfusionists work in operating rooms, where their main responsibility is to operate heart-lung machines. During many heart surgeries, the heart itself must be stopped. In these situations, a heart-lung machine keeps the patient alive by aerating the blood with oxygen and removing carbon dioxide. The perfusionist monitors both the machine and the status of the blood, notifying the surgeon and the anesthetist of any concerns and taking corrective action if the status of the blood becomes abnormal.

Despite the narrow parameters of their specialty, perfusionists must be highly trained. Certified perfusion education programs require a student to learn anatomy, physiology, pathology, chemistry, pharmacology, math, and physics. A college degree is usually required. Some perfusionists work with other external artificial organs, such as hemodialysis machines and artificial livers.

CONCEPT REVIEW EXERCISES

1. What are the colligative properties of solutions?
2. Explain how the following properties of solutions differ from those of the pure solvent: vapor pressure, boiling point, freezing point, and osmotic pressure.

ANSWERS

1. Colligative properties are characteristics that a solution has that depend on the number, not the identity, of solute particles.
2. In solutions, the vapor pressure is lower, the boiling point is higher, the freezing point is lower, and the osmotic pressure is higher.

KEY TAKEAWAY

- Certain properties of solutions differ from those of pure solvents in predictable ways.

EXERCISES

1. In each pair of aqueous systems, which will have the lower vapor pressure?
   a. pure water or 1.0 M NaCl
   b. 1.0 M NaCl or 1.0 M $C_6H_{12}O_6$
   c. 1.0 M $CaCl_2$ or 1.0 M $(NH_4)_3PO_4$
2. In each pair of aqueous systems, which will have the lower vapor pressure?
   a. 0.50 M $Ca(NO_3)_2$ or 1.0 M KBr
   b. 1.5 M $C_{12}H_{22}O_{11}$ or 0.75 M $Ca(OH)_2$
   c. 0.10 M $Cu(NO_3)_2$ or pure water
3. In each pair of aqueous systems, which will have the higher boiling point?
   a. pure water or a 1.0 M NaCl
   b. 1.0 M NaCl or 1.0 M $C_6H_{12}O_6$
   c. 1.0 M $CaCl_2$ or 1.0 M $(NH_4)_3PO_4$
4. In each pair of aqueous systems, which will have the higher boiling point?
   a. 1.0 M KBr
   b. 1.5 M $C_{12}H_{22}O_{11}$ or 0.75 M $Ca(OH)_2$
   c. 0.10 M $Cu(NO_3)_2$ or pure water
5. Estimate the boiling point of each aqueous solution. The boiling point of pure water is 100.0°C.
   a. 0.50 M NaCl
   b. 1.5 M Na_2SO_4
   c. 2.0 M $C_6H_{12}O_6$
6. Estimate the freezing point of each aqueous solution. The freezing point of pure water is 0.0°C.
   a. 0.50 M NaCl
   b. 1.5 M Na_2SO_4
   c. 2.0 M $C_6H_{12}O_6$
7. Explain why salt (NaCl) is spread on roads and sidewalks to inhibit ice formation in cold weather.

8. Salt (NaCl) and calcium chloride ($CaCl_2$) are used widely in some areas to minimize the formation of ice on sidewalks and roads. One of these ionic compounds is better, mole for mole, at inhibiting ice formation. Which is that likely to be? Why?
9. What is the osmolarity of each aqueous solution?
   a. 0.500 M NH_2CONH_2
   b. 0.500 M NaBr
   c. 0.500 M $Ca(NO_3)_2$
10. What is the osmolarity of each aqueous solution?
    a. 0.150 M KCl
    b. 0.450 M $(CH_3)_2CHOH$
    c. 0.500 M $Ca_3(PO_4)_2$
11. A 1.0 M solution of an unknown soluble salt has an osmolarity of 3.0 osmol. What can you conclude about the salt?
12. A 1.5 M NaCl solution and a 0.75 M $Al(NO_3)_3$ solution exist on opposite sides of a semipermeable membrane. Determine the osmolarity of each solution and the direction of solvent flow, if any, across the membrane.

ANSWERS

1. a. 1.0 M NaCl
   b. 1.0 M NaCl
   c. 1.0 M $(NH_4)_3PO_4$
3. a. 1.0 M NaCl
   b. 1.0 M NaCl
   c. 1.0 M $(NH_4)_3PO_4$
5. a. 100.5°C
   b. 102.3°C
   c. 101°C
7. NaCl lowers the freezing point of water, so it needs to be colder for the water to freeze.
9. a. 0.500 osmol
   b. 1.000 osmol
   c. 1.500 osmol
11. It must separate into three ions when it dissolves.

5. END-OF-CHAPTER MATERIAL

Chapter Summary

To ensure that you understand the material in this chapter, you should review the meanings of the bold terms in the following summary and ask yourself how they relate to the topics in the chapter.

A **solution** is a homogeneous mixture. The major component is the **solvent**, while the minor component is the **solute**. Solutions can have any phase; for example, an **alloy** is a solid solution. Solutes are **soluble** or **insoluble**, meaning they dissolve or do not dissolve in a particular solvent. The terms **miscible** and **immiscible**, instead of soluble and insoluble, are used for liquid solutes and solvents. The statement *like dissolves like* is a useful guide to predicting whether a solute will dissolve in a given solvent.

The amount of solute in a solution is represented by the **concentration** of the solution. The maximum amount of solute that will dissolve in a given amount of solvent is called the **solubility** of the solute. Such solutions are **saturated**. Solutions that have less than the maximum amount are **unsaturated**. Most solutions are unsaturated, and there are various ways of stating their concentrations. **Mass/mass percent**, **volume/volume percent**, and **mass/volume percent** indicate the percentage of the overall solution that is solute. **Parts per million (ppm)** and **parts per billion (ppb)** are used to describe very small concentrations of a solute. **Molarity**, defined as the number of moles of solute per liter of solution, is a common concentration unit in the chemistry laboratory. **Equivalents** express concentrations in terms of moles of charge on ions. When a solution is diluted, we use the fact that the amount of solute remains constant to be able to determine the volume or concentration of the final diluted solution.

Dissolving occurs by **solvation**, the process in which particles of a solvent surround the individual particles of a solute, separating them to make a solution. For water solutions, the word **hydration** is used. If the solute is molecular, it dissolves into individual molecules. If the solute is ionic, the individual ions separate from each other, forming a solution that conducts electricity. Such solutions are called **electrolytes**. If the dissociation of ions is complete, the solution is a **strong electrolyte**. If the dissociation is only partial, the solution is a **weak electrolyte**. Solutions of molecules do not conduct electricity and are called **nonelectrolytes**.

Solutions have properties that differ from those of the pure solvent. Some of these are **colligative** properties, which are due to the number of solute particles dissolved, not the chemical identity of the solute. Colligative properties include **vapor pressure depression**, **boiling point elevation**, **freezing point depression**, and **osmotic pressure**. Osmotic pressure is particularly important in biological systems. It is caused by **osmosis**, the passage of solvents through certain membranes like cell walls. The **osmolarity** of a solution is the product of a solution's molarity and the number of particles a solute separates into when it dissolves. Osmosis can be reversed by the application of pressure; this reverse osmosis is used to make fresh water from saltwater in some parts of the world. Because of osmosis, red blood cells placed in hypotonic or hypertonic solutions lose function through either hemolysis or crenation. If they are placed in isotonic solutions, however, the cells are unaffected because osmotic pressure is equal on either side of the cell membrane.

ADDITIONAL EXERCISES

1. Calcium nitrate reacts with sodium carbonate to precipitate solid calcium carbonate:

   $$Ca(NO_3)_2(aq) + Na_2CO_3(aq) \rightarrow CaCO_3(s) + NaNO_3(aq)$$

   a. Balance the chemical equation.
   b. How many grams of Na_2CO_3 are needed to react with 50.0 mL of 0.450 M $Ca(NO_3)_2$?
   c. Assuming that the Na_2CO_3 has a negligible effect on the volume of the solution, find the osmolarity of the $NaNO_3$ solution remaining after the $CaCO_3$ precipitates from solution.
2. The compound HCl reacts with sodium carbonate to generate carbon dioxide gas:

   $$HCl(aq) + Na_2CO_3(aq) \rightarrow H_2O(\ell) + CO_2(g) + NaCl(aq)$$

   a. Balance the chemical equation.
   b. How many grams of Na_2CO_3 are needed to react with 250.0 mL of 0.755 M HCl?
   c. Assuming that the Na_2CO_3 has a negligible effect on the volume of the solution, find the osmolarity of the NaCl solution remaining after the reaction is complete.
3. Estimate the freezing point of concentrated aqueous HCl, which is usually sold as a 12 M solution. Assume complete ionization into H^+ and Cl^- ions.
4. Estimate the boiling point of concentrated aqueous H_2SO_4, which is usually sold as an 18 M solution. Assume complete ionization into H^+ and HSO_4^- ions.
5. Seawater can be approximated by a 3.0% m/m solution of NaCl in water. Determine the molarity and osmolarity of seawater. Assume a density of 1.0 g/mL.
6. Human blood can be approximated by a 0.90% m/m solution of NaCl in water. Determine the molarity and osmolarity of blood. Assume a density of 1.0 g/mL.
7. How much water must be added to 25.0 mL of a 1.00 M NaCl solution to make a resulting solution that has a concentration of 0.250 M?
8. Sports drinks like Gatorade are advertised as capable of resupplying the body with electrolytes lost by vigorous exercise. Find a label from a sports drink container and identify the electrolytes it contains. You should be able to identify several simple ionic compounds in the ingredients list.
9. Occasionally we hear a sensational news story about people stranded in a lifeboat on the ocean who had to drink their own urine to survive. While distasteful, this act was probably necessary for survival. Why not simply drink the ocean water? (Hint: See Exercise 5 and Exercise 6 above. What would happen if the two solutions in these exercises were on opposite sides of a semipermeable membrane, as we would find in our cell walls?)

ANSWERS

1. a. $Ca(NO_3)_2(aq) + Na_2CO_3(aq) \rightarrow CaCO_3(s) + 2NaNO_3(aq)$
   b. 2.39 g
   c. 1.80 osmol
3. −45.6°C
5. 0.513 M; 1.026 osmol
7. 75.0 mL
9. The osmotic pressure of seawater is too high. Drinking seawater would cause water to go from inside our cells into the more concentrated seawater, ultimately killing the cells.

CHAPTER 10
Acids and Bases

Opening Essay

One of the most concentrated acids in the body is stomach acid, which can be approximated as a 0.05 M hydrochloric acid solution. Special cells in the stomach wall secrete this acid, along with special enzymes, as part of the digestion process. In a laboratory, a 0.05 M solution of hydrochloric acid would dissolve some metals. How does the stomach survive the presence of such a reactive acid?

Actually, the stomach has several mechanisms for withstanding this chemical onslaught. First, the lining of the stomach is coated with a thin layer of mucus that contains some bicarbonate ions (HCO_3^-). These react with the hydrochloric acid to produce water, carbon dioxide, and harmless chloride ions. If any acid penetrates through the mucus, it can attack the surface layer of stomach cells, called the *gastric epithelium*. Cells in the gastric epithelium are being constantly shed, so damaged cells are quickly removed and replaced with healthy cells.

However, if the gastric epithelium is destroyed faster than it can be replaced, the acid may reach the wall of the stomach, resulting in ulcers. If an ulcer grows large enough, it can expose blood vessels in the stomach wall, causing bleeding. In extreme situations, the loss of blood through a severe ulcer can threaten a person's health.

Ulcers can also result from the presence of a certain bacterium—*Helicobacter pylori*—in the stomach. The mechanism for this ulcer formation is not the same as that for ulcers caused by stomach acid and is not completely understood. However, there are two main treatments for ulcers: (1) *antacids* to react chemically with excess hydrochloric acid in the stomach and (2) *antibiotics* to destroy the *H. pylori* bacteria in the stomach.

Many of us are familiar with the group of chemicals called *acids*. But do you know what it takes for a compound to be an acid? Actually, there are several different definitions of *acid* that chemistry uses, and each definition is appropriate under different circumstances. Less familiar—but just as important to chemistry and ultimately to us—is the group of chemicals known as *bases*. Both acids and bases are important enough that we devote an entire chapter to them—their properties and their reactions. Figure 10.1 illustrates how common acids and bases are in everyday life.

FIGURE 10.1 Prevalence of Acids and Bases

The products shown in this photograph, all acids or bases, give an idea of how prevalent and important acids and bases are in everyday life.

1. ARRHENIUS DEFINITION OF ACIDS AND BASES

LEARNING OBJECTIVE

1. **Recognize a compound as an Arrhenius acid or an Arrhenius base.**

One way to define a class of compounds is by describing the various characteristics its members have in common. In the case of the compounds known as acids, the common characteristics include a sour taste, the ability to change the color of the vegetable dye *litmus* to red, and the ability to dissolve certain metals and simultaneously produce hydrogen gas. For the compounds called bases, the common characteristics are a slippery texture, a bitter taste, and the ability to change the color of litmus to blue. Acids and bases also react with each other to form compounds generally known as salts.

Note

Although we include their tastes among the common characteristics of acids and bases, we never advocate tasting an unknown chemical!

Arrhenius acid

A compound that increases the concentration of hydrogen ion (H^+) in aqueous solution.

Arrhenius base

A compound that increases the concentration of hydroxide ion (OH^-) in aqueous solution.

Chemists prefer, however, to have definitions for acids and bases in chemical terms. The Swedish chemist Svante Arrhenius developed the first chemical definitions of acids and bases in the late 1800s. Arrhenius defined an **acid** as a compound that increases the concentration of hydrogen ion (H^+) in aqueous solution. Many acids are simple compounds that release a hydrogen cation into solution when they dissolve. Similarly, Arrhenius defined a **base** as a compound that increases the concentration of hydroxide ion (OH^-) in aqueous solution. Many bases are ionic compounds that have the hydroxide ion as their anion, which is released when the base dissolves in water.

Many bases and their aqueous solutions are named using the normal rules of ionic compounds that were presented in Chapter 3, [Unsupported Reference Type: chapter-section]; that is, they are named as hydroxide compounds. For example, the base sodium hydroxide (NaOH) is both an ionic compound and an aqueous solution. However, aqueous solutions of acids have their own naming rules. The names of *binary acids* (compounds with hydrogen and one other element in their formula) are based on the root of the name of the other element preceded by the prefix *hydro-* and followed by the suffix *-ic acid*. Thus, an aqueous solution of HCl [designated "HCl(aq)"] is called hydrochloric acid, H_2S(aq) is called hydrosulfuric acid, and so forth. Acids composed of more than two elements (typically hydrogen and oxygen and some other element) have names based on the name of the other element, followed by the suffix *-ic acid* or *-ous acid*, depending on the number of oxygen atoms in the acid's formula. Other prefixes, like *per-* and *hypo-*, also appear in the names for some acids. Unfortunately, there is no strict rule for the number of oxygen atoms that are associated with the *-ic acid* suffix; the names of these acids are best memorized. Table 10.1 lists some acids and bases and their names. Note that acids have hydrogen written first, as if it were the cation, while most bases have the negative hydroxide ion, if it appears in the formula, written last.

Note

The name *oxygen* comes from the Latin meaning "acid producer" because its discoverer, Antoine Lavoisier, thought it was the essential element in acids. Lavoisier was wrong, but it is too late to change the name now.

TABLE 10.1 Formulas and Names for Some Acids and Bases

Formula	Name
Acids	
HCl(aq)	hydrochloric acid
HBr(aq)	hydrobromic acid
HI(aq)	hydriodic acid
H_2S(aq)	hydrosulfuric acid
$HC_2H_3O_2$(aq)	acetic acid
HNO_3(aq)	nitric acid
HNO_2(aq)	nitrous acid
H_2SO_4(aq)	sulfuric acid
H_2SO_3(aq)	sulfurous acid
$HClO_3$(aq)	chloric acid
$HClO_4$(aq)	perchloric acid
$HClO_2$(aq)	chlorous acid
H_3PO_4(aq)	phosphoric acid
H_3PO_3(aq)	phosphorous acid
Bases	
NaOH(aq)	sodium hydroxide
KOH(aq)	potassium hydroxide
$Mg(OH)_2$(aq)	magnesium hydroxide
$Ca(OH)_2$(aq)	calcium hydroxide
NH_3(aq)	ammonia

EXAMPLE 1

Name each substance.

1. HF(aq)
2. $Sr(OH)_2$(aq)

Solution

1. This acid has only two elements in its formula, so its name includes the *hydro-* prefix. The stem of the other element's name, fluorine, is *fluor*, and we must also include the *-ic acid* ending. Its name is hydrofluoric acid.
2. This base is named as an ionic compound between the strontium ion and the hydroxide ion: strontium hydroxide.

SKILL-BUILDING EXERCISE

Name each substance.

1. $H_2Se(aq)$
2. $Ba(OH)_2(aq)$

Notice that one base listed in Table 10.1—ammonia—does not have hydroxide as part of its formula. How does this compound increase the amount of hydroxide ion in aqueous solution? Instead of dissociating into hydroxide ions, ammonia molecules react with water molecules by taking a hydrogen ion from the water molecule to produce an ammonium ion and a hydroxide ion:

$$NH_3(aq) + H_2O(\ell) \rightarrow NH_4^+(aq) + OH^-(aq)$$

Because this reaction of ammonia with water causes an increase in the concentration of hydroxide ions in solution, ammonia satisfies the Arrhenius definition of a base. Many other nitrogen-containing compounds are bases because they too react with water to produce hydroxide ions in aqueous solution.

As we noted previously, acids and bases react chemically with each other to form *salts*. A salt is a general chemical term for any ionic compound formed from an acid and a base. In reactions where the acid is a hydrogen ion containing compound and the base is a hydroxide ion containing compound, water is also a product. The general reaction is as follows:

$$\text{acid} + \text{base} \rightarrow \text{water} + \text{salt}$$

neutralization

The reaction of acid and base to make water and a salt.

The reaction of acid and base to make water and a salt is called **neutralization**. Like any chemical equation, a neutralization chemical equation must be properly balanced. For example, the neutralization reaction between sodium hydroxide and hydrochloric acid is as follows:

$$NaOH(aq) + HCl(aq) \rightarrow NaCl(aq) + H_2O(\ell)$$

with coefficients all understood to be one. The neutralization reaction between sodium hydroxide and sulfuric acid is as follows:

$$2NaOH(aq) + H_2SO_4(aq) \rightarrow Na_2SO_4(aq) + 2H_2O(\ell)$$

Once a neutralization reaction is properly balanced, we can use it to perform stoichiometry calculations, such as the ones we practiced in Chapter 5 and Chapter 6.

EXAMPLE 2

Nitric acid [$HNO_3(aq)$] can be neutralized by calcium hydroxide [$Ca(OH)_2(aq)$].

1. Write a balanced chemical equation for the reaction between these two compounds and identify the salt it produces.
2. For one reaction, 16.8 g of HNO_3 is present initially. How many grams of $Ca(OH)_2$ are needed to neutralize that much HNO_3?
3. In a second reaction, 805 mL of 0.672 M $Ca(OH)_2$ is present initially. What volume of 0.432 M HNO_3 solution is necessary to neutralize the $Ca(OH)_2$ solution?

Solution

1. Because there are two OH^- ions in the formula for $Ca(OH)_2$, we need two moles of HNO_3 to provide H^+ ions. The balanced chemical equation is as follows:

$$Ca(OH)_2(aq) + 2HNO_3(aq) \rightarrow Ca(NO_3)_2(aq) + 2H_2O(\ell)$$

The salt formed is calcium nitrate.

2. This calculation is much like the calculations we did in Chapter 6. First we convert the mass of HNO_3 to moles using its molar mass of 1.01 + 14.00 + 3(16.00) = 63.01 g/mol; then we use the balanced chemical equation to determine the related number of moles of $Ca(OH)_2$ needed to neutralize it; and then we convert that number of moles of $Ca(OH)_2$ to the mass of $Ca(OH)_2$ using its molar mass of 40.08 + 2(1.01) + 2(16.00) = 74.10 g/mol.

$$16.8 \text{ g } \cancel{HNO_3} \times \frac{1 \text{ mol } \cancel{HNO_3}}{63.01 \text{ g } \cancel{HNO_3}} \times \frac{1 \text{ mol } \cancel{Ca(OH)_2}}{2 \text{ mol } \cancel{HNO_3}} \times \frac{74.10 \text{ g } Ca(OH)_2}{1 \text{ mol } \cancel{Ca(OH)_2}} = 9.88 \text{ g } Ca(OH)_2 \text{ needed}$$

3. Having concentration information allows us to employ the skills we developed in Chapter 9. First, we use the concentration and volume data to determine the number of moles of $Ca(OH)_2$ present. Recognizing that 805 mL = 0.805 L,

$$0.672 \text{ M } Ca(OH)_2 = \frac{\text{mol } Ca(OH)_2}{0.805 \text{ L soln}}$$

$$(0.672 \text{ M } CaOH)_2 \times (0.805 \text{ L soln}) = \text{mol } Ca(OH)_2 = 0.541 \text{ mol } Ca(OH)_2$$

We combine this information with the proper ratio from the balanced chemical equation to determine the number of moles of HNO_3 needed:

$$0.541 \text{ } \cancel{\text{mol } Ca(OH)_2} \times \frac{2 \text{ mol } HNO_3}{1 \text{ } \cancel{\text{mol } Ca(OH)_2}} = 1.08 \text{ mol } HNO_3$$

Now, using the definition of molarity one more time, we determine the volume of acid solution needed:

$$0.432 \text{ M } HNO_3 = \frac{1.08 \text{ mol } HNO_3}{\text{volume of } HNO_3}$$

$$\text{volume of } HNO_3 = \frac{1.08 \text{ mol } HNO_3}{0.432 \text{ M } HNO_3} = 2.50 \text{ L} = 2.50 \times 10^3 \text{ mL } HNO_3$$

SKILL-BUILDING EXERCISE

Hydrocyanic acid [$HCN(aq)$] can be neutralized by potassium hydroxide [$KOH(aq)$].

1. Write a balanced chemical equation for the reaction between these two compounds and identify the salt it produces.
2. For one reaction, 37.5 g of HCN is present initially. How many grams of KOH are needed to neutralize that much HCN?
3. In a second reaction, 43.0 mL of 0.0663 M KOH is present initially. What volume of 0.107 M HCN solution is necessary to neutralize the KOH solution?

Note

Hydrocyanic acid (HCN) is one exception to the acid-naming rules that specify using the prefix *hydro-* for binary acids (acids composed of hydrogen and only one other element).

CONCEPT REVIEW EXERCISES

1. Give the Arrhenius definitions of an acid and a base.
2. What is neutralization?

ANSWERS

1. Arrhenius acid: a compound that increases the concentration of hydrogen ion (H^+) in aqueous solution; Arrhenius base: a compound that increases the concentration of hydroxide ion (OH^-) in aqueous solution.
2. the reaction of an acid and a base

KEY TAKEAWAY

- An Arrhenius acid increases the H^+ ion concentration in water, while an Arrhenius base increases the OH^- ion concentration in water.

EXERCISES

1. Give two examples of Arrhenius acids.
2. Give two examples of Arrhenius bases.
3. List the general properties of acids.
4. List the general properties of bases.
5. Name each compound.
   a. HBr(aq)
   b. $Ca(OH)_2$(aq)
   c. HNO_3(aq)
   d. $Fe(OH)_3$(aq)
6. Name each compound.
   a. HI(aq)
   b. $Cu(OH)_2$(aq)
   c. H_3PO_4(aq)
   d. CsOH(aq)
7. Propose a name for water (H_2O) using the rules for naming acids.
8. Propose a name for hydrogen peroxide (H_2O_2) using the rules for naming acids.
9. Write a balanced chemical equation for the neutralization of $Ba(OH)_2$(aq) with HNO_3(aq).
10. Write a balanced chemical equation for the neutralization of H_2SO_4(aq) with $Cr(OH)_3$(aq).
11. How many moles of sodium hydroxide (NaOH) are needed to neutralize 0.844 mol of acetic acid ($HC_2H_3O_2$)? (Hint: begin by writing a balanced chemical equation for the process.)
12. How many moles of perchloric acid ($HClO_4$) are needed to neutralize 0.052 mol of calcium hydroxide [$Ca(OH)_2$]? (Hint: begin by writing a balanced chemical equation for the process.)
13. Hydrazoic acid (HN_3) can be neutralized by a base.
    a. Write the balanced chemical equation for the reaction between hydrazoic acid and calcium hydroxide.
    b. How many milliliters of 0.0245 M $Ca(OH)_2$ are needed to neutralize 0.564 g of HN_3?
14. Citric acid ($H_3C_6H_5O_7$) has three hydrogen atoms that can form hydrogen ions in solution.
    a. Write the balanced chemical equation for the reaction between citric acid and sodium hydroxide.
    b. If an orange contains 0.0675 g of $H_3C_6H_5O_7$, how many milliliters of 0.00332 M NaOH solution are needed to neutralize the acid?

15. Magnesium hydroxide [$Mg(OH)_2$] is an ingredient in some antacids. How many grams of $Mg(OH)_2$ are needed to neutralize the acid in 158 mL of 0.106 M HCl(aq)? It might help to write the balanced chemical equation first.

16. Aluminum hydroxide [$Al(OH)_3$] is an ingredient in some antacids. How many grams of $Al(OH)_3$ are needed to neutralize the acid in 96.5 mL of 0.556 M H_2SO_4(aq)? It might help to write the balanced chemical equation first.

ANSWERS

1. HCl and HNO_3 (answers will vary)
3. sour taste, react with metals, react with bases, and turn litmus red
5. a. hydrobromic acid
   b. calcium hydroxide
   c. nitric acid
   d. iron(III) hydroxide
7. perhaps hydroxic acid
9. $2HNO_3(aq) + Ba(OH)_2(aq) \rightarrow Ba(NO_3)_2(aq) + 2H_2O$
11. 0.844 mol
13. a. $2HN_3(aq) + Ca(OH)_2 \rightarrow Ca(N_3)_2 + 2H_2O$
    b. 268 mL
15. 0.488 g

2. BRØNSTED-LOWRY DEFINITION OF ACIDS AND BASES

LEARNING OBJECTIVES

1. **Recognize a compound as a Brønsted-Lowry acid or a Brønsted-Lowry base.**
2. **Illustrate the proton transfer process that defines a Brønsted-Lowry acid-base reaction.**

Ammonia (NH_3) increases the hydroxide ion concentration in aqueous solution by reacting with water rather than releasing hydroxide ions directly. In fact, the Arrhenius definitions of an acid and a base focus on hydrogen ions and hydroxide ions. Are there more fundamental definitions for acids and bases?

In 1923, the Danish scientist Johannes Brønsted and the English scientist Thomas Lowry independently proposed new definitions for acids and bases. Rather than considering both hydrogen and hydroxide ions, they focused on the hydrogen ion only. A **Brønsted-Lowry acid** is a compound that supplies a hydrogen ion in a reaction. A **Brønsted-Lowry base**, conversely, is a compound that accepts a hydrogen ion in a reaction. Thus, the Brønsted-Lowry definitions of an acid and a base focus on the movement of hydrogen ions in a reaction, rather than on the production of hydrogen ions and hydroxide ions in an aqueous solution.

Brønsted-Lowry acid

A compound that supplies a hydrogen ion (H^+) in a reaction; a proton donor.

Brønsted-Lowry base

A compound that accepts a hydrogen ion (H^+) in a reaction; a proton acceptor.

Let us use the reaction of ammonia in water to demonstrate the Brønsted-Lowry definitions of an acid and a base. Ammonia and water molecules are reactants, while the ammonium ion and the hydroxide ion are products:

$$NH_3(aq) + H_2O(\ell) \rightarrow NH_4^+(aq) + OH^-(aq)$$

What has happened in this reaction is that the original water molecule has donated a hydrogen ion to the original ammonia molecule, which in turn has accepted the hydrogen ion. We can illustrate this as follows:

$$NH_3 + H_2O \rightarrow NH_4^+ + OH^-$$

Hydrogen ion acceptor: B-L base

Hydrogen ion donor: B-L acid

Because the water molecule donates a hydrogen ion to the ammonia, it is the Brønsted-Lowry acid, while the ammonia molecule—which accepts the hydrogen ion—is the Brønsted-Lowry base. Thus, ammonia acts as a base in both the Arrhenius sense and the Brønsted-Lowry sense.

Is an Arrhenius acid like hydrochloric acid still an acid in the Brønsted-Lowry sense? Yes, but it requires us to understand what really happens when HCl is dissolved in water. Recall that the hydrogen *atom* is a single proton surrounded by a single electron. To make the hydrogen *ion*, we remove the electron, leaving a bare proton. Do we *really* have bare protons floating around in aqueous solution? No, we do not. What really happens is that the H^+ ion attaches itself to H_2O to make H_3O^+, which is called the *hydronium ion*. For most purposes, H^+ and H_3O^+ represent the same species, but writing H_3O^+ instead of H^+ shows that we understand that there are no bare protons floating around in solution. Rather, these protons are actually attached to solvent molecules.

Note

A proton in aqueous solution may be surrounded by more than one water molecule, leading to formulas like $H_5O_2^+$ or $H_9O_4^+$ rather than H_3O^+. It is simpler, however, to use H_3O^+.

With this in mind, how do we define HCl as an acid in the Brønsted-Lowry sense? Consider what happens when HCl is dissolved in H_2O:

$$HCl + H_2O(\ell) \rightarrow H_3O^+(aq) + Cl^-(aq)$$

We can depict this process using Lewis electron dot diagrams:

$$H{-}Cl + H{-}O{-}H \rightarrow Cl^- + H_3O^+$$

Now we see that a hydrogen ion is transferred from the HCl molecule to the H_2O molecule to make chloride ions and hydronium ions. As the hydrogen ion donor, HCl acts as a Brønsted-Lowry acid; as a hydrogen ion acceptor, H_2O is a Brønsted-Lowry base. So HCl is an acid not just in the Arrhenius sense but also in the Brønsted-Lowry sense. Moreover, by the Brønsted-Lowry definitions, H_2O is a base in the formation of aqueous HCl. So the Brønsted-Lowry definitions of an acid and a base classify the dissolving of HCl in water as a reaction between an acid and a base—although the Arrhenius definition would not have labeled H_2O a base in this circumstance.

Note

All Arrhenius acids and bases are Brønsted-Lowry acids and bases as well. But not all Brønsted-Lowry acids and bases are Arrhenius acids and bases.

EXAMPLE 3

Aniline ($C_6H_5NH_2$) is slightly soluble in water. It has a nitrogen atom that can accept a hydrogen ion from a water molecule just like the nitrogen atom in ammonia does. Write the chemical equation for this reaction and identify the Brønsted-Lowry acid and base.

Solution

$C_6H_5NH_2$ and H_2O are the reactants. When $C_6H_5NH_2$ accepts a proton from H_2O, it gains an extra H and a positive charge and leaves an OH^- ion behind. The reaction is as follows:

$$C_6H_5NH_2(aq) + H_2O(\ell) \rightarrow C_6H_5NH_3^+(aq) + OH^-(aq)$$

Because $C_6H_5NH_2$ accepts a proton, it is the Brønsted-Lowry base. The H_2O molecule, because it donates a proton, is the Brønsted-Lowry acid.

SKILL-BUILDING EXERCISE

1. Caffeine ($C_8H_{10}N_4O_2$) is a stimulant found in coffees and teas. When dissolved in water, it can accept a proton from a water molecule. Write the chemical equation for this process and identify the Brønsted-Lowry acid and base.

The Brønsted-Lowry definitions of an acid and a base can be applied to chemical reactions that occur in solvents other than water. The following example illustrates.

EXAMPLE 4

Sodium amide ($NaNH_2$) dissolves in methanol (CH_3OH) and separates into sodium ions and amide ions (NH_2^-). The amide ions react with methanol to make ammonia and the methoxide ion (CH_3O^-). Write a balanced chemical equation for this process and identify the Brønsted-Lowry acid and base.

Solution

The equation for the reaction is between NH_2^- and CH_3OH to make NH_3 and CH_3O^- is as follows:

$$NH_2^-(solv) + CH_3OH(\ell) \rightarrow NH_3(solv) + CH_3O^-(solv)$$

The label *(solv)* indicates that the species are dissolved in some solvent, in contrast to *(aq)*, which specifies an aqueous (H_2O) solution. In this reaction, we see that the NH_2^- ion accepts a proton from a CH_3OH molecule to make an NH_3 molecule. Thus, as the proton acceptor, NH_2^- is the Brønsted-Lowry base. As the proton donor, CH_3OH is the Brønsted-Lowry acid.

SKILL-BUILDING EXERCISE

1. Pyridinium chloride (C_5H_5NHCl) dissolves in ethanol (C_2H_5OH) and separates into pyridinium ions ($C_5H_5NH^+$) and chloride ions. The pyridinium ion can transfer a hydrogen ion to a solvent molecule. Write a balanced chemical equation for this process and identify the Brønsted-Lowry acid and base.

To Your Health: Brønsted-Lowry Acid-Base Reactions in Pharmaceuticals

There are many interesting applications of Brønsted-Lowry acid-base reactions in the pharmaceutical industry. For example, drugs often need to be water soluble for maximum effectiveness. However, many complex organic compounds are not soluble or are only slightly soluble in water. Fortunately, those drugs that contain proton-accepting nitrogen atoms (and there are a lot of them) can be reacted with dilute hydrochloric acid [HCl(aq)]. The nitrogen atoms—acting as Brønsted-Lowry bases—accept the hydrogen ions from the acid to make an ion, which is usually much more soluble in water. The modified drug molecules can then be isolated as chloride salts:

$$RN(sl\ aq) + H^+(aq) \rightarrow RNH^+(aq) \xrightarrow{Cl^-(aq)} RNHCl(s)$$

where RN represents some organic compound containing nitrogen. The label *(sl aq)* means "slightly aqueous," indicating that the compound RN is only slightly soluble. Drugs that are modified in this way are called *hydrochloride salts*. Examples include the powerful painkiller codeine, which is commonly administered as codeine hydrochloride. Acids other than hydrochloric acid are also used. Hydrobromic acid, for example, gives *hydrobromide salts*. Dextromethorphan, an ingredient in many cough medicines, is dispensed as dextromethorphan hydrobromide. The accompanying figure shows another medication as a hydrochloride salt.

The name of this medicine makes it clear that it exists as the hydrochloride salt.

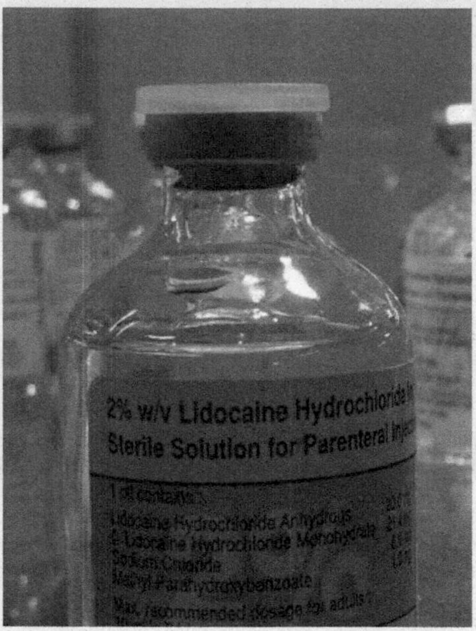

© *Thinkstock*

CONCEPT REVIEW EXERCISE

1. Give the definitions of a Brønsted-Lowry acid and a Brønsted-Lowry base.

ANSWER

1. A Brønsted-Lowry acid is a proton donor, while a Brønsted-Lowry base is a proton acceptor.

KEY TAKEAWAYS

- A Brønsted-Lowry acid is a proton donor, and a Brønsted-Lowry base is a proton acceptor.
- Brønsted-Lowry acid-base reactions are essentially proton transfer reactions.

EXERCISES

1. Label each reactant as a Brønsted-Lowry acid or a Brønsted-Lowry base.

   $HCl(aq) + NH_3(aq) \rightarrow NH_4^+(aq) + Cl^-(aq)$

2. Label each reactant as a Brønsted-Lowry acid or a Brønsted-Lowry base.

   $H_2O(\ell) + N_2H_4(aq) \rightarrow N_2H_5^+(aq) + OH^-(aq)$

3. Explain why a Brønsted-Lowry acid can be called a proton donor.
4. Explain why a Brønsted-Lowry base can be called a proton acceptor.
5. Write the chemical equation of the reaction of ammonia in water and label the Brønsted-Lowry acid and base.
6. Write the chemical equation of the reaction of methylamine (CH_3NH_2) in water and label the Brønsted-Lowry acid and base.
7. Demonstrate that the dissolution of HNO_3 in water is actually a Brønsted-Lowry acid-base reaction by describing it with a chemical equation and labeling the Brønsted-Lowry acid and base.
8. Identify the Brønsted-Lowry acid and base in the following chemical equation:

$$C_3H_7NH_2(aq) + H_3O^+(aq) \rightarrow C_3H_7NH_3^+(aq) + H_2O(\ell)$$

9. Write the chemical equation for the reaction that occurs when cocaine hydrochloride ($C_{17}H_{22}ClNO_4$) dissolves in water and donates a proton to a water molecule. (When hydrochlorides dissolve in water, they separate into chloride ions and the appropriate cation.)
10. If codeine hydrobromide has the formula $C_{18}H_{22}BrNO_3$, what is the formula of the parent compound codeine?

ANSWERS

1. HCl: Brønsted-Lowry acid; NH_3: Brønsted-Lowry base
3. A Brønsted-Lowry acid gives away an H^+ ion—nominally, a proton—in an acid-base reaction.
5. $NH_3 + H_2O \rightarrow NH_4^+ + OH^-$; NH_3: Brønsted-Lowry base; H_2O: Brønsted-Lowry acid
7. $HNO_3 + H_2O \rightarrow H_3O^+ + NO_3^-$; HNO_3: Brønsted-Lowry acid; H_2O: Brønsted-Lowry base
9. $C_{17}H_{22}NO_4+ + H_2O \rightarrow H_3O^+ + C_{17}H_{21}NO_4$

3. WATER: BOTH AN ACID AND A BASE

LEARNING OBJECTIVE

1. **Write chemical equations for water acting as an acid and as a base.**

Water (H_2O) is an interesting compound in many respects. Here, we will consider its ability to behave as an acid or a base.

In some circumstances, a water molecule will accept a proton and thus act as a Brønsted-Lowry base. We saw an example in the dissolving of HCl in H_2O:

$$HCl + H_2O(\ell) \rightarrow H_3O^+(aq) + Cl^-(aq)$$

In other circumstances, a water molecule can donate a proton and thus act as a Brønsted-Lowry acid. For example, in the presence of the amide ion (see Example 4 in Section 2), a water molecule donates a proton, making ammonia as a product:

$$H_2O(\ell) + NH_2^-(aq) \rightarrow OH^-(aq) + NH_3(aq)$$

In this case, NH_2^- is a Brønsted-Lowry base (the proton acceptor).

So, depending on the circumstances, H_2O can act as either a Brønsted-Lowry acid or a Brønsted-Lowry base. Water is not the only substance that can react as an acid in some cases or a base in others, but it is certainly the most common example—and the most important one. A substance that can either donate or accept a proton, depending on the circumstances, is called an **amphiprotic** compound.

amphiprotic

A substance that can either donate or accept a proton, depending on the circumstances.

A water molecule can act as an acid or a base even in a sample of pure water. About 6 in every 100 million (6 in 10^8) water molecules undergo the following reaction:

$$H_2O(\ell) + H_2O(\ell) \rightarrow H_3O^+(aq) + OH^-(aq)$$

autoionization of water

The process by which water ionizes into hydronium ions and hydroxide ions as it acts as an acid and a base.

This process is called the **autoionization of water** (Figure 10.2) and occurs in every sample of water, whether it is pure or part of a solution. Autoionization occurs to some extent in any amphiprotic liquid. (For comparison, liquid ammonia undergoes autoionization as well, but only about 1 molecule in a million billion (1 in 10^{15}) reacts with another ammonia molecule.)

FIGURE 10.2 Autoionization

A small fraction of water molecules—approximately 6 in 100 million—ionize spontaneously into hydronium ions and hydroxide ions. This picture necessarily overrepresents the amount of autoionization that really occurs in pure water.

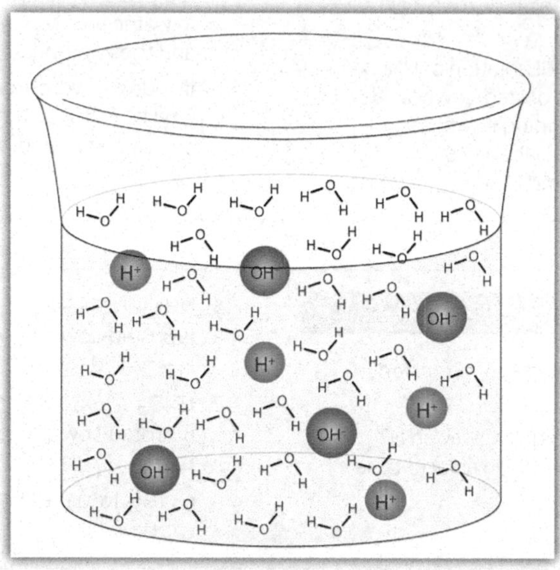

EXAMPLE 5

Identify water as either a Brønsted-Lowry acid or a Brønsted-Lowry base.

1. $H_2O(\ell) + NO_2^-(aq) \rightarrow HNO_2(aq) + OH^-(aq)$
2. $HC_2H_3O_2(aq) + H_2O(\ell) \rightarrow H_3O^+(aq) + C_2H_3O_2^-(aq)$

Solution

1. In this reaction, the water molecule donates a proton to the NO_2^- ion, making $OH^-(aq)$. As the proton donor, H_2O acts as a Brønsted-Lowry acid.
2. In this reaction, the water molecule accepts a proton from $HC_2H_3O_2$, becoming $H_3O^+(aq)$. As the proton acceptor, H_2O is a Brønsted-Lowry base.

SKILL-BUILDING EXERCISE

Identify water as either a Brønsted-Lowry acid or a Brønsted-Lowry base.

1. $HCOOH(aq) + H_2O(\ell) \rightarrow H_3O^+(aq) + HCOO^-(aq)$
2. $H_2O(\ell) + PO_4^{3-}(aq) \rightarrow OH^-(aq) + HPO_4^{2-}(aq)$

CONCEPT REVIEW EXERCISES

1. Explain how water can act as an acid.
2. Explain how water can act as a base.

ANSWERS

1. Under the right conditions, H_2O can donate a proton, making it a Brønsted-Lowry acid.
2. Under the right conditions, H_2O can accept a proton, making it a Brønsted-Lowry base.

KEY TAKEAWAY

- Water molecules can act as both an acid and a base, depending on the conditions.

EXERCISES

1. Is $H_2O(\ell)$ acting as an acid or a base?

$$H_2O(\ell) + NH_4^+(aq) \rightarrow H_3O^+(aq) + NH_3(aq)$$

2. Is $H_2O(\ell)$ acting as an acid or a base?

$$CH_3^-(aq) + H_2O(\ell) \rightarrow CH_4(aq) + OH^-(aq)$$

3. In the aqueous solutions of some salts, one of the ions from the salt can react with water molecules. In some $C_2H_3O_2^-$ solutions, the following reaction can occur:

$$C_2H_3O_2^-(aq) + H_2O(\ell) \rightarrow HC_2H_3O_2(aq) + OH^-(aq)$$

Is H_2O acting as an acid or a base in this reaction?

4. In the aqueous solutions of some salts, one of the ions from the salt can react with water molecules. In some NH_4^+ solutions, the following reaction can occur:

$$NH_4^+(aq) + H_2O \rightarrow NH_3(aq) + H_3O^+(aq)$$

Is H_2O acting as an acid or a base in this reaction?

5. Aluminum hydroxide [$Al(OH)_3$] is *amphoteric*; it reacts with both acids and bases. Propose the chemical equations for the reactions of $Al(OH)_3$ with H^+ and with OH^-.
6. Based on the information in this section, does ammonia (NH_3) autoionize more or less than water? Write the chemical equation for the autoionization of ammonia.

ANSWERS

1. base
3. acid
5. $Al(OH)_3 + H^+ \rightarrow HAl(OH)_3^+$; $Al(OH)_3 + OH^- \rightarrow Al(OH)_4^-$

4. THE STRENGTHS OF ACIDS AND BASES

LEARNING OBJECTIVES

1. **Describe the difference between strong and weak acids and bases.**
2. **Describe how a chemical reaction reaches chemical equilibrium.**
3. **Define the pH scale and use it to describe acids and bases.**

Acids and bases do not all demonstrate the same degree of chemical activity in solution. Different acids and bases have different strengths.

4.1 Strong and Weak Acids

Let us consider the strengths of acids first. A small number of acids ionize completely in aqueous solution. For example, when HCl dissolves in water, every molecule of HCl separates into a hydronium ion and a chloride ion:

$$HCl + H_2O(\ell) \xrightarrow{\sim 100\%} H_3O^+(aq) + Cl^-(aq)$$

strong acid

An acid that is 100% ionized in aqueous solution.

$HCl(aq)$ is one example of a **strong acid**, which is a compound that is essentially 100% ionized in aqueous solution. There are very few strong acids. The important ones are listed in Table 10.2.

TABLE 10.2 Strong Acids and Bases (All in Aqueous Solution)

Acids	Bases
HCl	$LiOH$
HBr	$NaOH$
HI	KOH
HNO_3	$Mg(OH)_2$
H_2SO_4	$Ca(OH)_2$
$HClO_4$	

strong base

A base that is 100% ionized in aqueous solution.

weak acid

An acid that is less than 100% ionized in aqueous solution.

weak base

A base that is less than 100% ionized in aqueous solution.

By analogy, a **strong base** is a compound that is essentially 100% ionized in aqueous solution. As with acids, there are only a few strong bases, which are also listed in Table 10.2.

If an acid is not listed in Table 10.2, it is likely a **weak acid**, which is a compound that is not 100% ionized in aqueous solution. Similarly, a **weak base** is a compound that is not 100% ionized in aqueous solution. For example, acetic acid ($HC_2H_3O_2$) is a weak acid. The ionization reaction for acetic acid is as follows:

$$HC_2H_3O_2(aq) + H_2O(\ell) \rightarrow H_3O^+(aq) + C_2H_3O_2^-(aq)$$

Depending on the concentration of $HC_2H_3O_2$, the ionization reaction may occur only for 1%–5% of the acetic acid molecules.

Looking Closer: Household Acids and Bases

Many household products are acids or bases. For example, the owner of a swimming pool may use muriatic acid to clean the pool. Muriatic acid is another name for hydrochloric acid [$HCl(aq)$]. Vinegar has already been mentioned as a dilute solution of acetic acid [$HC_2H_3O_2(aq)$]. In a medicine chest, one may find a bottle of vitamin C tablets; the chemical name of vitamin C is ascorbic acid ($HC_6H_7O_6$).

One of the more familiar household bases is ammonia (NH_3), which is found in numerous cleaning products. As we mentioned previously, ammonia is a base because it increases the hydroxide ion concentration by reacting with water:

$$NH_3(aq) + H_2O(\ell) \rightarrow NH_4^+(aq) + OH^-(aq)$$

Many soaps are also slightly basic because they contain compounds that act as Brønsted-Lowry bases, accepting protons from water and forming excess hydroxide ions. This is one reason that soap solutions are slippery.

Perhaps the most dangerous household chemical is the lye-based drain cleaner. Lye is a common name for sodium hydroxide, although it is also used as a synonym for potassium hydroxide. Lye is an extremely caustic chemical that can react with grease, hair, food particles, and other substances that may build up and form a clog in a pipe. Unfortunately, lye can also attack tissues and other substances in our bodies. Thus, when we use lye-based drain cleaners, we must be very careful not to touch any of the solid drain cleaner or spill the water it was poured into. Safer, nonlye drain cleaners use peroxide compounds to react on the materials in the clog and clear the drain.

Drain cleaners can be made from a reactive material that is less caustic than a base.

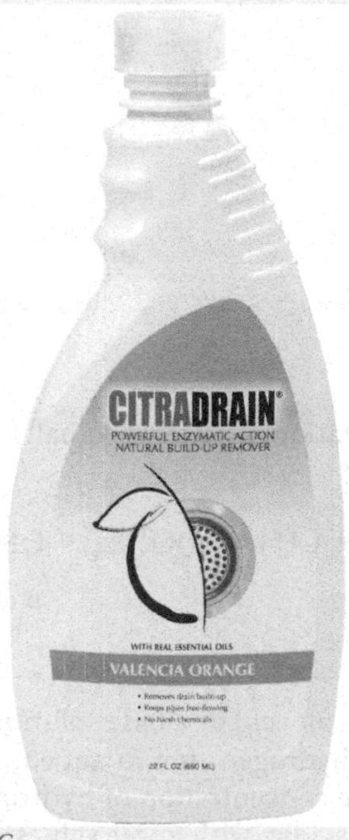

Source: Photo used by permission of Citrasolv, LLC.

4.2 Chemical Equilibrium

The behavior of weak acids and bases illustrates a key concept in chemistry. Does the chemical reaction describing the ionization of a weak acid or base just stop when the acid or base is done ionizing? Actually, no. Rather, the reverse process—the reformation of the molecular form of the acid or base—occurs, ultimately at the same rate as the ionization process. For example, the ionization of the weak acid $HC_2H_3O_2$ (aq) is as follows:

$$HC_2H_3O_2(aq) + H_2O(\ell) \rightarrow H_3O^+(aq) + C_2H_3O_2^-(aq)$$

The reverse process also begins to occur:

$$H_3O^+(aq) + C_2H_3O_2^-(aq) \rightarrow HC_2H_3O_2(aq) + H_2O(\ell)$$

Eventually, there is a balance between the two opposing processes, and no additional change occurs. The chemical reaction is better represented at this point with a double arrow:

$$HC_2H_3O_2(aq) + H_2O(\ell) \leftrightarrows H_3O^+(aq) + C_2H_3O_2^-(aq)$$

The $\leftrightarrows$ implies that both the forward and reverse reactions are occurring, and their effects cancel each other out. A process at this point is considered to be at **chemical equilibrium (or equilibrium)**. It is important to note that the processes do not stop. They balance out each other so that there is no further net change; that is, chemical equilibrium is a *dynamic equilibrium*.

chemical equilibrium (equilibrium)

The condition in which the extent of a chemical reaction does not change any further.

EXAMPLE 6

Write the equilibrium chemical equation for the partial ionization of each weak acid or base.

1. $HNO_2(aq)$
2. $C_5H_5N(aq)$

Solution

1. $HNO_2(aq) + H_2O(\ell) \leftrightarrows NO_2^-(aq) + H_3O^+(aq)$
2. $C_5H_5N(aq) + H_2O(\ell) \leftrightarrows C_5H_5NH^+(aq) + OH^-(aq)$

SKILL-BUILDING EXERCISE

Write the equilibrium chemical equation for the partial ionization of each weak acid or base.

1. HF(aq)
2. AgOH(aq)

Note

Hydrofluoric acid [HF(aq)] is one chemical that reacts directly with glass. (Very few chemicals react with glass.) Hydrofluoric acid is used in glass etching.

Finally, you may realize that the autoionization of water is actually an equilibrium process, so it is more properly written with the double arrow:

$$H_2O(\ell) + H_2O(\ell) \leftrightarrows H_3O^+(aq) + OH^-(aq)$$

4.3 The pH Scale

pH scale

A logarithmic scale that relates the concentration of the hydrogen ion in solution.

One qualitative measure of the strength of an acid or a base solution is the **pH scale**, which is based on the concentration of the hydronium (or hydrogen) ion in aqueous solution. A neutral (neither acidic nor basic) solution, one that has the same concentration of hydrogen and hydroxide ions, has a pH of 7. A pH below 7 means that a solution is acidic, with lower values of pH corresponding to increasingly acidic solutions. A pH greater than 7 indicates a basic solution, with higher values of pH corresponding to increasingly basic solutions. Thus, given the pH of several solutions, you can state which ones are acidic, which ones are basic, and which are more acidic or basic than others. Table 10.3 lists the pH of several common solutions. Notice that some biological fluids are nowhere near neutral.

TABLE 10.3 The pH Values of Some Common Solutions

Solution	pH
battery acid	0.3
stomach acid	1–2
lemon or lime juice	2.1
vinegar	2.8–3.0
Coca-Cola	3
wine	2.8–3.8
beer	4–5
coffee	5
milk	6
urine	6
pure H_2O	7
(human) blood	7.3–7.5
sea water	8
antacid (milk of magnesia)	10.5
NH_3 (1 M)	11.6
bleach	12.6
NaOH (1 M)	14.0

Weak acids and bases are relatively common. You may notice from Table 10.3 that many food products are slightly acidic. They are acidic because they contain solutions of weak acids. If the acid components of these foods were strong acids, the food would likely be inedible.

CONCEPT REVIEW EXERCISES

1. Explain the difference between a strong acid or base and a weak acid or base.
2. Explain what is occurring when a chemical reaction reaches equilibrium.
3. Define *pH.*

ANSWERS

1. A strong acid or base is 100% ionized in aqueous solution; a weak acid or base is less than 100% ionized.
2. The overall reaction progress stops because the reverse process balances out the forward process.
3. pH is a measure of the hydrogen ion concentration.

KEY TAKEAWAYS

- Acids and bases can be strong or weak depending on the extent of ionization in solution.
- Most chemical reactions reach equilibrium at which point there is no net change.
- The pH scale is used to succinctly communicate the acidity or basicity of a solution.

EXERCISES

1. Name a strong acid and a weak acid.
2. Name a strong base and a weak base.
3. Is each compound a strong acid or a weak acid? Assume all are in aqueous solution.
    a. HF
    b. $HC_2H_3O_2$
    c. HCl
    d. $HClO_4$
4. Is each compound a strong acid or a weak acid? Assume all are in aqueous solution.
    a. H_2SO_4
    b. HSO_4^-
    c. HPO_4^{2-}
    d. HNO_3
5. Is each compound a strong base or a weak base? Assume all are in aqueous solution.
    a. NH_3
    b. NaOH
    c. $Mg(OH)_2$
    d. $Cu(OH)_2$
6. Is each compound a strong base or a weak base? Assume all are in aqueous solution.
    a. KOH
    b. H_2O
    c. $Fe(OH)_2$
    d. $Fe(OH)_3$
7. Write the chemical equation for the equilibrium process for each weak acid in Exercise 3.
8. Write the chemical equation for the equilibrium process for each weak acid in Exercise 4.
9. Write the chemical equation for the equilibrium process for each weak base in Exercise 5.
10. Write the chemical equation for the equilibrium process for each weak base in Exercise 6.
11. Which is the stronger acid—HCl(aq) or HF(aq)?
12. Which is the stronger base—KOH(aq) or $Ni(OH)_2$(aq)?
13. Consider the two acids in Exercise 11. For solutions that have the same concentration, which one would you expect to have a lower pH?
14. Consider the two bases in Exercise 12. For solutions that have the same concentration, which one would you expect to have a higher pH?
15. Consider the list of substances in Table 10.3. What is the most acidic substance on the list that you have encountered recently?
16. Consider the list of substances in Table 10.3. What is the most basic substance on the list that you have encountered recently?

ANSWERS

1. strong acid: HCl; weak acid: $HC_2H_3O_2$ (answers will vary)
3. a. weak
   b. weak
   c. strong
   d. strong
5. a. weak
   b. strong
   c. strong
   d. weak
7. 3a: $HF(aq) \leftrightarrows H^+(aq) + F^-(aq)$; 3b: $HC_2H_3O_2(aq) \leftrightarrows H^+(aq) + C_2H_3O_2^-(aq)$
9. 5a: $NH_3(aq) + H_2O \leftrightarrows NH_4^+(aq) + OH^-(aq)$; 5d: $Cu(OH)_2(aq) \leftrightarrows Cu^{2+}(aq) + 2OH^-(aq)$
11. HCl(aq)
13. HCl(aq)
15. (answers will vary)

5. BUFFERS

LEARNING OBJECTIVE

1. **Define *buffer* and describe how it reacts with an acid or a base.**

As indicated in Section 4, weak acids are relatively common, even in the foods we eat. But we occasionally come across a strong acid or base, such as stomach acid, that has a strongly acidic pH of 1–2. By definition, strong acids and bases can produce a relatively large amount of hydrogen or hydroxide ions and, as a consequence, have a marked chemical activity. In addition, very small amounts of strong acids and bases can change the pH of a solution very quickly. If 1 mL of stomach acid [which we will approximate as 0.05 M HCl(aq)] is added to the bloodstream, and if no correcting mechanism is present, the pH of the blood would go from about 7.4 to about 4.9—a pH that is not conducive to continued living. Fortunately, the body has a mechanism for minimizing such dramatic pH changes.

buffer

A solution that resists dramatic changes in pH.

The mechanism involves a **buffer**, a solution that resists dramatic changes in pH. Buffers do so by being composed of certain pairs of solutes: either a weak acid plus a salt derived from that weak acid or a weak base plus a salt of that weak base. For example, a buffer can be composed of dissolved acetic acid ($HC_2H_3O_2$, a weak acid) and sodium acetate ($NaC_2H_3O_2$, a salt derived from that acid). Another example of a buffer is a solution containing ammonia (NH_3, a weak base) and ammonium chloride (NH_4Cl, a salt derived from that base).

Let us use an acetic acid–sodium acetate buffer to demonstrate how buffers work. If a strong base—a source of $OH^-(aq)$ ions—is added to the buffer solution, those hydroxide ions will react with the acetic acid in an acid-base reaction:

$$HC_2H_3O_2(aq) + OH^-(aq) \rightarrow H_2O(\ell) + C_2H_3O_2^-(aq)$$

Rather than changing the pH dramatically by making the solution basic, the added hydroxide ions react to make water, and the pH does not change much.

Note

Many people are aware of the concept of buffers from *buffered aspirin*, which is aspirin that also has magnesium carbonate, calcium carbonate, magnesium oxide, or some other salt. The salt acts like a base, while aspirin is itself a weak acid.

If a strong acid—a source of H^+ ions—is added to the buffer solution, the H^+ ions will react with the anion from the salt. Because $HC_2H_3O_2$ is a weak acid, it is not ionized much. This means that if lots of hydrogen ions and acetate ions (from sodium acetate) are present in the same solution, they will come together to make acetic acid:

$$H^+(aq) + C_2H_3O_2^-(aq) \rightarrow HC_2H_3O_2(aq)$$

Rather than changing the pH dramatically and making the solution acidic, the added hydrogen ions react to make molecules of a weak acid. Figure 10.3 illustrates both actions of a buffer.

FIGURE 10.3 The Action of Buffers

Buffers can react with both strong acids (top) and strong bases (bottom) to minimize large changes in pH.

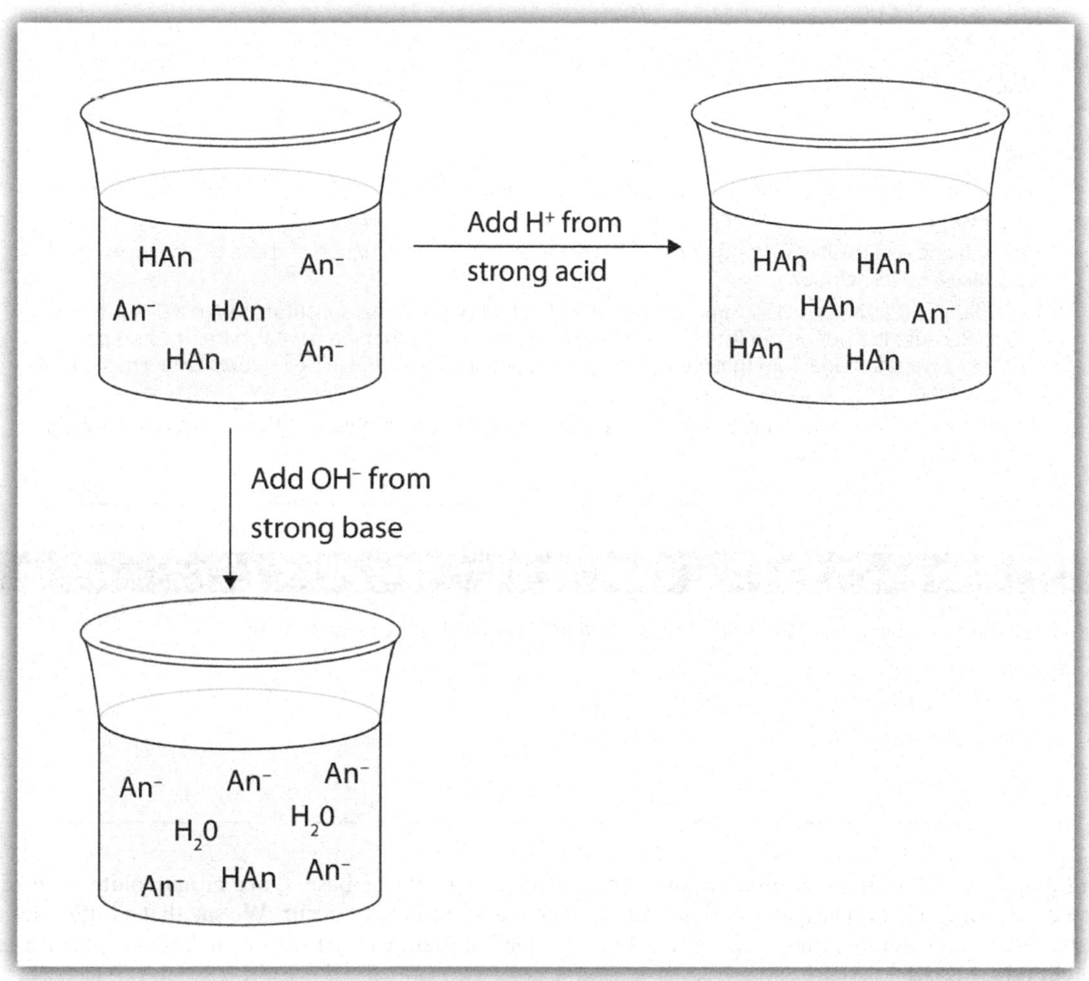

Buffers made from weak bases and salts of weak bases act similarly. For example, in a buffer containing NH_3 and NH_4Cl, ammonia molecules can react with any excess hydrogen ions introduced by strong acids:

$$NH_3(aq) + H^+(aq) \rightarrow NH_4^+(aq)$$

while the ammonium ion [$NH_4^+(aq)$] can react with any hydroxide ions introduced by strong bases:

$$NH_4^+(aq) + OH^-(aq) \rightarrow NH_3(aq) + H_2O(\ell)$$

EXAMPLE 7

Which solute combinations can make a buffer solution? Assume all are aqueous solutions.

1. $HCHO_2$ and $NaCHO_2$
2. HCl and NaCl
3. CH_3NH_2 and CH_3NH_3Cl
4. NH_3 and NaOH

Solution

1. Formic acid ($HCHO_2$) is a weak acid, while $NaCHO_2$ is the salt made from the anion of the weak acid—the formate ion (CHO_2^-). The combination of these two solutes would make a buffer solution.
2. Hydrochloric acid (HCl) is a strong acid, not a weak acid, so the combination of these two solutes would not make a buffer solution.
3. Methylamine (CH_3NH_2) is like ammonia with one of its hydrogen atoms substituted with a CH_3 (methyl) group. Because it is not on our list of strong bases, we can assume that it is a weak base. The compound CH_3NH_3Cl is a salt made from that weak base, so the combination of these two solutes would make a buffer solution.
4. Ammonia (NH_3) is a weak base, but NaOH is a strong base. The combination of these two solutes would not make a buffer solution.

SKILL-BUILDING EXERCISE

Which solute combinations can make a buffer solution? Assume all are aqueous solutions.

1. $NaHCO_3$ and NaCl
2. H_3PO_4 and NaH_2PO_4
3. NH_3 and $(NH_4)_3PO_4$
4. NaOH and NaCl

capacity

The amount of strong acid or base a buffer can counteract.

Buffers work well only for limited amounts of added strong acid or base. Once either solute is all reacted, the solution is no longer a buffer, and rapid changes in pH may occur. We say that a buffer has a certain **capacity**. Buffers that have more solute dissolved in them to start with have larger capacities, as might be expected.

Human blood has a buffering system to minimize extreme changes in pH. One buffer in blood is based on the presence of HCO_3^- and H_2CO_3 [H_2CO_3 is another way to write $CO_2(aq)$]. With this buffer present, even if some stomach acid were to find its way directly into the bloodstream, the change in the pH of blood would be minimal. Inside many of the body's cells, there is a buffering system based on phosphate ions.

Career Focus: Blood Bank Technology Specialist

At this point in this text, you should have the idea that the chemistry of blood is fairly complex. Because of this, people who work with blood must be specially trained to work with it properly.

A blood bank technology specialist is trained to perform routine and special tests on blood samples from blood banks or transfusion centers. This specialist measures the pH of blood, types it (according to the blood's ABO+/− type, Rh factors, and other typing schemes), tests it for the presence or absence of various diseases, and uses the blood to determine if a patient has any of several medical problems, such as anemia. A blood bank technology specialist may also interview and prepare donors to give blood and may actually collect the blood donation.

Blood bank technology specialists are well trained. Typically, they require a college degree with at least a year of special training in blood biology and chemistry. In the United States, training must conform to standards established by the American Association of Blood Banks.

CONCEPT REVIEW EXERCISE

1. Explain how a buffer prevents large changes in pH.

ANSWER

1. A buffer has components that react with both strong acids and strong bases to resist sudden changes in pH.

KEY TAKEAWAY

- A buffer is a solution that resists sudden changes in pH.

EXERCISES

1. Describe a buffer. What two related chemical components are required to make a buffer?
2. Can a buffer be made by combining a strong acid with a strong base? Why or why not?
3. Which solute combinations can make a buffer? Assume all are aqueous solutions.
   a. HCl and NaCl
   b. HNO_2 and $NaNO_2$
   c. NH_4NO_3 and HNO_3
   d. NH_4NO_3 and NH_3
4. Which solute combinations can make a buffer? Assume all are aqueous solutions.
   a. H_3PO_4 and Na_3PO_4
   b. $NaHCO_3$ and Na_2CO_3
   c. $NaNO_3$ and $Ca(NO_3)_2$
   d. HN_3 and NH_3
5. For each combination in Exercise 3 that is a buffer, write the chemical equations for the reactions of the buffer components when a strong acid and a strong base is added.
6. For each combination in Exercise 4 that is a buffer, write the chemical equations for the reaction of the buffer components when a strong acid and a strong base is added.
7. The complete phosphate buffer system is based on four substances: H_3PO_4, $H_2PO_4^-$, HPO_4^{2-}, and PO_4^{3-}. What different buffer solutions can be made from these substances?
8. Explain why NaBr cannot be a component in either an acidic or a basic buffer.
9. Two solutions are made containing the same concentrations of solutes. One solution is composed of phosphoric acid and sodium phosphate, while the other is composed of hydrocyanic acid and sodium cyanide. Which solution should have the larger capacity as a buffer?
10. Two solutions are made containing the same concentrations of solutes. One solution is composed of ammonia and ammonium nitrate, while the other is composed of sulfuric acid and sodium sulfate. Which solution should have the larger capacity as a buffer?

ANSWERS

1. A buffer resists sudden changes in pH. It has a weak acid or base and a salt of that weak acid or base.
3. a. not a buffer
   b. buffer
   c. not a buffer
   d. buffer
5. 3b: strong acid: $H^+ + NO_2^- \rightarrow HNO_2$; strong base: $OH^- + HNO_2 \rightarrow H_2O + NO_2^-$; 3d: strong acid: $H^+ + NH_3 \rightarrow NH_4^+$; strong base: $OH^- + NH_4^+ \rightarrow H_2O + NH_3$
7. Buffers can be made by combining H_3PO_4 and $H_2PO_4^-$, $H_2PO_4^-$ and HPO_4^{2-}, and HPO_4^{2-} and PO_4^{3-}.
9. the phosphoric acid–phosphate buffer

6. END-OF-CHAPTER MATERIAL

Chapter Summary

To ensure that you understand the material in this chapter, you should review the meanings of the bold terms in the following summary and ask yourself how they relate to the topics in the chapter.

The earliest chemical definition of an acid, the **Arrhenius definition**, says that an **acid** is a compound that increases the amount of hydrogen ion (H^+) in aqueous solution. An **Arrhenius base** is a compound that increases the amount of hydroxide ion (OH^-) in aqueous solution. While most bases are named as ionic hydroxide compounds, aqueous acids have a naming system unique to acids. Acids and bases react together in a characteristic chemical reaction called **neutralization**, in which the products are water and a salt. The principles of stoichiometry, along with the balanced chemical equation for a reaction between an acid and a base, can be used to determine how much of one compound will react with a given amount of the other.

A **Brønsted-Lowry acid** is any substance that donates a proton to another substance. A **Brønsted-Lowry base** is any substance that accepts a proton from another substance. The reaction of ammonia with water to make ammonium ions and hydroxide ions can be used to illustrate Brønsted-Lowry acid and base behavior.

Some compounds can either donate or accept protons, depending on the circumstances. Such compounds are called **amphiprotic**. Water is one example of an amphiprotic compound. One result of water being amphiprotic is that a water molecule can donate a proton to another water molecule to make a hydronium ion and a hydroxide ion. This process is called the **autoionization of water** and occurs in any sample of water.

Not all acids and bases are equal in chemical strength. A **strong acid** is an acid whose molecules are all dissociated into ions in aqueous solution. Hydrochloric acid is an example of a strong acid. Similarly, a **strong base** is a base whose molecules are dissociated into ions in aqueous solution. Sodium hydroxide is an example of a strong base. Any acid or base whose molecules are not all dissociated into ions in aqueous solution is a **weak acid** or a **weak base**. Solutions of weak acids and weak bases reach a **chemical equilibrium** between the un-ionized form of the compound and the dissociated ions. It is a dynamic equilibrium because acid and base molecules are constantly dissociating into ions and reassociating into neutral molecules.

The **pH** scale is a scale used to express the concentration of hydrogen ions in solution. A neutral solution, neither acidic nor basic, has a pH of 7. Acidic solutions have a pH lower than 7, while basic solutions have a pH higher than 7.

Buffers are solutions that resist dramatic changes in pH when an acid or a base is added to them. They contain a weak acid and a salt of that weak acid, or a weak base and a salt of that weak base. When a buffer is present, any strong acid reacts with the anion of the salt, forming a weak acid and minimizing the presence of hydrogen ions in solution. Any strong base reacts with the weak acid, minimizing the amount of additional hydroxide ions in solution. However, buffers only have limited **capacity**; there is a limit to the amount of strong acid or strong base any given amount of buffer will react with.

ADDITIONAL EXERCISES

1. The properties of a 1.0 M HCl solution and a 1.0 M $HC_2H_3O_2$ solution are compared. Measurements show that the hydrochloric acid solution has a higher osmotic pressure than the acetic acid solution. Explain why.
2. Of a 0.50 M HNO_3 solution and a 0.50 M $HC_2H_3O_2$ solution, which should have the higher boiling point? Explain why.
3. The reaction of sulfuric acid [H_2SO_4(aq)] with sodium hydroxide [NaOH(aq)] can be represented by two separate steps, with only one hydrogen ion reacting in each step. Write the chemical equation for each step.
4. The reaction of aluminum hydroxide [$Al(OH)_3$(aq)] with hydrochloric acid [HCl(aq)] can be represented by three separate steps, with only one hydroxide ion reacting in each step. Write the chemical equation for each step.
5. A friend brings you a small sample of an unknown chemical. Assuming that the chemical is soluble in water, how would you determine if the chemical is an acid or a base?
6. A neutral solution has a hydrogen ion concentration of about 1×10^{-7} M. What is the concentration of the hydroxide ion in a neutral solution?
7. The Lewis definitions of an acid and a base are based on electron pairs, not protons. A Lewis acid is an electron pair acceptor, while a Lewis base is an electron pair donor. Use Lewis diagrams to show that

$$H^+(aq) + OH^-(aq) \rightarrow H_2O(\ell)$$

is an acid-base reaction in the Lewis sense as well as in the Arrhenius and Brønsted-Lowry senses.
8. Given the chemical reaction

$$NH_3(g) + BF_3(g) \rightarrow NH_3\text{—}BF_3(s)$$

show that the reaction illustrated by this equation is an acid-base reaction if we use the Lewis definitions of an acid and a base (see Exercise 7). The product contains a bond between the N and B atoms.

ANSWERS

1. HCl is a strong acid and yields more ions in solution.
3. $H_2SO_4 + NaOH \rightarrow NaHSO_4 + H_2O$; $NaHSO_4 + NaOH \rightarrow Na_2SO_4 + H_2O$
5. One way is to add it to $NaHCO_3$; if it bubbles, it is an acid. Alternatively, add the sample to litmus and look for a characteristic color change (red for acid, blue for base).
7. $$H^+ + {}^-\!:\!\ddot{\underset{..}{O}}\!:\!H \longrightarrow H_2O$$

   The O atom is donating an electron pair to the H^+ ion, making the base an electron pair donor and the acid an electron pair acceptor.

CHAPTER 11

Nuclear Chemistry

Opening Essay

Most of us may not be aware of a device in our homes that guards our safety and, at the same time, depends on radioactivity to operate properly. This device is a smoke detector.

A typical smoke detector contains an electric circuit that includes two metal plates about 1 cm apart. A battery in the circuit creates a voltage between the plates. Next to the plates is a small disk containing a tiny amount (~0.0002 g) of the radioactive element americium (Am). The radioactivity of the americium ionizes the air between the plates, causing a tiny current to constantly flow between them. (This constant drain on the battery explains why the batteries in smoke detectors should be replaced on a regular basis, whether the alarm has been triggered or not.)

When particles of smoke from a fire enter the smoke detector, they interfere with the ions between the metal plates, interrupting the tiny flow of current. When the current drops beneath a set value, another circuit triggers a loud alarm, warning of the possible presence of fire.

Although radioactive, the americium in a smoke detector is embedded in plastic and is not harmful unless the plastic package is taken apart, which is unlikely. Although many people experience an unfounded fear of radioactivity, smoke detectors provide an application of radioactivity that saves thousands of lives every year.

Many people think of nuclear chemistry in connection with the nuclear power industry and atomic bombs but do not realize that most smoke detectors rely on nuclear chemistry and save countless lives every year. The applications of nuclear chemistry may be more widespread than you think.

© *Thinkstock*

Most chemists pay little attention to the nucleus of an atom except to consider the number of protons it contains because that determines an element's identity. However, in nuclear chemistry, the composition of the nucleus and the changes that occur there are very important.

Applications of nuclear chemistry may be more widespread than you realize. Many people are aware of nuclear power plants and nuclear bombs, but nuclear chemistry also has applications ranging from smoke detectors to medicine, from the sterilization of food to the analysis of ancient artifacts. In this chapter, we will examine some of the basic concepts of nuclear chemistry and some of the nuclear reactions that are important in our everyday lives.

1. RADIOACTIVITY

LEARNING OBJECTIVE

1. Define and give examples of the major types of radioactivity.

We saw in Chapter 2 that atoms are composed of subatomic particles—protons, neutrons, and electrons. Protons and neutrons are located in the nucleus and provide most of the mass of the atom, while electrons circle the nucleus in shells and subshells and account for an atom's size.

We also introduced in Chapter 2 the notation for succinctly representing an isotope of a particular atom:

$$^{12}_{6}\text{C}$$

The element in this example, represented by the symbol C, is carbon. Its atomic number, 6, is the lower left subscript on the symbol and is the number of protons in the atom. The mass number, the superscript to the upper left of the symbol, is the sum of the number of protons and neutrons in the nucleus of this particular isotope. In this case, the mass number is 12, which means that the number of neutrons in the atom is 12 − 6 = 6 (that is, the mass number of the atom minus the number of protons in the nucleus equals the number of neutrons). Occasionally, the atomic number is omitted in this notation because the symbol of the element itself conveys its characteristic atomic number. The two isotopes of hydrogen, ^{2}H and ^{3}H, are given their own names: deuterium (D) and tritium (T), respectively. Another way of expressing a particular isotope is to list the mass number after the element name, like carbon-12 or hydrogen-3.

radioactivity

Emanations of particles and radiation from atomic nuclei.

Atomic theory in the 19th century presumed that nuclei had fixed compositions. But in 1896, the French scientist Henri Becquerel found that a uranium compound placed near a photographic plate made an image on the plate, even if the compound was wrapped in black cloth. He reasoned that the uranium compound was emitting some kind of radiation that passed through the cloth to expose the photographic plate. Further investigations showed that the radiation was a combination of particles and electromagnetic rays, with its ultimate source as the atomic nucleus. These emanations were ultimately called, collectively, **radioactivity**.

alpha particle

A type of radioactive emission that is equivalent to a helium atom nucleus.

There are three main forms of radioactive emissions. The first is called an **alpha particle**, which is symbolized by the Greek letter α. An alpha particle is composed of two protons and two neutrons, and so is the same as a helium nucleus. (We often use $^{4}_{2}$He to represent an alpha particle.) It has a 2+ charge. When a radioactive atom emits an alpha particle, the original atom's atomic number decreases by two (because of the loss of two protons), and its mass number decreases by four (because of the loss of four nuclear particles). We can represent the emission of an alpha particle with a chemical equation—for example, the alpha-particle emission of uranium-235 is as follows:

$$^{235}_{92}\text{U} \rightarrow {}^{4}_{2}\text{He} + {}^{231}_{90}\text{Th}$$

How do we know that a product of the reaction is $^{231}_{90}$Th? We use the law of conservation of matter, which says that matter cannot be created or destroyed. This means we must have the same number of protons and neutrons on both sides of the chemical equation. If our uranium nucleus loses 2 protons, there are 90 protons remaining, identifying the element as thorium. Moreover, if we lose 4 nuclear particles of the original 235, there are 231 remaining. Thus, we use subtraction to identify the isotope of the thorium atom—in this case, $^{231}_{90}$Th.

Chemists often use the names *parent isotope* and *daughter isotope* to represent the original atom and the product other than the alpha particle. In the previous example, $^{235}_{92}$U is the parent isotope, and $^{231}_{90}$Th is the daughter isotope. When one element changes into another in this manner, it undergoes *radioactive decay*.

EXAMPLE 1

Write the nuclear equation that represents the radioactive decay of radon-222 by alpha particle emission and identify the daughter isotope.

Solution

Radon has an atomic number of 86, so the parent isotope is represented as $^{222}_{86}Rn$. We represent the alpha particle as $^{4}_{2}He$ and use subtraction (222 – 4 = 218 and 86 – 2 = 84) to identify the daughter isotope as an isotope of polonium, $^{218}_{84}Po$:

$$^{222}_{86}Rn \rightarrow ^{4}_{2}He + ^{218}_{84}Po$$

SKILL-BUILDING EXERCISE

1. Write the nuclear equation that represents the radioactive decay of polonium-209 by alpha particle emission and identify the daughter isotope.

The second major type of radioactive emission is called a **beta particle**, symbolized by the Greek letter β. A beta particle is an electron ejected from the nucleus (not from the shells of electrons about the nucleus) and has a 1– charge. We can also represent a beta particle as $^{0}_{-1}e$ or β^-. The net effect of beta particle emission on a nucleus is that a neutron is converted to a proton. The overall mass number stays the same, but because the number of protons increases by one, the atomic number goes up by one. Carbon-14 decays by emitting a beta particle:

beta particle

A type of radioactive emission that is equivalent to an electron.

$$^{14}_{6}C \rightarrow ^{14}_{7}N + ^{0}_{-1}e$$

Again, the sum of the atomic numbers is the same on both sides of the equation, as is the sum of the mass numbers. (Note that the electron is assigned an "atomic number" of 1–, equal to its charge.)

The third major type of radioactive emission is not a particle but rather a very energetic form of electromagnetic radiation called **gamma rays**, symbolized by the Greek letter γ. Gamma rays themselves do not carry an overall electrical charge, but they may knock electrons out of atoms in a sample of matter and make it electrically charged (for which gamma rays are termed *ionizing radiation*). For example, in the radioactive decay of radon-222, both alpha and gamma radiation are emitted, with the latter having an energy of 8.2×10^{-14} J per nucleus decayed:

gamma ray

A type of radioactive emission that is a very energetic form of electromagnetic radiation.

$$^{222}_{86}Rn \rightarrow ^{218}_{84}Po + ^{4}_{2}He + \gamma$$

This may not seem like much energy, but if 1 mol of radon atoms were to decay, the gamma ray energy would be 49 million kJ!

EXAMPLE 2

Write the nuclear equation that represents the radioactive decay of boron-12 by beta particle emission and identify the daughter isotope. A gamma ray is emitted simultaneously with the beta particle.

Solution

The parent isotope is ${}^{12}_{5}\text{B},$ while one of the products is an electron, ${}^{0}_{-1}\text{e}.$ So that the mass and atomic numbers have the same value on both sides, the mass number of the daughter isotope must be 12, and its atomic number must be 6. The element having an atomic number of 6 is carbon. Thus, the complete nuclear equation is as follows:

$${}^{12}_{5}\text{B} \rightarrow {}^{12}_{6}\text{C} + {}^{0}_{-1}\text{e} + \gamma$$

The daughter isotope is ${}^{12}_{6}\text{C}.$

SKILL-BUILDING EXERCISE

1. Write the nuclear equation that represents the radioactive decay of iodine-131 by beta particle emission and identify the daughter isotope. A gamma ray is emitted simultaneously with the beta particle.

Alpha, beta, and gamma emissions have different abilities to penetrate matter. The relatively large alpha particle is easily stopped by matter (although it may impart a significant amount of energy to the matter it contacts). Beta particles penetrate slightly into matter, perhaps a few centimeters at most. Gamma rays can penetrate deeply into matter and can impart a large amount of energy into the surrounding matter. Table 11.1 summarizes the properties of the three main types of radioactive emissions.

TABLE 11.1 The Three Main Forms of Radioactive Emissions

Characteristic	Alpha Particles	Beta Particles	Gamma Rays
symbols	α, ${}^{4}_{2}\text{He}$	β, ${}^{0}_{-1}\text{e}$	γ
identity	helium nucleus	electron	electromagnetic radiation
charge	2+	1−	none
mass number	4	0	0
penetrating power	minimal (will not penetrate skin)	short (will penetrate skin and some tissues slightly)	deep (will penetrate tissues deeply)

spontaneous fission

The breaking apart of an atomic nucleus into smaller nuclei.

Occasionally, an atomic nucleus breaks apart into smaller pieces in a radioactive process called **spontaneous fission (or fission)**. Typically, the daughter isotopes produced by fission are a varied mix of products, rather than a specific isotope as with alpha and beta particle emission. Often, fission produces excess neutrons that will sometimes be captured by other nuclei, possibly inducing additional radioactive events. Uranium-235 undergoes spontaneous fission to a small extent. One typical reaction is

$${}^{235}_{92}\text{U} \rightarrow {}^{139}_{56}\text{Ba} + {}^{94}_{36}\text{Kr} + 2{}^{1}_{0}\text{n}$$

where ${}^{1}_{0}\text{n}$ is a neutron. As with any nuclear process, the sums of the atomic numbers and the mass numbers must be the same on both sides of the equation. Spontaneous fission is found only in large nuclei. The smallest nucleus that exhibits spontaneous fission is lead-208.

Note

Fission is the radioactive process used in nuclear power plants and one type of nuclear bomb.

CONCEPT REVIEW EXERCISE

1. What are the major types of radioactivity? Write chemical equations demonstrating each type.

ANSWER

1. The major types of radioactivity are alpha decay, beta decay, and gamma ray emission; alpha decay with gamma emission: ${}^{222}_{86}Rn \rightarrow {}^{218}_{84}Po + {}^{4}_{2}He + \gamma$; beta decay: ${}^{14}_{6}C \rightarrow {}^{14}_{7}N + {}^{0}_{-1}e$ (answers will vary)

KEY TAKEAWAY

- The major types of radioactivity include alpha particles, beta particles, and gamma rays.

EXERCISES

1. Define *radioactivity*.
2. Give an example of a radioactive isotope.
3. How many protons and neutrons are in each isotope?
   a. ${}^{11}_{5}B$
   b. ${}^{27}_{13}Al$
   c. ${}^{56}Fe$
   d. ${}^{224}Rn$
4. How many protons and neutrons are in each isotope?
   a. ${}^{2}_{1}H$
   b. ${}^{112}_{48}Cd$
   c. ${}^{252}Es$
   d. ${}^{40}K$
5. Describe an alpha particle. What nucleus is it equivalent to?
6. Describe a beta particle. What subatomic particle is it equivalent to?
7. Explain what gamma rays are.
8. Explain why it is inappropriate to refer to gamma rays as gamma "particles."
9. Plutonium has an atomic number of 94. Write the chemical equation for the alpha particle emission of ${}^{244}Pu$. What is the daughter isotope?
10. Francium has an atomic number of 87. Write the chemical equation for the alpha particle emission of ${}^{212}Fr$. What is the daughter isotope?
11. Tin has an atomic number of 50. Write the chemical equation for the beta particle emission of ${}^{121}Sn$. What is the daughter isotope?
12. Technetium has an atomic number of 43. Write the chemical equation for the beta particle emission of ${}^{99}Tc$. What is the daughter isotope?
13. Energies of gamma rays are typically expressed in units of megaelectron volts (MeV), where 1 MeV = 1.602×10^{-13} J. Using data provided in the text, calculate the energy, in megaelectron volts, of the gamma ray emitted when radon-222 decays.
14. The gamma ray emitted when oxygen-19 gives off a beta particle is 0.197 MeV. What is its energy in joules? (See Exercise 13 for the definition of a megaelectron volt.)
15. Which penetrates matter more deeply—alpha particles or beta particles? Suggest ways to protect yourself against both particles.
16. Which penetrates matter more deeply—alpha particles or gamma rays? Suggest ways to protect yourself against both emissions.
17. Define *nuclear fission*.
18. What general characteristic is typically necessary for a nucleus to undergo spontaneous fission?

ANSWERS

1. Radioactivity is the spontaneous emission of particles and radiation from atomic nuclei.
3. a. 5 protons; 6 neutrons
   b. 13 protons; 14 neutrons
   c. 26 protons; 30 neutrons
   d. 86 protons; 138 neutrons
5. An alpha particle is a combination of two protons and two neutrons and is equivalent to a helium nucleus.
7. Gamma rays are high-energy electromagnetic radiation given off in radioactive decay.
9. ${}^{244}_{94}\text{Pu} \rightarrow {}^{4}_{2}\text{He} + {}^{240}_{92}\text{U}$; the daughter isotope is ${}^{240}_{92}\text{U}$, an atom of uranium.
11. ${}^{121}_{50}\text{Sn} \rightarrow {}^{0}_{-1}\text{e} + {}^{121}_{51}\text{Sb}$; the daughter isotope is ${}^{121}_{51}\text{Sb}$, an atom of antimony.
13. 0.512 MeV
15. Beta particles; shielding of the appropriate thickness can protect against both alpha and beta particles.
17. Nuclear fission is when large nuclei break down into smaller nuclei.

2. HALF-LIFE

LEARNING OBJECTIVE

1. **Define *half-life*.**
2. **Determine the amount of radioactive substance remaining after a given number of half-lives.**

half-life

The amount of time it takes for one-half of a radioactive isotope to decay.

Whether or not a given isotope is radioactive is a characteristic of that particular isotope. Some isotopes are stable indefinitely, while others are radioactive and decay through a characteristic form of emission. As time passes, less and less of the radioactive isotope will be present, and the level of radioactivity decreases. An interesting and useful aspect of radioactive decay is half-life. The **half-life** of a radioactive isotope is the amount of time it takes for one-half of the radioactive isotope to decay. The half-life of a specific radioactive isotope is constant; it is unaffected by conditions and is independent of the initial amount of that isotope.

Consider the following example. Suppose we have 100.0 g of ^{3}H (tritium, a radioactive isotope of hydrogen). It has a half-life of 12.3 y. After 12.3 y, half of the sample will have decayed to ^{3}He by emitting a beta particle, so that only 50.0 g of the original ^{3}H remains. After another 12.3 y—making a total of 24.6 y—another half of the remaining ^{3}H will have decayed, leaving 25.0 g of ^{3}H. After another 12.3 y—now a total of 36.9 y—another half of the remaining ^{3}H will have decayed, leaving 12.5 g of ^{3}H. This sequence of events is illustrated in Figure 11.1.

FIGURE 11.1 Radioactive Decay

During each successive half-life, half of the initial amount will radioactively decay.

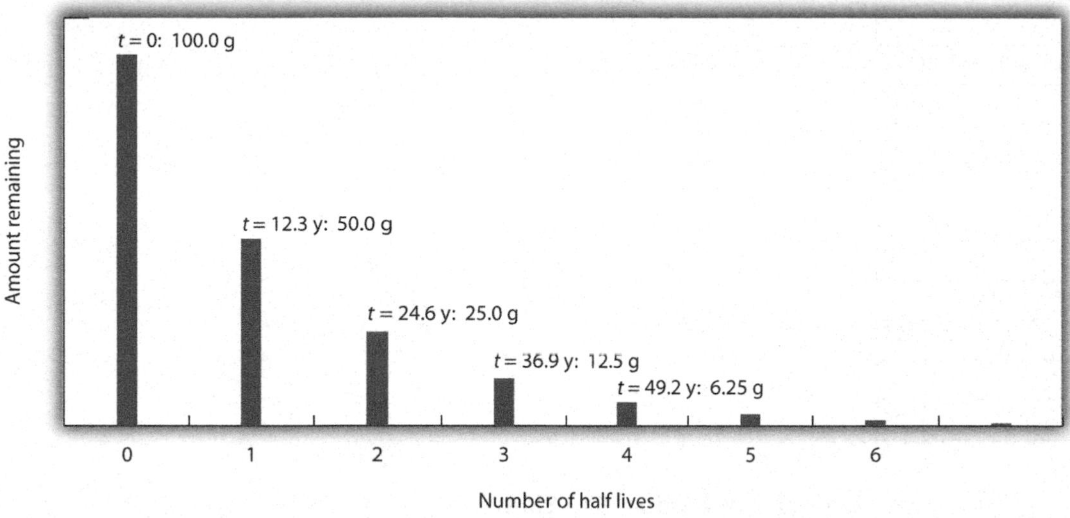

We can determine the amount of a radioactive isotope remaining after a given number half-lives by using the following expression:

$$\text{amount remaining} = \text{initial amount} \times \left(\frac{1}{2}\right)^n$$

where n is the number of half-lives. This expression works even if the number of half-lives is not a whole number.

EXAMPLE 3

The half-life of ^{20}F is 11.0 s. If a sample initially contains 5.00 g of ^{20}F, how much ^{20}F remains after 44.0 s?

Solution

If we compare the time that has passed to the isotope's half-life, we note that 44.0 s is exactly 4 half-lives, so using the previous equation, $n = 4$. Substituting and solving results in the following:

$$\text{amount remaining} = 5.00 \text{ g} \times \left(\frac{1}{2}\right)^4$$

$$\text{amount remaining} = 5.00 \text{ g} \times \frac{1}{16}$$

$$\text{amount remaining} = 0.313 \text{ g}$$

Less than one-third of a gram of ^{20}F remains.

SKILL-BUILDING EXERCISE

1. The half-life of ^{44}Ti is 60.0 y. A sample initially contains 0.600 g of ^{44}Ti. How much ^{44}Ti remains after 180.0 y?

Half-lives of isotopes range from fractions of a microsecond to billions of years. Table 11.2 lists the half-lives of some isotopes.

TABLE 11.2 Half-Lives of Various Isotopes

Isotope	Half-Life
^{3}H	12.3 y
^{14}C	5,730 y
^{40}K	1.26×10^9 y
^{51}Cr	27.70 d
^{90}Sr	29.1 y
^{131}I	8.04 d
^{222}Rn	3.823 d
^{235}U	7.04×10^8 y
^{238}U	4.47×10^9 y
^{241}Am	432.7 y
^{248}Bk	23.7 h
^{260}Sg	4 ms

Looking Closer: Half-Lives of Radioactive Elements

Many people think that the half-life of a radioactive element represents the amount of time an element is radioactive. In fact, it is the time required for half—not all—of the element to decay radioactively. Occasionally, however, the daughter element is also radioactive, so its radioactivity must also be considered.

The expected working life of an ionization-type smoke detector (described in the opening essay) is about 10 years. In that time, americium-241, which has a half-life of about 432 y, loses less than 4% of its radioactivity. A half-life of 432 y may seem long to us, but it is not very long as half-lives go. Uranium-238, the most common isotope of uranium, has a half-life of about 4.5×10^9 y, while thorium-232 has a half-life of 14×10^9 y.

On the other hand, some nuclei have extremely short half-lives, presenting challenges to the scientists who study them. The longest-lived isotope of lawrencium, ^{262}Lr, has a half-life of 3.6 h, while the shortest-lived isotope of lawrencium, ^{252}Lr, has a half-life of 0.36 s. As of this writing, the largest atom ever detected has atomic number 118, mass number 293, and a half-life of 120 ns. Can you imagine how quickly an experiment must be done to determine the properties of elements that exist for so short a time?

CONCEPT REVIEW EXERCISES

1. Define *half-life*.
2. Describe a way to determine the amount of radioactive isotope remaining after a given number of half-lives.

ANSWERS

1. Half-life is the amount of time needed for half of a radioactive material to decay.
2. take half of the initial amount for each half-life of time elapsed

KEY TAKEAWAYS

- Natural radioactive processes are characterized by a half-life, the time it takes for half of the material to decay radioactively.
- The amount of material left over after a certain number of half-lives can be easily calculated.

EXERCISES

1. Do all isotopes have a half-life? Explain.
2. Which is more radioactive—an isotope with a long half-life or an isotope with a short half-life?
3. How long does it take for 1.00 g of ^{103}Pd to decay to 0.125 g if its half-life is 17.0 d?
4. How long does it take for 2.00 g of ^{94}Nb to decay to 0.0625 g if its half-life is 20,000 y?
5. It took 75 y for 10.0 g of a radioactive isotope to decay to 1.25 g. What is the half-life of this isotope?
6. It took 49.2 s for 3.000 g of a radioactive isotope to decay to 0.1875 g. What is the half-life of this isotope?

ANSWERS

1. Only radioactive isotopes have half-lives.
3. 51.0 d
5. 25 y

3. UNITS OF RADIOACTIVITY

LEARNING OBJECTIVE

1. **Express amounts of radioactivity in a variety of units.**

In Section 2, we used mass to indicate the amount of radioactive substance present. This is only one of several units used to express amounts of radiation. Some units describe the number of radioactive events occurring per unit time, while others express the amount of a person's exposure to radiation.

Perhaps the direct way of reporting radioactivity is the number of radioactive decays per second. One decay per second is called one **becquerel (Bq)**. Even in a small mass of radioactive material, however, there are many thousands of decays or disintegrations per second. The unit **curie (Ci)**, now defined as 3.7×10^{10} decays per second, was originally defined as the number of decays per second in 1 g of radium. Many radioactive samples have activities that are on the order of microcuries (μCi) or more. Both the becquerel and curie can be used in place of grams to describe quantities of radioactive material. As an example, the amount of americium in an average smoke detector has an activity of 0.9 μCi.

becquerel (Bq)

A unit of radioactivity equal to one decay per second.

curie (Ci)

A unit of radioactivity equal to 3.7×10^{10} decays per second.

Note

The unit *becquerel* is named after Henri Becquerel, who discovered radioactivity in 1896. The unit *curie* is named after Polish scientist Marie Curie, who performed some of the initial investigations into radioactive phenomena in the early 1900s.

EXAMPLE 4

A sample of radium has an activity of 16.0 mCi (millicuries). If the half-life of radium is 1,600 y, how long before the sample's activity is 1.0 mCi?

Solution

The following table shows the activity of the radium sample over multiple half-lives:

Time in Years	Activity
0	16.0 mCi
1,600	8.0 mCi
3,200	4.0 mCi
4,800	2.0 mCi
6,400	1.0 mCi

Over a period of 4 half-lives, the activity of the radium will be halved four times, at which point its activity will be 1.0 mCi. Thus, it takes 4 half-lives, or 4 × 1,600 y = 6,400 y, for the activity to decrease to 1.0 mCi.

SKILL-BUILDING EXERCISE

1. A sample of radon has an activity of 60,000 Bq. If the half-life of radon is 15 h, how long before the sample's activity is 3,750 Bq?

Other measures of radioactivity are based on the effects it has on living tissue. Radioactivity can transfer energy to tissues in two ways: through the kinetic energy of the particles hitting the tissue and through the electromagnetic energy of the gamma rays being absorbed by the tissue. Either way, the transferred energy—like thermal energy from boiling water—can damage the tissue.

rad

A unit of radioactive exposure equal to 0.01 J/g of tissue.

The **rad** (an acronym for radiation absorbed dose) is a unit equivalent to a gram of tissue absorbing 0.01 J:

$$1 \text{ rad} = 0.01 \text{ J/g}$$

Another unit of radiation absorption is the gray (Gy):

$$1 \text{ Gy} = 100 \text{ rad}$$

The rad is more common. To get an idea of the amount of energy this represents, consider that the absorption of 1 rad by 70,000 g of H_2O (approximately the same mass as a 150 lb person) would increase its temperature by only 0.002°C. This may not seem like a lot, but it is enough energy to break about 1×10^{21} molecular C–C bonds in a person's body. That amount of damage would not be desirable.

rem

A unit of radioactive exposure that includes a factor to account for the type of radioactivity.

Predicting the effects of radiation is complicated by the fact that various tissues are affected differently by different types of emissions. To quantify these effects, the unit **rem** (an acronym for roentgen equivalent, man) is defined as

$$\text{rem} = \text{rad} \times \text{factor}$$

where *factor* is a number greater than or equal to 1 that takes into account the type of radioactive emission and sometimes the type of tissue being exposed. For beta particles, the factor equals 1. For alpha particles striking most tissues, the factor is 10, but for eye tissue, the factor is 30. Most radioactive emissions that people are exposed to are on the order of a few dozen millirems (mrem) or less; a medical X ray is about 20 mrem. A sievert (Sv) is a related unit and is defined as 100 rem.

What is a person's annual exposure to radioactivity and radiation? Table 11.3 lists the sources and annual amounts of radiation exposure. It may surprise you to learn that fully 82% of the radioactivity and radiation exposure we receive is from natural sources—sources we cannot avoid. Fully 10% of the exposure comes from our own bodies—largely from ^{14}C and ^{40}K.

TABLE 11.3 Average Annual Radiation Exposure (Approximate)

Source	Amount (mrem)
radon gas	200
medical sources	53
radioactive atoms in the body naturally	39
terrestrial sources	28
cosmic sources	28
consumer products	10
nuclear energy	0.05
Total	358

Note

Flying from New York City to San Francisco adds 5 mrem to your overall radiation exposure because the plane flies above much of the atmosphere, which protects us from most cosmic radiation.

The actual effects of radioactivity and radiation exposure on a person's health depend on the type of radioactivity, the length of exposure, and the tissues exposed. Table 11.4 lists the potential threats to health at various amounts of exposure over short periods of time (hours or days).

TABLE 11.4 Effects of Short-Term Exposure to Radioactivity and Radiation

Exposure (rem)	Effect
1 (over a full year)	no detectable effect
~20	increased risk of some cancers
~100	damage to bone marrow and other tissues; possible internal bleeding; decrease in white blood cell count
200–300	visible "burns" on skin, nausea, vomiting, and fatigue
>300	loss of white blood cells; hair loss
~600	death

One of the simplest ways of detecting radioactivity is by using a piece of photographic film embedded in a badge or a pen. On a regular basis, the film is developed and checked for exposure. A comparison of the exposure level of the film with a set of standard exposures indicates the amount of radiation a person was exposed to.

FIGURE 11.2
Detecting Radioactivity

A Geiger counter is a common instrument used to detect radioactivity.

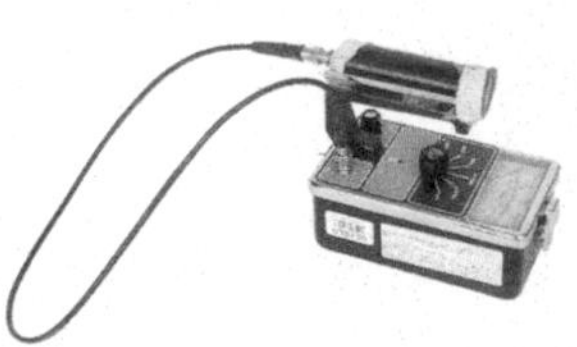

Another means of detecting radioactivity is an electrical device called a **Geiger counter** (Figure 11.2). It contains a gas-filled chamber with a thin membrane on one end that allows radiation emitted from radioactive nuclei to enter the chamber and knock electrons off atoms of gas (usually argon). The presence of electrons and positively charged ions causes a small current, which is detected by the Geiger counter and converted to a signal on a meter or, commonly, an audio circuit to produce an audible "click."

Geiger counter

An electrical device that detects radioactivity.

CONCEPT REVIEW EXERCISE

1. What units are used to quantify radioactivity?

ANSWER

1. the curie, the becquerel, the rad, the gray, the sievert, and the rem

KEY TAKEAWAY

- Radioactivity can be expressed in a variety of units, including rems, rads, and curies.

EXERCISES

1. Define *rad.*
2. Define *rem.*
3. How does a becquerel differ from a curie?
4. How is the curie defined?
5. A sample of radon gas has an activity of 140.0 mCi. If the half-life of radon is 1,500 y, how long before the activity of the sample is 8.75 mCi?
6. A sample of curium has an activity of 1,600 Bq. If the half-life of curium is 24.0 s, how long before its activity is 25.0 Bq?
7. If a radioactive sample has an activity of 65 µCi, how many disintegrations per second are occurring?
8. If a radioactive sample has an activity of 7.55×10^5 Bq, how many disintegrations per second are occurring?
9. Describe how a radiation exposure in rems is determined.
10. Which contributes more to the rems of exposure—alpha or beta particles? Why?
11. Use Table 11.4 to determine which sources of radiation exposure are inescapable and which can be avoided. What percentage of radiation is unavoidable?
12. What percentage of the approximate annual radiation exposure comes from radioactive atoms that are in the body naturally?
13. Explain how a film badge works to detect radiation.
14. Explain how a Geiger counter works to detect radiation.

ANSWERS

1. Known as the radiation absorbed dose, a rad is the absorption of 0.01 J/g of tissue.
3. A becquerel is smaller and equals 1 decay per second. A curie is 3.7×10^{10} Bq.
5. 6000 y
7. 2.41×10^6 disintegrations per second
9. The radiation exposure is determined by the number of rads times the quality factor of the radiation.
11. At least 16% (terrestrial and cosmic sources) of radioactivity is unavoidable; the rest depends on what else a person is exposed to.
13. A film badge uses film, which is exposed as it is subjected to radiation.

4. USES OF RADIOACTIVE ISOTOPES

LEARNING OBJECTIVE

1. Learn some applications of radioactivity.

Radioactive isotopes have a variety of applications. Generally, however, they are useful either because we can detect their radioactivity or we can use the energy they release.

Radioactive isotopes are effective tracers because their radioactivity is easy to detect. A **tracer** is a substance that can be used to follow the pathway of that substance through some structure. For instance, leaks in underground water pipes can be discovered by running some tritium-containing water through the pipes and then using a Geiger counter to locate any radioactive tritium subsequently present in the ground around the pipes. (Recall that tritium, ^3H, is a radioactive isotope of hydrogen.)

tracer

A substance that can be used to follow the pathway of that substance through some structure.

Tracers can also be used to follow the steps of a complex chemical reaction. After incorporating radioactive atoms into reactant molecules, scientists can track where the atoms go by following their radioactivity. One excellent example of this is the use of radioactive carbon-14 to determine the steps involved in the photosynthesis in plants. We know these steps because researchers followed the progress of the radioactive carbon-14 throughout the process.

Radioactive isotopes are useful for establishing the ages of various objects. The half-life of radioactive isotopes is unaffected by any environmental factors, so the isotope acts like an internal clock. For example, if a rock is analyzed and is found to contain a certain amount of uranium-235 and a certain amount of its daughter isotope, we can conclude that a certain fraction of the original uranium-235 has radioactively decayed. If half of the uranium has decayed, then the rock has an age of one half-life of uranium-235, or about 4.5×10^9 y. Many analyses like this, using a wide variety of isotopes, have indicated that the age of Earth itself is over 4×10^9 y. In another interesting example of radioactive dating, ^3H dating has been used to verify the stated vintages of some old fine wines.

Carbon-14 (half-life is 5,370 y) is particularly useful in determining the age of once-living artifacts (e.g., animal or plant matter). A tiny amount of carbon-14 is produced naturally in the upper reaches of the atmosphere, and living things incorporate some of it into their tissues, building up to a constant, although very low, level. Once a living thing dies, however, it no longer acquires carbon-14, and as time passes, the carbon-14 that was in the tissues decays. If a once-living artifact is discovered and analyzed many years after its death, with the remaining carbon-14 compared to the known constant level, an approximate age of the artifact can be determined. Using such methods, scientists determined that the age of the Shroud of Turin (made of linen, which comes from the flax plant, and purported by some to be the burial cloth of Jesus Christ; Figure 11.3) is about 600–700 y, not 2,000 y as claimed by some. Scientists were also able to use radiocarbon dating to show that the age of a mummified body found in the ice of the Alps was 5,300 y.

FIGURE 11.3
Shroud of Turin

In 1989, several groups of scientists used carbon-14 dating to demonstrate that the age of the Shroud of Turin was only 600–700 y. Many people still cling to a different notion, despite the scientific evidence.

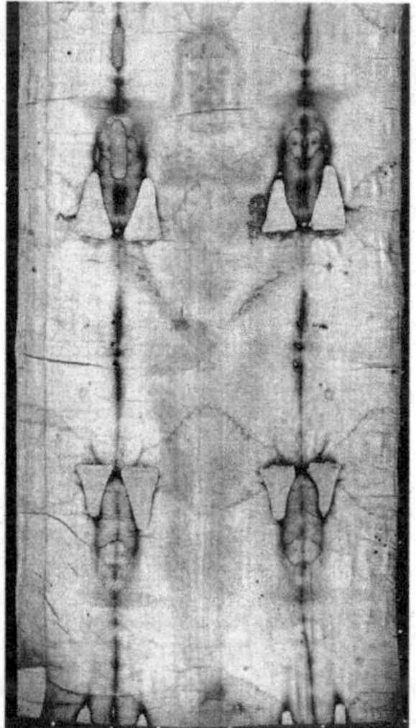

The radiation emitted by some radioactive substances can be used to kill microorganisms on a variety of foodstuffs, which extends the shelf life of these products. Produce such as tomatoes, mushrooms, sprouts, and berries are irradiated with the emissions from cobalt-60 or cesium-137. This exposure kills a lot of the bacteria that cause spoilage, so the produce stays fresh longer. Eggs and some meat, such as beef, pork, and poultry, can also be irradiated. Contrary to the belief of some people, irradiation of food *does not* make the food itself radioactive.

Radioactive isotopes have numerous medical applications—diagnosing and treating illnesses and diseases. One example of a diagnostic application is using radioactive iodine-131 to test for thyroid activity (Figure 11.4). The thyroid gland in the neck is one of the few places in the body with a significant concentration of iodine. To evaluate thyroid activity, a measured dose of iodine-131 is administered to a patient, and the next day a scanner is used to measure the amount of radioactivity in the thyroid gland. The amount of radioactive iodine that collects there is directly related to the activity of the thyroid, allowing trained physicians to diagnose both hyperthyroidism and hypothyroidism. Iodine-131 has a half-life of only 8 d, so the potential for damage due to exposure is minimal. Technetium-99 can also be used to test thyroid function. Bones, the heart, the brain, the liver, the lungs, and many other organs can be imaged in similar ways by using the appropriate radioactive isotope.

FIGURE 11.4 Medical Diagnostics

Radioactive iodine can be used to image the thyroid gland for diagnostic purposes.

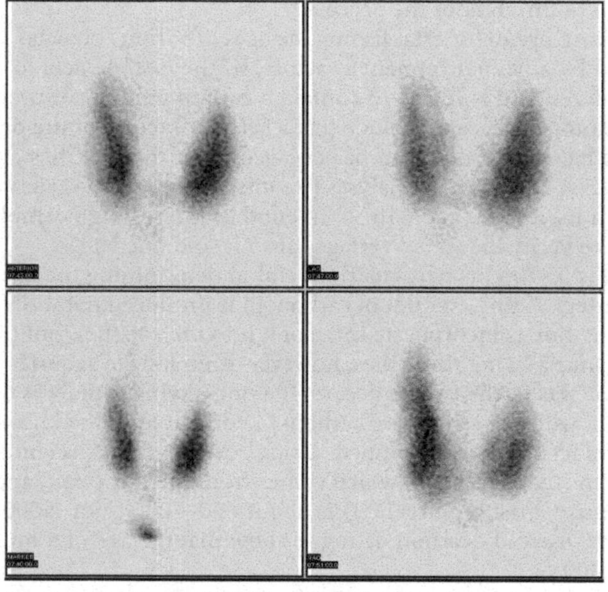

Source: Scan courtesy of Myo Han, http://en.wikipedia.org/wiki/File:Thyroid_scan.jpg.

Very little radioactive material is needed in these diagnostic techniques because the radiation emitted is so easy to detect. However, therapeutic applications usually require much larger doses because their purpose is to preferentially kill diseased tissues. For example, if a thyroid tumor is detected, a much larger infusion (thousands of rem, as opposed to a diagnostic dose of less then 40 rem) of iodine-131 could help destroy the tumor cells. Similarly, radioactive strontium is used to not only detect but also ease the pain of bone cancers. Table 11.5 lists several radioactive isotopes and their medical uses.

TABLE 11.5 Some Radioactive Isotopes That Have Medical Applications

Isotope	Use
^{32}P	cancer detection and treatment, especially in eyes and skin
^{59}Fe	anemia diagnosis
^{60}Co	gamma ray irradiation of tumors
^{99m}Tc	brain, thyroid, liver, bone marrow, lung, heart, and intestinal scanning; blood volume determination
^{131}I	diagnosis and treatment of thyroid function
^{133}Xe	lung imaging
^{198}Au	liver disease diagnosis

In addition to the direct application of radioactive isotopes to diseased tissue, the gamma ray emissions of some isotopes can be directed toward the tissue to be destroyed. Cobalt-60 is a useful isotope for this kind of procedure.

To Your Health: Positron Emission Tomography Scans

One relatively rare form of radioactivity is called *positron emission*. It is similar to beta particle emission, except that instead of emitting an electron, a nucleus emits a positively charged electron, called a *positron*. A positron is actually a piece of antimatter; therefore, when a positron encounters an electron, both particles are converted into high-energy gamma radiation.

Isotopes that emit positrons can be employed in a medical imaging technique called *positron emission tomography (PET)*. A patient receives a compound containing a positron-emitting isotope, either intravenously or by ingestion. The radioactive compound travels throughout the body, and the patient is then pushed slowly through a ring of sensors that detect the gamma radiation given off by the annihilation of positrons and electrons. A computer connected to the sensors constructs a three-dimensional image of the interior of part or all of the patient's body, allowing doctors to see organs or tumors or regulate the function of various organs (such as the brain or the heart) to diagnose the medical condition of the patient.

Two isotopes that undergo positron emission are carbon-11 and fluorine-18, with half-lives of 20.4 and 110 min, respectively. Both isotopes can be incorporated into sugar molecules and introduced into the body. Doctors can use the intensity of gamma ray emission to find tissues that metabolize the sugar faster than other tissues; fast-metabolizing tissue is one sign of a malignant (i.e., cancerous) tumor. Researchers use similar techniques to map areas of the brain that are most active during specific tasks, such as reading or speaking.

PET is one of many diagnostic and treatment methods that physicians use to improve the quality of our lives. It is one of the many positive uses of radioactivity in society.

This patient is undergoing a PET scan after having been injected with a positron-emitting isotope.

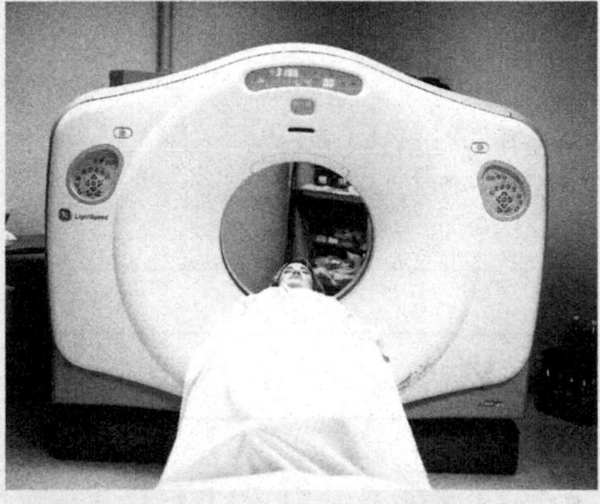

CONCEPT REVIEW EXERCISE

1. Describe some of the different ways that amounts of radioactivity are applied in society.

ANSWER

1. Radioactive isotopes are used in dating, as tracers, and in medicine as diagnostic and treatment tools.

KEY TAKEAWAY

- Radioactivity has several practical applications, including tracers, medical applications, dating once-living objects, and the preservation of food.

EXERCISES

1. Define *tracer* is and give an example of how tracers work.
2. Name two isotopes that have been used as tracers.
3. Explain how radioactive dating works.
4. Name an isotope that has been used in radioactive dating.
5. The current disintegration rate for carbon-14 is 14.0 Bq. A sample of burnt wood discovered in an archaeological excavation is found to have a carbon-14 decay rate of 3.5 Bq. If the half-life of carbon-14 is 5,700 y, approximately how old is the wood sample?
6. A small asteroid crashes to Earth. After chemical analysis, it is found to contain 1 g of technetium-99 to every 3 g of ruthenium-99, its daughter isotope. If the half-life of technetium-99 is 210,000 y, approximately how old is the asteroid?
7. What do you think are some of the positive aspects of irradiation of food?
8. What do you think are some of the negative aspects of irradiation of food?
9. Describe how iodine-131 is used to both diagnose and treat thyroid problems.
10. List at least five organs that can be imaged using radioactive isotopes.
11. Which radioactive emissions can be used therapeutically?
12. Which isotope is used in therapeutics primarily for its gamma ray emissions?

ANSWERS

1. A tracer follows the path of a chemical or a physical process. One of the uses of a tracer is following the path of water underground (answers will vary).
3. Radioactive dating works by comparing the amounts of parent and daughter isotopes and calculating back to how long ago all of the material was just the parent isotope.
5. about 11,400 y
7. increased shelf life (answers will vary)
9. Iodine-131 is preferentially absorbed by the thyroid gland and can be used to measure the gland's activity or destroy bad cells in the gland.
11. gamma rays, beta particles, or alpha particles

5. NUCLEAR ENERGY

LEARNING OBJECTIVES

1. **Explain where nuclear energy comes from.**
2. **Describe the difference between fission and fusion.**

Nuclear changes occur with a simultaneous release of energy. Where does this energy come from? If we could precisely measure the masses of the reactants and the products of a nuclear reaction, we would notice that the amount of mass drops slightly in the conversion from reactants to products. Consider the following nuclear reaction, in which the molar mass of each species is indicated to four decimal places:

$$\underset{235.0439}{^{235}\text{U}} \rightarrow \underset{138.9088}{^{139}\text{Ba}} + \underset{93.9343}{^{94}\text{Kr}} + \underset{2\times 1.0087}{2\,^{1}\text{n}}$$

If we compare the mass of the reactant (235.0439) to the masses of the products (sum = 234.8605), we notice a mass difference of −0.1834 g, or −0.0001834 kg. Where did this mass go?

According to Albert Einstein's theory of relativity, energy (E) and mass (m) are related by the following equation:

$$E = mc^2$$

where c is the speed of light, or 3.00×10^8 m/s. In the course of the uranium nuclear chemical reaction, the mass difference is converted to energy, which is given off by the reaction:

$$E = (-0.0001834\ \text{kg})(3.00 \times 10^8\ \text{m/s})^2 = -1.65 \times 10^{13}\ \text{J} = -1.65 \times 10^{10}\ \text{kJ}$$

That is, 16.5 billion kJ of energy are given off every time 1 mol of uranium-235 undergoes this nuclear reaction. This is an extraordinary amount of energy. Compare it to combustion reactions of hydrocarbons, which give off about 650 kJ/mol of energy for every CH_2 unit in the hydrocarbon—on the order of *hundreds* of kilojoules per mole. Nuclear reactions give off *billions* of kilojoules per mole.

If this energy could be properly harvested, it would be a significant source of energy for our society. **Nuclear energy** involves the controlled harvesting of energy from fission reactions. The reaction can be controlled because the fission of uranium-235 (and a few other isotopes, such as plutonium-239) can be artificially initiated by injecting a neutron into a uranium nucleus. The overall nuclear equation, with energy included as a product, is then as follows:

nuclear energy

The controlled harvesting of energy from fission reactions.

$$^{235}\text{U} + {}^{1}\text{n} \rightarrow {}^{139}\text{Ba} + {}^{94}\text{Kr} + 3\,{}^{1}\text{n} + \text{energy}$$

Thus, by the careful addition of extra neutrons into a sample of uranium, we can control the fission process and obtain energy that can be used for other purposes.

Note

Artificial or induced radioactivity was first demonstrated in 1934 by Irène Joliot-Curie and Frédéric Joliot, the daughter and son-in-law of Marie Curie.

EXAMPLE 5

Plutonium-239 can absorb a neutron and undergo a fission reaction to produce an atom of gold-204 and an atom of phosphorus-31. Write the balanced nuclear equation for the process and determine the number of neutrons given off as part of the reaction.

Solution

Using the data given, we can write the following initial equation:

$$^{1}_{0}\text{n} + {}^{239}_{94}\text{Pu} \rightarrow {}^{204}_{79}\text{Au} + {}^{31}_{15}\text{P} + ?{}^{1}_{0}\text{n}$$

In balanced nuclear equations, the sums of the subscripts on each sides of the equation are the same, as are the sums of the superscripts. The subscripts are already balanced: 0 + 94 = 94 and 79 + 15 = 94. The superscripts on the left equal 240 (1 + 239) but equal 235 (204 + 31) on the right. We need five more mass number units on the right. Five neutrons should be the products of the process for the mass numbers to balance. (Because the atomic number of a neutron is zero, including five neutrons on the right does not change the overall sum of the subscripts.) Thus, the balanced nuclear equation is as follows:

$$^{1}_{0}\text{n} + {}^{239}_{94}\text{Pu} \rightarrow {}^{204}_{79}\text{Au} + {}^{31}_{15}\text{P} + 5{}^{1}_{0}\text{n}$$

We predict that the overall process will give off five neutrons.

SKILL-BUILDING EXERCISE

1. Uranium-238 can absorb a neutron and undergo a fission reaction to produce an atom of cesium-135 and an atom of rubidium-96. Write the balanced nuclear equation for the process and determine the number of neutrons given off as part of the reaction.

nuclear reactor

An apparatus designed to carefully control the progress of a nuclear reaction and extract the resulting energy for useful purposes.

A **nuclear reactor** is an apparatus designed to carefully control the progress of a nuclear reaction and extract the resulting energy for useful purposes. Figure 11.5 shows a simplified diagram of a nuclear reactor. The energy from the controlled nuclear reaction converts liquid water into high-pressure steam, which is used to run turbines that generate electricity.

FIGURE 11.5 A Diagram of a Nuclear Power Plant for Generating Electricity

The two main components of the power plant are the nuclear reactor itself and the steam-driven turbine and electricity generator.

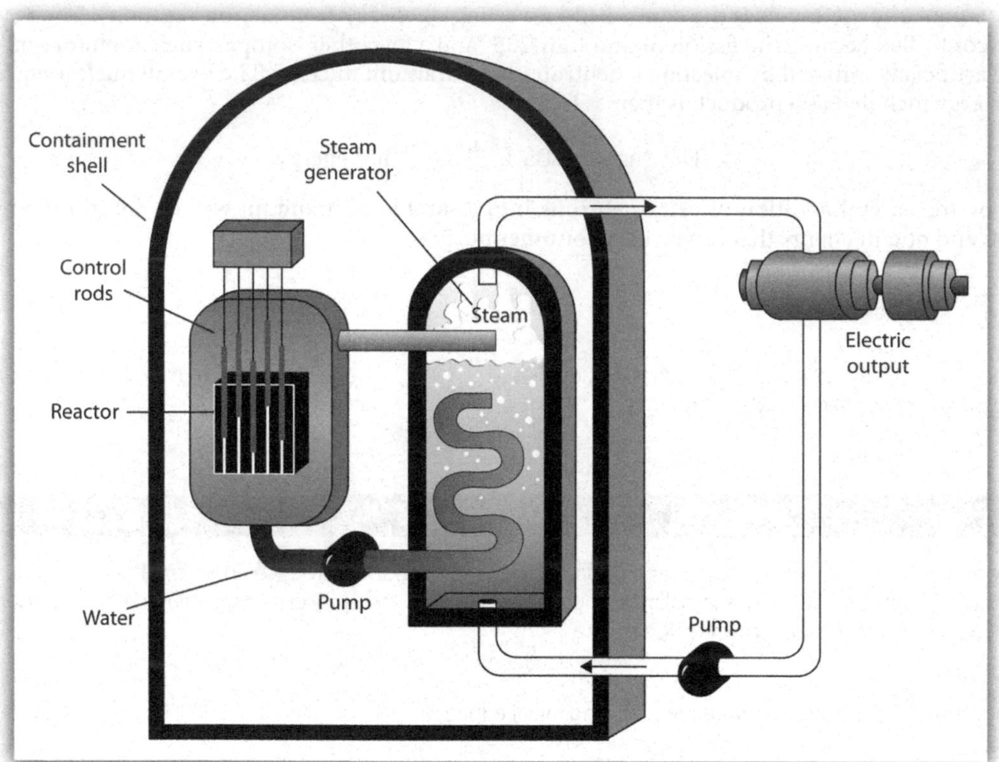

chain reaction

An exponential growth in a process.

Notice that the fission of uranium produces two more free neutrons than were present to begin with. These neutrons can themselves stimulate other uranium nuclei to undergo fission, releasing yet more energy and even more neutrons, which can in turn induce even more uranium fission. A single neutron can thus begin a process that grows exponentially in a phenomenon called a **chain reaction**:

$$1 \rightarrow 2 \rightarrow 4 \rightarrow 8 \rightarrow 16 \rightarrow 32 \rightarrow 64 \rightarrow 128 \rightarrow 256 \rightarrow 512 \rightarrow 1{,}024 \rightarrow 2{,}048 \rightarrow 4{,}096 \rightarrow 8{,}192 \rightarrow 16{,}384 \rightarrow \ldots$$

atomic bomb

A weapon that depends on a nuclear chain reaction to generate immense forces.

Because energy is produced with each fission event, energy is also produced exponentially and in an uncontrolled fashion. The quick production of energy creates an explosion. This is the mechanism behind the **atomic bomb**.

Note

The first controlled chain reaction was achieved on December 2, 1942, in an experiment supervised by Enrico Fermi in a laboratory underneath the football stadium at the University of Chicago.

Although fairly simple in theory, an atomic bomb is difficult to produce, in part because uranium-235, the isotope that undergoes fission, makes up only 0.7% of natural uranium; the rest is mostly uranium-238, which does not undergo fission. (Remember that the radioactive process that a nucleus undergoes is characteristic of the isotope.) To make uranium useful for nuclear reactors, the uranium in uranium-235 must be *enriched* to about 3%. Enrichment of uranium is a laborious and costly series of physical and chemical separations. To be useful in an atomic bomb, the uranium in uranium-235 must be enriched to 70% or more. At lesser concentrations, the chain reaction cannot sustain itself, so no explosion is produced.

Fusion is another nuclear process that can be used to produce energy. In this process, smaller nuclei are combined to make larger nuclei, with an accompanying release of energy. One example is the hydrogen fusion, which makes helium. While the steps of the process are complicated, the net reaction is:

fusion

A nuclear process in which small nuclei are combined into larger nuclei, releasing energy.

$$4\,^{1}\text{H} \rightarrow \,^{4}\text{He} + 2.58 \times 10^{12}\text{ J}$$

Notice that the amount of energy given off per mole of reactant is only a fraction of the amount given off by the fission of 1 mol of uranium-235. On a mass (per gram) basis, however, the hydrogen fusion emits many times more energy than fission does. In addition, the product of fission is helium gas, not a wide range of isotopes (some of which are also radioactive) produced by fission.

The practical problem is that to perform fusion, extremely high pressures and temperatures are necessary. Currently, the only known stable systems undergoing fusion are the interiors of stars. The conditions necessary for fusion can be created using an atomic bomb, but the resulting fusion is uncontrollable (and the basis for another type of bomb, a hydrogen bomb). Currently, researchers are looking for safe, controlled ways of producing useful energy using fusion.

Career Focus: Nuclear Medicine Technologist

Generally speaking, a radiological technician deals with X ray equipment and procedures. A *nuclear medicine technologist* has similar responsibilities, using compounds containing radioactive isotopes to help diagnose and treat disease.

Nuclear medicine technologists administer the substances containing the radioactive isotope and subsequently operate the apparatus that detects the radiation produced by radioactive decay. The apparatus may be as simple as a piece of photographic film or as complex as a series of computer-controlled electronic detectors. The images obtained by the technologist are interpreted by a specially trained physician.

One of the chief responsibilities of a nuclear medicine technologist is safety. Improper exposure to radioactivity can be harmful to both patient and technologist alike. Therefore, the technologist must adhere to strict safety standards to keep unnecessary exposure as low as possible. The technologist must also know how to dispose of waste materials safely and appropriately.

CONCEPT REVIEW EXERCISES

1. How is nuclear energy produced?
2. What is the difference between fission and fusion?

ANSWERS

1. Nuclear energy is produced by carefully controlling the speed of a fission reaction.
2. In fission, large nuclei break down into small ones; in fusion, small nuclei combine to make larger ones. In both cases, a lot of energy is emitted.

KEY TAKEAWAYS

- Nuclear energy comes from tiny mass changes in nuclei as radioactive processes occur.
- In fission, large nuclei break apart and release energy; in fusion, small nuclei merge together and release energy.

EXERCISES

1. In the spontaneous fission of uranium-233, the following reaction occurs:

   $$^{233}U + {}^{1}n \rightarrow {}^{142}Ce + {}^{82}Se + 10\,{}^{1}n$$

   For every mole of ^{233}U that decays, 0.1355 g of mass is lost. How much energy is given off per mole of ^{233}U reacted?

2. In the spontaneous fission of plutonium-241, the following reaction occurs:

   $$^{241}Pu + {}^{1}n \rightarrow {}^{104}Ru + {}^{124}Sn + 14\,{}^{1}n$$

   For every mole of ^{241}Pu that decays, 0.1326 g of mass is lost. How much energy is given off per mole of ^{241}Pu reacted?

3. The two rarer isotopes of hydrogen—deuterium and tritium—can also be fused to make helium by the following reaction:

   $$^{2}H + {}^{3}H \rightarrow {}^{4}He + {}^{1}n$$

   In the course of this reaction, 0.01888 g of mass is lost. How much energy is emitted in the reaction of 1 mol of deuterium and tritium?

4. A process called *helium burning* is thought to occur inside older stars, forming carbon:

   $$3\,{}^{4}He \rightarrow {}^{12}C$$

   If the reaction proceeds with 0.00781 g of mass lost on a molar basis, how much energy is given off?

5. Briefly describe how a nuclear reactor generates electricity.
6. Briefly describe the difference between how a nuclear reactor works and how a nuclear bomb works.
7. What is a chain reaction?
8. Why must uranium be enriched to supply nuclear energy?

ANSWERS

1. 1.22×10^{13} J
3. 1.70×10^{12} J
5. A nuclear reactor generates heat, which is used to generate steam that turns a turbine to generate electricity.
7. A chain reaction is an ever-expanding series of processes that, if left unchecked, can cause a runaway reaction and possibly an explosion.

6. END-OF-CHAPTER MATERIAL

Chapter Summary

To ensure that you understand the material in this chapter, you should review the meanings of the bold terms in the following summary and ask yourself how they relate to the topics in the chapter.

Some atoms have unstable nuclei that emit particles and high-energy electromagnetic radiation to form new elements that are more stable. This emission of particles and electromagnetic radiation is called **radioactivity**. There are three main types of spontaneous radioactive emission: **alpha particles**, which are equivalent to helium nuclei; **beta particles**, which are electrons; and **gamma radiation**, which is high-energy electromagnetic radiation. Another type of radioactive process is **spontaneous fission**, in which large nuclei spontaneously break apart into smaller nuclei and, often, neutrons. In all forms of radioactivity, new elements are formed from the radioactive reactants.

Radioactive isotopes decay at different rates. The rate of an isotope's decay is expressed as a **half-life**, which is the amount of time required for half of the original material to decay. The length of its half-life is a characteristic of the particular isotope and can range from less than microseconds to billions of years.

Amounts of radioactivity are measured in several different ways. A **becquerel** is equal to one radioactive decay per second. A **curie** represents 3.7×10^{10} decays per second. Other units describe the amount of energy absorbed by body tissues. One **rad** is equivalent to 0.01 joule of energy absorbed per gram of tissue. Different tissues react differently to different types of radioactivity. The **rem** unit takes into account not only the energy absorbed by the tissues, but also includes a numerical multiplication factor to account for the type of radioactivity and the type of tissue. The average annual radiation exposure of a person is less than 360 millirem, over 80% of which is from natural sources. Radioactivity can be detected using photographic film or other devices such as **Geiger counters**.

Radioactive isotopes have many useful applications. They can be used as **tracers** to follow the journey of a substance through a system, like an underground waterway or a metabolic pathway. Radioactive isotopes can be used to date objects, since the amount of parent and daughter isotopes can sometimes be measured very accurately. Radioactive emission can be used to sterilize food for a longer edible lifetime. There are also a number of diagnostic and therapeutic medical applications for radioactive isotopes.

Radioactive processes occur with simultaneous changes in energy. This **nuclear energy** can be used to generate power for human use. **Nuclear reactors** use the energy released by fission of large isotopes to generate electricity. When carefully controlled, fission can produce a **chain reaction** that facilitates the continuous production of energy. If not carefully controlled, a very quick production of energy can result, as in an **atomic bomb**. Natural uranium does not contain enough of the proper isotope of uranium to work in a nuclear reactor, so it must first be **enriched** in uranium-235. Forcing small nuclei together to make larger nuclei, a process called **fusion**, also gives off energy; however, scientists have yet to achieve a controlled fusion process.

ADDITIONAL EXERCISES

1. Given that many elements are metals, suggest why it would be unsafe to have radioactive materials in contact with acids.
2. Many alpha-emitting radioactive substances are relatively safe to handle, but inhaling radioactive dust can be very dangerous. Why?
3. Uranium can be separated from its daughter isotope thorium by dissolving a sample in acid and adding sodium iodide, which precipitates thorium(III) iodide:

   $$Th^{3+}(aq) + 3I^-(aq) \rightarrow ThI_3(s)$$

   If 0.567 g of Th^{3+} were dissolved in solution, how many milliliters of 0.500 M NaI(aq) would have to be added to precipitate all the thorium?
4. Thorium oxide can be dissolved in an acidic solution:

   $$ThO_2(s) + 4H^+ \rightarrow Th^{4+}(aq) + 2H_2O(\ell)$$

   How many milliliters of 1.55 M HCl(aq) are needed to dissolve 10.65 g of ThO_2?
5. Radioactive strontium is dangerous because it can chemically replace calcium in the human body. The bones are particularly susceptible to radiation damage. Write the nuclear equation for the beta emission of strontium-90.
6. Write the nuclear equation for the beta emission of iodine-131, the isotope used to diagnose and treat thyroid problems.
7. A common uranium compound is uranyl nitrate hexahydrate [$UO_2(NO_3)_2$_$6H_2O$]. What is the formula mass of this compound?
8. Plutonium forms three oxides: PuO, PuO_2, and Pu_2O_3. What are the formula masses of these three compounds?
9. A banana contains 600 mg of potassium, 0.0117% of which is radioactive potassium-40. If 1 g of potassium-40 has an activity of 2.626×10^5 Bq, what is the activity of a banana?
10. Smoke detectors typically contain about 0.25 mg of americium-241 as part of the smoke detection mechanism. If the activity of 1 g of americium-241 is 1.26×10^{11} Bq, what is the activity of americium-241 in the smoke detector?
11. Uranium hexafluoride (UF_6) reacts with water to make uranyl fluoride (UO_2F_2) and hydrogen fluoride (HF). Balance the following chemical equation:

    $$UF_6 + H_2O \rightarrow UO_2F_2 + HF$$

12. The cyclopentadienyl anion ($C_5H_5^-$) is an organic ion that can make ionic compounds with positive ions of radioactive elements, such as Np^{3+}. Balance the following chemical equation:

    $$NpCl_3 + Be(C_5H_5)_2 \rightarrow Np(C_5H_5)_3 + BeCl_2$$

ANSWERS

1. Acids can dissolve metals, making aqueous solutions.
3. 14.7 mL
5. $^{90}_{38}Sr \rightarrow ^{0}_{-1}e + ^{90}_{39}Y$
7. 502 g/mol
9. about 18 Bq
11. $UF_6 + 2H_2O \rightarrow UO_2F_2 + 4HF$

CHAPTER 12
Organic Chemistry: Alkanes and Halogenated Hydrocarbons

Opening Essay

Hydrocarbons are the simplest organic compounds, but they have interesting physiological effects. These effects depend on the size of the hydrocarbon molecules and where on or in the body they are applied. Alkanes of low molar mass—those with from 1 to approximately 10 or so carbon atoms—are gases or light liquids that act as anesthetics. Inhaling ("sniffing") these hydrocarbons in gasoline or aerosol propellants for their intoxicating effect is a major health problem that can lead to liver, kidney, or brain damage or to immediate death by asphyxiation by excluding oxygen.

Swallowed, liquid alkanes do little harm while in the stomach. In the lungs, however, they cause "chemical" pneumonia by dissolving fatlike molecules from cell membranes in the tiny air sacs (alveoli). The lungs become unable to expel fluids, just as in pneumonia caused by bacteria or viruses. People who swallow gasoline or other liquid alkane mixtures should not be made to vomit, as this would increase the chance of getting alkanes into the lungs. (There is no home-treatment antidote for gasoline poisoning; call a poison control center.)

Liquid alkanes with approximately 5–16 carbon atoms per molecule wash away natural skin oils and cause drying and chapping of the skin, while heavier liquid alkanes (those with approximately 17 or more carbon atoms per molecule) act as emollients (skin softeners). Such alkane mixtures as mineral oil and petroleum jelly can be applied as a protective film. Water and aqueous solutions such as urine will not dissolve such a film, which explains why petroleum jelly protects a baby's tender skin from diaper rash.

We begin our study of organic chemistry with the alkanes, compounds containing only two elements, carbon and hydrogen, and having only single bonds. There are several other kinds of hydrocarbons, distinguished by the types of bonding between carbon atoms and by the properties that result from that bonding. In Chapter 13 we will examine hydrocarbons with double bonds, with triple bonds, and with a special kind of bonding called *aromaticity*. Then in Chapter 14 we will study some compounds considered to be derived from hydrocarbons by replacing one or more hydrogen atoms with an oxygen-containing group. Chapter 15 focuses on organic acids and bases, after which we will be ready to look at the chemistry of life itself—biochemistry—in the remaining five chapters.

1. ORGANIC CHEMISTRY

LEARNING OBJECTIVE

1. **Recognize the composition and properties typical of organic and inorganic compounds.**

Scientists of the 18th and early 19th centuries studied compounds obtained from plants and animals and labeled them *organic* because they were isolated from "organized" (living) systems. Compounds isolated from nonliving systems, such as rocks and ores, the atmosphere, and the oceans, were labeled *inorganic*. For many years, scientists thought organic compounds could be made by only living organisms because they possessed a vital force found only in living systems. The vital force theory began to decline in 1828, when the German chemist Friedrich Wöhler synthesized urea from inorganic starting materials. He reacted silver cyanate (AgOCN) and ammonium chloride (NH_4Cl), expecting to get ammonium cyanate (NH_4OCN). What he expected is described by the following equation.

$$AgOCN + NH_4Cl \rightarrow AgCl + NH_4OCN$$

Instead, he found the product to be urea (NH_2CONH_2), a well-known organic material readily isolated from urine. This result led to a series of experiments in which a wide variety of organic compounds were made from inorganic starting materials. The vital force theory gradually went away as chemists learned that they could make many organic compounds in the laboratory.

organic chemistry

The study of the chemistry of carbon compounds.

inorganic chemistry

The study of the chemistry of all other elements.

Today **organic chemistry** is the study of the chemistry of the carbon compounds, and **inorganic chemistry** is the study of the chemistry of all other elements. It may seem strange that we divide chemistry into two branches—one that considers compounds of only one element and one that covers the 100-plus remaining elements. However, this division seems more reasonable when we consider that of tens of millions of compounds that have been characterized, the overwhelming majority are carbon compounds.

Note

The word *organic* has different meanings. Organic fertilizer, such as cow manure, is organic in the original sense; it is derived from living organisms. Organic foods generally are foods grown without synthetic pesticides or fertilizers. Organic chemistry is the chemistry of compounds of carbon.

Carbon is unique among the other elements in that its atoms can form stable covalent bonds with each other and with atoms of other elements in a multitude of variations. The resulting molecules can contain from one to millions of carbon atoms. In Chapter 12 through Chapter 15, we survey organic chemistry by dividing its compounds into families based on functional groups. (For general information about organic functional groups, see Chapter 4, [Unsupported Reference Type: chapter-section].) We begin with the simplest members of a family and then move on to molecules that are organic in the original sense—that is, they are made by and found in living organisms. These complex molecules (all containing carbon) determine the forms and functions of living systems and are the subject of biochemistry, a topic presented in Chapter 16 through Chapter 20.

Organic compounds, like inorganic compounds, obey all the natural laws. Often there is no clear distinction in the chemical or physical properties among organic and inorganic molecules. Nevertheless, it is useful to compare typical members of each class, as in Table 12.1. (Keep in mind, however, that there are exceptions to every category in this table.) To further illustrate typical differences among organic and inorganic compounds, Table 12.1 also lists properties of the inorganic compound sodium chloride (common table salt, NaCl) and the organic compound hexane (C_6H_{14}), a solvent that is used to extract soybean oil from soybeans (among other uses). Many compounds can be classified as organic or inorganic by the presence or absence of certain typical properties, as illustrated in Table 12.1.

TABLE 12.1 General Contrasting Properties and Examples of Organic and Inorganic Compounds

Organic	Hexane		Inorganic	NaCl
low melting points	−95°C		high melting points	801°C
low boiling points	69°C		high boiling points	1,413°C
low solubility in water; high solubility in nonpolar solvents	insoluble in water; soluble in gasoline		greater solubility in water; low solubility in nonpolar solvents	soluble in water; insoluble in gasoline
flammable	highly flammable		nonflammable	nonflammable
aqueous solutions do not conduct electricity	nonconductive		aqueous solutions conduct electricity	conductive in aqueous solution
exhibit covalent bonding	covalent bonds		exhibit ionic bonding	ionic bonds

CONCEPT REVIEW EXERCISES

1. Classify each compound as organic or inorganic.
   a. C_3H_8O
   b. $CaCl_2$
   c. $Cr(NH_3)_3Cl_3$
   d. $C_{30}H_{48}O_3N$
2. Which compound is likely organic and which is likely inorganic?
   a. a flammable compound that boils at 80°C and is insoluble in water
   b. a compound that does not burn, melts at 630°C, and is soluble in water

ANSWERS

1. a. organic
   b. inorganic
   c. inorganic
   d. organic
2. a. organic
   b. inorganic

KEY TAKEAWAY

- Organic chemistry is the study of carbon compounds, nearly all of which also contain hydrogen atoms.

EXERCISES

1. Classify each compound as organic or inorganic.
   a. C_6H_{10}
   b. $CoCl_2$
   c. $C_{12}H_{22}O_{11}$
2. Classify each compound as organic or inorganic.
   a. CH_3NH_2
   b. $NaNH_2$
   c. $Cu(NH_3)_6Cl_2$
3. Which member of each pair has a higher melting point?
   a. CH_3OH and NaOH
   b. CH_3Cl and KCl
4. Which member of each pair has a higher melting point?
   a. C_2H_6 and $CoCl_2$
   b. CH_4 and LiH

ANSWERS

1. a. organic
   b. inorganic
   c. organic
3. a. NaOH
   b. KCl

2. STRUCTURES AND NAMES OF ALKANES

LEARNING OBJECTIVE

1. **Identify and name simple (straight-chain) alkanes given formulas and write formulas for straight-chain alkanes given their names.**

hydrocarbon

The simplest organic compound, composed of carbon and hydrogen atoms only.

alkane (saturated hydrocarbon)

A hydrocarbon with only carbon-to-carbon single bonds and existing as a continuous chain of carbon atoms also bonded to hydrogen atoms

We began our study of organic chemistry in Chapter 4 with the **hydrocarbons**, the simplest organic compounds, which are composed of carbon and hydrogen atoms only. As we noted, there are several different kinds of hydrocarbons. They are distinguished by the types of bonding between carbon atoms and the properties that result from that bonding. Hydrocarbons with only carbon-to-carbon single bonds (C–C) and existing as a continuous chain of carbon atoms also bonded to hydrogen atoms are called **alkanes (or saturated hydrocarbons)**. *Saturated*, in this case, means that each carbon atom is bonded to four other atoms (hydrogen or carbon)—the most possible; there are no double or triple bonds in the molecules.

Note

The word *saturated* has the same meaning for hydrocarbons as it does for the dietary fats and oils: the molecule has no carbon-to-carbon double bonds (C=C). (For more information about fats and oils, see Chapter 17, [Unsupported Reference Type: chapter-section] and [Unsupported Reference Type: chapter-section].)

We introduced the three simplest alkanes—methane (CH_4), ethane (C_2H_6), and propane (C_3H_8)—in Chapter 4, [Unsupported Reference Type: chapter-section]. They are shown again in Figure 12.1. The flat representations shown do not accurately portray bond angles or molecular geometry. Methane has a tetrahedral shape that chemists often portray with wedges indicating bonds coming out toward you and dashed lines indicating bonds that go back away from you. (For more information about the shape of molecules, see Chapter 4, [Unsupported Reference Type: chapter-section].) An ordinary solid line indicates a bond in the plane of the page.

FIGURE 12.1 The Three Simplest Alkanes

```
     H             H   H              H   H   H
     |             |   |              |   |   |
  H—C—H         H—C—C—H           H—C—C—C—H
     |             |   |              |   |   |
     H             H   H              H   H   H

  Methane         Ethane            Propane
```

Recall from Chapter 4, [Unsupported Reference Type: chapter-section] that the VSEPR theory correctly predicts a tetrahedral shape for the methane molecule (Figure 12.2).

FIGURE 12.2 The Tetrahedral Methane Molecule

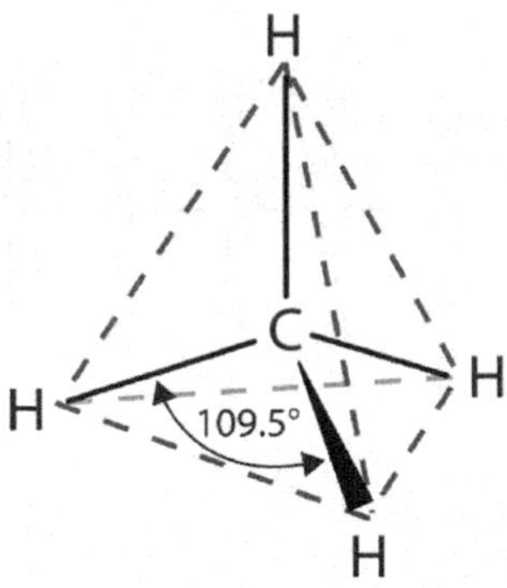

Methane (CH_4), ethane (C_2H_6), and propane (C_3H_8) are the beginning of a series of compounds in which any two members in a sequence differ by one carbon atom and two hydrogen atoms—namely, a CH_2 unit. The first 10 members of this series are given in Table 12.2.

TABLE 12.2 The First 10 Straight-Chain Alkanes

Name	Molecular Formula (C_nH_{2n+2})	Condensed Structural Formula	Number of Possible Isomers
methane	CH_4	CH_4	—
ethane	C_2H_6	CH_3CH_3	—
propane	C_3H_8	$CH_3CH_2CH_3$	—
butane	C_4H_{10}	$CH_3CH_2CH_2CH_3$	2
pentane	C_5H_{12}	$CH_3CH_2CH_2CH_2CH_3$	3
hexane	C_6H_{14}	$CH_3CH_2CH_2CH_2CH_2CH_3$	5
heptane	C_7H_{16}	$CH_3CH_2CH_2CH_2CH_2CH_2CH_3$	9
octane	C_8H_{18}	$CH_3CH_2CH_2CH_2CH_2CH_2CH_2CH_3$	18
nonane	C_9H_{20}	$CH_3CH_2CH_2CH_2CH_2CH_2CH_2CH_2CH_3$	35
decane	$C_{10}H_{22}$	$CH_3CH_2CH_2CH_2CH_2CH_2CH_2CH_2CH_2CH_3$	75

Consider the series in Figure 12.3. The sequence starts with C_3H_8, and a CH_2 unit is added in each step moving up the series. Any family of compounds in which adjacent members differ from each other by a definite factor (here a CH_2 group) is called a **homologous series.** The members of such a series, called *homologs*, have properties that vary in a regular and predictable manner. The principle of *homology* gives organization to organic chemistry in much the same way that the periodic table gives organization to inorganic chemistry. Instead of a bewildering array of individual carbon compounds, we can study a few members of a homologous series and from them deduce some of the properties of other compounds in the series.

homologous series

Any family of compounds in which adjacent members differ from each other by a definite factor.

FIGURE 12.3 Members of a Homologous Series

Each succeeding formula incorporates one carbon atom and two hydrogen atoms more than the previous formula.

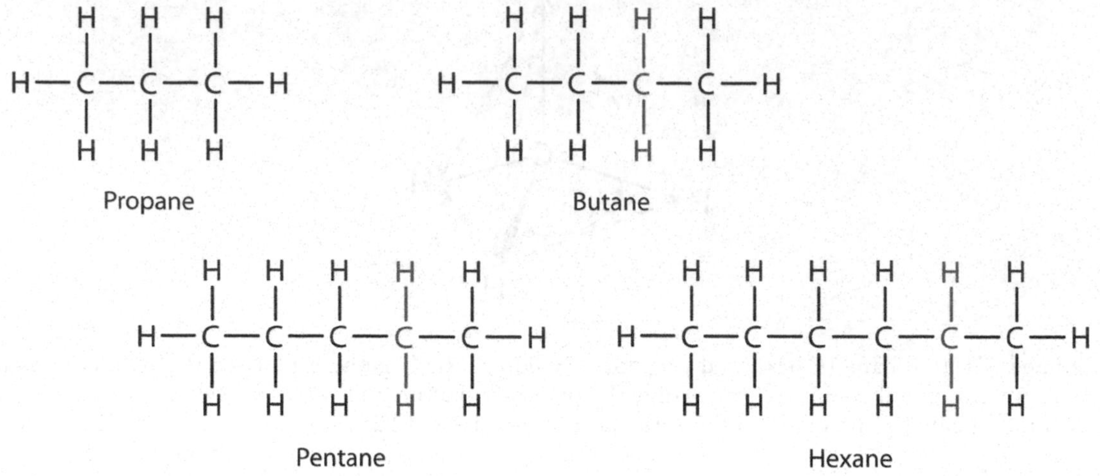

Propane

Butane

Pentane

Hexane

The principle of homology allows us to write a general formula for alkanes: C_nH_{2n+2}. Using this formula, we can write a molecular formula for any alkane with a given number of carbon atoms. For example, an alkane with eight carbon atoms has the molecular formula $C_8H_{(2 \times 8) + 2} = C_8H_{18}$.

CONCEPT REVIEW EXERCISES

1. In the homologous series of alkanes, what is the molecular formula for the member just above C_8H_{18}?
2. Use the general formula for alkanes to write the molecular formula of the alkane with 12 carbon atoms.

ANSWERS

1. C_9H_{20}
2. $C_{12}H_{26}$

KEY TAKEAWAY

- Simple alkanes exist as a homologous series, in which adjacent members differ by a CH_2 unit.

EXERCISES

1. What compounds contain fewer carbon atoms than C_3H_8 and are its homologs?
2. What compounds contain five to eight carbon atoms and are homologs of C_4H_{10}?

ANSWER

1. CH_4 and C_2H_6

3. BRANCHED-CHAIN ALKANES

LEARNING OBJECTIVE

1. **Learn how alkane molecules can have branched chains and recognize compounds that are isomers.**

We can write the structure of butane (C_4H_{10}) by stringing four carbon atoms in a row,

–C–C–C–C–

and then adding enough hydrogen atoms to give each carbon atom four bonds:

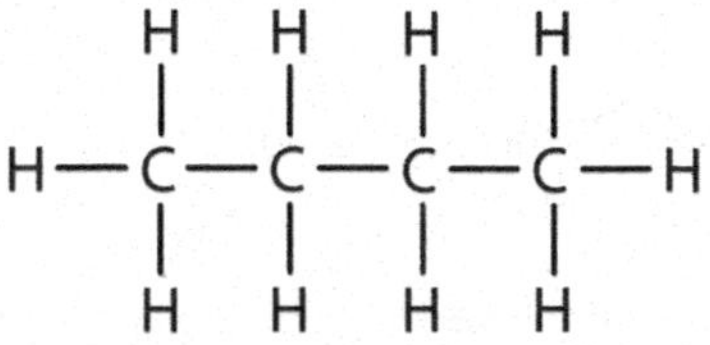

```
     H   H   H   H
     |   |   |   |
 H — C — C — C — C — H
     |   |   |   |
     H   H   H   H
```

The compound butane has this structure, but there is another way to put 4 carbon atoms and 10 hydrogen atoms together. Place 3 of the carbon atoms in a row and then branch the fourth one off the middle carbon atom:

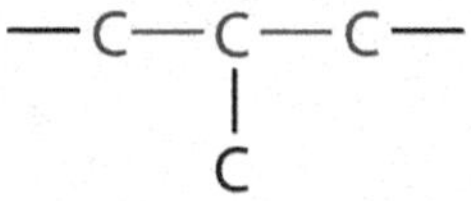

```
— C — C — C —
      |
      C
```

Now we add enough hydrogen atoms to give each carbon four bonds.

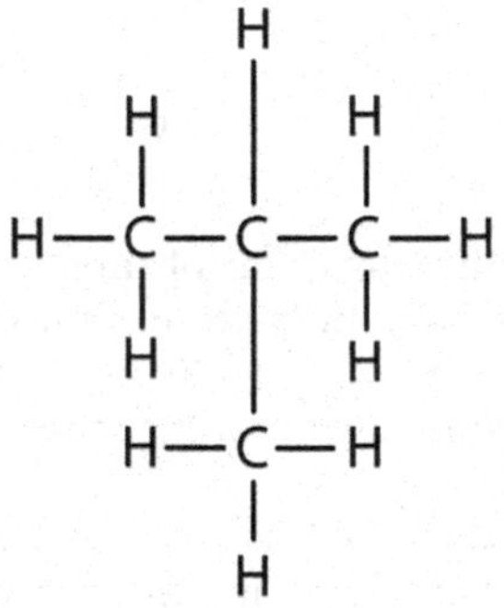

```
          H
     H    |    H
     |    |    |
 H — C —  C  — C — H
     |    |    |
     H    |    H
      H — C — H
          |
          H
```

There is a hydrocarbon that corresponds to this structure, which means that two different compounds have the same molecular formula: C_4H_{10}. The two compounds have different properties—for example, one boils at −0.5°C; the other at −11.7°C. Different compounds having the same molecular formula are called **isomers**. The compound with this branched chain is called *isobutane* (Figure 12.4).

isomers

Compounds having the same molecular formula but different structural formulas and properties.

FIGURE 12.4 Butane and Isobutane

The ball-and-stick models of these two compounds show them to be isomers; both have the molecular formula C_4H_{10}.

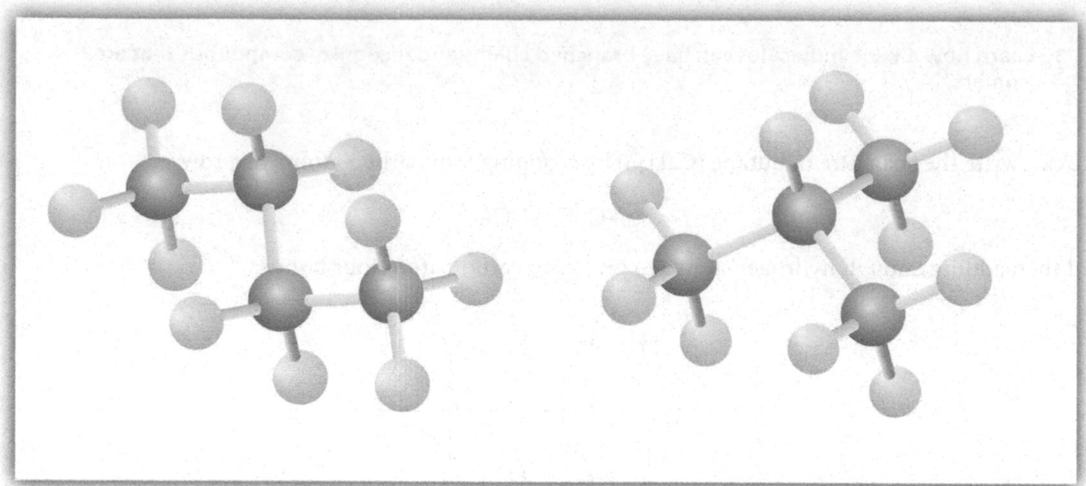

Notice that C_4H_{10} is depicted with a bent chain in Figure 12.4. The four-carbon chain may be bent in various ways because the groups can rotate freely about the C–C bonds. However, this rotation does not change the identity of the compound. It is important to realize that bending a chain does *not* change the identity of the compound; all of the following represent the same compound:

```
        C      C
        |      |
  C—C—C        C—C—C        C—C—C—C

  C—C—C        C—C—C        C—C
  |                |        |  |
  C                C        C  C
```

The formula of isobutane shows a continuous chain of three carbon atoms only, with the fourth attached as a branch off the middle carbon atom of the continuous chain.

Unlike C_4H_{10}, the compounds methane (CH_4), ethane (C_2H_6), and propane (C_3H_8) do not exist in isomeric forms because there is only one way to arrange the atoms in each formula so that each carbon atom has four bonds.

Next beyond C_4H_{10} in the homologous series is pentane. Each compound has the same molecular formula: C_5H_{12}. (Table 12.2 has a column identifying the number of possible isomers for the first 10 straight-chain alkanes.) The compound at the far left is pentane because it has all five carbon atoms in a continuous chain. The compound in the middle is isopentane; like isobutane, it has a one CH_3 branch off the second carbon atom of the continuous chain. The compound at the far right, discovered after the other two, was named neopentane (from the Greek *neos*, meaning "new"). Although all three have the same molecular formula, they have different properties, including boiling points: pentane, 36.1°C; isopentane, 27.7°C; and neopentane, 9.5°C.

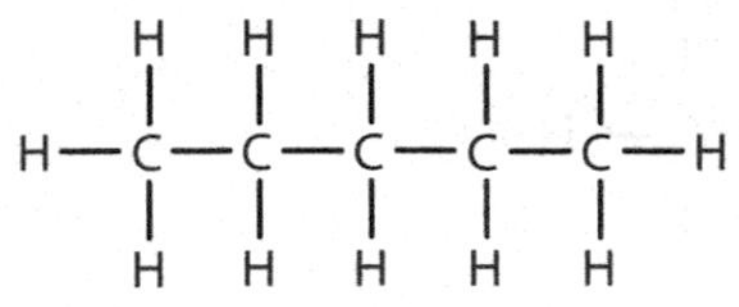

Pentane 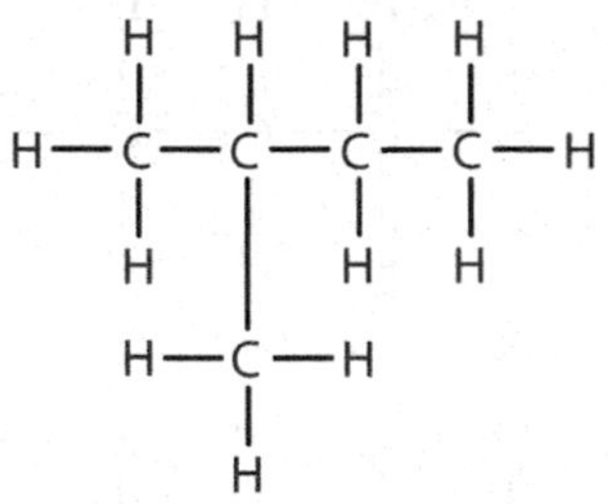 Isopentane 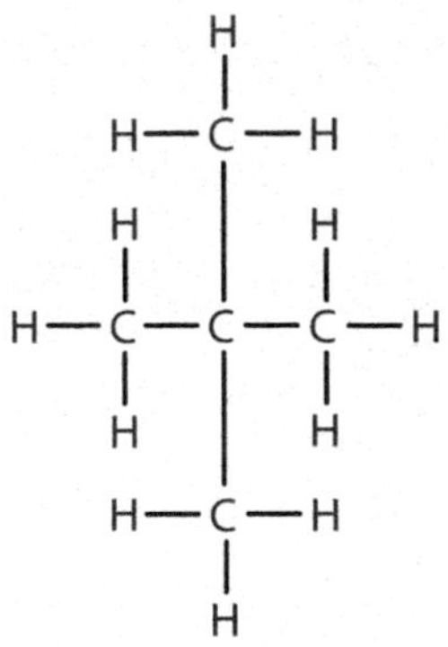 Neopentane

Note

A continuous (unbranched) chain of carbon atoms is often called a *straight chain* even though the tetrahedral arrangement about each carbon gives it a zigzag shape. Straight-chain alkanes are sometimes called *normal alkanes*, and their names are given the prefix *n*-. For example, butane is called *n*-butane. We will not use that prefix here because it is not a part of the system established by the International Union of Pure and Applied Chemistry.

CONCEPT REVIEW EXERCISES

1. In alkanes, can there be a two-carbon branch off the second carbon atom of a four-carbon chain? Explain.
2. A student is asked to write structural formulas for two different hydrocarbons having the molecular formula C_5H_{12}. She writes one formula with all five carbon atoms in a horizontal line and the other with four carbon atoms in a line, with a CH_3 group extending down from the first attached to the third carbon atom. Do these structural formulas represent different molecular formulas? Explain why or why not.

ANSWERS

1. No; the branch would make the longest continuous chain of five carbon atoms.
2. No; both are five-carbon continuous chains.

KEY TAKEAWAY

- Alkanes with four or more carbon atoms can exist in isomeric forms.

EXERCISES

1. Briefly identify the important distinctions between a straight-chain alkane and a branched-chain alkane.
2. How are butane and isobutane related? How do they differ?

3. Name each compound.
   a.

```
    H   H   H   H   H
    |   |   |   |   |
H — C — C — C — C — C — H
    |   |   |   |   |
    H   H   H   H   H
```

   b.

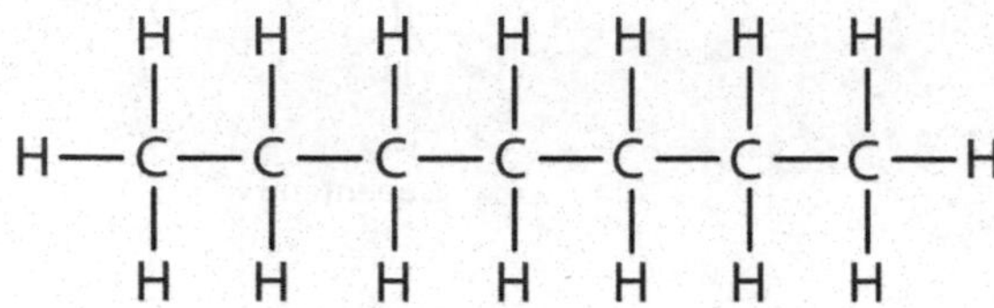

4. Write the structural formula for each compound.
   a. hexane
   b. octane
5. Indicate whether the structures in each set represent the same compound or isomers.
   a. $CH_3CH_2CH_2CH_3$ and

```
CH3CH2CH2CH2
           |
          CH2
```

   b. $CH_3CH_2CH_2CH_2CH_3$ and

```
CH3CH2CHCH3
        |
       CH3
```

ANSWERS

1. Straight-chain alkanes and branched-chain alkanes have different properties as well as different structures.
3. a. pentane
   b. heptane
5. a. no
   b. yes

4. CONDENSED STRUCTURAL AND LINE-ANGLE FORMULAS

LEARNING OBJECTIVES

1. **Write condensed structural formulas for alkanes given complete structural formulas.**
2. **Draw line-angle formulas given structural formulas.**

We use several kinds of formulas to describe organic compounds. A *molecular formula* shows only the kinds and numbers of atoms in a molecule. For example, the molecular formula C_4H_{10} tells us there are 4 carbon atoms and 10 hydrogen atoms in a molecule, but it doesn't distinguish between butane and isobutane. A **structural formula** shows all the carbon and hydrogen atoms and the bonds attaching them. Thus, structural formulas identify the specific isomers by showing the order of attachment of the various atoms.

structural formula

A chemical formula that shows how the atoms of a molecule are attached to one another.

Unfortunately, structural formulas are difficult to type/write and take up a lot of space. Chemists often use **condensed structural formulas** to alleviate these problems. The condensed formulas show hydrogen atoms right next to the carbon atoms to which they are attached, as illustrated for butane:

condensed structural formula

An organic chemical formula that shows the hydrogen atoms (or other atoms or groups) right next to the carbon atoms to which they are attached.

```
    H   H   H   H
    |   |   |   |
H — C — C — C — C — H
    |   |   |   |
    H   H   H   H
```

condenses to $CH_2CH_2CH_2CH_2$

The ultimate condensed formula is a **line-angle formula**, in which carbon atoms are implied at the corners and ends of lines, and each carbon atom is understood to be attached to enough hydrogen atoms to give each carbon atom four bonds. For example, we can represent pentane ($CH_3CH_2CH_2CH_2CH_3$) and isopentane [$(CH_3)_2CHCH_2CH_3$] as follows:

line-angle formula

An organic chemical formula in which carbon atoms are implied at the corners and ends of lines. Each carbon atom is understood to be attached to enough hydrogen atoms to give each carbon atom four bonds.

Pentane   Isopentane

Note

Parentheses in condensed structural formulas indicate that the enclosed grouping of atoms is attached to the adjacent carbon atom.

KEY TAKEAWAYS

- Condensed chemical formulas show the hydrogen atoms (or other atoms or groups) right next to the carbon atoms to which they are attached.
- Line-angle formulas imply a carbon atom at the corners and ends of lines. Each carbon atom is understood to be attached to enough hydrogen atoms to give each carbon atom four bonds.

EXERCISES

1. Write the condensed structural formula for each structural formula.

   a.

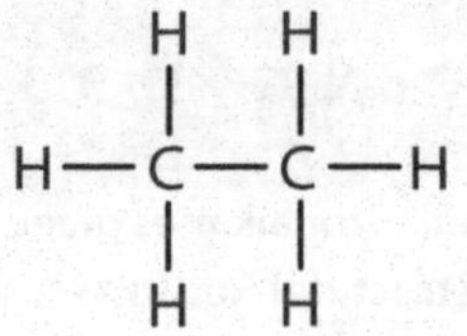

   b.

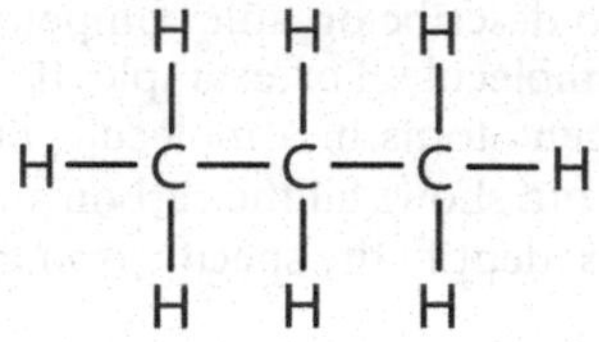

   c.

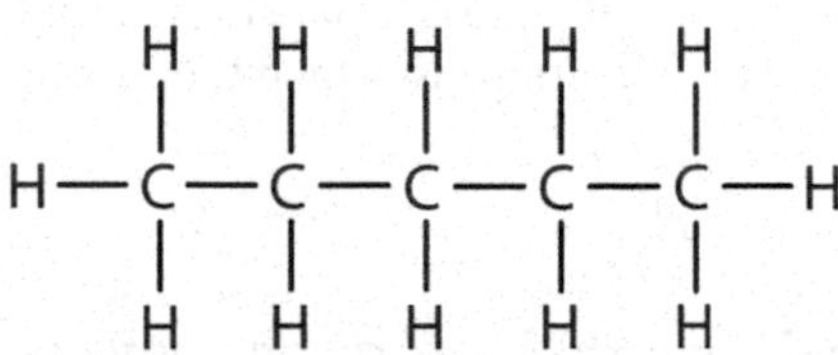

2. A condensed structural formula for isohexane can be written as $(CH_3)_2CHCH_2CH_2CH_3$. Draw the line-angle formula for isohexane.
3. Draw a line-angle formula for the compound $CH_3CH_2CH(CH_3)CH_2CH_2CH_3$.
4. Give the structural formula for the compound represented by this line-angle formula:

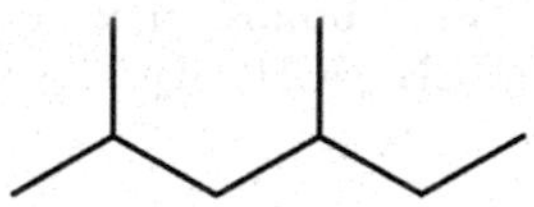

ANSWERS

1. a. CH_3CH_3

   b. $CH_3CH_2CH_3$

   c. $CH_3CH_2CH_2CH_2CH_3$

3.

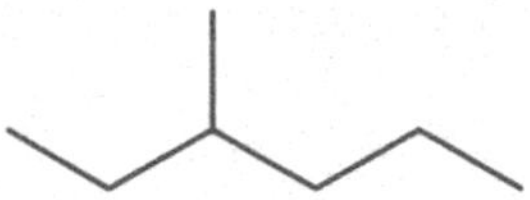

5. IUPAC NOMENCLATURE

LEARNING OBJECTIVE

1. **Name alkanes by the IUPAC system and write formulas for alkanes given IUPAC names.**

As noted in Table 12.2, the number of isomers increases rapidly as the number of carbon atoms increases. There are 3 pentanes, 5 hexanes, 9 heptanes, and 18 octanes. It would be difficult to assign unique individual names that we could remember. A systematic way of naming hydrocarbons and other organic compounds has been devised by the International Union of Pure and Applied Chemistry (IUPAC). These rules, used worldwide, are known as the **IUPAC System of Nomenclature**. (Some of the names we used earlier, such as isobutane, isopentane, and neopentane, do not follow these rules and are called *common names.*) A stem name (Table 12.3) indicates the number of carbon atoms in the longest continuous chain (LCC). Atoms or groups attached to this carbon chain, called *substituents*, are then named, with their positions indicated by numbers. For now, we will consider only those substituents called alkyl groups.

IUPAC System of Nomenclature

A systematic way of naming chemical substances so that each has a unique name.

TABLE 12.3 Stems That Indicate the Number of Carbon Atoms in Organic Molecules

Stem	Number
meth-	1
eth-	2
prop-	3
but-	4
pent-	5
hex-	6
hept-	7
oct-	8
non-	9
dec-	10

An **alkyl group** is a group of atoms that results when one hydrogen atom is removed from an alkane. The group is named by replacing the *-ane* suffix of the parent hydrocarbon with *-yl*. For example, the CH_3 group derived from methane (CH_4) results from subtracting one hydrogen atom and is called a *methyl group*.

The alkyl groups we will use most frequently are listed in Table 12.4. Alkyl groups are not independent molecules; they are parts of molecules that we consider as a unit to name compounds systematically.

alkyl group

A hydrocarbon group derived from an alkane by removal of a hydrogen atom.

TABLE 12.4 Common Alkyl Groups

Parent Alkane		Alkyl Group		Condensed Structural Formula
methane		methyl		CH_3–
ethane		ethyl		CH_3CH_2–
propane		propyl		$CH_3CH_2CH_2$–
		isopropyl		$(CH_3)_2CH$–
butane		butyl*		$CH_3CH_2CH_2CH_2$–

***There are four butyl groups, two derived from butane and two from isobutane. We will introduce the other three where appropriate.**

Simplified IUPAC rules for naming alkanes are as follows (demonstrated in Example 12.1).

1. **Name alkanes according to the LCC of carbon atoms in the molecule (rather than the total number of carbon atoms).** This LCC, considered the parent chain, determines the base name, to which we add the suffix *-ane* to indicate that the molecule is an alkane.
2. **If the hydrocarbon is branched, number the carbon atoms of the LCC.** Numbers are assigned in the direction that gives the lowest numbers to the carbon atoms with attached substituents. Hyphens are used to separate numbers from the names of substituents; commas separate numbers from each other. (The LCC need not be written in a straight line; for example, the LCC in the following has five carbon atoms.)

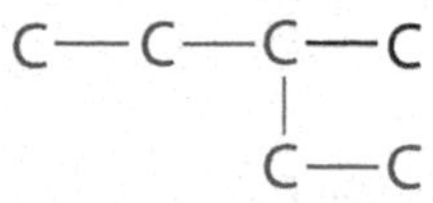

```
C—C—C—C
    |
    C—C
```

3. **Place the names of the substituent groups in alphabetical order before the name of the parent compound.** If the same alkyl group appears more than once, the numbers of all the carbon atoms to which it is attached are expressed. If the same group appears more than once on the same carbon atom, the number of that carbon atom is repeated as many times as the group appears. Moreover, the number of identical groups is indicated by the Greek prefixes *di-*, *tri-*, *tetra-*, and so on. These prefixes are *not* considered in determining the alphabetical order of the substituents. For example, ethyl is listed before dimethyl; the di- is simply ignored. The last alkyl group named is prefixed to the name of the parent alkane to form one word.

When these rules are followed, every unique compound receives its own exclusive name. The rules enable us to not only name a compound from a given structure but also draw a structure from a given name. The best way to learn how to use the IUPAC system is to put it to work, not just memorize the rules. It's easier than it looks.

EXAMPLE 1

Name each compound.

1. 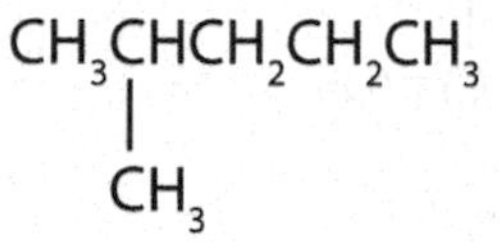 $CH_3CH(CH_3)CH_2CH_2CH_3$

```
CH3CHCH2CH2CH3
   |
   CH3
```

2. $CH_3CH(CH_3)CH_2CH_2CH(CH_3)CH_3$

```
CH3CHCH2CH2CHCH3
   |        |
   CH3      CH3
```

3. $CH_3CH_2CH_2C(CH_2CH_3)(CH_3)CH_2CH_2CH_2CH_3$

```
          CH2CH3
          |
CH3CH2CH2CCH2CH2CH2CH3
          |
          CH3
```

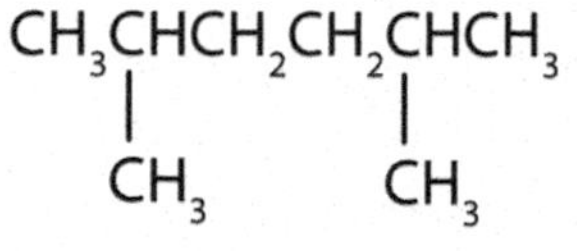

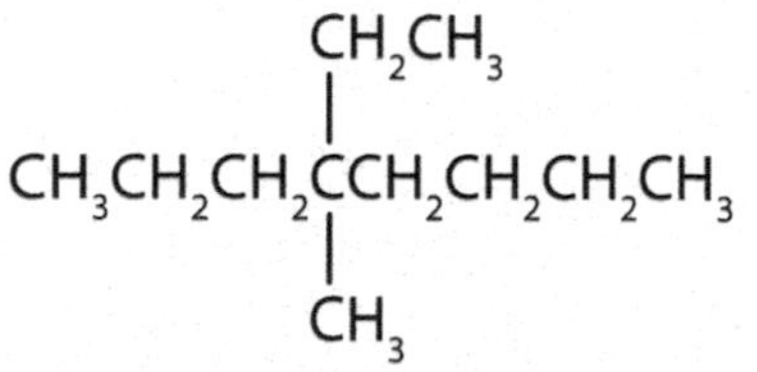

Solution

1. The LCC has five carbon atoms, and so the parent compound is pentane (rule 1). There is a methyl group (rule 2) attached to the second carbon atom of the pentane chain. The name is therefore 2-methylpentane.
2. The LCC has six carbon atoms, so the parent compound is hexane (rule 1). Methyl groups (rule 2) are attached to the second and fifth carbon atoms. The name is 2,5-dimethylhexane.
3. The LCC has eight carbon atoms, so the parent compound is octane (rule 1). There are methyl and ethyl groups (rule 2), both attached to the fourth carbon atom (counting from the *right* gives this carbon atom a lower number; rule 3). The correct name is thus 4-ethyl-4-methyloctane.

SKILL-BUILDING EXERCISE

Name each compound.

1.

$$\begin{array}{l} CH_3CH_2\underset{\displaystyle |}{C}HCH_2CH_3 \\ \quad\quad\quad\;\; CH_3 \end{array}$$

2.

$$\begin{array}{c} CH_3 \\ | \\ CH_3CCH_2CH_2CH_3 \\ | \\ CH_3 \end{array}$$

3.

$$\begin{array}{l} \quad\quad CH_3 \\ \quad\quad\;\; | \\ CH_3CH_2CCH_2CH_2CH_2CH_2CH_3 \\ \quad\quad\;\; | \\ \quad\quad CH_2CH_3 \end{array}$$

EXAMPLE 2

Draw the structure for each compound.

1. 2,3-dimethylbutane
2. 4-ethyl-2-methylheptane

Solution

In drawing structures, always start with the parent chain.

1. The parent chain is butane, indicating four carbon atoms in the LCC.

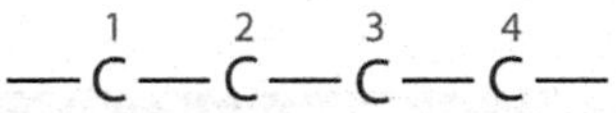

```
  1   2   3   4
—C—C—C—C—
```

Then add the groups at their proper positions. You can number the parent chain from either direction as long as you are consistent; just don't change directions before the structure is done. The name indicates two methyl (CH_3) groups, one on the second carbon atom and one on the third.

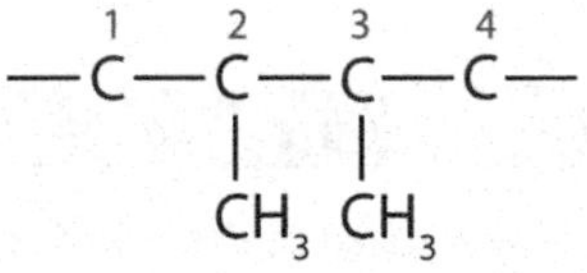

```
  1   2   3   4
—C—C—C—C—
      |    |
     CH3 CH3
```

Finally, fill in all the hydrogen atoms, keeping in mind that each carbon atom must have four bonds.

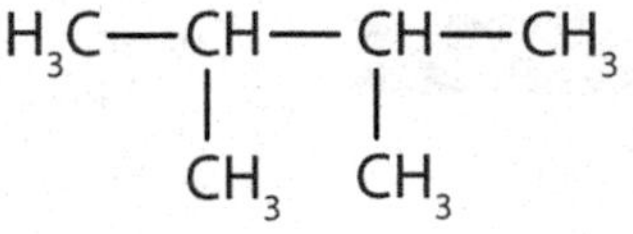

```
H3C—CH—CH—CH3
     |    |
    CH3  CH3
```

2. The parent chain is heptane in this case, indicating seven carbon atoms in the LCC.

–C–C–C–C–C–C–C–

Adding the groups at their proper positions gives

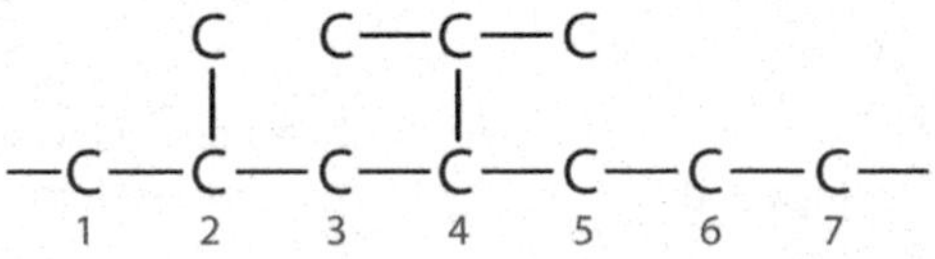

```
     C   C—C—C
     |       |
—C—C—C—C—C—C—C—
 1  2  3  4  5  6  7
```

Filling in all the hydrogen atoms gives the following condensed structural formulas:

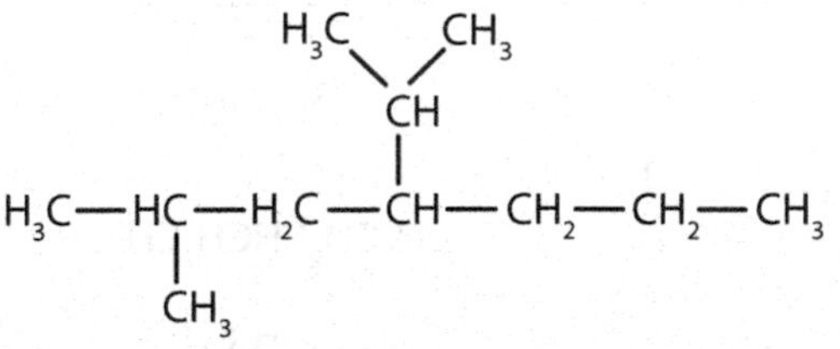

```
            H3C   CH3
               \ /
               CH                                   H
               |                              H3C—C—CH3
H3C—HC—H2C—CH—CH2—CH2—CH3    or                  |
     |                              CH3CHCH2CHCH2CH2CH2CH3
    CH3                                |
                                      CH3
```

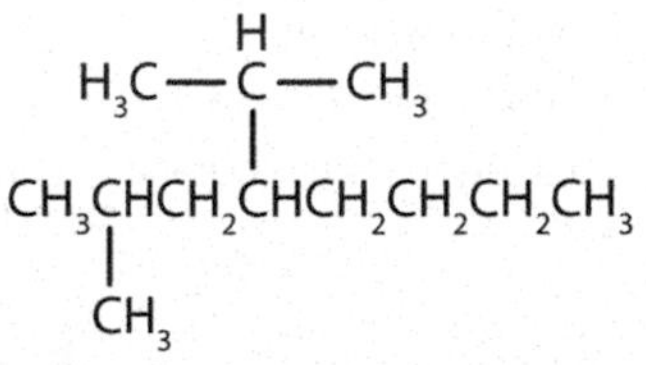

Note that the bonds (dashes) can be shown or not; sometimes they are needed for spacing.

SKILL-BUILDING EXERCISE

Draw the structure for each compound.

1. 4-ethyloctane
2. 3-ethyl-2-methylpentane

3. 3,3,5-trimethylheptane

CONCEPT REVIEW EXERCISES

1. What is a CH_3 group called when it is attached to a chain of carbon atoms—a substituent or a functional group?
2. Which type of name uses numbers to locate substituents—common names or IUPAC names?

ANSWERS

1. substituent
2. IUPAC names

KEY TAKEAWAY

- Alkanes have both common names and systematic names, specified by IUPAC.

EXERCISES

1. Briefly identify the important distinctions between an alkane and an alkyl group.
2. How many carbon atoms are present in each molecule?
   a. 2-methylbutane
   b. 3-ethylpentane
3. How many carbon atoms are present in each molecule?
   a. 2,3-dimethylbutane
   b. 3-ethyl-2-methylheptane
4. Draw the structure for each compound.
   a. 3-methylpentane
   b. 2,2,5-trimethylhexane
   c. 4-ethyl-3-methyloctane
5. Draw the structure for each compound.
   a. 2-methylpentane
   b. 4-ethyl-2-methylhexane
   c. 2,2,3,3-tetramethylbutane
6. Name each compound according to the IUPAC system.
   a.

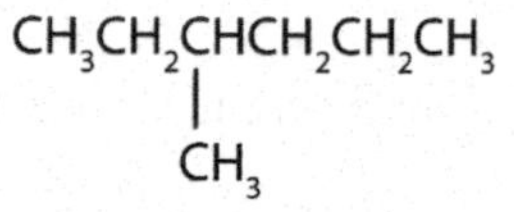

   $CH_3CH_2CHCH_2CH_2CH_3$ (with CH_3 attached to the third carbon)

   b.

   $CH_3CHCH_2CH_2CHCH_2CH_3$ (with CH_3 attached to the second carbon and CH_3 attached to the fifth carbon)

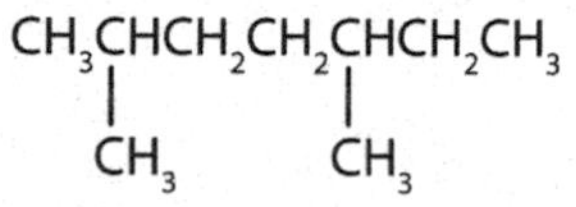

7. Name each compound according to the IUPAC system.
   a.

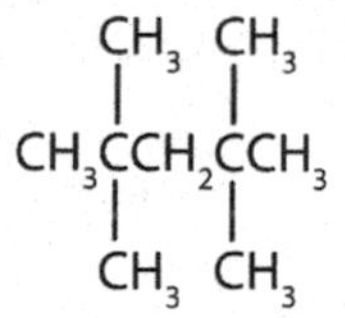

   $CH_3CCH_2CCH_3$ (with two CH_3 groups attached to the second carbon and two CH_3 groups attached to the fourth carbon)

   b.

   $CH_3CH_2CHCH_2CH_2CH_3$ (with CH_2CH_3 attached to the third carbon)

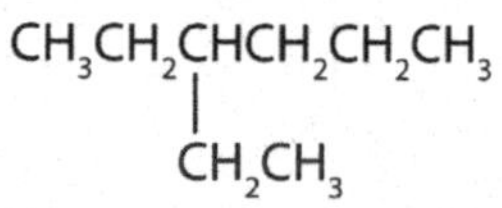

8. What is a substituent? How is the location of a substituent indicated in the IUPAC system?
9. Briefly identify the important distinctions between a common name and an IUPAC name.

ANSWERS

1. An alkane is a molecule; an alkyl group is not an independent molecule but rather a part of a molecule that we consider as a unit.
3. a. 6
   b. 10
5. a.

$$\begin{array}{l} CH_3CHCH_2CH_2CH_3 \\ \quad\;\; | \\ \quad\;\; CH_3 \end{array}$$

   b.

$$\begin{array}{l} \quad\;\; CH_3 \quad\;\; CH_2CH_3 \\ \quad\;\; | \qquad\quad\; | \\ CH_3CHCH_2CHCH_2CH_3 \end{array}$$

   c.

$$\begin{array}{l} \quad\;\; CH_3\; CH_3 \\ \quad\;\; | \qquad | \\ CH_3C\!-\!CCH_3 \\ \quad\;\; | \qquad | \\ \quad\;\; CH_3\; CH_3 \end{array}$$

7. a. 2,2,4,4-tetramethylpentane
   b. 3-ethylhexane
9. Common names are widely used but not very systematic; IUPAC names identify a parent compound and name other groups as substituents.

6. PHYSICAL PROPERTIES OF ALKANES

LEARNING OBJECTIVE

1. **Identify the physical properties of alkanes and describe trends in these properties.**

Because alkanes have relatively predictable physical properties and undergo relatively few chemical reactions other than combustion, they serve as a basis of comparison for the properties of many other organic compound families. Let's consider their physical properties first.

Table 12.5 describes some of the properties of some of the first 10 straight-chain alkanes. Because alkane molecules are nonpolar, they are insoluble in water, which is a polar solvent, but are soluble in nonpolar and slightly polar solvents. (For more information about solubility, see Chapter 9, [Unsupported Reference Type: chapter-section].) Consequently, alkanes themselves are commonly used as solvents for organic substances of low polarity, such as fats, oils, and waxes. Nearly all alkanes have densities less than 1.0 g/mL and are therefore less dense than water (the density of H_2O is 1.00 g/mL at 20°C). These properties explain why oil and grease do not mix with water but rather float on its surface.

TABLE 12.5 Physical Properties of Some Alkanes

Molecular Name	Formula	Melting Point (°C)	Boiling Point (°C)	Density (20°C)*	Physical State (at 20°C)
methane	CH_4	−182	−164	0.668 g/L	gas
ethane	C_2H_6	−183	−89	1.265 g/L	gas
propane	C_3H_8	−190	−42	1.867 g/L	gas
butane	C_4H_{10}	−138	−1	2.493 g/L	gas
pentane	C_5H_{12}	−130	36	0.626 g/mL	liquid
hexane	C_6H_{14}	−95	69	0.659 g/mL	liquid
octane	C_8H_{18}	−57	125	0.703 g/mL	liquid
decane	$C_{10}H_{22}$	−30	174	0.730 g mL	liquid

***Note the change in units going from gases (grams per liter) to liquids (grams per milliliter). Gas densities are at 1 atm pressure.**

FIGURE 12.5
Oil Spills

Crude oil coats the water's surface in the Gulf of Mexico after the *Deepwater Horizon* oil rig sank following an explosion. The leak was a mile below the surface, making it difficult to estimate the size of the spill. One liter of oil can create a slick 2.5 hectares (6.3 acres) in size. This and similar spills provide a reminder that hydrocarbons and water don't mix.

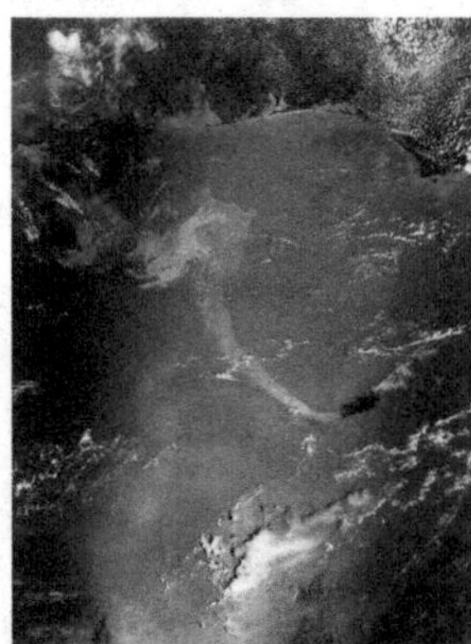

Source: Photo courtesy of NASA Goddard / MODIS Rapid Response Team, http://www.nasa.gov/topics/earth/features/oilspill/oil-20100519a.html.

Looking Closer: Gas Densities and Fire Hazards

Table 12.5 indicates that the first four members of the alkane series are gases at ordinary temperatures. Natural gas is composed chiefly of methane, which has a density of about 0.67 g/L. The density of air is about 1.29 g/L. Because natural gas is less dense than air, it rises. When a natural-gas leak is detected and shut off in a room, the gas can be removed by opening an upper window. On the other hand, bottled gas can be either propane (density 1.88 g/L) or butanes (a mixture of butane and isobutane; density about 2.5 g/L). Both are much heavier than air (density 1.2 g/L). If bottled gas escapes into a building, it collects near the floor. This presents a much more serious fire hazard than a natural-gas leak because it is more difficult to rid the room of the heavier gas.

As shown in Table 12.5, the boiling points of the straight-chain alkanes increase with increasing molar mass. This general rule holds true for the straight-chain homologs of all organic compound families. Larger molecules have greater surface areas and consequently interact more strongly; more energy is therefore required to separate them. For a given molar mass, the boiling points of alkanes are relatively low because these nonpolar molecules have only weak dispersion forces to hold them together in the liquid state.

Looking Closer: An Alkane Basis for Properties of Other Compounds

An understanding of the physical properties of the alkanes is important in that petroleum and natural gas and the many products derived from them—gasoline, bottled gas, solvents, plastics, and more—are composed primarily of alkanes. This understanding is also vital because it is the basis for describing the properties of other organic and biological compound families. For example, large portions of the structures of lipids consist of nonpolar alkyl groups. Lipids include the dietary fats and fatlike compounds called phospholipids and sphingolipids that serve as structural components of living tissues. (For more information about lipids, see Chapter 17.). These compounds have both polar and nonpolar groups, enabling them to bridge the gap between water-soluble and water-insoluble phases. This characteristic is essential for the selective permeability of cell membranes.

Tripalmitin (a), a typical fat molecule, has long hydrocarbon chains typical of most lipids. Compare these chains to hexadecane (b), an alkane with 16 carbon atoms.

(a)

$$H_2C-O-C(=O)-CH_2CH_2CH_2CH_2CH_2CH_2CH_2CH_2CH_2CH_2CH_2CH_2CH_2CH_2CH_3$$
$$HC-O-C(=O)-CH_2CH_2CH_2CH_2CH_2CH_2CH_2CH_2CH_2CH_2CH_2CH_2CH_2CH_2CH_3$$
$$H_2C-O-C(=O)-CH_2CH_2CH_2CH_2CH_2CH_2CH_2CH_2CH_2CH_2CH_2CH_2CH_2CH_2CH_3$$

(b)

$$CH_3CH_2CH_2CH_2CH_2CH_2CH_2CH_2CH_2CH_2CH_2CH_2CH_2CH_2CH_2CH_3$$

CONCEPT REVIEW EXERCISES

1. Without referring to a table, predict which has a higher boiling point—hexane or octane. Explain.

2. If 25 mL of hexane were added to 100 mL of water in a beaker, which of the following would you expect to happen? Explain.
   a. Hexane would dissolve in water.
   b. Hexane would not dissolve in water and would float on top.
   c. Hexane would not dissolve in water and would sink to the bottom of the container.

ANSWERS

1. octane because of its greater molar mass
2. b; hexane is insoluble in water and less dense than water.

KEY TAKEAWAY

- Alkanes are nonpolar compounds that are low boiling and insoluble in water.

EXERCISES

1. Without referring to a table or other reference, predict which member of each pair has the higher boiling point.
   a. pentane or butane
   b. heptane or nonane
2. For which member of each pair is hexane a good solvent?
   a. pentane or water
   b. sodium chloride or soybean oil

ANSWER

1. a. pentane
   b. nonane

7. CHEMICAL PROPERTIES OF ALKANES

LEARNING OBJECTIVE

1. **Identify the main chemical properties of alkanes.**

Alkane molecules are nonpolar and therefore generally do not react with ionic compounds such as most laboratory acids, bases, oxidizing agents, or reducing agents. Consider butane as an example:

$$\underset{\text{butane}}{CH_3CH_2CH_2CH_3} + OH^- \longrightarrow \text{no reaction}$$

$$+ H^+ \longrightarrow \text{no reaction}$$

$$+ MnO_4^- \longrightarrow \text{no reaction}$$

Neither positive ions nor negative ions are attracted to a nonpolar molecule. In fact, the alkanes undergo so few reactions that they are sometimes called *paraffins*, from the Latin *parum affinis*, meaning "little affinity."

combustion reaction

A chemical reaction in which a substance combines with molecular oxygen to make oxygen-containing compounds of other elements in the reaction.

Two important reactions that the alkanes do undergo are combustion and halogenation. Nothing happens when alkanes are merely mixed with oxygen (O_2) at room temperature, but when a flame or spark provides the activation energy, a highly exothermic **combustion reaction** proceeds vigorously. For methane (CH_4), the reaction is as follows:

$$CH_4 + 2O_2 \rightarrow CO_2 + 2H_2O + \text{heat}$$

If the reactants are adequately mixed and there is sufficient oxygen, the only products are carbon dioxide (CO_2), water (H_2O), and heat—heat for cooking foods, heating homes, and drying clothes. Because conditions are rarely ideal, however, other products are frequently formed. When the oxygen supply is limited, carbon monoxide (CO) is a by-product:

$$2CH_4 + 3O_2 \rightarrow 2CO + 4H_2O$$

This reaction is responsible for dozens of deaths each year from unventilated or improperly adjusted gas heaters. (Similar reactions with similar results occur with kerosene heaters.)

Alkanes also react with the halogens chlorine (Cl_2) and bromine (Br_2) in the presence of ultraviolet light or at high temperatures to yield chlorinated and brominated alkanes. For example, chlorine reacts with excess methane (CH_4) to give methyl chloride (CH_3Cl).

$$CH_4 + Cl_2 \rightarrow CH_3Cl + HCl$$

With more chlorine, a mixture of products is obtained: CH_3Cl, CH_2Cl_2, $CHCl_3$, and CCl_4.

Fluorine (F_2), the lightest halogen, combines explosively with most hydrocarbons. Iodine (I_2) is relatively unreactive. Fluorinated and iodinated alkanes are produced by indirect methods. We will discuss the names and uses of halogenated hydrocarbons in Section 8.

CONCEPT REVIEW EXERCISES

1. Why are alkanes sometimes called paraffins?
2. Which halogen reacts most readily with alkanes? Which reacts least readily?

ANSWERS

1. Alkanes do not react with many common chemicals. They are sometimes called paraffins, from the Latin *parum affinis*, meaning "little affinity."
2. most readily: F_2; least readily: I_2

KEY TAKEAWAY

- Alkanes react with oxygen (combustion) and with halogens (halogenation).

EXERCISES

1. Why do alkanes usually not react with ionic compounds such as most laboratory acids, bases, oxidizing agents, or reducing agents?
2. Write an equation for the complete combustion of methane (CH_4, the main component of natural gas).
3. What is the most important reaction of alkanes?
4. Name some substances other than oxygen that react readily with alkanes.

ANSWERS

1. Alkanes are nonpolar; they do not attract ions.

3. combustion

8. HALOGENATED HYDROCARBONS

LEARNING OBJECTIVE

1. **Name halogenated hydrocarbons given formulas and write formulas for these compounds given names.**

Many organic compounds are closely related to the alkanes. As we noted in Section 7, alkanes react with halogens to produce halogenated hydrocarbons, the simplest of which have a single halogen atom substituted for a hydrogen atom of the alkane. Even more closely related are the cycloalkanes, compounds in which the carbon atoms are joined in a ring, or cyclic fashion.

The reactions of alkanes with halogens produce **halogenated hydrocarbons**, compounds in which one or more hydrogen atoms of a hydrocarbon have been replaced by halogen atoms:

halogenated hydrocarbon

A hydrocarbon in which one or more hydrogen atoms has been replaced by a halogen atom.

CH_3CH_2Cl $CH_3CHBrCH_2Br$ CH_3CHICH_2Cl

The replacement of only one hydrogen atom gives an **alkyl halide (or haloalkane)**. The *common names* of alkyl halides consist of two parts: the name of the alkyl group plus the stem of the name of the halogen, with the ending *-ide*. The IUPAC system uses the name of the parent alkane with a prefix indicating the halogen substituents, preceded by number indicating the substituent's location. The prefixes are *fluoro-*, *chloro-*, *bromo-*, and *iodo-*. Thus CH_3CH_2Cl has the common name ethyl chloride and the IUPAC name chloroethane. Alkyl halides with simple alkyl groups (one to four carbon atoms) are often called by common names. Those with a larger number of carbon atoms are usually given IUPAC names.

alkyl halide (haloalkane)

A compound resulting from the replacement of a hydrogen atom of an alkane with a halogen atom.

EXAMPLE 3

Give the common and IUPAC names for each compound.

1. $CH_3CH_2CH_2Br$
2. $(CH_3)_2CHCl$

Solution

1. The alkyl group ($CH_3CH_2CH_2$–) is a propyl group, and the halogen is bromine (Br). The common name is therefore propyl bromide. For the IUPAC name, the prefix for bromine (bromo) is combined with the name for a three-carbon chain (propane), preceded by a number identifying the carbon atom to which the Br atom is attached, so the IUPAC name is 1-bromopropane.
2. The alkyl group [$(CH_3)_2CH$–] has three carbon atoms, with a chlorine (Cl) atom attached to the middle carbon atom. The alkyl group is therefore isopropyl, and the common name of the compound is isopropyl chloride. For the IUPAC name, the Cl atom (prefix *chloro-*) attached to the middle (second) carbon atom of a propane chain results in 2-chloropropane.

SKILL-BUILDING EXERCISE

Give common and IUPAC names for each compound.

1. CH_3CH_2I
2. $CH_3CH_2CH_2CH_2F$

EXAMPLE 4

Give the IUPAC name for each compound.

1. $CH_3CHCH_2CH_2CH_3$ with Br on the second carbon

2. $CH_3CHCH_2CHCH_2CH_3$ with CH_3 on the second carbon and Br on the fourth carbon

Solution

1. The parent alkane has five carbon atoms in the longest continuous chain; it is pentane. A bromo (Br) group is attached to the second carbon atom of the chain. The IUPAC name is 2-bromopentane.
2. The parent alkane is hexane. Methyl (CH_3) and bromo (Br) groups are attached to the second and fourth carbon atoms, respectively. Listing the substituents in alphabetical order gives the name 4-bromo-2-methylhexane.

SKILL-BUILDING EXERCISE

Give the IUPAC name for each compound.

1. $CH_3CHCHCH_3$ with Cl on the second carbon and CH_3 on the third carbon

2. $CH_3CHCH_2CHCH_2Br$ with CH_3 on the second carbon and Cl on the fourth carbon

A wide variety of interesting and often useful compounds have one or more halogen atoms per molecule. For example, methane (CH_4) can react with chlorine (Cl_2), replacing one, two, three, or all four hydrogen atoms with Cl atoms. Several halogenated products derived from methane and ethane (CH_3CH_3) are listed in Table 12.6, along with some of their uses.

TABLE 12.6 Some Halogenated Hydrocarbons

Formula	Common Name	IUPAC Name	Some Important Uses
Derived from CH_4			
CH_3Cl	methyl chloride	chloromethane	refrigerant; the manufacture of silicones, methyl cellulose, and synthetic rubber
CH_2Cl_2	methylene chloride	dichloromethane	laboratory and industrial solvent
$CHCl_3$	chloroform	trichloromethane	industrial solvent
CCl_4	carbon tetrachloride	tetrachloromethane	dry-cleaning solvent and fire extinguishers (but no longer recommended for use)
$CBrF_3$	halon-1301	bromotrifluoromethane	fire extinguisher systems
CCl_3F	chlorofluorocarbon-11 (CFC-11)	trichlorofluoromethane	foaming plastics
CCl_2F_2	chlorofluorocarbon-12 (CFC-12)	dichlorodifluoromethane	refrigerant
Derived from CH_3CH_3			
CH_3CH_2Cl	ethyl chloride	chloroethane	local anesthetic
$ClCH_2CH_2Cl$	ethylene dichloride	1,2-dichloroethane	solvent for rubber
CCl_3CH_3	methylchloroform	1,1,1-trichloroethane	solvent for cleaning computer chips and molds for shaping plastics

To Your Health: Halogenated Hydrocarbons

Once widely used in consumer products, many chlorinated hydrocarbons are suspected carcinogens (cancer-causing substances) and also are known to cause severe liver damage. An example is carbon tetrachloride (CCl_4), once used as a dry-cleaning solvent and in fire extinguishers but no longer recommended for either use. Even in small amounts, its vapor can cause serious illness if exposure is prolonged. Moreover, it reacts with water at high temperatures to form deadly phosgene ($COCl_2$) gas, which makes the use of CCl_4 in fire extinguishers particularly dangerous.

Ethyl chloride, in contrast, is used as an external local anesthetic. When sprayed on the skin, it evaporates quickly, cooling the area enough to make it insensitive to pain. It can also be used as an emergency general anesthetic.

Bromine-containing compounds are widely used in fire extinguishers and as fire retardants on clothing and other materials. Because they too are toxic and have adverse effects on the environment, scientists are engaged in designing safer substitutes for them, as for many other halogenated compounds.

To Your Health: Chlorofluorocarbons and the Ozone Layer

Alkanes substituted with both fluorine (F) and chlorine (Cl) atoms have been used as the dispersing gases in aerosol cans, as foaming agents for plastics, and as refrigerants. Two of the best known of these chlorofluorocarbons (CFCs) are listed in Table 12.6.

Chlorofluorocarbons contribute to the greenhouse effect in the lower atmosphere. They also diffuse into the stratosphere, where they are broken down by ultraviolet (UV) radiation to release Cl atoms. These in turn break down the ozone (O_3) molecules that protect Earth from harmful UV radiation. Worldwide action has reduced the use of CFCs and related compounds. The CFCs and other Cl- or bromine (Br)-containing ozone-destroying compounds are being replaced with more benign substances. Hydrofluorocarbons (HFCs), such as CH_2FCF_3, which have no Cl or Br to form radicals, are one alternative. Another is hydrochlorofluorocarbons (HCFCs), such as $CHCl_2CF_3$. HCFC molecules break down more readily in the troposphere, and fewer ozone-destroying molecules reach the stratosphere.

Ozone in the upper atmosphere shields Earth's surface from UV radiation from the sun, which can cause skin cancer in humans and is also harmful to other animals and to some plants. Ozone "holes" in the upper atmosphere (the gray, pink, and purple areas at the center) are large areas of substantial ozone depletion. They occur mainly over Antarctica from late August through early October and fill in about mid-November. Ozone depletion has also been noted over the Arctic regions. The largest ozone hole ever observed occurred on 24 September 2006.

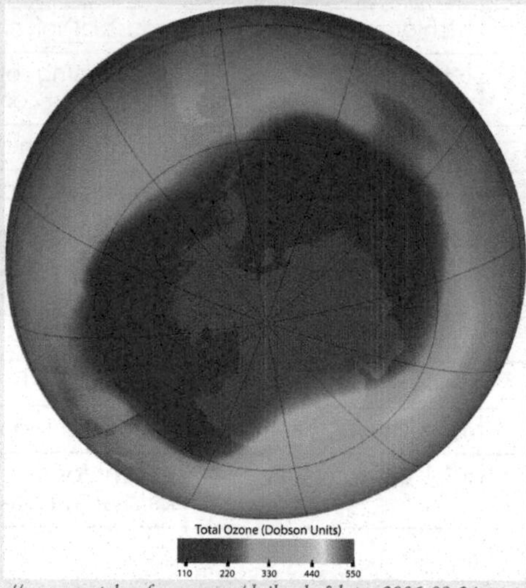

Source: Image courtesy of NASA, http://ozonewatch.gsfc.nasa.gov/daily.php?date=2006-09-24.

CONCEPT REVIEW EXERCISES

1. What is the IUPAC name for the HFC that has the formula CH_2FCF_3? (Hint: you must use a number to indicate the location of each substituent F atom.)
2. What is the IUPAC name for the HCFC that has the formula $CHCl_2CF_3$?

ANSWERS

1. 1,1,1,2-tetrafluoroethane
2. 1,1,1-trifluoro-2,2-dichloroethane

KEY TAKEAWAY

- The replacement of an hydrogen atom on an alkane by a halogen atom—F, Cl, Br, or I—forms a halogenated compound.

EXERCISES

1. Write the condensed structural formula for each compound.
   a. methyl chloride
   b. chloroform
2. Write the condensed structural formula for each compound.
   a. ethyl bromide
   b. carbon tetrachloride
3. Write the condensed structural formulas for the two isomers that have the molecular formula C_3H_7Br. Give the common name and the IUPAC name of each.
4. Write the condensed structural formulas for the four isomers that have the molecular formula C_4H_9Br. Give the IUPAC name of each.
5. What is a CFC? How are CFCs involved in the destruction of the ozone layer?

6. Explain why each compound is less destructive to the ozone layer than are CFCs.
   a. fluorocarbons
   b. HCFCs

ANSWERS

1. a. CH_3Cl
   b. $CHCl_3$
3. $CH_3CH_2CH_2Br$, propyl bromide, 1-bromopropane; $CH_3CHBrCH_3$, isopropyl bromide, 2-bromopropane
5. compounds containing Cl, F, and C; by releasing Cl atoms in the stratosphere

9. CYCLOALKANES

LEARNING OBJECTIVE

1. **Name cycloalkanes given their formulas and write formulas for these compounds given their names.**

The hydrocarbons we have encountered so far have been composed of molecules with open-ended chains of carbon atoms. When a chain contains three or more carbon atoms, the atoms can join to form *ring* or *cyclic* structures. The simplest of these **cyclic hydrocarbons** has the formula C_3H_6. Each carbon atom has two hydrogen atoms attached (Figure 12.6) and is called cyclopropane.

cyclic hydrocarbon

A hydrocarbon with a ring of carbon atoms.

FIGURE 12.6 Ball-and-Spring Model of Cyclopropane

The springs are bent to join the carbon atoms.

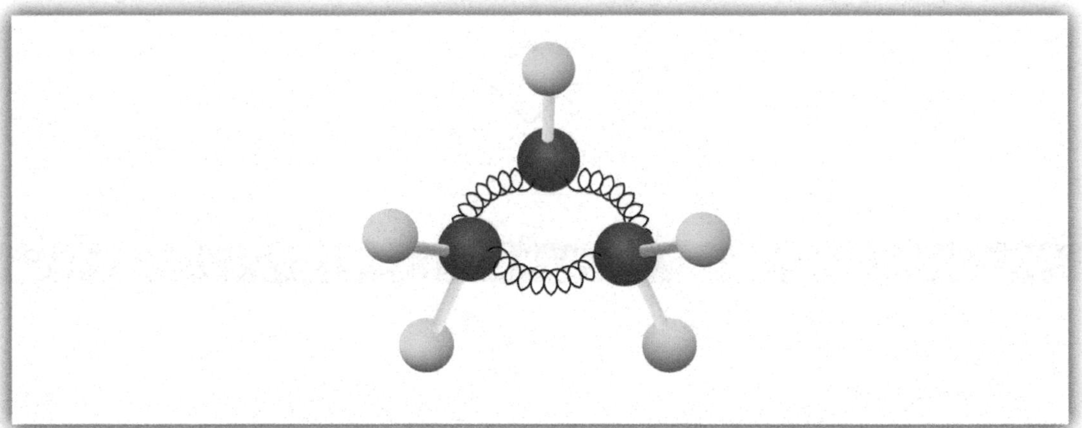

To Your Health: Cyclopropane as an Anesthetic

With its boiling point of −33°C, cyclopropane is a gas at room temperature. It is also a potent, quick-acting anesthetic with few undesirable side effects in the body. It is no longer used in surgery, however, because it forms explosive mixtures with air at nearly all concentrations.

The **cycloalkanes**—cyclic hydrocarbons with only single bonds—are named by adding the prefix *cyclo-* to the name of the open-chain compound having the same number of carbon atoms as there are in the ring. Thus the name for the cyclic compound C_4H_8 is cyclobutane. The carbon atoms in cyclic compounds can be represented by *line-angle formulas* that result in regular geometric figures. Keep in

cycloalkane

A cyclic hydrocarbon with only single bonds.

mind, however, that each corner of the geometric figure represents a carbon atom plus as many hydrogen atoms as needed to give each carbon atom four bonds.

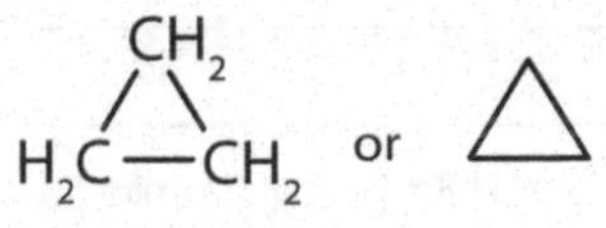

cyclopropane

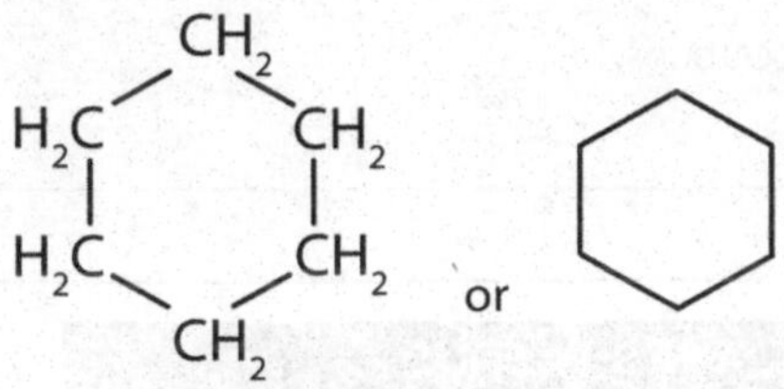

cyclohexane

Some cyclic compounds have substituent groups attached. Example 5 interprets the name of a cycloalkane with a single substituent group.

EXAMPLE 5

Draw the structure for each compound.

1. cyclopentane
2. methylcyclobutane

Solution

1. The name *cyclopentane* indicates a cyclic (cyclo) alkane with five (pent-) carbon atoms. It can be represented as a pentagon.

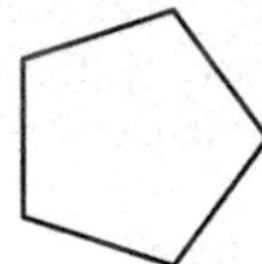

2. The name *methylcyclobutane* indicates a cyclic alkane with four (but-) carbon atoms in the cyclic part. It can be represented as a square with a CH_3 group attached.

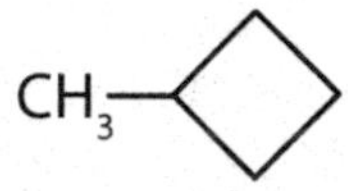

SKILL-BUILDING EXERCISE

1. Draw the structure for each compound.
   a. cycloheptane
   b. ethylcyclohexane

The properties of cyclic hydrocarbons are generally quite similar to those of the corresponding open-chain compounds. So cycloalkanes (with the exception of cyclopropane, which has a highly strained ring) act very much like noncyclic alkanes. Cyclic structures containing five or six carbon atoms, such as cyclopentane and cyclohexane, are particularly stable. We will see in Chapter 16 that some carbohydrates (sugars) form five- or six-membered rings in solution.

Note

The cyclopropane ring is strained because the C–C–C angles are 60°, and the preferred (tetrahedral) bond angle is 109.5°. (This strain is readily evident when you try to build a ball-and-stick model of cyclopropane; see Figure 12.6.) Cyclopentane and cyclohexane rings have little strain because the C–C–C angles are near the preferred angles.

CONCEPT REVIEW EXERCISES

1. What is the molecular formula of cyclooctane?
2. What is the IUPAC name for this compound?

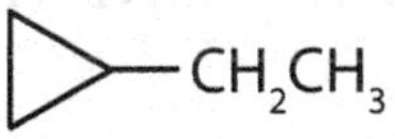

CH_2CH_3

ANSWERS

1. C_8H_{16}
2. ethylcyclopropane

KEY TAKEAWAY

- Many organic compounds have cyclic structures.

EXERCISES

1. Draw the structure for each compound.
   a. ethylcyclobutane
   b. propylcyclopropane
2. Draw the structure for each compound.
   a. methylcyclohexane
   b. butylcyclobutane
3. Cycloalkyl groups can be derived from cycloalkanes in the same way that alkyl groups are derived from alkanes. These groups are named as cyclopropyl, cyclobutyl, and so on. Name each cycloalkyl halide.
   a. 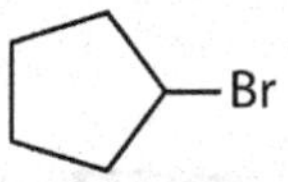
   Br
   b. 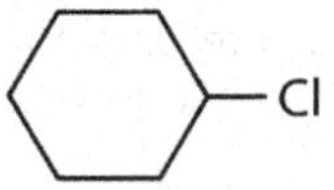
   Cl
4. Halogenated cycloalkanes can be named by the IUPAC system. As with alkyl derivatives, monosubstituted derivatives need no number to indicate the position of the halogen. To name disubstituted derivatives, the carbon atoms are numbered starting at the position of one substituent (C1) and proceeding to the second substituted atom by the shortest route. Name each compound.
   a. 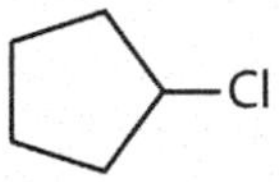
   Cl
   b.
   Br Br

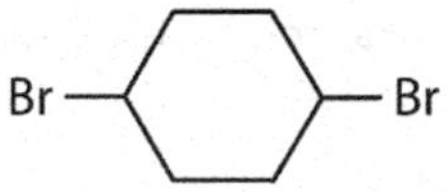

ANSWERS

1. a.

   (cyclobutane ring)—CH_2CH_3

   b.

   (cyclopropane ring)—$CH_2CH_2CH_3$

3. a. cyclopentyl bromide
   b. cyclohexyl chloride

10. END-OF-CHAPTER MATERIAL

Chapter Summary

To ensure that you understand the material in this chapter, you should review the meanings of the following bold terms in the summary and ask yourself how they relate to the topics in the chapter.

Organic chemistry is the chemistry of carbon compounds, and **inorganic chemistry** is the chemistry of all the other elements. Carbon atoms can form stable covalent bonds with other carbon atoms and with atoms of other elements, and this property allows the formation the tens of millions of organic compounds. **Hydrocarbons** contain only hydrogen and carbon atoms.

Hydrocarbons in which each carbon atom is bonded to four other atoms are called **alkanes** or **saturated hydrocarbons**. They have the general formula C_nH_{2n+2}. Any given alkane differs from the next one in a series by a CH_2 unit. Any family of compounds in which adjacent members differ from each other by a definite factor is called a **homologous series**.

Carbon atoms in alkanes can form straight chains or branched chains. Two or more compounds having the same molecular formula but different structural formulas are **isomers** of each other. There are no isomeric forms for the three smallest alkanes; beginning with C_4H_{10}, all other alkanes have isomeric forms.

A **structural formula** shows all the carbon and hydrogen atoms and how they are attached to one another. A **condensed structural formula** shows the hydrogen atoms right next to the carbon atoms to which they are attached. A **line-angle formula** is a formula in which carbon atoms are implied at the corners and ends of lines. Each carbon atom is understood to be attached to enough hydrogen atoms to give each carbon atom four bonds.

The **IUPAC System of Nomenclature** provides rules for naming organic compounds. An **alkyl group** is a unit formed by removing one hydrogen atom from an alkane.

The physical properties of alkanes reflect the fact that alkane molecules are nonpolar. Alkanes are insoluble in water and less dense than water.

Alkanes are generally unreactive toward laboratory acids, bases, oxidizing agents, and reducing agents. They do burn (undergo **combustion reactions**).

Alkanes react with halogens by substituting one or more halogen atoms for hydrogen atoms to form **halogenated hydrocarbons**. An **alkyl halide (haloalkane)** is a compound resulting from the replacement of a hydrogen atom of an alkane with a halogen atom.

Cycloalkanes are hydrocarbons whose molecules are closed rings rather than straight or branched chains. A **cyclic hydrocarbon** is a hydrocarbon with a ring of carbon atoms.

ADDITIONAL EXERCISES

1. You find an unlabeled jar containing a solid that melts at 48°C. It ignites readily and burns readily. The substance is insoluble in water and floats on the surface. Is the substance likely to be organic or inorganic?
2. Give the molecular formulas for methylcyclopentane, 2-methylpentane, and cyclohexane. Which are isomers?

3. What is wrong with each name? (Hint: first write the structure *as if* it were correct.) Give the correct name for each compound.
   a. 2-dimethylpropane
   b. 2,3,3-trimethylbutane
   c. 2,4-diethylpentane
   d. 3,4-dimethyl-5-propylhexane
4. What is the danger in swallowing a liquid alkane?
5. Distinguish between lighter and heavier liquid alkanes in terms of their effects on the skin.
6. Following is the line formula for an alkane. Draw its structure and give its name.

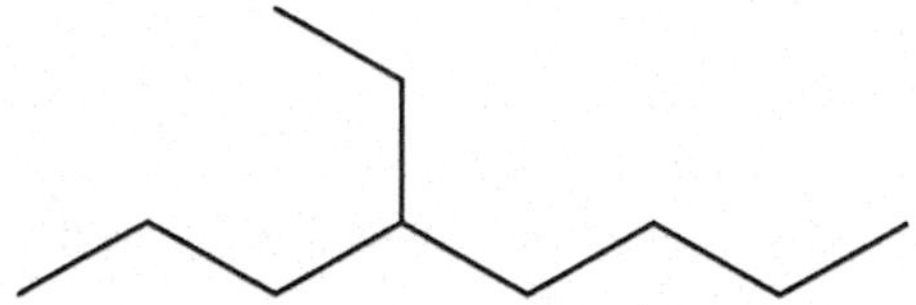

7. Write equations for the complete combustion of each compound.
   a. propane (a bottled gas fuel)
   b. octane (a typical hydrocarbon in gasoline).
8. The density of a gasoline sample is 0.690 g/mL. On the basis of the complete combustion of octane, calculate the amount in grams of carbon dioxide (CO_2) and water (H_2O) formed per gallon (3.78 L) of the gasoline when used in an automobile.
9. Draw the structures for the five isomeric hexanes (C_6H_{14}). Name each by the IUPAC system.
10. Indicate whether the structures in each set represent the same compound or isomers.
    a.

CH_3CH_2 (with CH_3 attached below the CH_2) and $CH_3CH_2CH_3$

    b.

$CH_3CH_2CHCH_2$ (with CH_3 attached above and CH_3 attached below the CH) and $CH_2CH_2CHCH_3$ (with CH_3 attached below the first CH_2 and CH_3 attached below the CH)

    c.

$CH_3CH_2CHCH_2CH_3$ (with CH_3 attached below the CH) and $CH_3CHCH_2CH_2CH_3$ (with CH_3 attached below the CH)

11. Consider the line-angle formulas shown here and answer the questions.

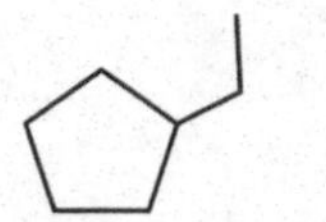

(i) 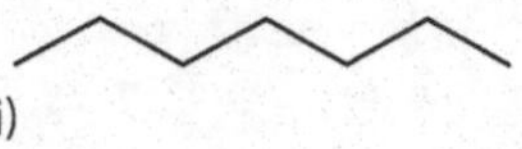 (ii)

(iii) (iv) Cl

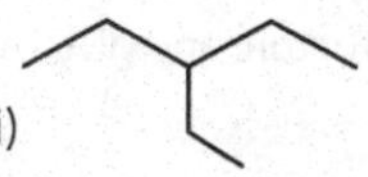

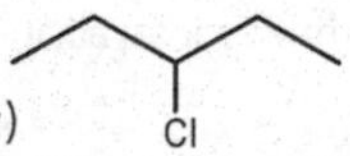

a. Which pair of formulas represents isomers? Draw each structure.
b. Which formula represents an alkyl halide? Name the compound and write its condensed structural formula.
c. Which formula represents a cyclic alkane? Name the compound and draw its structure.
d. What is the molecular formula of the compound represented by (i)?

ANSWERS

1. organic
3. a. Two numbers are needed to indicate two substituents; 2,2-dimethylpropane.
   b. The lowest possible numbers were not used; 2,2,3-trimethylbutane.
   c. An ethyl substituent is not possible on the second carbon atom; 3,5-dimethylheptane.
   d. A propyl substituent is not possible on the fifth carbon atom; 3,4,5-trimethyloctane.
5. Lighter alkanes wash away protective skin oils; heavier alkanes form a protective layer.
7. a. $C_3H_8 + 5O_2 \rightarrow 3CO_2 + 4H_2O$
   b. $2C_8H_{18} + 25O_2 \rightarrow 16CO_2 + 18H_2O$
9. $CH_3CH_2CH_2CH_2CH_2CH_3$; hexane

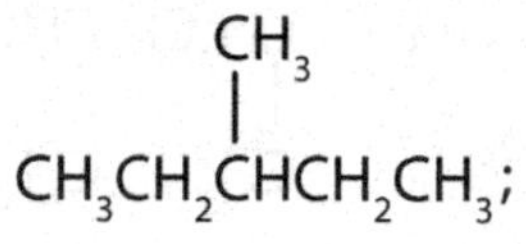

CH_3 (on C-3)
$CH_3CH_2CHCH_2CH_3$; 3-methylpentane

$CH_3CHCH_2CH_2CH_3$; 2-methylpentane
CH_3 (on C-2)

CH_3 (on C-2)
$CH_3CCH_2CH_3$; 2,2-dimethylbutane 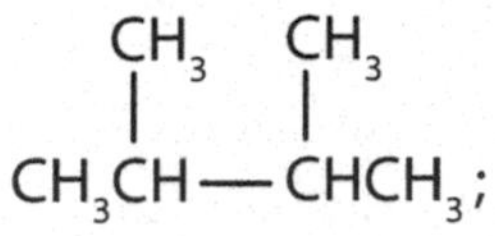
CH_3 (on C-2)

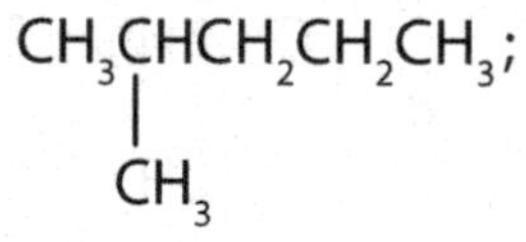

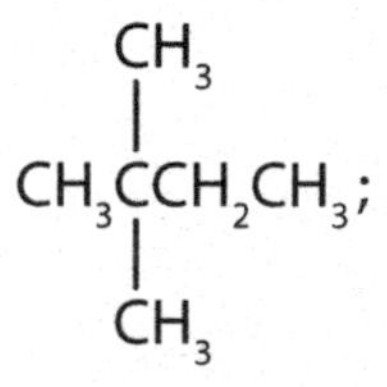

CH_3 CH_3
$CH_3CH—CHCH_3$; 2,3-dimethylbutane

11. a. ii and iii; $CH_3CH_2CH_2CH_2CH_2CH_2CH_3$ and

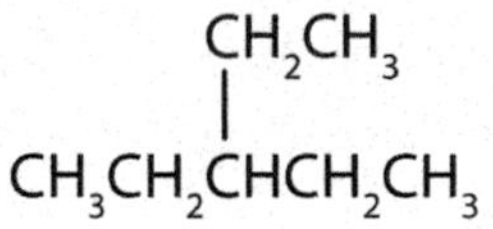

$$\begin{array}{c} CH_2CH_3 \\ | \\ CH_3CH_2CHCH_2CH_3 \end{array}$$

b. iv; 3-chloropentane; $CH_3CH_2CHClCH_2CH_3$

c. i; ethylcyclopentane;

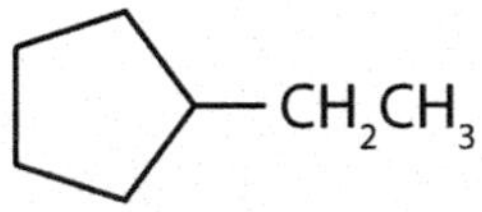

(cyclopentane ring)—CH_2CH_3

d. C_7H_{14}

CHAPTER 13
Unsaturated and Aromatic Hydrocarbons

Opening Essay

Our modern society is based to a large degree on the chemicals we discuss in this chapter. Most are made from petroleum. In Chapter 12 we noted that alkanes—saturated hydrocarbons—have relatively few important chemical properties other than that they undergo combustion and react with halogens. Unsaturated hydrocarbons—hydrocarbons with double or triple bonds—on the other hand, are quite reactive. In fact, they serve as building blocks for many familiar plastics—polyethylene, vinyl plastics, acrylics—and other important synthetic materials (e.g., alcohols, antifreeze, and detergents). Aromatic hydrocarbons have formulas that can be drawn as cyclic alkenes, making them appear unsaturated, but their structure and properties are generally quite different, so they are not considered to be alkenes. Aromatic compounds serve as the basis for many drugs, antiseptics, explosives, solvents, and plastics (e.g., polyesters and polystyrene).

The two simplest unsaturated compounds—ethylene (ethene) and acetylene (ethyne)—were once used as anesthetics and were introduced to the medical field in 1924. However, it was discovered that acetylene forms explosive mixtures with air, so its medical use was abandoned in 1925. Ethylene was thought to be safer, but it too was implicated in numerous lethal fires and explosions during anesthesia. Even so, it remained an important anesthetic into the 1960s, when it was replaced by nonflammable anesthetics such as halothane ($CHBrClCF_3$).

1. ALKENES: STRUCTURES AND NAMES

LEARNING OBJECTIVE

1. **Name alkenes given formulas and write formulas for alkenes given names.**

As we noted in Chapter 4, **alkenes** are hydrocarbons with carbon-to-carbon double bonds ($R_2C{=}CR_2$) and **alkynes** are hydrocarbons with carbon-to-carbon triple bonds ($R{-}C{\equiv}C{-}R$). Collectively, they are called **unsaturated hydrocarbons** because they have fewer hydrogen atoms than does an alkane with the same number of carbon atoms, as is indicated in the following general formulas:

alkene

A hydrocarbon with one or more carbon–carbon double bonds.

alkyne

A hydrocarbon with a carbon–carbon triple bond.

unsaturated hydrocarbon

An alkene or alkyne having one or more multiple (double or triple) bonds between carbon atoms.

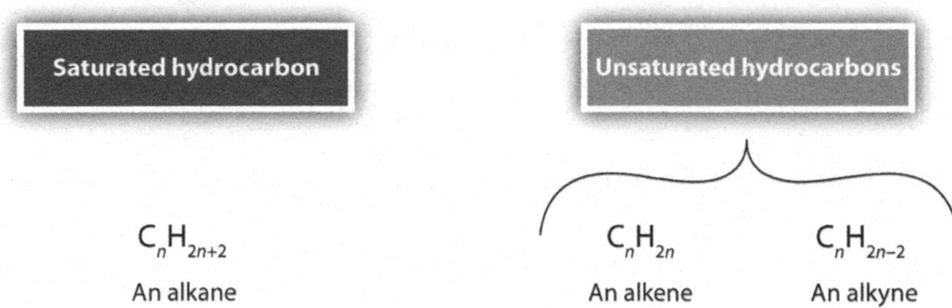

Some representative alkenes—their names, structures, and physical properties—are given in Table 13.1.

TABLE 13.1 Physical Properties of Some Selected Alkenes

IUPAC Name	Molecular Formula	Condensed Structural Formula	Melting Point (°C)	Boiling Point (°C)
ethene	C_2H_4	$CH_2{=}CH_2$	−169	−104
propene	C_3H_6	$CH_2{=}CHCH_3$	−185	−47
1-butene	C_4H_8	$CH_2{=}CHCH_2CH_3$	−185	−6
1-pentene	C_5H_{10}	$CH_2{=}CH(CH_2)_2CH_3$	−138	30
1-hexene	C_6H_{12}	$CH_2{=}CH(CH_2)_3CH_3$	−140	63
1-heptene	C_7H_{14}	$CH_2{=}CH(CH_2)_4CH_3$	−119	94
1-octene	C_8H_{16}	$CH_2{=}CH(CH_2)_5CH_3$	−102	121

We used only condensed structural formulas in Table 13.1. Thus, $CH_2{=}CH_2$ stands for

The double bond is shared by the two carbon atoms and does not involve the hydrogen atoms, although the condensed formula does not make this point obvious. Note that the molecular formula for ethene is C_2H_4, whereas that for ethane is C_2H_6.

The first two alkenes in Table 13.1—ethene and propene (Figure 13.1)—are most often called by their common names—ethylene and propylene, respectively. Ethylene is a major commercial chemical. The US chemical industry produces about 25 billion kilograms of ethylene annually, more than any other synthetic organic chemical. More than half of this ethylene goes into the manufacture of polyethylene, one of the most familiar plastics. (For more information about polymers and plastics, see Section 5.) Propylene is also an important industrial chemical. It is converted to plastics, isopropyl alcohol, and a variety of other products. (For more information about alcohols, see Chapter 14, [Unsupported Reference Type: chapter-section].)

FIGURE 13.1 Ethene and Propene

The ball-and-spring models of ethene/ethylene (a) and propene/propylene (b) show their respective shapes, especially bond angles.

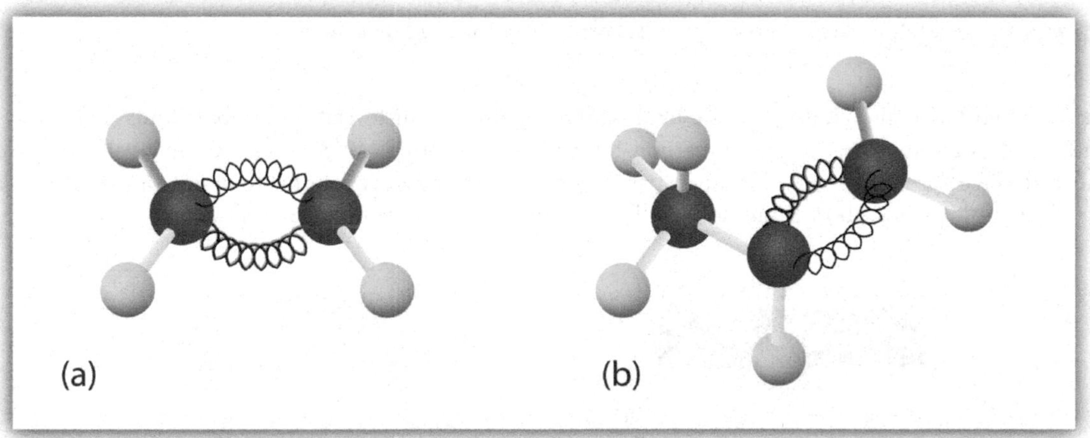

Note

Although there is only one alkene with the formula C_2H_4 (ethene) and only one with the formula C_3H_6 (propene), there are several alkenes with the formula C_4H_8. Section 2 begins a discussion of butenes.

Here are some basic rules for naming alkenes from the International Union of Pure and Applied Chemistry (IUPAC):

1. The longest chain of carbon atoms *containing the double bond* is considered the parent chain. It is named using the same stem as the alkane having the same number of carbon atoms but ends in *-ene* to identify it as an alkene. Thus the compound $CH_2{=}CHCH_3$ is *propene.*
2. If there are four or more carbon atoms in a chain, we must indicate the position of the double bond. The carbons atoms are numbered so that the first of the two that are doubly bonded is given the lower of the two possible numbers. The compound $CH_3CH{=}CHCH_2CH_3$, for example, has the double bond between the second and third carbon atoms. Its name is 2-pentene (not 3-pentene).
3. Substituent groups are named as with alkanes, and their position is indicated by a number. Thus,

6 5 4 3 2 1
$CH_3CHCH_2CH{=}CHCH_3$ (with CH_3 on carbon 5)

Methyl group

is 5-methyl-2-hexene. Note that the numbering of the parent chain is always done in such a way as to give the double bond the lowest number, even if that causes a substituent to have a higher number. *The double bond always has priority in numbering.*

EXAMPLE 1

Name each compound.

1. $CH_3CH{=}CHCHCH_3$ (with CH_3 on carbon 4)

2. $CH_2{=}CCH_2CH_3$ (with CH_2CH_3 on carbon 2)

Solution

1. The longest chain containing the double bond has five carbon atoms, so the compound is a *pentene* (rule 1). To give the first carbon atom of the double bond the lowest number (rule 2), we number from the left, so the compound is a 2-pentene. There is a methyl group on the fourth carbon atom (rule 3), so the compound's name is 4-methyl-2-pentene.
2. The longest chain containing the double bond has four carbon atoms, so the parent compound is a *butene* (rule 1). (The longest chain overall has five carbon atoms, but it does not contain the double bond, so the parent name is not *pentene.*) To give the first carbon atom of the double bond the lowest number (rule 2), we number from the left, so the compound is a 1-butene. There is an ethyl group on the second carbon atom (rule 3), so the compound's name is 2-ethyl-1-butene.

SKILL-BUILDING EXERCISE

Name each compound.

1. $CH_3CH_2CH_2CH_2CH_2CH{=}CHCH_3$

2.

$$\begin{array}{l} CH_3CH_2\underset{\displaystyle CH_3}{\underset{|}{C}}HCH{=}CHCH_2CH_3 \end{array}$$

Just as there are cycloalkanes, there are *cycloalkenes*. These compounds are named like alkenes, but with the prefix *cyclo*- attached to the beginning of the parent alkene name.

EXAMPLE 2

Draw the structure for each compound.

1. 3-methyl-2-pentene
2. cyclohexene

Solution

1. First write the parent chain of five carbon atoms: C–C–C–C–C. Then add the double bond between the second and third carbon atoms:

$$\overset{1}{C}{-}\overset{2}{C}{=}\overset{3}{C}{-}\overset{4}{C}{-}\overset{5}{C}$$

Now place the methyl group on the third carbon atom and add enough hydrogen atoms to give each carbon atom a total of four bonds.

$$CH_3CH{=}\underset{\displaystyle CH_3}{\underset{|}{C}}CH_2CH_3$$

2. First, consider what each of the three parts of the name means. *Cyclo* means a ring compound, *hex* means 6 carbon atoms, and *-ene* means a double bond.

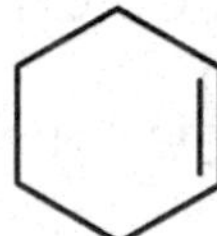

SKILL-BUILDING EXERCISE

Draw the structure for each compound.

1. 2-ethyl-1-hexene
2. cyclopentene

CONCEPT REVIEW EXERCISES

1. Briefly identify the important distinctions between a saturated hydrocarbon and an unsaturated hydrocarbon.
2. Briefly identify the important distinctions between an alkene and an alkane.

3. Classify each compound as saturated or unsaturated. Identify each as an alkane, an alkene, or an alkyne.
   a.

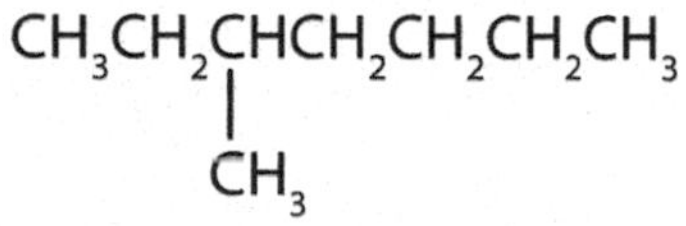

$$CH_3CH_2\underset{\displaystyle CH_3}{\underset{|}{C}}HCH_2CH_2CH_2CH_3$$

   b. $CH_3CH_2C{\equiv}CCH_3$
   c.

$$CH_3CH{=}\underset{\displaystyle CH_3}{\underset{|}{C}}CH_2CH_2CH_2CH_3$$

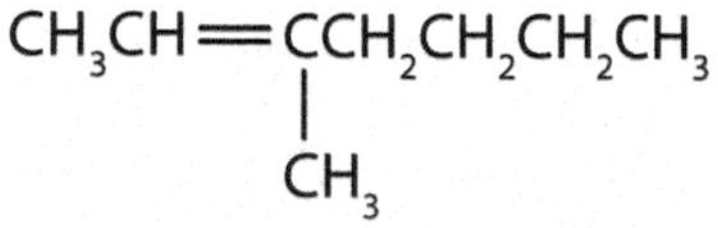

ANSWERS

1. Unsaturated hydrocarbons have double or triple bonds and are quite reactive; saturated hydrocarbons have only single bonds and are rather unreactive.
2. An alkene has a double bond; an alkane has single bonds only.
3. a. saturated; alkane
   b. unsaturated; alkyne
   c. unsaturated; alkene

KEY TAKEAWAY

- Alkenes are hydrocarbons with a carbon-to-carbon double bond.

EXERCISES

1. Draw the structure for each compound.
   a. 2-methyl-2-pentene
   b. 2,3-dimethyl-1-butene
   c. cyclohexene
2. Draw the structure for each compound.
   a. 5-methyl-1-hexene
   b. 3-ethyl-2-pentene
   c. 4-methyl-2-hexene
3. Name each compound according to the IUPAC system.
   a.

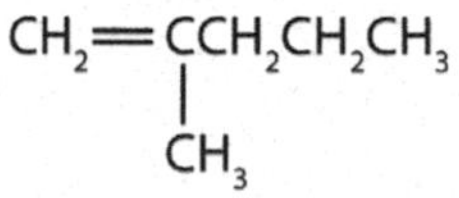

$$CH_2{=}\underset{\displaystyle CH_3}{\underset{|}{C}}CH_2CH_2CH_3$$

   b.

$$CH_3\underset{\displaystyle CH_3}{\underset{|}{C}}{=}CHCH_2CH_3$$

   c.

$$CH_3\underset{\displaystyle CH_3}{\underset{|}{C}}{=}CHCH_2\underset{\displaystyle CH_3}{\underset{|}{C}}HCH_3$$

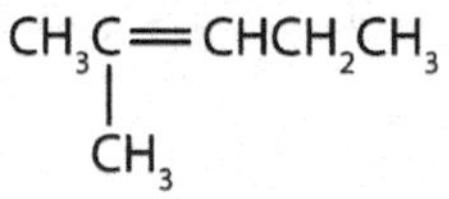

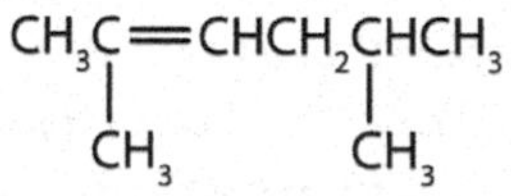

4. Name each compound according to the IUPAC system.

   a.

   $$CH_2{=}\underset{\displaystyle CH_3}{\underset{|}{C}}CH_2CH_3$$

   b.

   $$CH_3CH{=}CHCH_2\underset{\displaystyle CH_3}{\underset{|}{C}H}CH_2CH_3$$

   c.

   $$CH_3\overset{\displaystyle CH_3}{\overset{|}{\underset{\displaystyle CH_3}{\underset{|}{C}}}}CH{=}\underset{\displaystyle CH_3}{\underset{|}{C}}CH_2CH_3$$

ANSWERS

1. a.

   $$CH_3\underset{\displaystyle CH_3}{\underset{|}{C}}{=}CHCH_2CH_3$$

   b.

   $$CH_2{=}\overset{\displaystyle CH_3}{\overset{|}{\underset{\displaystyle CH_3}{\underset{|}{C}}}}CHCH_3$$

   c.

   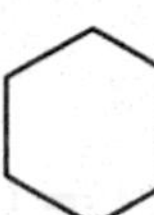

3. a. 2-methyl-2-pentene
   b. 3-methyl-2-heptene
   c. 2,5-dimethyl-2-hexene

2. CIS-TRANS ISOMERS (GEOMETRIC ISOMERS)

LEARNING OBJECTIVES

1. **Recognize that alkenes that can exist as cis-trans isomers.**
2. **Classify isomers as cis or trans.**
3. **Draw structures for cis-trans isomers given their names.**

As noted in Chapter 12, there is free rotation about the carbon-to-carbon single bonds (C–C) in alkanes. In contrast, the structure of alkenes requires that the carbon atoms of a double bond and the two atoms bonded to each carbon atom all lie in a single plane, and that each doubly bonded carbon atom lies in the center of a triangle. This part of the molecule's structure is rigid; rotation about doubly bonded carbon atoms is *not* possible without rupturing the bond. Look at the two chlorinated hydrocarbons in Figure 13.2.

FIGURE 13.2 Rotation about Bonds

In 1,2-dichloroethane (a), free rotation about the C–C bond allows the two structures to be interconverted by a twist of one end relative to the other. In 1,2-dichloroethene (b), restricted rotation about the double bond means that the relative positions of substituent groups above or below the double bond are significant.

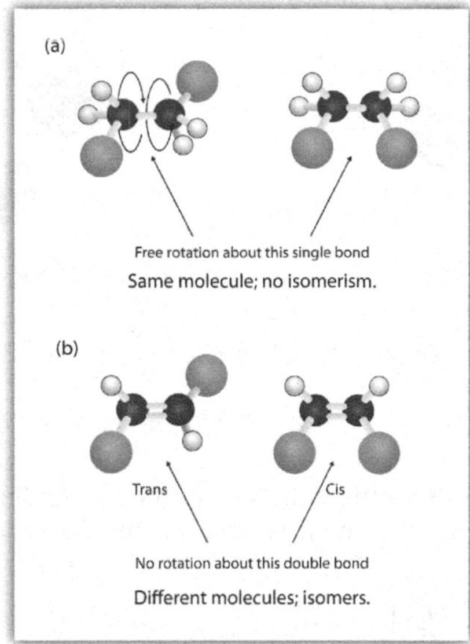

In 1,2-dichloroethane (part (a) of Figure 13.2), there is free rotation about the C–C bond. The two models shown represent exactly the same molecule; they are *not* isomers. You can draw structural formulas that look different, but if you bear in mind the possibility of this free rotation about single bonds, you should recognize that these two structures represent the same molecule:

$$\begin{array}{ccccccc} & & Cl & & H & & \\ & & | & & | & & \\ H & — & C & — & C & — & H \\ & & | & & | & & \\ & & H & & Cl & & \end{array} \qquad \begin{array}{ccccccc} & & H & & H & & \\ & & | & & | & & \\ H & — & C & — & C & — & H \\ & & | & & | & & \\ & & Cl & & Cl & & \end{array}$$

In 1,2-dichloroethene (part (b) of Figure 13.2), however, restricted rotation about the double bond means that the relative positions of substituent groups above or below the double bond become significant. This leads to a special kind of isomerism. The isomer in which the two chlorine (Cl) atoms lie on the same side of the molecule is called the **cis isomer** (Latin *cis*, meaning "on this side") and is named cis-1,2-dichloroethene. The isomer with the two Cl atoms on opposite sides of the molecule is the **trans isomer** (Latin *trans*, meaning "across") and is named *trans*-1,2-dichloroethene. These two compounds are **cis-trans isomers (or geometric isomers)**, compounds that have different configurations (groups permanently in different places in space) because of the presence of a rigid structure in their molecule.

Consider the alkene with the condensed structural formula $CH_3CH{=}CHCH_3$. We could name it 2-butene, but there are actually two such compounds; the double bond results in cis-trans isomerism (Figure 13.3).

cis isomer

An isomer in which two substituent groups are attached on the same side of a double bond or ring in an organic molecule.

trans isomer

An isomer in which two substituent groups are attached to opposite sides of a double bond or ring in a molecule.

cis-trans isomers (or geometric isomers)

Isomers that have different configurations because of the presence of a rigid structure such as a double bond or ring.

FIGURE 13.3 Ball-and-Spring Models of (a) Cis-2-Butene and (b) Trans-2-Butene

Cis-trans isomers have different physical, chemical, and physiological properties.

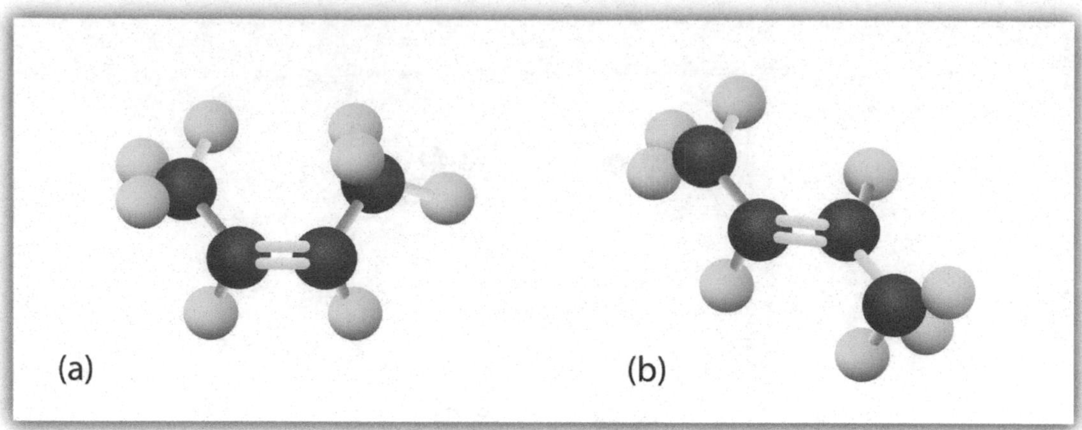

Cis-2-butene has both methyl groups on the same side of the molecule. *Trans*-2-butene has the methyl groups on opposite sides of the molecule. Their structural formulas are as follows:

CH_3, CH_3, C=C, H, H

cis-2-butene

H, CH_3, C=C, CH_3, H

trans-2-butene

Note, however, that the presence of a double bond does not necessarily lead to cis-trans isomerism. We can draw two *seemingly* different propenes:

CH_3, H, C=C, H, H

H, H, C=C, CH_3, H

However, these two structures are not really different from each other. If you could pick up either molecule from the page and flip it over top to bottom, you would see that the two formulas are identical.

Thus there are two requirements for cis-trans isomerism:

1. Rotation must be restricted in the molecule.
2. There must be two nonidentical groups on *each* doubly bonded carbon atom.

In these propene structures, the second requirement for cis-trans isomerism is not fulfilled. One of the doubly bonded carbon atoms does have two different groups attached, but the rules require that *both* carbon atoms have two different groups.

In general, the following statements hold true in cis-trans isomerism:

- Alkenes with a $C{=}CH_2$ unit do not exist as cis-trans isomers.
- Alkenes with a $C{=}CR_2$ unit, where the two R groups are the same, do not exist as cis-trans isomers.
- Alkenes of the type R–CH=CH–R can exist as cis and trans isomers; cis if the two R groups are on the same side of the carbon-to-carbon double bond, and trans if the two R groups are on opposite sides of the carbon-to-carbon double bond.

Cis-trans isomerism also occurs in cyclic compounds. In ring structures, groups are unable to rotate about any of the ring carbon–carbon bonds. Therefore, groups can be either on the same side of the ring (cis) or on opposite sides of the ring (trans). For our purposes here, we represent all cycloalkanes as planar structures, and we indicate the positions of the groups, either above or below the plane of the ring.

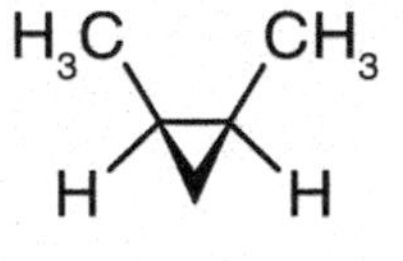

H_3C CH_3 / H H

Cis-1,2-dimethylcyclopropane

H_3C H / H CH_3

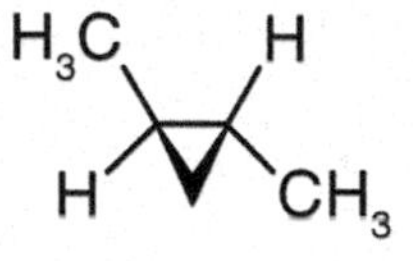

Trans-1,2-dimethylcyclopropane

EXAMPLE 3

Which compounds can exist as cis-trans (geometric) isomers? Draw them.

1. $CHCl{=}CHBr$
2. $CH_2{=}CBrCH_3$
3. $(CH_3)_2C{=}CHCH_2CH_3$
4. $CH_3CH{=}CHCH_2CH_3$

Solution

All four structures have a double bond and thus meet rule 1 for cis-trans isomerism.

1. This compound meets rule 2; it has two nonidentical groups on *each* carbon atom (H and Cl on one and H and Br on the other). It exists as both cis and trans isomers:

Cl, H on one carbon; Br, H on the other (C=C) — Cl, H on one carbon; H, Br on the other (C=C)

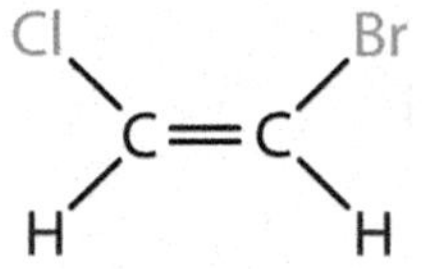

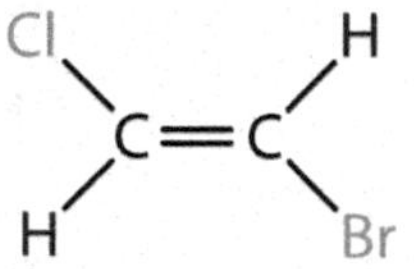

2. This compound has two hydrogen atoms on one of its doubly bonded carbon atoms; it fails rule 2 and does not exist as cis and trans isomers.
3. This compound has two methyl (CH_3) groups on one of its doubly bonded carbon atoms. It fails rule 2 and does not exist as cis and trans isomers.
4. This compound meets rule 2; it has two nonidentical groups on *each* carbon atom and exists as both cis and trans isomers:

H_3C, H on one carbon; CH_2CH_3, H on the other (C=C) — H_3C, H on one carbon; H, CH_2CH_3 on the other (C=C)

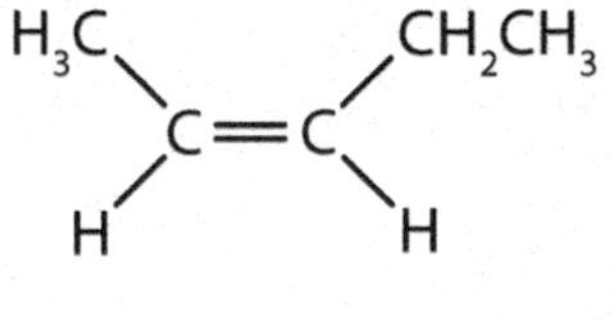

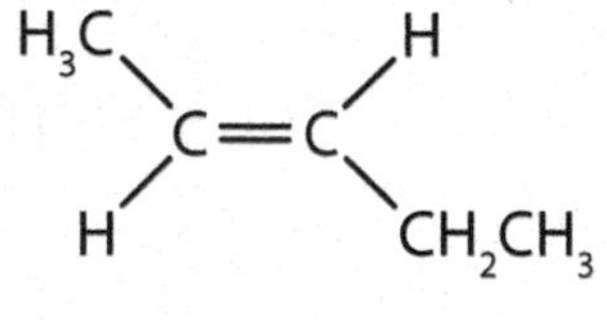

SKILL-BUILDING EXERCISE

1. Which compounds can exist as cis-trans isomers? Draw them.
   a. CH_2=$CHCH_2CH_2CH_3$
   b. CH_3CH=$CHCH_2CH_3$
   c. CH_3CH_2CH=$CHCH_2CH_3$
   d.

$$CH_2{=}\underset{\displaystyle |\atop \displaystyle CH_3}{C}CH_2CH_3$$

   e.

$$CH_3\underset{\displaystyle |\atop \displaystyle CH_3}{C}{=}CHCH_3$$

CONCEPT REVIEW EXERCISES

1. What are cis-trans (geometric) isomers? What two types of compounds can exhibit cis-trans isomerism?
2. Classify each compound as a cis isomer, a trans isomer, or neither.
   a.

CH_3CH_2(H)C=C(H)CH_2CH_3 — upper left CH_3CH_2, upper right H, lower left H, lower right CH_2CH_3

   b.

CH_3CH_2(H)C=C(H)CH_2CH_3 — upper left CH_3CH_2, upper right CH_2CH_3, lower left H, lower right H

   c.

upper left CH_3CH_2, upper right CH_2CH_3, lower left H_3C, lower right H

   d.

upper left H, upper right $\underset{}{CHCH_2CH_3}$ (bearing CH_3), lower left H, lower right H

ANSWERS

1. Cis-trans isomers are compounds that have different configurations (groups permanently in different places in space) because of the presence of a rigid structure in their molecule. Alkenes and cyclic compounds can exhibit cis-trans isomerism.

2. a. trans
   b. cis
   c. cis
   d. neither

KEY TAKEAWAY

- Cis-trans (geometric) isomerism exists when there is restricted rotation in a molecule and there are two nonidentical groups on *each* doubly bonded carbon atom.

EXERCISES

1. Draw the structures of the cis-trans isomers for each compound. Label them cis and trans. If no cis-trans isomers exist, write none.
   a. 2-bromo-2-pentene
   b. 3-heptene
   c. 4-methyl-2-pentene
   d. 1,1-dibromo-1-butene
   e. 2-butenoic acid (CH3CH=CHCOOH)
2. Draw the structures of the cis-trans isomers for each compound. Label them cis and trans. If no cis-trans isomers exist, write none.
   a. 2,3-dimethyl-2-pentene
   b. 1,1-dimethyl-2-ethylcyclopropane
   c. 1,2-dimethylcyclohexane
   d. 5-methyl-2-hexene
   e. 1,2,3-trimethylcyclopropane

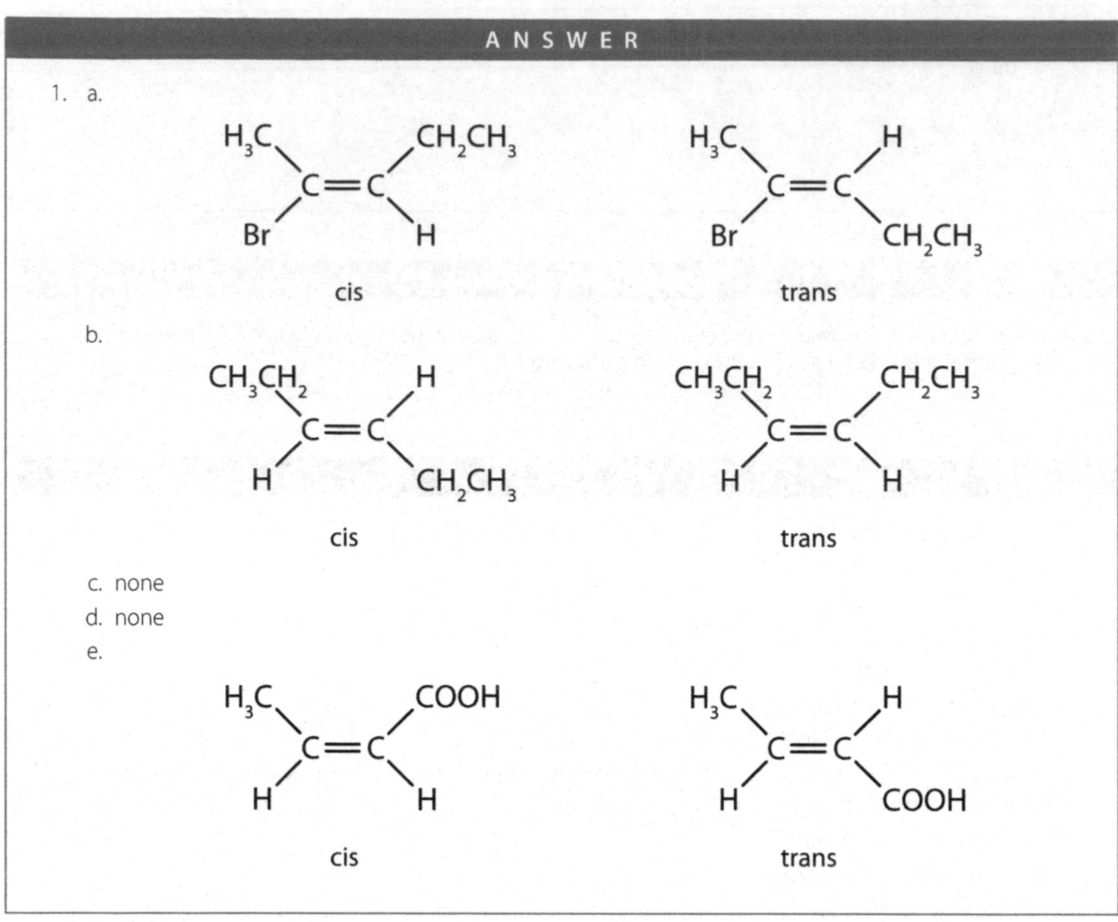

3. PHYSICAL PROPERTIES OF ALKENES

LEARNING OBJECTIVE

1. **Identify the physical properties of alkenes and describe trends in these properties.**

The physical properties of alkenes are similar to those of the alkanes. Table 13.1 (in Section 1) shows that the boiling points of straight-chain alkenes increase with increasing molar mass, just as with alkanes. For molecules with the same number of carbon atoms and the same general shape, the boiling points usually differ only slightly, just as we would expect for substances whose molar mass differs by only 2 u (equivalent to two hydrogen atoms). Like other hydrocarbons, the alkenes are insoluble in water but soluble in organic solvents.

Looking Closer: Environmental Note

Alkenes occur widely in nature. Ripening fruits and vegetables give off ethylene, which triggers further ripening. Fruit processors artificially introduce ethylene to hasten the ripening process; exposure to as little as 0.1 mg of ethylene for 24 h can ripen 1 kg of tomatoes. Unfortunately, this process does not exactly duplicate the ripening process, and tomatoes picked green and treated this way don't taste much like vine-ripened tomatoes fresh from the garden.

Other alkenes that occur in nature include 1-octene, a constituent of lemon oil, and octadecene ($C_{18}H_{36}$) found in fish liver. Dienes (two double bonds) and polyenes (three or more double bonds) are also common. Butadiene ($CH_2{=}CHCH{=}CH_2$) is found in coffee. Lycopene and the carotenes are isomeric polyenes ($C_{40}H_{56}$) that give the attractive red, orange, and yellow colors to watermelons, tomatoes, carrots, and other fruits and vegetables. Vitamin A, essential to good vision, is derived from a carotene. The world would be a much less colorful place without alkenes.

The bright red color of tomatoes is due to lycopene—a polyene.

CONCEPT REVIEW EXERCISES

1. Briefly describe the physical properties of alkenes. How do these properties compare to those of the alkanes?
2. Without consulting tables, arrange the following alkenes in order of increasing boiling point: 1-butene, ethene, 1-hexene, and propene.

ANSWERS

1. Alkenes have physical properties (low boiling points, insoluble in water) quite similar to those of their corresponding alkanes.
2. ethene < propene < 1-butene < 1-hexene

KEY TAKEAWAY

- The physical properties of alkenes are much like those of the alkanes: their boiling points increase with increasing molar mass, and they are insoluble in water.

EXERCISES

1. Without referring to a table or other reference, predict which member of each pair has the higher boiling point.
   a. 1-pentene or 1-butene
   b. 3-heptene or 3-nonene
2. Which is a good solvent for cyclohexene, pentane or water?

ANSWER

1. a. 1-pentene
   b. 3-nonene

4. CHEMICAL PROPERTIES OF ALKENES

LEARNING OBJECTIVE

1. Write equations for the addition reactions of alkenes with hydrogen, halogens, and water.

addition reaction

A reaction in which substituent groups join to hydrocarbon molecules at points of unsaturation—the double or triple bonds.

hydrogenation

A reaction in which hydrogen gas reacts at a carbon-to-carbon double or triple bond or a carbon-to-oxygen double bond to add hydrogen atoms to carbon atoms.

Alkenes are valued mainly for **addition reactions**, in which one of the bonds in the double bond is broken. Each of the carbon atoms in the bond can then attach another atom or group while remaining joined to each other by a single bond.

Perhaps the simplest addition reaction is **hydrogenation**—a reaction with hydrogen (H_2) in the presence of a catalyst such as nickel (Ni) or platinum (Pt).

$$H_2C{=}CH_2 + H_2 \longrightarrow H{-}CH_2{-}CH_2{-}H$$

Ethylene | Hydrogen | Ethane

The product is an alkane having the same carbon skeleton as the alkene. (The use of hydrogenation to convert unsaturated vegetable oils to saturated fats is discussed in Chapter 17, [Unsupported Reference Type: chapter-section].)

halogenation

A reaction in which a halogen reacts at a carbon-to-carbon double or triple bond to add halogen atoms to carbon atoms.

Alkenes also readily undergo **halogenation**—the addition of halogens. Indeed, the reaction with bromine (Br_2) can be used to test for alkenes. Bromine solutions are brownish red. When we add a Br_2 solution to an alkene, the color of the solution disappears because the alkene reacts with the bromine:

$$H_2C{=}CH_2 + Br_2 \longrightarrow H{-}CH_2Br{-}CH_2Br{-}H$$

Ethylene | Bromine (brownish-red) | 1,2-Dibromoethane (colorless)

hydration

The addition of water to a substance; in organic chemistry, the addition of water across the carbon-to-carbon double bond of an alkene or the carbon-to-oxygen double bond of an aldehyde or ketone.

Another important addition reaction is that between an alkene and water to form an alcohol. This reaction, called **hydration**, requires a catalyst—usually a strong acid, such as sulfuric acid (H_2SO_4):

$$H_2C{=}CH_2 + H_2O \longrightarrow H{-}CH_2{-}CH_2OH$$

Ethylene | Water | Ethanol

The hydration reaction is discussed further in Chapter 14, [Unsupported Reference Type: chapter-section], where we deal with this reaction in the synthesis of alcohols.

EXAMPLE 4

Write the equation for the reaction between $CH_3CH=CHCH_3$ and each substance.

1. H_2 (Ni catalyst)
2. Br_2
3. H_2O (H_2SO_4 catalyst)

Solution

In each reaction, the reagent adds across the double bond.

1. $$CH_3CH{=}CHCH_3 + H_2 \longrightarrow CH_3\underset{\displaystyle H}{\underset{|}{C}}H{-}\underset{\displaystyle H}{\underset{|}{C}}HCH_3 \quad \text{or} \quad CH_3CH_2CH_2CH_3$$

2. $$CH_3CH{=}CHCH_3 + Br_2 \longrightarrow CH_3\underset{\displaystyle Br}{\underset{|}{C}}H{-}\underset{\displaystyle Br}{\underset{|}{C}}HCH_3 \quad \text{or} \quad CH_3CHBrCHBrCH_3$$

3. $$CH_3CH{=}CHCH_3 + H_2O \longrightarrow CH_3\underset{\displaystyle H}{\underset{|}{C}}H{-}\underset{\displaystyle OH}{\underset{|}{C}}HCH_3 \quad \text{or} \quad CH_3CH_2CHOHCH_3$$

SKILL-BUILDING EXERCISE

Write the equation for each reaction.

1. $CH_3CH_2CH=CH_2$ with H_2 (Ni catalyst)
2. $CH_3CH=CH_2$ with Cl_2
3. $CH_3CH_2CH=CHCH_2CH_3$ with H_2O (H_2SO_4 catalyst)

CONCEPT REVIEW EXERCISES

1. What is the principal difference in properties between alkenes and alkanes? How are they alike?
2. If $C_{12}H_{24}$ reacts with HBr in an addition reaction, what is the molecular formula of the product?

ANSWERS

1. Alkenes undergo addition reactions; alkanes do not. Both burn.
2. $C_{12}H_{24}Br_2$

KEY TAKEAWAY

- Alkenes undergo addition reactions, adding such substances as hydrogen, bromine, and water across the carbon-to-carbon double bond.

EXERCISES

1. Complete each equation.
   a. $(CH3)\ 2C{=}CH2 + Br2 \rightarrow$
   b. $CH_2{=}C(CH_3)CH_2CH_3 + H_2 \xrightarrow{Ni}$
   c. $\text{cyclohexene} + H_2O \xrightarrow{H_2SO_4}$

2. Complete each equation.
   a. $CH_2{=}CHCH{=}CH_2 + 2H_2 \xrightarrow{Ni}$
   b. $(CH_3)_2C{=}C(CH_3)_2 + H_2O \xrightarrow{H_2SO_4}$
   c. $\text{cyclobutene} + CL_2 \rightarrow$

ANSWER

1. a. (CH3)2CBrCH2Br
   b. CH3CH(CH3)CH2CH3
   c. cyclohexanol (OH on cyclohexane ring)

5. POLYMERS

LEARNING OBJECTIVE

1. **Draw structures for monomers that can undergo addition polymerization and for four-monomer-unit sections of an addition polymer.**

The most important commercial reactions of alkenes are *polymerizations*, reactions in which small molecules, referred to in general as **monomers** (from the Greek *monos*, meaning "one," and *meros*, meaning "parts"), are assembled into giant molecules referred to as **polymers** (from the Greek *poly*, meaning "many," and *meros*, meaning "parts"). A polymer is as different from its monomer as a long strand of spaghetti is from a tiny speck of flour. For example, polyethylene, the familiar waxy material used to make plastic bags, is made from the monomer ethylene—a gas.

monomer

A small molecule that can be combined with other small molecules to make polymers.

polymer

A giant molecule formed by the combination of monomers in a repeating manner.

The Production of Polyethylene

Polyethylene pellets are melted, formed into a giant bubble, and then made into a film that is used in packaging, consumer products, and food services.

View the video online at: http://www.youtube.com/embed/JpF4zgJHOJg

There are two general types of polymerization reactions: addition polymerization and condensation polymerization. (For more information about condensation polymerization, see Chapter 15, [Unsupported Reference Type: chapter-section].) In **addition polymerization**, the monomers add to one another in such a way that the polymer contains all the atoms of the starting monomers. Ethylene molecules are joined together in long chains. The polymerization can be represented by the reaction of a few monomer units:

addition polymerization

A reaction in which monomers add to one another to produce a polymeric product that contains all the atoms of the starting monomers.

$$H_2C{=}CH_2 + H_2C{=}CH_2 + H_2C{=}CH_2 + \ldots \longrightarrow -CH_2-CH_2-CH_2-CH_2-CH_2-CH_2-$$

The bond lines extending at the ends in the formula of the product indicate that the structure extends for many units in each direction. Notice that all the atoms—two carbon atoms and four hydrogen atoms—of each monomer molecule are incorporated into the polymer structure. Because displays such as the one above are cumbersome, the polymerization is often abbreviated as follows:

$$nCH_2{=}CH_2 \rightarrow -\!\!\!+CH_2CH_2+\!\!\!-_n$$

Note

Many natural materials—such as proteins, cellulose and starch, and complex silicate minerals—are polymers. (For more information about proteins and cellulose/starch, see Chapter 18, [Unsupported Reference Type: chapter-section], and Chapter 16, [Unsupported Reference Type: chapter-section], respectively.) Artificial fibers, films, plastics, semisolid resins, and rubbers are also polymers. More than half the compounds produced by the chemical industry are synthetic polymers.

Some common addition polymers are listed in Table 13.2. Note that all the monomers have carbon-to-carbon double bonds. Many polymers are mundane (e.g., plastic bags, food wrap, toys, and tableware), but there are also polymers that conduct electricity, have amazing adhesive properties, or are stronger than steel but much lighter in weight.

TABLE 13.2 Some Addition Polymers

Monomer	Polymer	Polymer Name	Some Uses
CH2=CH2	~CH2CH2CH2CH2CH2CH2~	polyethylene	plastic bags, bottles, toys, electrical insulation
CH2=CHCH3	~$CH_2CHCH_2CHCH_2CH$~ (with CH_3 on each CH)	polypropylene	carpeting, bottles, luggage, exercise clothing
CH2=CHCl	~$CH_2CHCH_2CHCH_2CH$~ (with Cl on each CH)	polyvinyl chloride	bags for intravenous solutions, pipes, tubing, floor coverings
CF2=CF2	~CF2CF2CF2CF2CF2CF2~	polytetrafluoroethylene	nonstick coatings, electrical insulation

5.1 Medical Uses of Polymers

An interesting use of polymers is the replacement of diseased, worn out, or missing parts in the body. For example, about a 250,000 hip joints and 500,000 knees are replaced in US hospitals each year. The artificial ball-and-socket hip joints are made of a special steel (the ball) and plastic (the socket). People crippled by arthritis or injuries gain freedom of movement and relief from pain. Patients with heart and circulatory problems can be helped by replacing worn out heart valves with parts based on synthetic polymers. These are only a few of the many biomedical uses of polymers.

FIGURE 13.4 Hip Joint Replacement

Synthetic polymers are an important part of a hip joint replacement. The hip is much like a ball-and-socket joint, and total hip replacements mimic this with a metal ball that fits in a plastic cup.

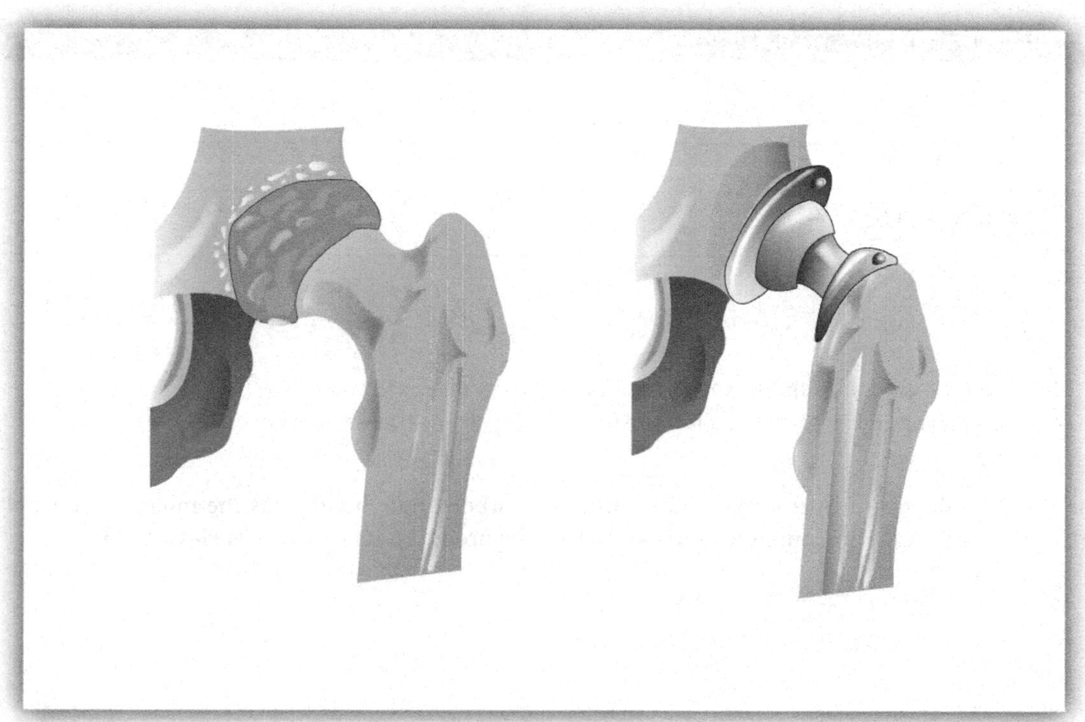

CONCEPT REVIEW EXERCISES

1. What is a monomer? What is a polymer? How do polymer molecules differ from the molecules we have discussed in earlier sections of this chapter?
2. What is addition polymerization? What structural feature usually characterizes molecules used as monomers in addition polymerization?
3. What is the molecular formula of a polymer molecule formed by the addition polymerization of 175 molecules of vinyl chloride ($CH_2{=}CHCl$)?

ANSWERS

1. Monomers are small molecules that can be assembled into giant molecules referred to as polymers, which are much larger than the molecules we discussed earlier in this chapter.
2. In addition polymerization, the monomers add to one another in such a way that the polymer contains all the atoms of the starting monomers.
3. $C_{350}H_{525}Cl_{175}$

KEY TAKEAWAY

- Molecules having carbon-to-carbon double bonds can undergo addition polymerization.

EXERCISES

1. Write the condensed structural formula of the monomer from which Saran is formed. A segment of the Saran molecule has the following structure: $CH_2CCl_2CH_2CCl_2CH_2CCl_2CH_2CCl_2$.

2. Write the condensed structural formula for the section of a molecule formed from four units of the monomer $CH_2{=}CHF$.

ANSWER

1. $H_2C{=}CCl_2$

6. ALKYNES

LEARNING OBJECTIVES

1. **Describe the general physical and chemical properties of alkynes.**
2. **Name alkynes given formulas and write formulas for alkynes given names.**

The simplest alkyne—a hydrocarbon with carbon-to-carbon triple bond—has the molecular formula C_2H_2 and is known by its common name—acetylene (Figure 13.5). Its structure is H–C≡C–H.

FIGURE 13.5 Ball-and-Spring Model of Acetylene

Acetylene (ethyne) is the simplest member of the alkyne family.

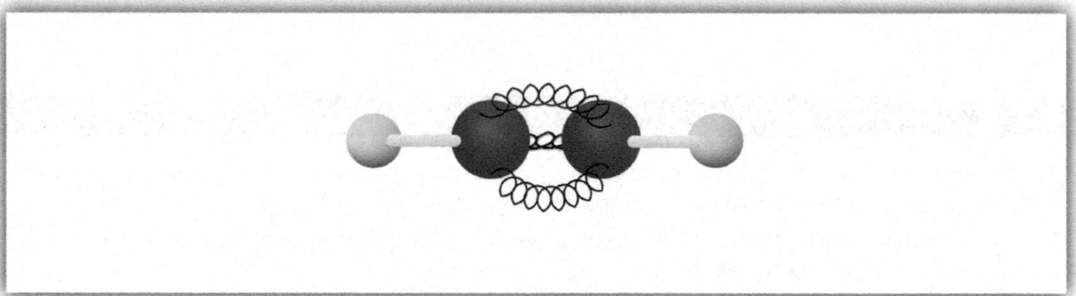

Note

Acetylene is used in oxyacetylene torches for cutting and welding metals. The flame from such a torch can be very hot. Most acetylene, however, is converted to chemical intermediates that are used to make vinyl and acrylic plastics, fibers, resins, and a variety of other products.

Alkynes are similar to alkenes in both physical and chemical properties. For example, alkynes undergo many of the typical addition reactions of alkenes. The International Union of Pure and Applied Chemistry (IUPAC) names for alkynes parallel those of alkenes, except that the family ending is *-yne* rather than *-ene*. The IUPAC name for acetylene is ethyne. The names of other alkynes are illustrated in the following exercises.

CONCEPT REVIEW EXERCISES

1. Briefly identify the important differences between an alkene and an alkyne. How are they similar?
2. The alkene $(CH_3)_2CHCH_2CH{=}CH_2$ is named 4-methyl-1-pentene. What is the name of $(CH_3)_2CHCH_2C{\equiv}CH$?
3. Do alkynes show cis-trans isomerism? Explain.

ANSWERS

1. Alkenes have double bonds; alkynes have triple bonds. Both undergo addition reactions.
2. 4-methyl-1-pentyne
3. No; a triply bonded carbon atom can form only one other bond. It would have to have two groups attached to show cis-trans isomerism.

KEY TAKEAWAY

- Alkynes are hydrocarbons with carbon-to-carbon triple bonds and properties much like those of alkenes.

EXERCISES

1. Draw the structure for each compound.
   a. acetylene
   b. 3-methyl-1-hexyne
2. Draw the structure for each compound.
   a. 4-methyl-2-hexyne
   b. 3-octyne
3. Name each alkyne.
   a. CH3CH2CH2C≡CH
   b. CH3CH2CH2C≡CCH3

ANSWERS

1. a. H–C≡C–H
   b.

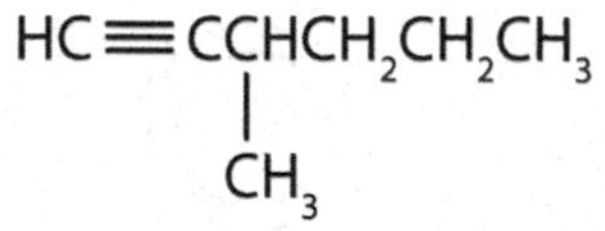

$$HC\equiv C\underset{\displaystyle CH_3}{\underset{|}{C}}HCH_2CH_2CH_3$$

3. a. 1-pentyne
   b. 2-hexyne

7. AROMATIC COMPOUNDS: BENZENE

LEARNING OBJECTIVE

1. **Describe the bonding in benzene and the way typical reactions of benzene differ from those of the alkenes.**

Next we consider a class of hydrocarbons with molecular formulas like those of unsaturated hydrocarbons, but which, unlike the alkenes, do not readily undergo addition reactions. These compounds comprise a distinct class, called **aromatic hydrocarbons**, with unique structures and properties. We start with the simplest of these compounds. Benzene (C_6H_6) is of great commercial importance, but it also has noteworthy health effects (see "To Your Health: Benzene and Us").

aromatic hydrocarbon

A hydrocarbon with a benzene-like structure.

The formula C_6H_6 seems to indicate that benzene has a high degree of unsaturation. (Hexane, the saturated hydrocarbon with six carbon atoms has the formula C_6H_{14}—eight more hydrogen atoms than benzene.) However, despite the seeming low level of saturation, benzene is rather unreactive. It does not, for example, react readily with bromine, which, as mentioned in Section 1, is a test for unsaturation.

Note

Benzene is a liquid that smells like gasoline, boils at 80°C, and freezes at 5.5°C. It is the aromatic hydrocarbon produced in the largest volume. It was formerly used to decaffeinate coffee and was a significant component of many consumer products, such as paint strippers, rubber cements, and home dry-cleaning spot removers. It was removed from many product formulations in the 1950s, but others continued to use benzene in products until the 1970s when it was associated with leukemia deaths. Benzene is still important in industry as a precursor in the production of plastics (such as Styrofoam and nylon), drugs, detergents, synthetic rubber, pesticides, and dyes. It is used as a solvent for such things as cleaning and maintaining printing equipment and for adhesives such as those used to attach soles to shoes. Benzene is a natural constituent of petroleum products, but because it is a known carcinogen, its use as an additive in gasoline is now limited.

To explain the surprising properties of benzene, chemists suppose the molecule has a cyclic, hexagonal, planar structure of six carbon atoms with one hydrogen atom bonded to each. We can write a structure with alternate single and double bonds, either as a full structural formula or as a line-angle formula:

However, these structures do not explain the unique properties of benzene. Furthermore, experimental evidence indicates that all the carbon-to-carbon bonds in benzene are equivalent, and the molecule is unusually stable.

Chemists often represent benzene as a hexagon with an inscribed circle:

The inner circle indicates that the valence electrons are shared equally by all six carbon atoms (that is, the electrons are *delocalized*, or spread out, over all the carbon atoms). It is understood that each corner of the hexagon is occupied by one carbon atom, and each carbon atom has one hydrogen atom attached to it. Any other atom or groups of atoms substituted for a hydrogen atom must be shown bonded to a particular corner of the hexagon. We use this modern symbolism, but many scientists still use the earlier structure with alternate double and single bonds.

To Your Health: Benzene and Us

Most of the benzene used commercially comes from petroleum. It is employed as a starting material for the production of detergents, drugs, dyes, insecticides, and plastics. Once widely used as an organic solvent, benzene is now known to have both short- and long-term toxic effects. The inhalation of large concentrations can cause nausea and even death due to respiratory or heart failure, while repeated exposure leads to a progressive disease in which the ability of the bone marrow to make new blood cells is eventually destroyed. This results in a condition called *aplastic anemia*, in which there is a decrease in the numbers of both the red and white blood cells.

CONCEPT REVIEW EXERCISES

1. How do the typical reactions of benzene differ from those of the alkenes?

2. Briefly describe the bonding in benzene.
3. What does the circle mean in the chemist's representation of benzene?

ANSWERS

1. Benzene is rather unreactive toward addition reactions compared to an alkene.
2. Valence electrons are shared equally by all six carbon atoms (that is, the electrons are delocalized).
3. The six electrons are shared equally by all six carbon atoms.

KEY TAKEAWAY

- Aromatic hydrocarbons appear to be unsaturated, but they have a special type of bonding and do not undergo addition reactions.

EXERCISES

1. Draw the structure of benzene as if it had alternate single and double bonds.
2. Draw the structure of benzene as chemists usually represent it today.

ANSWER

1.

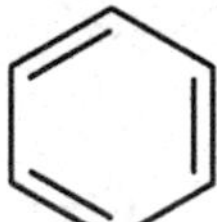

8. STRUCTURE AND NOMENCLATURE OF AROMATIC COMPOUNDS

LEARNING OBJECTIVES

1. **Recognize aromatic compounds from structural formulas.**
2. **Name aromatic compounds given formulas.**
3. **Write formulas for aromatic compounds given their names.**

Historically, benzene-like substances were called aromatic hydrocarbons because they had distinctive aromas. Today, an **aromatic compound** is any compound that contains a benzene ring or has certain benzene-like properties (but not necessarily a strong aroma). You can recognize the aromatic compounds in this text by the presence of one or more benzene rings in their structure. Some representative aromatic compounds and their uses are listed in Table 13.3, where the benzene ring is represented as C_6H_5.

aromatic compound

Any compound that contains a benzene ring or has certain benzene-like properties.

TABLE 13.3 Some Representative Aromatic Compounds

Name	Structure	Typical Uses
aniline	C6H5–NH2	starting material for the synthesis of dyes, drugs, resins, varnishes, perfumes; solvent; vulcanizing rubber
benzoic acid	C6H5–COOH	food preservative; starting material for the synthesis of dyes and other organic compounds; curing of tobacco
bromobenzene	C6H5–Br	starting material for the synthesis of many other aromatic compounds; solvent; motor oil additive
nitrobenzene	C6H5–NO2	starting material for the synthesis of aniline; solvent for cellulose nitrate; in soaps and shoe polish
phenol	C6H5–OH	disinfectant; starting material for the synthesis of resins, drugs, and other organic compounds
toluene	C6H5–CH3	solvent; gasoline octane booster; starting material for the synthesis of benzoic acid, benzaldehyde, and many other organic compounds

EXAMPLE 5

Which compounds are aromatic?

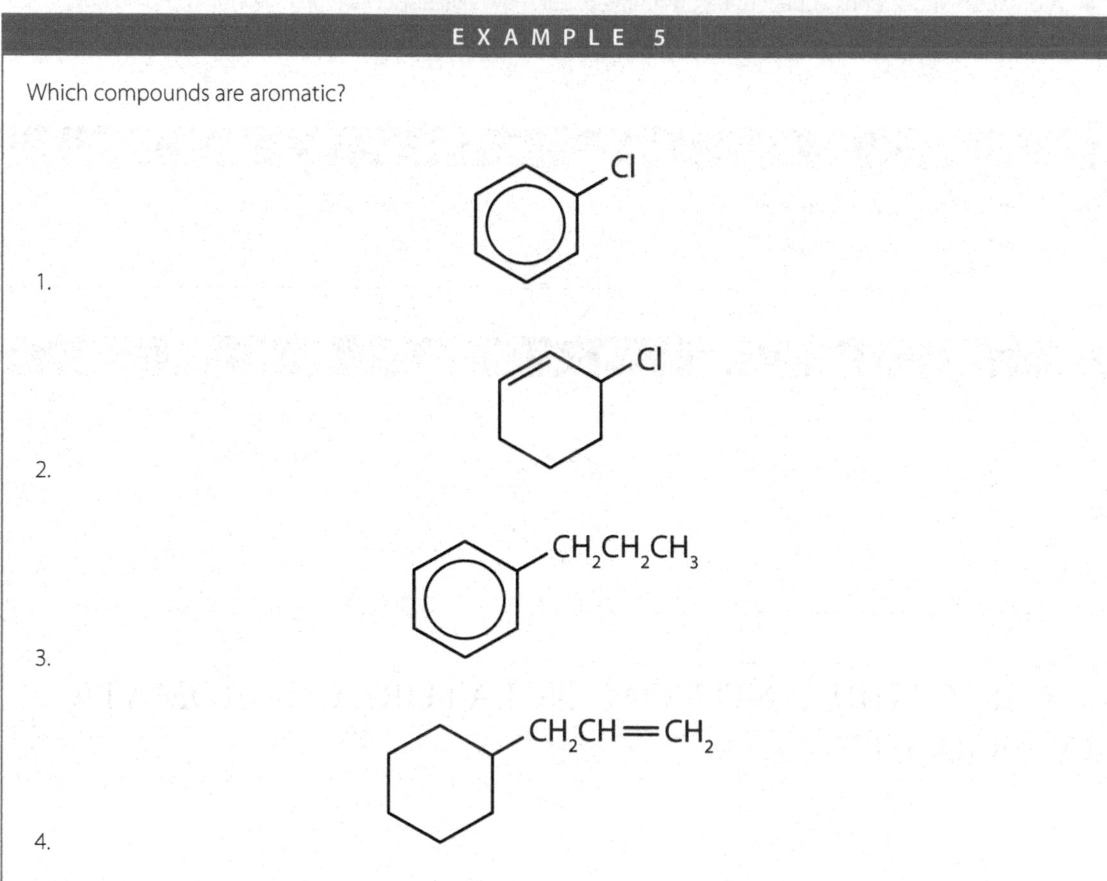

Solution

1. The compound has a benzene ring (with a chlorine atom substituted for one of the hydrogen atoms); it is aromatic.
2. The compound is cyclic, but it does not have a benzene ring; it is not aromatic.
3. The compound has a benzene ring (with a propyl group substituted for one of the hydrogen atoms); it is aromatic.
4. The compound is cyclic, but it does not have a benzene ring; it is not aromatic.

SKILL-BUILDING EXERCISE

Which compounds are aromatic?

1.

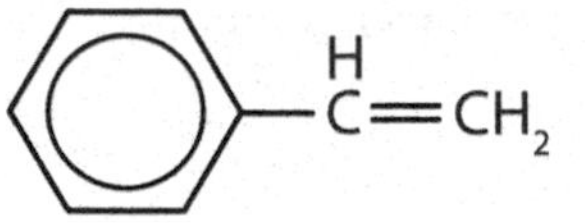

2.

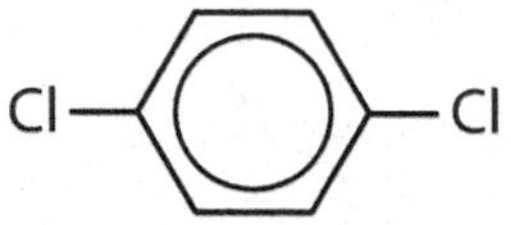

3.

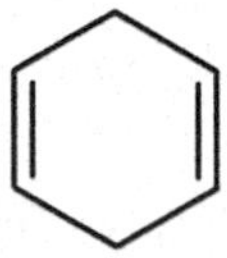

In the International Union of Pure and Applied Chemistry (IUPAC) system, aromatic hydrocarbons are named as derivatives of benzene. Figure 13.6 shows four examples. In these structures, it is immaterial whether the single substituent is written at the top, side, or bottom of the ring: a hexagon is symmetrical, and therefore all positions are equivalent.

FIGURE 13.6 Some Benzene Derivatives

These compounds are named in the usual way with the group that replaces a hydrogen atom named as a substituent group: Cl as chloro, Br as bromo, I as iodo, NO_2 as nitro, and CH_3CH_2 as ethyl.

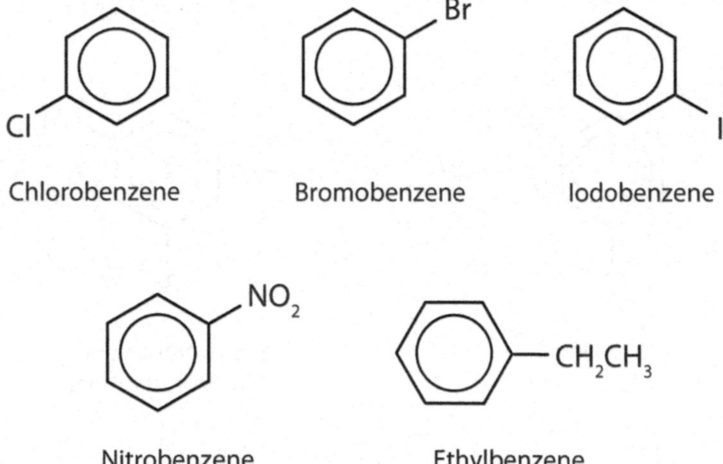

Although some compounds are referred to exclusively by IUPAC names, some are more frequently denoted by common names, as is indicated in Table 13.3.

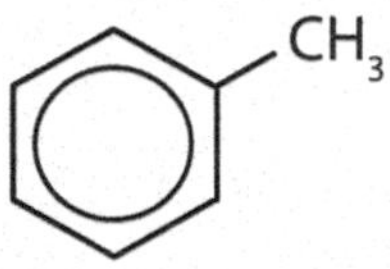

CH_3 OH NH_2

Toluene 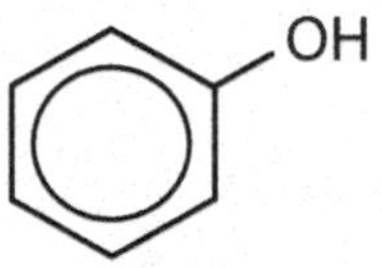 Phenol 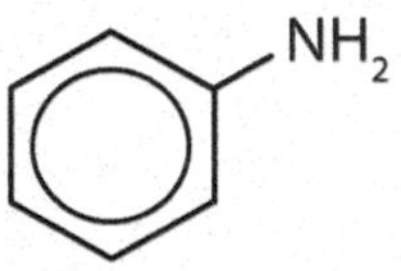 Aniline

When there is more than one substituent, the corners of the hexagon are no longer equivalent, so we must designate the relative positions. There are three possible disubstituted benzenes, and we can use numbers to distinguish them (Figure 13.7). We start numbering at the carbon atom to which one of the groups is attached and count toward the carbon atom that bears the other substituent group by the shortest path.

FIGURE 13.7 The Three Isomeric Dichlorobenzenes

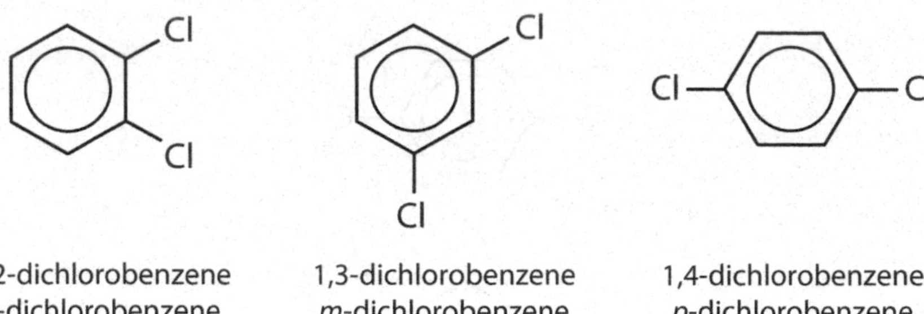

In Figure 13.7, common names are also used: the prefix *ortho* (*o*-) for 1,2-disubstitution, *meta* (*m*-) for 1,3-disubstitution, and *para* (*p*-) for 1,4-disubstitution.

The substituent names are listed in alphabetical order. The first substituent is given the lowest number. When a common name is used, the carbon atom that bears the group responsible for the name is given the number 1:

Br
Cl

1-Bromo-4-chlorobenzene
p-Bromochlorobenzene

OH
Br

2-Bromophenol
o-Bromophenol

NH_2
Cl

3-Chloroaniline
m-Chloroaniline

CH_3
Br

3-Bromotoluene
m-Bromotoluene

EXAMPLE 6

Name each compound using both the common name and the IUPAC name.

1.

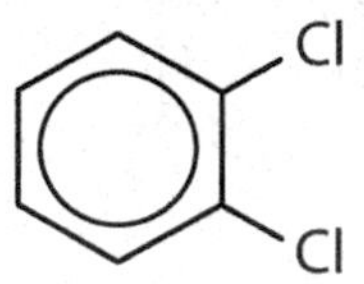

2.

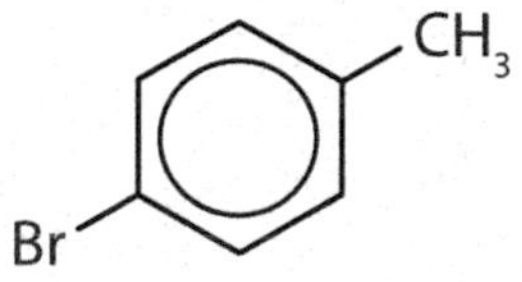

3.

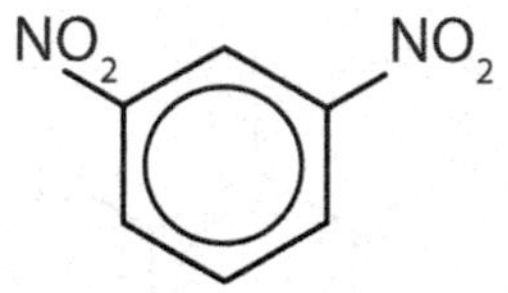

Solution

1. The benzene ring has two chlorine atoms (dichloro) in the first and second positions. The compound is *o*-dichlorobenzene or 1,2-dichlorobenzene.
2. The benzene ring has a methyl (CH_3) group. The compound is therefore named as a derivative of toluene. The bromine atom is on the fourth carbon atom, counting from the methyl group. The compound is *p*-bromotoluene or 4-bromotoluene.
3. The benzene ring has two nitro (NO_2) groups in the first and third positions. It is *m*-dinitrobenzene or 1,3-dinitrobenzene.

Note

The nitro (NO_2) group is a common substituent in aromatic compounds. Many nitro compounds are explosive, most notably 2,4,6-trinitrotoluene (TNT).

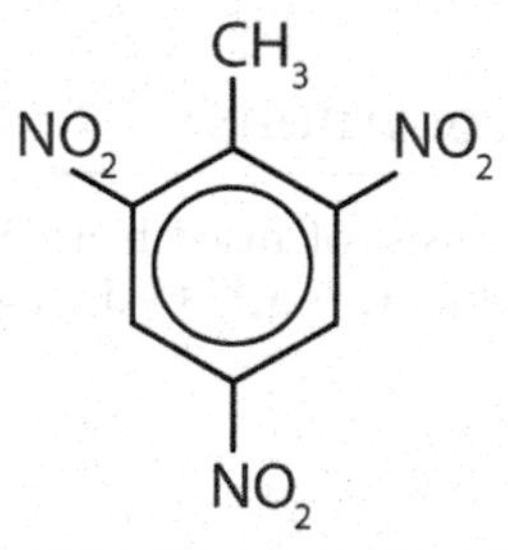

SKILL-BUILDING EXERCISE

Name each compound using both the common name and the IUPAC name.

1.

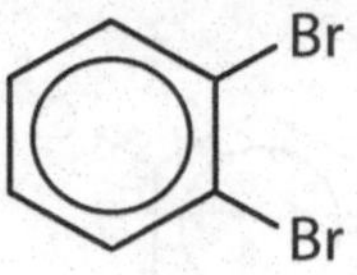

2.

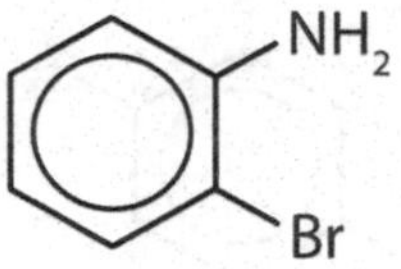

3.

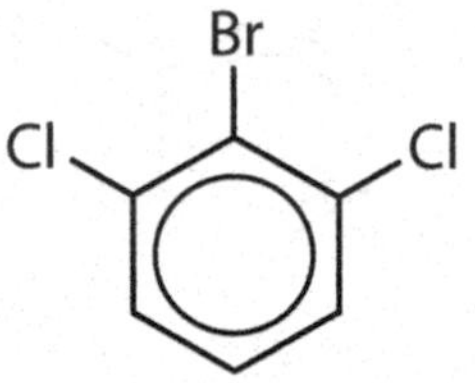

aryl group

A group derived from an aromatic hydrocarbon by the removal of a hydrogen atom.

Sometimes an aromatic group is found as a substituent bonded to a nonaromatic entity or to another aromatic ring. The group of atoms remaining when a hydrogen atom is removed from an aromatic compound is called an **aryl group**. The most common aryl group is derived from benzene (C_6H_6) by removing one hydrogen atom (C_6H_5) and is called a *phenyl* group, from *pheno*, an old name for benzene.

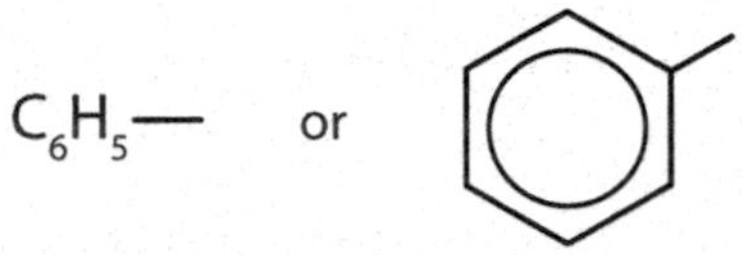

Phenyl group

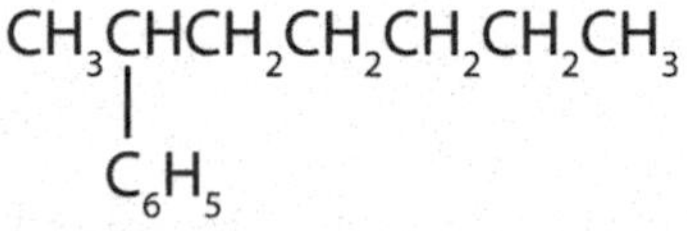

2-Phenylheptane

8.1 Polycyclic Aromatic Hydrocarbons

polycyclic aromatic hydrocarbon (PAH)

An aromatic hydrocarbon consisting of fused benzene rings sharing a common side.

Some common aromatic hydrocarbons consist of fused benzene rings—rings that share a common side. These compounds are called **polycyclic aromatic hydrocarbons (PAHs)**.

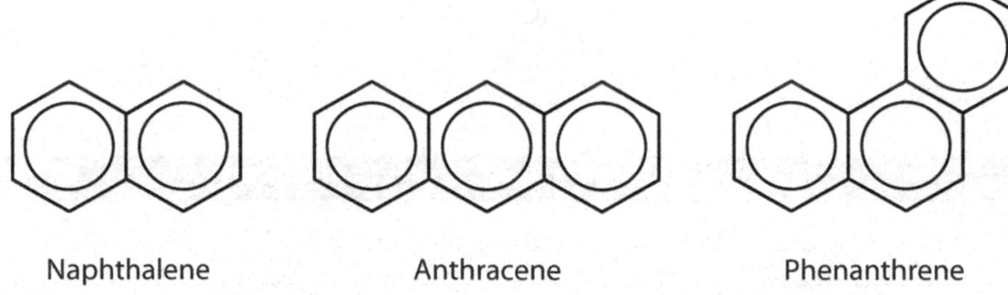

Naphthalene Anthracene Phenanthrene

The three examples shown here are colorless, crystalline solids generally obtained from coal tar. Naphthalene has a pungent odor and is used in mothballs. Anthracene is used in the manufacture of certain dyes. Steroids, a large group of naturally occurring substances, contain the phenanthrene structure.

(For more information about steroids, see Chapter 17, [Unsupported Reference Type: chapter-section].)

To Your Health: Polycyclic Aromatic Hydrocarbons and Cancer

The intense heating required for distilling coal tar results in the formation of PAHs. For many years, it has been known that workers in coal-tar refineries are susceptible to a type of skin cancer known as tar cancer. Investigations have shown that a number of PAHs are carcinogens. One of the most active carcinogenic compounds, benzopyrene, occurs in coal tar and has also been isolated from cigarette smoke, automobile exhaust gases, and charcoal-broiled steaks. It is estimated that more than 1,000 t of benzopyrene are emitted into the air over the United States each year. Only a few milligrams of benzopyrene per kilogram of body weight are required to induce cancer in experimental animals.

8.2 Biologically Important Compounds with Benzene Rings

Substances containing the benzene ring are common in both animals and plants, although they are more abundant in the latter. Plants can synthesize the benzene ring from carbon dioxide, water, and inorganic materials. Animals cannot synthesize it, but they are dependent on certain aromatic compounds for survival and therefore must obtain them from food. Phenylalanine, tyrosine, and tryptophan (essential amino acids) and vitamins K, B_2 (riboflavin), and B_9 (folic acid) all contain the benzene ring. (For more information about vitamins, see Chapter 18, [Unsupported Reference Type: chapter-section].) Many important drugs, a few of which are shown in Table 13.4, also feature a benzene ring.

Note

So far we have studied only aromatic compounds with carbon-containing rings. However, many cyclic compounds have an element other than carbon atoms in the ring. These compounds, called *heterocyclic compounds*, are discussed in Chapter 15, [Unsupported Reference Type: chapter-section]. Some of these are heterocyclic aromatic compounds.

TABLE 13.4 Some Drugs That Contain a Benzene Ring

Name	Structure
aspirin	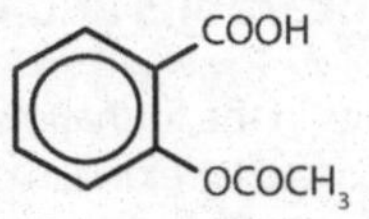 $COOH$, $OCOCH_3$
acetaminophen	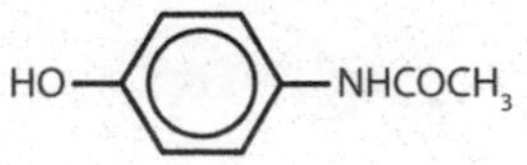 HO–, –$NHCOCH_3$
ibuprofen	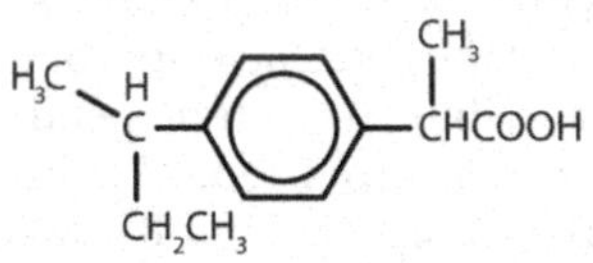 H_3C, H, C, CH_2CH_3, CH_3, $CHCOOH$
amphetamine	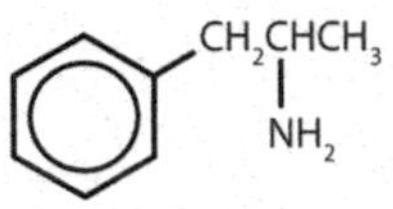 CH_2CHCH_3, NH_2
sulfanilamide	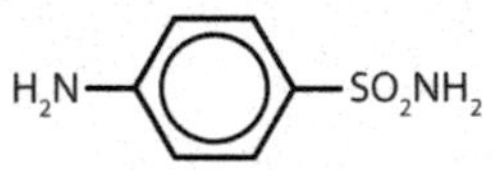 H_2N–, –SO_2NH_2

CONCEPT REVIEW EXERCISES

1. Briefly identify the important characteristics of an aromatic compound.
2. What is meant by the prefixes *meta*, *ortho*, or *para*? Give the name and draw the structure for a compound that illustrates each.
3. What is a phenyl group? Give the structure for 3-phenyloctane.

ANSWERS

1. An aromatic compound is any compound that contains a benzene ring or has certain benzene-like properties.

2. meta = 1,3 disubstitution; (answers will vary)

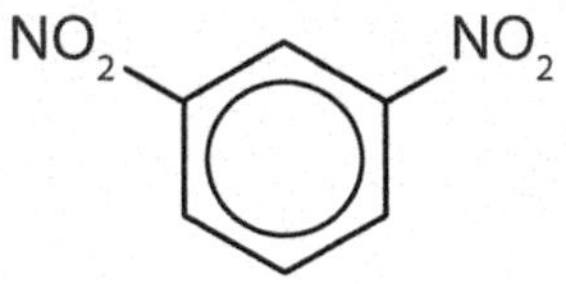

NO_2 NO_2

m-dinitrobenzene or 1,3-dinitrobenzene

ortho = 1,2 disubstitution

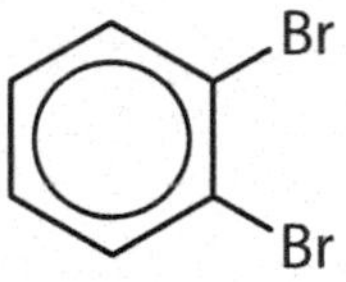

Br

Br

o-dibromobenzene or 1,2-dibromobenzene

para = 1,4 disubstitution or 1-bromo-4-chlorobenzene

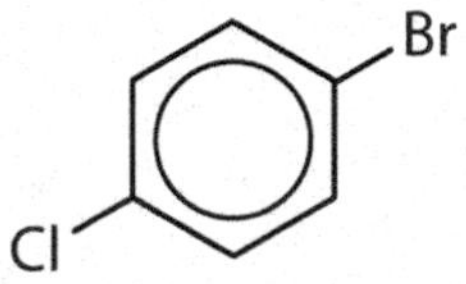

Br

Cl

p-bromochlorobenzene or 1-bromo-2-chlorobenzene

3. phenyl group: C_6H_5 or

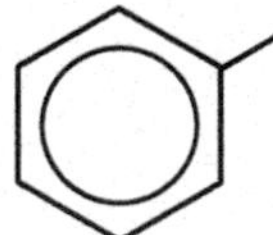

3-phenyloctane:

$$\begin{array}{l} CH_3CH_2\underset{\displaystyle C_6H_5}{\underset{|}{C}}HCH_2CH_2CH_2CH_2CH_3 \end{array}$$

KEY TAKEAWAY

- Aromatic compounds contain a benzene ring or have certain benzene-like properties; for our purposes, you can recognize aromatic compounds by the presence of one or more benzene rings in their structure.

EXERCISES

1. Is each compound aromatic?
   a.
   NO_2
   b.
   Br
2. Is each compound aromatic?
   a.
   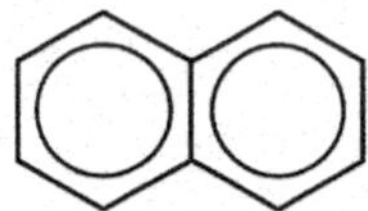
   b.
3. Draw the structure for each compound.
   a. toluene
   b. *m*-diethylbenzene
   c. 3,5-dinitrotoluene
4. Draw the structure for each compound.
   a. *p*-dichlorobenzene
   b. naphthalene
   c. 1,2,4-trimethylbenzene
5. Name each compound with its IUPAC name.
   a.
   CH_2CH_3
   b.
   CH_3
   $CHCH_3$
   c.
   CH_3
   Br
   d.
   Cl CH_3
   Cl
6. Name each compound with its IUPAC name.
   a.
   $CH_2CH_2CH_3$
   b.
   CH_3
   Cl
   Cl
   c.
   Br Br
   Br
   d.
   NO_2 CH_3

ANSWERS

1. a. yes
   b. no

3. a. [benzene ring]—CH_3

b. [benzene ring with CH_2CH_3 substituents in meta positions]

c. [benzene ring with NO_2, CH_3, and NO_2 substituents]

5. a. ethylbenzene
   b. isopropylbenzene
   c. *o*-bromotoluene
   d. 3,5-dichlorotoluene

9. END-OF-CHAPTER MATERIAL

Chapter Summary

To ensure that you understand the material in this chapter, you should review the meanings of the bold terms in the following summary and ask yourself how they relate to the topics in the chapter.

Any hydrocarbon containing either a double or triple bond is an **unsaturated hydrocarbon**. **Alkenes** have a carbon-to-carbon double bond. The general formula for alkenes with one double bond is C_nH_{2n}. Alkenes can be straight chain, branched chain, or cyclic. Simple alkenes often have common names, but all alkenes can be named by the system of the International Union of Pure and Applied Chemistry.

Cis-trans isomers (or geometric isomers) are characterized by molecules that differ only in their configuration around a rigid part of the structure, such as a carbon–to-carbon double bond or a ring. The molecule having two identical (or closely related) atoms or groups on the same side is the **cis isomer**; the one having the two groups on opposite sides is the **trans isomer**.

The physical properties of alkenes are quite similar to those of alkanes. Like other hydrocarbons, alkenes are insoluble in water but soluble in organic solvents.

More reactive than alkanes, alkenes undergo **addition reactions** across the double bond:

- Addition of hydrogen (**hydrogenation**):

$$CH_2{=}CH_2 + H_2 \rightarrow CH_3CH_3$$

- Addition of halogen (**halogenation**):

$$CH_2{=}CH_2 + X_2 \rightarrow XCH_2CH_2X$$

  where X = F, Cl, Br, or I.
- Addition of water (**hydration**):

$$CH_2{=}CH_2 + HOH \rightarrow HCH_2CH_2OH$$

Alkenes also undergo **addition polymerization**, molecules joining together to form long-chain molecules.

$$\ldots CH_2{=}CH_2 + CH_2{=}CH_2 + CH_2{=}CH_2 + \ldots \rightarrow \ldots CH_2CH_2{-}CH_2CH_2{-}CH_2CH_2{-}\ldots$$

The reactant units are **monomers**, and the product is a **polymer**.

Alkynes have a carbon-to-carbon triple bond. The general formula for alkynes is C_nH_{2n-2}. The properties of alkynes are quite similar to those of alkenes. They are named much like alkenes but with the ending *-yne*.

The cyclic hydrocarbon *benzene* (C_6H_6) has a ring of carbon atoms. The molecule seems to be unsaturated, but it does not undergo the typical reactions expected of alkenes. The electrons that might be fixed in three double bonds are instead *delocalized* over all six carbon atoms.

A hydrocarbon containing one or more benzene rings (or other similarly stable electron arrangements) is an **aromatic hydrocarbon**, and any related substance is an **aromatic compound**. One or more of the hydrogen atoms on a benzene ring can be replaced by other atoms. When two hydrogen atoms are replaced, the product name is based on the relative position of the replacement atoms (or atom groups). A 1,2-disubstituted benzene is designated as an *ortho* (*o*-) isomer; 1,3-, a *meta* (*m*-) isomer; and 1,4-, a *para* (*p*-) isomer. An aromatic group as a substituent is called an **aryl** group.

A **polycyclic aromatic hydrocarbon (PAH)** has fused benzene rings sharing a common side.

ADDITIONAL EXERCISES

1. Classify each compound as saturated or unsaturated.
   a.

      $CH_2{=}C(CH_3)CH_3$

   b. $CH_3C{\equiv}CCH_3$
2. Classify each compound as saturated or unsaturated.
   a.

      $CH_3C(CH_3)_2CH_3$

   b.
3. Give the molecular formula for each compound.
   a.

      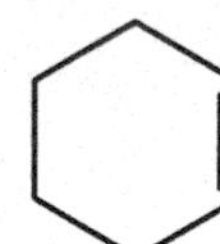

   b.

      CH_2 ring: CH_2—CH(—CH_3)—CH_2 (cyclopropane ring with CH_3 substituent)
4. When three isomeric pentenes—X, Y, and Z—are hydrogenated, all three form 2-methylbutane. The addition of Cl_2 to Y gives 1,2-dichloro-3-methylbutane, and the addition of Cl_2 to Z gives 1,2-dichloro-2-methylbutane. Draw the original structures for X, Y, and Z.
5. Pentane and 1-pentene are both colorless, low-boiling liquids. Describe a simple test that distinguishes the two compounds. Indicate what you would observe.
6. Draw and name all the alkene cis-trans isomers corresponding to the molecular formula C_5H_{10}. (Hint: there are only two.)

7. The complete combustion of benzene forms carbon dioxide and water:

$$C_6H_6 + O_2 \rightarrow CO_2 + H_2O$$

Balance the equation. What mass, in grams, of carbon dioxide is formed by the complete combustion of 39.0 g of benzene?

8. Describe a physiological effect of some PAHs.
9. What are some of the hazards associated with the use of benzene?
10. What is wrong with each name? Draw the structure and give the correct name for each compound.
    a. 2-methyl-4-heptene
    b. 2-ethyl-2-hexene
    c. 2,2-dimethyl-3-pentene
11. What is wrong with each name?
    a. 2-bromobenzene
    b. 3,3-dichlorotoluene
    c. 1,4-dimethylnitrobenzene
12. Following are line-angle formulas for three compounds. Draw the structure and give the name for each.
    a. 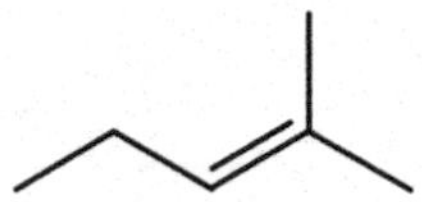
    b. 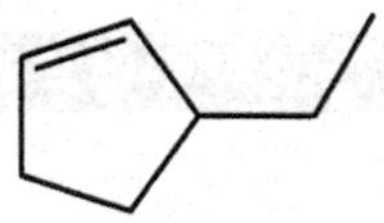
    c.

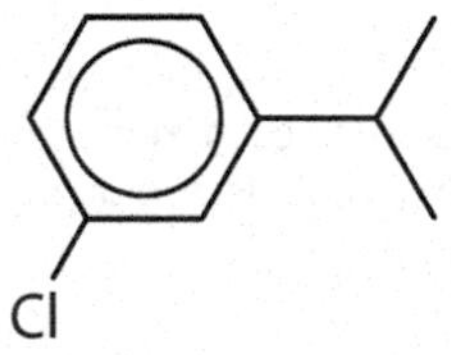

Cl

13. Following are ball-and-stick molecular models for three compounds (blue balls represent H atoms; red balls are C atoms). Write the condensed structural formula and give the name for each.

    a.

    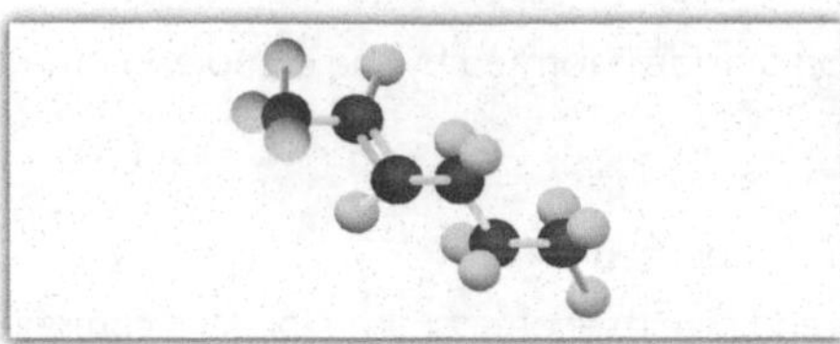

    b.

    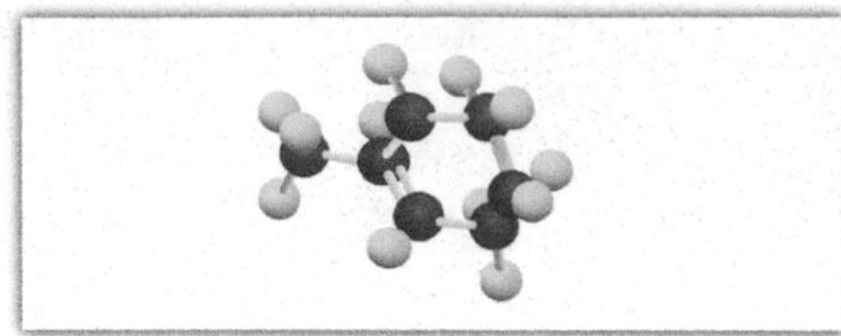

    c.

    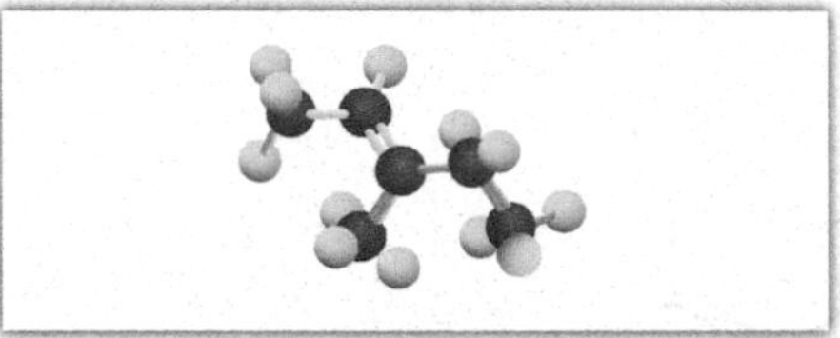

ANSWERS

1. a. unsaturated
   b. unsaturated
3. a. C_6H_{10}
   b. C_4H_8
5. Add bromine solution (reddish-brown) to each. Pentane will not react, and the reddish-brown color persists; 1-pentene will react, leaving a colorless solution.
7. $2C_6H_6 + 15O_2 \rightarrow 12CO_2 + 6H_2O$; 132 g
9. carcinogenic, flammable
11. a. number not needed
    b. can't have two groups on one carbon atom on a benzene ring
    c. can't have a substituent on the same carbon atom as the nitro group
13. a. $CH_3CH{=}CHCH_2CH_2CH_3$; 2-hexene
    b.

    CH_3

    c.

    $CH_3CH{=}CCH_2CH_3$

    CH_3

CHAPTER 14

Organic Compounds of Oxygen

Opening Essay

One of the more familiar chemical compounds on Earth is ethyl alcohol (ethanol). As the intoxicant in alcoholic beverages, ethanol is often simply called alcohol. If ethanol is diluted, as it is in wine, beer, or mixed drinks with about 1 oz of liquor, and if it is consumed in small quantities, it is relatively safe. In excess—four or more drinks in a few hours—it causes intoxication, which is characterized by a loss of coordination, nausea and vomiting, and memory blackouts.

Excessive ingestion of ethanol over a long period of time leads to cirrhosis of the liver, alteration of brain cell function, nerve damage, and strong physiological addiction. Alcoholism—an addiction to ethanol—is the most serious drug problem in the United States. Heavy drinking shortens a person's life span by contributing to diseases of the liver, the cardiovascular system, and virtually every other organ of the body.

In small quantities—one or two drinks a day—ethanol might promote health. In addition to the possible benefits of modest amounts of ethanol, a chemical in red wines, resveratrol, is thought to lower the risk of heart disease. Resveratrol, found in red grapes, is an antioxidant. It inhibits the oxidation of cholesterol and subsequent clogging of the arteries. One need not drink wine to get the benefits of resveratrol, however. It can be obtained by eating the grapes or drinking red grape juice.

Ethanol and resveratrol, a phenol, are representatives of two of the families of oxygen-containing compounds that we consider in this chapter. Two other classes, aldehydes and ketones, are formed by the oxidation of alcohols. Ethers, another class, are made by the dehydration of alcohols.

1. ORGANIC COMPOUNDS WITH FUNCTIONAL GROUPS

LEARNING OBJECTIVE

1. **Describe functional groups and explain why they are useful in the study of organic chemistry.**

In Chapter 12 and Chapter 13, we considered several kinds of hydrocarbons. Now we examine some of the many organic compounds that contain functional groups. We first introduced the idea of the **functional group**, a specific structural arrangement of atoms or bonds that imparts a characteristic chemical reactivity to the molecule, in Chapter 4, [Unsupported Reference Type: chapter-section]. If you understand the behavior of a particular functional group, you will know a great deal about the general properties of that class of compounds. In this chapter and Chapter 15, we make a brief yet systematic study of some of organic compound families. Each family is based on a common, simple functional group that contains an oxygen atom or a nitrogen atom. Some common functional groups are listed in Table 14.1.

functional group

A structural arrangement of atoms and/or bonds that imparts a wide range of important properties to organic compounds.

TABLE 14.1 Selected Organic Functional Groups

Name of Family	General Formula	Functional Group	Suffix*
alkane	RH	none	*-ane*
alkene	$R_2C{=}CR_2$	$>C{=}C<$	*-ene*
alkyne	RC≡CR	–C≡C–	*-yne*
alcohol	ROH	–OH	*-ol*
thiol	RSH	–SH	*-thiol*
ether	ROR	–O–	ether
aldehyde	$R{-}C({=}O){-}H$	$-C({=}O){-}H$	*-al*
ketone	$R{-}C({=}O){-}R$	$-C({=}O)-$	*-one*
carboxylic acid	$R{-}C({=}O){-}OH$	$-C({=}O){-}OH$	*-oic acid*

***Ethers do not have a suffix in their common name; all ethers end with the word** *ether*.

CONCEPT REVIEW EXERCISES

1. What is the functional group of an alkene? An alkyne?
2. Does $CH_3CH_2CH_2CH_2CH_2CH_2CH_2CH_2CH_2CH_2CH_3$ have a functional group? Explain.

ANSWERS

1. carbon-to-carbon double bond; carbon-to-carbon triple bond
2. No; it has nothing but carbon and hydrogen atoms and all single bonds.

KEY TAKEAWAY

- The functional group, a structural arrangement of atoms and/or bonds, is largely responsible for the properties of organic compound families.

EXERCISES

1. What is the functional group of 1-butanol ($CH_3CH_2CH_2CH_2OH$)?
2. What is the functional group of butyl bromide, $CH_3CH_2CH_2CH_2Br$?

ANSWER

1. OH

2. ALCOHOLS: NOMENCLATURE AND CLASSIFICATION

LEARNING OBJECTIVES

1. **Identify the general structure for an alcohol.**
2. **Identify the structural feature that classifies alcohols as primary, secondary, or tertiary.**
3. **Name alcohols with both common names and IUPAC names.**

As noted in Chapter 4, an **alcohol** is an organic compound with a hydroxyl (OH) functional group on an aliphatic carbon atom. Because OH is the functional group of all alcohols, we often represent alcohols by the general formula ROH, where R is an alkyl group. (For more information about alkyl groups, see Chapter 12, [Unsupported Reference Type: chapter-section]. Table 12.4 presents some common alkyl groups.)

alcohol

An organic compound with an OH functional group on an aliphatic carbon atom.

Alcohols are common in nature. Most people are familiar with ethyl alcohol (ethanol), the active ingredient in alcoholic beverages, but this compound is only one of a family of organic compounds known as alcohols. The family also includes such familiar substances as cholesterol and the carbohydrates.

As we noted in Chapter 4, [Unsupported Reference Type: chapter-section], methanol (CH_3OH) and ethanol (CH_3CH_2OH) are the first two members of the homologous series of alcohols.

2.1 Nomenclature of Alcohols

Alcohols with one to four carbon atoms are frequently called by common names, in which the name of the alkyl group is followed by the word *alcohol*:

CH_3OH	CH_3CH_2OH	$CH_3CH_2CH_2OH$	CH_3CHOH with CH_3 on the CH
Methyl alcohol	Ethyl alcohol	Propyl alcohol	Isopropyl alcohol

According to the International Union of Pure and Applied Chemistry (IUPAC), alcohols are named by changing the ending of the parent alkane name (Chapter 12, [Unsupported Reference Type: chapter-section]) to *-ol*. Here are some basic IUPAC rules for naming alcohols:

1. The longest continuous chain (LCC) of carbon atoms containing the OH group is taken as the parent compound—an alkane with the same number of carbon atoms. The chain is numbered from the end nearest the OH group.
2. The number that indicates the position of the OH group is prefixed to the name of the parent hydrocarbon, and the *-e* ending of the parent alkane is replaced by the suffix *-ol*. (In cyclic alcohols, the carbon atom bearing the OH group is designated C1, but the 1 is not used in the name.) Substituents are named and numbered as in alkanes.
3. If more than one OH group appears in the same molecule (polyhydroxy alcohols), suffixes such as *-diol* and *-triol* are used. In these cases, the *-e* ending of the parent alkane is retained.

Figure 14.1 shows some examples of the application of these rules.

FIGURE 14.1 IUPAC Rules for Alcohols

The names and structures of some alcohols demonstrate the use of IUPAC rules.

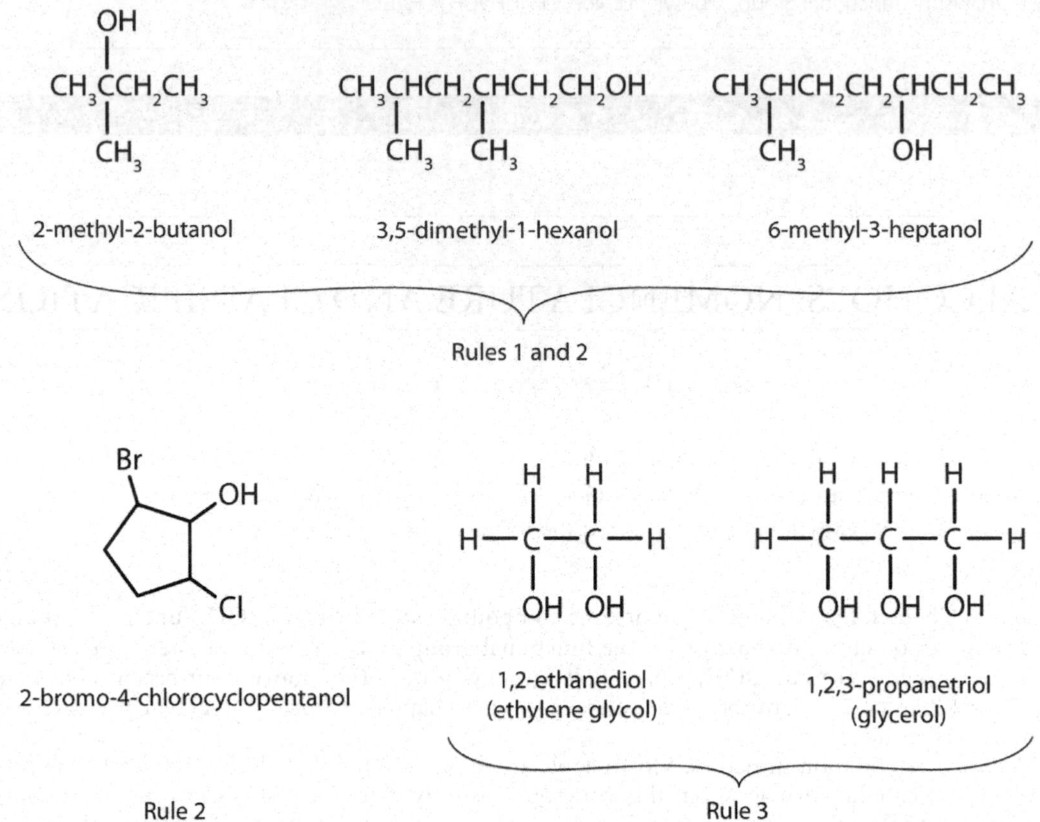

EXAMPLE 1

Give the IUPAC name for each compound.

1.

$$\begin{array}{l} CH_3CH_2\underset{\displaystyle CH_3}{\underset{|}{C}}HCH_2\underset{\displaystyle CH_3}{\underset{|}{C}}HCH_2CH_2\underset{\displaystyle OH}{\underset{|}{C}}HCH_2CH_3 \end{array}$$

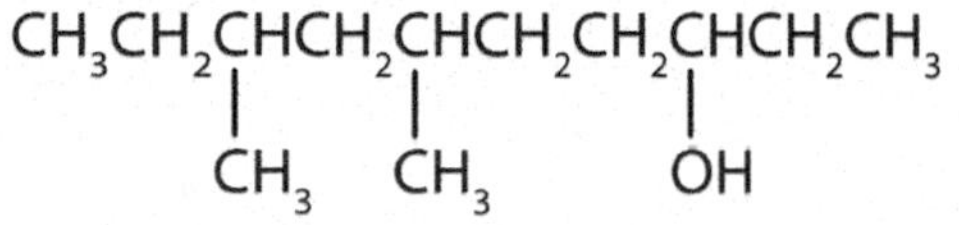

2. $HOCH_2CH_2CH_2CH_2CH_2OH$

Solution

1. Ten carbon atoms in the LCC makes the compound a derivative of decane (rule 1), and the OH on the third carbon atom makes it a 3-decanol (rule 2).

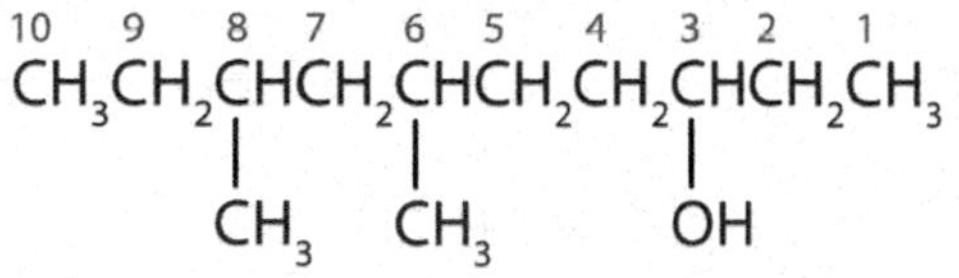

$$\begin{array}{l} \overset{10}{C}H_3\overset{9}{C}H_2\underset{\displaystyle CH_3}{\underset{|}{\overset{8}{C}}}H\overset{7}{C}H_2\underset{\displaystyle CH_3}{\underset{|}{\overset{6}{C}}}H\overset{5}{C}H_2\overset{4}{C}H_2\underset{\displaystyle OH}{\underset{|}{\overset{3}{C}}}H\overset{2}{C}H_2\overset{1}{C}H_3 \end{array}$$

The carbon atoms are numbered from the end closest to the OH group. That fixes the two methyl (CH_3) groups at the sixth and eighth positions. The name is 6,8-dimethyl-3-decanol (not 3,5-dimethyl-8-decanol).

2. Five carbon atoms in the LCC make the compound a derivative of pentane. Two OH groups on the first and fifth carbon atoms make the compound a diol and give the name 1,5-pentanediol (rule 3).

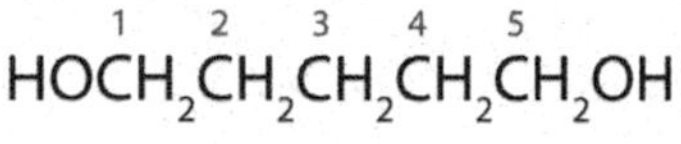

$$HO\overset{1}{C}H_2\overset{2}{C}H_2\overset{3}{C}H_2\overset{4}{C}H_2\overset{5}{C}H_2OH$$

SKILL-BUILDING EXERCISE

Give the IUPAC name for each compound.

1.

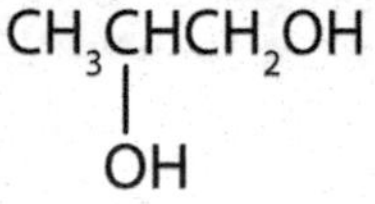

$$CH_3\underset{\displaystyle OH}{\underset{|}{C}}HCH_2OH$$

2.

(cyclopentane ring bearing OH and CH_3 on the same carbon)

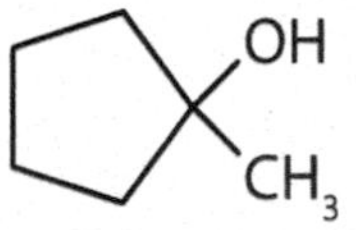

EXAMPLE 2

Draw the structure for each compound.

1. 2-hexanol
2. 3-methyl-2-pentanol

Solution

1. The ending *-ol* indicates an alcohol (the OH functional group), and the *hex-* stem tells us that there are six carbon atoms in the LCC. We start by drawing a chain of six carbon atoms: –C–C–C–C–C–C–.

   The 2 indicates that the OH group is attached to the second carbon atom.

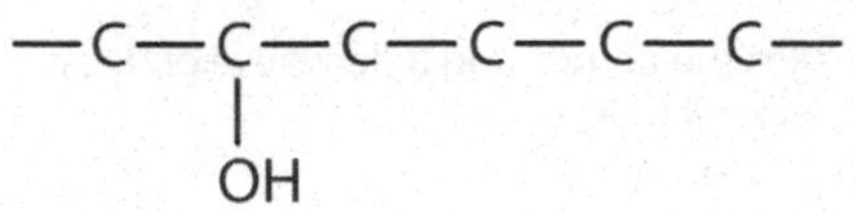

   —C—C—C—C—C—C—
   (OH on the second carbon)

   Finally, we add enough hydrogen atoms to give each carbon atom four bonds.

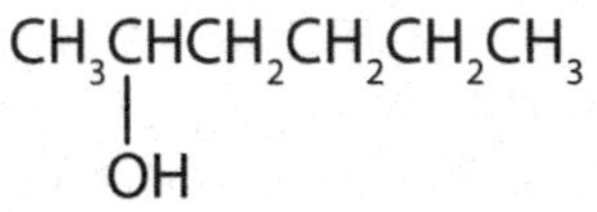

   $CH_3CH(OH)CH_2CH_2CH_2CH_3$

2. The ending *-ol* indicates an OH functional group, and the *pent-* stem tells us that there are five carbon atoms in the LCC. We start by drawing a chain of five carbon atoms:

   -C-C-C-C-C-

   The numbers indicate that there is a methyl (CH_3) group on the third carbon atom and an OH group on the second carbon atom.

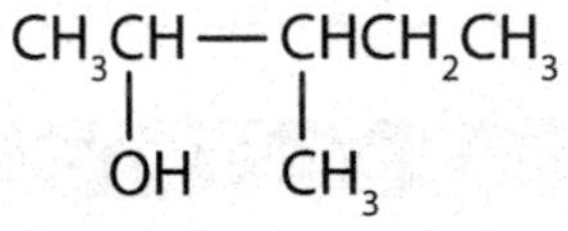

   $CH_3CH(OH)—CH(CH_3)CH_2CH_3$

SKILL-BUILDING EXERCISE

Draw the structure for each compound.

1. 3-heptanol
2. 2-methyl-3-hexanol

2.2 Classification of Alcohols

Some of the properties of alcohols depend on the number of carbon atoms attached to the specific carbon atom that is attached to the OH group. Alcohols can be grouped into three classes on this basis.

primary (1°) alcohol

A compound with an OH group on a carbonatom that is attached to only one other carbon atom.

- A **primary (1°) alcohol** is one in which the carbon atom (in red) with the OH group is attached to *one* other carbon atom (in blue). Its general formula is RCH_2OH.

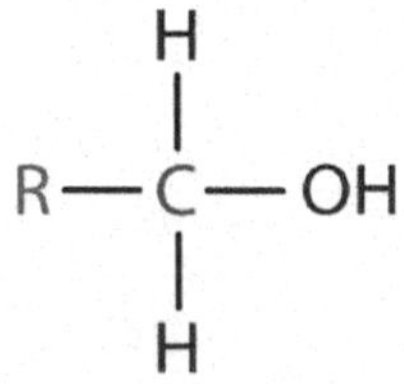

$$R—\underset{H}{\overset{H}{C}}—OH$$

- A **secondary (2°) alcohol** is one in which the carbon atom (in red) with the OH group is attached to *two* other carbon atoms (in blue). Its general formula is R_2CHOH.

secondary (2°) alcohol

A compound with an OH group on a carbon atom that is attached to two other carbon atoms.

$$\begin{array}{c} R \\ | \\ R—C—OH \\ | \\ H \end{array}$$

- A **tertiary (3°) alcohol** is one in which the carbon atom (in red) with the OH group is attached to *three* other carbon atoms (in blue). Its general formula is R_3COH.

tertiary (3°) alcohol

A compond with an OH group on a carbon atom that is attached to three other carbon atoms.

$$\begin{array}{c} R \\ | \\ R—C—OH \\ | \\ R \end{array}$$

Table 14.2 names and classifies some of the simpler alcohols. Some of the common names reflect a compound's classification as secondary (*sec*-) or tertiary (*tert*-). These designations are not used in the IUPAC nomenclature system for alcohols. Note that there are four butyl alcohols in the table, corresponding to the four butyl groups: the butyl group ($CH_3CH_2CH_2CH_2$) introduced in Chapter 12, [Unsupported Reference Type: chapter-section], and three others:

$CH_3CHCH_2—$ (with CH_3 on the second carbon)

Isobutyl group

$CH_3CHCH_2CH_3$ (with a bond on the second carbon)

Sec-butyl group

$CH_3C—$ (with two CH_3 on the central carbon)

Tert-butyl group

TABLE 14.2 Classification and Nomenclature of Some Alcohols

Condensed Structural Formula	Class of Alcohol	Common Name	IUPAC Name
CH_3OH	—	methyl alcohol	methanol
CH_3CH_2OH	primary	ethyl alcohol	ethanol
$CH_3CH_2CH_2OH$	primary	propyl alcohol	1-propanol
$(CH_3)_2CHOH$	secondary	isopropyl alcohol	2-propanol
$CH_3CH_2CH_2CH_2OH$	primary	butyl alcohol	1-butanol
$CH_3CH_2CHOHCH_3$	secondary	*sec*-butyl alcohol	2-butanol
$(CH_3)_2(CH_3)_2CHCH_2OH$	primary	isobutyl alcohol	2-methyl-1-propanol
$(CH_3)_3COH$	tertiary	*tert*-butyl alcohol	2-methyl-2-propanol
(cyclohexane ring)—OH	secondary	cyclohexyl alcohol	cyclohexanol

CONCEPT REVIEW EXERCISES

1. Is isobutyl alcohol primary, secondary, or tertiary? Explain.

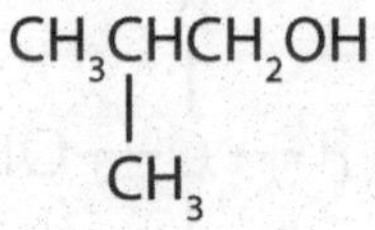

$$\begin{array}{l} CH_3\underset{\displaystyle CH_3}{\underset{|}{C}}HCH_2OH \end{array}$$

2. What is the LCC in 2-ethyl-1-hexanol? What is taken as the LCC in naming the compound? Explain.

ANSWERS

1. primary; the carbon atom bearing the OH group is attached to only one other carbon atom
2. 7 carbon atoms; the 6-atom chain includes the carbon atom bearing the OH group

KEY TAKEAWAYS

- In the IUPAC system, alcohols are named by changing the ending of the parent alkane name to *-ol*.
- Alcohols are classified according to the number of carbon atoms attached to the carbon atom that is attached to the OH group.

EXERCISES

1. Name each alcohol and classify it as primary, secondary, or tertiary.
   a. CH3CH2CH2CH2CH2CH2OH
   b. 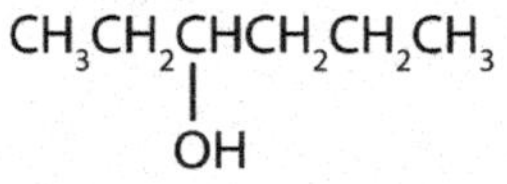
   $$CH_3CH_2\underset{\displaystyle OH}{\underset{|}{C}}HCH_2CH_2CH_3$$
   c.
   $$CH_3\underset{\displaystyle OH}{\underset{|}{\overset{\displaystyle CH_3}{\overset{|}{C}}}}—\underset{\displaystyle Br}{\underset{|}{\overset{\displaystyle Br}{\overset{|}{C}}}}CH_3$$
2. Name each alcohol and classify it as primary, secondary, or tertiary.
   a. 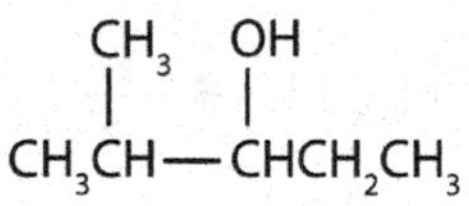
   $$CH_3\overset{\displaystyle CH_3}{\overset{|}{C}}H—\overset{\displaystyle OH}{\overset{|}{C}}HCH_2CH_3$$
   b.
   $$CH_3\underset{\displaystyle CH_3}{\underset{|}{C}}HCH_2CH_2OH$$
   c. (cyclopentane ring)—OH
3. Draw the structure for each alcohol.
   a. 3-hexanol
   b. 3,3-dimethyl-2-butanol
   c. cyclobutanol
4. Draw the structure for each alcohol.
   a. cyclopentanol
   b. 4-methyl-2-hexanol
   c. 4,5-dimethyl-3-heptanol

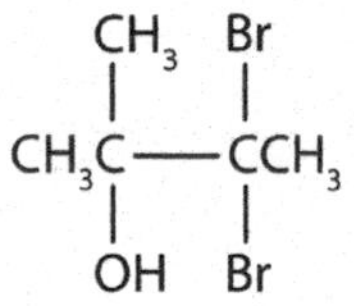

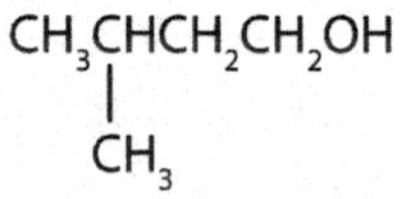

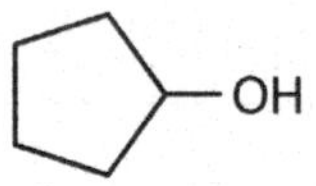

ANSWERS

1. a. 1-hexanol; primary
   b. 3-hexanol; secondary
   c. 3,3-dibromo-2-methyl-2-butanol; tertiary

3. a.

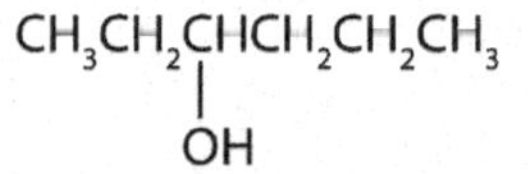

$$CH_3CH_2CHCH_2CH_2CH_3 \text{ (OH on C3)}$$

b.

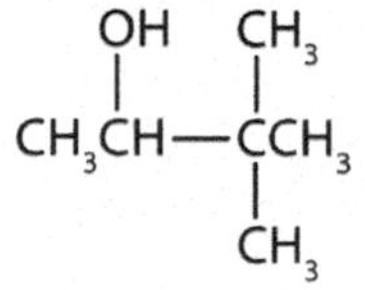

$$CH_3CH(OH)—C(CH_3)_2CH_3$$

c.

(cyclobutane ring)—OH

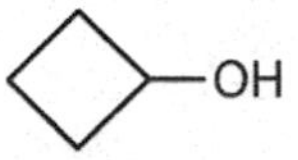

3. PHYSICAL PROPERTIES OF ALCOHOLS

LEARNING OBJECTIVES

1. **Explain why the boiling points of alcohols are higher than those of ethers and alkanes of similar molar masses.**
2. **Explain why alcohols and ethers of four or fewer carbon atoms are soluble in water while comparable alkanes are not soluble.**

Alcohols can be considered derivatives of water (H_2O; also written as HOH).

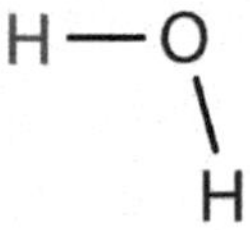

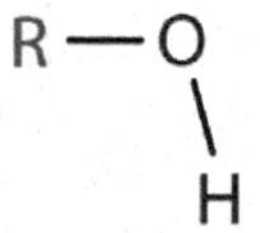

H—O—H   R—O—H

Like the H–O–H bond in water, the R–O–H bond is bent, and alcohol molecules are polar. This relationship is particularly apparent in small molecules and reflected in the physical and chemical properties of alcohols with low molar mass.

Replacing a hydrogen atom from an alkane with an OH group allows the molecules to associate through hydrogen bonding (Figure 14.2). Recall from Chapter 8 that physical properties are determined to a large extent by the type of intermolecular forces. Table 14.3 lists the molar masses and the boiling points of some common compounds. The table shows that substances with similar molar masses can have quite different boiling points. Alkanes are nonpolar and are thus associated only through relatively weak dispersion forces. Alkanes with one to four carbon atoms are gases at room temperature. In contrast, even methanol (with one carbon atom) is a liquid at room temperature. Hydrogen bonding greatly increases the boiling points of alcohols compared to hydrocarbons of comparable molar mass. The boiling point is a rough measure of the amount of energy necessary to separate a liquid molecule from its nearest neighbors. If the molecules interact through hydrogen bonding, a relatively large quantity of energy must be supplied to break those intermolecular attractions. Only then can the molecule escape from the liquid into the gaseous state.

FIGURE 14.2 Intermolecular Hydrogen Bonding in Methanol

The OH groups of alcohol molecules make hydrogen bonding possible.

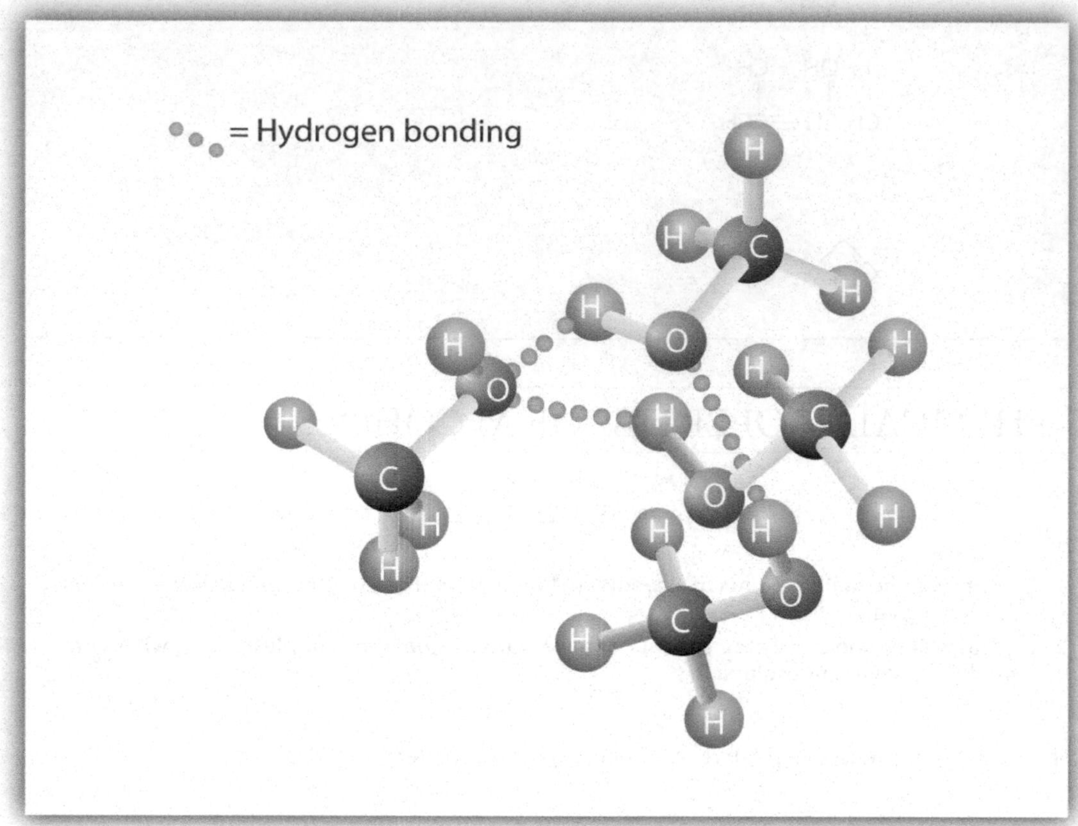

TABLE 14.3 Comparison of Boiling Points and Molar Masses

Formula	Name	Molar Mass	Boiling Point (°C)
CH_4	methane	16	−164
HOH	water	18	100
C_2H_6	ethane	30	−89
CH_3OH	methanol	32	65
C_3H_8	propane	44	−42
CH_3CH_2OH	ethanol	46	78
C_4H_{10}	butane	58	−1
$CH_3CH_2CH_2OH$	1-propanol	60	97

Alcohols can also engage in hydrogen bonding with water molecules (Figure 14.3). Thus, whereas the hydrocarbons are insoluble in water, alcohols with one to three carbon atoms are completely soluble. As the length of the chain increases, however, the solubility of alcohols in water decreases; the molecules become more like hydrocarbons and less like water. The alcohol 1-decanol ($CH_3CH_2CH_2CH_2CH_2CH_2CH_2CH_2CH_2CH_2OH$) is essentially insoluble in water. We frequently find that the borderline of solubility in a family of organic compounds occurs at four or five carbon atoms.

FIGURE 14.3 Hydrogen Bonding between Methanol Molecules and Water Molecules

Hydrogen bonding between the OH of methanol and water molecules accounts for the solubility of methanol in water.

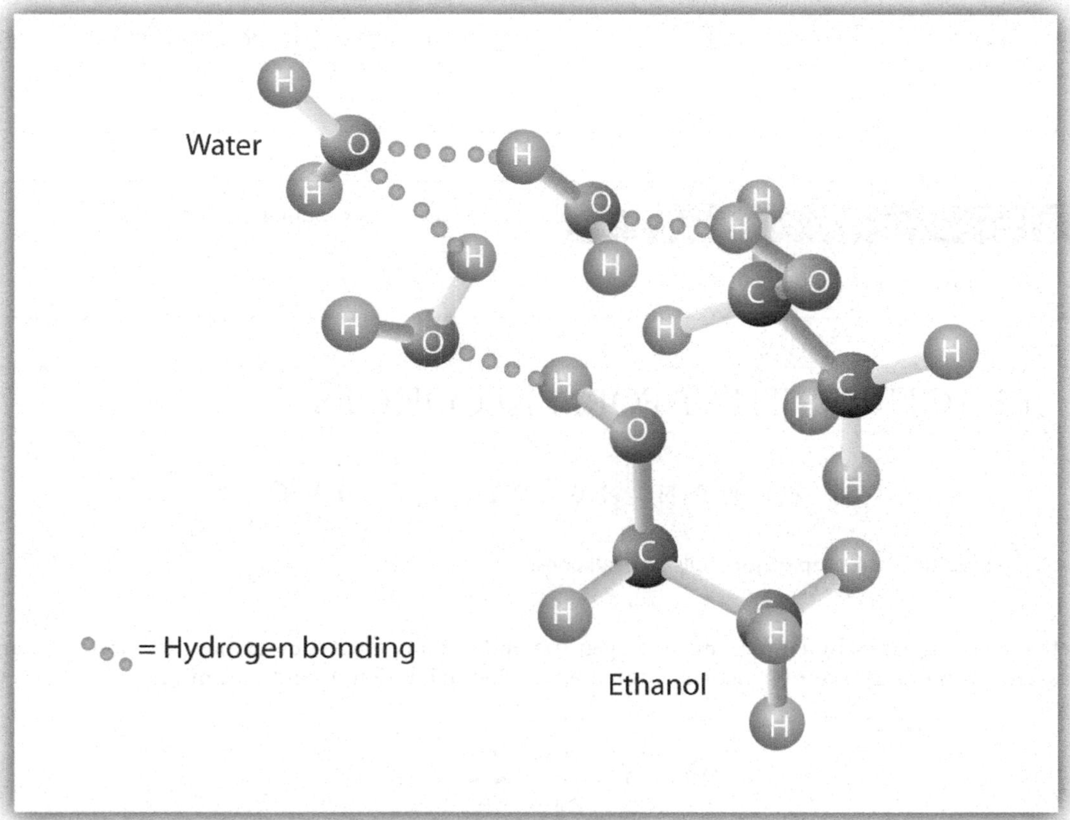

CONCEPT REVIEW EXERCISES

1. Why is ethanol more soluble in water than 1-hexanol?
2. Why does 1-butanol have a lower boiling point than 1-hexanol?

ANSWERS

1. Ethanol has an OH group and only 2 carbon atoms; 1-hexanol has one OH group for 6 carbon atoms and is thus more like a (nonpolar) hydrocarbon than ethanol is.
2. The molar mass of 1-hexanol is greater than that of 1-butanol.

KEY TAKEAWAYS

- Alcohols have higher boiling points than do ethers and alkanes of similar molar masses because the OH group allows alcohol molecules to engage in hydrogen bonding.
- Alcohols of four or fewer carbon atoms are soluble in water because the alcohol molecules engage in hydrogen bonding with water molecules; comparable alkane molecules cannot engage in hydrogen bonding.

EXERCISES

Answer the following exercises without consulting tables in the text.

1. Arrange these alcohols in order of increasing boiling point: ethanol, methanol, and 1-propanol.
2. Which has the higher boiling point—butane or 1-propanol?
3. Arrange these alcohols in order of increasing solubility in water: 1-butanol, methanol, and 1-octanol.
4. Arrange these compounds in order of increasing solubility in water: 1-butanol, ethanol, and pentane.

ANSWERS

1. methanol < ethanol < 1-propanol
3. 1-octanol < 1-butanol < methanol

4. REACTIONS THAT FORM ALCOHOLS

LEARNING OBJECTIVE

1. **Describe how to prepare alcohols from alkenes.**

Methanol is prepared by combining hydrogen gas and carbon monoxide at high temperatures and pressures in the presence of a catalyst composed of zinc oxide (ZnO) and chromium oxide (Cr_2O_3) catalyst:

$$2H_2 + CO \xrightarrow[ZnO,\ Cr_2O_3]{200\ \text{atm},\ 350^\circ C} CH_3OH$$

Methanol is an important solvent and is used as an automotive fuel, either as the pure liquid—as in some racing cars—or as an additive in gasoline.

Note

Nearly 2 billion gallons of methanol are produced each year in the United States by the catalytic reduction of carbon monoxide with hydrogen gas.

Many simple alcohols are made by the hydration of alkenes. (For more information about the hydration of alkenes, see Chapter 13, [Unsupported Reference Type: chapter-section].) Ethanol is made by the hydration of ethylene in the presence of a catalyst such as sulfuric acid (H_2SO_4).

$$H_2C{=}CH_2 + H_2O \xrightarrow{H^+} CH_3CH_2OH$$

Ethylene Water Ethanol

In a similar manner, isopropyl alcohol is produced by the addition of water to propene (propylene).

$$CH_2{=}CH{-}CH_3 + H{-}OH \xrightarrow{H_2SO_4} CH_3{-}\underset{\displaystyle OH}{\underset{|}{CH}}{-}CH_3$$

Propylene — Isopropyl alcohol (2-propanol)

Note

Additional Exercise 19 describes how to use a generalization called Markovnikov's rule to predict the results when the addition of water to an alcohol has two possible products.

EXAMPLE 3

Write the equation for the reaction of 2-butene with water to form 2-butanol. Indicate that sulfuric acid is used as a catalyst.

Solution

First write the condensed structural formula of 2-butene and indicate that it reacts with water. Then write the condensed structural formula of 2-butanol after the reaction arrow to indicate that it is the product. Finally, write the formula for the catalyst above the arrow.

$$CH_3CH{=}CHCH_3 + H_2O \xrightarrow{H_2SO_4} CH_3\underset{\displaystyle OH}{\underset{|}{C}}HCH_2CH_3$$

SKILL-BUILDING EXERCISE

1. Write the equation for the reaction of cyclopentene with water to form cyclopentanol. Indicate that phosphoric acid (H3PO4) is used as a catalyst.

Note

Many OH compounds in living systems are formed by alkene hydration. Here is an example that occurs in the Krebs cycle: fumarate is hydrated to form malate. (For more information about the Krebs cycle, see Chapter 20, [Unsupported Reference Type: chapter-section].)

$$HOOCCH{-}CHCOO^- + HOH \xrightleftharpoons{enzyme} HOOCCH_2CHOHCOO^-$$

In addition to its preparation from ethylene, ethanol is made by the fermentation of sugars or starch from various sources (potatoes, corn, wheat, rice, etc.). Fermentation is catalyzed by enzymes found in yeast and proceeds by an elaborate multistep mechanism. We can represent the overall process as follows:

$$(C_6H_{10}O_5)_x \xrightarrow{\text{enzymes}} C_6H_{12}O_6 \xrightarrow{\text{enzymes}} 2CH_3CH_2OH + 2CO_2$$

Starch Glucose Ethanol

To Your Health: The Physiological Effects of Alcohols

Methanol is quite poisonous to humans. Ingestion of as little as 15 mL of methanol can cause blindness, and 30 mL (1 oz) can cause death. However, the usual fatal dose is 100 to 150 mL. The main reason for methanol's toxicity is that we have liver enzymes that catalyze its oxidation to formaldehyde, the simplest member of the aldehyde family (Section 9):

$$CH_3OH \xrightarrow{\text{liver enzymes}} H{-}\overset{\overset{\large O}{\|}}{C}{-}H$$

Methanol Formaldehyde

Formaldehyde reacts rapidly with the components of cells, coagulating proteins in much the same way that cooking coagulates an egg. This property of formaldehyde accounts for much of the toxicity of methanol.

Note

Organic and biochemical equations are frequently written showing only the organic reactants and products. In this way, we focus attention on the organic starting material and product, rather than on balancing complicated equations.

Ethanol is oxidized in the liver to acetaldehyde:

$$CH_3CH_2OH \xrightarrow{\text{liver enzymes}} CH_3{-}\overset{\overset{\large O}{\|}}{C}{-}H$$

Ethanol Acetaldehyde

The acetaldehyde is in turn oxidized to acetic acid ($HC_2H_3O_2$), a normal constituent of cells, which is then oxidized to carbon dioxide and water. Even so, ethanol is potentially toxic to humans. The rapid ingestion of 1 pt (about 500 mL) of pure ethanol would kill most people, and acute ethanol poisoning kills several hundred people each year—often those engaged in some sort of drinking contest. Ethanol freely crosses into the brain, where it depresses the respiratory control center, resulting in failure of the respiratory muscles in the lungs and hence suffocation. Ethanol is believed to act on nerve cell membranes, causing a diminution in speech, thought, cognition, and judgment.

Rubbing alcohol is usually a 70% aqueous solution of isopropyl alcohol. It has a high vapor pressure, and its rapid evaporation from the skin produces a cooling effect. It is toxic when ingested but, compared to methanol, is less readily absorbed through the skin.

CONCEPT REVIEW EXERCISES

1. Why is methanol more toxic than ethanol?
2. How does rubbing alcohol cool a feverish patient?

ANSWERS

1. Methanol is oxidized to formaldehyde, which destroys tissue; ethanol is oxidized to acetaldehyde and then acetic acid, a normal metabolite.
2. Evaporation removes heat.

KEY TAKEAWAYS

- Many alcohols are made by the hydration of alkenes.
- Ethanol can be made by the fermentation of sugars or starch from various sources.

EXERCISES

1. From what alkene is ethanol made? Draw its condensed structural formula.
2. Can methanol be made from an alkene? Explain.

ANSWER

1. ethylene; $CH_2{=}CH_2$

5. REACTIONS OF ALCOHOLS

LEARNING OBJECTIVES

1. **Give two major types of reactions of alcohols.**
2. **Describe the result of the oxidation of a primary alcohol.**
3. **Describe the result of the oxidation of a secondary alcohol.**

Chemical reactions in alcohols occur mainly at the functional group, but some involve hydrogen atoms attached to the OH-bearing carbon atom or to an adjacent carbon atom. Of the three major kinds of alcohol reactions, which are summarized in Figure 14.4, two—dehydration and oxidation—are considered here. The third reaction type—esterification—is covered in Chapter 15, [Unsupported Reference Type: chapter-section].

FIGURE 14.4 Reactions of Alcohols

Oxidation and dehydration of alcohols are considered here.

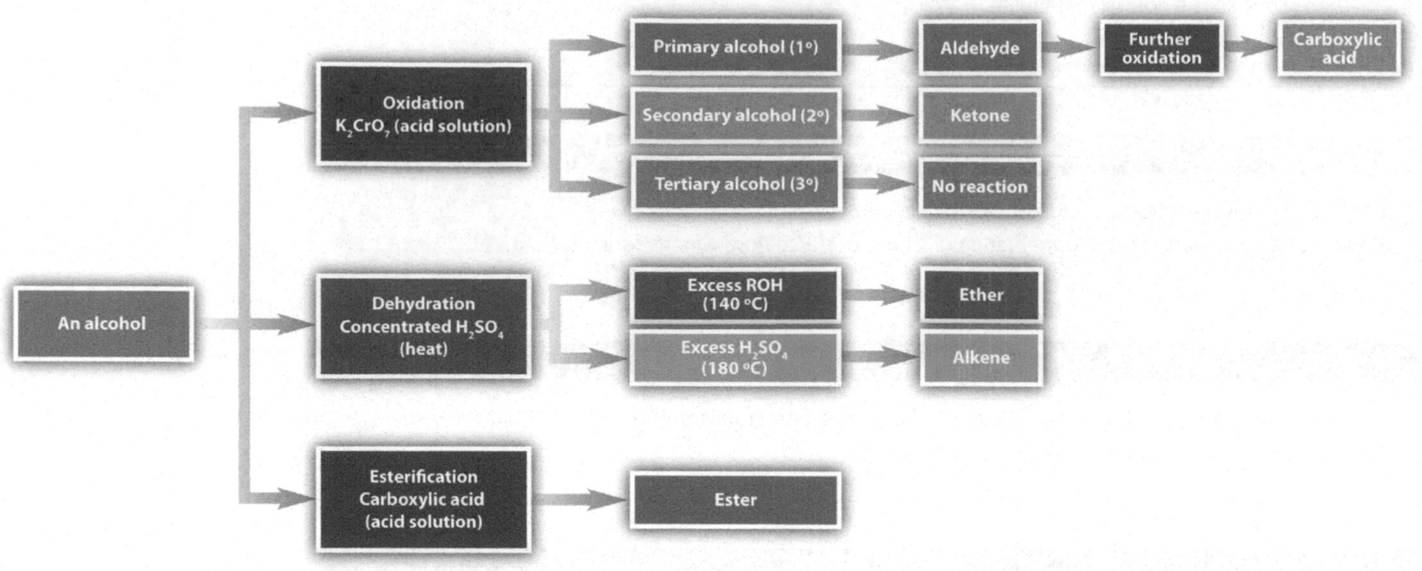

5.1 Dehydration

As noted in Figure 14.4, an alcohol undergoes dehydration in the presence of a catalyst to form an alkene and water. The reaction removes the OH group from the alcohol carbon atom and a hydrogen atom from an adjacent carbon atom in the same molecule:

$$H_3C\text{—}CH_2OH \xrightarrow[\text{excess acid}]{\text{concd } H_2SO_4\text{, 180°C}} H_2C{=}CH_2 + HOH$$

Ethanol Ethylene

Under the proper conditions, it is possible for the dehydration to occur between *two* alcohol molecules. The entire OH group of one molecule and only the hydrogen atom of the OH group of the second molecule are removed. The two ethyl groups attached to an oxygen atom form an ether molecule.

$$CH_3CH_2OH + HOCH_2CH_3 \xrightarrow[\text{140°C, excess ethanol}]{\text{concd } H_2SO_4} CH_3CH_2\text{—}O\text{—}CH_2CH_3 + H_2O$$

Two molecules of ethanol Diethyl ether

(Ethers are discussed in Section 4.) Thus, depending on conditions, one can prepare either alkenes or ethers by the dehydration of alcohols.

Note

Both dehydration and hydration reactions occur continuously in cellular metabolism, with enzymes serving as catalysts and at a temperature of about 37°C. (For more information about hydration reactions, see Chapter 13, [Unsupported Reference Type: chapter-section].) The following reaction occurs in the Embden–Meyerhof pathway. (For more information about metabolic reactions, see Chapter 20.)

$$H-\underset{H}{\overset{OH}{C}}-\underset{OPO_3^{2-}}{\overset{H}{C}}-COO^- \xrightarrow{\text{enzyme}} \begin{matrix} H & & COO^- \\ & C{=}C & \\ H & & OPO_3^{2-} \end{matrix} + HOH$$

2-Phosphoglycerate — Phosphoenolpyruvate

Although the participating compounds are complex, the reaction is the same: elimination of water from the starting material. The idea is that if you know the chemistry of a particular functional group, you know the chemistry of hundreds of different compounds.

5.2 Oxidation

Primary and secondary alcohols are readily oxidized. We saw earlier how methanol and ethanol are oxidized by liver enzymes to form aldehydes. Because a variety of oxidizing agents can bring about oxidation, we can indicate an oxidizing agent without specifying a particular one by writing an equation with the symbol [O] above the arrow. For example, we write the oxidation of ethanol—a primary alcohol—to form acetaldehyde—an aldehyde—as follows:

$$CH_3CH_2OH \xrightarrow{[O]} CH_3CH{=}O$$

Ethanol (a primary alcohol) — Acetaldehyde (an aldehyde)

We shall see (in Section 9) that aldehydes are even more easily oxidized than alcohols and yield carboxylic acids.

Secondary alcohols are oxidized to *ketones*. The oxidation of isopropyl alcohol by potassium dichromate ($K_2Cr_2O_7$) gives acetone, the simplest ketone:

$$CH_3\overset{OH}{\overset{|}{C}}HCH_3 \xrightarrow[H^+]{K_2Cr_2O_7} CH_3-\overset{O}{\overset{\|}{C}}-CH_3$$

Isopropyl alcohol (a secondary alcohol) — Acetone (a ketone)

Unlike aldehydes, ketones are relatively resistant to further oxidation (Section 9), so no special precautions are required to isolate them as they form.

Note that in oxidation of both primary (RCH_2OH) and secondary (R_2CHOH) alcohols, two hydrogen atoms are removed from the alcohol molecule, one from the OH group and other from the carbon atom that bears the OH group.

Note

These reactions can also be carried out in the laboratory with chemical oxidizing agents. One such oxidizing agent is potassium dichromate. The balanced equation (showing only the species involved in the reaction) in this case is as follows:

$$8H^+ + Cr_2O_7^{2-} + 3CH_3CH_2OH \longrightarrow 3CH_3CHO + 2Cr^{3+} + 7H_2O$$

Alcohol oxidation is important in living organisms. Enzyme-controlled oxidation reactions provide the energy cells need to do useful work. One step in the metabolism of carbohydrates involves the oxidation of the secondary alcohol group in isocitric acid to a ketone group:

$$\begin{array}{c} CH_2\text{—}COOH \\ | \\ CH\text{—}COOH \\ | \\ HO\text{—}CH\text{—}COOH \end{array} \xrightarrow{\text{enzyme}} \begin{array}{c} CH_2\text{—}COOH \\ | \\ CH\text{—}COOH \\ | \\ O{=}C\text{—}CH_3 \end{array}$$

Isocitrate　　　　Oxalosuccinate

Note that the overall type of reaction is the same as that in the conversion of isopropyl alcohol to acetone. (For more information on metabolic reactions, see Chapter 20.)

Tertiary alcohols (R3COH) are resistant to oxidation because the carbon atom that carries the OH group does not have a hydrogen atom attached but is instead bonded to other carbon atoms. The oxidation reactions we have described involve the formation of a carbon-to-oxygen double bond. Thus, the carbon atom bearing the OH group must be able to release one of its attached atoms to form the double bond. The carbon-to-hydrogen bonding is easily broken under oxidative conditions, but carbon-to-carbon bonds are not. Therefore tertiary alcohols are not easily oxidized.

EXAMPLE 4

Write an equation for the oxidation of each alcohol. Use [O] above the arrow to indicate an oxidizing agent. If no reaction occurs, write "no reaction" after the arrow.

1. $CH_3CH_2CH_2CH_2CH_2OH$
2.

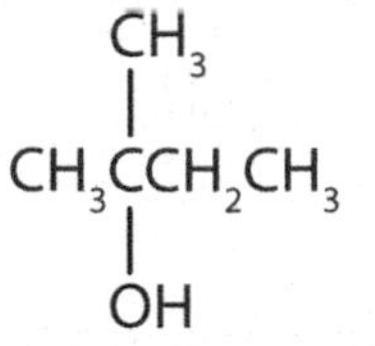

$$\begin{array}{c} CH_3 \\ | \\ CH_3CCH_2CH_3 \\ | \\ OH \end{array}$$

3.

$$\begin{array}{l} CH_3CHCH_2CH_2CH_2CH_3 \\ \quad\;\, | \\ \quad OH \end{array}$$

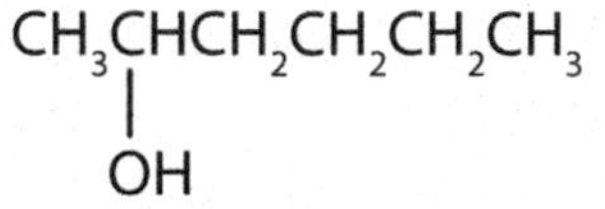

Solution

The first step is to recognize the class of each alcohol as primary, secondary, or tertiary.

1. This alcohol has the OH group on a carbon atom that is attached to only *one* other carbon atom, so it is a primary alcohol. Oxidation forms first an aldehyde and further oxidation forms a carboxylic acid.

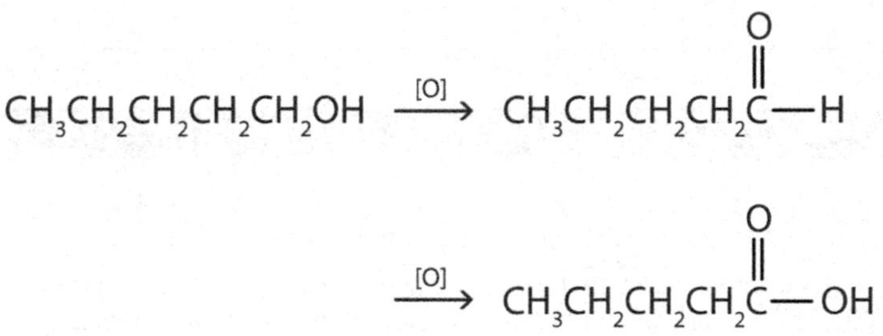

$$CH_3CH_2CH_2CH_2CH_2OH \xrightarrow{[O]} CH_3CH_2CH_2CH_2\overset{\overset{\displaystyle O}{\|}}{C}—H$$

$$\xrightarrow{[O]} CH_3CH_2CH_2CH_2\overset{\overset{\displaystyle O}{\|}}{C}—OH$$

2. This alcohol has the OH group on a carbon atom that is attached to three other carbon atoms, so it is a tertiary alcohol. No reaction occurs.

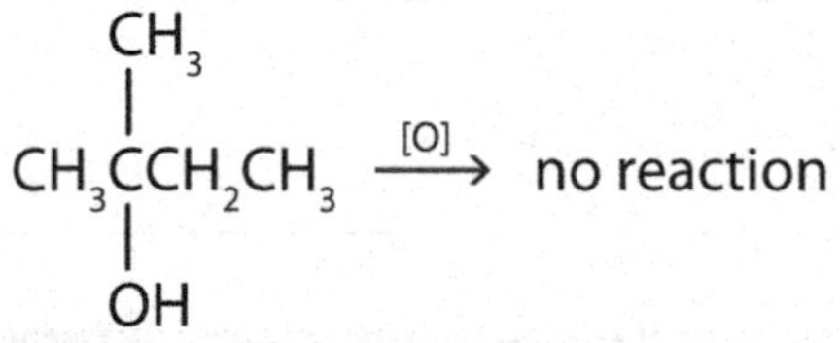

$$\begin{array}{c} CH_3 \\ | \\ CH_3CCH_2CH_3 \\ | \\ OH \end{array} \xrightarrow{[O]} \text{no reaction}$$

3. This alcohol has the OH group on a carbon atom that is attached to two other carbon atoms, so it is a secondary alcohol; oxidation gives a ketone.

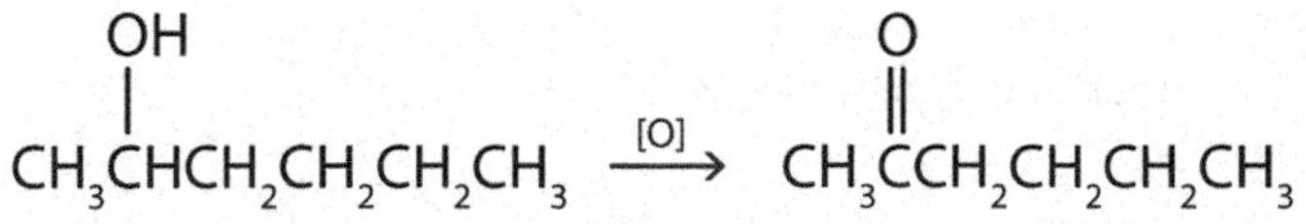

$$CH_3\overset{\overset{\displaystyle OH}{|}}{C}HCH_2CH_2CH_2CH_3 \xrightarrow{[O]} CH_3\overset{\overset{\displaystyle O}{\|}}{C}CH_2CH_2CH_2CH_3$$

SKILL-BUILDING EXERCISE

Write an equation for the oxidation of each alcohol. Use [O] above the arrow to indicate an oxidizing agent. If no reaction occurs, write "no reaction" after the arrow.

1.

$$CH_3CH_2C(OH)(CH_3)CH_2CH_2CH_3$$

2.

$$CH_3CHCH(CH_3)CH_2OH$$

3.

$$CH_3CH(CH_3)CH(OH)CH_2CH_2CH_3$$

CONCEPT REVIEW EXERCISES

1. In a reaction, compound W with the molecular formula $C_4H_{10}O$ is converted to compound X with the formula C_4H_8O. Is W oxidized, reduced, dehydrated, or none of these? Explain.
2. In a reaction, 2 mol of compound Y with the molecular formula $C_4H_{10}O$ is converted to 1 mol of compound Z with the formula $C_8H_{18}O$. Is Y oxidized, reduced, or neither? Explain.

ANSWERS

1. oxidized; H is removed
2. neither; water is removed

KEY TAKEAWAYS

- Alcohols can be dehydrated to form either alkenes (higher temperature, excess acid) or ethers (lower temperature, excess alcohol).
- Primary alcohols are oxidized to form aldehydes.
- Secondary alcohols are oxidized to form ketones.
- Tertiary alcohols are not readily oxidized.

EXERCISES

1. Name the three major types of chemical reactions of alcohols.
2. Why do tertiary alcohols not undergo oxidation? Can a tertiary alcohol undergo dehydration?

3. Draw the structure of the product for each reaction.

   a.

$$CH_3C(CH_3)(OH)CH_3 \xrightarrow[\text{excess acid}]{\text{concd } H_2SO_4,\ 180°C}$$

   b.

$$CH_3CH(OH)CH_2CH_2CH_3 \xrightarrow[H^+]{K_2Cr_2O_7}$$

4. Draw the structure of the product for each reaction.

   a.

$$CH_3CH(OH)CH(CH_3)CH_2CH_2CH_3 \xrightarrow[H^+]{K_2Cr_2O_7}$$

   b.

$$\text{cyclopentyl}-OH + \xrightarrow[\text{excess acid}]{\text{concd } H_2SO_4,\ 180°C}$$

5. Write an equation for the dehydration of 2-propanol to yield each compound type.
   a. an alkene
   b. an ether
6. Draw the structure of the alkene formed by the dehydration of cyclohexanol.

ANSWERS

1. dehydration, oxidation, and esterification
3. a.

$$CH_3C(CH_3)=CH_2$$

   b.

$$CH_3-C(=O)-CH_2CH_2CH_3$$

   a. $CH_3CHOHCH_3 \xrightarrow[180\,°C,\ \text{excess acid}]{\text{conc } H_2SO_4} CH_3COCH_3 + H_2O$

5. b. $2CH_3CHOHCH_3 \xrightarrow[180\,°C,\ \text{excess acid}]{\text{conc } H_2SO_4} (CH_3)_2CHOCH(CH_3)_2 + H_2O$

6. GLYCOLS AND GLYCEROL

LEARNING OBJECTIVE

1. Describe the structure and uses of some common polyhydric alcohols.

glycol

An alcohol with two OH functional groups.

Alcohols with two OH groups on adjacent carbon atoms are commonly known as **glycols**. The most important of these is 1,2-ethanediol (the common name is ethylene glycol), a sweet, colorless, somewhat viscous liquid.

$$HOCH_2CH_2OH$$

Ethylene glycol

Another common glycol, 1,2-propanediol, is commonly called propylene glycol. Its physical properties are quite similar to those of ethylene glycol.

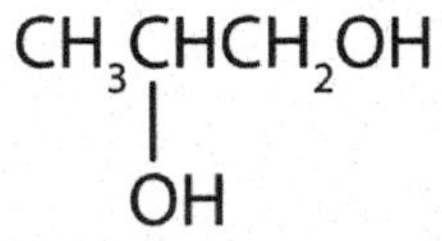

$$CH_3CH(OH)CH_2OH$$

Propylene glycol

Commonly called glycerol or glycerin, 1,2,3-propanetriol is the most important trihydroxy alcohol. Like the two glycols, it is a sweet, syrupy liquid. Glycerol is a product of the hydrolysis of fats and oils. (For more information about fats and oils, see Chapter 17, [Unsupported Reference Type: chapter-section].)

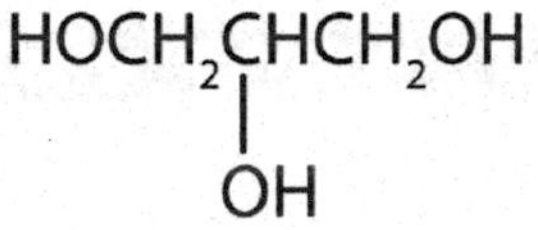

$$HOCH_2CH(OH)CH_2OH$$

Glycerol

Ethylene glycol is the main ingredient in many antifreeze mixtures for automobile radiators. The two OH groups lead to extensive intermolecular hydrogen bonding. This results in a high boiling point—198°C; thus ethylene glycol does not boil away when it is used as an antifreeze. It is also completely miscible with water. A solution of 60% ethylene glycol in water freezes at −49°C (−56°F) and thus protects an automobile radiator down to that temperature. Ethylene glycol is also used in the manufacture of polyester fiber and magnetic film used in tapes for recorders and computers.

To Your Health: Glycols and Human Health

Ethylene glycol is quite toxic. Because it is sweet, pets often lap up spills of leaked antifreeze from a garage floor or driveway. Sometimes people, especially children, drink it. As with methanol, its toxicity is due to a metabolite. Liver enzymes oxidize ethylene glycol to oxalate ion.

$$HOCH_2CH_2OH \xrightarrow{[O]} {}^-O-\overset{\overset{O}{\|}}{C}-\overset{\overset{O}{\|}}{C}-O^-$$

Ethylene glycol — Oxalate ion

In the kidneys, the oxalate ion combines with the calcium (Ca^{2+}) ion, precipitating as calcium oxalate (CaC_2O_4).

$Ca^{2+}(aq) + C_2O_4{}^{2-}(aq) \rightarrow CaC_2O_4(s)$

These crystals cause renal damage and can lead to kidney failure and death.

Although propylene glycol has physical properties much like those of ethylene glycol, its physiological properties are quite different. Propylene glycol is essentially nontoxic, and it can be used as a solvent for drugs and as a moisturizing agent for foods. Like other alcohols, propylene glycol is oxidized by liver enzymes.

$$CH_3\underset{\underset{OH}{|}}{C}HCH_2OH \xrightarrow{[O]} CH_3-\overset{\overset{O}{\|}}{C}-\overset{\overset{O}{\|}}{C}-O^-$$

Propylene glycol — Pyruvate ion

In this case, however, the product is pyruvate ion, a normal intermediate in carbohydrate metabolism. (For more information about metabolic reactions, see Chapter 20.)

Glycerol, a product of fat metabolism, is essentially nontoxic.

CONCEPT REVIEW EXERCISES

1. In the oxidation of propylene glycol to pyruvic acid, what functional groups in the reactant are involved? What new functional groups appear in the product?
2. Oxalate ion is formed by the oxidation of ethylene glycol. In what kind of reaction is the oxalate ion involved?

ANSWERS

1. two OH groups; a ketone group and a carboxylic acid group
2. precipitation

KEY TAKEAWAYS

- Glycols are alcohols with two OH groups on adjacent carbon atoms.
- Glycerol is the most important trihydroxy alcohol.

EXERCISES

1. What is a glycol?
2. Why is ethylene glycol so much more toxic to humans than propylene glycol?
3. Draw the structure for each compound.
    a. 1,5-pentanediol
    b. propylene glycol
4. Draw the structure for each compound.
    a. 1,3-hexandiol
    b. glycerol

ANSWERS

1. an alcohol with two OH groups on adjacent carbon atoms

3. a. $HOCH_2CH_2CH_2CH_2CH_2OH$
   b. $CH_3CH(OH)CH_2OH$

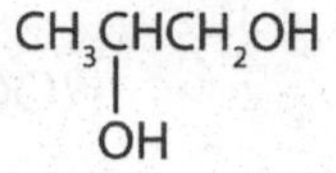

7. PHENOLS

LEARNING OBJECTIVE

1. **Describe the structure and uses of some phenols.**

phenol

An aromatic compound with an OH group attached directly to a benzene ring.

Compounds in which an OH group is attached directly to an aromatic ring are designated ArOH and called **phenols**. Phenols differ from alcohols in that they are slightly acidic in water. They react with aqueous sodium hydroxide (NaOH) to form salts.

$$ArOH(aq) + NaOH(aq) \rightarrow ArONa(aq) + H_2O$$

The parent compound, C_6H_5OH, is itself called phenol. (An old name, emphasizing its slight acidity, was *carbolic acid*.) Phenol is a white crystalline compound that has a distinctive ("hospital smell") odor.

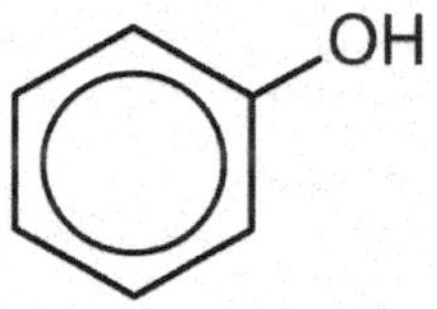

OH

To Your Health: Phenols and Us

Phenols are widely used as antiseptics (substances that kill microorganisms on living tissue) and as disinfectants (substances intended to kill microorganisms on inanimate objects such as furniture or floors). The first widely used antiseptic was phenol. Joseph Lister used it for antiseptic surgery in 1867. Phenol is toxic to humans, however, and can cause severe burns when applied to the skin. In the bloodstream, it is a systemic poison—that is, one that is carried to and affects all parts of the body. Its severe side effects led to searches for safer antiseptics, a number of which have been found.

One safer phenolic antiseptic is 4-hexylresorcinol (4-hexyl-1,3-dihydroxybenzene; resorcinol is the common name for 1,3-dihydroxybenzene, and 4-hexylresorcinol has a hexyl group on the fourth carbon atom of the resorcinol ring). It is much more powerful than phenol as a germicide and has fewer undesirable side effects. Indeed, it is safe enough to be used as the active ingredient in some mouthwashes and throat lozenges.

(a) Phenolic compounds help to ensure antiseptic conditions in hospital operating rooms. (b) The compound 4-hexylresorcinol is mild enough to be used as the active ingredient in antiseptic preparations for use on the skin.

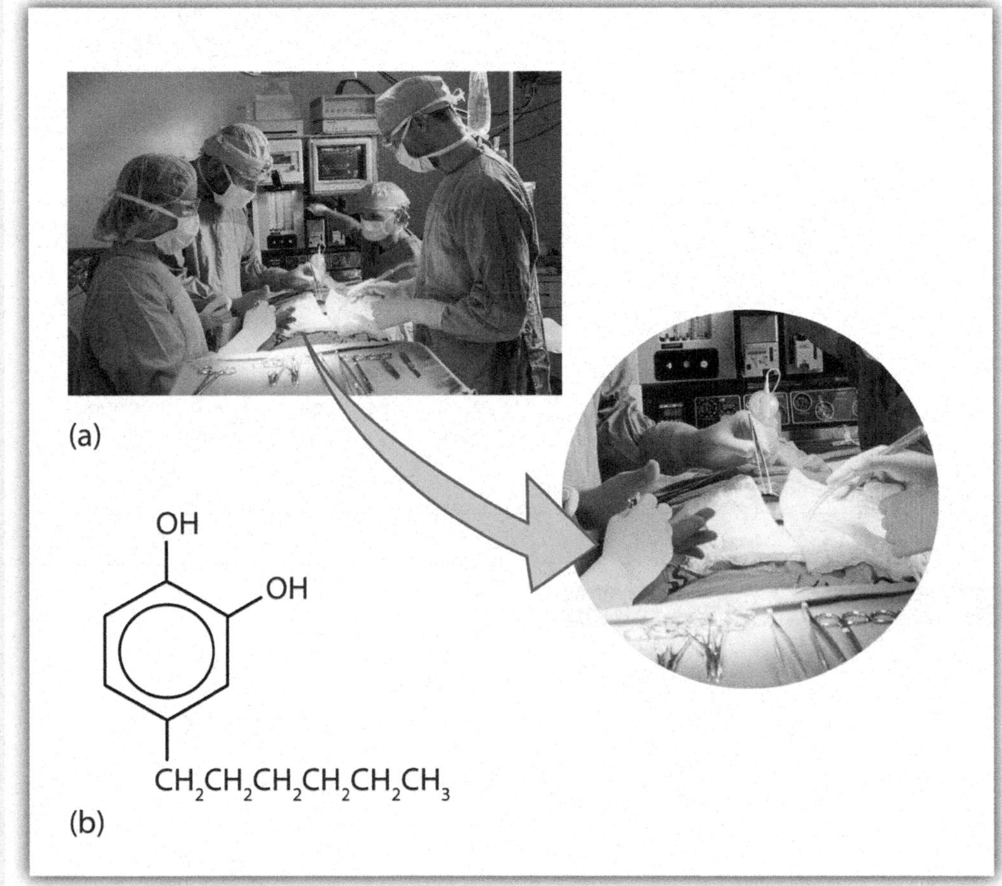

Source: Photo © Thinkstock

CONCEPT REVIEW EXERCISES

1. How do phenols differ from alcohols in terms of structure and properties?
2. How do phenols differ in properties from aromatic hydrocarbons?

ANSWERS

1. Phenols have an OH group attached directly to an aromatic ring. Phenols are weakly acidic.
2. Phenols have an OH group and are somewhat soluble in water.

KEY TAKEAWAYS

- Phenols are compounds in which an OH group is attached directly to an aromatic ring.
- Many phenols are used as antiseptics.

EXERCISES

1. Name each compound.
   a. 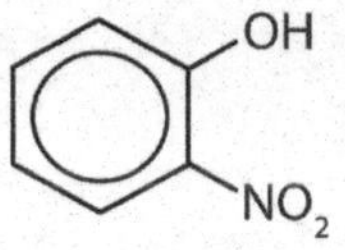
   b. 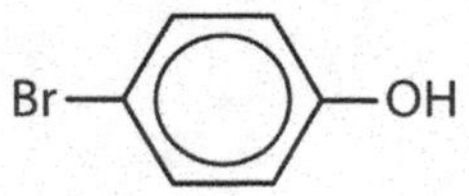
2. Name each compound.
   a. 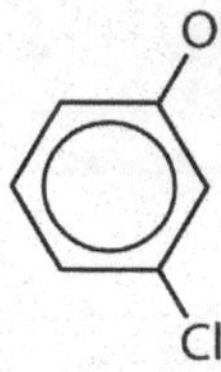
   b. 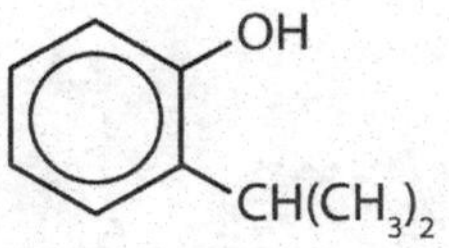
3. Draw the structure for each compound.
   a. *m*-iodophenol
   b. *p*-methylphenol (*p*-cresol)
4. Draw the structure for each compound.
   a. 2,4,6-trinitrophenol (picric acid)
   b. 3,5-diethylphenol

ANSWERS

1. a. *o*-nitrophenol
   b. *p*-bromophenol
3. a. 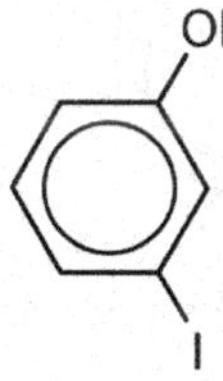
   b.

8. ETHERS

LEARNING OBJECTIVES

1. **Describe the structural difference between an alcohol and an ether that affects physical characteristics and reactivity of each.**
2. **Name simple ethers.**
3. **Describe the structure and uses of some ethers.**

ether

An organic compound that has an oxygen atom between two hydrocarbon groups.

With the general formula ROR′, an **ether** may be considered a derivative of water in which both hydrogen atoms are replaced by alkyl or aryl groups. It may also be considered a derivative of an alcohol (ROH) in which the hydrogen atom of the OH group is been replaced by a second alkyl or aryl group:

$$\text{HOH} \xrightarrow[\text{H atoms}]{\text{replace both}} \text{ROR}' \xleftarrow[\text{of OH group}]{\text{replace H atom}} \text{ROH}$$

Simple ethers have simple common names, formed from the names of the groups attached to oxygen atom, followed by the generic name *ether*. For example, $CH_3–O–CH_2CH_2CH_3$ is methyl propyl ether. If both groups are the same, the group name should be preceded by the prefix *di-*, as in dimethyl ether ($CH_3–O–CH_3$) and diethyl ether $CH_3CH_2–O–CH_2CH_3$.

Ether molecules have no hydrogen atom on the oxygen atom (that is, no OH group). Therefore there is no intermolecular hydrogen bonding between ether molecules, and ethers therefore have quite low boiling points for a given molar mass. Indeed, ethers have boiling points about the same as those of alkanes of comparable molar mass and much lower than those of the corresponding alcohols (Table 14.4).

TABLE 14.4 Comparison of Boiling Points of Alkanes, Alcohols, and Ethers

Condensed Structural Formula	Name	Molar Mass	Boiling Point (°C)	Intermolecular Hydrogen Bonding in Pure Liquid?
$CH_3CH_2CH_3$	propane	44	–42	no
CH_3OCH_3	dimethyl ether	46	–25	no
CH_3CH_2OH	ethyl alcohol	46	78	yes
$CH_3CH_2CH_2CH_2CH_3$	pentane	72	36	no
$CH_3CH_2OCH_2CH_3$	diethyl ether	74	35	no
$CH_3CH_2CH_2CH_2OH$	butyl alcohol	74	117	yes

Ether molecules do have an oxygen atom, however, and engage in hydrogen bonding with water molecules. Consequently, an ether has about the same solubility in water as the alcohol that is isomeric with it. For example, dimethyl ether and ethanol (both having the molecular formula C_2H_6O) are completely soluble in water, whereas diethyl ether and 1-butanol (both $C_4H_{10}O$) are barely soluble in water (8 g/100 mL of water).

EXAMPLE 5

What is the common name for each ether?

1. $CH_3CH_2CH_2OCH_2CH_2CH_3$
2. CH_3CHOCH_3 (with CH_3 attached to the CH)

Solution

1. The carbon groups on either side of the oxygen atom are propyl ($CH_3CH_2CH_2$) groups, so the compound is dipropyl ether.
2. The three-carbon group is attached by the middle carbon atom, so it is an isopropyl group. The one-carbon group is a methyl group. The compound is isopropyl methyl ether.

SKILL-BUILDING EXERCISE

What is the common name for each ether?

1. $CH_3CH_2CH_2CH_2OCH_2CH_2CH_2CH_3$
2.

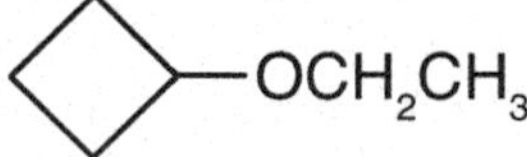

To Your Health: Ethers as General Anesthetics

A *general anesthetic* acts on the brain to produce unconsciousness and a general insensitivity to feeling or pain. Diethyl ether ($CH_3CH_2OCH_2CH_3$) was the first general anesthetic to be used.

William Morton, a Boston dentist, introduced diethyl ether into surgical practice in 1846. This painting shows an operation in Boston in 1846 in which diethyl ether was used as an anesthetic. Inhalation of ether vapor produces unconsciousness by depressing the activity of the central nervous system.

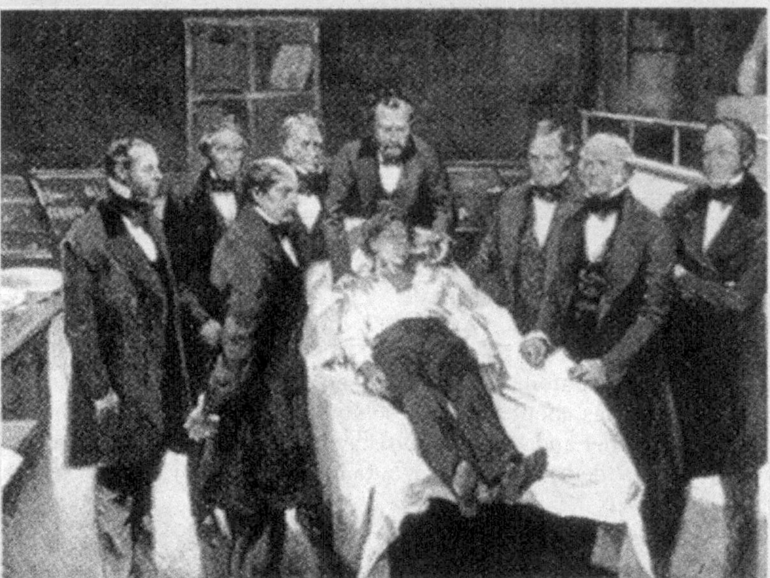

Source: Painting of William Morton by Ernest Board, from http://commons.wikimedia.org/wiki/File:Morton_Ether_1846.jpg.

Diethyl ether is relatively safe because there is a fairly wide gap between the dose that produces an effective level of anesthesia and the lethal dose. However, because it is highly flammable and has the added disadvantage of causing nausea, it has been replaced by newer inhalant anesthetics, including the fluorine-containing compounds halothane, enflurane, and isoflurane. Unfortunately, the safety of these compounds for operating room personnel has been questioned. For example, female operating room workers exposed to halothane suffer a higher rate of miscarriages than women in the general population.

These three modern, inhalant, halogen-containing, anesthetic compounds are less flammable than diethyl ether.

```
   Br F             F       F  H                F       H  F
   |  |             |       |  |                |       |  |
H—C—C—F        H—C—O—C—C—Cl          H—C—O—C—C—F
   |  |             |       |  |                |       |  |
   Cl F             F       F  F                F       Cl F
```

Halothane Enflurane Isoflurane

CONCEPT REVIEW EXERCISES

1. Why does diethyl ether ($CH_3CH_2OCH_2CH_3$) have a much lower boiling point than 1-butanol ($CH_3CH_2CH_2CH_2OH$)?
2. Which is more soluble in water—ethyl methyl ether ($CH_3CH_2OCH_3$) or 1-butanol ($CH_3CH_2CH_2CH_2OH$)? Explain.

ANSWERS

1. Diethyl ether has no intermolecular hydrogen bonding because there is no OH group; 1-butanol has an OH and engages in intermolecular hydrogen bonding.
2. Ethyl methyl ether (three carbon atoms, one oxygen atom) is more soluble in water than 1-butanol (four carbon atoms, one oxygen atom), even though both can engage in hydrogen bonding with water.

KEY TAKEAWAYS

- To give ethers common names, simply name the groups attached to the oxygen atom, followed by the generic name *ether*. If both groups are the same, the group name should be preceded by the prefix *di-*.
- Ether molecules have no OH group and thus no intermolecular hydrogen bonding. Ethers therefore have quite low boiling points for a given molar mass.
- Ether molecules have an oxygen atom and can engage in hydrogen bonding with water molecules. An ether molecule has about the same solubility in water as the alcohol that is isomeric with it.

EXERCISES

1. How can ethanol give two different products when heated with sulfuric acid? Name these products.
2. Which of these ethers is isomeric with ethanol—$CH_3CH_2OCH_2CH_3$, $CH_3OCH_2CH_3$, or CH_3OCH_3?
3. Name each compound.
   a. $CH_3OCH_2CH_2CH_3$
   b.
   $$\begin{array}{l} CH_3\underset{\displaystyle CH_3}{\underset{|}{C}}HOCH_2CH_3 \end{array}$$
4. Name each compound.
   a. $CH_3CH_2CH_2CH_2OCH_3$
   b. $CH_3CH_2OCH_2CH_2CH_3$
5. Draw the structure for each compound.
   a. methyl ethyl ether
   b. *tert*-butyl ethyl ether
6. Draw the structure for each compound.
   a. diisopropyl ether
   b. cyclopropyl propyl ether

ANSWERS

1. Intramolecular (both the H and the OH come from the same molecule) dehydration gives ethylene; intermolecular (the H comes from one molecule and the OH comes from another molecule) dehydration gives diethyl ether.
3. a. methyl propyl ether
   b. ethyl isopropyl ether
5. a. $CH_3OCH_2CH_3$
   b.
   $$CH_3\overset{\displaystyle CH_3}{\overset{|}{\underset{\displaystyle CH_3}{\underset{|}{C}}}}—OCH_2CH_3$$

9. ALDEHYDES AND KETONES: STRUCTURE AND NAMES

LEARNING OBJECTIVES

1. **Identify the general structure for an aldehyde and a ketone.**
2. **Use common names to name aldehydes and ketones.**
3. **Use the IUPAC system to name aldehydes and ketones.**

carbonyl group

A compound with an carbon-to-oxygen double bond.

The next functional group we consider, the **carbonyl group**, has a carbon-to-oxygen double bond.

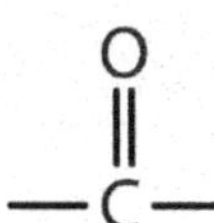

Carbonyl groups define two related families of organic compounds: the aldehydes and the ketones.

Note

The carbonyl group is ubiquitous in biological compounds. It is found in carbohydrates, fats, proteins, nucleic acids, hormones, and vitamins—organic compounds critical to living systems.

ketone

An organic compound whose molecules have a carbonyl functional group between two hydrocarbon groups.

In a **ketone**, two carbon groups are attached to the carbonyl carbon atom. The following general formulas, in which R represents an alkyl group and Ar stands for an aryl group, represent ketones.

R—C(=O)—R Ar—C(=O)—R Ar—C(=O)—Ar

aldehyde

An organic compound with a carbonyl functional group that has an hydrogen atom attached and either a hydrocarbon group or a second hydrogen atom.

In an **aldehyde**, at least one of the attached groups must be a hydrogen atom. The following compounds are aldehydes:

H—C(=O)—H R—C(=O)—H Ar—C(=O)—H

In condensed formulas, we use CHO to identify an aldehyde rather than COH, which might be confused with an alcohol. This follows the general rule that in condensed structural formulas H comes after the atom it is attached to (usually C, N, or O).

—CHO —CO—

An aldehyde A ketone

The carbon-to-oxygen double bond is not shown but understood to be present.

Because they contain the same functional group, aldehydes and ketones share many common properties, but they still differ enough to warrant their classification into two families.

9.1 Naming Aldehydes and Ketones

Both common and International Union of Pure and Applied Chemistry (IUPAC) names are frequently used for aldehydes and ketones, with common names predominating for the lower homologs. The common names of aldehydes are taken from the names of the acids into which the aldehydes can be converted by oxidation. (For more information about carboxylic acids, see Chapter 15, [Unsupported Reference Type: chapter-section] through [Unsupported Reference Type: chapter-section].)

$$H{-}\overset{\displaystyle O}{\overset{\|}{C}}{-}H \xrightarrow{[O]} H{-}\overset{\displaystyle O}{\overset{\|}{C}}{-}OH$$

Formaldehyde Formic acid

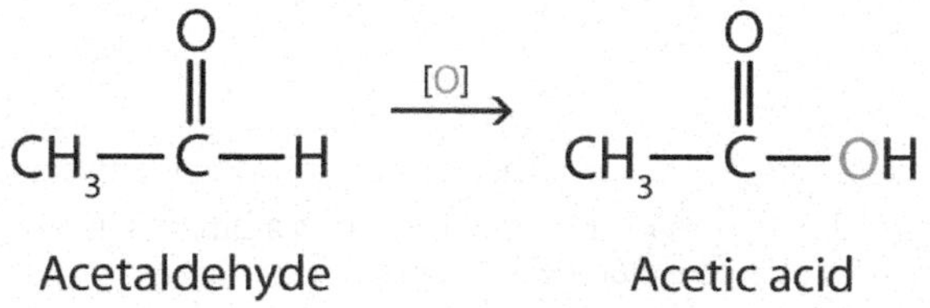

$$CH_3{-}\overset{\displaystyle O}{\overset{\|}{C}}{-}H \xrightarrow{[O]} CH_3{-}\overset{\displaystyle O}{\overset{\|}{C}}{-}OH$$

Acetaldehyde Acetic acid

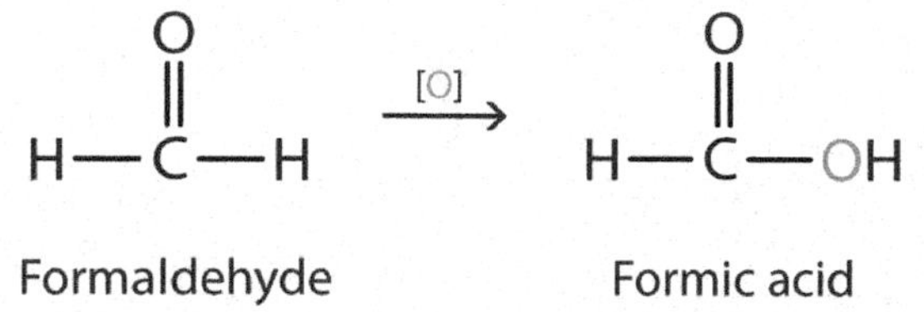

Note

The stems for the common names of the first four aldehydes are as follows:

- 1 carbon atom: *form-*
- 2 carbon atoms: *acet-*
- 3 carbon atoms: *propion-*
- 4 carbon atoms: *butyr-*

Because the carbonyl group in a ketone must be attached to two carbon groups, the simplest ketone has three carbon atoms. It is widely known as *acetone*, a unique name unrelated to other common names for ketones.

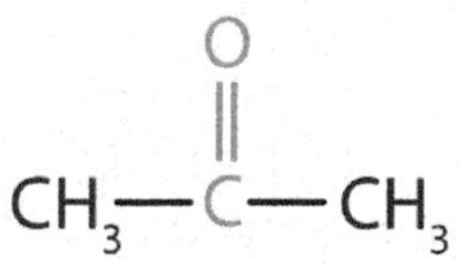

$$CH_3{-}\overset{\displaystyle O}{\overset{\|}{C}}{-}CH_3$$

Acetone

Generally, the common names of ketones consist of the names of the groups attached to the carbonyl group, followed by the word *ketone*. (Note the similarity to the naming of ethers.) Another name for acetone, then, is *dimethyl ketone*. The ketone with four carbon atoms is ethyl methyl ketone.

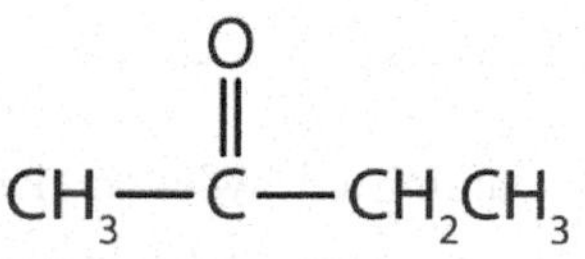

$$CH_3{-}\overset{\displaystyle O}{\overset{\|}{C}}{-}CH_2CH_3$$

Ethyl methyl ketone

EXAMPLE 6

Classify each compound as an aldehyde or a ketone. Give the common name for each ketone.

1. $CH_3CH_2CH_2-C(=O)-H$
2. $CH_3CH_2CH_2-C(=O)-CH_2CH_2CH_3$
3. $CH_3-C(=O)-CH(CH_3)CH_3$

Solution

1. This compound has the carbonyl group on an end carbon atom, so it is an aldehyde.
2. This compound has the carbonyl group on an interior carbon atom, so it is a ketone. Both alkyl groups are propyl groups. The name is therefore dipropyl ketone.
3. This compound has the carbonyl group between two alkyl groups, so it is a ketone. One alkyl group has three carbon atoms and is attached by the middle carbon atom; it is an isopropyl group. A group with one carbon atom is a methyl group. The name is therefore isopropyl methyl ketone.

SKILL-BUILDING EXERCISE

Classify each compound as an aldehyde or a ketone. Give the common name for each ketone.

1. $CH_3CH_2CH_2-C(=O)-CH_2CH_3$
2. $CH_3CH_2CH(CH_3)-C(=O)-H$
3. cyclobutyl$-C(=O)-CH_3$

Here are some simple IUPAC rules for naming aldehydes and ketones:

1. The stem names of aldehydes and ketones are derived from those of the parent alkanes, defined by the longest continuous chain (LCC) of carbon atoms that contains the functional group.
2. For an aldehyde, drop the *-e* from the alkane name and add the ending *-al*. Methanal is the IUPAC name for formaldehyde, and ethanal is the name for acetaldehyde.
3. For a ketone, drop the *-e* from the alkane name and add the ending *-one*. Propanone is the IUPAC name for acetone, and butanone is the name for ethyl methyl ketone.

4. To indicate the position of a substituent on an aldehyde, the carbonyl carbon atom is always considered to be C1; it is unnecessary to designate this group by number.
5. To indicate the position of a substituent on a ketone, number the chain in the manner that gives the carbonyl carbon atom the lowest possible number. In cyclic ketones, it is understood that the carbonyl carbon atom is C1.

EXAMPLE 7

Give the IUPAC name for each compound.

1. 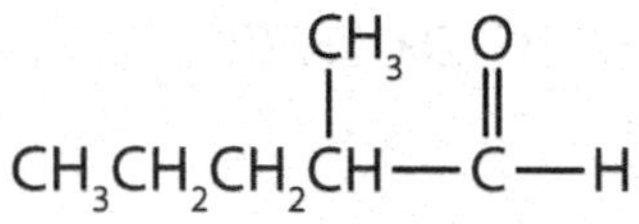 $CH_3CH_2CH_2CH(CH_3){-}C({=}O){-}H$

2. $CH_3CH(CH_3){-}C({=}O){-}CH(CH_3)CH_3$

3. (cyclohexane ring with =O)

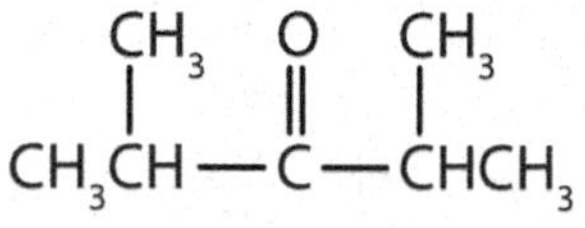

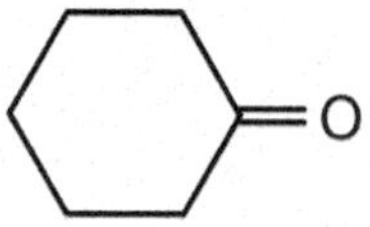

Solution

1. There are five carbon atoms in the LCC. The methyl group (CH_3) is a substituent on the second carbon atom of the chain; the aldehyde carbon atom is always C1. The name is derived from pentane. Dropping the *-e* and adding the ending *-al* gives pentanal. The methyl group on the second carbon atom makes the name 2-methylpentanal.
2. There are five carbon atoms in the LCC. The carbonyl carbon atom is C3, and there are methyl groups on C2 and C4. The IUPAC name is 2,4-dimethyl-3-pentanone.
3. There are six carbon atoms in the ring. The compound is cyclohexanone. No number is needed to indicate the position of the carbonyl group because all six carbon atoms are equivalent.

SKILL-BUILDING EXERCISE

Give the IUPAC name for each compound.

1. 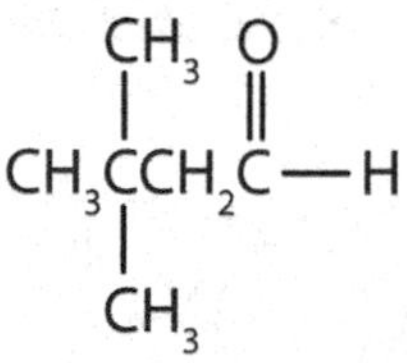 $CH_3C(CH_3)_2CH_2C({=}O){-}H$

2. $CH_3CH(CH_3){-}C({=}O){-}CH_2CH_2CH_3$

3. (cyclobutane ring with =O)

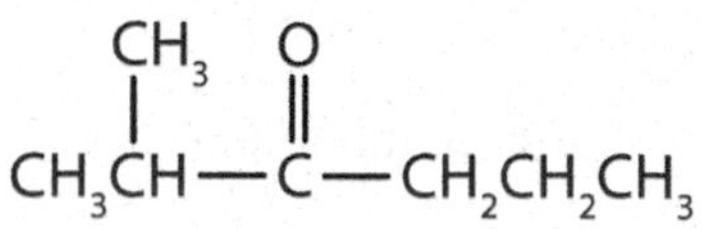

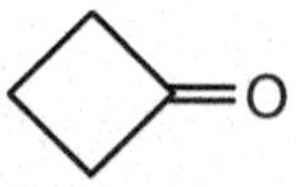

EXAMPLE 8

Draw the structure for each compound.

1. 7-chlorooctanal
2. 4-methyl–3-hexanone

Solution

1. The *octan-* part of the name tells us that the LCC has eight carbon atoms. There is a chlorine (Cl) atom on the seventh carbon atom; numbering from the carbonyl group and counting the carbonyl carbon atom as C1, we place the Cl atom on the seventh carbon atom.

$$CH_3\underset{\displaystyle Cl}{\underset{|}{C}}HCH_2CH_2CH_2CH_2CH_2CHO$$

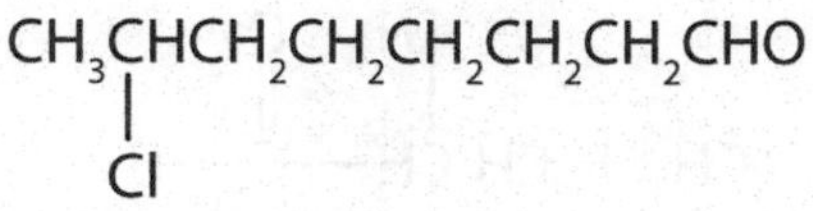

2. The *hexan-* part of the name tells us that the LCC has six carbon atoms. The 3 means that the carbonyl carbon atom is C3 in this chain, and the 4 tells us that there is a methyl (CH_3) group at C4:

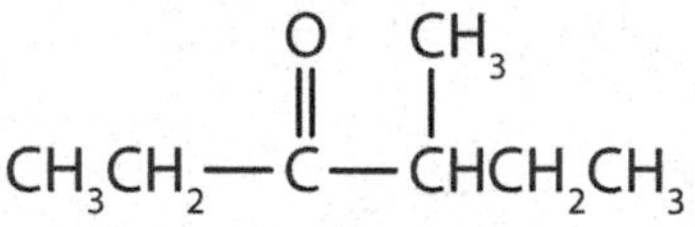

$$CH_3CH_2—\overset{\displaystyle O}{\overset{\|}{C}}—\overset{\displaystyle CH_3}{\overset{|}{C}}HCH_2CH_3$$

SKILL-BUILDING EXERCISE

Draw the structure for each compound.

1. 5-bromo-3-iodoheptanal
2. 5-bromo-4-ethyl-2-heptanone

CONCEPT REVIEW EXERCISES

1. Give the structure and IUPAC name for the compound that has the common name *m*-bromobenzaldehyde (see Figure 14.6 for the structure of benzaldehyde).
2. Give the IUPAC name for glyceraldehyde, ($HOCH_2CHOHCHO$). (Hint: as a substituent, the OH group is named *hydroxy*.)

ANSWERS

1.

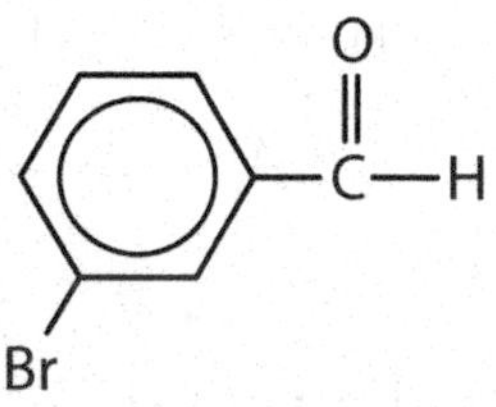

O
||
—C—H
Br

3-Bromobenzaldehyde

3-bromobenzaldehyde

2. 2,3-dihydroxypropanal

KEY TAKEAWAYS

- The common names of aldehydes are taken from the names of the corresponding carboxylic acids: formaldehyde, acetaldehyde, and so on.
- The common names of ketones, like those of ethers, consist of the names of the groups attached to the carbonyl group, followed by the word *ketone.*
- Stem names of aldehydes and ketones are derived from those of the parent alkanes, using an *-al* ending for an aldehydes and an *-one* ending for a ketone.

EXERCISES

1. Name each compound.
   a. $CH_3CH_2{-}\overset{\overset{\displaystyle O}{\|}}{C}{-}H$
   b. $CH_3CH_2CH_2{-}\overset{\overset{\displaystyle O}{\|}}{C}{-}H$
   c. $CH_3CH_2{-}\overset{\overset{\displaystyle O}{\|}}{C}{-}CH_2CH_3$
   d. $C_6H_5{-}\overset{\overset{\displaystyle O}{\|}}{C}{-}H$
2. Name each compound.
   a. $CH_3{-}\overset{\overset{\displaystyle O}{\|}}{C}{-}\overset{\overset{\displaystyle CH_3}{|}}{C}HCH_3$
   b. CH3CH2CH2CH2CH2CHO
   c. $CH_3\overset{\overset{\displaystyle Br}{|}}{C}HCH_2CH_2{-}\overset{\overset{\displaystyle O}{\|}}{C}{-}H$
   d. $CH_3CH_2{-}\overset{\overset{\displaystyle O}{\|}}{C}{-}CH_2CH_2CH_2CH_3$
3. Draw the structure for each compound.
   a. butyraldehyde
   b. 2-hexanone
   c. *p*-nitrobenzaldehyde

4. Draw the structure for each compound.
   a. 5-ethyloctanal
   b. 2-chloropropanal
   c. 2-hydroxy-3-pentanone

ANSWERS

1. a. propanal or propionaldehyde
   b. butanal or butyraldehyde
   c. 3-pentanone or diethyl ketone
   d. benzaldehyde
3. a. CH3CH2CH2CHO
   b.

$$CH_3-\overset{\overset{\displaystyle O}{\|}}{C}-CH_2CH_2CH_2CH_3$$

   c.

$$O_2N-C_6H_4-CHO$$

10. PROPERTIES OF ALDEHYDES AND KETONES

LEARNING OBJECTIVES

1. **Explain why the boiling points of aldehydes and ketones are higher than those of ethers and alkanes of similar molar masses but lower than those of comparable alcohols.**
2. **Compare the solubilities in water of aldehydes and ketones of four or fewer carbon atoms with the solubilities of comparable alkanes and alcohols.**
3. **Name the typical reactions take place with aldehydes and ketones.**
4. **Describe some of the uses of common aldehydes and ketones.**

The carbon-to-oxygen double bond is quite polar, more polar than a carbon-to-oxygen single bond. The electronegative oxygen atom has a much greater attraction for the bonding electron pairs than does the carbon atom. The carbon atom has a partial positive charge, and the oxygen atom has a partial negative charge:

$$\begin{matrix} R \\ \delta+\ C{=}O\ \delta- \\ R \end{matrix}$$

In aldehydes and ketones, this charge separation leads to dipole-dipole interactions that are great enough to significantly affect the boiling points. Table 14.5 shows that the polar single bonds in ethers have little such effect, whereas hydrogen bonding between alcohol molecules is even stronger.

TABLE 14.5 Boiling Points of Compounds Having Similar Molar Masses but Different Types of Intermolecular Forces

Compound	Family	Molar Mass	Type of Intermolecular Forces	Boiling Point (°C)
$CH_3CH_2CH_2CH_3$	alkane	58	dispersion only	−1
$CH_3OCH_2CH_3$	ether	60	weak dipole	6
CH_3CH_2CHO	aldehyde	58	strong dipole	49
$CH_3CH_2CH_2OH$	alcohol	60	hydrogen bonding	97

Formaldehyde is a gas at room temperature. Acetaldehyde boils at 20°C; in an open vessel, it boils away in a warm room. Most other common aldehydes are liquids at room temperature.

Note

Although the lower members of the homologous series have pungent odors, many higher aldehydes have pleasant odors and are used in perfumes and artificial flavorings. As for the ketones, acetone has a pleasant odor, but most of the higher homologs have rather bland odors.

The oxygen atom of the carbonyl group engages in hydrogen bonding with a water molecule.

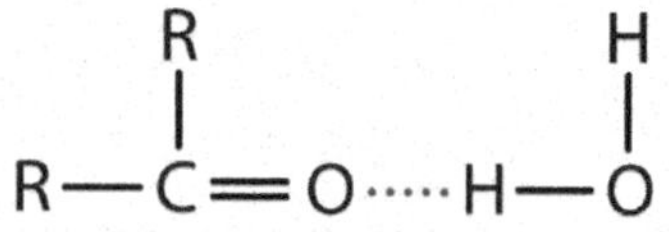

$$R_2C{=}O \cdots H{-}O{-}H$$

The solubility of aldehydes is therefore about the same as that of alcohols and ethers. Formaldehyde, acetaldehyde, and acetone are soluble in water. As the carbon chain increases in length, solubility in water decreases. The borderline of solubility occurs at about four carbon atoms per oxygen atom. All aldehydes and ketones are soluble in organic solvents and, in general, are less dense than water.

10.1 Oxidation of Aldehydes and Ketones

Aldehydes and ketones are much alike in many of their reactions, owing to the presence of the carbonyl functional group in both. They differ greatly, however, in one most important type of reaction: oxidation. Aldehydes are readily oxidized to carboxylic acids, whereas ketones resist oxidation.

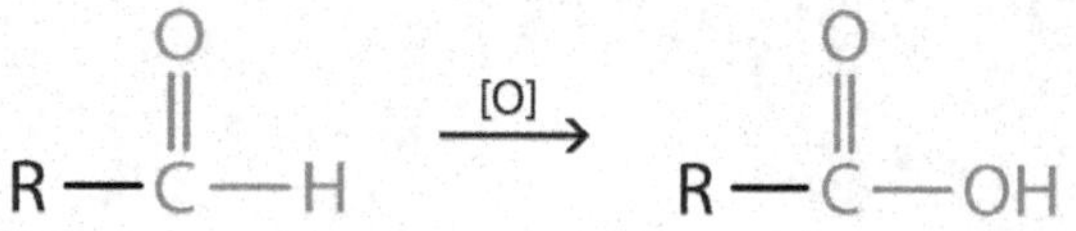

$$R{-}C({=}O){-}H \xrightarrow{[O]} R{-}C({=}O){-}OH$$

An aldehyde → A carboxylic acid

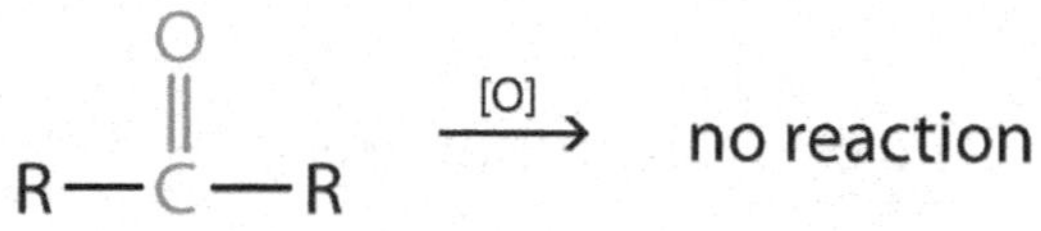

$$R{-}C({=}O){-}R \xrightarrow{[O]} \text{no reaction}$$

A ketone

The aldehydes are, in fact, among the most easily oxidized of organic compounds. They are oxidized by oxygen (O_2) in air to carboxylic acids.

$$2RCHO + O_2 \rightarrow 2RCOOH$$

The ease of oxidation helps chemists identify aldehydes. A sufficiently mild oxidizing agent can distinguish aldehydes not only from ketones but also from alcohols. Tollens' reagent, for example, is an alkaline solution of silver (Ag^+) ion complexed with ammonia (NH_3), which keeps the Ag^+ ion in solution.

$$H_3N—Ag^+—NH_3$$

When Tollens' reagent oxidizes an aldehyde, the Ag^+ ion is reduced to free silver (Ag).

$$\underset{\text{An aldehyde}}{RCHO(aq)} + 2Ag(NH_3)_2{}^+(aq) + 3OH^-(aq) \longrightarrow RCOO^-(aq) + \underset{\text{Free silver}}{2Ag(s)} + 4NH_3(aq) + 2H_2O$$

Deposited on a clean glass surface, the silver produces a mirror (Figure 14.5). Ordinary ketones do not react with Tollens' reagent.

FIGURE 14.5 Aldehyde Reactions

A reaction related to the Tollens' reaction is often used to silver mirrors. These ornaments were silvered by such a reaction. Glucose, a simple sugar with an aldehyde functional group, is used as the reducing agent.

Source: Photo courtesy of Krebs Glas Lauscha, http://commons.wikimedia.org/wiki/File:Silvering.jpg.

Although ketones resist oxidation by ordinary laboratory oxidizing agents, they undergo combustion, as do aldehydes.

10.2 Some Common Carbonyl Compounds

Formaldehyde has an irritating odor. Because of its reactivity, it is difficult to handle in the gaseous state. For many uses, it is therefore dissolved in water and sold as a 37% to 40% aqueous solution called *formalin*. Formaldehyde denatures proteins, rendering them insoluble in water and resistant to bacterial decay. (For more information about proteins, see Chapter 18, [Unsupported Reference Type: chapter-section].) For this reason, formalin is used in embalming solutions and in preserving biological specimens.

Aldehydes are the active components in many other familiar substances. Large quantities of formaldehyde are used to make phenol-formaldehyde resins for gluing the wood sheets in plywood and as adhesives in other building materials. Sometimes the formaldehyde escapes from the materials and causes health problems in some people. While some people seem unaffected, others experience coughing, wheezing, eye irritation, and other symptoms.

Acetaldehyde is an extremely volatile, colorless liquid. It is a starting material for the preparation of many other organic compounds. Acetaldehyde is formed as a metabolite in the fermentation of sugars and in the detoxification of alcohol in the liver. Aldehydes are the active components of many other familiar materials (Figure 14.6).

Note

The odor of green leaves is due in part to a carbonyl compound, *cis*-3-hexenal, which with related compounds is used to impart a "green" herbal odor to shampoos and other products.

FIGURE 14.6 Some Interesting Aldehydes

(a) Benzaldehyde is an oil found in almonds; (b) cinnamaldehyde is oil of cinnamon; (c) vanillin gives vanilla its flavor; (d) *cis*-3-hexenal provides an herbal odor; and (e) *trans*-2-*cis*-6-nonadienal gives a cucumber odor.

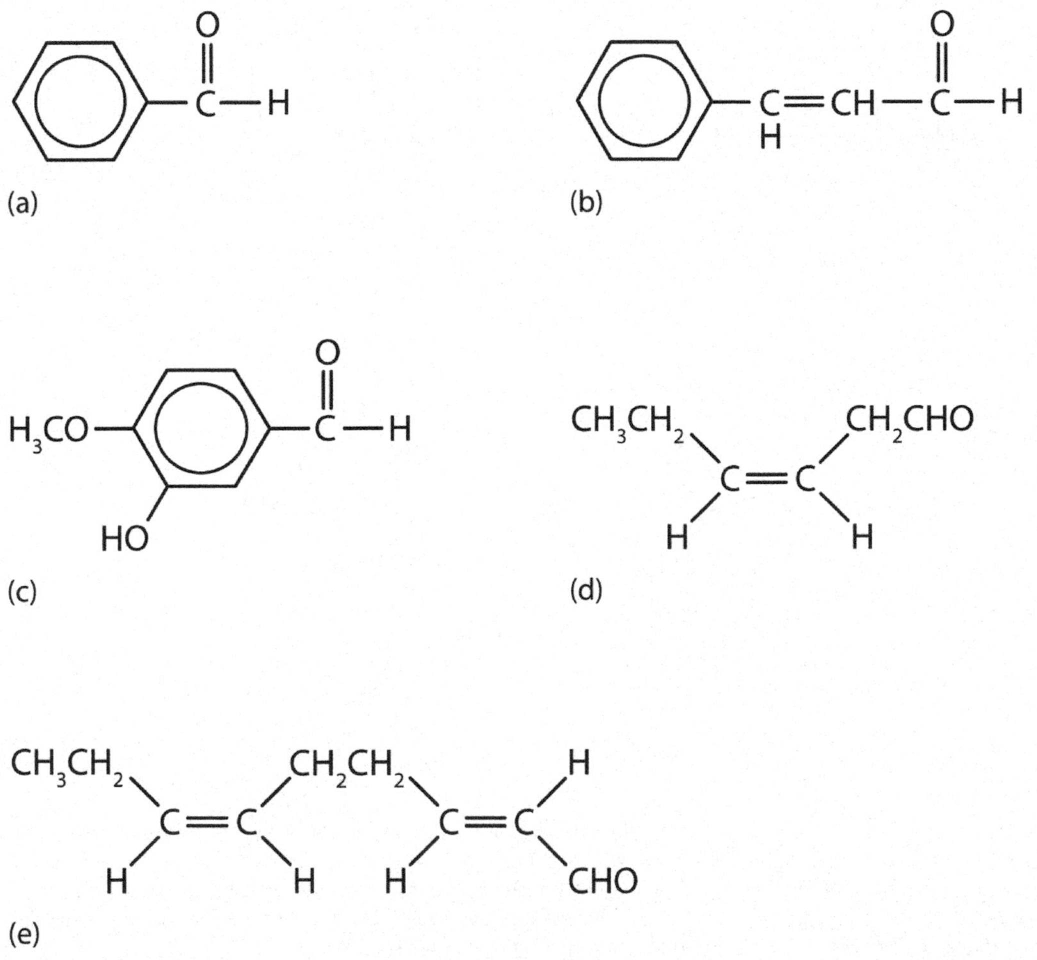

Acetone is the simplest and most important ketone. Because it is miscible with water as well as with most organic solvents, its chief use is as an industrial solvent (for example, for paints and lacquers). It is also the chief ingredient in some brands of nail polish remover.

To Your Health: Acetone in Blood, Urine, and Breath

Acetone is formed in the human body as a by-product of lipid metabolism. (For more information about metabolic reactions, see Chapter 20.) Normally, acetone does not accumulate to an appreciable extent because it is oxidized to carbon dioxide and water. The normal concentration of acetone in the human body is less than 1 mg/100 mL of blood. In certain disease states, such as uncontrolled diabetes mellitus, the acetone concentration rises to higher levels. It is then excreted in the urine, where it is easily detected. In severe cases, its odor can be noted on the breath.

Ketones are also the active components of other familiar substances, some of which are noted in the accompanying figure.

Some ketones have interesting properties: (a) Butter flavoring comes from 2,3-butanedione; (b) β-ionone is responsible for the odor of violets; (c) muscone is musk oil, an ingredient in perfumes; and (d) camphor is used in some insect repellents.

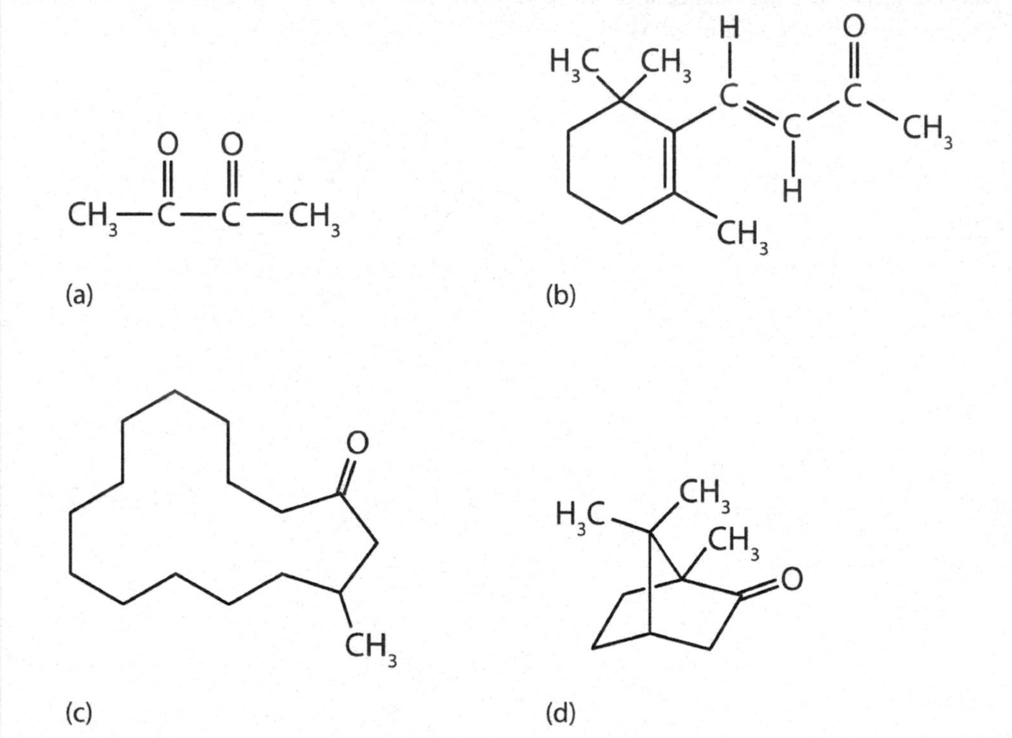

$$CH_3-\overset{\overset{\large O}{\|}}{C}-\overset{\overset{\large O}{\|}}{C}-CH_3$$

(a)

(b)

(c)

(d)

Note

Certain steroid hormones have the ketone functional group as a part of their structure. Two examples are progesterone, a hormone secreted by the ovaries that stimulates the growth of cells in the uterine wall and prepares it for attachment of a fertilized egg, and testosterone, the main male sex hormone. These and other sex hormones affect our development and our lives in fundamental ways. (For more information about the sex hormones, see Chapter 17, [Unsupported Reference Type: chapter-section].)

CONCEPT REVIEW EXERCISES

1. What feature of their structure makes aldehydes easier to oxidize than ketones?
2. How does the carbon-to-oxygen bond of aldehydes and ketones differ from the carbon-to-carbon bond of alkenes?

ANSWERS

1. the H on the carbonyl carbon atom
2. The carbon-to-oxygen double bond is polar; the carbon-to-carbon double bond is nonpolar.

KEY TAKEAWAYS

- The polar carbon-to-oxygen double bond causes aldehydes and ketones to have higher boiling points than those of ethers and alkanes of similar molar masses but lower than those of comparable alcohols that engage in intermolecular hydrogen bonding.
- Aldehydes are readily oxidized to carboxylic acids, whereas ketones resist oxidation.

EXERCISES

1. Which compound in each pair has the higher boiling point?
   a. acetone or 2-propanol
   b. dimethyl ether or acetaldehyde
2. Which compound in each pair has the higher boiling point?
   a. butanal or 1-butanol
   b. acetone or isobutane
3. Draw the structure of the alcohol that could be oxidized to each compound.
   a. cyclohexanone
   b. 2-methyl-1-propanal
4. Draw the structure of the alcohol that could be oxidized to each compound.
   a. 2-pentanone
   b. *o*-methylbenzaldehyde
5. Acetaldehyde is treated with each substance.
   a. $Ag^+(aq)$—What inorganic product, if any, is formed?
   b. $K_2Cr_2O_7$ in an acid solution—What organic product, if any, is formed?
6. Acetone is treated with each substance.
   a. $Ag^+(aq)$ —What inorganic product, if any, is formed?
   b. $K_2Cr_2O_7$ in an acid solution—What organic product, if any, is formed?

ANSWERS

1. a. 2-propanol
   b. acetaldehyde

3. a.

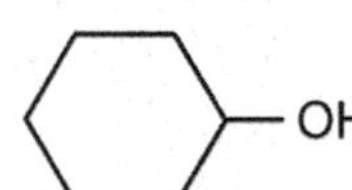

   b.

$$\begin{array}{c} CH_3CHCHO \\ | \\ CH_3 \end{array}$$

5. a. silver metal (Ag)
   b. acetic acid (CH_3COOH)

11. ORGANIC SULFUR COMPOUNDS

LEARNING OBJECTIVES

1. **Identify thiols (mercaptans) by the presence of an SH group.**
2. **The mild oxidation of thiols gives disulfides.**

Because sulfur is in the same group (6A) of the periodic table as oxygen, the two elements have some similar properties. We might expect sulfur to form organic compounds related to those of oxygen, and indeed it does.

thiol

A compound with an SH functional group.

Thiols (also called mercaptans), which are sulfur analogs of alcohols, have the general formula RSH. Methanethiol (also called methyl mercaptan), has the formula CH_3SH. Ethanethiol (ethyl mercaptan) is the most common odorant for liquid propane (LP) gas.

The mild oxidation of thiols gives compounds called disulfides.

$$2\ RSH \xrightarrow{[O]} RSSR$$

As we note in Chapter 18, [Unsupported Reference Type: chapter-section], the amino acids cysteine [$HSCH_2CH(NH_2)COOH$] and methionine [$CH_3SCH_2CH_2CH(NH_2)COOH$] contain sulfur atoms, as do all proteins that contain these amino acids. Disulfide linkages (–S–S–) between protein chains are extremely important in protein structure.

Thioethers, which are sulfur analogs of ethers, have the form general formula RSR′. An example is dimethylsulfide (CH_3SCH_3), which is responsible for the sometimes unpleasant odor of cooking cabbage and related vegetables. Note that methionine has a thioether functional group.

Career Focus: Paramedic

Paramedics are highly trained experts at providing emergency medical treatment. Their critical duties often include rescue work and emergency medical procedures in a wide variety of settings, sometimes under extremely harsh and difficult conditions. Like other science-based professions, their work requires knowledge, ingenuity, and complex thinking, as well as a great deal of technical skill. The recommended courses for preparation in this field include anatomy, physiology, medical terminology, and—not surprisingly—chemistry. An understanding of basic principles of organic chemistry, for example, is useful when paramedics have to deal with such traumas as burns from fuel (hydrocarbons) or solvent (alcohols, ethers, esters, and so on) fires and alcohol and drug overdoses.

To become a paramedic requires 2–4 y of training and usually includes a stint as an emergency medical technician (EMT). An EMT provides basic care, can administer certain medications and treatments, such as oxygen for respiratory problems and epinephrine (adrenalin) for allergic reactions, and has some knowledge of common medical conditions. A paramedic, in contrast, must have extensive knowledge of common medical problems and be trained to administer a wide variety of emergency drugs.

Paramedics usually work under the direction of a medical doctor with a title such as "medical director." Some paramedics are employed by fire departments and may work from a fire engine that carries medical equipment as well as fire-fighting gear. Some work from hospital-sponsored ambulances and continue to care for their patients after reaching the hospital emergency room. Still other paramedics work for a government department responsible for emergency health care in a specific geographical area. Finally, some work for private companies that contract to provide service for a government body.

An experienced paramedic has a broad range of employment options, including training for mountain or ocean rescue, working with police department special weapons and tactics (SWAT) teams, or working in isolated settings such as on oil rigs. With their expertise at treating and stabilizing patients before quickly moving them to a hospital, paramedics often provide the first critical steps in saving an endangered life. The following quotation, inscribed on the Arlington National Cemetery headstone of Army Lieutenant R. Adams Cowley, who is often called the "father" of shock trauma medicine, serves as the motto for many paramedic units: "Next to creating a life the finest thing a man can do is save one." —Abraham Lincoln

CONCEPT REVIEW EXERCISES

1. What is the functional group of a thiol? Write the condensed structural formula for ethanethiol (ethyl mercaptan).
2. What is the functional group of a disulfide? Write the condensed structural formula for dipropyl disulfide.

ANSWERS

1. SH; CH_3CH_2SH
2. –S–S–; $CH_3CH_2CH_2SSCH_2CH_2CH_3$

KEY TAKEAWAY

- Thiols, thioethers, and disulfides are common in biological compounds.

EXERCISES

1. A common natural gas odorant is *tert*-butyl mercaptan. What is its condensed structural formula?
2. Write the equation for the oxidation of ethanethiol to diethyl disulfide.

ANSWER

1. $(CH_3)_3CSH$

12. END-OF-CHAPTER MATERIAL

Chapter Summary

To ensure that you understand the material in this chapter, you should review the meanings of the following bold terms in the summary and ask yourself how they relate to the topics in the chapter.

A **functional group** is any atom or atom group that confers characteristic properties to a family of compounds.

The hydroxyl group (OH) is the functional group of the **alcohols**. The alcohols are represented by the general formula ROH. Alcohols are derived from alkanes by replacing one or more hydrogen atoms by an OH group. A **primary (1°) alcohol** (RCH_2OH) has the OH group on a carbon atom attached to one other carbon atom; a **secondary (2°) alcohol** (R_2CHOH) has the OH group on a carbon atom attached to two other carbon atoms; and a **tertiary (3°) alcohol** (R_3COH) has the OH group on a carbon atom attached to three other carbon atoms.

The ability to engage in hydrogen bonding greatly increases the boiling points of alcohols compared to hydrocarbons of comparable molar mass. Alcohols can also engage in hydrogen bonding with water molecules, and those with up to about four carbon atoms are soluble in water.

Many alcohols can be synthesized by the hydration of alkenes. Common alcohols include methanol, ethanol, and isopropyl alcohol. Methanol is quite poisonous. It can cause blindness or even death. Ethanol can be prepared from ethylene or made by fermentation. It is the "alcohol" in alcoholic beverages. On occasion, people drink methanol by mistake, thinking it is the beverage alcohol. On occasion, unscrupulous bootleggers, sell methanol to unsuspecting customers. In either case, the results are often tragic.

Rubbing alcohol is usually a 70% aqueous solution of isopropyl alcohol. Ethanol is also used in some rubbing alcohol formulations.

When water is removed from an alcohol in a dehydration step, the result is either an alkene or an ether, depending on the reaction conditions. Primary alcohols are oxidized to aldehydes or carboxylic acids, and secondary alcohols are oxidized to ketones. Tertiary alcohols are not easily oxidized.

Alcohols containing two OH groups on adjacent carbon atoms are called **glycols**.

Phenols (ArOH) are compounds having the OH group attached to an aromatic ring.

Ethers (ROR′, ROAr, ArOAr) are compounds in which an oxygen atom is joined to two organic groups.

The **carbonyl group**, a carbon-to-oxygen double bond, is the defining feature of **aldehydes** and **ketones**. In aldehydes at least one bond on the carbonyl group is a carbon-to-hydrogen bond; in ketones, both available bonds on the carbonyl carbon atom are carbon-to-carbon bonds. Aldehydes are synthesized by the oxidation of primary alcohols. The aldehyde can be further oxidized to a carboxylic acid. Ketones are prepared by the oxidation of secondary alcohols. Mild oxidizing agents oxidize aldehydes to carboxylic acids. Ketones are not oxidized by these reagents.

A **thiol** is a compound with an SH functional group.

ADDITIONAL EXERCISES

1. Describe two ways that ethanol can be prepared. Which method is used to produce alcoholic beverages?
2. Give the structure of the alkene from which isopropyl alcohol is made by reaction with water in an acidic solution.
3. Ethanol is used as a solvent for some drugs that are not soluble in water. Why is methanol not used in medicines?
4. Give the structure of the alkene that is made from *tert*-butyl alcohol [$(CH_3)_3COH$] by reaction with water in an acidic solution.
5. Classify each conversion as oxidation, dehydration, or hydration (only the organic starting material and product are shown):
   a. $CH_3OH \rightarrow HCHO$
   b. $CH_3CHOHCH_3 \rightarrow CH_3CH{=}CH_2$
   c. $CH_2{=}CHCH_2CH_3 \rightarrow CH_3CHOHCH_2CH_3$
6. Classify each conversion as oxidation, dehydration, or hydration (only the organic starting material and product are shown.):
   a. $CH_3CHOHCH_3 \rightarrow CH_3COCH_3$
   b. $HOOCCH{=}CHCOOH \rightarrow HOOCCH_2CHOHCOOH$
   c. $2\ CH_3OH \rightarrow CH_3OCH_3$
7. Why is methanol so much more toxic to humans than ethanol?
8. Each of the four isomeric butyl alcohols is treated with potassium dichromate ($K_2Cr_2O_7$) in acid. Give the product (if any) expected from each reaction.
9. Draw the structures and give IUPAC names for the four isomeric aldehydes having the formula $C_5H_{10}O$.
10. Write an equation for the reaction of phenol with aqueous NaOH.
11. Write an equation for the ionization of phenol in water.
12. Draw the structures and give the common and IUPAC names for the three isomeric ketones having the formula $C_5H_{10}O$.
13. As we shall see in Chapter 16, 2,3-dihydroxypropanal and 1,3-dihydroxyacetone are important carbohydrates. Draw their structures.
14. Glutaraldehyde (pentanedial) is a germicide that is replacing formaldehyde as a sterilizing agent. It is less irritating to the eyes, the nose, and skin. Write the condensed structural formula of glutaraldehyde.
15. Why does the oxidation of isopropyl alcohol give a ketone, whereas the oxidation of isobutyl alcohol gives an aldehyde?
16. Identify each compound as an alcohol, a phenol, or an ether. Classify any alcohols as primary (1°), secondary (2°), or tertiary (3°).
   a. $CH_3CH_2CH_2OH$
   b.

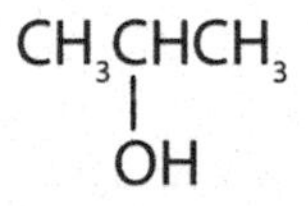

      CH_3CHCH_3 (with OH on the central C)

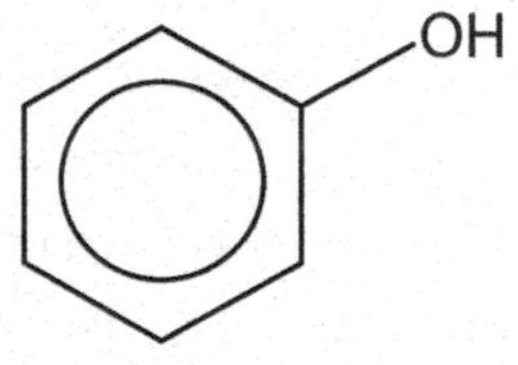

      OH
   c.

      OH (on a benzene ring)
   d.

      CH_3CHOCH_3 (with CH_3 on the central C)

      CH_3

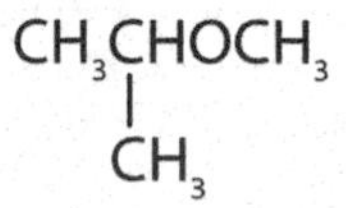

17. Identify each compound as an alcohol, a phenol, or an ether. Classify any alcohols as primary, secondary, or tertiary.
    a. $CH_3CH_2OCH_2CH_3$
    b.

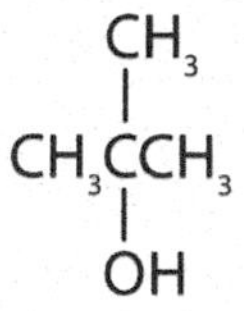

$$\begin{array}{c} CH_3 \\ | \\ CH_3CCH_3 \\ | \\ OH \end{array}$$

    c.

Cl–C_6H_4–OH (para-chlorophenol ring structure)

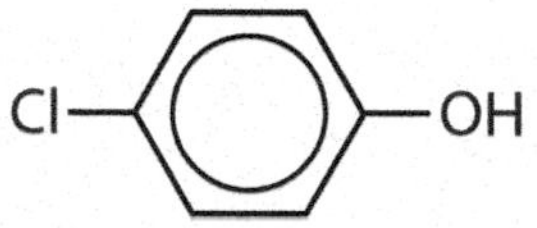

    d.

$$\begin{array}{l} CH_3CHCH_2CH_2CH_3 \\ \quad\;\; | \\ \quad\; OH \end{array}$$

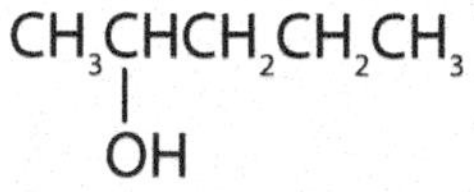

18. Tell whether each compound forms an acidic, a basic, or a neutral solution in water.
    a.

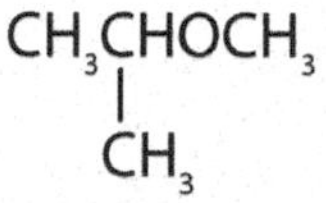

$$\begin{array}{l} CH_3CHOCH_3 \\ \quad\;\; | \\ \quad\; CH_3 \end{array}$$

    b.

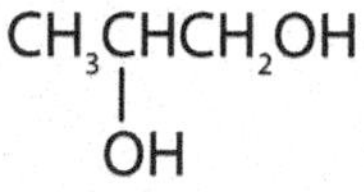

$$\begin{array}{l} CH_3CHCH_2OH \\ \quad\;\; | \\ \quad\; OH \end{array}$$

    c.

C_6H_5–OH (benzene ring with OH)

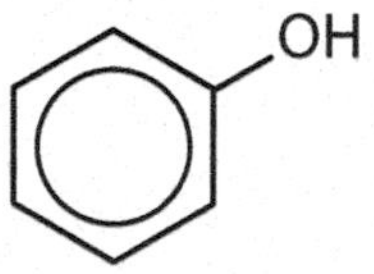

19. When water is added to ethylene in the presence of an acid catalyst, only one product—ethanol—is possible. However, when water is added to propylene, two products are possible—1-propanol and 2-propanol—but only 2-propanol is formed. In 1870, the Russian chemist Vladimir V. Markovnikov proposed a rule to predict the products of such reactions: Considering water to be HOH, the hydrogen atom of water goes on the carbon atom (of the two involved in the double bond) that has the most hydrogen atoms already bonded to it. The OH group goes on the carbon atom with fewer hydrogen atoms. Use Markovnikov's rule to predict the product of the addition of water to each compound.
    a. 2-methylpropene
    b. 1-butene
    c. 2-methyl-1-pentene
    d. 2-methyl-2-pentene
20. Ethyl alcohol, like rubbing alcohol (isopropyl alcohol), is often used for sponge baths. What property of alcohols makes them useful for this purpose?
21. In addition to ethanol, the fermentation of grain produces other organic compounds collectively called fusel oils (FO). The four principal FO components are 1-propanol, isobutyl alcohol, 3-methyl-1-butanol, and 2-methyl-1-butanol. Draw a structure for each. (FO is quite toxic and accounts in part for hangovers.)
22. Draw and name the isomeric ethers that have the formula $C_5H_{12}O$.

23. Menthol is an ingredient in mentholated cough drops and nasal sprays. It produces a cooling, refreshing sensation when rubbed on the skin and so is used in shaving lotions and cosmetics. Thymol, the aromatic equivalent of menthol, is the flavoring constituent of thyme.

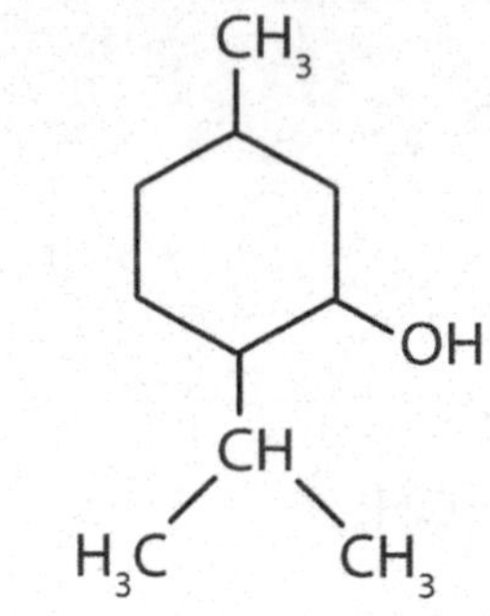

    Menthol 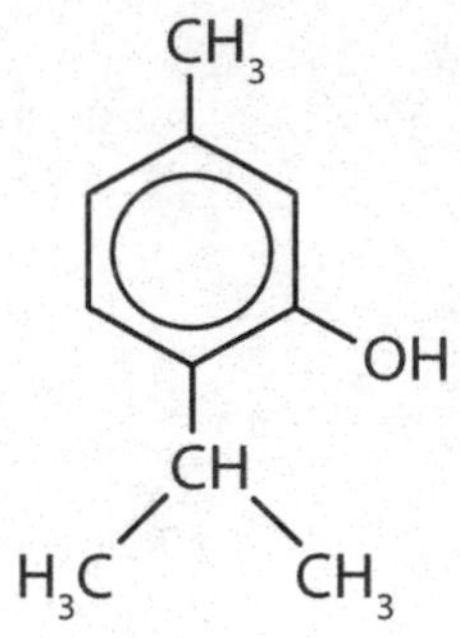   Thymol

    a. To what class of compounds does each belong?
    b. Give an alternate name for thymol.
24. Write the equation for the production of ethanol by the addition of water to ethylene. How much ethanol can be made from 14.0 kg of ethylene?
25. Methanol is not particularly toxic to rats. If methanol were newly discovered and tested for toxicity in laboratory animals, what would you conclude about its safety for human consumption?
26. The amino acid cysteine has the formula $HSCH_2CH(NH_2)COOH$. What is the sulfur-containing functional group in the cysteine molecule?
27. The amino acid methionine has the formula $CH_3SCH_2CH_2CH(NH_2)COOH$. What functional groups are in methionine?
28. Tetrahydrocannabinol is the principal active ingredient in marijuana. What functional groups are present in this molecule?

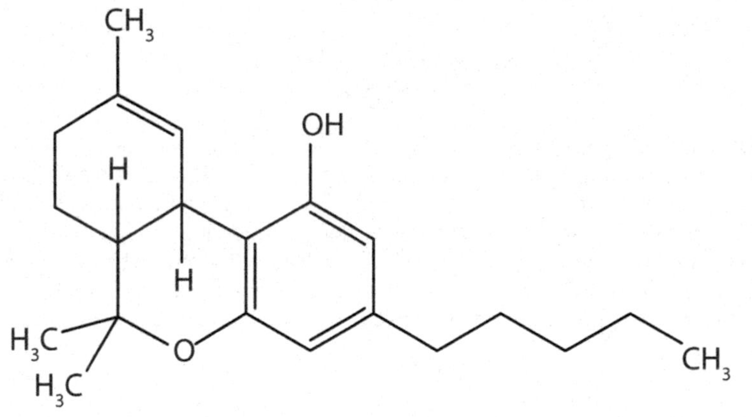

ANSWERS

1. addition of water to ethylene; fermentation (for beverages)
3. Methanol is too toxic.
5. a. oxidation
   b. dehydration
   c. hydration
7. Methanol is oxidized in the body to toxic formaldehyde; ethanol is oxidized to the less toxic acetaldehyde.

9.

$CH_3CH_2CH_2CH_2CHO$

Pentanal

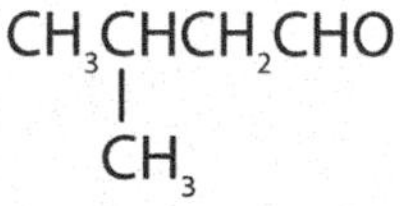

CH_3CHCH_2CHO (with CH_3 on C2)

3-Methylbutanal

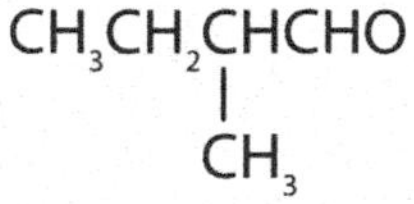

CH_3CH_2CHCHO (with CH_3 on C2)

2-Methylbutanal

CH_3CCHO (with two CH_3 on C2)

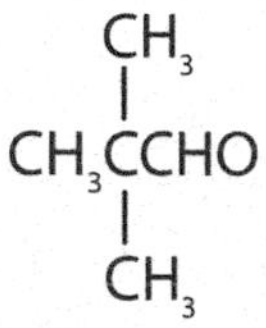

2,2-Dimethylpropanal

11. $C_6H_5OH + H_2O \rightarrow C_6H_5O^- + H_3O^+$

13.

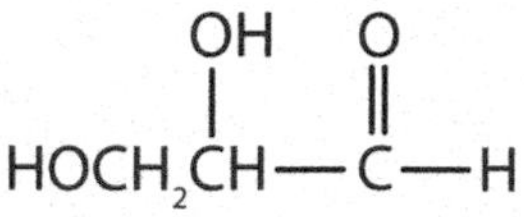

$HOCH_2CH(OH){-}C(=O){-}H$ and $HOCH_2{-}C(=O){-}CH_2OH$

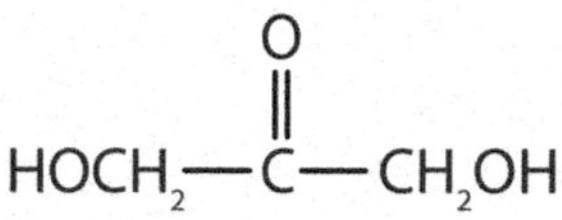

15. Isopropyl alcohol is a secondary alcohol, whereas isobutyl alcohol is a primary alcohol.

17. a. ether
    b. tertiary alcohol
    c. phenol
    d. secondary alcohol

19. a. *tert*-butyl alcohol
    b. 2-butanol
    c. 2-methyl-2-pentanol
    d. 2-methyl-2-pentanol

21.

$CH_3CH_2CH_2OH$

1-Propanol

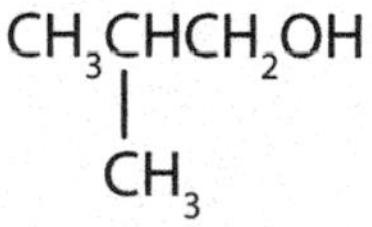

CH_3CHCH_2OH (with CH_3 on C2)

Isobutyl alcohol

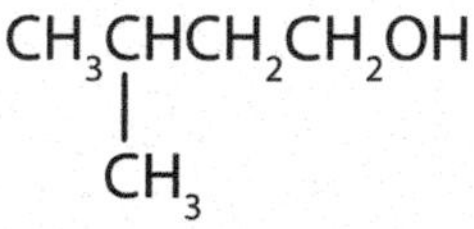

$CH_3CHCH_2CH_2OH$ (with CH_3 on C2)

3-Methyl-1-butanol

$CH_3CH_2CHCH_2OH$ (with CH_3 on C3)

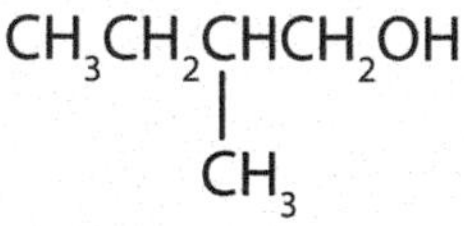

2-Methyl-1-butanol

23. a. menthol: alcohol; thymol: phenol
    b. 2-isopropyl-5-methylphenol

25. It might be ruled safe until tested on humans.

27. sulfide, amino, and carboxylic acid

CHAPTER 15

Organic Acids and Bases and Some of Their Derivatives

Opening Essay

Organic acids have been known for ages. Prehistoric people likely made acetic acid when their fermentation reactions went awry and produced vinegar instead of wine. The Sumerians (2900–1800 BCE) used vinegar as a condiment, a preservative, an antibiotic, and a detergent. Citric acid was discovered by an Islamic alchemist, Jabir Ibn Hayyan (also known as Geber), in the 8th century, and crystalline citric acid was first isolated from lemon juice in 1784 by the Swedish chemist Carl Wilhelm Scheele. Medieval scholars in Europe were aware that the crisp, tart flavor of citrus fruits is caused by citric acid. Naturalists of the 17th century knew that the sting of a red ant's bite was due to an organic acid that the ant injected into the wound. The acetic acid of vinegar, the formic acid of red ants, and the citric acid of fruits all belong to the same family of compounds—carboxylic acids. Soaps are salts of long-chain carboxylic acids. (For more information about soaps, see Chapter 17, [Unsupported Reference Type: chapter-section].)

Prehistoric people also knew about organic bases—by smell if not by name; amines are the organic bases produced when animal tissue decays.

The organic compounds that we consider in this chapter are organic acids and bases. We will also consider two derivatives of carboxylic acids: esters and amides. An *ester* is derived from a carboxylic acid and an alcohol. Fats and oils are esters, as are many important fragrances and flavors. (For more information about fats and oils, see Chapter 17, [Unsupported Reference Type: chapter-section].) An amide is derived from a carboxylic acid and either ammonia or an amine. Proteins, often called "the stuff of life," are polyamides. (For more information about proteins, see Chapter 18, [Unsupported Reference Type: chapter-section].)

1. FUNCTIONAL GROUPS OF THE CARBOXYLIC ACIDS AND THEIR DERIVATIVES

LEARNING OBJECTIVES

1. **Identify the general structure for a carboxylic acid, an ester, an amine, and an amide.**
2. **Identify the functional group for a carboxylic acid, an ester, an amine, and an amide.**

We introduced the carbonyl group (C=O)—the functional group of aldehydes and ketones—in Chapter 14. The carbonyl group is also found in carboxylic acids, esters, and amides. However, in these compounds, the carbonyl group is only *part* of the functional group.

carboxylic acid

An organic compound that has a carboxyl group.

carboxyl group

A functional group that contains a carbon–oxygen bond and an OH group also attached to the same carbon atom.

A **carboxylic acid** is an organic compound that has a **carboxyl group**. The carboxyl group is a functional group that contains a carbon–oxygen double bond and an OH group also attached to the same carbon atom, but it has characteristic properties of its own. As with aldehydes and ketones, carboxylic acid formulas can be written to show the carbon-to-oxygen double bond explicitly, or the carboxyl group can be written in condensed form on one line. In general, carboxylic acids are represented by the formula RCOOH, where R is a hydrocarbon group.

$$R-\overset{\overset{\large O}{\|}}{C}-OH \quad \text{or} \quad RCOOH \qquad\qquad -\overset{\overset{\large O}{\|}}{C}-OH \quad \text{or} \quad -COOH$$

A carboxylic acid

A carboxyl group

ester

An organic compound derived from a carboxylic acid and an alcohol in which the OH of the acid is replaced by an OR group.

Esters are represented by the formula RCOOR', where R and R' are hydrocarbon groups. The **ester**, which is organic compound derived from a carboxylic acid and an alcohol in which the OH of the acid is replaced by an OR group, looks somewhat like an ether and also somewhat like a carboxylic acid. Even so, compounds in this group react *neither* like carboxylic acids nor like ethers; they make up a distinctive family. Unlike ethers, esters have a carbonyl group. Unlike carboxylic acids, esters have no acidic hydrogen atom; they have a hydrocarbon group in its place.

$$R-\overset{\overset{\large O}{\|}}{C}-OR' \quad \text{or} \quad RCOOR' \qquad\qquad -\overset{\overset{\large O}{\|}}{C}-OR \quad \text{or} \quad -COOR$$

An ester

An ester group

amine

An organic compound derived from ammonia by the replacement of one, two, or three of the hydrogens atoms by alkyl or aryl groups.

An **amine** is a compound derived from ammonia (NH_3); it has one, two, or all three of the hydrogen atoms of NH_3 replaced by an alkyl (or an aryl) group. Like NH_3, amines are weak bases. The functional group of an amine is a nitrogen atom with a lone pair of electrons and with one, two, or three alkyl or aryl groups attached.

$$-\underset{|}{N}-$$

An amine

amide

An organic compound with a carbonyl group joined to a nitrogen atom from ammonia or an amine.

The **amide** functional group has a carbonyl group joined to a nitrogen atom from ammonia or an amine. The properties of the amide functional group differ from those of the simple carbonyl group, NH_3, and amines.

$$R-\overset{\overset{\large O}{\|}}{C}-\underset{|}{N}- \quad \text{or} \quad RCO\underset{|}{N}- \qquad\qquad -\overset{\overset{\large O}{\|}}{C}-\underset{|}{N}- \quad \text{or} \quad -CO\underset{|}{N}-$$

An amide

An amide group

Esters and amides are considered to be *derivatives* of carboxylic acids because the OH in the carboxyl group is replaced with another group. These functional groups are listed in Table 15.1, along with an example (identified by common and International Union of Pure and Applied Chemistry [IUPAC] names) for each type of compound.

Note

Most familiar carboxylic acids have an even number of carbon atoms. As we shall see in Chapter 17, these acids—called fatty acids—are synthesized in nature by adding two carbon atoms at a time.

TABLE 15.1 Organic Acids, Bases, and Acid Derivatives

Family	Functional Group	Example	Common Name	IUPAC Name
carboxylic acid	$-C(=O)-OH$	$CH_3-C(=O)-OH$	acetic acid	ethanoic acid
amine	$-\ddot{N}-$ (with third bond)	CH3NH2	methylamine	methanamine (aminomethane)
amide	$-C(=O)-N<$	$CH_3-C(=O)-NH_2$	acetamide	ethanamide
ester	$-C(=O)-O-C<$	$CH_3-C(=O)-OCH_3$	methyl acetate	methyl ethanoate

CONCEPT REVIEW EXERCISES

1. How is the carboxyl group related to the carbonyl group and the OH group?
2. How is the amide group related to the carboxyl group and amines?

ANSWERS

1. The carboxyl group has a carbonyl group joined to an OH group.
2. The amide group has a carboxyl group joined to an amino group.

KEY TAKEAWAY

- Knowledge of carboxylic acids, esters, amines, and amides underlies an understanding of biologically important molecules.

EXERCISES

1. Draw the functional group in each class of compounds.
   a. aldehydes
   b. esters
   c. carboxylic acids
2. How are the functional groups in Exercise 1 alike and different?
3. Draw the functional group in each class of compounds.
   a. amides
   b. ketones
   c. ethers
4. How are the functional groups in Exercise 2 alike and different?

ANSWERS

1. a. $-\overset{\overset{\displaystyle O}{\|}}{C}-H$

   b. $-\overset{\overset{\displaystyle O}{\|}}{C}-OR$

   c. $-\overset{\overset{\displaystyle O}{\|}}{C}-OH$

3. a. $-\overset{\overset{\displaystyle O}{\|}}{C}-\underset{|}{N}-$

   b. $-\overset{\overset{\displaystyle O}{\|}}{C}-$

   c. $-O-$

2. CARBOXYLIC ACIDS: STRUCTURES AND NAMES

LEARNING OBJECTIVES

1. **Name carboxylic acids with common names.**
2. **Name carboxylic acids according to IUPAC nomenclature.**

Carboxylic acids occur widely in nature, often combined with alcohols or other functional groups, as in fats, oils, and waxes. They are components of many foods, medicines, and household products (Figure 15.1). Not surprisingly, many of them are best known by common names based on Latin and Greek words that describe their source. What you learn in this chapter about the chemistry of carboxylic acids will help you understand biochemistry (Chapter 16 through Chapter 20).

FIGURE 15.1 Carboxylic Acids in the Home

Carboxylic acids occur in many common household items. (a) Vinegar contains acetic acid, (b) aspirin is acetylsalicylic acid, (c) vitamin C is ascorbic acid, (d) lemons contain citric acid, and (e) spinach contains oxalic acid.

The simplest carboxylic acid, formic acid (HCOOH), was first obtained by the distillation of ants (Latin *formica*, meaning "ant"). The bites of some ants inject formic acid, and the stings of wasps and bees contain formic acid (as well as other poisonous materials).

$$\mathrm{H{-}\overset{\overset{\displaystyle O}{\|}}{C}{-}OH}$$

Formic acid

The next higher homolog is acetic acid, which is made by fermenting cider and honey in the presence of oxygen. This fermentation produces vinegar, a solution containing 4%–10% acetic acid, plus a number of other compounds that add to its flavor. Acetic acid is probably the most familiar weak acid used in educational and industrial chemistry laboratories.

$$\mathrm{CH_3{-}\overset{\overset{\displaystyle O}{\|}}{C}{-}OH}$$

Acetic acid

Note

Pure acetic acid solidifies at 16.6°C, only slightly below normal room temperature. In the poorly heated laboratories of the late 19th and early 20th centuries in northern North America and Europe, acetic acid often "froze" on the storage shelf. For that reason, pure acetic acid (sometimes called concentrated acetic acid) came to be known as *glacial acetic acid*, a name that survives to this day.

The third homolog, propionic acid (CH_3CH_2COOH), is seldom encountered in everyday life. The fourth homolog, butyric acid ($CH_3CH_2CH_2COOH$), is one of the most foul-smelling substances imaginable. It is found in rancid butter and is one of the ingredients of body odor. By recognizing extremely small amounts of this and other chemicals, bloodhounds are able to track fugitives. Models of the first four carboxylic acids are shown in Figure 15.2.

FIGURE 15.2 Ball-and-Stick Models of Carboxylic Acids

Carboxylic acids feature a carbon atom doubly bonded to an oxygen atom and also joined to an OH group. The four acids illustrated here are formic acid (a), acetic acid (b), propionic acid (c), and butyric acid (d).

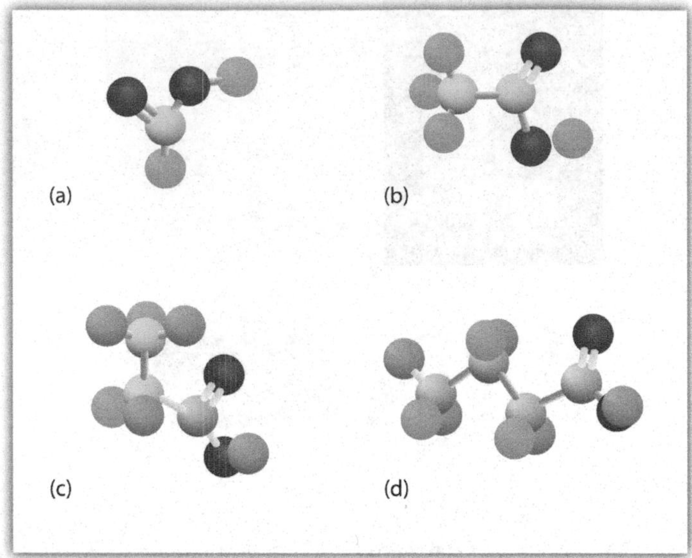

The acid with the carboxyl group attached directly to a benzene ring is called benzoic acid (C_6H_5COOH).

O
||
—C—OH

Benzoic acid

The common names of carboxylic acids use Greek letters (α, β, γ, δ, and so forth), not numbers, to designate the position of substituent groups in acids. These letters refer to the position of the carbon atom in relation to the carboxyl carbon atom.

δ γ β α
C—C—C—C—COOH

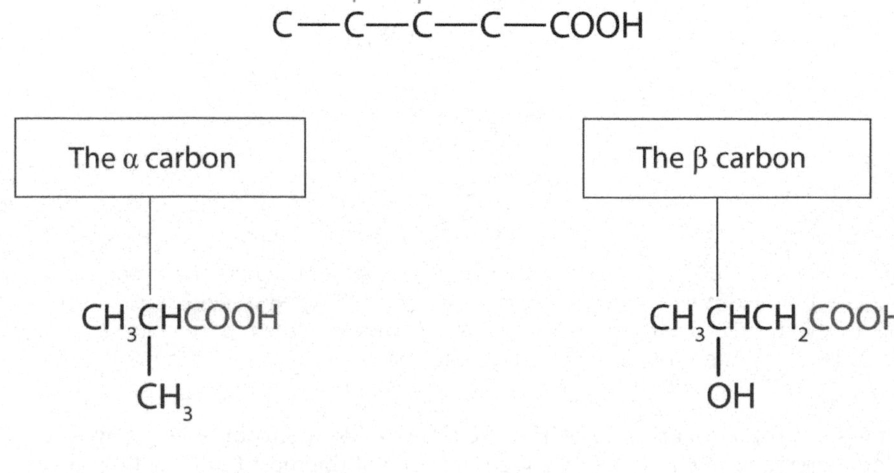

In the nomenclature system of the International Union of Pure and Applied Chemistry (IUPAC), the parent hydrocarbon is the one that corresponds to the longest continuous chain (LCC) containing the carboxyl group. The *-e* ending of the parent alkane is replaced by the suffix *-oic* and the word *acid*. For example, the carboxylic acid derived from pentane is pentanoic acid ($CH_3CH_2CH_2CH_2COOH$). As with aldehydes, the carboxyl carbon atom is counted first; numbers are used to indicate any substituted carbon atoms in the parent chain.

Note

Greek letters are used with common names; numbers are used with IUPAC names.

EXAMPLE 1

Give the common and IUPAC names for each compound.

1. $ClCH_2CH_2CH_2COOH$
2. 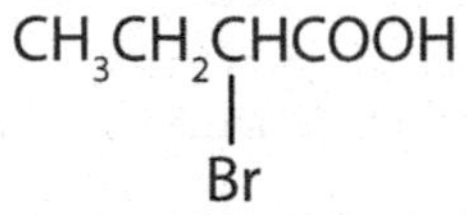 $CH_3CH_2CHCOOH$ with Br on the CH carbon

$$\begin{array}{c} CH_3CH_2\underset{\displaystyle Br}{\underset{|}{C}}HCOOH \end{array}$$

Solution

1. The LCC contains four carbon atoms; the compound is therefore named as a substituted butyric (or butanoic) acid.

$$\overset{4}{\underset{}{}}\;\;\overset{\gamma}{}\quad Cl-\overset{\overset{4}{\gamma}}{C}-\overset{\overset{3}{\beta}}{C}-\overset{\overset{2}{\alpha}}{C}-\overset{1}{COOH}$$

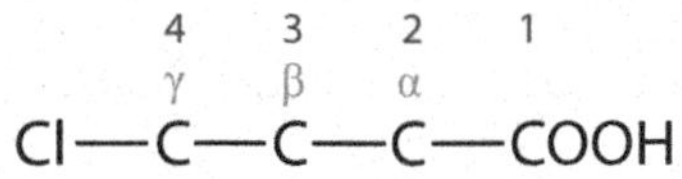

The chlorine atom is attached to the γ-carbon in the common system or C4 in the IUPAC system. The compound is γ-chlorobutyric acid or 2-bromobutanoic acid.

2. The LCC contains four carbon atoms; the compound is therefore named as a substituted butyric (or butanoic) acid.

$$\overset{\overset{4}{\gamma}}{C}-\overset{\overset{3}{\beta}}{C}-\underset{\underset{\displaystyle Br}{|}}{\overset{\overset{2}{\alpha}}{C}}-\overset{1}{COOH}$$

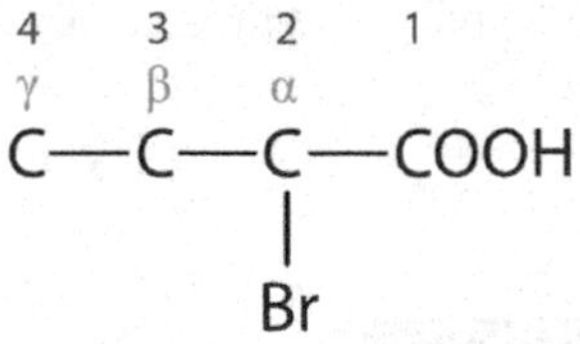

The bromine (Br) atom is at the α-carbon in the common system or C2 in the IUPAC system. The compound is α-bromobutyric acid or 4-chlorobutanoic acid.

SKILL-BUILDING EXERCISE

Give the IUPAC name for each compound.

1. $ClCH_2CH_2CH_2CH_2COOH$
2. $(CH_3)_2CHCH_2CHBrCOOH$

EXAMPLE 2

Write the condensed structural formula for β-chloropropionic acid.

Solution

Propionic acid has three carbon atoms: C–C–COOH. Attach a chlorine (Cl) atom to the parent chain at the beta carbon atom, the second one from the carboxyl group: Cl–C–C–COOH. Then add enough hydrogen atoms to give each carbon atom four bonds: $ClCH_2CH_2COOH$.

SKILL-BUILDING EXERCISE

1. Write the condensed structural formula for 4-bromo-5-methylhexanoic acid.

CONCEPT REVIEW EXERCISES

1. What is the IUPAC name for the straight-chain carboxylic acid with six carbon atoms?
2. The straight-chain aldehyde with five carbon atoms has the common name valeraldehyde. What is the common name of the corresponding straight-chain carboxylic acid?

ANSWERS

1. hexanoic acid
2. valeric acid

KEY TAKEAWAYS

- Simple carboxylic acids are best known by common names based on Latin and Greek words that describe their source (e.g., formic acid, Latin *formica*, meaning "ant").
- Greek letters, not numbers, designate the position of substituted acids in the common naming convention.
- IUPAC names are derived from the LCC of the parent hydrocarbon with the *-e* ending of the parent alkane replaced by the suffix *-oic* and the word *acid*.

EXERCISES

1. Draw the structure for each compound.
   a. heptanoic acid
   b. 3-methylbutanoic acid
   c. 2,3-dibromobenzoic acid
   d. β-hydroxybutyric acid
2. Draw the structure for each compound.
   a. *o*-nitrobenzoic acid
   b. *p*-chlorobenzoic acid
   c. 3-chloropentanoic acid
   d. α-chloropropionic acid
3. Name each compound with either the IUPAC name, the common name, or both.
   a. $(CH_3)_2CHCH_2COOH$
   b. $(CH_3)_3CCH(CH_3)CH_2COOH$
   c. $CH_2OHCH_2CH_2COOH$
4. Name each compound with its IUPAC name.
   a. $CH_3(CH_2)_8COOH$
   b. $(CH_3)_2CHCCl_2CH_2CH_2COOH$
   c. $CH_3CHOHCH(CH_2CH_3)CHICOOH$

ANSWERS

1. a. CH3CH2CH2CH2CH2CH2COOH

   b.

$$\begin{array}{l} CH_3CHCH_2COOH \\ \quad\;\;| \\ \quad CH_3 \end{array}$$

   c.

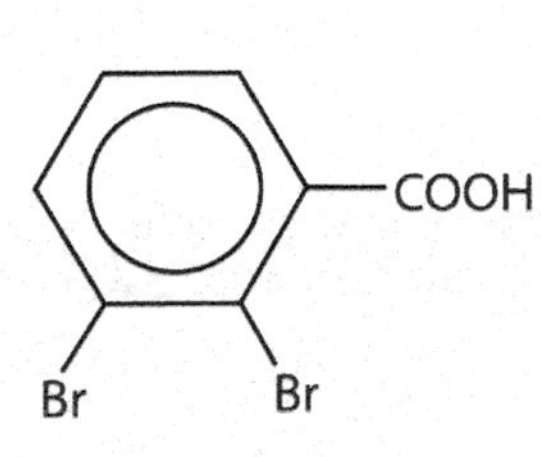

   d.

$$\begin{array}{l} CH_3CHCH_2COOH \\ \quad\;\;| \\ \quad OH \end{array}$$

3. a. 3-methylbutanoic acid; β-methylbutyric acid
   b. 3,4,4-trimethylpentanoic acid
   c. 4-hydroxybutanoic acid; γ-hydroxybutyric acid

3. THE FORMATION OF CARBOXYLIC ACIDS

LEARNING OBJECTIVE

1. **Describe the preparation of carboxylic acids.**

As we noted in Chapter 14, the oxidation of aldehydes or primary alcohols forms carboxylic acids:

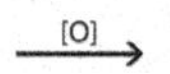

$$\underset{\text{A primary alcohol}}{RCH_2OH} \xrightarrow{[O]} \underset{\text{An aldehyde}}{RCHO} \xrightarrow{[O]} \underset{\text{A carboxylic acid}}{RCOOH}$$

In the presence of an oxidizing agent, ethanol is oxidized to acetaldehyde, which is then oxidized to acetic acid.

$$\underset{\text{Ethanol}}{CH_3CH_2OH} \xrightarrow[H^+]{K_2Cr_2O_7} \underset{\text{Acetaldehyde}}{CH_3CHO} \xrightarrow[H^+]{K_2Cr_2O_7} \underset{\text{Acetic acid}}{CH_3COOH}$$

This process also occurs in the liver, where enzymes catalyze the oxidation of ethanol to acetic acid.

$$CH_3CH_2OH \xrightarrow[\text{oxidizing agent}]{\text{alcohol dehydrogenase}} CH_3CHO \xrightarrow[\text{oxidizing agent}]{\text{alcohol dehydrogenase}} CH_3COOH$$

Acetic acid can be further oxidized to carbon dioxide and water.

CONCEPT REVIEW EXERCISES

1. Caproic acid (hexanoic acid) can be prepared in an oxidation reaction from
   a. what alcohol?
   b. what aldehyde?
2. Give the structures of the aldehyde and the carboxylic acid formed by the oxidation of isobutyl alcohol [(CH3)2CHCH2OH].

ANSWERS

1. a. $CH_3CH_2CH_2CH_2CH_2CH_2OH$
   b. $CH_3CH_2CH_2CH_2CH_2CHO$
2. $CH_3CH(CH_3)CHO$ and $CH_3CH(CH_3)COOH$

KEY TAKEAWAY

- Whether in the laboratory or in the body, the oxidation of aldehydes or primary alcohols forms carboxylic acids.

EXERCISES

1. Caprylic acid (octanoic acid) can be prepared in an oxidation reaction from
   a. what alcohol?
   b. what aldehyde?
2. Give the structures of the aldehyde and the carboxylic acid formed by the oxidation of 1,4-butanediol ($HOCH_2CH_2CH_2CH_2OH$).

ANSWER

1. a. $CH_3CH_2CH_2CH_2CH_2CH_2CH_2CH_2OH$
   b. $CH_3CH_2CH_2CH_2CH_2CH_2CH_2CHO$

4. PHYSICAL PROPERTIES OF CARBOXYLIC ACIDS

LEARNING OBJECTIVES

1. **Compare the boiling points of carboxylic acids with alcohols of similar molar mass.**
2. **Compare the solubilities of carboxylic acids in water with the solubilities of comparable alkanes and alcohols in water.**

Many carboxylic acids are colorless liquids with disagreeable odors. The carboxylic acids with 5 to 10 carbon atoms all have "goaty" odors (explaining the odor of Limburger cheese). These acids are also produced by the action of skin bacteria on human sebum (skin oils), which accounts for the odor of poorly ventilated locker rooms. The acids with more than 10 carbon atoms are waxlike solids, and their odor diminishes with increasing molar mass and resultant decreasing volatility.

Carboxylic acids exhibit strong hydrogen bonding between molecules. They therefore have high boiling points compared to other substances of comparable molar mass.

The carboxyl group readily engages in hydrogen bonding with water molecules (Figure 15.3). The acids with one to four carbon atoms are completely miscible with water. Solubility decreases as the carbon chain length increases because dipole forces become less important and dispersion forces become more predominant. Hexanoic acid [$CH_3(CH_2)_4COOH$] is barely soluble in water (about 1.0 g/100 g of water). Palmitic acid [$CH_3(CH_2)_{14}COOH$], with its large nonpolar hydrocarbon component, is essentially insoluble in water. The carboxylic acids generally are soluble in such organic solvents as ethanol, toluene, and diethyl ether.

FIGURE 15.3 Hydrogen Bonding between an Acetic Acid Molecule and Water Molecules

Carboxylic acids of low molar mass are quite soluble in water.

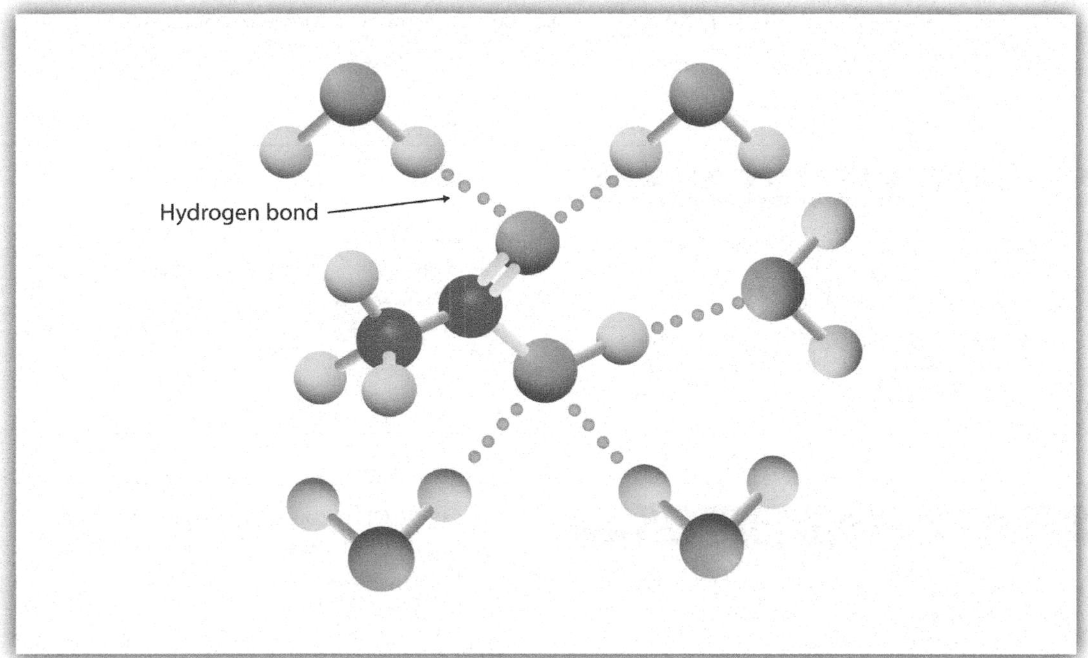

Table 15.2 lists some physical properties for selected carboxylic acids. The first six are homologs. Notice that the boiling points increase with increasing molar mass, but the melting points show no regular pattern.

TABLE 15.2 Physical Constants of Carboxylic Acids

Condensed Structural Formula	Name of Acid	Melting Point (°C)	Boiling Point (°C)	Solubility (g/100 g of Water)
HCOOH	formic acid	8	100	miscible
CH_3COOH	acetic acid	17	118	miscible
CH_3CH_2COOH	propionic acid	−22	141	miscible
$CH_3(CH_2)_2COOH$	butyric acid	−5	163	miscible
$CH_3(CH_2)_3COOH$	valeric acid	−35	187	5
$CH_3(CH_2)_4COOH$	caproic acid	−3	205	1.1
C_6H_5COOH	benzoic acid	122	249	0.29

CONCEPT REVIEW EXERCISES

1. Which compound has the higher boiling point—butanoic acid (molar mass 88) or 2-pentanone (molar mass 86)? Explain.
2. Would you expect butyric acid (butanoic acid) to be more or less soluble than 1-butanol in water? Explain.

ANSWERS

1. butyric acid because of hydrogen bonding (There is no intermolecular hydrogen bonding in 2-pentanone.)
2. more soluble because there is more extensive hydrogen bonding

KEY TAKEAWAYS

- Carboxylic acids have high boiling points compared to other substances of comparable molar mass. Boiling points increase with molar mass.
- Carboxylic acids having one to four carbon atoms are completely miscible with water. Solubility decreases with molar mass.

EXERCISES

1. Which compound has the higher boiling point—$CH_3CH_2CH_2OCH_2CH_3$ or $CH_3CH_2CH_2COOH$? Explain.
2. Which compound has the higher boiling point—$CH_3CH_2CH_2CH_2CH_2OH$ or $CH_3CH_2CH_2COOH$? Explain.
3. Which compound is more soluble in water—CH_3COOH or $CH_3CH_2CH_2CH_3$? Explain.
4. Which compound is more soluble in water—CH_3CH_2COOH or $CH_3CH_2CH_2CH_2CH_2COOH$? Explain.

ANSWERS

1. $CH_3CH_2CH_2COOH$ because of hydrogen bonding (There is no intermolecular hydrogen bonding with $CH_3CH_2CH_2OCH_2CH_3$.)
3. CH_3COOH because it engages in hydrogen bonding with water (There is no intermolecular hydrogen bonding with $CH_3CH_2CH_2CH_3$.)

5. CHEMICAL PROPERTIES OF CARBOXYLIC ACIDS: IONIZATION AND NEUTRALIZATION

LEARNING OBJECTIVES

1. **Name the typical reactions that take place with carboxylic acids.**
2. **Describe how carboxylic acids react with basic compounds.**

Water-soluble carboxylic acids ionize slightly in water to form moderately acidic solutions.

$$RCOOH + H_2O \rightleftarrows RCOO^- + H_3O^+$$

Their aqueous solutions exhibit the typical properties of acids, such as changing litmus from blue to red.

Note

The anion formed when a carboxylic acid dissociates is called the *carboxylate* anion ($RCOO^-$).

Whether soluble in water or not, carboxylic acids react with aqueous solutions of sodium hydroxide (NaOH), sodium carbonate (Na_2CO_3), and sodium bicarbonate ($NaHCO_3$) to form salts:

$$RCOOH + NaOH(aq) \rightarrow RCOO^-Na^+(aq) + H_2O$$

$$2RCOOH + Na_2CO_3(aq) \rightarrow 2RCOO^-Na^+(aq) + H_2O + CO_2(g)$$

$$RCOOH + NaHCO_3(aq) \rightarrow RCOO^-Na^+(aq) + H_2O + CO_2(g)$$

In these reactions, the carboxylic acids act like inorganic acids: they neutralize basic compounds. With solutions of carbonate (CO_3) and bicarbonate (HCO_3) ions, they also form carbon dioxide gas.

Carboxylic acid salts are named in the same manner as inorganic salts: the name of the cation is followed by the name of the organic anion. The name of the anion is obtained by dropping the *-ic* ending of the acid name and replacing it with the suffix *-ate*. This rule applies whether we are using common names or International Union of Pure and Applied Chemistry (IUPAC) names:

$CH_3COO^-Li^+$	$CH_3CH_2CH_2COO^-K^+$	$C_6H_5COO^-Na^+$
Lithium acetate (lithium ethanoate)	Potassium butyrate (potassium butanoate)	Sodium benzoate

Note

The salts of long-chain carboxylic acids are called soaps. We discuss the chemistry of soaps further in Chapter 17, [Unsupported Reference Type: chapter-section].

$$CH_3(CH_2)_{13}CH_2COO^-Na^+$$

Sodium palmitate (a soap)

EXAMPLE 3

Write an equation for each reaction.

1. the ionization of propionic acid in water (H_2O)
2. the neutralization of propionic acid with aqueous sodium hydroxide (NaOH)

Solution

Propionic acid has three carbon atoms, so its formula is CH_2CH_2COOH.

1. Propionic acid ionizes in water to form a propionate ion and a hydronium (H_3O^+) ion.

$$CH_3CH_2COOH(aq) + H_2O(\ell) \rightarrow CH_3CH_2COO^-(aq) + H_3O^+(aq)$$

2. Propionic acid reacts with NaOH(aq) to form sodium propionate and water.

$$CH_3CH_2COOH(aq) + NaOH(aq) \rightarrow CH_3CH_2COO^-Na^+(aq) + H_2O(\ell)$$

SKILL-BUILDING EXERCISE

Write an equation for each reaction.

1. the ionization of formic acid in water
2. the ionization of *p*-chlorobenzoic acid in water

EXAMPLE 4

Write an equation for the reaction of decanoic acid with each compound.

1. aqueous sodium hydoxide (NaOH)
2. aqueous sodium bicarbonate ($NaHCO_3$)

Solution

1. Decanoic acid has 10 carbon atoms. It reacts with NaOH to form a salt and water (H_2O).

$$CH_3(CH_2)_8COOH + NaOH(aq) \rightarrow CH_3(CH_2)_8COO^-Na^+(aq) + H_2O(\ell)$$

2. With $NaHCO_3$, the products are a salt, H_2O, and carbon dioxide (CO_2).

$$CH_3(CH_2)_8COOH + NaHCO_3(aq) \rightarrow CH_3(CH_2)_8COO^-Na^+(aq) + H_2O(\ell) + CO_2(g)$$

SKILL-BUILDING EXERCISE

Write an equation for the reaction of benzoic acid with each compound.

1. aqueous sodium hydroxide (NaOH)
2. aqueous sodium bicarbonate ($NaHCO_3$)

To Your Health: Organic Salts as Preservatives

Some organic salts are used as preservatives in food products. They prevent spoilage by inhibiting the growth of bacteria and fungi. Calcium and sodium propionate, for example, are added to processed cheese and bakery goods; sodium benzoate is added to cider, jellies, pickles, and syrups; and sodium sorbate and potassium sorbate are added to fruit juices, sauerkraut, soft drinks, and wine. Look for them on ingredient labels the next time you shop for groceries.

$$(CH_3CH_2COO^-)_2\ Ca^{2+}$$

Calcium propionate

$$CH_3CH{=}CHCH{=}CHCOO^-K^+$$

Potassium sorbate

CONCEPT REVIEW EXERCISES

1. How does the neutralization of a carboxylic acid differ from that of an inorganic acid? How are they similar?
2. What products are formed when a carboxylic acid is neutralized with a strong base? What additional product is formed when a carboxylic acid is neutralized with a carbonate or a bicarbonate?

ANSWERS

1. Insoluble carboxylic acids often form soluble carboxylate salts. Both form a salt and water.
2. a carboxylate salt and water; carbon dioxide

KEY TAKEAWAYS

- Soluble carboxylic acids are weak acids in aqueous solutions.
- Carboxylic acids neutralize bases to form salts.

EXERCISES

1. Write the equation for the ionization of $CH_3CH_2CH_2COOH$ in water.
2. Write the equation for the neutralization of $CH_3CH_2CH_2COOH$ with sodium hydroxide [NaOH(aq)].
3. Write the equation for the reaction of CH_3COOH with sodium carbonate [Na_2CO_3(aq)].
4. Write the equation for the reaction of CH_3CH_2COOH with sodium bicarbonate [$NaHCO_3$(aq)].
5. Write the equation for the ionization of propionic acid in water.
6. Write the equation for the ionization of γ-chloropentanoic acid in water.
7. Write an equation for the reaction of butyric acid with each compound.
   a. aqueous NaOH
   b. aqueous $NaHCO_3$
8. Write the condensed structural formula for each compound.
   a. potassium acetate
   b. calcium propanoate
9. Name each compound.
   a. $CH_3CH_2CH_2COO^-Li^+$
   b. $CH_3CH_2CH_2COO^-NH_4^+$

ANSWERS

1. $CH_3CH_2CH_2COOH(aq) + H_2O(\ell) \rightarrow CH_3CH_2CH_2COO^-(aq) + H_3O^+(aq)$

3. $2CH_3COOH + Na_2CO_3(aq) \rightarrow 2CH_3COO^-Na^+(aq) + H_2O(\ell) + CO_2(g)$

5. $CH_3CH_2COOH(aq) + H_2O(\ell) \rightarrow CH_3CH_2COO^-(aq) + H_3O^+(aq)$

7. a. $CH_3CH_2CH_2COOH(aq) + NaOH(aq) \rightarrow CH_3CH_2CH_2COO^-Na^+(aq) + H_2O(\ell)$
   b. $CH_3(CH_2)_2COOH + NaHCO_3(aq) \rightarrow CH_3(CH_2)COO^-Na^+(aq) + H_2O(\ell) + CO_2(g)$

9. a. lithium butyrate (lithium butanoate)
   b. ammonium butanoate or ammonium butyrate

6. ESTERS: STRUCTURES AND NAMES

LEARNING OBJECTIVES

1. **Identify the general structure for an ester.**
2. **Use common names to name esters.**
3. **Name esters according to the IUPAC system.**

Esters have the general formula RCOOR′, where R may be a hydrogen atom, an alkyl group, or an aryl group, and R′ may be an alkyl group or an aryl group but *not* a hydrogen atom. (If it were hydrogen atom, the compound would be a carboxylic acid.) Figure 15.4 shows models for two common esters.

FIGURE 15.4 The Structure of Esters

Esters feature a carbon-to-oxygen double bond that is also singly bonded to a second oxygen atom, which is then joined to an alkyl or an aryl group. The esters shown here are ethyl acetate (a) and methyl butyrate (b).

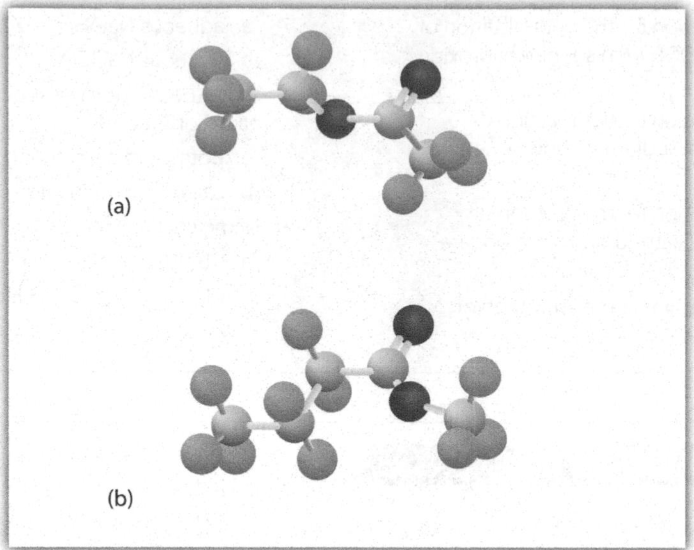

Esters occur widely in nature. Unlike carboxylic acids, esters generally have pleasant odors and are often responsible for the characteristic fragrances of fruits and flowers. Once a flower or fruit has been chemically analyzed, flavor chemists can attempt to duplicate the natural odor or taste. Both natural and synthetic esters are used in perfumes and as flavoring agents.

Note

Fats and vegetable oils are esters of long-chain fatty acids and glycerol. Esters of phosphoric acid are of the utmost importance to life. (For more information about fats/oils and esters, see Chapter 17, [Unsupported Reference Type: chapter-section], and Section 10, respectively.)

6.1 Names of Esters

Although esters are covalent compounds and salts are ionic, esters are named in a manner similar to that used for naming salts. The group name of the alkyl or aryl portion is given first and is followed by the name of the acid portion. In both common and International Union of Pure and Applied Chemistry (IUPAC) nomenclature, the *-ic* ending of the parent acid is replaced by the suffix *-ate* (Table 15.3).

TABLE 15.3 Nomenclature of Esters

Condensed Structural Formula	Common Name	IUPAC Name
$HCOOCH_3$	methyl formate	methyl methanoate
CH_3COOCH_3	methyl acetate	methyl ethanoate
$CH_3COOCH_2CH_3$	ethyl acetate	ethyl ethanoate
$CH_3CH_2COOCH_2CH_3$	ethyl propionate	ethyl propanoate
$CH_3CH_2CH_2COOCH(CH_3)_2$	isopropyl butyrate	isopropyl butanoate
$C_6H_5-C(=O)-OCH_2CH_3$	ethyl benzoate	ethyl benzoate

EXAMPLE 5

Give the common and IUPAC names for each compound.

1. $CH_3CH_2\overset{\overset{\displaystyle O}{\|}}{C}OCH_2CH_2CH_2CH_3$

2. $C_6H_5-\overset{\overset{\displaystyle O}{\|}}{C}-O\underset{\underset{\displaystyle CH_3}{|}}{C}HCH_3$

Solution

1. The alkyl group attached directly to the oxygen atom is a butyl group (in green).

$$CH_3CH_2\overset{\overset{\displaystyle O}{\|}}{C}OCH_2CH_2CH_2CH_3$$

   The part of the molecule derived from the carboxylic acid (in red) has three carbon atoms. It is called propionate (common) or propanoate (IUPAC). The ester is therefore butyl propionate or butyl propanoate.

2. An alkyl group (in green) is attached directly to the oxygen atom by its middle carbon atom; it is an isopropyl group. The part derived from the acid (that is, the benzene ring and the carbonyl group, in red) is benzoate. The ester is therefore isopropyl benzoate (both the common name and the IUPAC name).

$$C_6H_5-\overset{\overset{\displaystyle O}{\|}}{C}-O\underset{\underset{\displaystyle CH_3}{|}}{C}HCH_3$$

SKILL-BUILDING EXERCISE

Give the common and IUPAC names for each compound.

1. $CH_3CH_2CH_2CH_2\overset{\overset{\displaystyle O}{\|}}{C}-OCH_2CH_3$

2. $CH_3CH_2\overset{\overset{\displaystyle O}{\|}}{C}OCH_2CH_2CH_3$

EXAMPLE 6

Draw the structure for ethyl pentanoate.

Solution

Start with the portion from the acid. Draw the pentanoate (five carbon atoms) group first; keeping in mind that the last carbon atom is a part of the carboxyl group.

$$CH_3CH_2CH_2CH_2\overset{\overset{\displaystyle O}{\|}}{C}—O—$$

Then attach the ethyl group to the bond that ordinarily holds the hydrogen atom in the carboxyl group.

$$CH_3CH_2CH_2CH_2\overset{\overset{\displaystyle O}{\|}}{C}—OCH_2CH_3$$

SKILL-BUILDING EXERCISE

1. Draw the structure for phenyl pentanoate.

CONCEPT REVIEW EXERCISES

1. From what carboxylic acid and what alcohol can isopropyl hexanoate be made?
2. From what carboxylic acid and what alcohol can cyclobutyl butyrate be made?

ANSWERS

1. hexanoic acid and isopropyl alcohol
2. butyric acid and cyclobutyl alcohol

KEY TAKEAWAY

- An ester has an OR group attached to the carbon atom of a carbonyl group.

EXERCISES

1. Draw the structure for each compound.
   a. methyl acetate
   b. ethyl pentanoate
   c. phenyl acetate
   d. isopropyl propionate
2. Draw the structure for each compound.
   a. ethyl hexanoate
   b. ethyl benzoate
   c. phenyl benzoate
   d. ethyl 3-methylhexanoate
3. Name each compound with both the common name and the IUPAC name.

   a.

   $$H—\overset{\overset{\displaystyle O}{\|}}{C}—OCH_3$$

   b.

   $$CH_3CH_2\overset{\overset{\displaystyle O}{\|}}{C}OCH_2CH_3$$

4. Name each compound with both the common name and the IUPAC name.
   a. $CH_3CH_2CH_2OC(=O)CH_3$
   b. $CH_3CH_2C(=O)OCH_2CH_2CH_3$

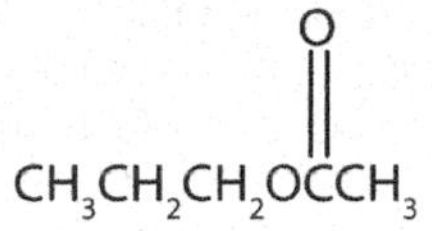

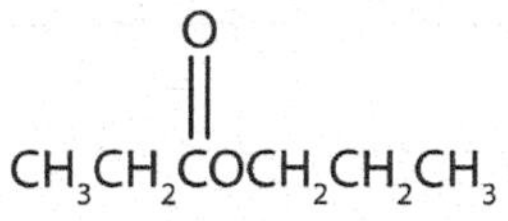

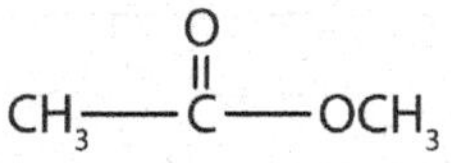

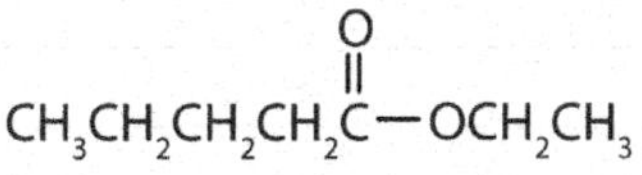

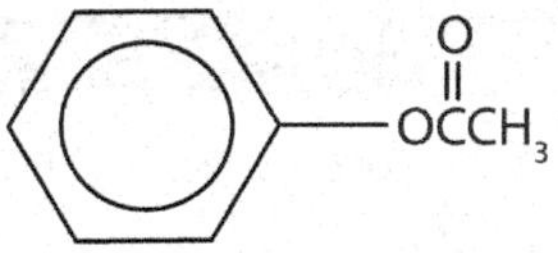

ANSWERS

1. a. $CH_3—C(=O)—OCH_3$
   b. $CH_3CH_2CH_2CH_2C(=O)—OCH_2CH_3$
   c. $C_6H_5—OC(=O)CH_3$
   d. $CH_3CH_2—C(=O)—CH(CH_3)CH_3$
3. a. methyl formate; methyl methanoate
   b. ethyl propionate; ethyl propanoate

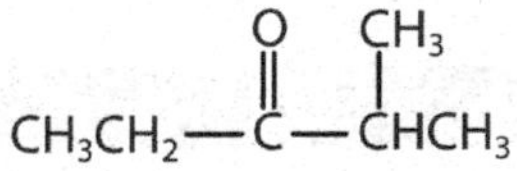

7. PHYSICAL PROPERTIES OF ESTERS

LEARNING OBJECTIVES

1. **Compare the boiling points of esters with alcohols of similar molar mass.**
2. **Compare the solubilities of esters in water with the solubilities of comparable alkanes and alcohols in water.**

Ester molecules are polar but have no hydrogen atom attached directly to an oxygen atom. They are therefore incapable of engaging in intermolecular hydrogen bonding with one another and thus have considerably lower boiling points than their isomeric carboxylic acids counterparts. Because ester molecules can engage in hydrogen bonding with water molecules, however, esters of low molar mass are somewhat soluble in water. Borderline solubility occurs in those molecules that have three to five carbon atoms. Table 15.4 lists the physical properties of some common esters.

Note

Esters are common solvents. Ethyl acetate is used to extract organic solutes from aqueous solutions—for example, to remove caffeine from coffee. It also is used to remove nail polish and paint. Cellulose nitrate is dissolved in ethyl acetate and butyl acetate to form lacquers. The solvent evaporates as the lacquer "dries," leaving a thin film on the surface. High boiling esters are used as softeners (plasticizers) for brittle plastics.

TABLE 15.4 Physical Properties of Some Esters

Condensed Structural Formula	Name	Molar Mass	Melting Point (°C)	Boiling Point (°C)	Aroma
$HCOOCH_3$	methyl formate	60	−99	32	
$HCOOCH_2CH_3$	ethyl formate	74	−80	54	rum
CH_3COOCH_3	methyl acetate	74	−98	57	
$CH_3COOCH_2CH_3$	ethyl acetate	88	−84	77	
$CH_3CH_2CH_2COOCH_3$	methyl butyrate	102	−85	102	apple
$CH_3CH_2CH_2COOCH_2CH_3$	ethyl butyrate	116	−101	121	pineapple
$CH_3COO(CH_2)_4CH_3$	pentyl acetate	130	−71	148	pear
$CH_3COOCH_2CH_2CH(CH_3)_2$	isopentyl acetate	130	−79	142	banana
$CH_3COOCH_2C_6H_5$	benzyl acetate	150	−51	215	jasmine
$CH_3CH_2CH_2COO(CH_2)_4CH_3$	pentyl butyrate	158	−73	185	apricot
$CH_3COO(CH_2)_7CH_3$	octyl acetate	172	−39	210	orange

CONCEPT REVIEW EXERCISES

1. Which compound has the higher boiling point—$CH_3CH_2CH_2CH_2OH$ or CH_3COOCH_3? Explain.
2. Which compound is more soluble in water—methyl butyrate or butyric acid? Explain.

ANSWERS

1. $CH_3CH_2CH_2CH_2OH$ because there is intermolecular hydrogen bonding (There is no intermolecular hydrogen bonding in CH_3COOCH_3.)
2. butyric acid because of hydrogen bonding with water

KEY TAKEAWAYS

- Esters have polar bonds but do not engage in hydrogen bonding and are therefore intermediate in boiling points between the nonpolar alkanes and the alcohols, which engage in hydrogen bonding.
- Ester molecules can engage in hydrogen bonding with water, so esters of low molar mass are therefore somewhat soluble in water.

EXERCISES

1. Which compound has the higher boiling point—$CH_3CH_2CH_2COOH$ or $CH_3CH_2CH_2COOCH_3$? Explain.
2. Which compound is more soluble in water—methyl acetate or octyl acetate? Explain.

ANSWER

1. CH3CH2CH2COOH because there is intermolecular hydrogen bonding (There is no intermolecular hydrogen bonding in CH3CH2COOCH3.)

8. PREPARATION OF ESTERS

LEARNING OBJECTIVE

1. **Identify and describe the substances from which most esters are prepared.**

Some esters can be prepared by **esterification**, a reaction in which a carboxylic acid and an alcohol, heated in the presence of a mineral acid catalyst, form an ester and water:

$$R{-}\overset{\overset{\displaystyle O}{\|}}{C}{-}OH + ROH \overset{H^+}{\rightleftharpoons} R{-}\overset{\overset{\displaystyle O}{\|}}{C}{-}OR + H_2O$$

The reaction is reversible. As a specific example of an esterification reaction, butyl acetate can be made from acetic acid and 1-butanol.

$$\underset{\text{Acetic acid}}{CH_3{-}\overset{\overset{\displaystyle O}{\|}}{C}{-}OH} + \underset{\text{1-Butanol}}{CH_3CH_2CH_2CH_2OH} \overset{H^+}{\rightleftharpoons} \underset{\text{Butyl acetate}}{CH_3\overset{\overset{\displaystyle O}{\|}}{C}OCH_2CH_2CH_2CH_3} + H_2O$$

esterification

The formation of an ester from a carboxylic acid and an alcohol.

A Closer Look: Condensation Polymers

A commercially important esterification reaction is condensation polymerization, in which a reaction occurs between a dicarboxylic acid and a dihydric alcohol (diol), with the elimination of water. Such a reaction yields an ester that contains a free (unreacted) carboxyl group at one end and a free alcohol group at the other end. Further condensation reactions then occur, producing polyester polymers.

The most important polyester, polyethylene terephthalate (PET), is made from terephthalic acid and ethylene glycol monomers:

$$\underset{\text{Ethylene glycol}}{n\ HOCH_2CH_2OH} + \underset{\text{Terephthalic acid}}{n\ HOOC{-}C_6H_4{-}COOH} \longrightarrow$$

$$\underset{\text{Polyethylene terephthalate}}{\left[CO{-}C_6H_4{-}COOCH_2CH_2O\right]_n} + n\ H_2O$$

Polyester molecules make excellent fibers and are used in many fabrics. A knitted polyester tube, which is biologically inert, can be used in surgery to repair or replace diseased sections of blood vessels. PET is used to make bottles for soda pop and other beverages. It is also formed into films called Mylar. When magnetically coated, Mylar tape is used in audio- and videocassettes. Synthetic arteries can be made from PET, polytetrafluoroethylene, and other polymers.

CONCEPT REVIEW EXERCISES

1. From what carboxylic acid and what alcohol can the ester isopropyl nonanoate be made?
2. From what carboxylic acid and what alcohol can the ester cyclobutyl butyrate be made?

ANSWERS

1. nonanoic acid and isopropyl alcohol
2. butyric acid and cyclobutyl alcohol

KEY TAKEAWAY

- Esters are made by the reaction of a carboxylic acid with an alcohol, a process that is called esterification.

EXERCISES

1. Write the equation for the reaction of acetic acid with each compound.
   a. ethanol
   b. 1-butanol in the presence of a mineral acid catalyst
2. Write the equation for the reaction of benzoic acid with each compound.
   a. methanol
   b. 1-propanol in the presence of a mineral acid catalyst

ANSWER

1. a.

$$CH_3\text{—}\overset{\overset{\displaystyle O}{\|}}{C}\text{—}OH + CH_3CH_2OH \xrightarrow{H^+} CH_3\overset{\overset{\displaystyle O}{\|}}{C}OCH_2CH_3 + H_2O$$

   b.

$$CH_3\text{—}\overset{\overset{\displaystyle O}{\|}}{C}\text{—}OH + CH_3CH_2CH_2CH_2OH \xrightarrow{H^+} CH_3\overset{\overset{\displaystyle O}{\|}}{C}OCH_2CH_2CH_2CH_3 + H_2O$$

9. HYDROLYSIS OF ESTERS

LEARNING OBJECTIVES

1. **Describe the typical reaction that takes place with esters.**
2. **Identify the products of an acidic hydrolysis of an ester.**
3. **Identify the products of a basic hydrolysis of an ester.**

Esters are neutral compounds, unlike the acids from which they are formed. In typical reactions, the alkoxy (OR′) group of an ester is replaced by another group. One such reaction is **hydrolysis**, literally "splitting with water." The hydrolysis of esters is catalyzed by either an acid or a base.

hydrolysis

The reaction of a substance with water.

Acidic hydrolysis is simply the reverse of esterification. The ester is heated with a large excess of water containing a strong-acid catalyst. Like esterification, the reaction is reversible and does not go to completion.

$$\underset{\text{An ester}}{R{-}\overset{O}{\overset{\|}{C}}{-}OR} + \underset{\text{Water}}{H_2O} \xrightleftharpoons{H^+} \underset{\text{A carboxylic acid}}{R{-}\overset{O}{\overset{\|}{C}}{-}OH} + \underset{\text{An alcohol}}{ROH}$$

As a specific example, butyl acetate and water react to form acetic acid and 1-butanol. The reaction is reversible and does not go to completion.

$$\underset{\text{Butyl acetate}}{CH_3\overset{O}{\overset{\|}{C}}OCH_2CH_2CH_2CH_3} + \underset{\text{Water}}{H_2O} \xrightleftharpoons{H^+} \underset{\text{Acetic acid}}{CH_3{-}\overset{O}{\overset{\|}{C}}{-}OH} + \underset{\text{1-Butanol (butyl alcohol)}}{CH_3CH_2CH_2CH_2OH}$$

EXAMPLE 7

Write an equation for the acidic hydrolysis of ethyl butyrate ($CH_3CH_2CH_2COOCH_2CH_3$) and name the products.

Solution

Remember that in acidic hydrolysis, water (HOH) splits the ester bond. The H of HOH joins to the oxygen atom in the OR part of the original ester, and the OH of HOH joins to the carbonyl carbon atom:

$$CH_3CH_2CH_2\overset{O}{\overset{\|}{C}}OCH_2CH_3 + H_2O \xrightleftharpoons{H^+} CH_3CH_2CH_2{-}\overset{O}{\overset{\|}{C}}{-}OH + CH_3CH_2OH$$

The products are butyric acid (butanoic acid) and ethanol.

SKILL-BUILDING EXERCISE

1. Write an equation for the acidic hydrolysis of methyl butanoate and name the products.

When a base (such as sodium hydroxide [NaOH] or potassium hydroxide [KOH]) is used to hydrolyze an ester, the products are a carboxylate salt and an alcohol. Because soaps are prepared by the alkaline hydrolysis of fats and oils, alkaline hydrolysis of esters is called **saponification** (Latin *sapon*, meaning "soap," and *facere*, meaning "to make"). In a saponification reaction, the base is a reactant, not simply a catalyst. The reaction goes to completion:

saponification

The hydrolysis of fats and oils in the presence of a base to make soap.

$$\underset{\text{An ester}}{R{-}\overset{O}{\overset{\|}{C}}{-}OR} + \underset{\text{A base}}{NaOH\,(aq)} \longrightarrow \underset{\text{A carboxylate salt}}{R{-}\overset{O}{\overset{\|}{C}}{-}ONa\,(aq)} + \underset{\text{An alcohol}}{ROH}$$

As a specific example, ethyl acetate and NaOH react to form sodium acetate and ethanol:

$$\underset{\text{Ethyl acetate}}{CH_3\overset{O}{\overset{\|}{C}}OCH_2CH_3} + \underset{\text{Sodium hydroxide}}{NaOH\ (aq)} \longrightarrow \underset{\text{Sodium acetate}}{CH_3-\overset{O}{\overset{\|}{C}}-ONa\ (aq)} + \underset{\text{Ethanol (ethyl alcohol)}}{CH_3CH_2OH}$$

EXAMPLE 8

Write an equation for the hydrolysis of methyl benzoate in a potassium hydroxide solution.

Solution

In basic hydrolysis, the molecule of the base splits the ester linkage. The acid portion of the ester ends up as the *salt* of the acid (in this case, the potassium salt). The alcohol portion of the ester ends up as the free alcohol.

$$C_6H_5-\overset{O}{\overset{\|}{C}}-OCH_3 + KOH\ (aq) \longrightarrow C_6H_5-\overset{O}{\overset{\|}{C}}-OK + CH_3OH$$

SKILL-BUILDING EXERCISE

1. Write the equation for the hydrolysis of ethyl propanoate in a sodium hydroxide solution.

CONCEPT REVIEW EXERCISES

1. How do acidic hydrolysis and basic hydrolysis of an ester differ in terms of
   a. products obtained?
   b. the extent of reaction?
2. What is saponification?

ANSWERS

1. a. acidic hydrolysis: carboxylic acid + alcohol; basic hydrolysis: carboxylate salt + alcohol
   b. basic hydrolysis: completion; acidic hydrolysis: incomplete reaction
2. the basic hydrolysis of an ester

KEY TAKEAWAYS

- Hydrolysis is a most important reaction of esters.
- Acidic hydrolysis of an ester gives a carboxylic acid and an alcohol.
- Basic hydrolysis of an ester gives a carboxylate salt and an alcohol.

EXERCISES

1. Write an equation for the acid-catalyzed hydrolysis of ethyl acetate.
2. Write an equation for the base-catalyzed hydrolysis of ethyl acetate.

3. Complete each equation.
   a. 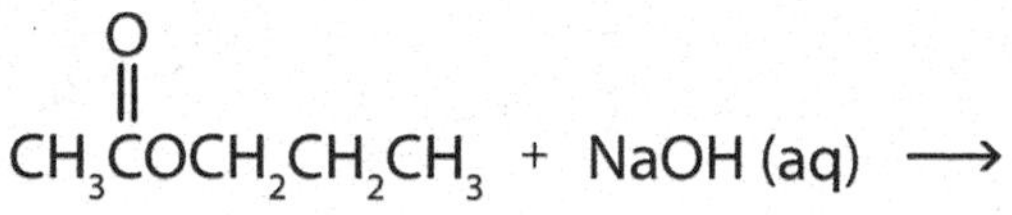
$$CH_3\overset{\overset{\displaystyle O}{\|}}{C}OCH_2CH_2CH_3 + NaOH\,(aq) \longrightarrow$$
   b. 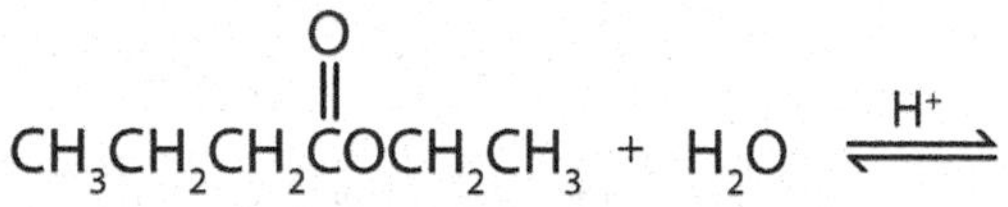
$$CH_3CH_2CH_2\overset{\overset{\displaystyle O}{\|}}{C}OCH_2CH_3 + H_2O \xrightleftharpoons{H^+}$$
4. Complete each equation.
   a. $(CH_3)_2CHCOOCH_2CH_3 + H_2O \overset{H^+}{\rightleftarrows}$
   b. $CH_3COOCH(CH_3)_2 + KOH(aq) \rightarrow$

ANSWERS

1. $CH_3COOCH_2CH_3 + H_2O \xrightarrow{H^+} CH_3COOH + CH_3CH_2OH$
3. a. $CH_3COONa(aq) + CH_3CH_2CH_2OH$
   b. $CH_3CH_2CH_2COOH + CH_3CH_2OH$

10. ESTERS OF PHOSPHORIC ACID

LEARNING OBJECTIVES

1. **Describe phosphate esters.**
2. **Understand why phosphate esters are important in living cells.**

Just as carboxylic acids do, inorganic acids such as nitric acid (HNO_3), sulfuric acid (H_2SO_4), and phosphoric acid (H_3PO_4) also form esters. The esters of phosphoric acid are especially important in biochemistry. A phosphoric acid molecule can form a monoalkyl, a dialkyl, or a trialkyl ester by reaction with one, two, or three molecules of an alcohol.

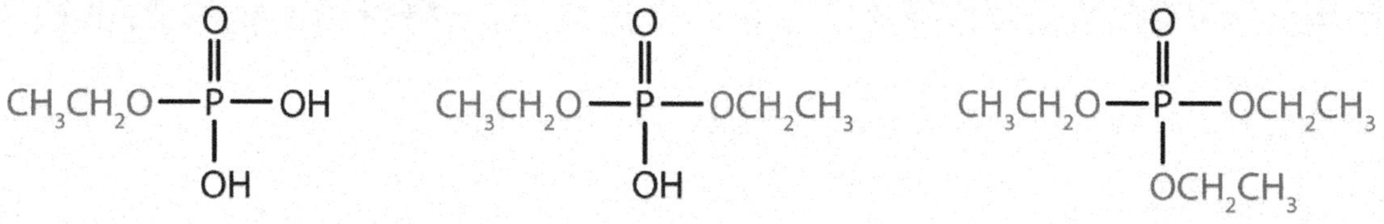

$$CH_3CH_2O-\overset{\overset{\displaystyle O}{\|}}{\underset{\underset{\displaystyle OH}{|}}{P}}-OH \qquad CH_3CH_2O-\overset{\overset{\displaystyle O}{\|}}{\underset{\underset{\displaystyle OH}{|}}{P}}-OCH_2CH_3 \qquad CH_3CH_2O-\overset{\overset{\displaystyle O}{\|}}{\underset{\underset{\displaystyle OCH_2CH_3}{|}}{P}}-OCH_2CH_3$$

Ethyl dihydrogen phosphate | **Diethyl hydrogen phosphate** | **Triethyl phosphate**

Esters of pyrophosphoric acid and triphosphoric acid are also important in biochemistry.

$$HO-\overset{\overset{O}{\|}}{\underset{\underset{OH}{|}}{P}}-OH \qquad HO-\overset{\overset{O}{\|}}{\underset{\underset{OH}{|}}{P}}-O-\overset{\overset{O}{\|}}{\underset{\underset{OH}{|}}{P}}-OH \qquad HO-\overset{\overset{O}{\|}}{\underset{\underset{OH}{|}}{P}}-O-\overset{\overset{O}{\|}}{\underset{\underset{OH}{|}}{P}}-O-\overset{\overset{O}{\|}}{\underset{\underset{OH}{|}}{P}}-OH$$

Phosphoric acid Pyrophosphoric acid Triphosphoric acid

Esters of these acids are present in every plant and animal cell. They are biochemical intermediates in the transformation of food into usable energy. The bonds between phosphate units in adenosine triphosphate (ATP) are called *phosphoanhydride* bonds. These are high-energy bonds that store energy from the metabolism of foods. Hydrolysis of ATP releases energy as it is needed for biochemical processes (for instance, for muscle contraction). Phosphate esters are also important structural constituents of phospholipids and nucleic acids. (For more information about phospholipids and nucleic acids, see Chapter 17, [Unsupported Reference Type: chapter-section], and Chapter 19, respectively.)

Note

The explosive nitroglycerin (glyceryl trinitrate) is an ester formed from glycerol and nitric acid. It is used in medicine to relieve chest pain in heart disease.

$$\begin{array}{c} CH_2OH \\ | \\ CHOH \\ | \\ CH_2OH \end{array} + 3\ HONO_2 \longrightarrow \begin{array}{c} CH_2ONO_2 \\ | \\ CHONO_2 \\ | \\ CH_2ONO_2 \end{array} + 3\ H_2O$$

Glycerol Glycerol trinitrate (nitroglycerin)

CONCEPT REVIEW EXERCISE

1. What compounds combine to form phosphate esters?

ANSWER

1. phosphoric acids and alcohols

KEY TAKEAWAYS

- Inorganic acids such as H3PO4 form esters.
- The esters of phosphoric acid are especially important in biochemistry.

EXERCISES

1. Draw the structure for each compound.
   a. diethyl hydrogen phosphate
   b. methyl dihydrogen phosphate
   c. 1-glycerol phosphate

2. Name each compound.

a.

$$HO-\overset{\overset{\displaystyle O}{\|}}{\underset{\underset{\displaystyle OH}{|}}{P}}-O-\overset{\overset{\displaystyle O}{\|}}{\underset{\underset{\displaystyle OH}{|}}{P}}-OH$$

b.

$$CH_3CH_2O-\overset{\overset{\displaystyle O}{\|}}{\underset{\underset{\displaystyle OH}{|}}{P}}-OH$$

c.

$$CH_3CH_2O-\overset{\overset{\displaystyle O}{\|}}{\underset{\underset{\displaystyle OH}{|}}{P}}-O-\overset{\overset{\displaystyle O}{\|}}{\underset{\underset{\displaystyle OH}{|}}{P}}-OH$$

ANSWER

1. a.

$$CH_3CH_2O-\overset{\overset{\displaystyle O}{\|}}{\underset{\underset{\displaystyle OH}{|}}{P}}-OCH_2CH_3$$

b.

$$CH_3O-\overset{\overset{\displaystyle O}{\|}}{\underset{\underset{\displaystyle OH}{|}}{P}}-OH$$

c.

$$\begin{array}{l} CH_2OPO_3H \\ | \\ CHOH \\ | \\ CH_2OH \end{array}$$

11. AMINES: STRUCTURES AND NAMES

LEARNING OBJECTIVES

1. **Identify the general structure for an amine.**
2. **Identify the functional group for amines.**
3. **Determine the structural feature that classifies amines as primary, secondary, or tertiary.**
4. **Use nomenclature systems to name amines.**

primary (1°) amine

A compound that has only one alkyl or aryl group on the nitrogen atom.

secondary (2°) amine

A compound that has two alkyl or aryl groups on the nitrogen atom.

tertiary (3°) amine

A compound that has three alkyl or aryl groups on the nitrogen atom.

Amines are classified according to the number of carbon atoms bonded directly to the nitrogen atom. A **primary (1°) amine** has one alkyl (or aryl) group on the nitrogen atom, a **secondary (2°) amine** has two, and a **tertiary (3°) amine** has three (Figure 15.5).

FIGURE 15.5 The Structure of Amines Compared to Water, an Alcohol, and an Ether

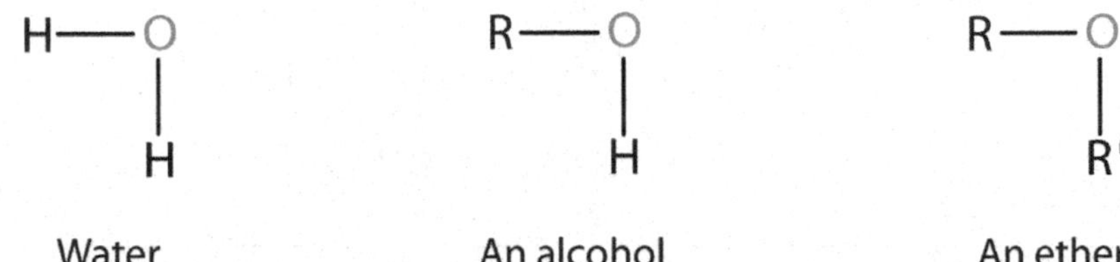

H—N—H, H — Ammonia

R—N—H, H — A 1° amine

R—N—R, H — A 2° amine

R—N—R, R — A 3° amine

Note

To classify alcohols, we look at the number of carbon atoms bonded to the *carbon atom* bearing the OH group, not the oxygen atom itself. Thus, although isopropylamine looks similar to isopropyl alcohol, the former is a *primary* amine, while the latter is a *secondary* alcohol.

CH_3CHCH_3 with NH_2 — Isopropylamine (a primary amine)

CH_3CHCH_3 with OH — Isopropyl alcohol (a secondary alcohol)

amino group

An NH_2 unit.

The common names for simple aliphatic amines consist of an alphabetic list of alkyl groups attached to the nitrogen atom, followed by the suffix *-amine*. (Systematic names are often used by some chemists.) The **amino group** (NH_2) is named as a substituent in more complicated amines, such as those that incorporate other functional groups or in which the alkyl groups cannot be simply named.

EXAMPLE 9

Name and classify each compound.

1. $CH_3CH_2CH_2NH_2$
2. $CH_3CH_2NCH_3$ with a CH_3 group attached to N
3. $CH_3CH_2NHCH_2CH_3$
4. $CH_3CH_2CH_2NHCH_3$

Solution

1. There is only one alkyl group attached to the nitrogen atom, so the amine is primary. A group of three carbon atoms (a propyl group) is attached to the NH_2 group through an end carbon atom, so the name is propylamine.
2. There are two methyl groups and one ethyl group on the nitrogen atom. The compound is ethyldimethylamine, a tertiary amine.
3. There are two ethyl groups attached to the nitrogen atom; the amine is secondary, so the compound is diethylamine.
4. The nitrogen atom has a methyl group and a propyl group, so the compound is methylpropylamine, a secondary amine.

SKILL-BUILDING EXERCISE

Name and classify each compound.

1. $CH_3CHNHCH_3$ with a CH_3 group attached to the second C
2. $CH_3CH_2NCH_2CH_3$ with a CH_3 group attached to N
3. $CH_3CH_2CH_2CH_2NH_2$
4. $CH_3CH_2CH_2NHCH_2CH_2 CH_3$

EXAMPLE 10

Draw the structure for each compound and classify.

1. isopropyldimethylamine
2. dipropylamine

Solution

1. The name indicates that there are an isopropyl group (in red) and two methyl groups (in green) attached to the nitrogen atom; the amine is tertiary.

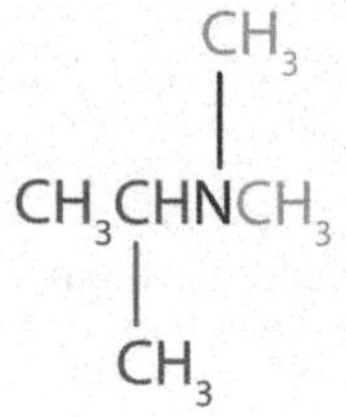

$$
\begin{array}{c}
\quad\quad CH_3 \\
\quad\quad | \\
CH_3CHNCH_3 \\
| \quad\quad \\
CH_3 \quad\quad
\end{array}
$$

2. The name indicates that there are two propyl groups attached to the nitrogen atom; the amine is secondary. (The third bond on the nitrogen atom goes to a hydrogen atom.)

$$CH_3CH_2CH_2NHCH_2CH_2CH_3$$

SKILL-BUILDING EXERCISE

Draw the structure for each compound and classify.

1. ethylisopropylamine
2. diethylpropylamine

The primary amine in which the nitrogen atom is attached directly to a benzene ring has a special name—aniline. Aryl amines are named as derivatives of aniline.

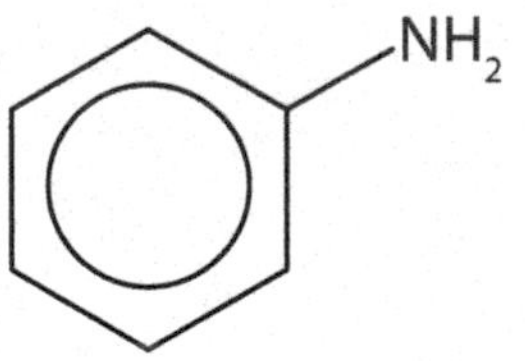

NH_2 NH_2 NH_2 Cl Cl I

Aniline 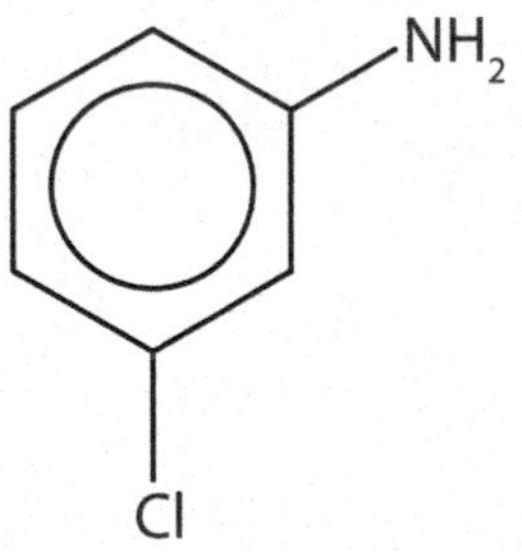 *M*-chloroaniline 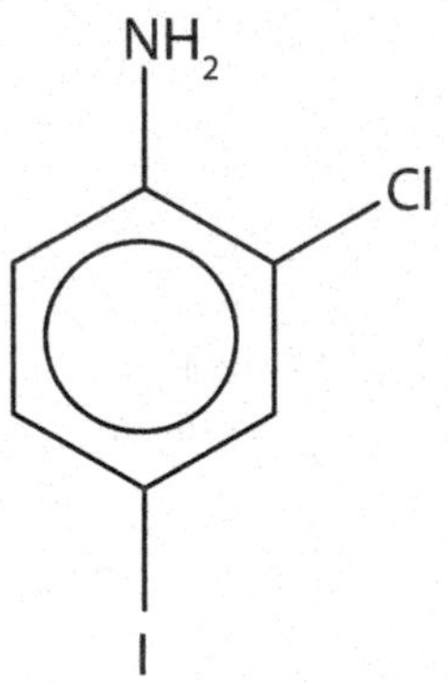 2-Chloro-4-iodoaniline

EXAMPLE 11

Name this compound.

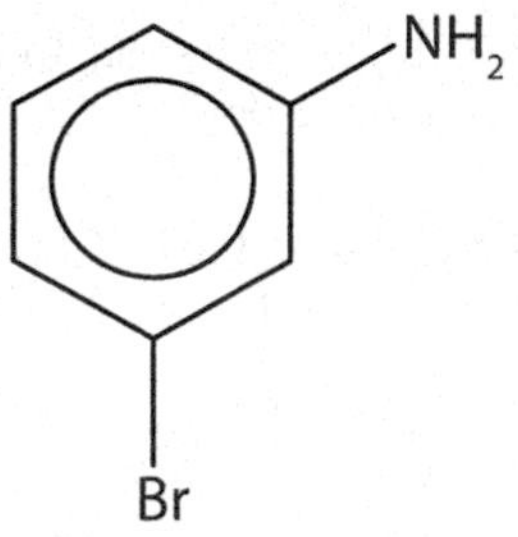

NH2

Br

Solution

The benzene ring with an amino (NH_2) group is aniline. The compound is named as a derivative of aniline: 3-bromoaniline or *m*-bromoaniline.

SKILL-BUILDING EXERCISE

1. Name this compound.

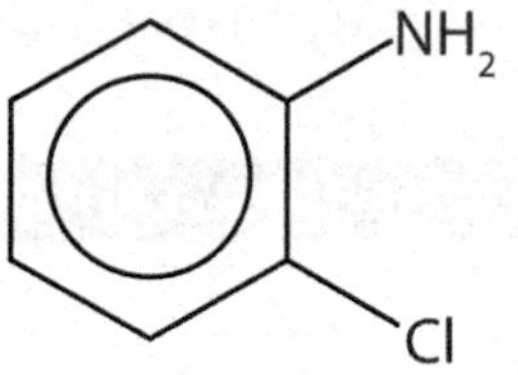

NH2

Cl

EXAMPLE 12

Draw the structure for *p*-ethylaniline and classify.

Solution

The compound is a derivative of aniline. It is a primary amine having an ethyl group located *para* to the amino (NH_2) group.

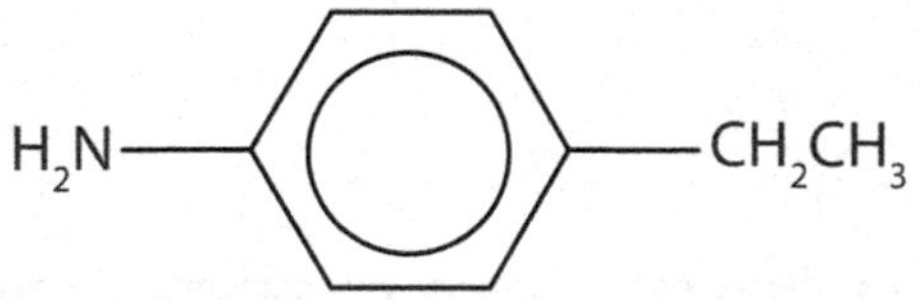

H_2N— —CH_2CH_3

SKILL-BUILDING EXERCISE

1. Draw the structure for *p*-isopropylaniline and classify.

EXAMPLE 13

Draw the structure for 2-amino-3-methylpentane.

Solution

Always start with the parent compound: draw the pentane chain. Then attach a methyl group at the third carbon atom and an amino group at the second carbon atom.

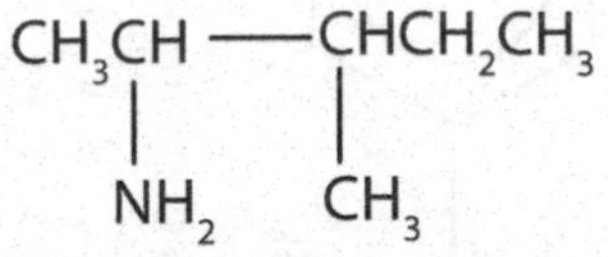

$$\begin{array}{lll} CH_3CH & - & CHCH_2CH_3 \\ \quad | & & \ \ | \\ \ NH_2 & & CH_3 \end{array}$$

SKILL-BUILDING EXERCISE

1. Draw the structure for 2-amino-3-ethyl-1-chloroheptane.

Ammonium (NH_4^+) ions, in which one or more hydrogen atoms are replaced with alkyl groups, are named in a manner analogous to that used for simple amines. The alkyl groups are named as substituents, and the parent species is regarded as the NH_4^+ ion. For example, $CH_3NH_3^+$ is the methylammonium ion. The ion formed from aniline ($C_6H_5NH_3^+$) is called the anilinium ion.

EXAMPLE 14

Name each ion.

1. $CH_3NH_3^+$
2. $(CH_3)_2NH_2^+$
3. $(CH_3)_3NH^+$
4. $(CH_3)_4N^+$

Solution

The ions have one, two, three, and four methyl (CH_3) groups attached to a nitrogen atom. Their names are as follows:

1. methylammonium ion
2. dimethylammonium ion
3. trimethylammonium ion
4. tetramethylammonium ion

SKILL-BUILDING EXERCISE

Name each ion.

1. $CH_3CH_2NH_3^+$
2. $(CH_3CH_2)_3NH^+$
3. $(CH_3CH_2CH_2)_2NH_2^+$
4. $(CH_3CH_2CH_2CH_2)_4N^+$

CONCEPT REVIEW EXERCISES

1. To what inorganic compound are the amines related?
2. How are amines classified?

ANSWERS

1. ammonia
2. by the number of hydrocarbon groups on the nitrogen atom: primary amine, one group; secondary amine, two groups; tertiary amine, three groups

KEY TAKEAWAYS

- An amine is a derivative of ammonia in which one, two, or all three hydrogen atoms are replaced by hydrocarbon groups.
- The amine functional group is as follows:

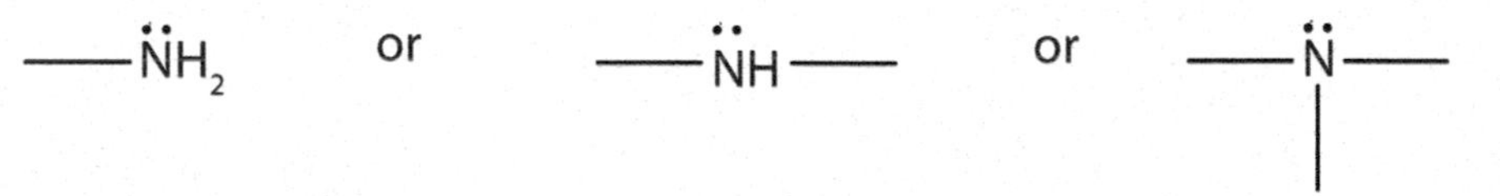

- Amines are classified as primary, secondary, or tertiary by the number of hydrocarbon groups attached to the nitrogen atom.
- Amines are named by naming the alkyl groups attached to the nitrogen atom, followed by the suffix *-amine.*

EXERCISES

1. Draw the structure for each compound and classify the amine as primary, secondary, or tertiary.
   a. dimethylamine
   b. diethylmethylamine
   c. 2-aminoethanol
2. Draw the structure for each compound and classify the amine as primary, secondary, or tertiary.
   a. 3-aminopentane
   b. 1,6-diaminohexane
   c. ethylphenylamine
3. Draw the structure for each compound.
   a. aniline
   b. *m*-bromoaniline
4. Draw the structure for each compound.
   a. 2-chloroaniline
   b. 3,5-dichloroaniline
5. Name each compound.
   a. $CH_3CH_2CH_2NH_2$
   b.

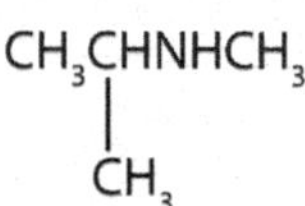

   c.

   $CH_3CHCH_2CH_2CH_3$ (with NH_2 on C-2)

6. Name each compound.
   a. $(CH_3CH_2)_3N$
   b. $(CH_3CH_2)_2NCH_3$
7. Draw the structure for each compound.
   a. dimethylammonium chloride
   b. anilinium chloride
8. Draw the structure for each compound.
   a. ethylmethylammonium chloride
   b. anilinium nitrate
9. Name each compound.
   a. $[CH_3CH_2NH_2CH_2CH_3]^+Br^-$
   b. $[(CH_3CH_2)_3NH]^+I^-$
10. Name each compound.
    a. $[(CH_3)_3NH]^+NO_3^-$
    b. $[(CH_3CH_2)_2NH_2]^+Cl^-$

ANSWERS

1. a. CH_3NHCH_3; secondary
   b. tertiary

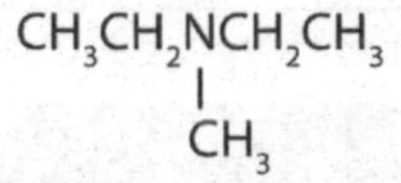

   $CH_3CH_2NCH_2CH_3$ with CH_3 on N

   c. $HOCH_2CH_2NH_2$; primary
3. a.

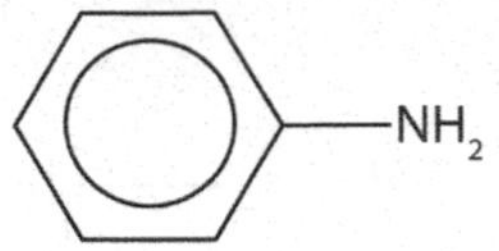

   NH_2

   b.

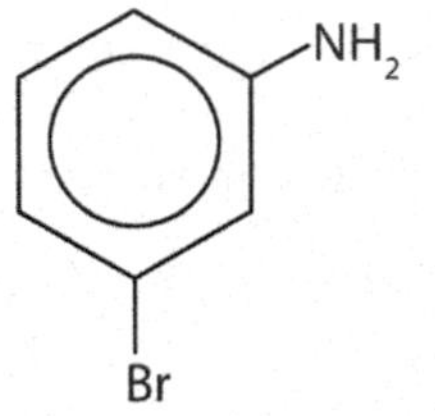

   NH_2

   Br
5. a. propylamine
   b. isopropylmethylamine
   c. 2-aminopentane
7. a. $[(CH_3)_2NH_2^+]Cl^-$
   b.

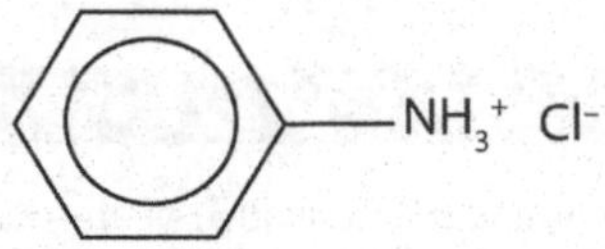

   NH_3^+ Cl^-
9. a. diethylammonium bromide
   b. triethylammonium iodide

12. PHYSICAL PROPERTIES OF AMINES

LEARNING OBJECTIVES

1. **Explain why the boiling points of primary and secondary amines are higher than those of alkanes or ethers of similar molar mass but are lower than those of alcohols.**
2. **Compare the boiling points of tertiary amines with alcohols, alkanes, and ethers of similar molar mass.**
3. **Compare the solubilities in water of amines of five or fewer carbon atoms with the solubilities of comparable alkanes and alcohols in water.**

Primary and secondary amines have hydrogen atoms bonded to an nitrogen atom and are therefore capable of hydrogen bonding (part (a) of Figure 15.6), although not as strongly as alcohol molecules (which have hydrogen atoms bonded to an oxygen atom, which is more electronegative than nitrogen). These amines boil at higher temperatures than alkanes but at lower temperatures than alcohols of comparable molar mass. For example, compare the boiling point of methylamine (CH_3NH_2; −6°C) with those of ethane (CH_3CH_3; −89°C) and methanol (CH_3OH; 65°C). Tertiary amines have no hydrogen atom bonded to the nitrogen atom and so cannot participate in intermolecular hydrogen bonding. They have boiling points comparable to those of ethers (Table 15.5).

FIGURE 15.6 Hydrogen Bonding

(a) Amine molecules are associated through hydrogen bonding. (b) An amine molecule can form a hydrogen bond with water molecules.

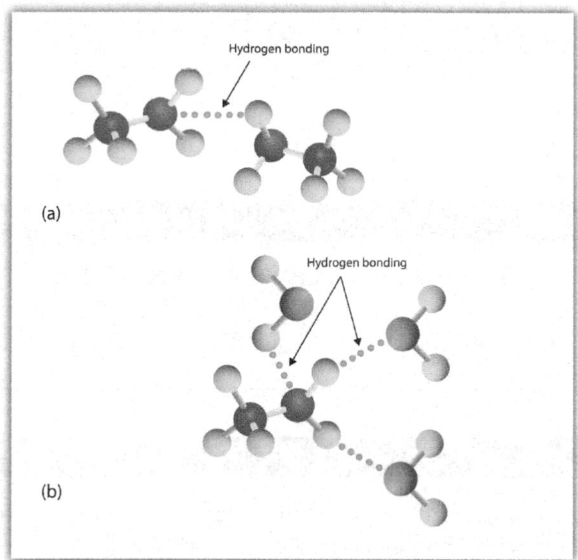

TABLE 15.5 Physical Properties of Some Amines and Comparable Oxygen-Containing Compounds

Name	Condensed Structural Formula	Class	Molar Mass	Boiling Point (°C)	Solubility at 25°C (g/100 g Water)
butylamine	CH3CH2CH2CH2NH2	1°	73	78	miscible
diethylamine	(CH3CH2)2NH	2°	73	55	miscible
butyl alcohol	CH3CH2CH2CH2OH	—	74	118	8
dipropylamine	(CH3CH2CH2)2NH	2°	101	111	4
triethylamine	(CH3CH2)3N	3°	101	90	14
dipropyl ether	(CH3CH2CH2)2O	—	102	91	0.25

All three classes of amines can engage in hydrogen bonding with water (part (b) of Figure 15.6). Amines of low molar mass are quite soluble in water; the borderline of solubility in water is at five or six carbon atoms.

To Your Health: Amines in Death and Life

Amines have "interesting" odors. The simple ones smell very much like ammonia. Higher aliphatic amines smell like decaying fish. Or perhaps we should put it the other way around: Decaying fish give off odorous amines. The stench of rotting fish is due in part to two diamines: putrescine and cadaverine. They arise from the decarboxylation of ornithine and lysine, respectively, amino acids that are found in animal cells. (For more information about lysine, see Chapter 18, [Unsupported Reference Type: chapter-section].)

$$HOCH_2CH_2OH$$

Aromatic amines generally are quite toxic. They are readily absorbed through the skin, and workers must exercise caution when handling these compounds. Several aromatic amines, including β-naphthylamine, are potent carcinogens.

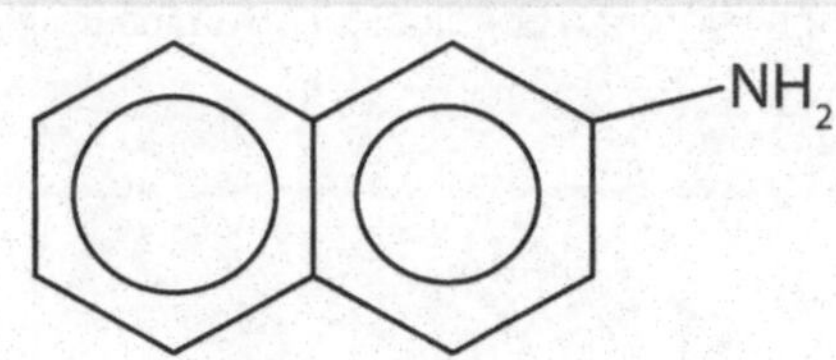

CONCEPT REVIEW EXERCISES

1. Which compound has the higher boiling point, $CH_3CH_2CH_2CH_2CH_2NH_2$ or $CH_3CH_2CH_2CH_2CH_2CH_3$? Explain.
2. Which compound is more soluble in water, $CH_3CH_2CH_2CH_2CH_3$ or $CH_3CH_2NHCH_2CH_3$? Explain.

ANSWERS

1. $CH_3CH_2CH_2CH_2CH_2NH_2$ because the nitrogen-to-hydrogen (N–H) bonds can engage in hydrogen bonding; $CH_3CH_2CH_2CH_2CH_2CH_3$ cannot engage in hydrogen bonding
2. $CH_3CH_2NHCH_2CH_3$ because amines can engage in hydrogen bonding with water; alkanes cannot engage in hydrogen bonding

KEY TAKEAWAYS

- Primary and secondary amines have higher boiling points than those of alkanes or ethers of similar molar mass because they can engage in intermolecular hydrogen bonding. Their boiling points are lower than those of alcohols because alcohol molecules have hydrogen atoms bonded to an oxygen atom, which is more electronegative.
- The boiling points of tertiary amines, which cannot engage in hydrogen bonding because they have no hydrogen atom on the nitrogen atom, are comparable to those of alkanes and ethers of similar molar mass.
- Because all three classes of amines can engage in hydrogen bonding with water, amines of low molar mass are quite soluble in water.

EXERCISES

1. Which compound of each pair has the higher boiling point? Explain.
   a. butylamine or pentane
   b. CH_3NH_2 or $CH_3CH_2CH_2CH_2CH_2NH_2$
2. Which compound of each pair has the higher boiling point? Explain.
   a. butylamine or butyl alcohol
   b. trimethylamine or propylamine
3. Which compound is more soluble in water—$CH_3CH_2CH_3$ or $CH_3CH_2NH_2$? Explain.
4. Which compound is more soluble in water—$CH_3CH_2CH_2NH_2$ or $CH_3CH_2CH_2CH_2CH_2CH_2NH_2$? Explain.

ANSWERS

1. a. butylamine because the N–H bonds can engage in hydrogen bonding; pentane cannot engage in hydrogen bonding
   b. $CH_3CH_2CH_2CH_2CH_2NH_2$ because it has a greater molar mass than CH_3NH_2
3. $CH_3CH_2NH_2$ because amines can engage in hydrogen bonding with water; alkanes cannot engage in hydrogen bonding

13. AMINES AS BASES

LEARNING OBJECTIVES

1. **Name the typical reactions that take place with amines.**
2. **Describe heterocyclic amines.**

Recall that ammonia (NH_3) acts as a base because the nitrogen atom has a lone pair of electrons that can accept a proton. Amines also have a lone electron pair on their nitrogen atoms and can accept a proton from water to form substituted ammonium (NH_4^+) ions and hydroxide (OH^-) ions:

$$R_2\ddot{N}R + H_2O \rightleftharpoons [R_2NHR]^+ + OH^-$$

As a specific example, methylamine reacts with water to form the methylammonium ion and the OH^- ion.

$$\underset{\text{Methylamine}}{CH_3NH_2(aq)} + H_2O \rightleftharpoons \underset{\text{Methylammonium ion}}{CH_3NH_3^+(aq)} + OH^-(aq)$$

Nearly all amines, including those that are not very soluble in water, will react with strong acids to form salts soluble in water.

$$\underset{\text{Octylamine (insoluble)}}{CH_3(CH_2)_6NH_2(l)} + HNO_3(aq) \longrightarrow \underset{\text{Octylammonium nitrate (soluble)}}{CH_3(CH_2)_6NH_3^+NO_3^-(aq)}$$

Amine salts are named like other salts: the name of the cation is followed by the name of the anion.

EXAMPLE 15

What are the formulas of the acid and base that react to form $[CH_3NH_2CH_2CH_3]^+CH_3COO^-$?

Solution

The cation has two groups—methyl and ethyl—attached to the nitrogen atom. It comes from ethylmethylamine ($CH_3NHCH_2CH_3$). The anion is the acetate ion. It comes from acetic acid (CH_3COOH).

SKILL-BUILDING EXERCISE

1. What are the formulas of the acid and base that react to form $(CH_3CH_2CH_2)_3NH^+I^-$?

To Your Health: Amine Salts as Drugs

Salts of aniline are properly named as *anilinium* compounds, but an older system, still in use for naming drugs, identifies the salt of aniline and hydrochloric acid as "aniline hydrochloride." These compounds are ionic—they are salts—and the properties of the compounds (solubility, for example) are those characteristic of salts. Many drugs that are amines are converted to hydrochloride salts to increase their solubility in aqueous solution.

13.1 Heterocyclic Amines

heterocyclic compound

A cyclic compound in which one or more atoms in the ring is an element other than a carbon atom.

alkaloid

A nitrogen-containing organic compound obtained from plants that has physiological properties.

Looking back at the various cyclic hydrocarbons introduced in Chapter 12 and Chapter 13, we see that all the atoms in the rings of these compounds are carbon atoms. In other cyclic compounds, called **heterocyclic compounds** (Greek *heteros*, meaning "other"), nitrogen, oxygen, sulfur, or some other atom is incorporated in the ring. Many heterocyclic compounds are important in medicine and biochemistry. Some compose part of the structure of the nucleic acids, which in turn compose the genetic material of cells and direct protein synthesis. (For more information about nucleic acids, see Chapter 19.)

Many heterocyclic amines occur naturally in plants. Like other amines, these compounds are basic. Such a compound is an **alkaloid**, a name that means "like alkalis." Many alkaloids are physiologically active, including the familiar drugs caffeine, nicotine, and cocaine.

To Your Health: Three Well-Known Alkaloids

Caffeine is a stimulant found in coffee, tea, and some soft drinks. Its mechanism of action is not well understood, but it is thought to block the activity of adenosine, a heterocyclic base that acts as a neurotransmitter, a substance that carries messages across a tiny gap (synapse) from one nerve cell (neuron) to another cell. The effective dose of caffeine is about 200 mg, corresponding to about two cups of strong coffee or tea.

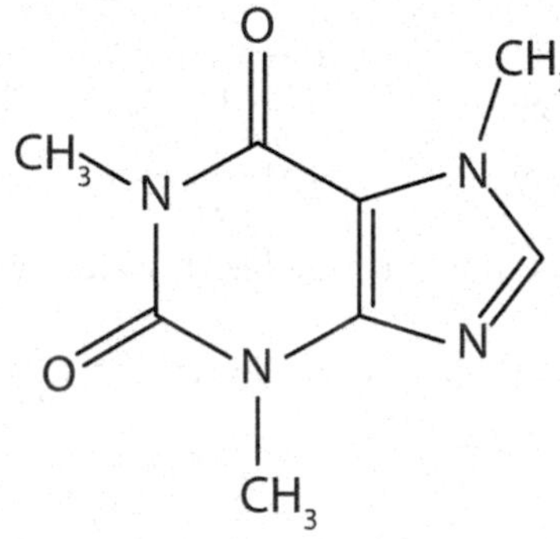

O CH$_3$ CH$_3$ N N N N O CH$_3$

Caffeine

Nicotine acts as a stimulant by a different mechanism; it probably mimics the action of the neurotransmitter acetylcholine. People ingest this drug by smoking or chewing tobacco. Its stimulant effect seems transient, as this initial response is followed by depression. Nicotine is highly toxic to animals. It is especially deadly when injected; the lethal dose for a human is estimated to be about 50 mg. Nicotine has also been used in agriculture as a contact insecticide.

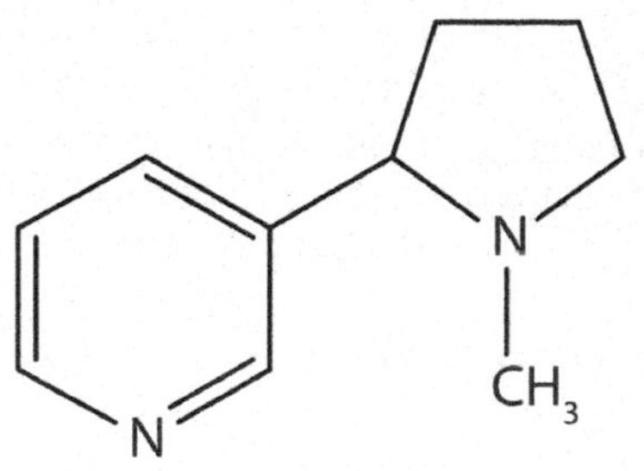

Nicotine

Cocaine acts as a stimulant by preventing nerve cells from taking up dopamine, another neurotransmitter, from the synapse. High levels of dopamine are therefore available to stimulate the pleasure centers of the brain. The enhancement of dopamine action is thought to be responsible for cocaine's "high" and its addictive properties. After the binge, dopamine is depleted in less than an hour. This leaves the user in a pleasureless state and (often) craving more cocaine.

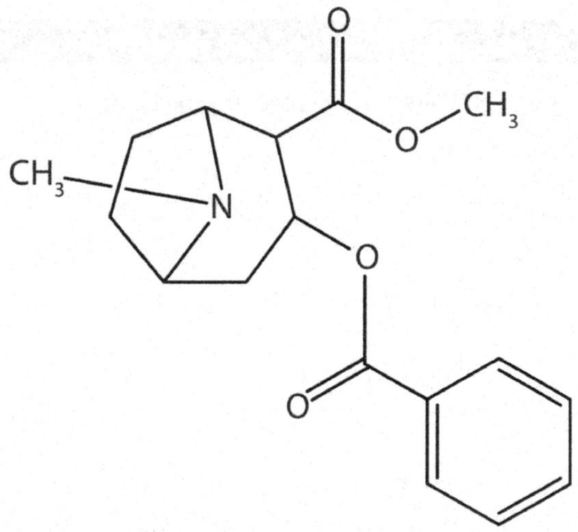

Cocaine

Cocaine is used as the salt cocaine hydrochloride and in the form of broken lumps of the free (unneutralized) base, which is called *crack cocaine*.

$$\underset{\text{Cocaine (freebase)}}{C_{17}H_{21}O_4N} + HCl \longrightarrow \underset{\text{Cocaine hydrochloride}}{C_{17}H_{21}O_4NH^+Cl^-}$$

Because it is soluble in water, cocaine hydrochloride is readily absorbed through the watery mucous membranes of the nose when it is snorted. Crack cocaine is more volatile than cocaine hydrochloride. It vaporizes at the temperature of a burning cigarette. When smoked, cocaine reaches the brain in 15 s.

CONCEPT REVIEW EXERCISES

1. Explain the basicity of amines.
2. Contrast the physical properties of amines with those of alcohols and alkanes.
3. What is a heterocyclic compound?

ANSWERS

1. Amines have a lone pair of electrons on the nitrogen atom and can thus act as proton acceptors (bases).
2. The solubilities of amines are similar to those of alcohols; the boiling points of primary and secondary amines are similar to those of alcohols; the boiling points of tertiary amines, which cannot engage in hydrogen bonding because they do not have a hydrogen atom on the nitrogen atom, are comparable to those of alkanes.
3. Heterocyclic compounds are ring compounds with atoms other than carbon atoms in the ring.

KEY TAKEAWAYS

- Amines are bases; they react with acids to form salts.
- Salts of aniline are properly named as *anilinium* compounds, but an older system is used to name drugs: the salts of amine drugs and hydrochloric acid are called "hydrochlorides."
- Heterocyclic amines are cyclic compounds with one or more nitrogen atoms in the ring.

EXERCISES

1. What salt is formed in each reaction? Write its condensed structural formula.
   a. $CH_3NH_2(aq) + HBr(aq) \rightarrow$
   b. $CH_3NHCH_3(aq) + HNO_3(aq) \rightarrow$
2. What salt is formed in each reaction? Draw its structure.
   a.

$$\underset{\displaystyle CH_3}{CH_3\overset{|}{C}HNH_2} + HBr\,(aq) \longrightarrow$$

   b.

$$\text{(azetidine, four-membered ring with NH)} + HBr\,(aq) \longrightarrow$$

ANSWER

1.
   a. $CH_3NH_3{}^+Br^-(aq)$
   b. $[CH_3NH_2CH_3]^+NO_3{}^-(aq)$

14. AMIDES: STRUCTURES AND NAMES

LEARNING OBJECTIVES

1. **Identify the general structure for an amide.**
2. **Identify the functional group for an amide.**
3. **Names amides with common names.**
4. **Name amides according to the IUPAC system.**

The amide functional group has an nitrogen atom attached to a carbonyl carbon atom. If the two remaining bonds on the nitrogen atom are attached to hydrogen atoms, the compound is a *simple amide*. If one or both of the two remaining bonds on the atom are attached to alkyl or aryl groups, the compound is a *substituted amide*.

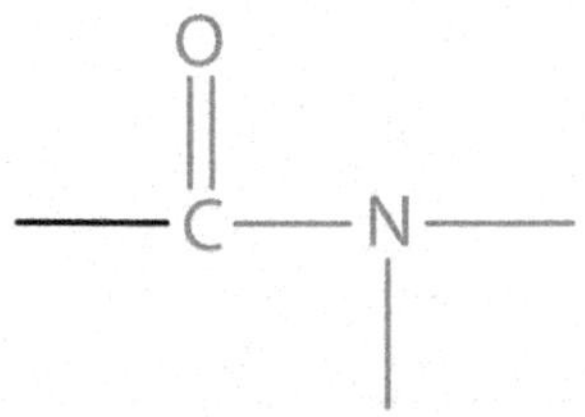

$$-\overset{O}{\overset{\|}{C}}-\underset{|}{N}- \qquad -\overset{O}{\overset{\|}{C}}-NH_2 \qquad -\overset{O}{\overset{\|}{C}}-\overset{H}{N}-R$$

The amide group 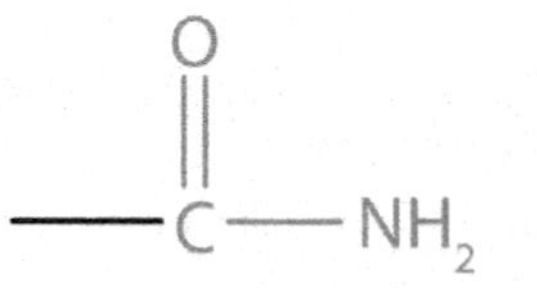 A simple amide 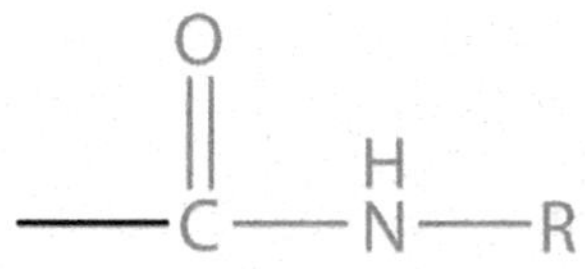 A substituted amide

Note

The carbonyl carbon-to-nitrogen bond is called an *amide linkage*. This bond is quite stable and is found in the repeating units of protein molecules, where it is called a *peptide linkage*. (For more about peptide linkages, see Chapter 18, [Unsupported Reference Type: chapter-section].)

Simple amides are named as derivatives of carboxylic acids. The *-ic* ending of the common name or the *-oic* ending of the International Union of Pure and Applied Chemistry (IUPAC) name of the carboxylic acid is replaced with the suffix *-amide*.

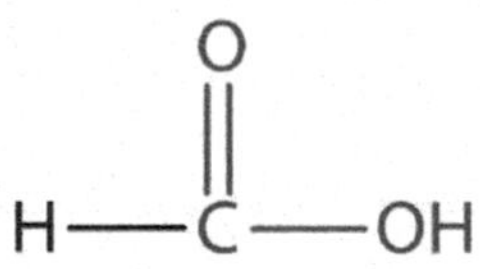

$$H-\overset{O}{\overset{\|}{C}}-OH \qquad H-\overset{O}{\overset{\|}{C}}-NH_2$$

Formic acid (methanoic acid)

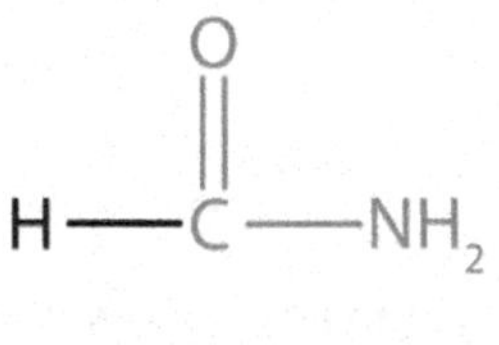

Formamide (methanamide)

EXAMPLE 16

Name each compound with the common name, the IUPAC name, or both.

1. 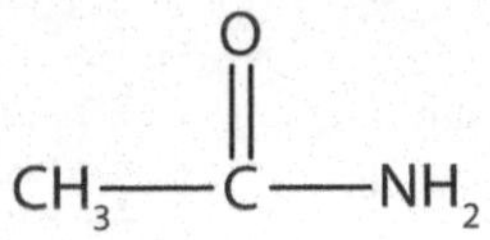 $CH_3{-}C({=}O){-}NH_2$

2. $C_6H_5{-}C({=}O){-}NH_2$

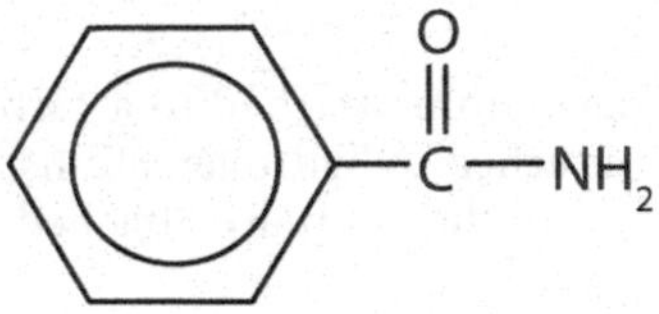

Solution

1. This amide has two carbon atoms and is thus derived from acetic acid. The OH of acetic acid is replaced by an NH_2 group. The *-ic* from *acetic* (or *-oic* from ethanoic) is dropped, and *-amide* is added to give *acetamide* (or ethanamide in the IUPAC system).
2. This amide is derived from benzoic acid. The *-oic* is dropped, and *-amide* is added to give benzamide.

SKILL-BUILDING EXERCISE

Name each compound with the common name, the IUPAC name, or both.

1. 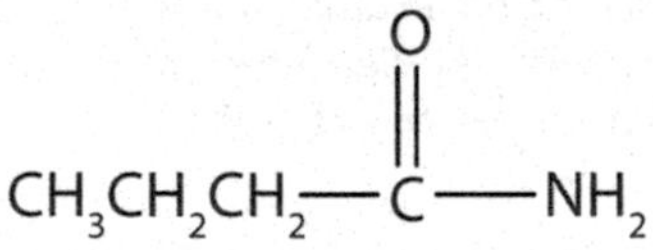 $CH_3CH_2CH_2{-}C({=}O){-}NH_2$

2. $CH_3CH_2CH_2CH_2CH_2CH_2C({=}O){-}NH_2$

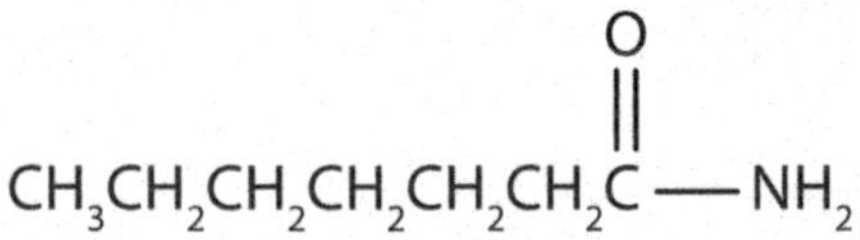

CONCEPT REVIEW EXERCISES

1. Name this compound with the common name and the IUPAC name.

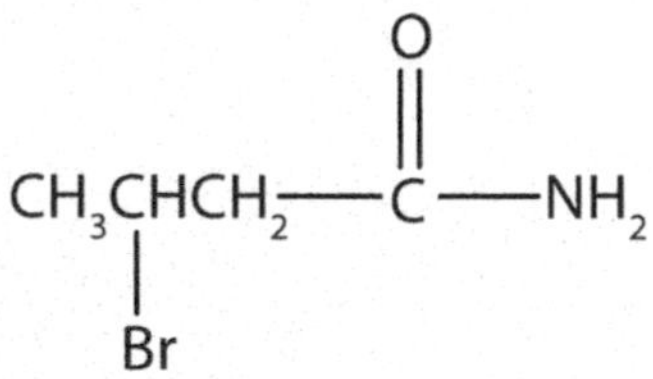

   $CH_3CH(Br)CH_2{-}C({=}O){-}NH_2$

2. Draw a the structural formulae for pentanamide.

ANSWERS

1. β-bromobutyramide (3-bromobutanamide)

2.

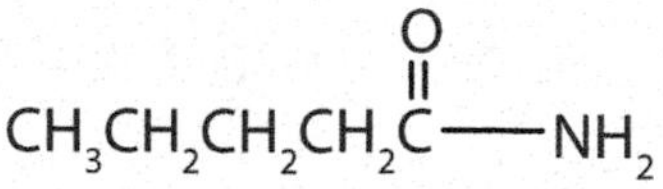

$$CH_3CH_2CH_2CH_2\overset{\overset{\displaystyle O}{\|}}{C}—NH_2$$

KEY TAKEAWAYS

- Amides have a general structure in which a nitrogen atom is bonded to a carbonyl carbon atom.
- The functional group for an amide is as follows:

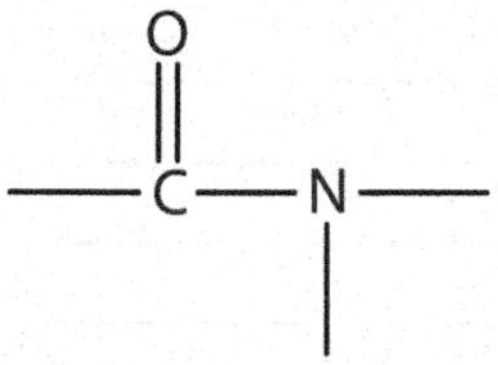

$$—\overset{\overset{\displaystyle O}{\|}}{C}—\underset{|}{N}—$$

- In names for amides, the *-ic acid* of the common name or the *-oic* ending of the IUPAC for the corresponding carboxylic acid is replaced by *-amide*.

EXERCISES

1. Draw the structure for each compound.
   a. formamide
   b. hexanamide
2. Draw the structure for each compound.
   a. propionamide
   b. butanamide
3. Name each compound with the common name, the IUPAC name, or both.
   a. 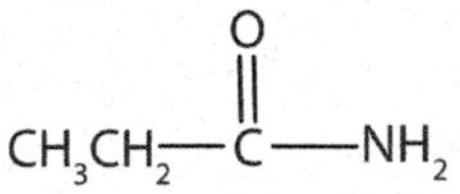
   $$CH_3CH_2—\overset{\overset{\displaystyle O}{\|}}{C}—NH_2$$
   b. 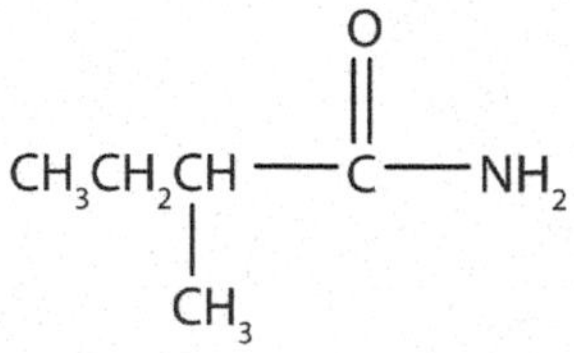
   $$CH_3CH_2\underset{\underset{\displaystyle CH_3}{|}}{CH}—\overset{\overset{\displaystyle O}{\|}}{C}—NH_2$$
4. Name the compound.

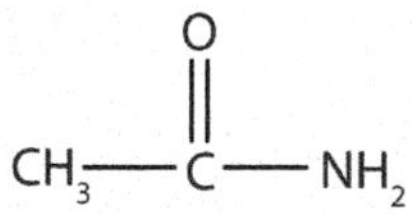

$$CH_3—\overset{\overset{\displaystyle O}{\|}}{C}—NH_2$$

ANSWERS

1. a. 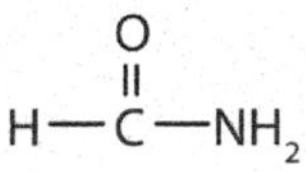
   $$H—\overset{\overset{\displaystyle O}{\|}}{C}—NH_2$$
   b. 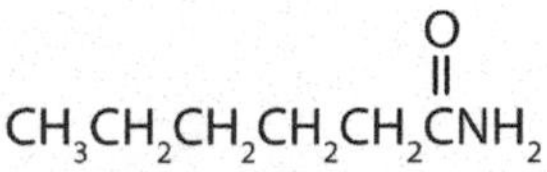
   $$CH_3CH_2CH_2CH_2CH_2\overset{\overset{\displaystyle O}{\|}}{C}NH_2$$
3. a. propionamide (propanamide)
   b. α-methylbutyramide (2-methylbutanamide)

15. PHYSICAL PROPERTIES OF AMIDES

LEARNING OBJECTIVES

1. Compare the boiling points of amides with alcohols of similar molar mass.
2. Compare the solubilities in water of amides of five or fewer carbon atoms with the solubilities of comparable alkanes and alcohols in water.

With the exception of formamide ($HCONH_2$), which is a liquid, all simple amides are solids (Table 15.6). The lower members of the series are soluble in water, with borderline solubility occurring in those that have five or six carbon atoms. Like the esters, solutions of amides in water usually are neutral—neither acidic nor basic.

TABLE 15.6 Physical Constants of Some Unsubstituted Amides

Condensed Structural Formula	Name	Melting Point (°C)	Boiling Point (°C)	Solubility in Water
$HCONH_2$	formamide	2	193	soluble
CH_3CONH_2	acetamide	82	222	soluble
$CH_3CH_2CONH_2$	propionamide	81	213	soluble
$CH_3CH_2CH_2CONH_2$	butyramide	115	216	soluble
$C_6H_5CONH_2$	benzamide	132	290	slightly soluble

The amides generally have high boiling points and melting points. These characteristics and their solubility in water result from the polar nature of the amide group and hydrogen bonding (Figure 15.7). (Similar hydrogen bonding plays a critical role in determining the structure and properties of proteins, deoxyribonucleic acid [DNA], ribonucleic acid [RNA], and other giant molecules so important to life processes. See Chapter 19.)

FIGURE 15.7 Hydrogen Bonding in Amides

Amide molecules can engage in hydrogen bonding with water molecules (a). Those amides with a hydrogen atom on the nitrogen atom can also engage in hydrogen bonding (b). Both hydrogen bonding networks extend in all directions.

(a)

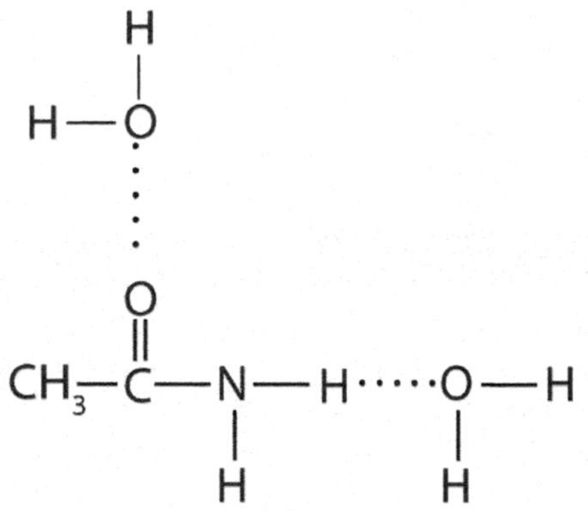

$$\begin{array}{c} H \\ | \\ H{-}O \\ \vdots \\ O \\ \| \\ CH_3{-}C{-}N{-}H\cdots O{-}H \\ \quad\quad | \quad\quad\quad | \\ \quad\quad H \quad\quad\quad H \end{array}$$

(b)

$$CH_3{-}\overset{\overset{O}{\|}}{C}{-}\underset{\underset{H}{|}}{N}{-}H\cdots O{=}\underset{\underset{CH_3}{|}}{C}{-}\overset{\overset{H}{|}}{N}{-}H$$

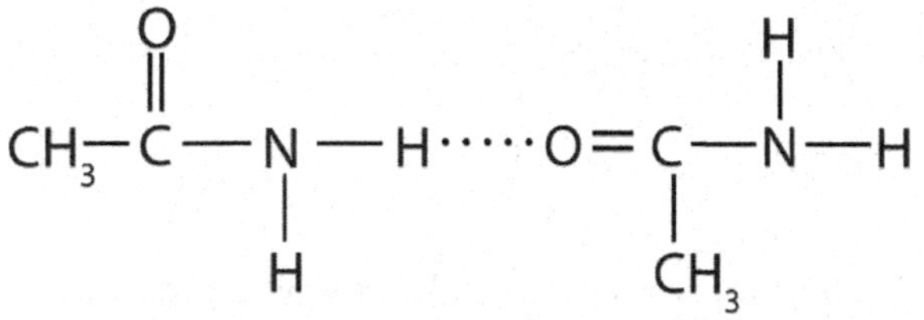

CONCEPT REVIEW EXERCISES

1. Which compound has the higher boiling point—pentanamide ($CH_3CH_2CH_2CH_2CONH_2$) or propyl acetate ($CH_3COOCH_2CH_2CH_3$)? Explain.
2. Which compound is more soluble in water—propanamide ($CH_3CH_2CONH_2$) or 1-pentene ($CH_2{=}CHCH_2CH_2CH_3$)? Explain.

ANSWERS

1. pentanamide because the nitrogen-to-hydrogen (N–H) and the carbon-to-oxygen double (C=O) bonds can engage in hydrogen bonding; propyl acetate cannot engage in hydrogen bonding
2. propanamide because the N–H and C=O bonds can engage in hydrogen bonding with water; 1-pentene cannot engage in hydrogen bonding with water

KEY TAKEAWAYS

- Most amides are solids at room temperature; the boiling points of amides are much higher than those of alcohols of similar molar mass.
- Amides of five or fewer carbon atoms are soluble in water?.

EXERCISES

1. Which compound has the higher boiling point—butyramide ($CH_3CH_2CH_2CONH_2$) or ethyl acetate ($CH_3COOCH_2CH_3$)? Explain.
2. Which compound has the higher boiling point—butyramide or dimethylacetamide [$CH_3CON(CH_3)_2$]? Explain.
3. Which compound is more soluble in water—acetamide (CH_3CONH_2) or 1-butene ($CH_2{=}CHCH_2CH_3$)? Explain.
4. Which compound is more soluble in water—$CH_3CONHCH_3$ or 2-methylbutane [$CH_3CH(CH_3)CH_2CH_3$]? Explain.

ANSWERS

1. butyramide because the nitrogen-to-hydrogen (N–H) and the carbon-to-oxygen double (C=O) bonds can engage in hydrogen bonding; ethyl acetate cannot engage in hydrogen bonding
3. acetamide because the N–H and C=O bonds can engage in hydrogen bonding with water; 1-butene cannot engage in hydrogen bonding with water

16. FORMATION OF AMIDES

LEARNING OBJECTIVE

1. **Describe the preparation procedure for amides.**

The addition of ammonia (NH_3) to a carboxylic acid forms an amide, but the reaction is very slow in the laboratory at room temperature. Water molecules are split out, and a bond is formed between the nitrogen atom and the carbonyl carbon atom.

$$\underset{\text{Acetic acid}}{CH_3COOH} + NH_3 \longrightarrow \underset{\text{Acetamide}}{CH_3CONH_2} + H_2O$$

In living cells, amide formation is catalyzed by enzymes. Proteins are polyamides; they are formed by joining amino acids into long chains. In proteins, the amide functional group is called a *peptide bond*. (For more information about proteins, see Chapter 18, [Unsupported Reference Type: chapter-section].)

16.1 Polyamides

polyamide

A condensation polymer in which the monomer units are joined by an amide linkage.

Just as the reaction of a diol and a diacid forms a polyester (Section 8), the reaction of a diacid and a diamine yields a **polyamide**. The two difunctional monomers often employed are adipic acid and 1,6-hexanediamine. The monomers condense by splitting out water to form a new product, which is still difunctional and thus can react further to yield a polyamide polymer.

$$n\,\underset{\text{1,6-Hexanediamine}}{H_2NCH_2CH_2CH_2CH_2CH_2CH_2NH_2} + n\,\underset{\text{Adipic acid}}{HOOCCH_2CH_2CH_2CH_2COOH} \longrightarrow$$

$$\underset{\text{Nylon 66 (a polyamide)}}{—HN[COCH_2CH_2CH_2CH_2CONHCH_2CH_2CH_2CH_2CH_2CH_2NH]_nCO—} + 2n\,H_2O$$

Some polyamides are known as *nylons*. Nylons are among the most widely used synthetic fibers—for example, they are used in ropes, sails, carpets, clothing, tires, brushes, and parachutes. They also can be molded into blocks for use in electrical equipment, gears, bearings, and valves.

CONCEPT REVIEW EXERCISES

1. Write the condensed structural formulas and give names of the two compounds from which butanamide ($CH_3CH_2CH_2CONH_2$) is formed.

2. Write the condensed structural formulas and names of the two compounds from which $CH_3CH_2CH_2CH_2CH_2CONHCH_2CH_2CH_3$ is formed.

ANSWERS

1. $CH_3CH_2CH_2COOH$ (butanoic acid) and NH_3 (ammonia)
2. $CH_3CH_2CH_2CH_2CH_2COOH$ (hexanoic acid) and $CH_3CH_2CH_2NH_2$ (propylamine)

KEY TAKEAWAY

- Amides are prepared by the reaction of a carboxylic acid with ammonia or an amine.

EXERCISES

1. Write the condensed structural formulas and names of the two compounds from which pentanamide ($CH_3CH_2CH_2CH_2CONH_2$) is formed.
2. Write the condensed structural formulas and names of the two compounds from which $CH_3CONHCH_3$ is formed.

ANSWER

1. $CH_3CH_2CH_2CH_2COOH$ (pentanoic acid) and NH_3 (ammonia)

17. CHEMICAL PROPERTIES OF AMIDES: HYDROLYSIS

LEARNING OBJECTIVE

1. **Identify the typical reaction that amides undergo.**

Generally, amides resist hydrolysis in plain water, even after prolonged heating. In the presence of added acid or base, however, hydrolysis proceeds at a moderate rate. In living cells, amide hydrolysis is catalyzed by enzymes. Amide hydrolysis is illustrated in the following example:

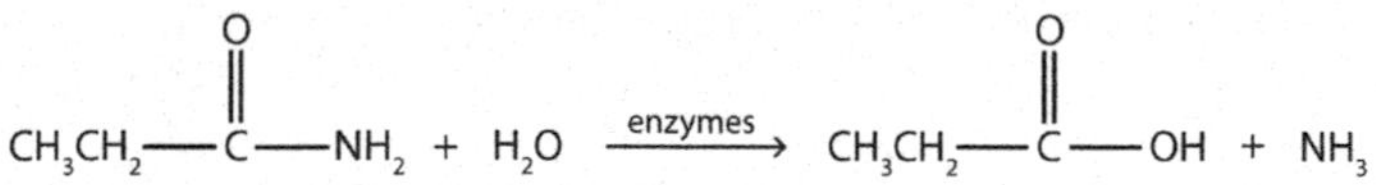

$$CH_3CH_2-\overset{\overset{O}{\|}}{C}-NH_2 + H_2O \xrightarrow{\text{enzymes}} CH_3CH_2-\overset{\overset{O}{\|}}{C}-OH + NH_3$$

Note

Hydrolysis of an amide in acid solution actually gives a carboxylic acid and the *salt* of ammonia or an amine (the ammonia or amine initially formed is neutralized by the acid). Basic hydrolysis gives a salt of the carboxylic acid and ammonia or an amine.

EXAMPLE 17

Write the equation for the hydrolysis of each compound.

1. butyramide
2. benzamide

Solution

1. The hydrolysis of a simple amide produces an organic acid and ammonia. Butyramide thus yields butyric acid and ammonia.

$$CH_3CH_2CH_2{-}\overset{\overset{\displaystyle O}{\|}}{C}{-}NH_2 + H_2O \longrightarrow CH_3CH_2CH_2{-}\overset{\overset{\displaystyle O}{\|}}{C}{-}OH + NH_3$$

2. The hydrolysis of an amide produces an organic acid and ammonia. Benzamide thus yields benzoic acid and ammonia.

$$C_6H_5{-}\overset{\overset{\displaystyle O}{\|}}{C}{-}NH_2 + H_2O \longrightarrow C_6H_5{-}\overset{\overset{\displaystyle O}{\|}}{C}{-}OH + NH_3$$

SKILL-BUILDING EXERCISE

Write the equation for the hydrolysis of each compound.

1. propionamide (propanamide)
2. hexanamide

Career Focus: Athletic Trainer

Athletic training is an allied health-care profession recognized by the American Medical Association. The athletic trainer's role is to recognize, evaluate, and provide immediate care for athletic injuries; prevent athletic injuries by taping, bandaging, and bracing vulnerable body parts; make referrals to medical doctors when necessary; and rehabilitate injured athletes. Athletic trainers work in high schools, colleges, and other organizations where athletics programs are found. Athletic trainers usually have a degree from an accredited athletic training program whose curriculum includes such basic science courses as biology, chemistry, and physics. These studies provide the necessary background for more applied courses, such as anatomy and physiology, exercise physiology, kinesiology, and nutrition. Knowledge of chemistry is necessary for understanding pharmacological and medical terminology. For example, athletic trainers must understand the action of numerous drugs, many of which are esters, amines, or amides like those mentioned in this chapter.

Athletic trainers may have administrative duties, such as the responsibility for ordering supplies. They also need to be able to evaluate nutritional supplements because providing the wrong one can get an athlete banned from competition and may bring sanctions against a school. In short, the athletic trainer is responsible for the overall health and well-being of the athletes in his or her charge.

CONCEPT REVIEW EXERCISES

1. What are the products of the hydrolysis of an amide?
2. When the amide CH3CH2CH2CH2CONH2 is hydrolyzed in an NaOH solution, the products are CH3CH2CH2CH2COO$^-$Na$^+$ and NH3. What products are obtained when CH3CH2CH2CH2CONH2 is hydrolyzed in an hydrochloric acid solution?

ANSWERS

1. a carboxylic acid and ammonia or an amine
2. CH3CH2CH2CH2COOH and NH4Cl

KEY TAKEAWAY

- The hydrolysis of an amide produces a carboxylic acid and ammonia or an amine.

EXERCISES

1. Complete each equation.
   a. 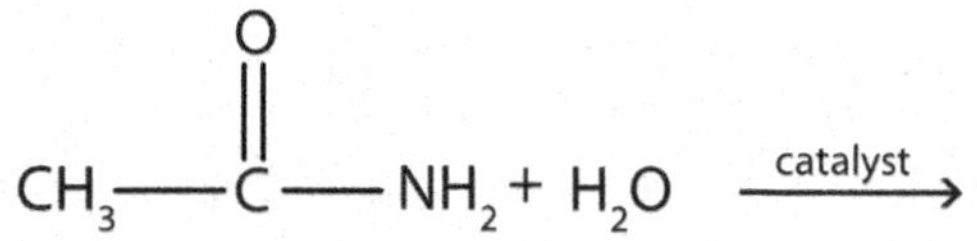
   $$CH_3{-}\overset{\displaystyle O}{\overset{\|}{C}}{-}NH_2 + H_2O \xrightarrow{\text{catalyst}}$$
   b. 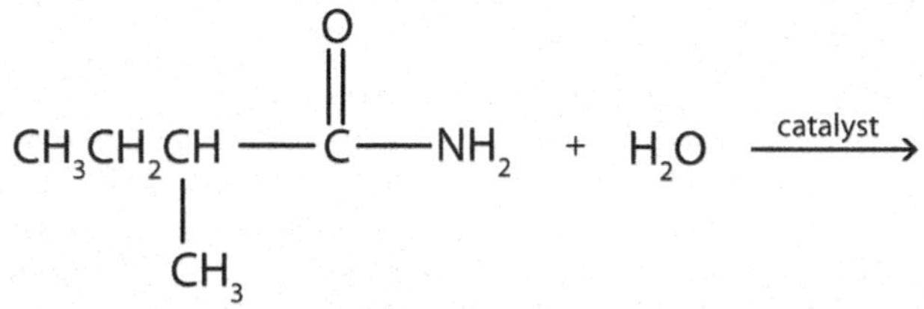
   $$\underset{\displaystyle CH_3}{CH_3CH_2\underset{|}{C}H}{-}\overset{\displaystyle O}{\overset{\|}{C}}{-}NH_2 + H_2O \xrightarrow{\text{catalyst}}$$
2. Complete each equation.
   a. 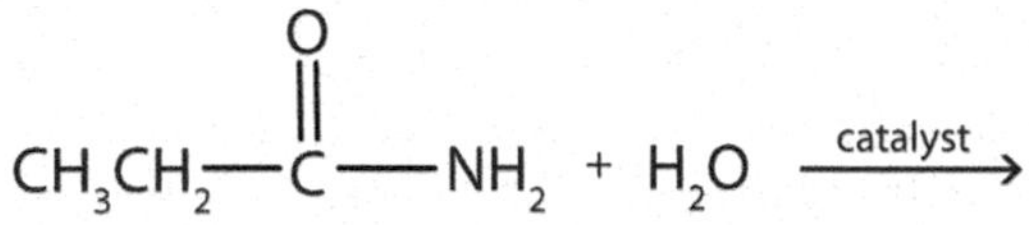
   $$CH_3CH_2{-}\overset{\displaystyle O}{\overset{\|}{C}}{-}NH_2 + H_2O \xrightarrow{\text{catalyst}}$$
   b.
   $$CH_3CH_2CH_2{-}\overset{\displaystyle O}{\overset{\|}{C}}{-}NH_2 + H_2O \xrightarrow{\text{catalyst}}$$

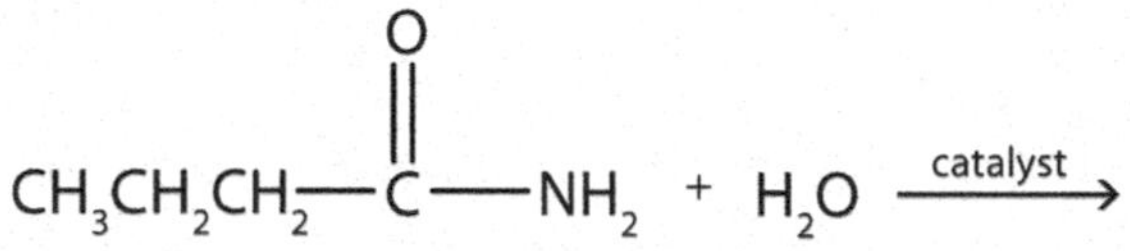

ANSWER

1. a. CH3COOH + NH3
   b.
   $$\underset{\displaystyle CH_3}{CH_3CH_2\underset{|}{C}H}{-}\overset{\displaystyle O}{\overset{\|}{C}}{-}OH{-}NH_2$$

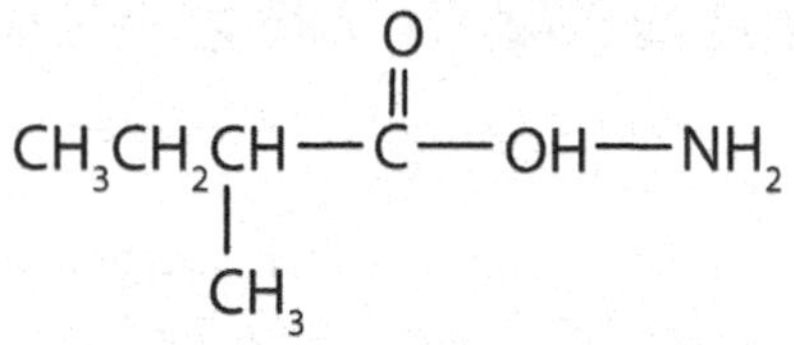

18. END-OF-CHAPTER MATERIAL

Chapter Summary

To ensure that you understand the material in this chapter, you should review the meanings of the following bold terms in the summary and ask yourself how they relate to the topics in the chapter.

A **carboxylic acid** (RCOOH) contains the functional group COOH, called the **carboxyl group**, which has an OH group attached to a carbonyl carbon atom. An **ester** (RCOOR′) has an OR′ group attached to a carbonyl carbon atom. An **amine** is derived from ammonia (NH_3), with one, two, or all three of the hydrogen atoms of NH_3 replaced by an alkyl (or an aryl) group. The **amide** functional group has a carbonyl group joined to a nitrogen atom from NH_3 or an amine.

There are many familiar carboxylic acids. The R group may be a hydrogen atom (as in formic acid, HCOOH), an alkyl group (as in acetic acid, CH_2COOH), or an aryl group (as in benzoic acid, C_6H_5COOH). The location of substituents along the carbon chain is indicated by a Greek letter (for common names) or a number (for names from the International Union of Pure and Applied Chemistry).

A carboxylic acid is formed by the oxidation of an aldehyde with the same number of carbon atoms. Because aldehydes are formed from primary alcohols, these alcohols are also a starting material for carboxylic acids.

Carboxylic acids have strong, often disagreeable, odors. They are highly polar molecules and readily engage in hydrogen bonding, so they have relatively high boiling points.

Carboxylic acids are weak acids. They react with bases to form salts and with carbonates and bicarbonates to form carbon dioxide gas and the salt of the acid.

Esters are pleasant-smelling compounds that are responsible for the fragrances of flowers and fruits. They have lower boiling points than comparable carboxylic acids because, even though ester molecules are somewhat polar, they cannot engage in hydrogen bonding. However, with water, esters can engage in hydrogen bonding; consequently, the low molar mass esters are soluble in water. Esters can be synthesized by **esterification**, in which a carboxylic acid and an alcohol are combined under acidic conditions. Esters are neutral compounds that undergo **hydrolysis**, a reaction with water. Under acidic conditions, hydrolysis is essentially the reverse of esterification. When carried out under basic conditions, the process is called **saponification**.

Inorganic acids also react with alcohols to form esters. Some of the most important esters in biochemistry are those formed from phosphoric acid.

Amines are nitrogen-containing organic molecules derived from ammonia (NH_3). A **primary (1°) amine** (RNH_2) has one organic group bonded to the nitrogen atom, a **secondary (2°) amine** (R_2NH) has two organic groups bonded to the nitrogen atom, and a **tertiary (3°) amine** (R_3N) has three organic groups bonded to the nitrogen atom. Amines are basic compounds that react with strong acids to produce ammonium (NH_4^+) salts. A cyclic compound in which the ring contains one or more noncarbon atoms is called a **heterocyclic compound**. There are many heterocyclic amines, including many physiologically important ones. **Alkaloids** are heterocyclic amines found in many plants. Caffeine, nicotine, and cocaine are familiar alkaloids.

Organic compounds containing a carbonyl group bonded to a nitrogen atom are amides, and the carbon-to-nitrogen bond is an amide linkage (or a peptide linkage). Most amides are colorless and odorless, and the lighter ones are soluble in water. Because they are polar molecules, amides have comparatively high boiling points and melting points. Amides are synthesized from carboxylic acids and NH_3 or amines. Amides are neutral compounds. They resist hydrolysis in water, but acids, bases, and enzymes catalyze the reaction.

ADDITIONAL EXERCISES

1. Of the families of organic compounds discussed in this chapter, which are known for their typically unpleasant odors? Which for their characteristically pleasant aromas?
2. What is esterification of a carboxylic acid? How does it differ from neutralization?
3. Like alcohols, phenols form esters with carboxylic acids. The hydrocarbon group from phenol is called phenyl. Draw the structure of phenyl acetate.
4. Describe the hydrogen bonding in carboxylic acids, both acid-acid and acid-water. How does this influence their physical properties?
5. Which compound is more soluble in water—benzoic acid or sodium benzoate? Explain.
6. Dicarboxylic acids have two carboxyl groups and are named with the ending *-dioic acid*. Give the equation for the reaction of 1,5-pentanedioic acid ($HOOCCH_2CH_2CH_2COOH$; common name, glutaric acid) with each of the following:
   a. 1 mol of NaOH
   b. 2 mol of NaOH
7. Without consulting tables, arrange the following compounds in order of increasing boiling point: butyl alcohol, methyl acetate, pentane, and propionic acid.

8. From which alcohol might each acid be prepared via oxidation with acidic dichromate?
   a. CH_3CH_2COOH
   b. HCOOH
   c. $HOOCH_2COOH$
   d. $(CH_3)_2CHCH_2COOH$
9. The distinctive aroma and flavor of oranges are due in part to octyl acetate, an ester formed from 1-octanol (octyl alcohol) and acetic acid. Write the condensed structural formula for octyl acetate.
10. A lactone is a cyclic ester. What product is formed in following reaction?

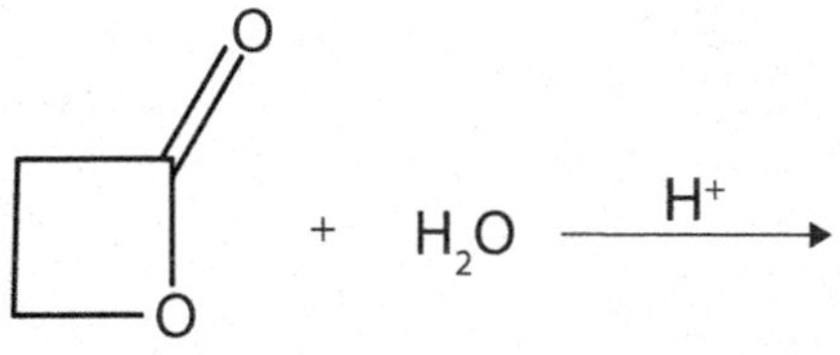

$$\text{(4-membered lactone)} + H_2O \xrightarrow{H^+}$$

11. A lactam is a cyclic amide. What product is formed in the following reaction?

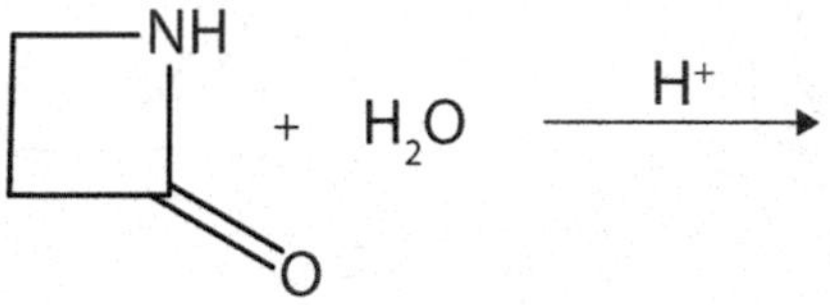

$$\text{(4-membered lactam, NH)} + H_2O \xrightarrow{H^+}$$

12. Draw the structures for the eight isomeric amines that have the molecular formula $C_4H_{11}N$. Give each a common name and classify it as primary, secondary, or tertiary.
13. Draw the structures for the five isomeric amines that have the molecular formula C_7H_9N and contain a benzene ring. Classify each compound as primary, secondary, or tertiary.
14. Cocaine is usually used in the form of the salt cocaine hydrochloride and sniffed up the nose. Some prefer to ingest their cocaine by smoking it (mixed with tobacco, for example). Before smoking, the cocaine hydrochloride must be converted back to the free base (that is, to the molecular form). Explain the choice of dosage form for each route of administration.
15. Draw the structures all the isomeric amides that have the molecular formula C_4H_9NO.
16. An ester with the molecular formula $C_6H_{12}O_2$ was hydrolyzed in aqueous acid to yield an acid Y and an alcohol Z. Oxidation of the alcohol with potassium dichromate ($K_2Cr_2O_7$) gave the identical acid Y. What is the condensed structural formula of the ester?
17. The neutralization of 125 mL of a 0.400 M NaOH solution requires 5.10 g of a monocarboxylic acid. Draw all the possible structures for the acid.
18. If 3.00 g of acetic acid reacts with excess methanol, how many grams of methyl acetate are formed?
19. How many milliliters of a 0.100 M barium hydroxide solution are required to neutralize 0.500 g of dichloroacetic acid?

ANSWERS

1. unpleasant: carboxylic acids; pleasant: esters
3.

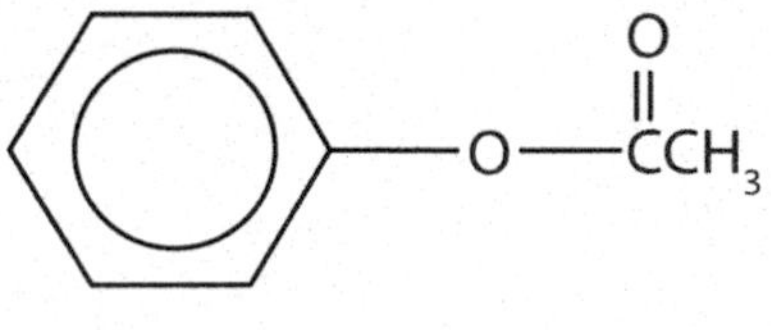

$$C_6H_5\text{—O—}\overset{O}{\overset{\|}{C}}CH_3$$

5. sodium benzoate because it is ionic and forms ion-dipole forces with water; benzoic acid can engage in hydrogen bonding only with water
7. pentane < methyl acetate < butyl alcohol < propionic acid
9. $CH_3COOCH_2CH_2CH_2CH_2CH_2CH_2CH_2CH_3$

11. $H_3N^+CH_2CH_2COOH$
13.

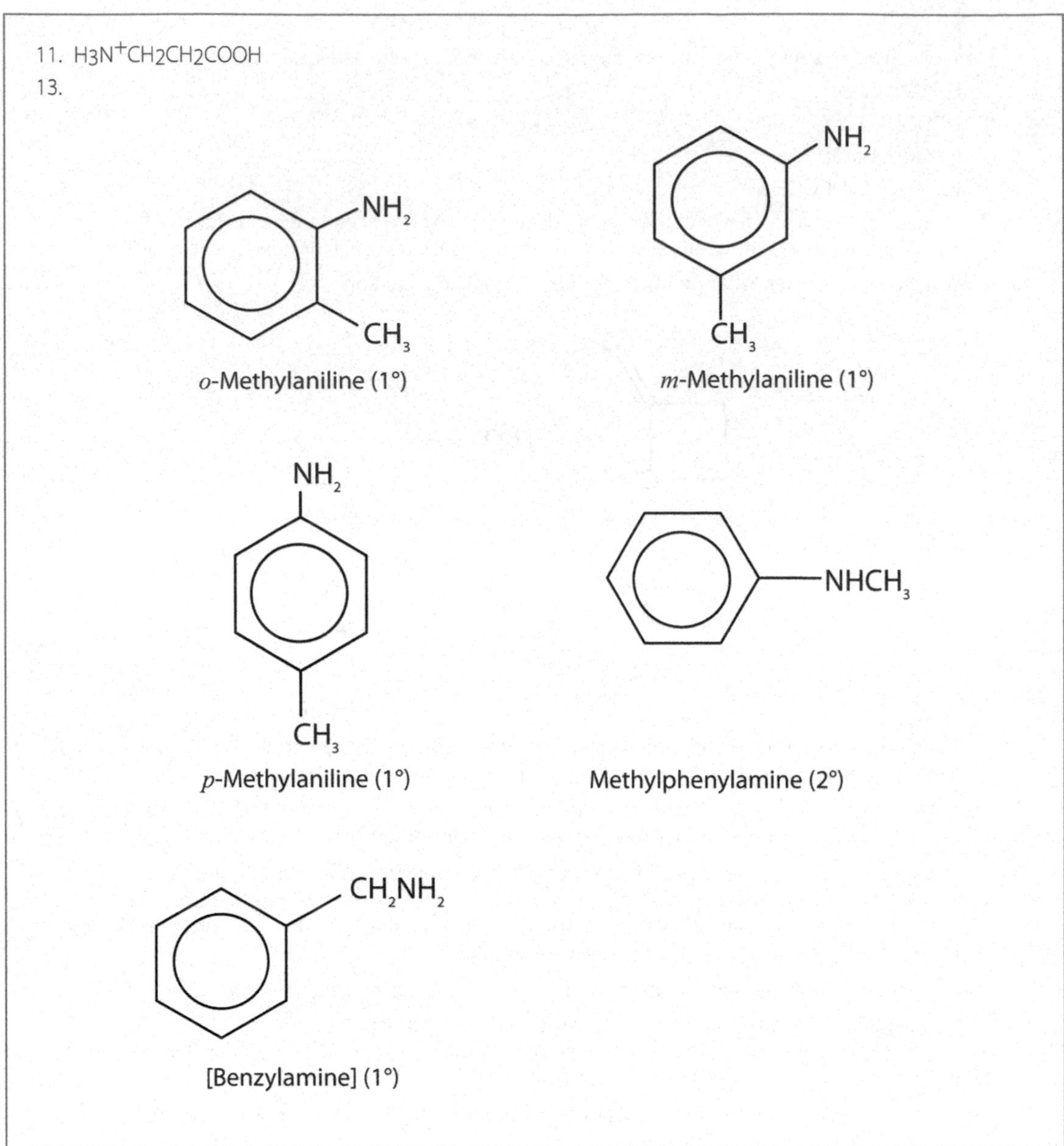

15.

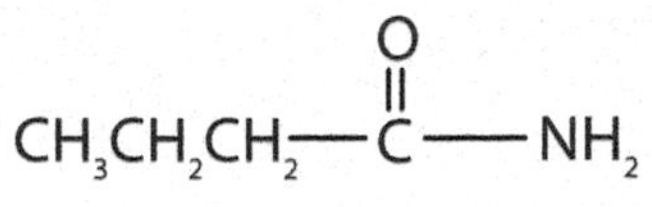

$CH_3CH_2CH_2{-}C({=}O){-}NH_2$

Butanamide

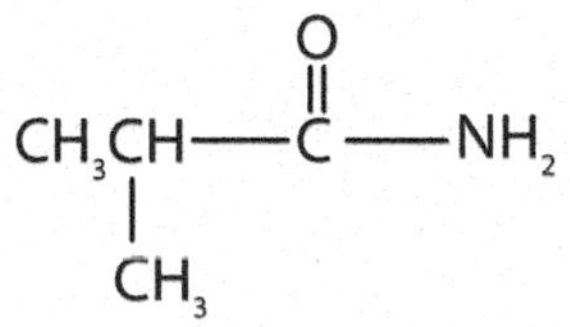

$CH_3CH(CH_3){-}C({=}O){-}NH_2$

2-Methylpropanamide

$H_3C{-}C({=}O){-}N(CH_3){-}CH_3$

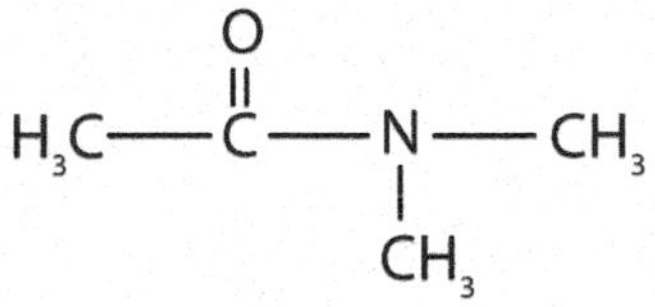

N,N-dimethylethanamide

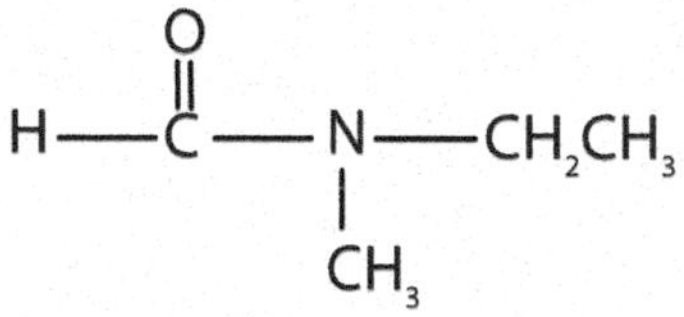

$H{-}C({=}O){-}N(CH_3){-}CH_2CH_3$

N-ethyl-N-methylmethanamide

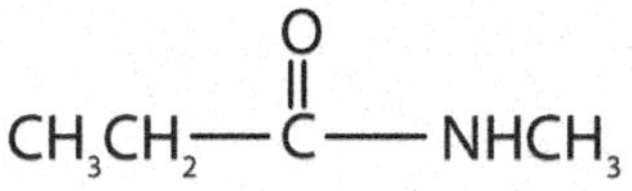

$CH_3CH_2{-}C({=}O){-}NHCH_3$

N-methylpropanamide

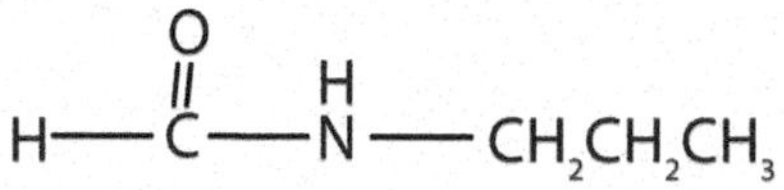

$H{-}C({=}O){-}N(H){-}CH_2CH_2CH_3$

N-propylmethanamide

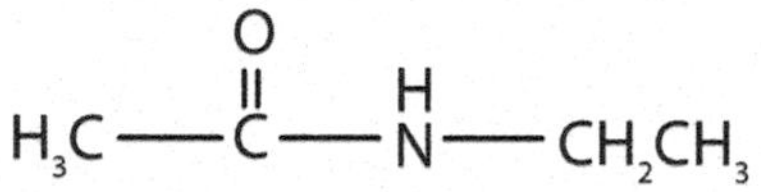

$H_3C{-}C({=}O){-}N(H){-}CH_2CH_3$

N-ethylethanamide

$H{-}C({=}O){-}N(H){-}CH(CH_3)CH_3$

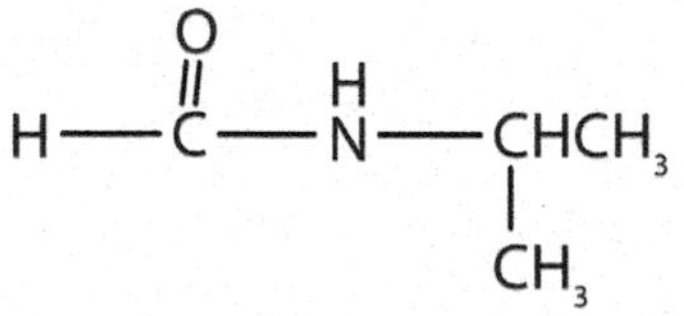

N-isopropylmethanamide

17.

$CH_3CH_2CH_2CH_2COOH$

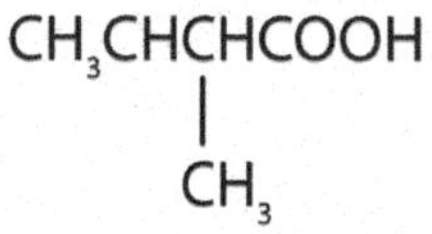

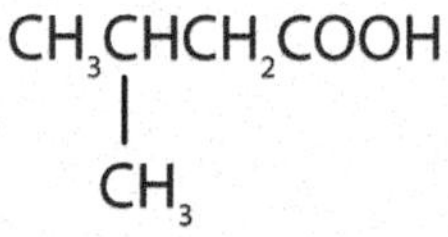

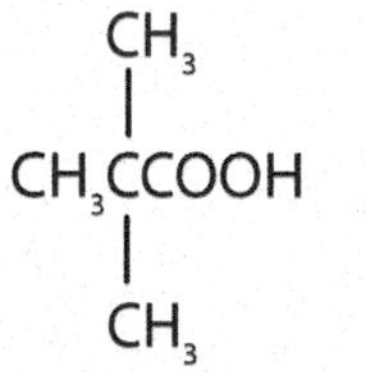

$CH_3CHCHCOOH$ (with CH_3 on the third carbon)

CH_3CHCH_2COOH (with CH_3 on the second carbon)

$CH_3C(CH_3)_2COOH$

19. 20.0 mL

CHAPTER 16
Carbohydrates

Opening Essay

In the United States, 17.9 million people have been diagnosed with diabetes, and experts estimate that at least another 5.7 million people have the disease but have not been diagnosed. In 2006, diabetes was the seventh leading cause of death, listed on 72,507 death certificates. Moreover, it was a contributing factor in over 200,000 deaths in which the cause was listed as something else, such as heart or kidney disease.

People with diabetes are impaired in their ability to metabolize glucose, a sugar needed by the body for energy; as a result, excessive quantities of glucose accumulate in the blood and the urine. The characteristic symptoms of diabetes are weight loss, constant hunger, extreme thirst, and frequent urination (the kidneys excrete large amounts of water in an attempt to remove the excess sugar from the blood).

An important diagnostic test for diabetes is the *oral glucose tolerance test*, which measures the level of glucose in blood plasma. A first measurement is made after a fast of at least 8 h, followed by another measurement 2 h after the person drinks a flavored solution of 75 g of glucose dissolved in water. At the second measurement, the glucose plasma level should be no higher than 139 mg/dL. Individuals with a value between 140 and 199 mg/dL are diagnosed with prediabetes, while those with a value of 200 mg/dL or above are diagnosed with diabetes. Following a diagnosis of diabetes a person will need to monitor his or her blood glucose levels daily (or more often) using a glucose meter.

Using a Glucose Meter to Test Blood Glucose Level

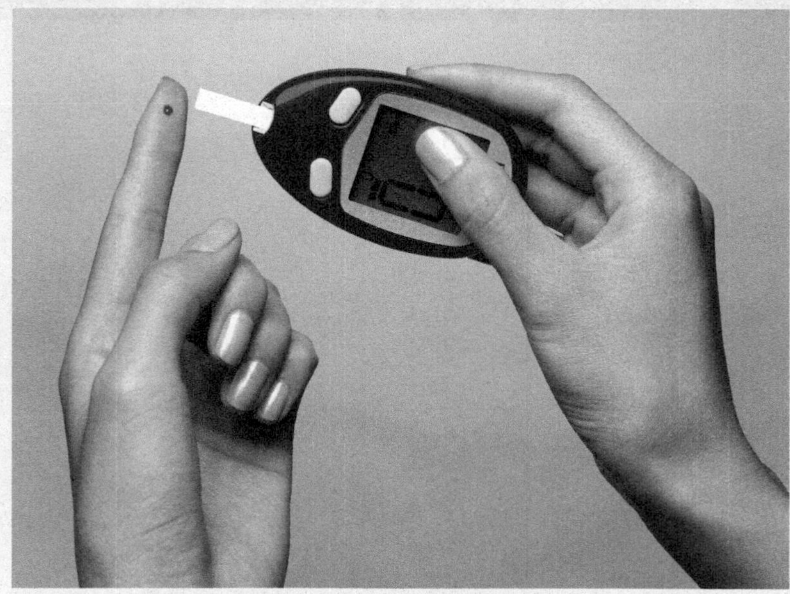

Glucose is one of the carbohydrates you will learn about in this chapter as we begin the study of **biochemistry**—the chemistry of molecules found in living organisms. Later we will study the other three major types of macromolecules found in living organisms: lipids, proteins, and nucleic acids.

biochemistry

The chemistry of molecules found in living organisms.

1. CARBOHYDRATES

LEARNING OBJECTIVE

1. Recognize carbohydrates and classify them as mono-, di-, or polysaccharides.

carbohydrate

A compound composed of carbon, hydrogen, and oxygen atoms that is a polyhydroxy aldehyde or ketone or a compound that can be broken down to form such a compound. It is one of the three main components of the human diet.

All **carbohydrates** consist of carbon, hydrogen, and oxygen atoms and are polyhydroxy aldehydes or ketones or are compounds that can be broken down to form such compounds. Examples of carbohydrates include starch, fiber, the sweet-tasting compounds called sugars, and structural materials such as cellulose. The term *carbohydrate* had its origin in a misinterpretation of the molecular formulas of many of these substances. For example, because its formula is $C_6H_{12}O_6$, glucose was once thought to be a "carbon hydrate" with the structure $C_6·6H_2O$.

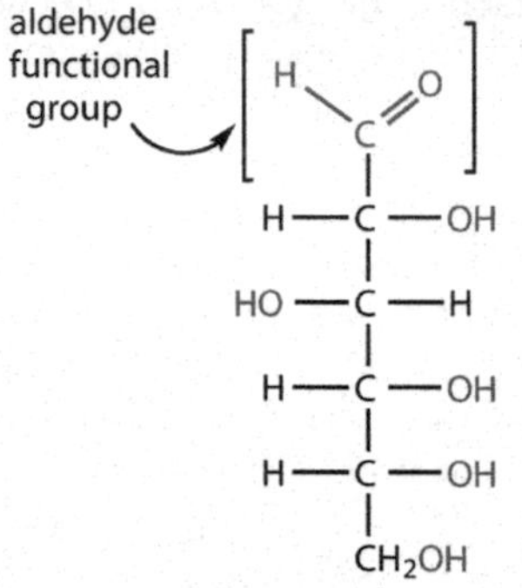

aldehyde functional group

H—C—OH
HO—C—H
H—C—OH
H—C—OH
CH_2OH

Because glucose has an aldehyde functional group and several -OH (hydroxyl) groups, it is described as a polyhydroxy aldehyde.

EXAMPLE 1

Which compounds would be classified as carbohydrates?

1. 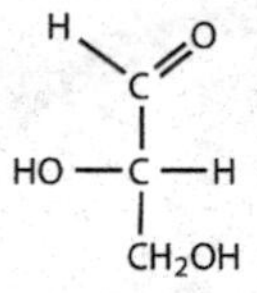 HCO—CHOH—CH_2OH (H, O; HO—C—H; CH_2OH)
2. 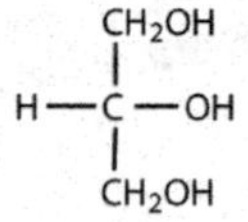 CH_2OH; H—C—OH; CH_2OH
3. 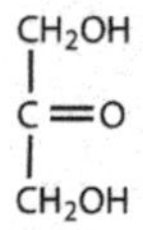 CH_2OH; C=O; CH_2OH
4. 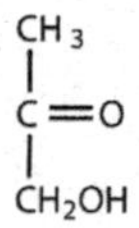 CH_3; C=O; CH_2OH

Solution

1. This is a carbohydrate because the molecule contains an aldehyde functional group with OH groups on the other two carbon atoms.
2. This is not a carbohydrate because the molecule does not contain an aldehyde or a ketone functional group.
3. This is a carbohydrate because the molecule contains a ketone functional group with OH groups on the other two carbon atoms.
4. This is not a carbohydrate; although it has a ketone functional group, one of the other carbons atoms does not have an OH group attached.

SKILL-BUILDING EXERCISE

Which compounds would be classified as carbohydrates?

1.

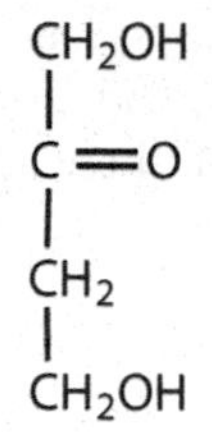

CH_2OH
|
$C{=}O$
|
CH_2
|
CH_2OH

2.

H   O
 \ //
  C
  |
HO—C—H
  |
H—C—OH
  |
CH_2OH

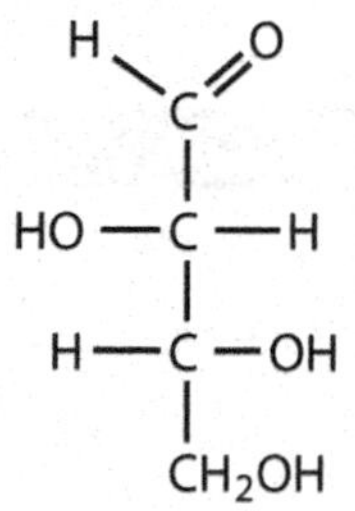

3.

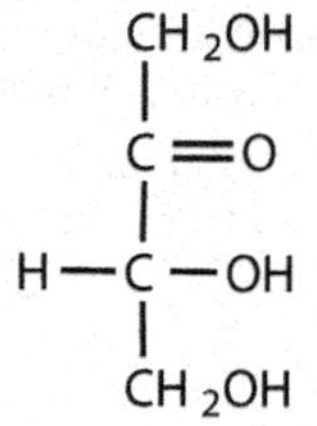

CH_2OH
|
$C{=}O$
|
H—C—OH
|
CH_2OH

4.

CH_2OH
|
H—C—OH
|
CH_2
|
CH_2OH

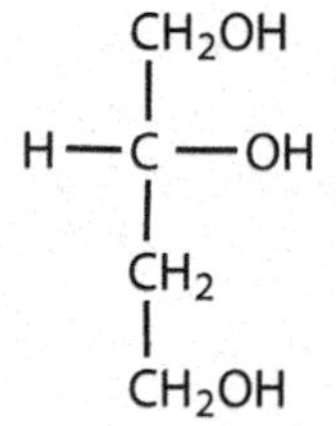

Green plants are capable of synthesizing glucose ($C_6H_{12}O_6$) from carbon dioxide (CO_2) and water (H_2O) by using solar energy in the process known as **photosynthesis**:

$$6CO_2 + 6H_2O + 686 \text{ kcal} \rightarrow C_6H_{12}O_6 + 6O_2$$

(The 686 kcal come from solar energy.) Plants can use the glucose for energy or convert it to larger carbohydrates, such as starch or cellulose. Starch provides energy for later use, perhaps as nourishment for a plant's seeds, while cellulose is the structural material of plants. We can gather and eat the parts of a plant that store energy—seeds, roots, tubers, and fruits—and use some of that energy ourselves. Carbohydrates are also needed for the synthesis of nucleic acids and many proteins and lipids.

photosynthesis
The process by which plants use solar energy to convert carbon dioxide and water to glucose.

Animals, including humans, cannot synthesize carbohydrates from carbon dioxide and water and are therefore dependent on the plant kingdom to provide these vital compounds. We use carbohydrates not only for food (about 60%–65% by mass of the average diet) but also for clothing (cotton, linen, rayon), shelter (wood), fuel (wood), and paper (wood).

monosaccharide

The simplest carbohydrate that cannot be hydrolyzed to produce smaller carbohydrate molecules.

disaccharide

A carbohydrate containing two monosaccharide units.

polysaccharide

A carbohydrate containing many monosaccharide units.

The simplest carbohydrates—those that cannot be hydrolyzed to produce even smaller carbohydrates—are called **monosaccharides**. Two or more monosaccharides can link together to form chains that contain from two to several hundred or thousand monosaccharide units. Prefixes are used to indicate the number of such units in the chains. **Disaccharide** molecules have two monosaccharide units, *trisaccharide* molecules have three units, and so on. Chains with many monosaccharide units joined together are called **polysaccharides**. All these so-called higher saccharides can be hydrolyzed back to their constituent monosaccharides.

Note

Compounds that cannot be hydrolyzed will not react with water to form two or more smaller compounds.

CONCEPT REVIEW EXERCISES

1. Why is photosynthesis important?
2. Identify the differences among monosaccharides, disaccharides, and polysaccharides.

ANSWERS

1. Photosynthesis is the process by which solar energy is used to reduce carbon dioxide to carbohydrates, which are needed for energy by plants and other living organisms that eat plants.
2. A monosaccharide is the simplest carbohydrate and cannot be hydrolyzed to produce a smaller carbohydrate; a disaccharide is composed of two monosaccharide units; and a polysaccharide contains many saccharide units.

KEY TAKEAWAYS

- Carbohydrates are an important group of biological molecules that includes sugars and starches.
- Photosynthesis is the process by which plants use energy from sunlight to synthesize carbohydrates.
- A monosaccharide is the simplest carbohydrate and cannot be hydrolyzed to produce a smaller carbohydrate molecule. Disaccharides contain two monosaccharide units, and polysaccharides contain many monosaccharide units.

EXERCISES

1. When an aqueous solution of trehalose is heated, two molecules of glucose are produced for each molecule of trehalose. Is trehalose a monosaccharide, a disaccharide, or a polysaccharide?
2. When an aqueous solution of arabinose is heated, no other molecules are produced. Is arabinose a monosaccharide, a disaccharide, or a polysaccharide?

ANSWER

1. Trehalose is a disaccharide because it is hydrolyzed into two molecules of glucose (a monosaccharide).

2. CLASSES OF MONOSACCHARIDES

LEARNING OBJECTIVES

1. **Classify monosaccharides as aldoses or ketoses and as trioses, tetroses, pentoses, or hexoses.**
2. **Distinguish between a D sugar and an L sugar.**

The naturally occurring monosaccharides contain three to seven carbon atoms per molecule. Monosaccharides of specific sizes may be indicated by names composed of a stem denoting the number of carbon atoms and the suffix *-ose*. For example, the terms *triose*, *tetrose*, *pentose*, and *hexose* signify monosaccharides with, respectively, three, four, five, and six carbon atoms. Monosaccharides are also classified as aldoses or ketoses. Those monosaccharides that contain an aldehyde functional group are called **aldoses**; those containing a ketone functional group on the second carbon atom are **ketoses**. Combining these classification systems gives general names that indicate both the type of carbonyl group *and* the number of carbon atoms in a molecule. Thus, monosaccharides are described as aldotetroses, aldopentoses, ketopentoses, ketoheptoses, and so forth. Glucose and fructose are specific examples of an aldohexose and a ketohexose, respectively.

aldose

A monosaccharide that contains an aldehyde functional group.

ketose

A monosaccharide that contains a ketone functional group on the second carbon atom.

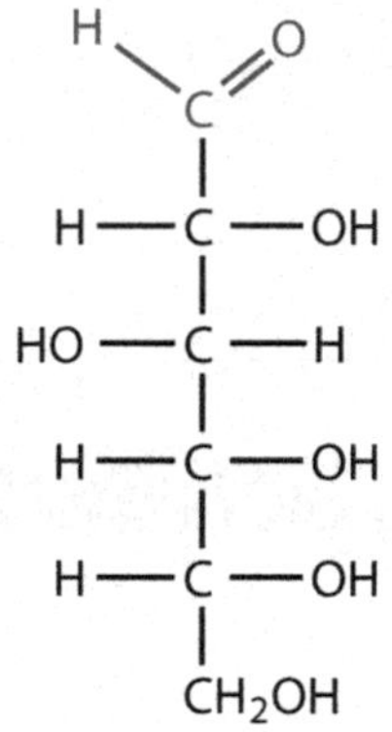

H—C=O
H—C—OH
HO—C—H
H—C—OH
H—C—OH
CH_2OH

Glucose
(an aldohexose)

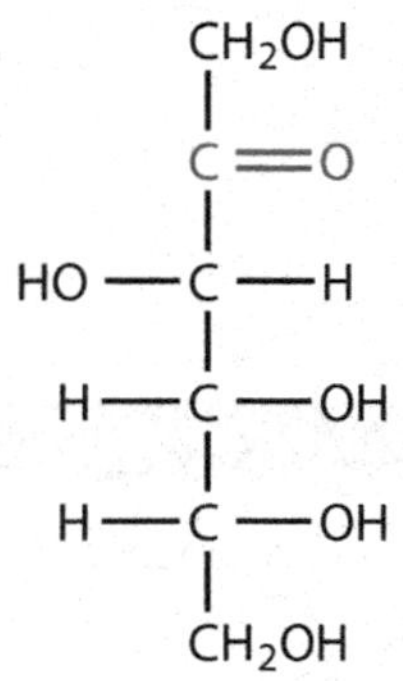

CH_2OH
C=O
HO—C—H
H—C—OH
H—C—OH
CH_2OH

Fructose
(a ketohexose)

EXAMPLE 2

Draw an example of each type of compound.

1. a ketopentose
2. an aldotetrose

Solution

1. The structure must have five carbon atoms with the second carbon atom being a carbonyl group and the other four carbon atoms each having an OH group attached. Several structures are possible, but one example is shown.

```
       CH2OH
        |
        C=O
        |
    H—C—OH
        |
  HO—C—H
        |
       CH2OH
```

2. The structure must have four carbon atoms with the first carbon atom part of the aldehyde functional group. The other three carbon atoms each have an OH group attached. Several structures are possible, but one example is shown.

```
     H    O
      \ //
        C
        |
  HO—C—H
        |
  HO—C—H
        |
       CH2OH
```

SKILL-BUILDING EXERCISE

Draw an example of each type of compound.

1. an aldohexose
2. a ketotetrose

stereoisomer

An isomer that has the same structural formula but differs in the arrangement of atoms or groups of atoms in three-dimensional space.

enantiomers

Stereoisomers that are nonsuperimposable mirror images of each other.

The simplest sugars are the trioses. The possible trioses are shown in part (a) of Figure 16.2; glyceraldehyde is an aldotriose, while dihydroxyacetone is a ketotriose. Notice that two structures are shown for glyceraldehyde. These structures are **stereoisomers**, isomers having the same structural formula but differing in the arrangement of atoms or groups of atoms in three-dimensional space. If you make models of the two stereoisomers of glyceraldehyde, you will find that you cannot place one model on top of the other and have each functional group point in the same direction. However, if you place one of the models in front of a mirror, the image in the mirror will be identical to the second stereoisomer in part (b) of Figure 16.2. Molecules that are nonsuperimposable (nonidentical) mirror images of each other are a type of stereoisomer called **enantiomers** (Greek *enantios*, meaning "opposite").

Note

Cis-trans (geometric) isomers were discussed in Chapter 13, [Unsupported Reference Type: chapter-section]. These are another type of stereoisomers.

FIGURE 16.2 Structures of the Trioses

(a) D- and L-glyceraldehyde are mirror images of each other and represent a pair of enantiomers. (b) A ball-and-stick model of D-glyceraldehyde is reflected in a mirror. Note that the reflection has the same structure as L-glyceraldehyde.

(a)

H—C(=O) / H—C—OH / CH_2OH
D-(+)-Glyceraldehyde

O=C—H / H—C—OH / CH_2OH
L-(-)-Glyceraldehyde

CH_2OH / C=O / CH_2OH
Dihydoxyacetone

(b)

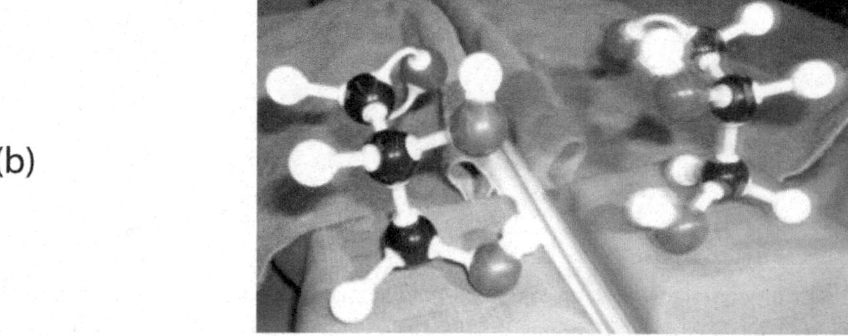

A key characteristic of enantiomers is that they have a carbon atom to which four different groups are attached. Note, for example, the four different groups attached to the central carbon atom of glyceraldehyde (part (a) of Figure 16.2). A carbon atom that has four different groups attached is a **chiral carbon**. If a molecule contains one or more chiral carbons, it is likely to exist as two or more stereoisomers. Dihydroxyacetone does not contain a chiral carbon and thus does not exist as a pair of stereoisomers. Glyceraldehyde, however, has a chiral carbon and exists as a pair of enantiomers. Except for the direction in which each enantiomer rotates plane-polarized light, these two molecules have identical physical properties. One enantiomer has a specific rotation of +8.7°, while the other has a specific rotation of −8.7°.

chiral carbon

A carbon atom that has four different groups attached to it.

H. Emil Fischer, a German chemist, developed the convention commonly used for writing two-dimensional representations of the monosaccharides, such as those in part (a) of Figure 16.2. In these structural formulas, the aldehyde group is written at the top, and the hydrogen atoms and OH groups that are attached to each chiral carbon are written to the right or left. (If the monosaccharide is a ketose, the ketone functional group is the second carbon atom.) Vertical lines represent bonds pointing away from you, while horizontal lines represent bonds coming toward you. The formulas of chiral molecules represented in this manner are referred to as *Fischer projections*.

The two enantiomers of glyceraldehyde are especially important because monosaccharides with more than three carbon atoms can be considered as being derived from them. Thus, D- and L-glyceraldehyde provide reference points for designating and drawing all other monosaccharides. Sugars whose Fischer projections terminate in the same configuration as D-glyceraldehyde are designated as **D sugars**; those derived from L-glyceraldehyde are designated as **L sugars**.

D sugar

A sugar whose Fischer projection terminates in the same configuration as D-glyceraldehyde.

L sugar

A sugar whose Fischer projection terminates in the same configuration as L-glyceraldehyde.

Note

By convention, the penultimate (next-to-last) carbon atom has been chosen as the carbon atom that determines if a sugar is D or L. It is the chiral carbon farthest from the aldehyde or ketone functional group.

Looking Closer: Polarized Light

A beam of ordinary light can be pictured as a bundle of waves; some move up and down, some sideways, and others at all other conceivable angles. When a beam of light has been polarized, however, the waves in the bundle all vibrate in a single plane. Light altered in this way is called *plane-polarized light*. Much of what chemists know about stereoisomers comes from studying the effects they have on plane-polarized light. In this illustration, the light on the left is not polarized, while that on the right is polarized.

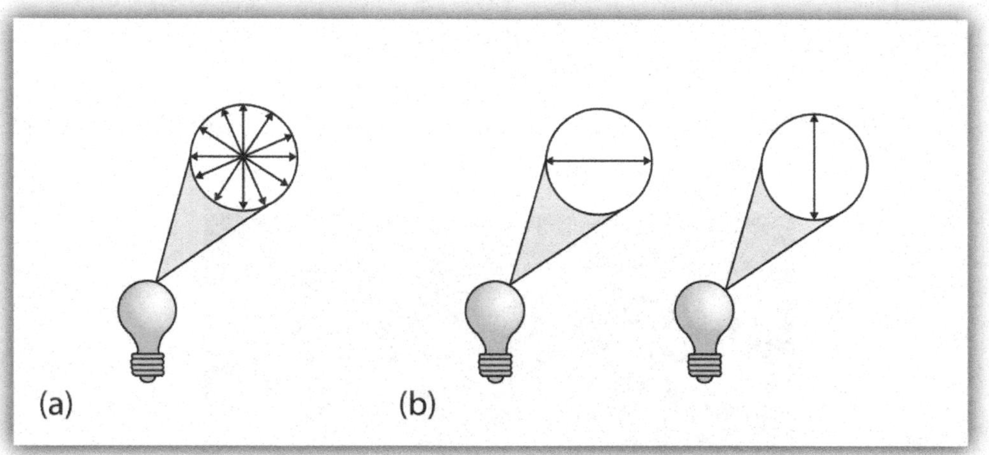

Sunlight, in general, is not polarized; light from an ordinary light bulb or an ordinary flashlight is not polarized. One way to polarize ordinary light is to pass it through Polaroid sheets, special plastic sheets containing carefully oriented organic compounds that permit only light vibrating in a single plane to pass through. To the eye, polarized light doesn't "look" any different from nonpolarized light. We can detect polarized light, however, by using a second sheet of polarizing material, as shown here.

In the photo on the left, two Polaroid sheets are aligned in the same direction; plane-polarized light from the first Polaroid sheet can pass through the second sheet. In the photo on the right, the top Polaroid sheet has been rotated 90° and now blocks the plane-polarized light that comes through the first Polaroid sheet.

Certain substances act on polarized light by rotating the plane of vibration. Such substances are said to be optically active. The extent of optical activity is measured by a polarimeter, an instrument that contains two polarizing lenses separated by a sample tube, as shown in the accompanying figure. With the sample tube empty, maximum light reaches the observer's eye when the two lenses are aligned so that both pass light vibrating in the same plane. When an optically active substance is placed in the sample tube, that substance rotates the plane of polarization of the light passing through it, so that the polarized light emerging from the sample tube is vibrating in a different direction than when it entered the tube. To see the maximum amount of light when the sample is in place, the observer must rotate one lens to accommodate the change in the plane of polarization.

Diagram of a Polarimeter

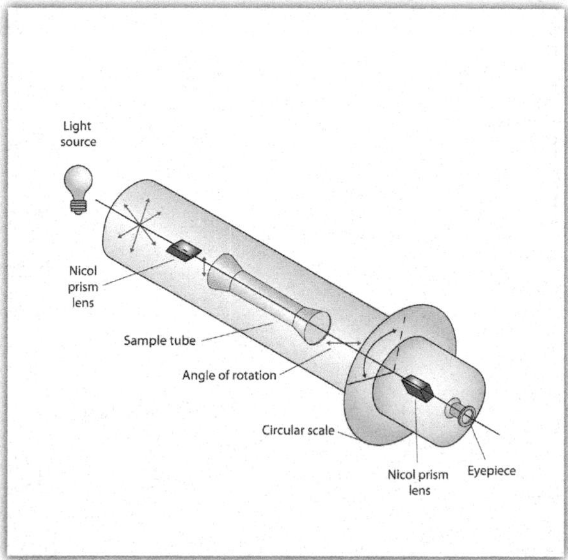

Some optically active substances rotate the plane of polarized light to the right (clockwise) from the observer's point of view. These compounds are said to be dextrorotatory; substances that rotate light to the left (counterclockwise) are levorotatory. To denote the direction of rotation, a positive sign (+) is given to dextrorotatory substances, and a negative sign (−) is given to levorotatory substances.

CONCEPT REVIEW EXERCISES

1. What is a chiral carbon?
2. Describe how enantiomers differ.

ANSWERS

1. A chiral carbon is a carbon atom with four different groups attached to it.
2. Enantiomers are mirror images of each other; they differ in the arrangements of atoms around a chiral carbon.

KEY TAKEAWAYS

- Monosaccharides can be classified by the number of carbon atoms in the structure and/or the type of carbonyl group they contain (aldose or ketose).
- Most monosaccharides contain at least one chiral carbon and can form stereoisomers.
- Enantiomers are a specific type of stereoisomers that are mirror images of each other.

EXERCISES

1. Identify each sugar as an aldose or a ketose and then as a triose, tetrose, pentose, or hexose.

   a. D-glucose

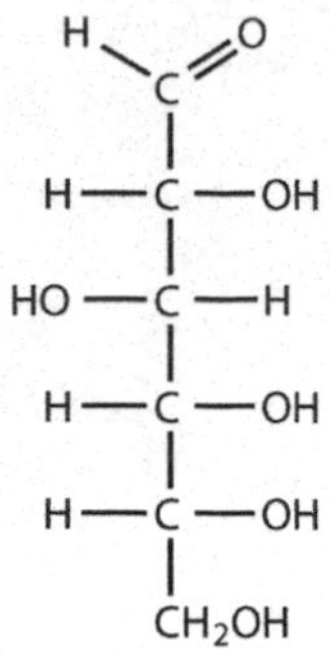

   H—C=O
   H—C—OH
   HO—C—H
   H—C—OH
   H—C—OH
   CH_2OH

   b. L-ribulose

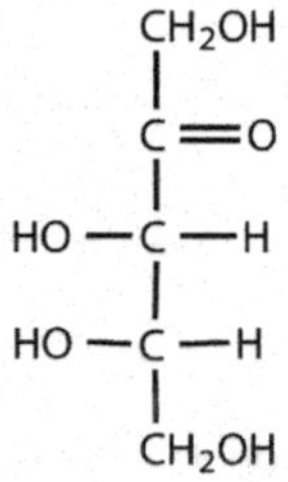

   CH_2OH
   C=O
   HO—C—H
   HO—C—H
   CH_2OH

   c. D-glyceraldehyde

   H—C=O
   H—C—OH
   CH_2OH

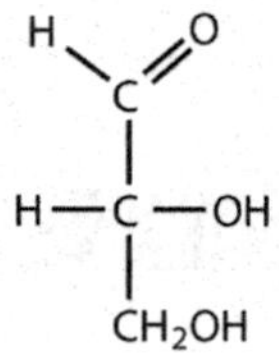

2. Identify each sugar as an aldose or a ketose and then as a triose, tetrose, pentose, or hexose.

   a. dihydroxyacetone

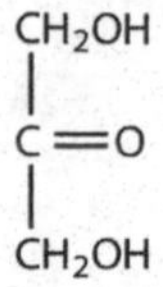

   CH_2OH
   C=O
   CH_2OH

   b. D-ribose

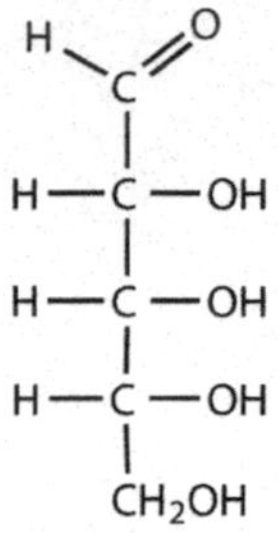

   H—C=O
   H—C—OH
   H—C—OH
   H—C—OH
   CH_2OH

   c. D-galactose

   H—C=O
   H—C—OH
   HO—C—H
   HO—C—H
   H—C—OH
   CH_2OH

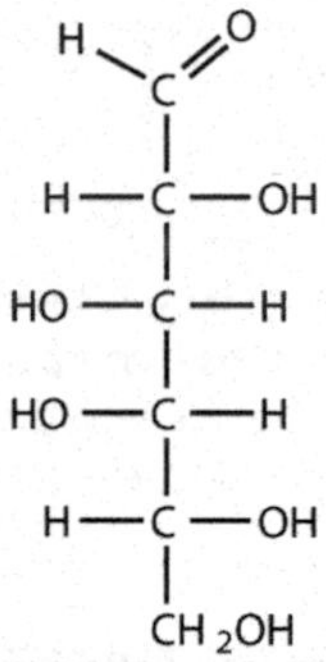

3. Identify each sugar as an aldose or a ketose and then as a D sugar or an L sugar.

   a.

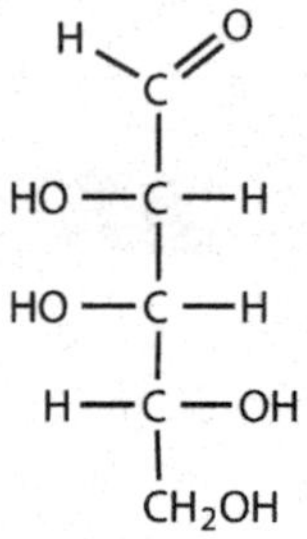

   H—C=O
   HO—C—H
   HO—C—H
   H—C—OH
   CH_2OH

   b.

   CH_2OH
   C=O
   HO—C—H
   CH_2OH

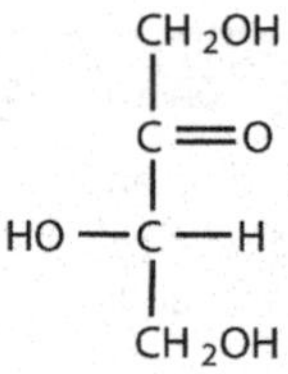

4. Identify each sugar as an aldose or a ketose and then as a D sugar or an L sugar.

   a.

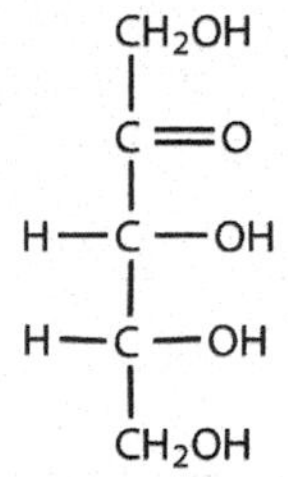

$$\begin{array}{c} CH_2OH \\ | \\ C{=}O \\ | \\ H{-}C{-}OH \\ | \\ H{-}C{-}OH \\ | \\ CH_2OH \end{array}$$

   b.

$$\begin{array}{c} H\diagdown\ \ \diagup\!\!\diagup O \\ C \\ | \\ HO{-}C{-}H \\ | \\ HO{-}C{-}H \\ | \\ HO{-}C{-}H \\ | \\ CH_2OH \end{array}$$

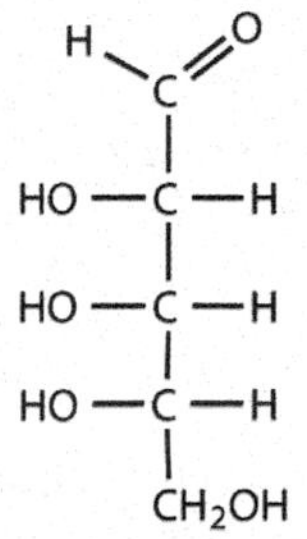

ANSWERS

1. a. aldose; hexose
   b. ketose; pentose
   c. aldose; triose

3. a. aldose; D sugar
   b. ketose; L sugar

3. IMPORTANT HEXOSES

LEARNING OBJECTIVE

1. **Identify the structures of D-glucose, D-galactose, and D-fructose and describe how they differ from each other.**

Although a variety of monosaccharides are found in living organisms, three hexoses are particularly abundant: D-glucose, D-galactose, and D-fructose (Figure 16.4). Glucose and galactose are both aldohexoses, while fructose is a ketohexose.

FIGURE 16.4 Structures of Three Important Hexoses

Each hexose is pictured with a food source in which it is commonly found.

Source: Photos © Thinkstock.

3.1 Glucose

D-Glucose, generally referred to as simply glucose, is the most abundant sugar found in nature; most of the carbohydrates we eat are eventually converted to it in a series of biochemical reactions that produce energy for our cells. It is also known by three other names: *dextrose*, from the fact that it rotates plane-polarized light in a clockwise (dextrorotatory) direction; *corn sugar* because in the United States corn-starch is used in the commercial process that produces glucose from the hydrolysis of starch; and *blood sugar* because it is the carbohydrate found in the circulatory system of animals. Normal blood sugar values range from 70 to 105 mg glucose/dL plasma, and normal urine may contain anywhere from a trace to 20 mg glucose/dL urine.

The Fischer projection of D-glucose is given in Figure 16.5. Glucose is a D sugar because the OH group on the fifth carbon atom (the chiral center farthest from the carbonyl group) is on the right. In fact, all the OH groups except the one on the third carbon atom are to the right.

3.2 Galactose

D-Galactose does not occur in nature in the uncombined state. It is released when lactose, a disaccharide found in milk, is hydrolyzed. The galactose needed by the human body for the synthesis of lactose is obtained by the metabolic conversion of D-glucose to D-galactose. Galactose is also an important constituent of the glycolipids that occur in the brain and the myelin sheath of nerve cells. (For more information about glycolipids, see Chapter 17, [Unsupported Reference Type: chapter-section].) For this reason it is also known as *brain sugar*. The structure of D-galactose is shown in Figure 16.4. Notice that the configuration differs from that of glucose only at the fourth carbon atom.

3.3 Fructose

D-Fructose, also shown in Figure 16.4, is the most abundant ketohexose. Note that from the third through the sixth carbon atoms, its structure is the same as that of glucose. It occurs, along with glucose and sucrose, in honey (which is 40% fructose) and sweet fruits. Fructose (from the Latin *fructus*, meaning "fruit") is also referred to as *levulose* because it has a specific rotation that is strongly levorotatory (−92.4°). It is the sweetest sugar, being 1.7 times sweeter than sucrose, although many nonsugars are several hundred or several thousand times as sweet (Table 16.1).

TABLE 16.1 The Relative Sweetness of Some Compounds (Sucrose = 100)

Compound	Relative Sweetness
lactose	16
maltose	32
glucose	74
sucrose	100
fructose	173
aspartame	18,000
acesulfame K	20,000
saccharin	30,000
sucralose	60,000

Looking Closer: Artificial Sweeteners

Although sweetness is commonly associated with mono- and disaccharides, it is not a property found only in sugars. Several other kinds of organic compounds have been synthesized that are far superior as sweetening agents. These so-called high-intensity or artificial sweeteners are useful for people with diabetes or other medical conditions that require them to control their carbohydrate intake. The synthetic compounds are noncaloric or used in such small quantities that they do not add significantly to the caloric value of food.

The first artificial sweetener—saccharin—was discovered by accident in 1879. It is 300 times sweeter than sucrose, but it passes through the body unchanged and thus adds no calories to the diet. After its discovery, saccharin was used until it was banned in the early 1900s. However, during the sugar-short years of World War I, the ban was lifted and was not reinstated at the war's end. One drawback to the use of saccharin is its bitter, metallic aftertaste. The initial solution to this problem was to combine saccharin with cyclamate, a second artificial sweetener discovered in 1937.

In the 1960s and 1970s, several clinical tests with laboratory animals implicated both cyclamate and saccharin as carcinogenic (cancer-causing) substances. The results from the cyclamate tests were completed first, and cyclamate was banned in the United States in 1969. Then a major study was released in Canada in 1977 indicating that saccharin increased the incidence of bladder cancer in rats. The US Food and Drug Administration (FDA) proposed a ban on saccharin that raised immediate public opposition because saccharin was the only artificial sweetener still available. In response, Congress passed the Saccharin Study and Labeling Act in 1977, permitting the use of saccharin as long as any product containing it was labeled with a consumer warning regarding the possible elevation of the risk of bladder cancer. Today this warning is no longer required; moreover, the FDA is currently reviewing the ban on cyclamate, as 75 additional studies and years of usage in other countries, such as Canada, have failed to show that it has any carcinogenic effect.

A third artificial sweetener, aspartame, was discovered in 1965. This white crystalline compound is about 180 times sweeter than sucrose and has no aftertaste. It was approved for use in 1981 and is used to sweeten a wide variety of foods because it blends well with other food flavors. Aspartame is not used in baked goods, however, because it is not heat stable.

In the body (or when heated), aspartame is initially hydrolyzed to three molecules: the amino acids aspartic acid and phenylalanine and an alcohol methanol. Repeated controversy regarding the safety of aspartame arises partly from the fact that the body metabolizes the released methanol to formaldehyde. It should be noted, though, that a glass of tomato juice has six times as much methanol as a similar amount of a diet soda containing aspartame. The only documented risk connected to aspartame use is for individuals with the genetic disease *phenylketonuria* (PKU); these individuals lack the enzyme needed to metabolize the phenylalanine released when aspartame is broken down by the body. Because of the danger to people with PKU, all products containing aspartame must carry a warning label.

Acesulfame K, discovered just two years after aspartame (1967), was approved for use in the United States in 1988. It is 200 times sweeter than sugar and, unlike aspartame, is heat stable. It has no lingering aftertaste.

One of the newest artificial sweeteners to gain FDA approval (April 1998) for use in the United States is sucralose, a white crystalline solid approximately 600 times sweeter than sucrose. Sucralose is synthesized from sucrose and has three chlorine atoms substituted for three OH groups. It is noncaloric because it passes through the body unchanged. It can be used in baking because it is heat stable.

All of the extensive clinical studies completed to date have indicated that these artificial sweeteners approved for use in the United States are safe for consumption by healthy individuals in moderate amounts.

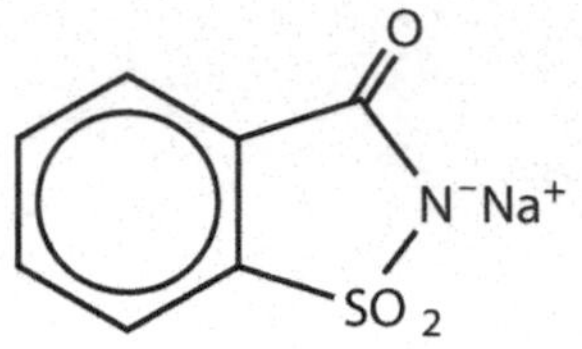

Saccharin

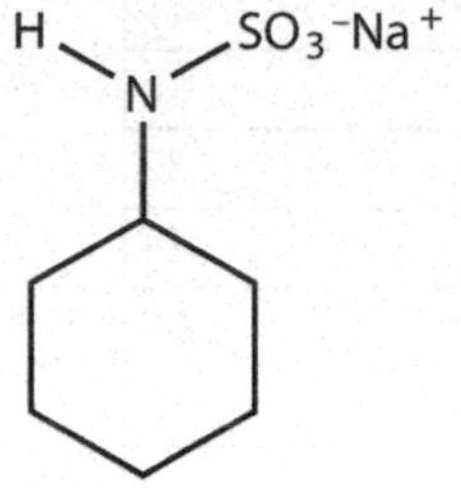

Cyclamate

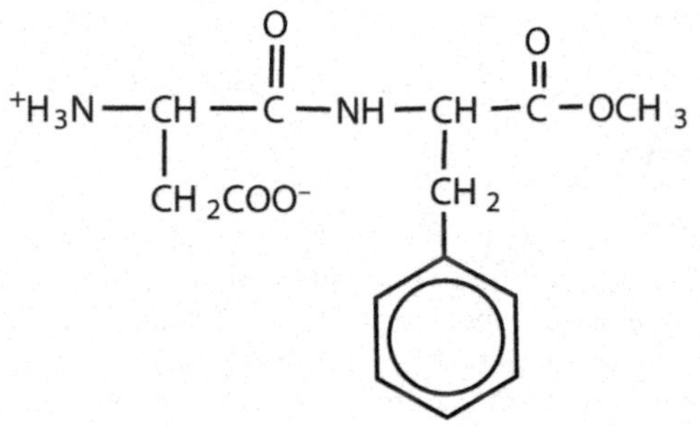

Aspartame

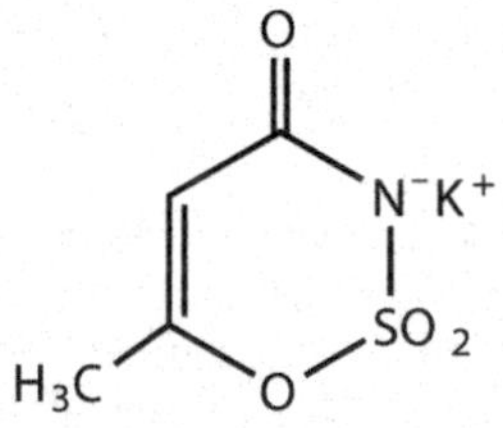

Acesulfame K

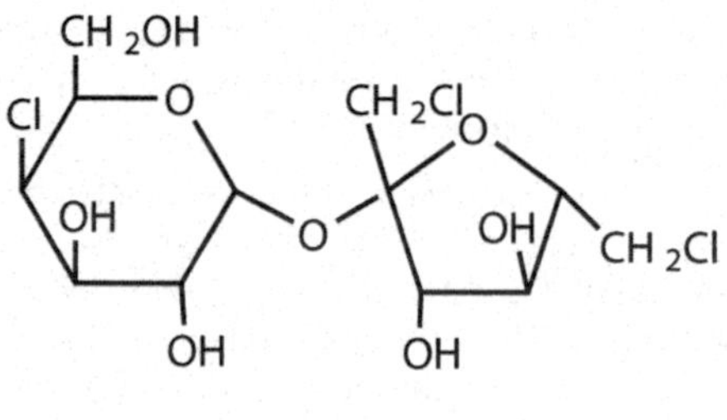

Sucralose

CONCEPT REVIEW EXERCISES

1. Describe the similarities and differences in the structures of D-glucose and D-galactose.
2. Describe similarities and differences in the structures of D-glucose and D-fructose.

ANSWERS

1. Both monosaccharides are aldohexoses. The two monosaccharides differ in the configuration around the fourth carbon atom.
2. Both monosaccharides are hexoses. D-glucose is an aldohexose, while D-fructose is a ketohexose.

KEY TAKEAWAY

- Three abundant hexoses in living organisms are the aldohexoses D-glucose and D-galactose and the ketohexose D-fructose.

EXERCISES

1. Identify each sugar by its common chemical name.
   a. blood sugar
   b. levulose
2. Identify each sugar by its common chemical name.
   a. dextrose
   b. brain sugar
3. Identify each sugar as an aldohexose or a ketohexose.
   a. glucose
   b. galactose
   c. fructose
4. What hexose would you expect to be most abundant in each food?
   a. honey
   b. milk
   c. cornstarch

ANSWERS

1. a. D-glucose
   b. D-fructose
3. a. aldohexose
   b. aldohexose
   c. ketohexose

4. CYCLIC STRUCTURES OF MONOSACCHARIDES

LEARNING OBJECTIVES

1. **Define what is meant by anomers and describe how they are formed.**
2. **Explain what is meant by mutarotation.**

So far we have represented monosaccharides as linear molecules, but many of them also adopt cyclic structures. This conversion occurs because of the ability of aldehydes and ketones to react with alcohols:

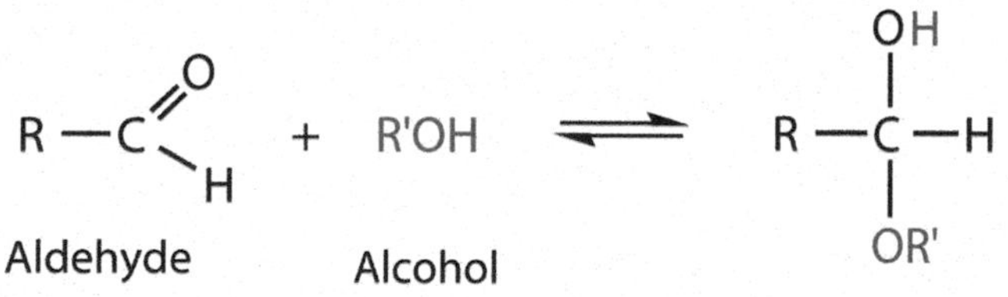

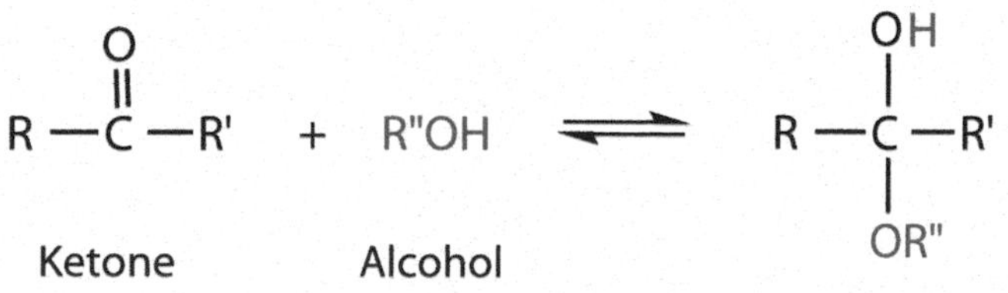

$$\underset{\text{Aldehyde}}{R{-}CHO} + \underset{\text{Alcohol}}{R'OH} \rightleftharpoons R{-}C(OH)(H){-}OR'$$

$$\underset{\text{Ketone}}{R{-}CO{-}R'} + \underset{\text{Alcohol}}{R''OH} \rightleftharpoons R{-}C(OH)(R'){-}OR''$$

In some cases, OH and carbonyl groups on the same molecule are able to react with one another in an intramolecular reaction. Thus, monosaccharides larger than tetroses exist mainly as cyclic compounds (Figure 16.5). You might wonder why the aldehyde reacts with the OH group on the fifth carbon atom rather than the OH group on the second carbon atom next to it. Recall from Chapter 12, [Unsupported Reference Type: chapter-section], that cyclic alkanes containing five or six carbon atoms in the ring are the most stable. The same is true for monosaccharides that form cyclic structures: rings consisting of five or six carbon atoms are the most stable.

FIGURE 16.5 Cyclization of D-Glucose

D-Glucose can be represented with a Fischer projection (a) or three dimensionally (b). By reacting the OH group on the fifth carbon atom with the aldehyde group, the cyclic monosaccharide (c) is produced.

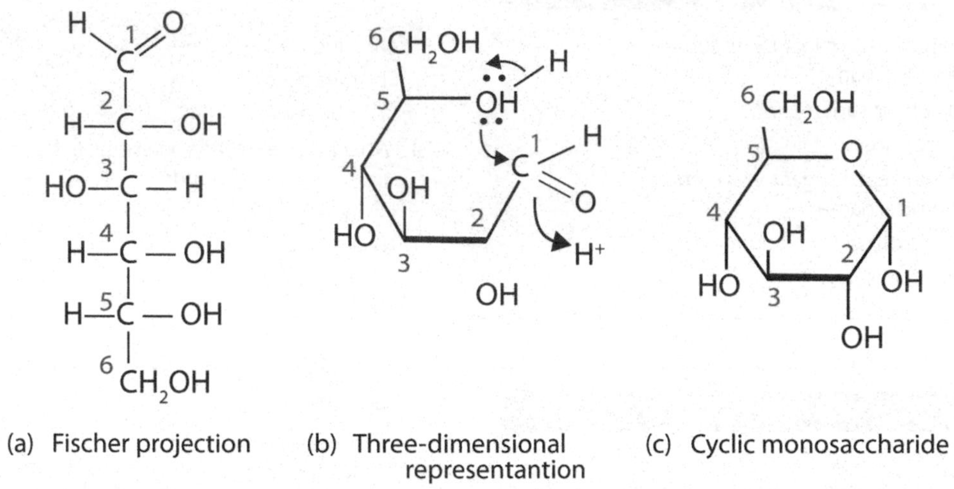

(a) Fischer projection (b) Three-dimensional representantion (c) Cyclic monosaccharide

anomers

Stereoisomers that differ in structure around what was the carbonyl carbon atom in the straight-chain form of a monosaccharide.

anomeric carbon

The carbon atom that was the carbonyl carbon atom in the straight-chain form of a monosaccharide.

When a straight-chain monosaccharide, such as any of the structures shown in Figure 16.4, forms a cyclic structure, the carbonyl oxygen atom may be pushed either up or down, giving rise to two stereoisomers, as shown in Figure 16.6. The structure shown on the left side of Figure 16.6, with the OH group on the first carbon atom projected downward, represent what is called the *alpha (α) form*. The structures on the right side, with the OH group on the first carbon atom pointed upward, is the *beta (β) form*. These two stereoisomers of a cyclic monosaccharide are known as **anomers**; they differ in structure around the **anomeric carbon**—that is, the carbon atom that was the carbonyl carbon atom in the straight-chain form.

FIGURE 16.6 Monosaccharides

In an aqueous solution, monosaccharides exist as an equilibrium mixture of three forms. The interconversion between the forms is known as *mutarotation*, which is shown for D-glucose (a) and D-fructose (b).

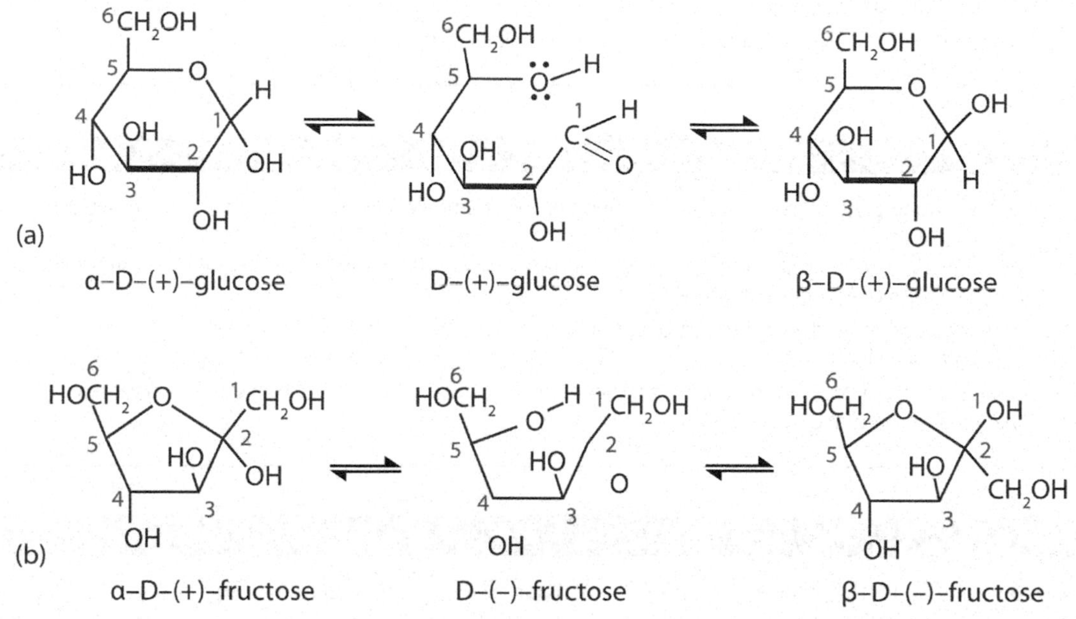

(a) α-D-(+)-glucose ⇌ D-(+)-glucose ⇌ β-D-(+)-glucose

(b) α-D-(+)-fructose ⇌ D-(–)-fructose ⇌ β-D-(–)-fructose

It is possible to obtain a sample of crystalline glucose in which all the molecules have the α structure or all have the β structure. The α form melts at 146°C and has a specific rotation of +112°, while the β form melts at 150°C and has a specific rotation of +18.7°. When the sample is dissolved in water, however, a mixture is soon produced containing both anomers as well as the straight-chain form, in dynamic equilibrium (part (a) of Figure 16.6). You can start with a pure crystalline sample of glucose consisting entirely of either anomer, but as soon as the molecules dissolve in water, they open to form the carbonyl group and then reclose to form either the α or the β anomer. The opening and closing repeats continuously in an ongoing interconversion between anomeric forms and is referred to as **mutarotation** (Latin *mutare*, meaning "to change"). At equilibrium, the mixture consists of about 36% α-D-glucose, 64% β-D-glucose, and less than 0.02% of the open-chain aldehyde form. The observed rotation of this solution is +52.7°.

mutarotation

The ongoing interconversion between anomeric forms of a monosaccharide to form an equilibrium mixture.

Even though only a small percentage of the molecules are in the open-chain aldehyde form at any time, the solution will nevertheless exhibit the characteristic reactions of an aldehyde. As the small amount of free aldehyde is used up in a reaction, there is a shift in the equilibrium to yield more aldehyde. Thus, *all* the molecules may eventually react, even though very little free aldehyde is present at a time.

In Figure 16.5 and Figure 16.6, and elsewhere in this book, the cyclic forms of sugars are depicted using a convention first suggested by Walter N. Haworth, an English chemist. The molecules are drawn as planar hexagons with a darkened edge representing the side facing toward the viewer. The structure is simplified to show only the functional groups attached to the carbon atoms. Any group written to the right in a Fischer projection appears below the plane of the ring in a Haworth projection, and any group written to the left in a Fischer projection appears above the plane in a Haworth projection.

The difference between the α and the β forms of sugars may seem trivial, but such structural differences are often crucial in biochemical reactions. This explains why we can get energy from the starch in potatoes and other plants but not from cellulose, even though both starch and cellulose are polysaccharides composed of glucose molecules linked together. We will examine the effects of these differences more closely in Section 7 and when we discuss enzyme specificity in Chapter 18, [Unsupported Reference Type: chapter-section].

CONCEPT REVIEW EXERCISES

1. Define each term.
   a. mutarotation
   b. anomer
   c. anomeric carbon
2. How can you prove that a solution of α-D-glucose exhibits mutarotation?

ANSWERS

1. a. the ongoing interconversion between anomers of a particular carbohydrate to form an equilibrium mixture
   b. a stereoisomer that differs in structure around what was the carbonyl carbon atom in the straight-chain form of a monosaccharide
   c. the carbon atom that was the carbonyl carbon atom in the straight-chain form of a monosaccharide
2. Place a sample of pure α-D-glucose in a polarimeter and measure its observed rotation. This value will change as mutarotation occurs.

KEY TAKEAWAYS

- Monosaccharides that contain five or more carbons atoms form cyclic structures in aqueous solution.
- Two cyclic stereoisomers can form from each straight-chain monosaccharide; these are known as anomers.
- In an aqueous solution, an equilibrium mixture forms between the two anomers and the straight-chain structure of a monosaccharide in a process known as mutarotation.

EXERCISES

1. Draw the cyclic structure for β-D-glucose. Identify the anomeric carbon.
2. Draw the cyclic structure for α-D-fructose. Identify the anomeric carbon.
3. Given that the aldohexose D-mannose differs from D-glucose only in the configuration at the second carbon atom, draw the cyclic structure for α-D-mannose.
4. Given that the aldohexose D-allose differs from D-glucose only in the configuration at the third carbon atom, draw the cyclic structure for β-D-allose.

ANSWERS

1.

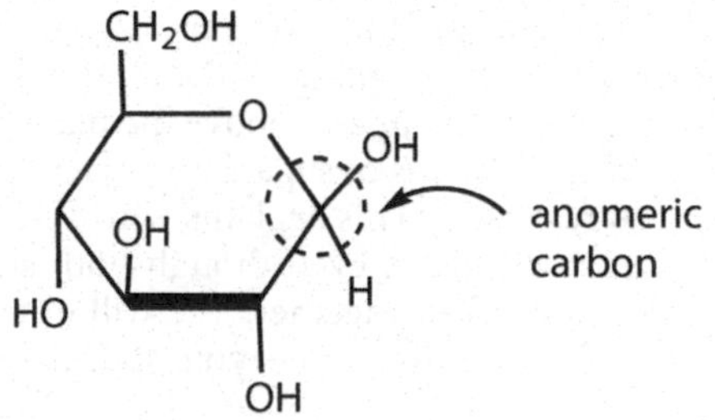

CH_2OH
O
OH
OH
anomeric carbon
H
HO
OH

3.

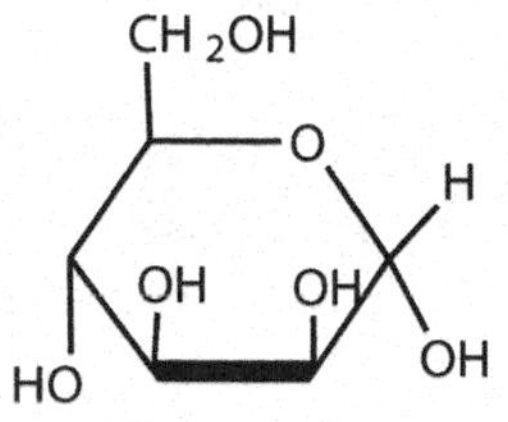

CH_2OH ... O ... H ... OH OH ... HO ... OH

5. PROPERTIES OF MONOSACCHARIDES

LEARNING OBJECTIVE

1. **Identify the physical and chemical properties of monosaccharides.**

Monosaccharides such as glucose and fructose are crystalline solids at room temperature, but they are quite soluble in water, each molecule having several OH groups that readily engage in hydrogen bonding. The chemical behavior of these monosaccharides is likewise determined by their functional groups.

An important reaction of monosaccharides is the oxidation of the aldehyde group, one of the most easily oxidized organic functional groups. Aldehyde oxidation can be accomplished with any mild oxidizing agent, such as Tollens' reagent or Benedict's reagent. (For more information about aldehyde oxidation, see Chapter 14, [Unsupported Reference Type: chapter-section].) With the latter, complexed copper(II) ions are reduced to copper(I) ions that form a brick-red precipitate [copper(I) oxide; Figure 16.7].

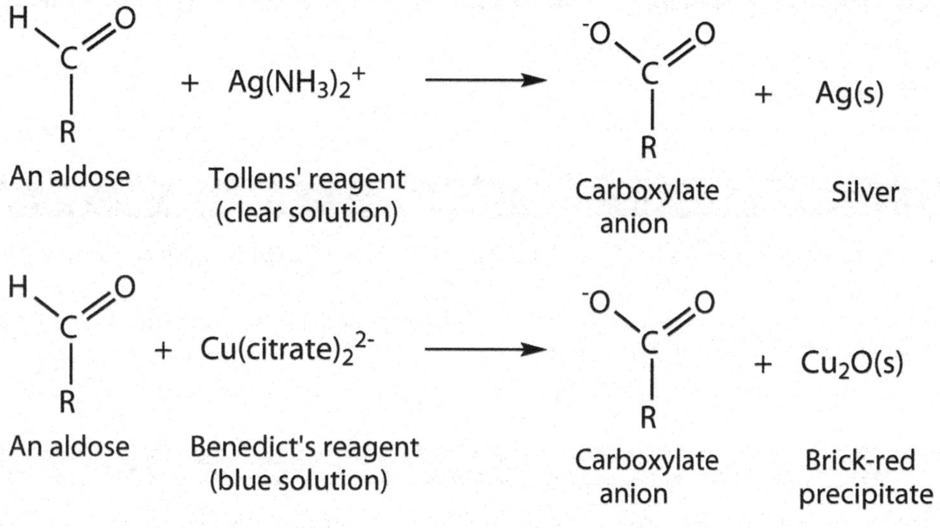

$$RCHO + Ag(NH_3)_2^+ \longrightarrow RCOO^- + Ag(s)$$

An aldose — Tollens' reagent (clear solution) — Carboxylate anion — Silver

$$RCHO + Cu(citrate)_2^{2-} \longrightarrow RCOO^- + Cu_2O(s)$$

An aldose — Benedict's reagent (blue solution) — Carboxylate anion — Brick-red precipitate

Any carbohydrate capable of reducing either Tollens' or Benedict's reagents without first undergoing hydrolysis is said to be a **reducing sugar**. Because both the Tollens' and Benedict's reagents are basic solutions, ketoses (such as fructose) also give positive tests due to an equilibrium that exists between ketoses and aldoses in a reaction known as *tautomerism*.

reducing sugar

Any carbohydrate capable of reducing a mild oxidizing agent, such as Tollens' or Benedict's reagents, without first undergoing hydrolysis.

FIGURE 16.7 Benedict's Test

Benedict's test was performed on three carbohydrates, depicted from left to right: fructose, glucose, and sucrose. The solution containing sucrose remains blue because sucrose is a nonreducing sugar.

These reactions have been used as simple and rapid diagnostic tests for the presence of glucose in blood or urine. For example, Clinitest tablets, which are used to test for sugar in the urine, contain copper(II) ions and are based on Benedict's test. A green color indicates very little sugar, whereas a brick-red color indicates sugar in excess of 2 g/100 mL of urine.

CONCEPT REVIEW EXERCISES

1. Why are monosaccharides soluble in water?
2. What is a reducing sugar?

ANSWERS

1. Monosaccharides are quite soluble in water because of the numerous OH groups that readily engage in hydrogen bonding with water.
2. any carbohydrate capable of reducing a mild oxidizing agent, such as Tollens' or Benedict's reagents, without first undergoing hydrolysis

KEY TAKEAWAYS

- Monosaccharides are crystalline solids at room temperature and quite soluble in water.
- Monosaccharides are reducing sugars; they reduce mild oxidizing agents, such as Tollens' or Benedict's reagents.

EXERCISES

1. Which gives a positive Benedict's test—L-galactose, levulose, or D-glucose?
2. Which gives a positive Benedict's test—D-glyceraldehyde, corn sugar, or L-fructose?
3. D-Galactose can be oxidized at the sixth carbon atom to yield D-galacturonic acid and at both the first and sixth carbon atoms to yield D-galactaric acid. Draw the Fischer projection for each oxidation product.

4. D-Glucose can be oxidized at the first carbon atom to form D-gluconic acid, at the sixth carbon atom to yield D-glucuronic acid, and at both the first and sixth carbon atoms to yield D-glucaric acid. Draw the Fischer projection for each oxidation product.

ANSWERS

1. All three will give a positive Benedict's test because they are all monosaccharides.
3.

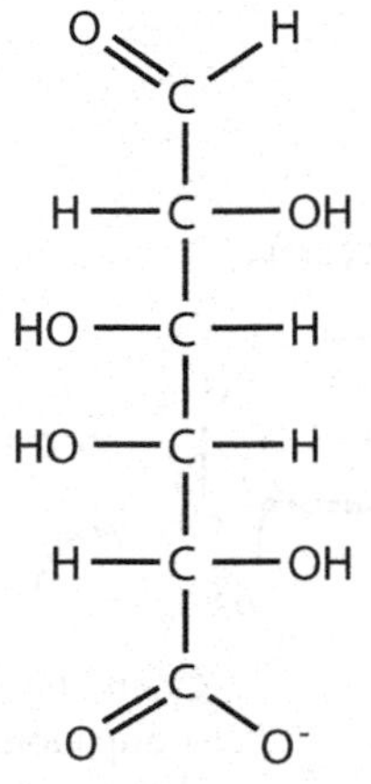

D-galacturonic acid

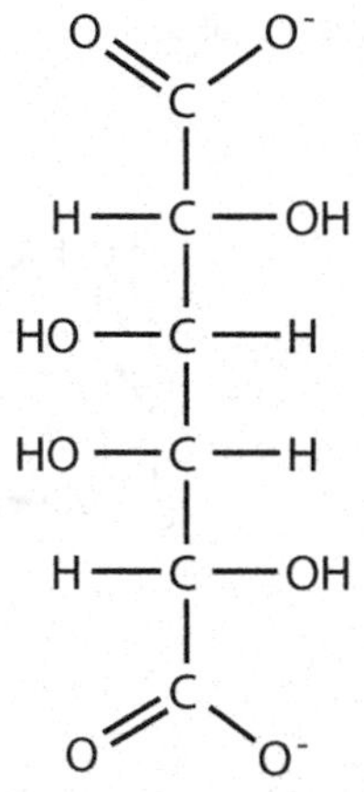

D-galactaric acid

6. DISACCHARIDES

LEARNING OBJECTIVES

1. **Identify the structures of sucrose, lactose, and maltose.**
2. **Identify the monosaccharides that are needed to form sucrose, lactose, and maltose.**

In Section 4, you learned that monosaccharides can form cyclic structures by the reaction of the carbonyl group with an OH group. These cyclic molecules can in turn react with another alcohol. Disaccharides ($C_{12}H_{22}O_{11}$) are sugars composed of two monosaccharide units that are joined by a carbon–oxygen-carbon linkage known as a **glycosidic linkage**. This linkage is formed from the reaction of the anomeric carbon of one cyclic monosaccharide with the OH group of a second monosaccharide.

glycosidic linkage

The carbon–oxygen-carbon linkage between monosaccharide units in more complex carbohydrates, such as disaccharides or polysaccharides.

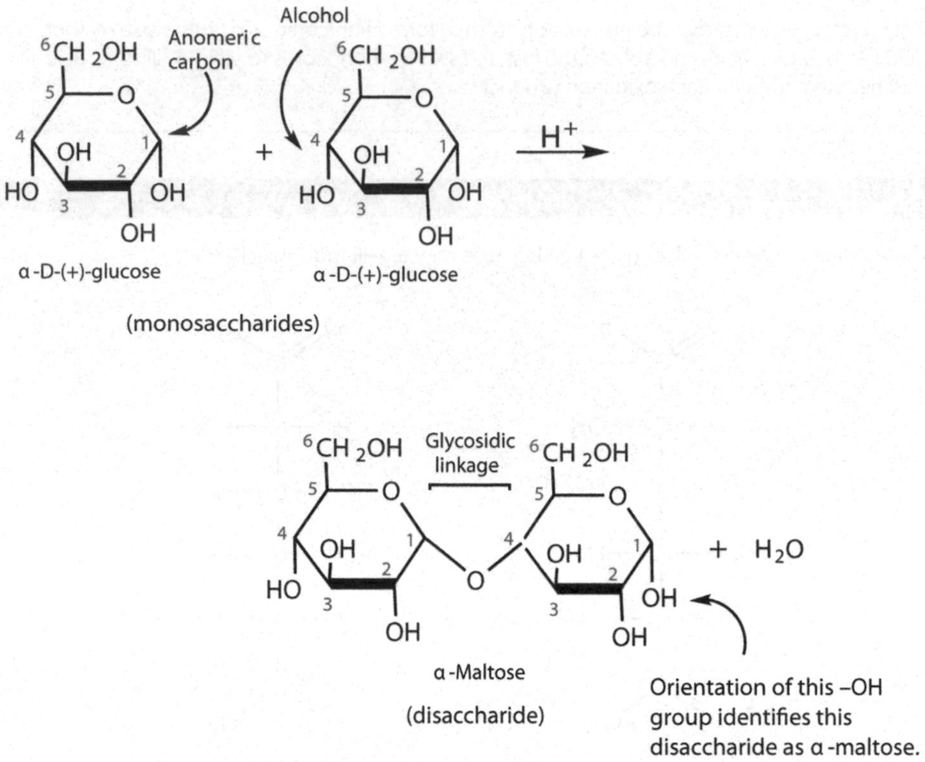

The disaccharides differ from one another in their monosaccharide constituents and in the specific type of glycosidic linkage connecting them. There are three common disaccharides: maltose, lactose, and sucrose. All three are white crystalline solids at room temperature and are soluble in water. We'll consider each sugar in more detail.

6.1 Maltose

Maltose occurs to a limited extent in sprouting grain. It is formed most often by the partial hydrolysis of starch and glycogen. In the manufacture of beer, maltose is liberated by the action of malt (germinating barley) on starch; for this reason, it is often referred to as *malt sugar*. Maltose is about 30% as sweet as sucrose. The human body is unable to metabolize maltose or any other disaccharide directly from the diet because the molecules are too large to pass through the cell membranes of the intestinal wall. Therefore, an ingested disaccharide must first be broken down by hydrolysis into its two constituent monosaccharide units. In the body, such hydrolysis reactions are catalyzed by enzymes such as *maltase*. The same reactions can be carried out in the laboratory with dilute acid as a catalyst, although in that case the rate is much slower, and high temperatures are required. Whether it occurs in the body or a glass beaker, the hydrolysis of maltose produces two molecules of D-glucose.

$$\text{maltose} \xrightarrow{H^+ \text{ or maltase}} 2 \text{ D-glucose}$$

Maltose is a reducing sugar. Thus, its two glucose molecules must be linked in such a way as to leave one anomeric carbon that can open to form an aldehyde group. The glucose units in maltose are joined in a *head-to-tail* fashion through an α-linkage from the first carbon atom of one glucose molecule to the fourth carbon atom of the second glucose molecule (that is, an α-1,4-glycosidic linkage; see Figure 16.8). The bond from the anomeric carbon of the first monosaccharide unit is directed downward, which is why this is known as an α-glycosidic linkage. The OH group on the anomeric carbon of the second glucose can be in either the α or the β position, as shown in Figure 16.8.

FIGURE 16.8 An Equilibrium Mixture of Maltose Isomers

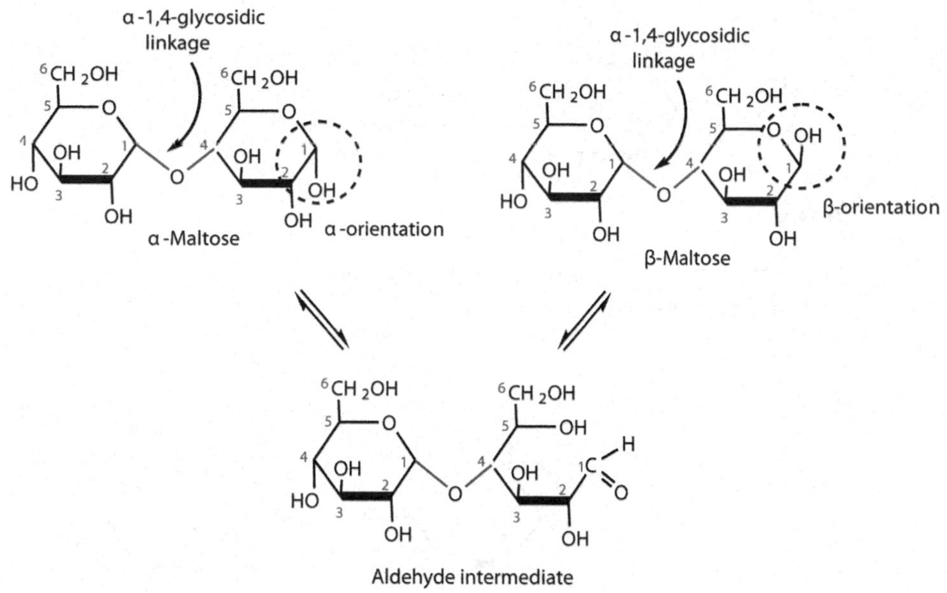

6.2 Lactose

Lactose is known as *milk sugar* because it occurs in the milk of humans, cows, and other mammals. In fact, the natural synthesis of lactose occurs only in mammary tissue, whereas most other carbohydrates are plant products. Human milk contains about 7.5% lactose, and cow's milk contains about 4.5%. This sugar is one of the lowest ranking in terms of sweetness, being about one-sixth as sweet as sucrose (see Table 16.1 in Section 3). Lactose is produced commercially from whey, a by-product in the manufacture of cheese. It is important as an infant food and in the production of penicillin.

Lactose is a reducing sugar composed of one molecule of D-galactose and one molecule of D-glucose joined by a β-1,4-glycosidic bond (the bond from the anomeric carbon of the first monosaccharide unit being directed upward). The two monosaccharides are obtained from lactose by acid hydrolysis or the catalytic action of the enzyme *lactase*:

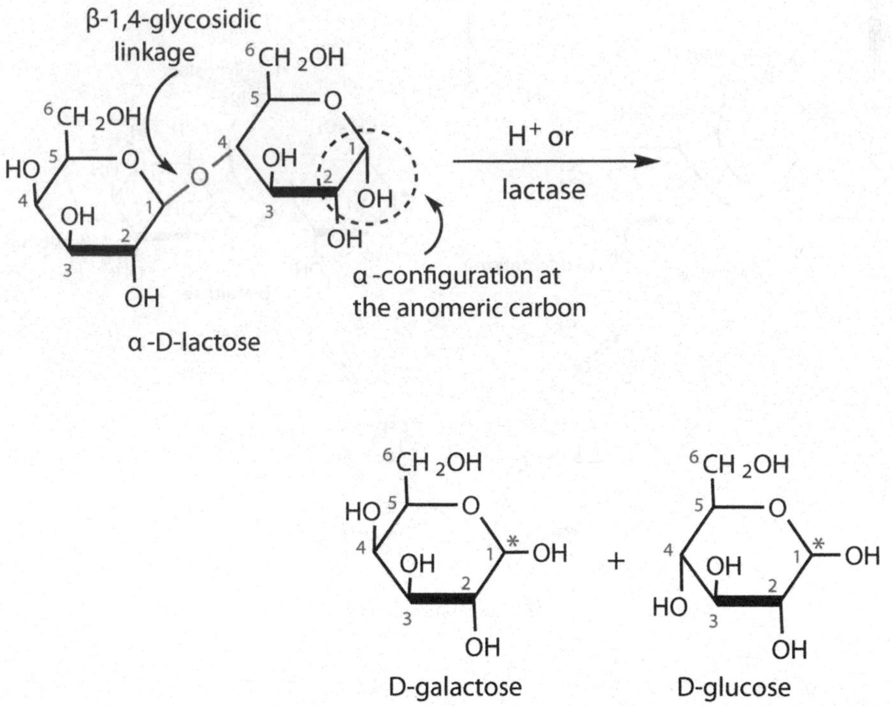

β-1,4-glycosidic linkage

α-configuration at the anomeric carbon

α-D-lactose

H^+ or lactase

D-galactose + D-glucose

*We use this convention for writing the hydroxyl group on the anomeric carbon when we do not wish to specify either the α or the β anomer.

lactose intolerant

The inability to digest the lactose found in milk or dairy products due to a deficiency of the enzyme lactase.

galactosemia

A genetic disease caused by the absence of one of the enzymes needed to convert galactose to glucose.

Many adults and some children suffer from a deficiency of lactase. These individuals are said to be **lactose intolerant** because they cannot digest the lactose found in milk. A more serious problem is the genetic disease **galactosemia**, which results from the absence of an enzyme needed to convert galactose to glucose. Certain bacteria can metabolize lactose, forming lactic acid as one of the products. This reaction is responsible for the "souring" of milk.

EXAMPLE 3

For this trisaccharide, indicate whether each glycosidic linkage is α or β.

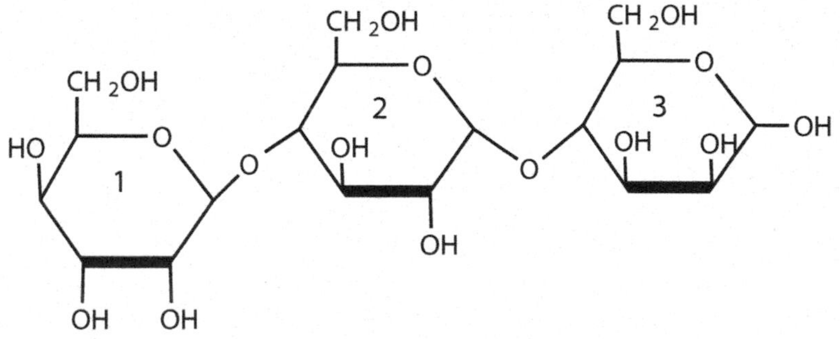

Solution

The glycosidic linkage between sugars 1 and 2 is β because the bond is directed up from the anomeric carbon. The glycosidic linkage between sugars 2 and 3 is α because the bond is directed down from the anomeric carbon.

SKILL-BUILDING EXERCISE

1. For this trisaccharide, indicate whether each glycosidic linkage is α or β.

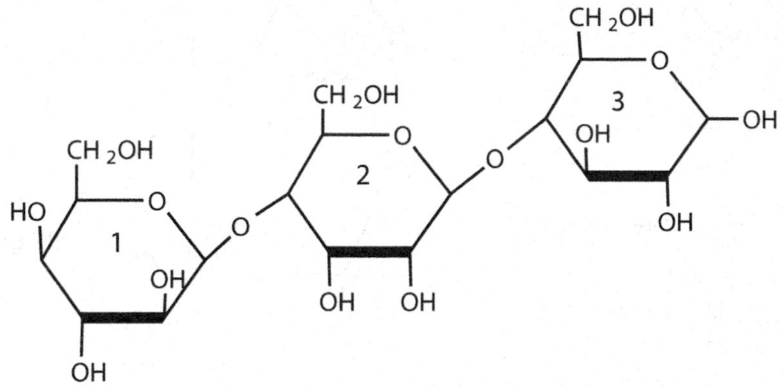

To Your Health: Lactose Intolerance and Galactosemia

Lactose makes up about 40% of an infant's diet during the first year of life. Infants and small children have one form of the enzyme lactase in their small intestines and can digest the sugar easily; however, adults usually have a less active form of the enzyme, and about 70% of the world's adult population has some deficiency in its production. As a result, many adults experience a reduction in the ability to hydrolyze lactose to galactose and glucose in their small intestine. For some people the inability to synthesize sufficient enzyme increases with age. Up to 20% of the US population suffers some degree of lactose intolerance.

In people with lactose intolerance, some of the unhydrolyzed lactose passes into the colon, where it tends to draw water from the interstitial fluid into the intestinal lumen by osmosis. At the same time, intestinal bacteria may act on the lactose to produce organic acids and gases. The buildup of water and bacterial decay products leads to abdominal distention, cramps, and diarrhea, which are symptoms of the condition.

The symptoms disappear if milk or other sources of lactose are excluded from the diet or consumed only sparingly. Alternatively, many food stores now carry special brands of milk that have been pretreated with lactase to hydrolyze the lactose. Cooking or fermenting milk causes at least partial hydrolysis of the lactose, so some people with lactose intolerance are still able to enjoy cheese, yogurt, or cooked foods containing milk. The most common treatment for lactose intolerance, however, is the use of lactase preparations (e.g., Lactaid), which are available in liquid and tablet form at drugstores and grocery stores. These are taken orally with dairy foods—or may be added to them directly—to assist in their digestion.

Galactosemia is a condition in which one of the enzymes needed to convert galactose to glucose is missing. Consequently, the blood galactose level is markedly elevated, and galactose is found in the urine. An infant with galactosemia experiences a lack of appetite, weight loss, diarrhea, and jaundice. The disease may result in impaired liver function, cataracts, mental retardation, and even death. If galactosemia is recognized in early infancy, its effects can be prevented by the exclusion of milk and all other sources of galactose from the diet. As a child with galactosemia grows older, he or she usually develops an alternate pathway for metabolizing galactose, so the need to restrict milk is not permanent. The incidence of galactosemia in the United States is 1 in every 65,000 newborn babies.

6.3 Sucrose

Sucrose, probably the largest-selling pure organic compound in the world, is known as *beet sugar*, *cane sugar*, *table sugar*, or simply *sugar*. Most of the sucrose sold commercially is obtained from sugar cane and sugar beets (whose juices are 14%–20% sucrose) by evaporation of the water and recrystallization. The dark brown liquid that remains after the recrystallization of sugar is sold as molasses.

The sucrose molecule is unique among the common disaccharides in having an α-1,β-2-glycosidic (head-to-head) linkage. Because this glycosidic linkage is formed by the OH group on the anomeric carbon of α-D-glucose and the OH group on the anomeric carbon of β-D-fructose, it ties up the anomeric carbons of both glucose and fructose.

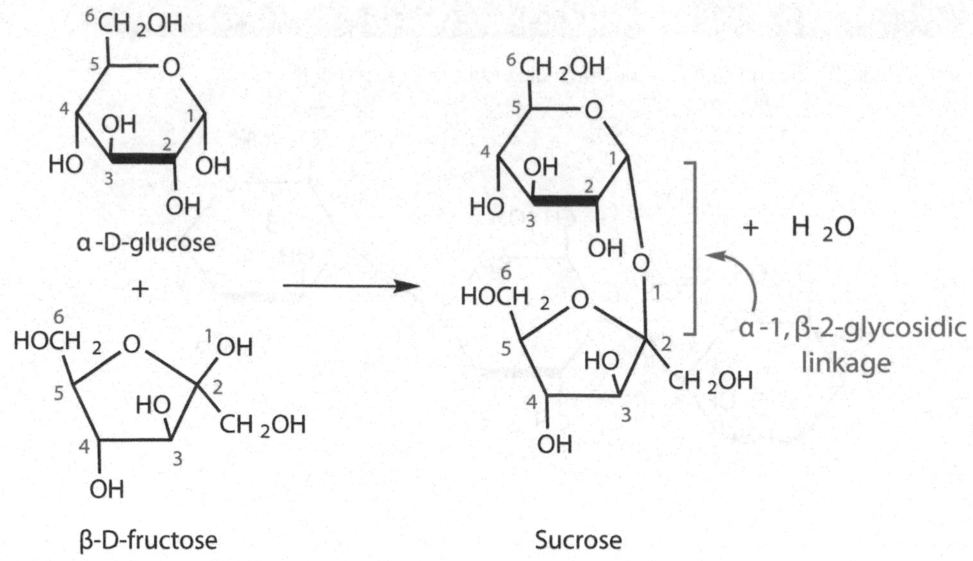

α-D-glucose

+

β-D-fructose

Sucrose

+ H_2O

α-1,β-2-glycosidic linkage

This linkage gives sucrose certain properties that are quite different from those of maltose and lactose. As long as the sucrose molecule remains intact, neither monosaccharide "uncyclizes" to form an open-chain structure. Thus, sucrose is incapable of mutarotation and exists in only one form both in the solid state and in solution. In addition, sucrose does not undergo reactions that are typical of aldehydes and ketones. Therefore, sucrose is a nonreducing sugar.

The hydrolysis of sucrose in dilute acid or through the action of the enzyme *sucrase* (also known as invertase) gives an equimolar mixture of glucose and fructose. This 1:1 mixture is referred to as *invert sugar* because it rotates plane-polarized light in the opposite direction than sucrose. The hydrolysis reaction has several practical applications. Sucrose readily recrystallizes from a solution, but invert sugar has a much greater tendency to remain in solution. In the manufacture of jelly and candy and in the canning of fruit, the recrystallization of sugar is undesirable. Therefore, conditions leading to the hydrolysis of sucrose are employed in these processes. Moreover, because fructose is sweeter than sucrose, the hydrolysis adds to the sweetening effect. Bees carry out this reaction when they make honey.

The average American consumes more than 100 lb of sucrose every year. About two-thirds of this amount is ingested in soft drinks, presweetened cereals, and other highly processed foods. The widespread use of sucrose is a contributing factor to obesity and tooth decay. Carbohydrates such as sucrose, are converted to fat when the caloric intake exceeds the body's requirements, and sucrose causes tooth decay by promoting the formation of plaque that sticks to teeth.

CONCEPT REVIEW EXERCISE

1. What monosaccharides are obtained by the hydrolysis of each disaccharide?
   a. sucrose
   b. maltose
   c. lactose

ANSWER

1. a. D-glucose and D-fructose
   b. two molecules of D-glucose
   c. D-glucose and D-galactose

KEY TAKEAWAYS

- Maltose is composed of two molecules of glucose joined by an α-1,4-glycosidic linkage. It is a reducing sugar that is found in sprouting grain.
- Lactose is composed of a molecule of galactose joined to a molecule of glucose by a β-1,4-glycosidic linkage. It is a reducing sugar that is found in milk.
- Sucrose is composed of a molecule of glucose joined to a molecule of fructose by an α-1,β-2-glycosidic linkage. It is a nonreducing sugar that is found in sugar cane and sugar beets.

EXERCISES

1. Identify each sugar by its common chemical name.
   a. milk sugar
   b. table sugar
2. Identify each sugar by its common chemical name.
   a. cane sugar
   b. malt sugar
3. For each disaccharide, indicate whether the glycosidic linkage is α or β.
   a.

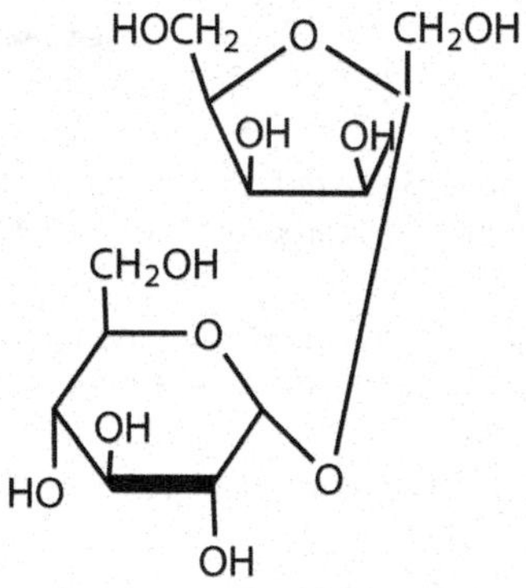

   $HOCH_2$ O CH_2OH OH OH CH_2OH O OH HO O OH

   b.

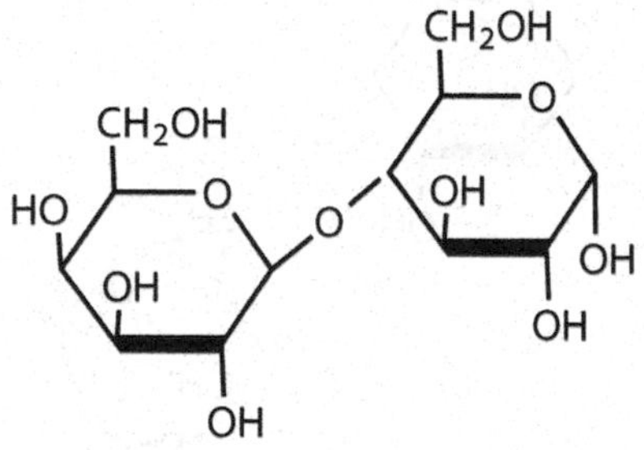

   CH_2OH O CH_2OH HO O O OH OH OH OH OH

4. For each disaccharide, indicate whether the glycosidic linkage is α or β.
   a.

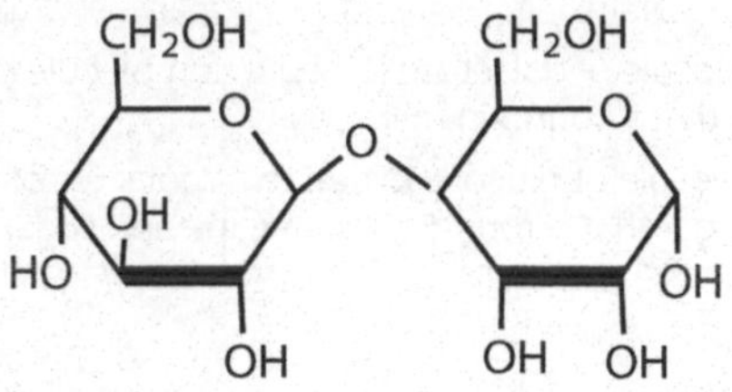

   b.

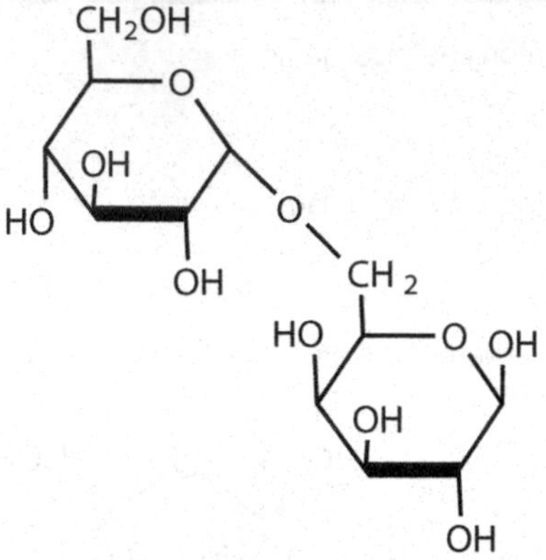

5. Identify each disaccharide in Exercise 3 as a reducing or nonreducing sugar. If it is a reducing sugar, draw its structure and circle the anomeric carbon. State if the OH group at the anomeric carbon is in the α or the β position.
6. Identify each disaccharide in Exercise 4 as a reducing or nonreducing sugar. If it is a reducing sugar, draw its structure and circle the anomeric carbon. State if the OH group at the anomeric carbon is in the α or β position.
7. Melibiose is a disaccharide that occurs in some plant juices. Its structure is as follows:

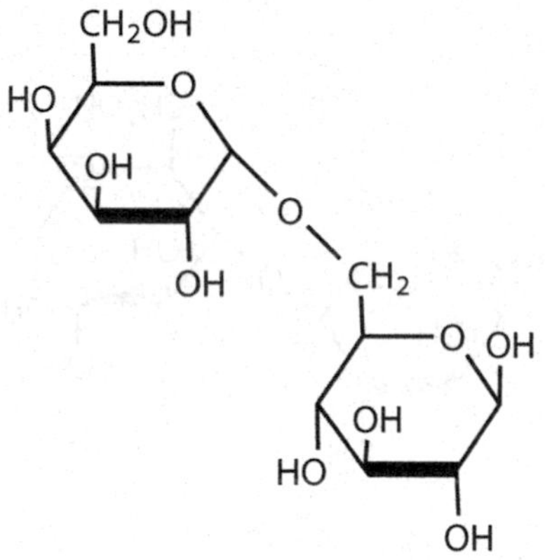

   a. What monosaccharide units are incorporated into melibiose?
   b. What type of linkage (α or β) joins the two monosaccharide units of melibiose?
   c. Melibiose has a free anomeric carbon and is thus a reducing sugar. Circle the anomeric carbon and indicate whether the OH group is α or β.
8. Cellobiose is a disaccharide composed of two glucose units joined by a β-1,4-glycosidic linkage.
   a. Draw the structure of cellobiose.
   b. Is cellobiose a reducing or nonreducing sugar? Justify your answer.

ANSWERS

1. a. lactose
   b. sucrose

3. a.

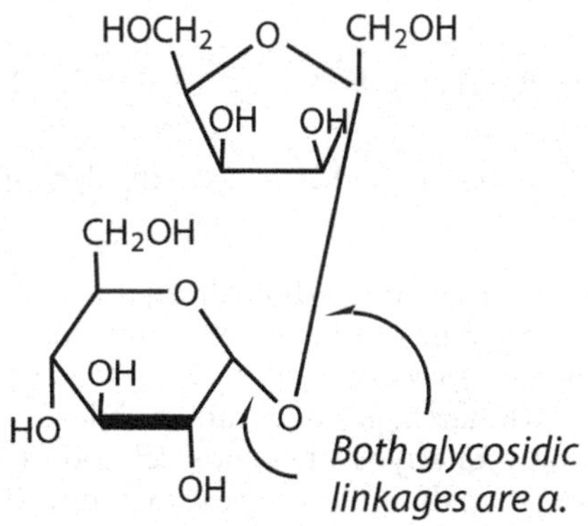

b.

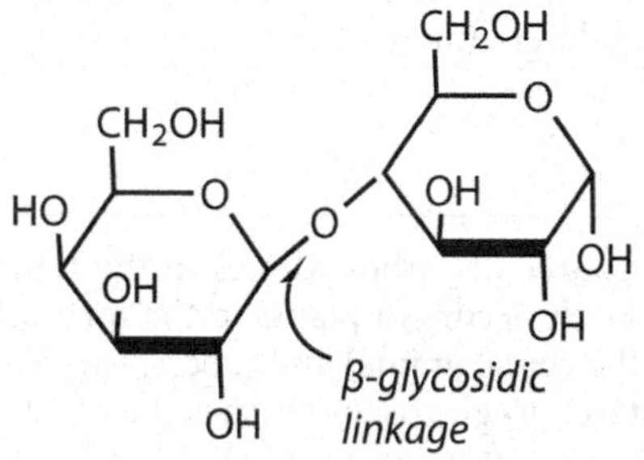

5. 3a: nonreducing; 3b: reducing

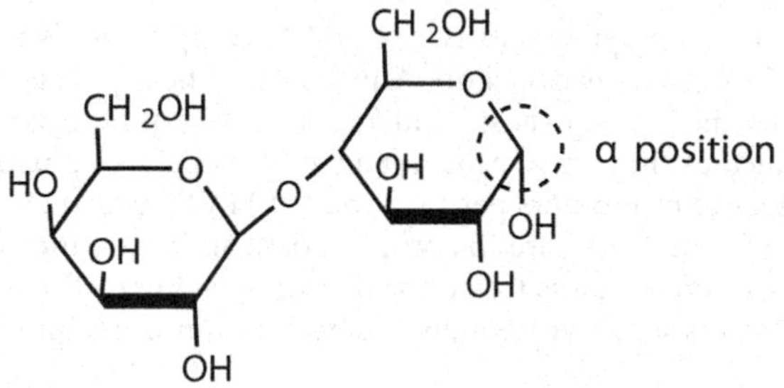

7. a. galactose and glucose
   b. α-glycosidic linkage
   c.

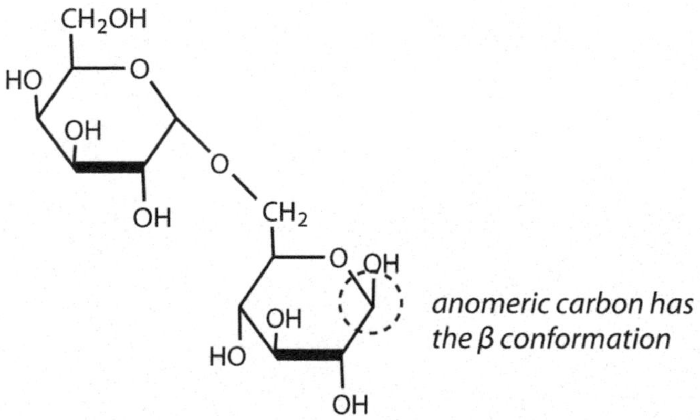

7. POLYSACCHARIDES

LEARNING OBJECTIVE

1. **Compare and contrast the structures and uses of starch, glycogen, and cellulose.**

The polysaccharides are the most abundant carbohydrates in nature and serve a variety of functions, such as energy storage or as components of plant cell walls. Polysaccharides are very large polymers composed of tens to thousands of monosaccharides joined together by glycosidic linkages. The three most abundant polysaccharides are starch, glycogen, and cellulose. These three are referred to as *homopolymers* because each yields only one type of monosaccharide (glucose) after complete hydrolysis. *Heteropolymers* may contain sugar acids, amino sugars, or noncarbohydrate substances in addition to monosaccharides. Heteropolymers are common in nature (gums, pectins, and other substances) but will not be discussed further in this textbook. The polysaccharides are nonreducing carbohydrates, are not sweet tasting, and do not undergo mutarotation.

7.1 Starch

Starch is the most important source of carbohydrates in the human diet and accounts for more than 50% of our carbohydrate intake. It occurs in plants in the form of granules, and these are particularly abundant in seeds (especially the cereal grains) and tubers, where they serve as a storage form of carbohydrates. The breakdown of starch to glucose nourishes the plant during periods of reduced photosynthetic activity. We often think of potatoes as a "starchy" food, yet other plants contain a much greater percentage of starch (potatoes 15%, wheat 55%, corn 65%, and rice 75%). Commercial starch is a white powder.

amylose

A linear polymer of glucose units found in starch.

amylopectin

A branched polymer of glucose units found in starch.

Starch is a mixture of two polymers: **amylose** and **amylopectin**. Natural starches consist of about 10%–30% amylase and 70%–90% amylopectin. Amylose is a linear polysaccharide composed entirely of D-glucose units joined by the α-1,4-glycosidic linkages we saw in maltose (part (a) of Figure 16.9). Experimental evidence indicates that amylose is not a straight chain of glucose units but instead is coiled like a spring, with six glucose monomers per turn (part (b) of Figure 16.9). When coiled in this fashion, amylose has just enough room in its core to accommodate an iodine molecule. The characteristic blue-violet color that appears when starch is treated with iodine is due to the formation of the amylose-iodine complex. This color test is sensitive enough to detect even minute amounts of starch in solution.

FIGURE 16.9 Amylose

(a) Amylose is a linear chain of α-D-glucose units joined together by α-1,4-glycosidic bonds. (b) Because of hydrogen bonding, amylose acquires a spiral structure that contains six glucose units per turn.

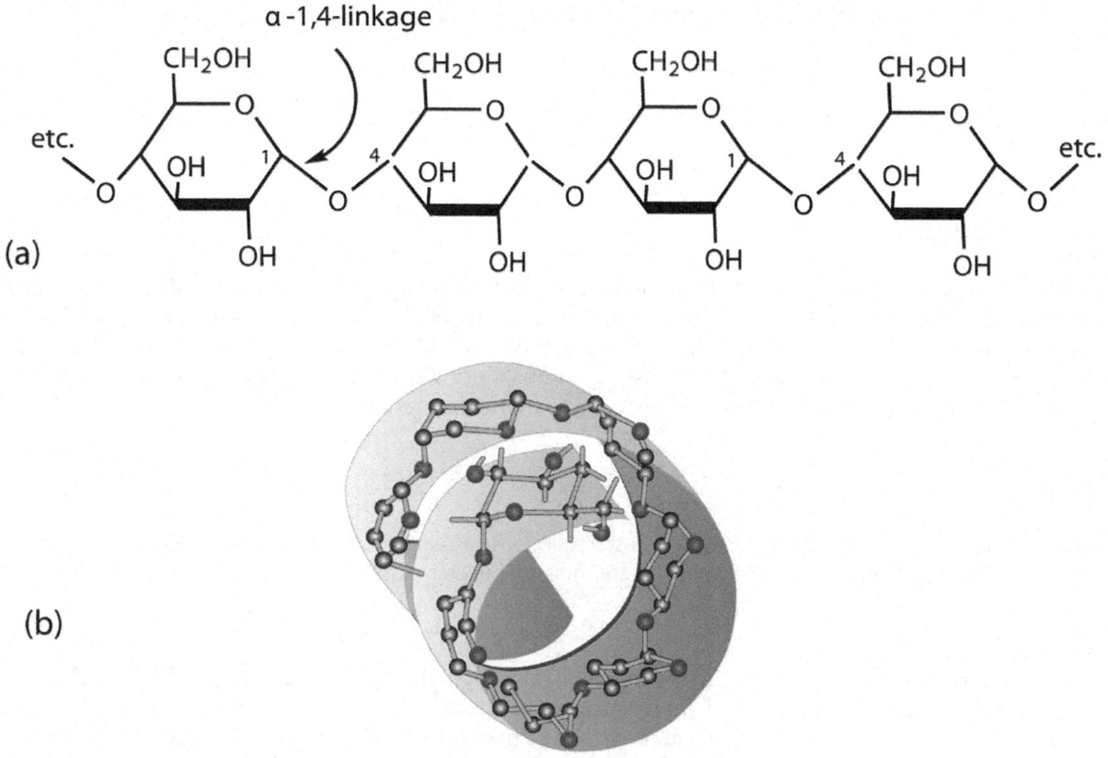

Amylopectin is a branched-chain polysaccharide composed of glucose units linked primarily by α-1,4-glycosidic bonds but with occasional α-1,6-glycosidic bonds, which are responsible for the branching. A molecule of amylopectin may contain many thousands of glucose units with branch points occurring about every 25–30 units (Figure 16.10). The helical structure of amylopectin is disrupted by the branching of the chain, so instead of the deep blue-violet color amylose gives with iodine, amylopectin produces a less intense reddish brown.

FIGURE 16.10 Representation of the Branching in Amylopectin and Glycogen

Both amylopectin and glycogen contain branch points that are linked through α-1,6-linkages. These branch points occur more often in glycogen.

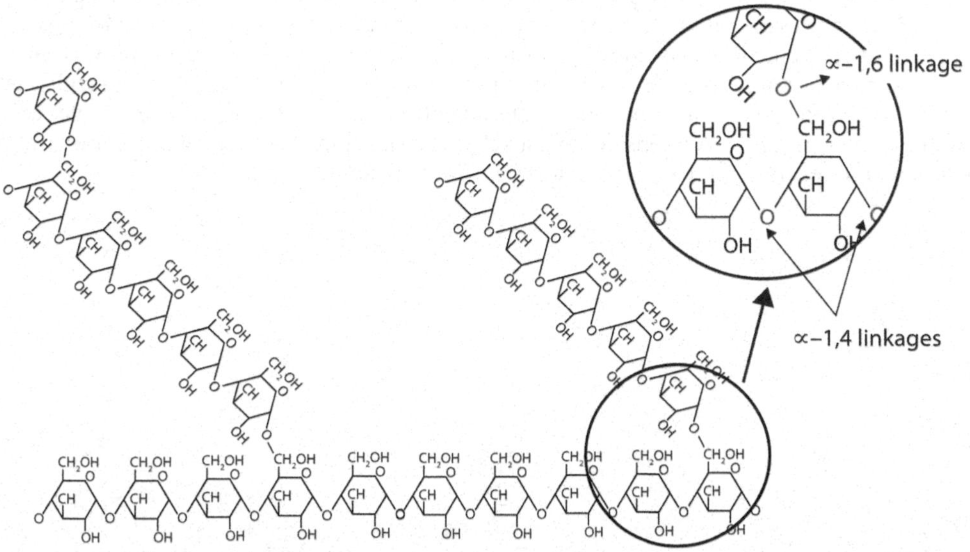

Dextrins are glucose polysaccharides of intermediate size. The shine and stiffness imparted to clothing by starch are due to the presence of dextrins formed when clothing is ironed. Because of their characteristic stickiness with wetting, dextrins are used as adhesives on stamps, envelopes, and labels; as binders to hold pills and tablets together; and as pastes. Dextrins are more easily digested than starch and are therefore used extensively in the commercial preparation of infant foods.

The complete hydrolysis of starch yields, in successive stages, glucose:

$$\text{starch} \rightarrow \text{dextrins} \rightarrow \text{maltose} \rightarrow \text{glucose}$$

In the human body, several enzymes known collectively as amylases degrade starch sequentially into usable glucose units.

7.2 Glycogen

Glycogen is the energy reserve carbohydrate of animals. Practically all mammalian cells contain some stored carbohydrates in the form of glycogen, but it is especially abundant in the liver (4%–8% by weight of tissue) and in skeletal muscle cells (0.5%–1.0%). Like starch in plants, glycogen is found as granules in liver and muscle cells. When fasting, animals draw on these glycogen reserves during the first day without food to obtain the glucose needed to maintain metabolic balance.

Note

About 70% of the total glycogen in the body is stored in muscle cells. Although the percentage of glycogen (by weight) is higher in the liver, the much greater mass of skeletal muscle stores a greater total amount of glycogen.

Glycogen is structurally quite similar to amylopectin, although glycogen is more highly branched (8–12 glucose units between branches) and the branches are shorter. When treated with iodine, glycogen gives a reddish brown color. Glycogen can be broken down into its D-glucose subunits by acid hydrolysis or by the same enzymes that catalyze the breakdown of starch. In animals, the enzyme phosphorylase catalyzes the breakdown of glycogen to phosphate esters of glucose.

7.3 Cellulose

Cellulose, a fibrous carbohydrate found in all plants, is the structural component of plant cell walls. Because the earth is covered with vegetation, cellulose is the most abundant of all carbohydrates, accounting for over 50% of all the carbon found in the vegetable kingdom. Cotton fibrils and filter paper are almost entirely cellulose (about 95%), wood is about 50% cellulose, and the dry weight of leaves is about 10%–20% cellulose. The largest use of cellulose is in the manufacture of paper and paper products. Although the use of noncellulose synthetic fibers is increasing, rayon (made from cellulose) and cotton still account for over 70% of textile production.

Like amylose, cellulose is a linear polymer of glucose. It differs, however, in that the glucose units are joined by β-1,4-glycosidic linkages, producing a more extended structure than amylose (part (a) of Figure 16.11). This extreme linearity allows a great deal of hydrogen bonding between OH groups on adjacent chains, causing them to pack closely into fibers (part (b) of Figure 16.11). As a result, cellulose exhibits little interaction with water or any other solvent. Cotton and wood, for example, are completely insoluble in water and have considerable mechanical strength. Because cellulose does not have a helical structure, it does not bind to iodine to form a colored product.

FIGURE 16.11 Cellulose

(a) There is extensive hydrogen bonding in the structure of cellulose. (b) In this electron micrograph of the cell wall of an alga, the wall consists of successive layers of cellulose fibers in parallel arrangement.

(a)

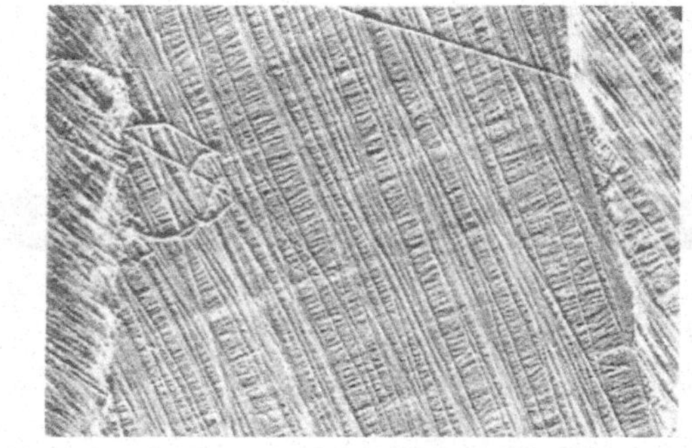

(b)

Cellulose yields D-glucose after complete acid hydrolysis, yet humans are unable to metabolize cellulose as a source of glucose. Our digestive juices lack enzymes that can hydrolyze the β-glycosidic linkages found in cellulose, so although we can eat potatoes, we cannot eat grass. However, certain microorganisms can digest cellulose because they make the enzyme cellulase, which catalyzes the hydrolysis of cellulose. The presence of these microorganisms in the digestive tracts of herbivorous animals (such as cows, horses, and sheep) allows these animals to degrade the cellulose from plant material into glucose for energy. Termites also contain cellulase-secreting microorganisms and thus can subsist on a wood diet. This example once again demonstrates the extreme stereospecificity of biochemical processes.

Career Focus: Certified Diabetes Educator

Certified diabetes educators come from a variety of health professions, such as nursing and dietetics, and specialize in the education and treatment of patients with diabetes. A diabetes educator will work with patients to manage their diabetes. This involves teaching the patient to monitor blood sugar levels, make good food choices, develop and maintain an exercise program, and take medication, if required. Diabetes educators also work with hospital or nursing home staff to improve the care of diabetic patients. Educators must be willing to spend time attending meetings and reading the current literature to maintain their knowledge of diabetes medications, nutrition, and blood monitoring devices so that they can pass this information to their patients.

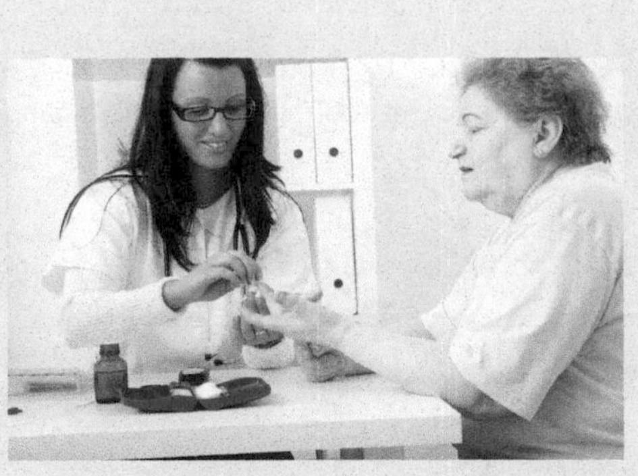

© *Thinkstock*

CONCEPT REVIEW EXERCISES

1. What purposes do starch and cellulose serve in plants?
2. What purpose does glycogen serve in animals?

ANSWERS

1. Starch is the storage form of glucose (energy) in plants, while cellulose is a structural component of the plant cell wall.
2. Glycogen is the storage form of glucose (energy) in animals.

KEY TAKEAWAYS

- Starch is a storage form of energy in plants. It contains two polymers composed of glucose units: amylose (linear) and amylopectin (branched).
- Glycogen is a storage form of energy in animals. It is a branched polymer composed of glucose units. It is more highly branched than amylopectin.
- Cellulose is a structural polymer of glucose units found in plants. It is a linear polymer with the glucose units linked through β-1,4-glycosidic bonds.

EXERCISES

1. What monosaccharide is obtained from the hydrolysis of each carbohydrate?
   a. starch
   b. cellulose
   c. glycogen
2. For each carbohydrate listed in Exercise 1, indicate whether it is found in plants or mammals.
3. Describe the similarities and differences between amylose and cellulose.
4. Describe the similarities and differences between amylopectin and glycogen.

ANSWERS

1. a. glucose
   b. glucose
   c. glucose
3. Amylose and cellulose are both linear polymers of glucose units, but the glycosidic linkages between the glucose units differ. The linkages in amylose are α-1,4-glycosidic linkages, while the linkages in cellulose they are β-1,4-glycosidic linkages.

8. END-OF-CHAPTER MATERIAL

Chapter Summary

To ensure that you understand the material in this chapter, you should review the meanings of the bold terms in the following summary and ask yourself how they relate to the topics in the chapter.

Carbohydrates, a large group of biological compounds containing carbon, hydrogen, and oxygen atoms, include sugars, starch, glycogen, and cellulose. All carbohydrates contain alcohol functional groups, and either an aldehyde or a ketone group (or a functional group that can be converted to an aldehyde or ketone). The simplest carbohydrates are **monosaccharides**. Those with two monosaccharide units are **disaccharides**, and those with many monosaccharide units are **polysaccharides**. Most sugars are either monosaccharides or disaccharides. Cellulose, glycogen, and starch are polysaccharides.

Many carbohydrates exist as **stereoisomers**, in which the three-dimensional spatial arrangement of the atoms in space is the only difference between the isomers. These particular stereoisomers contain at least one **chiral carbon**, a carbon atom that has four different groups bonded to it. A molecule containing a chiral carbon is nonsuperimposable on its mirror image, and two molecules that are nonsuperimposable mirror images of each other are a special type of stereoisomer called **enantiomers**. Enantiomers have the same physical properties, such as melting point, but differ in the direction they rotate polarized light.

A sugar is designated as being a D sugar or an L sugar according to how, in a Fischer projection of the molecule, the hydrogen atom and OH group are attached to the *penultimate* carbon atom, which is the carbon atom immediately before the terminal alcohol carbon atom. If the structure at this carbon atom is the same as that of D-glyceraldehyde (OH to the right), the sugar is a **D sugar**; if the configuration is the same as that of L-glyceraldehyde (OH to the left), the sugar is an **L sugar**.

Monosaccharides of five or more carbons atoms readily form cyclic structures when the carbonyl carbon atom reacts with an OH group on a carbon atom three or four carbon atoms distant. Consequently, glucose in solution exists as an equilibrium mixture of three forms, two of them cyclic (α- and β-) and one open chain. In Haworth projections, the *alpha* form is drawn with the OH group on the "former" carbonyl carbon atom (**anomeric carbon**) pointing downward; the *beta* form, with the OH group pointing upward; these two compounds are stereoisomers and are given the more specific term of **anomers**. Any solid sugar can be all alpha or all beta. Once the sample is dissolved in water, however, the ring opens up into the open-chain structure and then closes to form either the α- or the β-anomer. These interconversions occur back and forth until a dynamic equilibrium mixture is achieved in a process called **mutarotation**.

The carbonyl group present in monosaccharides is easily oxidized by Tollens' or Benedict's reagents (as well as others). Any mono- or disaccharide containing a free anomeric carbon is a **reducing sugar**. The disaccharide *maltose* contains two glucose units joined in an α-1,4-glycosidic linkage. The disaccharide *lactose* contains a galactose unit and a glucose unit joined by a β-1,4-glycosidic linkage. Both maltose and lactose contain a free anomeric carbon that can convert to an aldehyde functional group, so they are reducing sugars; they also undergo mutarotation. Many adults, and some children, have a deficiency of the enzyme lactase (which is needed to break down lactose) and are said to be **lactose intolerant**. A more serious problem is the genetic disease **galactosemia**, which results from the absence of an enzyme needed to convert galactose to glucose.

The disaccharide *sucrose* (table sugar) consists of a glucose unit and a fructose unit joined by a glycosidic linkage. The linkage is designated as an α-1,β-2-glycosidic linkage because it involves the OH group on the first carbon atom of glucose and the OH group on the second carbon atom of fructose. Sucrose is not a reducing sugar because it has no anomeric carbon that can reform a carbonyl group, and it cannot undergo mutarotation because of the restrictions imposed by this linkage.

Starch, the principal carbohydrate of plants, is composed of the polysaccharides **amylose** (10%–30%) and **amylopectin** (70%–90%). When ingested by humans and other animals, starch is hydrolyzed to glucose and becomes the body's energy source. *Glycogen* is the polysaccharide animals use to store excess carbohydrates from their diets. Similar in structure to amylopectin, glycogen is hydrolyzed to glucose whenever an animal needs energy for a metabolic process. The polysaccharide *cellulose* provides structure for plant cells. It is a linear polymer of glucose units joined by β-1,4-glycosidic linkages. It is indigestible in the human body but digestible by many microorganisms, including microorganisms found in the digestive tracts of many herbivores.

ADDITIONAL EXERCISES

1. Draw the Fischer projections for D-glucose and D-ribose. Identify all the functional groups in each structure.

2. Draw the Fischer projections for D-galactose and D-fructose. Identify all the functional groups in each structure.
3. L-Fucose is an aldohexose that is often incorporated into oligosaccharides attached to cell membranes. It is also known as 6-deoxy-L-galactose. Draw the structure of L-fucose.
4. D-glucitol, also known as sorbitol, is added to shredded coconut to keep it soft and to pharmaceutical products to increase the absorption of nutrients. It is prepared industrially by the reduction of D-glucose. Propose a structure for D-glucitol.
5. Which would give a positive Benedict's test—lactose, amylopectin, D-ribose, sucrose, D-glyceraldehyde, or amylose?
6. Which enzyme hydrolyzes each carbohydrate?
   a. maltose
   b. lactose
   c. cellulose
   d. sucrose
7. What structural characteristics are necessary if a disaccharide is to be a reducing sugar? Draw the structure of a hypothetical reducing disaccharide composed of two aldohexoses.
8. Raffinose, a trisaccharide found in beans and sugar beets, contains D-galactose, D-glucose, and D-fructose. The enzyme α-galactase catalyzes the hydrolysis of raffinose to galactose and sucrose. Draw the structure of raffinose. (The linkage from galactose to the glucose unit is α-1,6).
9. What reagent(s) could be used to carry out each conversion?
   a.

H, C=O
H—C—OH
H—C—OH
CH_2OH
?→
$^-$O, C=O
H—C—OH
H—C—OH
CH_2OH

   b.

H, C=O
H—C—OH
H—C—OH
CH_2OH
?→
OH
H—C—OCH_3
HO—C—H
H—C—OH
CH_2OH

10. What reagents are necessary to carry out each conversion?

a.

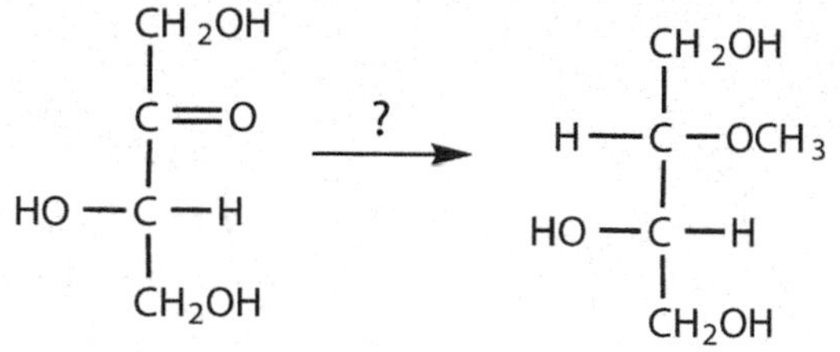

$$\begin{array}{c} CH_2OH \\ | \\ C{=}O \\ | \\ HO{-}C{-}H \\ | \\ CH_2OH \end{array} \xrightarrow{?} \begin{array}{c} CH_2OH \\ | \\ H{-}C{-}OCH_3 \\ | \\ HO{-}C{-}H \\ | \\ CH_2OH \end{array}$$

b.

$$\begin{array}{c} CH_2OH \\ | \\ C{=}O \\ | \\ HO{-}C{-}H \\ | \\ CH_2OH \end{array} \xrightarrow{?} \begin{array}{c} CH_2OH \\ | \\ H{-}C{-}OH \\ | \\ HO{-}C{-}H \\ | \\ CH_2OH \end{array}$$

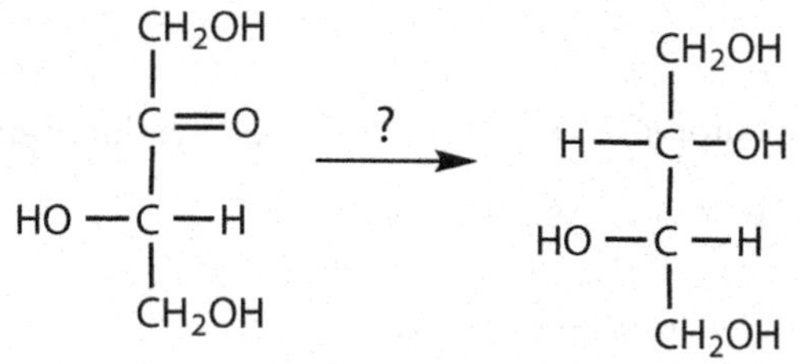

11. The structure of lactulose is shown here. What monosaccharide units compose this disaccharide?

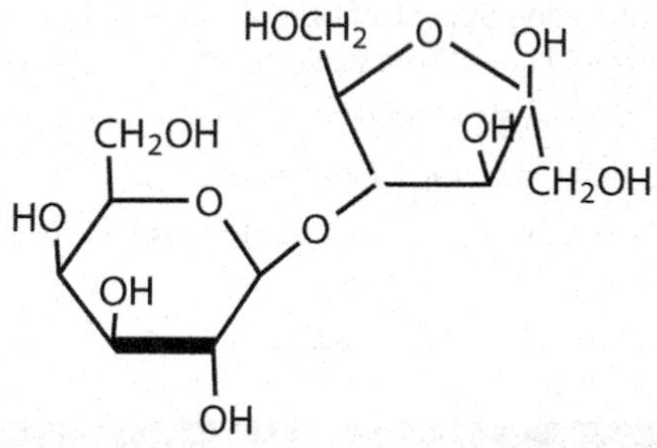

HOCH$_2$ O OH OH CH$_2$OH CH$_2$OH O HO O OH OH

12. N-acetylglucosamine is synthesized from D-glucosamine, which in turn is obtained from D-glucose. What reagents are needed for the conversion of D-glucosamine to N-acetylglucosamine?

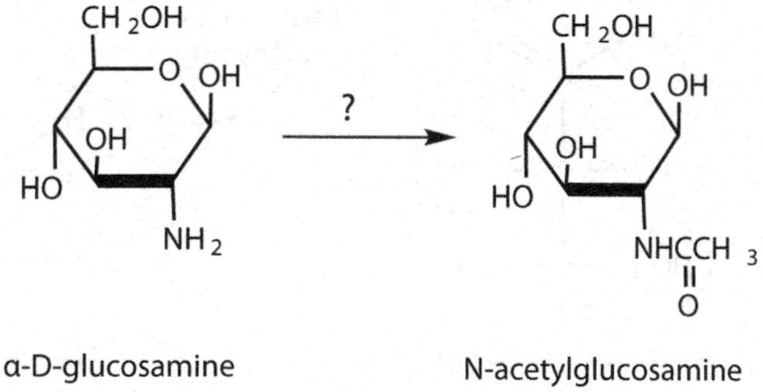

CH$_2$OH O OH OH HO NH$_2$ $\xrightarrow{?}$ CH$_2$OH O OH OH HO NHCCH$_3$ (C=O)

α-D-glucosamine N-acetylglucosamine

13. Hyaluronic acid is a heteropolymer that acts as a lubricating agent in the fluids of joints and the eyes. Its structure consists of repeating disaccharide units containing glucuronic acid and N-acetylglucosamine connected by a β-1,3-linkage. Draw the structure of the disaccharide unit found in hyaluronic acid.

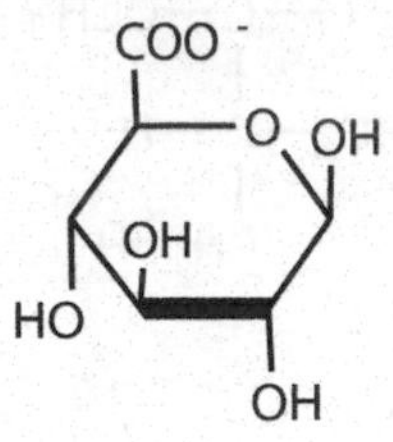

Glucuronic acid

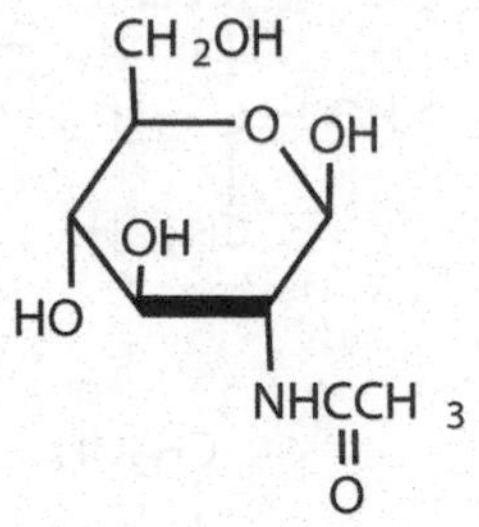

N-acetylglucosamine

14. Several artificial sweeteners are discussed in this chapter.
    a. Which are currently approved for use in the United States?
    b. Which has (or have) a bitter, metallic aftertaste?
    c. Which was (or were) most recently approved for use in the United States?
    d. Which contain(s) potassium?
15. If 3.0 mmol (3.0×10^{-3} mol) samples of saccharin, cyclamate, aspartame, and acesulfame K were each dissolved in separate beakers containing 500 mL of pure water, which solution would have the sweetest taste? Which solution would have the least sweet taste? Justify your answers.
16. Identify two functional groups found in aspartame, acesulfame K, and sucralose.
17. Why does a deficiency of lactase lead to cramps and diarrhea?
18. How does galactosemia differ from lactose intolerance in terms of the cause of the disease and its symptoms and severity?

ANSWERS

1.

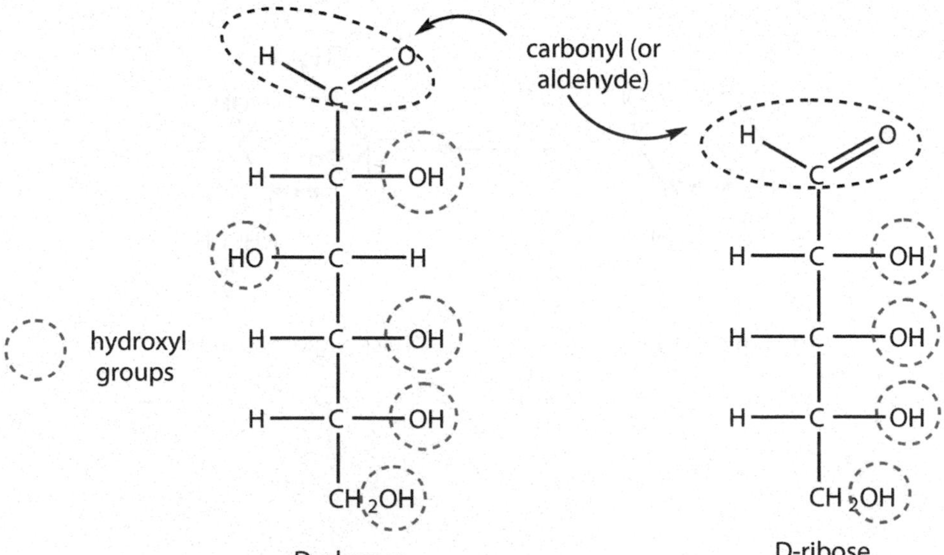

3.

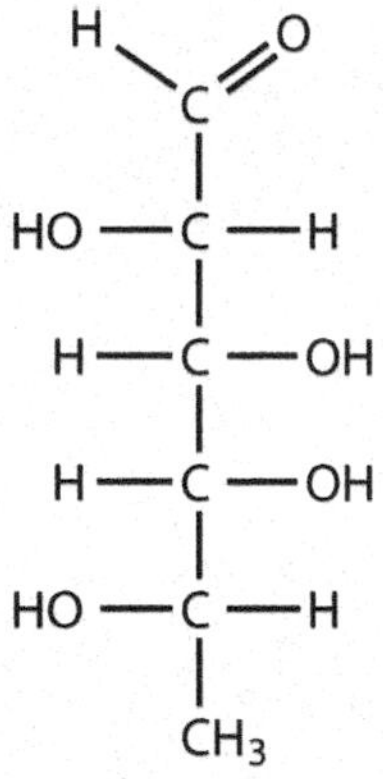

H
C=O
HO—C—H
H—C—OH
H—C—OH
HO—C—H
CH_3

L-fucose

5. Lactose, D-ribose, and D-glyceraldehyde would give a positive Benedict's test.

7. To be a reducing sugar, a disaccharide must contain an anomeric carbon atom that can open up to form an aldehyde functional group, as shown in this disaccharide (answers will vary).

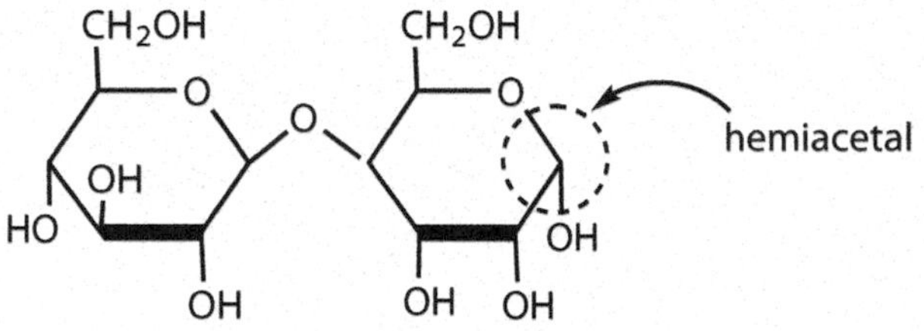

CH_2OH CH_2OH
O O O
OH hemiacetal
HO OH
OH OH OH

9. a. The carbohydrate is being oxidized; Tollens' or Benedict's reagent could be used.
   b. To form the compound shown, an aldehyde must react with methanol (CH3OH) and an acid catalyst.

11. galactose and fructose

13.

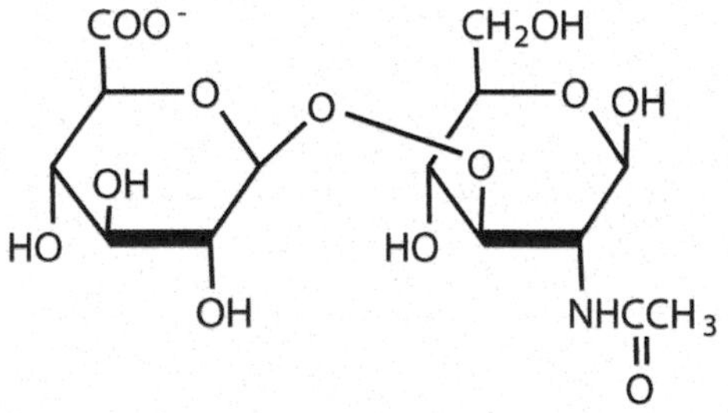

COO^- CH_2OH
O O O OH
OH O
HO HO
OH $NHCCH_3$
O

15. Sucralose would be expected to have the sweetest taste because its relative sweetness is the highest. Lactose would have the least sweet taste because it has the lowest relative sweetness.

17. Intestinal bacteria can act on the lactose present in the intestine to produce organic acids and gases. The buildup of water and bacterial decay products leads to cramps and diarrhea.

CHAPTER 17
Lipids

Opening Essay

On July 11, 2003, the Food and Drug Administration amended its food labeling regulations to require that manufacturers list the amount of *trans* fatty acids on Nutrition Facts labels of foods and dietary supplements, effective January 1, 2006. This amendment was a response to published studies demonstrating a link between the consumption of *trans* fatty acids and an increased risk of heart disease. *Trans* fatty acids are produced in the conversion of liquid oils to solid fats, as in the creation of many commercial margarines and shortenings. They have been shown to increase the levels of low-density lipoproteins (LDLs)—complexes that are often referred to as bad cholesterol—in the blood. In this chapter, you will learn about fatty acids and what is meant by a *trans* fatty acid, as well as the difference between fats and oils. You will also learn what cholesterol is and why it is an important molecule in the human body.

All food products must display the amount of *trans* fatty acids they contain. A listing of 0 g means that a serving contains less than 0.5 g of *trans* fatty acids.

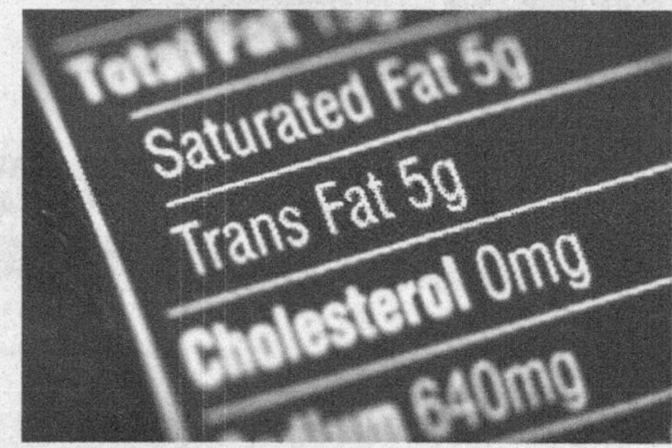

Fats and oils, found in many of the foods we eat, belong to a class of biomolecules known as lipids. Gram for gram, they pack more than twice the caloric content of carbohydrates: the oxidation of fats and oils supplies about 9 kcal of energy for every gram oxidized, whereas the oxidation of carbohydrates supplies only 4 kcal/g. Although the high caloric content of fats may be bad news for the dieter, it says something about the efficiency of nature's designs. Our bodies use carbohydrates, primarily in the form of glucose, for our *immediate* energy needs. Our capacity for storing carbohydrates for later use is limited to tucking away a bit of glycogen in the liver or in muscle tissue. We store our *reserve* energy in lipid form, which requires far less space than the same amount of energy stored in carbohydrate form.

Lipids have other biological functions besides energy storage. They are a major component of the membranes of the 10 trillion cells in our bodies. They serve as protective padding and insulation for vital organs. Furthermore, without lipids in our diets, we would be deficient in the fat-soluble vitamins A, D, E, and K.

Lipids are not defined by the presence of specific functional groups, as carbohydrates are, but by a physical property—solubility. Compounds isolated from body tissues are classified as **lipids** if they are more soluble in organic solvents, such as dichloromethane, than in water. By this criterion, the lipid category includes not only fats and oils, which are esters of the trihydroxy alcohol glycerol and fatty acids, but also compounds that incorporate functional groups derived from phosphoric acid, carbohydrates, or amino alcohols, as well as steroid compounds

lipid

A compound isolated from body tissues that is more soluble in organic solvents than in water.

such as cholesterol. (Figure 17.1 presents one scheme for classifying the various kinds of lipids.) We will discuss the various kinds of lipids by considering one subclass at a time and pointing out structural similarities and differences as we go.

FIGURE 17.1 Lipid Organization Based on Structural Relationships

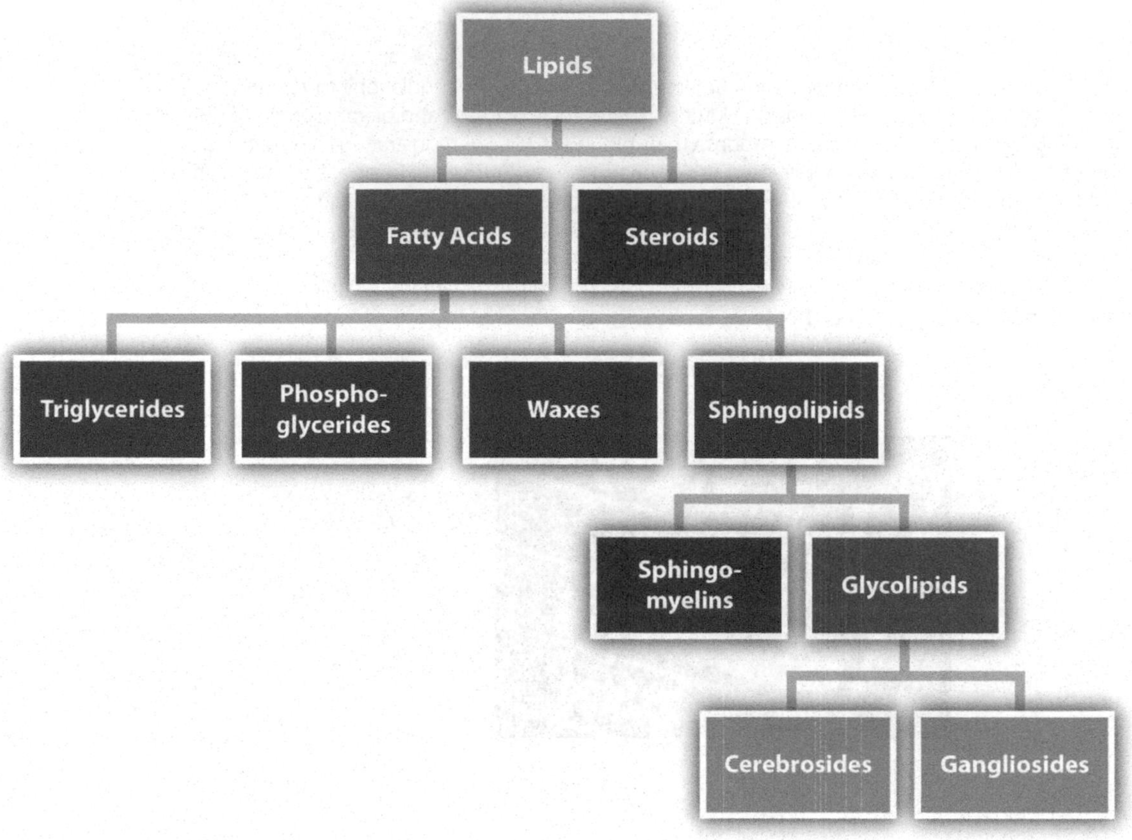

1. FATTY ACIDS

LEARNING OBJECTIVE

1. Recognize the structures of common fatty acids and classify them as saturated, monounsaturated, or polyunsaturated.

Fatty acids are carboxylic acids that are structural components of fats, oils, and all other categories of lipids, except steroids. More than 70 have been identified in nature. They usually contain an even number of carbon atoms (typically 12–20), are generally unbranched, and can be classified by the presence and number of carbon-to-carbon double bonds. Thus, **saturated fatty acids** contain no carbon-to-carbon double bonds, **monounsaturated fatty acids** contain one carbon-to-carbon double bond, and **polyunsaturated fatty acids** contain two or more carbon-to-carbon double bonds. Table 17.1 lists some common fatty acids and one important source for each. The atoms or groups around the double bonds in unsaturated fatty acids can be arranged in either the *cis* or *trans* isomeric form. Naturally occurring fatty acids are generally in the *cis* configuration. (For more information about cis-trans isomerism, see Chapter 13, [Unsupported Reference Type: chapter-section].)

fatty acid

A carboxylic acid that is a structural component of fats and oils.

saturated fatty acid

A fatty acid that has no carbon-to-carbon double bonds.

monounsaturated fatty acid

A fatty acid that has one carbon-to-carbon double bond.

polyunsaturated fatty acid

A fatty acid that has two or more carbon-to-carbon double bonds.

$CH_3(CH_2)_5$ / $(CH_2)_7COOH$ — C=C — H / H

cis fatty acid

H / $(CH_2)_7COOH$ — C=C — $CH_3(CH_2)_5$ / H

trans fatty acid

TABLE 17.1 Some Common Fatty Acids Found in Natural Fats

Name	Abbreviated Structural Formula	Condensed Structural Formula	Melting Point (°C)	Source
lauric acid	$C_{11}H_{23}COOH$	$CH_3(CH_2)_{10}COOH$	44	palm kernel oil
myristic acid	$C_{13}H_{27}COOH$	$CH_3(CH_2)_{12}COOH$	58	oil of nutmeg
palmitic acid	$C_{15}H_{31}COOH$	$CH_3(CH_2)_{14}COOH$	63	palm oil
palmitoleic acid	$C_{15}H_{29}COOH$	$CH_3(CH_2)_5CH=CH(CH_2)_7COOH$	0.5	macadamia oil
stearic acid	$C_{17}H_{35}COOH$	$CH_3(CH_2)_{16}COOH$	70	cocoa butter
oleic acid	$C_{17}H_{33}COOH$	$CH_3(CH_2)_7CH=CH(CH_2)_7COOH$	16	olive oil
linoleic acid	$C_{17}H_{31}COOH$	$CH_3(CH_2)_3(CH_2CH=CH)_2(CH_2)_7COOH$	−5	canola oil
α-linolenic acid	$C_{17}H_{29}COOH$	$CH_3(CH_2CH=CH)_3(CH_2)_7COOH$	−11	flaxseed
arachidonic acid	$C_{19}H_{31}COOH$	$CH_3(CH_2)_4(CH_2CH=CH)_4(CH_2)_2COOH$	−50	liver

Two polyunsaturated fatty acids—linoleic and α-linolenic acids—are termed **essential fatty acids** because humans must obtain them from their diets. Both substances are required for normal growth and development, but the human body does not synthesize them. The body uses linoleic acid to synthesize many of the other unsaturated fatty acids, such as arachidonic acid, a precursor for the synthesis of prostaglandins. In addition, the essential fatty acids are necessary for the efficient transport and metabolism of cholesterol. The average daily diet should contain about 4–6 g of the essential fatty acids.

essential fatty acid

A fatty acid that must be obtained from the diet because it cannot be synthesized by the human body.

To Your Health: Prostaglandins

Prostaglandins are chemical messengers synthesized in the cells in which their physiological activity is expressed. They are unsaturated fatty acids containing 20 carbon atoms and are synthesized from arachidonic acid—a polyunsaturated fatty acid—when needed by a particular cell. They are called *prostaglandins* because they were originally isolated from semen found in the prostate gland. It is now known that they are synthesized in nearly all mammalian tissues and affect almost all organs in the body. The five major classes of prostaglandins are designated as PGA, PGB, PGE, PGF, and PGI. Subscripts are attached at the end of these abbreviations to denote the number of double bonds outside the five-carbon ring in a given prostaglandin.

The prostaglandins are among the most potent biological substances known. Slight structural differences give them highly distinct biological effects; however, all prostaglandins exhibit some ability to induce smooth muscle contraction, lower blood pressure, and contribute to the inflammatory response. Aspirin and other nonsteroidal anti-inflammatory agents, such as ibuprofen, obstruct the synthesis of prostaglandins by inhibiting cyclooxygenase, the enzyme needed for the initial step in the conversion of arachidonic acid to prostaglandins.

Their wide range of physiological activity has led to the synthesis of hundreds of prostaglandins and their analogs. Derivatives of PGE_2 are now used in the United States to induce labor. Other prostaglandins have been employed clinically to lower or increase blood pressure, inhibit stomach secretions, relieve nasal congestion, relieve asthma, and prevent the formation of blood clots, which are associated with heart attacks and strokes.

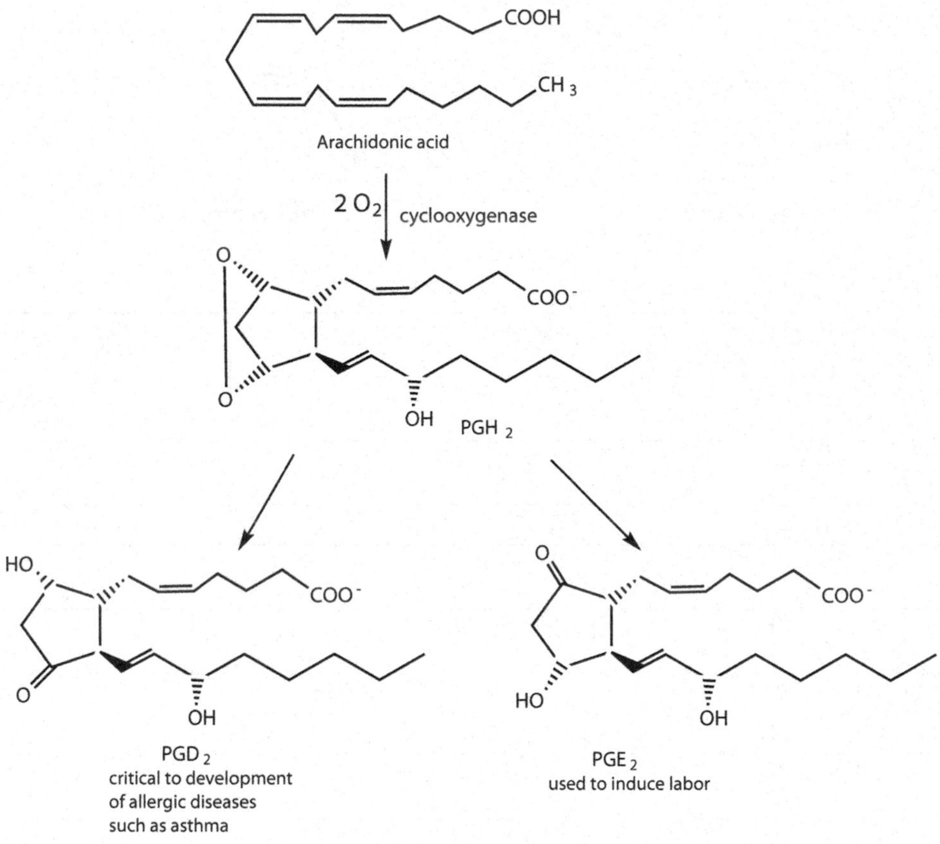

Although we often draw the carbon atoms in a straight line, they actually have more of a zigzag configuration (part (a) of Figure 17.2). Viewed as a whole, however, the saturated fatty acid molecule is relatively straight (part (b) of Figure 17.2). Such molecules pack closely together into a crystal lattice, maximizing the strength of dispersion forces and causing fatty acids and the fats derived from them to have relatively high melting points. In contrast, each *cis* carbon-to-carbon double bond in an unsaturated fatty acid produces a pronounced bend in the molecule, so that these molecules do not stack neatly. As a result, the intermolecular attractions of unsaturated fatty acids (and unsaturated fats) are weaker, causing these substances to have lower melting points. Most are liquids at room temperature.

FIGURE 17.2 The Structure of Saturated Fatty Acids

(a) There is a zigzag pattern formed by the carbon-to-carbon single bonds in the ball-and-stick model of a palmitic acid molecule. (b) A space-filling model of palmitic acid shows the overall straightness of a saturated fatty acid molecule.

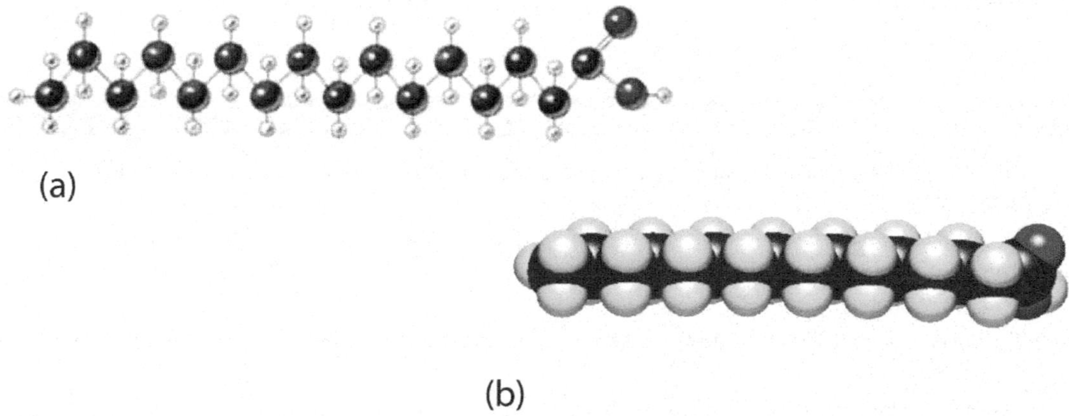

Waxes are esters formed from long-chain fatty acids and long-chain alcohols. Most natural waxes are mixtures of such esters. Plant waxes on the surfaces of leaves, stems, flowers, and fruits protect the plant from dehydration and invasion by harmful microorganisms. Carnauba wax, used extensively in floor waxes, automobile waxes, and furniture polish, is largely myricyl cerotate, obtained from the leaves of certain Brazilian palm trees. Animals also produce waxes that serve as protective coatings, keeping the surfaces of feathers, skin, and hair pliable and water repellent. In fact, if the waxy coating on the feathers of a water bird is dissolved as a result of the bird swimming in an oil slick, the feathers become wet and heavy, and the bird, unable to maintain its buoyancy, drowns.

$$\underbrace{CH_3(CH_2)_{24}C(=O)}_{\text{from a fatty acid}}-O-\underbrace{(CH_2)_{29}CH_3}_{\text{from a long-chain alcohol}}$$

Myricyl cerotate
(found in carnauba wax)

CONCEPT REVIEW EXERCISES

1. Give an example of each compound.
   a. saturated fatty acid
   b. polyunsaturated fatty acid
   c. monounsaturated fatty acid
2. Why do unsaturated fatty acids have lower melting points than saturated fatty acids?

ANSWERS

1. a. stearic acid (answers will vary)
   b. linoleic acid (answers will vary)
   c. palmitoleic acid (answers will vary)
2. Unsaturated fatty acids cannot pack as tightly together as saturated fatty acids due to the presence of the cis double bond that puts a "kink" or bend in the hydrocarbon chain.

KEY TAKEAWAYS

- Fatty acids are carboxylic acids that are the structural components of many lipids. They may be saturated or unsaturated.
- Most fatty acids are unbranched and contain an even number of carbon atoms.
- Unsaturated fatty acids have lower melting points than saturated fatty acids containing the same number of carbon atoms.

EXERCISES

1. Classify each fatty acid as saturated or unsaturated and indicate the number of carbon atoms in each molecule.
   a. palmitoleic acid
   b. myristic acid
   c. linoleic acid
2. Classify each fatty acid as saturated or unsaturated and indicate the number of carbon atoms in each molecule.
   a. stearic acid
   b. oleic acid
   c. palmitic acid
3. Write the condensed structural formula for each fatty acid.
   a. lauric acid
   b. palmitoleic acid
   c. linoleic acid
4. Write the condensed structural formulas for each fatty acid.
   a. oleic acid
   b. α-linolenic acid
   c. palmitic acid
5. Arrange these fatty acids (all contain 18 carbon atoms) in order of increasing melting point. Justify your arrangement.
   a.

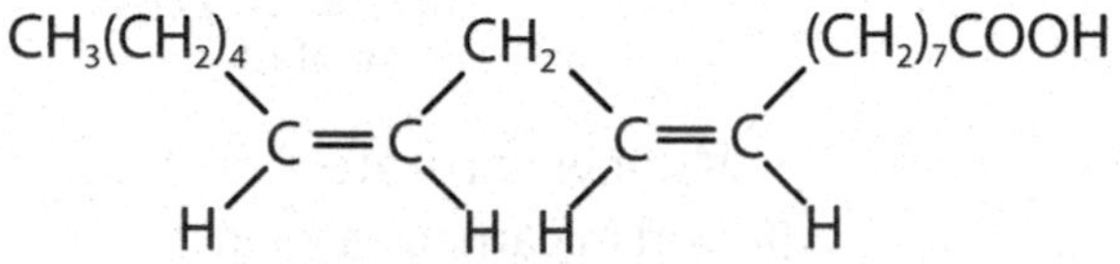

      $CH_3(CH_2)_4$ CH_2 $(CH_2)_7COOH$
      C=C C=C
      H H H H

   b.

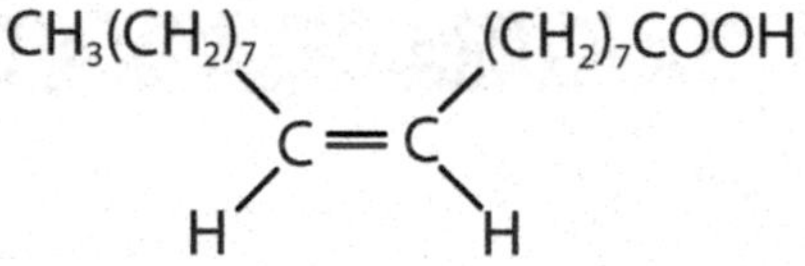

      $CH_3(CH_2)_7$ $(CH_2)_7COOH$
      C=C
      H H

   c.

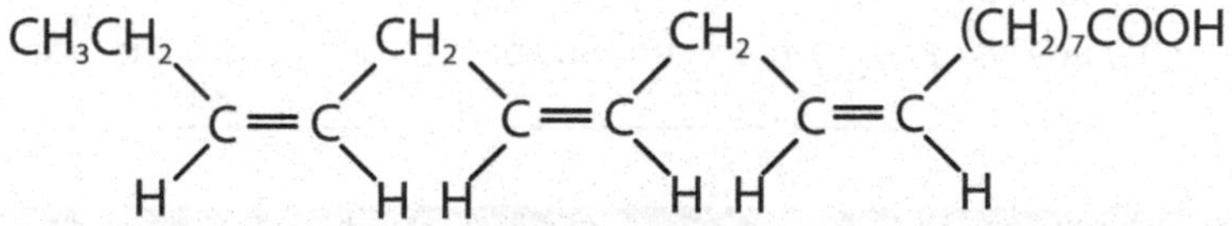

      CH_3CH_2 CH_2 CH_2 $(CH_2)_7COOH$
      C=C C=C C=C
      H H H H H H

6. Arrange these fatty acids (all contain 16 carbon atoms) in order of increasing melting point. Justify your arrangement.
   a. CH3(CH2)14COOH
   b.

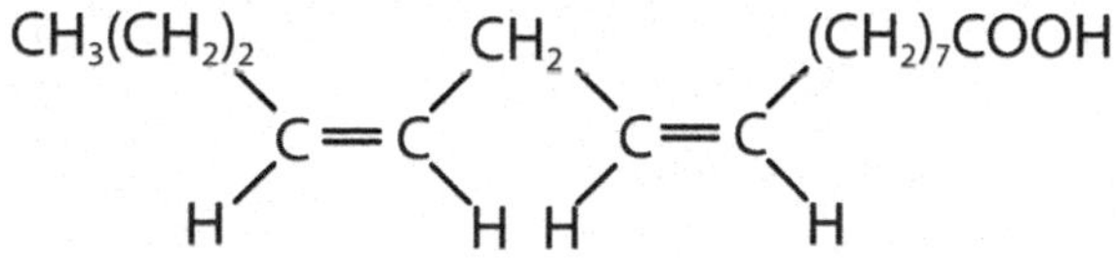

$$\underset{H}{\overset{CH_3(CH_2)_2}{C}}=\underset{H}{\overset{CH_2}{C}}\ \underset{H}{C}=\underset{H}{\overset{(CH_2)_7COOH}{C}}$$

   c.

$$\underset{H}{\overset{CH_3(CH_2)_5}{C}}=\underset{H}{\overset{(CH_2)_7COOH}{C}}$$

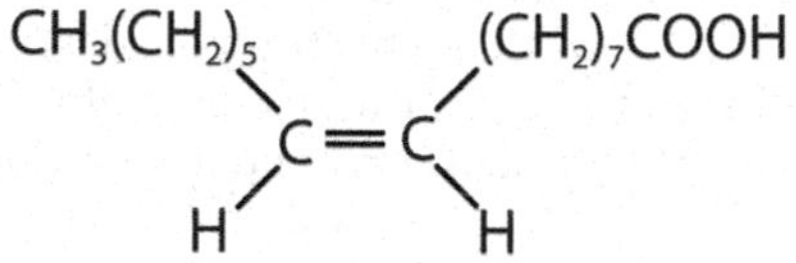

ANSWERS

1. a. unsaturated; 16 carbon atoms
   b. saturated; 14 carbon atoms
   c. unsaturated; 18 carbon atoms
3. a. CH3(CH2)10COOH
   b. CH3(CH2)5CH=CH(CH2)7COOH
   c. CH3(CH2)3(CH2CH=CH)2(CH2)7COOH
5. c < a < b; an increase in the number of double bonds will lower the melting point because it is more difficult to closely pack the fatty acids together.

2. FATS AND OILS

LEARNING OBJECTIVES

1. **Explain why fats and oils are referred to as triglycerides.**
2. **Explain how the fatty acid composition of the triglycerides determines whether a substance is a fat or oil.**
3. **Describe the importance of key reactions of triglycerides, such as hydrolysis, hydrogenation, and oxidation.**

Fats and oils are the most abundant lipids in nature. They provide energy for living organisms, insulate body organs, and transport fat-soluble vitamins through the blood.

2.1 Structures of Fats and Oils

Fats and oils are called **triglycerides** (or *triacylcylgerols*) because they are esters composed of three fatty acid units joined to *glycerol*, a trihydroxy alcohol:

triglyceride

An ester composed of three fatty acid units linked to glycerol and found in fats and oils.

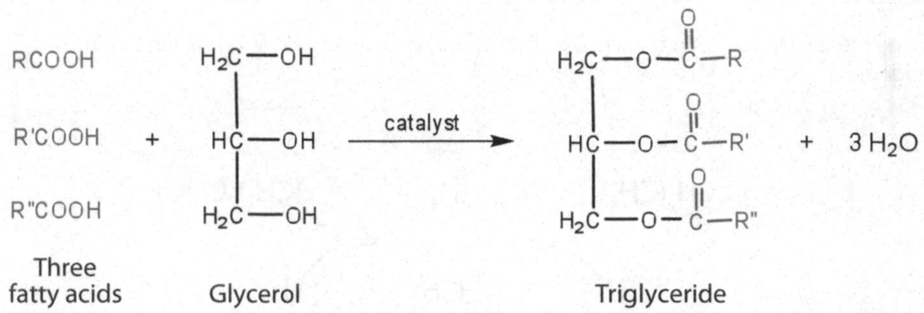

$$\begin{array}{l} RCOOH \\ R'COOH \\ R''COOH \end{array} + \begin{array}{l} H_2C-OH \\ HC-OH \\ H_2C-OH \end{array} \xrightarrow{\text{catalyst}} \begin{array}{l} H_2C-O-C(=O)-R \\ HC-O-C(=O)-R' \\ H_2C-O-C(=O)-R'' \end{array} + 3\,H_2O$$

Three fatty acids — Glycerol — Triglyceride

If all three OH groups on the glycerol molecule are esterified with the same fatty acid, the resulting ester is called a *simple triglyceride*. Although simple triglycerides have been synthesized in the laboratory, they rarely occur in nature. Instead, a typical triglyceride obtained from naturally occurring fats and oils contains two or three different fatty acid components and is thus termed a *mixed triglyceride*.

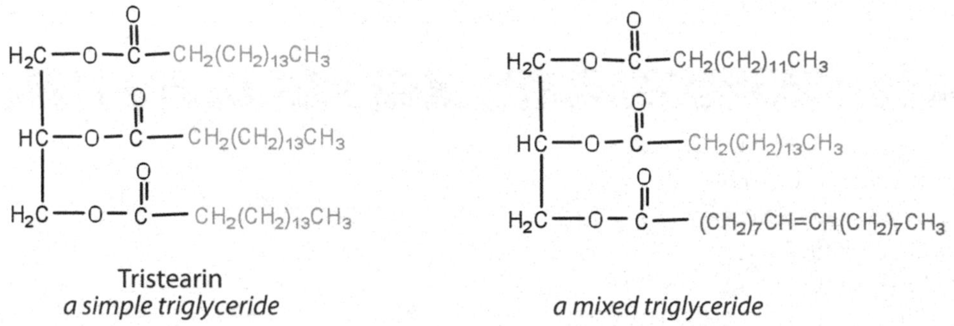

$$\begin{array}{l} H_2C-O-C(=O)-CH_2(CH_2)_{13}CH_3 \\ HC-O-C(=O)-CH_2(CH_2)_{13}CH_3 \\ H_2C-O-C(=O)-CH_2(CH_2)_{13}CH_3 \end{array} \qquad \begin{array}{l} H_2C-O-C(=O)-CH_2(CH_2)_{11}CH_3 \\ HC-O-C(=O)-CH_2(CH_2)_{13}CH_3 \\ H_2C-O-C(=O)-(CH_2)_7CH{=}CH(CH_2)_7CH_3 \end{array}$$

Tristearin
a simple triglyceride

a mixed triglyceride

fat

A compound composed of large hydrocarbon chains that supplies energy for the body. It is a triglyceride that is a solid at room temperature.

oil

A triglyceride that is a liquid at room temperature.

A triglyceride is called a **fat** if it is a solid at 25°C; it is called an **oil** if it is a liquid at that temperature. These differences in melting points reflect differences in the degree of unsaturation and number of carbon atoms in the constituent fatty acids. Triglycerides obtained from animal sources are usually solids, while those of plant origin are generally oils. Therefore, we commonly speak of animal fats and vegetable oils.

No single formula can be written to represent the naturally occurring fats and oils because they are highly complex mixtures of triglycerides in which many different fatty acids are represented. Table 17.2 shows the fatty acid compositions of some common fats and oils. The composition of any given fat or oil can vary depending on the plant or animal species it comes from as well as on dietetic and climatic factors. To cite just one example, lard from corn-fed hogs is more highly saturated than lard from peanut-fed hogs. Palmitic acid is the most abundant of the saturated fatty acids, while oleic acid is the most abundant unsaturated fatty acid.

TABLE 17.2 Average Fatty Acid Composition of Some Common Fats and Oils (%)*

	Lauric	Myristic	Palmitic	Stearic	Oleic	Linoleic	Linolenic
Fats							
butter (cow)	3	11	27	12	29	2	1
tallow		3	24	19	43	3	1
lard		2	26	14	44	10	
Oils							
canola oil			4	2	62	22	10
coconut oil†	47	18	9	3	6	2	
corn oil			11	2	28	58	1
olive oil			13	3	71	10	1
peanut oil			11	2	48	32	
soybean oil			11	4	24	54	7

***Totals less than 100% indicate the presence of fatty acids with fewer than 12 carbon atoms or more than 18 carbon atoms.**

†Coconut oil is highly saturated. It contains an unusually high percentage of the low-melting C_8, C_{10}, and C_{12} saturated fatty acids.

Terms such as *saturated fat* or *unsaturated oil* are often used to describe the fats or oils obtained from foods. Saturated fats contain a high proportion of saturated fatty acids, while unsaturated oils contain a high proportion of unsaturated fatty acids. The high consumption of saturated fats is a factor, along with the high consumption of cholesterol, in increased risks of heart disease. (For more information about cholesterol, see Section 4.)

2.2 Physical Properties of Fats and Oils

Contrary to what you might expect, *pure* fats and oils are colorless, odorless, and tasteless. The characteristic colors, odors, and flavors that we associate with some of them are imparted by foreign substances that are lipid soluble and have been absorbed by these lipids. For example, the yellow color of butter is due to the presence of the pigment carotene; the taste of butter comes from two compounds—diacetyl and 3-hydroxy-2-butanone—produced by bacteria in the ripening cream from which the butter is made.

$$H_3C-\overset{\overset{O}{\|}}{C}-\overset{\overset{O}{\|}}{C}-CH_3 \qquad\qquad H_3C-\overset{\overset{O}{\|}}{C}-\overset{\overset{OH}{|}}{CH}-CH_3$$

Diacetyl 3-hydroxy-2-butanone

Fats and oils are lighter than water, having densities of about 0.8 g/cm^3. They are poor conductors of heat and electricity and therefore serve as excellent insulators for the body, slowing the loss of heat through the skin.

2.3 Chemical Reactions of Fats and Oils

Fats and oils can participate in a variety of chemical reactions—for example, because triglycerides are esters, they can be hydrolyzed in the presence of an acid, a base, or specific enzymes known as lipases. The hydrolysis of fats and oils in the presence of a base is used to make soap and is called **saponification**. Today most soaps are prepared through the hydrolysis of triglycerides (often from tallow, coconut oil, or both) using water under high pressure and temperature [700 lb/in^2 ($\sim$50 atm or 5,000 kPa) and 200°C]. Sodium carbonate or sodium hydroxide is then used to convert the fatty acids to their sodium salts (soap molecules):

saponification

The hydrolysis of fats and oils in the presence of a base to make soap.

$$H_2C{-}O{-}C(=O){-}(CH_2)_{14}CH_3$$
$$HC{-}O{-}C(=O){-}(CH_2)_{14}CH_3 \xrightarrow[\text{Heat, pressure}]{H_2O} \text{Glycerol} + \begin{matrix} 2CH_3(CH_2)_{14}COOH \\ CH_3(CH_2)_{16}COOH \end{matrix} \xrightarrow{NaOH} \begin{matrix} 2CH_3(CH_2)_{14}COO^-Na^+ \\ CH_3(CH_2)_{16}COO^-Na^+ \end{matrix}$$
$$H_2C{-}O{-}C(=O){-}(CH_2)_{16}CH_3$$

Hydrolysis of triglycerides → *produces fatty acids* → *which react with a base to form soap molecules*

Looking Closer: Soaps

Ordinary soap is a mixture of the sodium salts of various fatty acids, produced in one of the oldest organic syntheses practiced by humans (second only to the fermentation of sugars to produce ethyl alcohol). Both the Phoenicians (600 BCE) and the Romans made soap from animal fat and wood ash. Even so, the widespread production of soap did not begin until the 1700s. Soap was traditionally made by treating molten lard or tallow with a slight excess of alkali in large open vats. The mixture was heated, and steam was bubbled through it. After saponification was completed, the soap was precipitated from the mixture by the addition of sodium chloride (NaCl), removed by filtration, and washed several times with water. It was then dissolved in water and reprecipitated by the addition of more NaCl. The glycerol produced in the reaction was also recovered from the aqueous wash solutions.

Pumice or sand is added to produce scouring soap, while ingredients such as perfumes or dyes are added to produce fragrant, colored soaps. Blowing air through molten soap produces a floating soap. Soft soaps, made with potassium salts, are more expensive but produce a finer lather and are more soluble. They are used in liquid soaps, shampoos, and shaving creams.

Dirt and grime usually adhere to skin, clothing, and other surfaces by combining with body oils, cooking fats, lubricating greases, and similar substances that act like glues. Because these substances are not miscible in water, washing with water alone does little to remove them. Soap removes them, however, because soap molecules have a dual nature. One end, called the *head*, carries an ionic charge (a carboxylate anion) and therefore dissolves in water; the other end, the *tail*, has a hydrocarbon structure and dissolves in oils. The hydrocarbon tails dissolve in the soil; the ionic heads remain in the aqueous phase, and the soap breaks the oil into tiny soap-enclosed droplets called *micelles*, which disperse throughout the solution. (For more information about cell structure, see Section 3.) The droplets repel each other because of their charged surfaces and do not coalesce. With the oil no longer "gluing" the dirt to the soiled surface (skin, cloth, dish), the soap-enclosed dirt can easily be rinsed away.

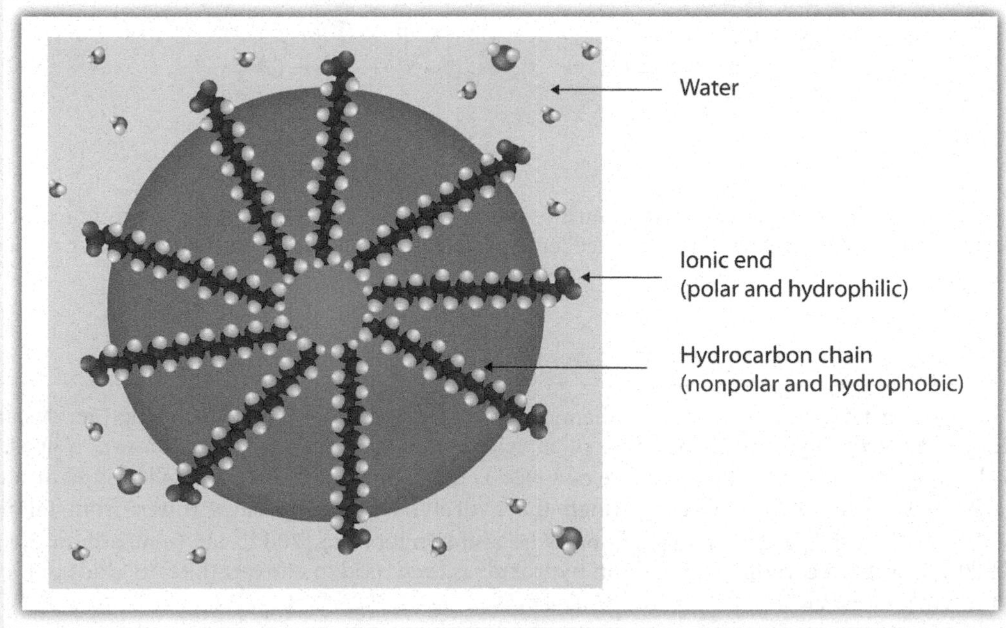

The double bonds in fats and oils can undergo hydrogenation and also oxidation. The hydrogenation of vegetable oils to produce semisolid fats is an important process in the food industry. Chemically, it is essentially identical to the catalytic hydrogenation reaction described for alkenes in Chapter 13, [Unsupported Reference Type: chapter-section].

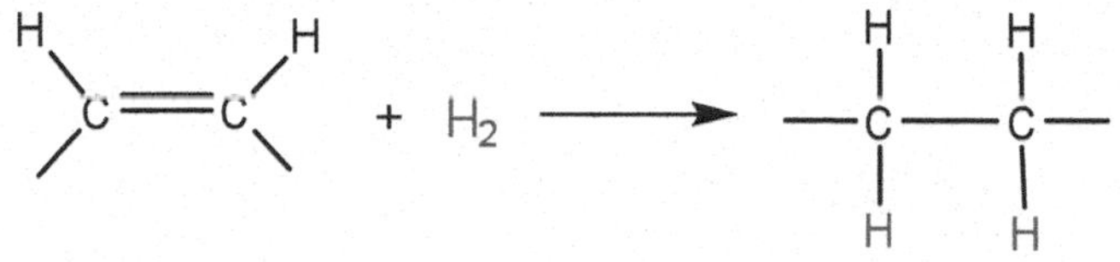

$$>C=C< + H_2 \longrightarrow -\underset{H}{\overset{H}{C}}-\underset{H}{\overset{H}{C}}-$$

In commercial processes, the number of double bonds that are hydrogenated is carefully controlled to produce fats with the desired consistency (soft and pliable). Inexpensive and abundant vegetable oils (canola, corn, soybean) are thus transformed into margarine and cooking fats. In the preparation of margarine, for example, partially hydrogenated oils are mixed with water, salt, and nonfat dry milk, along with flavoring agents, coloring agents, and vitamins A and D, which are added to approximate the look, taste, and nutrition of butter. (Preservatives and antioxidants are also added.) In most commercial peanut butter, the peanut oil has been partially hydrogenated to prevent it from separating out. Consumers could decrease the amount of saturated fat in their diet by using the original unprocessed oils on their foods, but most people would rather spread margarine on their toast than pour oil on it.

Many people have switched from butter to margarine or vegetable shortening because of concerns that saturated animal fats can raise blood cholesterol levels and result in clogged arteries. However, during the hydrogenation of vegetable oils, an isomerization reaction occurs that produces the *trans* fatty acids mentioned in the opening essay. However, studies have shown that *trans* fatty acids also raise cholesterol levels and increase the incidence of heart disease. *Trans* fatty acids do not have the bend in their structures, which occurs in *cis* fatty acids and thus pack closely together in the same way that the saturated fatty acids do. Consumers are now being advised to use polyunsaturated oils and soft or liquid margarine and reduce their total fat consumption to less than 30% of their total calorie intake each day.

Fats and oils that are in contact with moist air at room temperature eventually undergo oxidation and hydrolysis reactions that cause them to turn rancid, acquiring a characteristic disagreeable odor. One cause of the odor is the release of volatile fatty acids by hydrolysis of the ester bonds. Butter, for example, releases foul-smelling butyric, caprylic, and capric acids. Microorganisms present in the air furnish lipases that catalyze this process. Hydrolytic rancidity can easily be prevented by covering the fat or oil and keeping it in a refrigerator.

Another cause of volatile, odorous compounds is the oxidation of the unsaturated fatty acid components, particularly the readily oxidized structural unit

$$\sim CH{=}CH{-}CH_2{-}CH{=}CH\sim$$

in polyunsaturated fatty acids, such as linoleic and linolenic acids. One particularly offensive product, formed by the oxidative cleavage of both double bonds in this unit, is a compound called *malonaldehyde*.

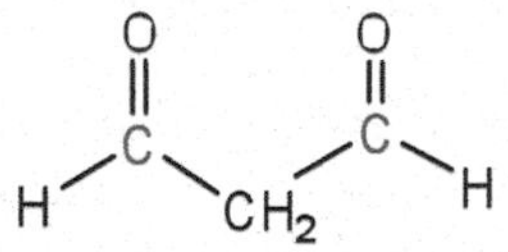

$$H-\overset{O}{\overset{\|}{C}}-CH_2-\overset{O}{\overset{\|}{C}}-H$$

Malonaldehyde

Rancidity is a major concern of the food industry, which is why food chemists are always seeking new and better **antioxidants**, substances added in very small amounts (0.001%–0.01%) to prevent oxidation and thus suppress rancidity. Antioxidants are compounds whose affinity for oxygen is greater than that of the lipids in the food; thus they function by preferentially depleting the supply of oxygen absorbed into the product. Because vitamin E has antioxidant properties, it helps reduce damage to lipids in the body, particularly to unsaturated fatty acids found in cell membrane lipids.

antioxidant

A compound that prevents oxidation.

CONCEPT REVIEW EXERCISES

1. What functions does fat serve in the body?
2. Which of these triglycerides would you expect to find in higher amounts in oils? In fats? Justify your choice.

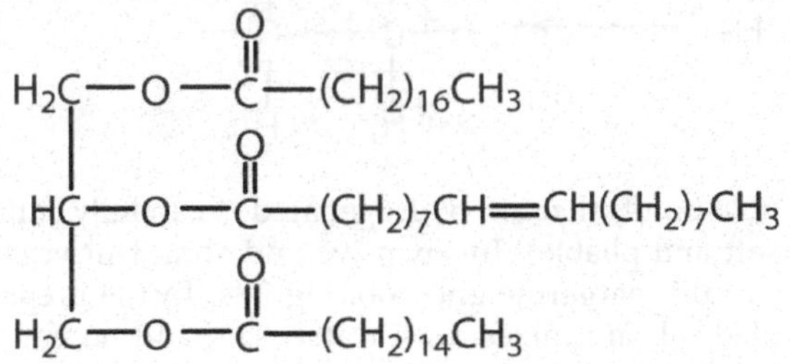

$$\begin{array}{l} H_2C-O-\overset{O}{\overset{\|}{C}}-(CH_2)_{16}CH_3 \\ HC-O-\overset{O}{\overset{\|}{C}}-(CH_2)_7CH{=}CH(CH_2)_7CH_3 \\ H_2C-O-\overset{O}{\overset{\|}{C}}-(CH_2)_{14}CH_3 \end{array}$$

(a)

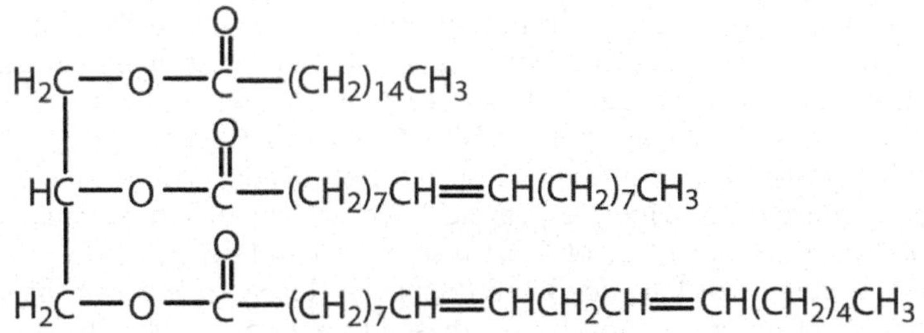

$$\begin{array}{l} H_2C-O-\overset{O}{\overset{\|}{C}}-(CH_2)_{14}CH_3 \\ HC-O-\overset{O}{\overset{\|}{C}}-(CH_2)_7CH{=}CH(CH_2)_7CH_3 \\ H_2C-O-\overset{O}{\overset{\|}{C}}-(CH_2)_7CH{=}CHCH_2CH{=}CH(CH_2)_4CH_3 \end{array}$$

(b)

ANSWERS

1. Fats provide energy for living organisms. They also provide insulation for body organs and transport fat-soluble vitamins.
2. The triglyceride on the left is expected to be present in higher amounts in fats because it is composed of a greater number of saturated fatty acids. The triglyceride on the right is expected to be present in higher amounts in oils because it is composed of a greater number of unsaturated fatty acids.

KEY TAKEAWAYS

- Fats and oils are composed of molecules known as triglycerides, which are esters composed of three fatty acid units linked to glycerol.
- An increase in the percentage of shorter-chain fatty acids and/or unsaturated fatty acids lowers the melting point of a fat or oil.
- The hydrolysis of fats and oils in the presence of a base makes soap and is known as saponification.
- Double bonds present in unsaturated triglycerides can be hydrogenated to convert oils (liquid) into margarine (solid).
- The oxidation of fatty acids can form compounds with disagreeable odors. This oxidation can be minimized by the addition of antioxidants.

EXERCISES

1. Draw the structure for each compound.
   a. trimyristin
   b. a triglyceride likely to be found in peanut oil

2. Draw the structure for each compound.
    a. tripalmitin
    b. a triglyceride likely to be found in butter
3. Draw structures to write the reaction for the complete hydrogenation of tripalmitolein (see Table 17.1 for the condensed structure of palmitoleic acid). Name the product formed.
4. Draw structures to write the reaction for the complete hydrogenation of trilinolein (see Table 17.1 for the condensed structure of linoleic acid). Name the product formed.
5. Draw structures to write the reaction for the hydrolysis of trilaurin in a basic solution (see Table 17.1 for the condensed structure of lauric acid).
6. Draw structures to write the reaction for the hydrolysis of tristearin in a basic solution (see Table 17.1 for the condensed structure of stearic acid).
7.
    a. What compounds with a disagreeable odor are formed when butter becomes rancid?
    b. How are these compounds formed?
    c. How can rancidity be prevented?
8.
    a. What compound with a disagreeable odor is formed when unsaturated fatty acids react with oxygen in the atmosphere?
    b. How can this process be prevented?

ANSWERS

1.

a.

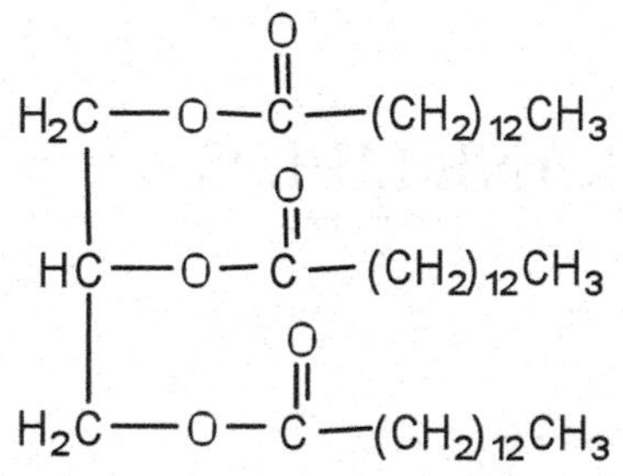

$$\begin{array}{l} H_2C-O-\overset{O}{\overset{\|}{C}}-(CH_2)_{12}CH_3 \\ \;| \\ HC-O-\overset{O}{\overset{\|}{C}}-(CH_2)_{12}CH_3 \\ \;| \\ H_2C-O-\overset{O}{\overset{\|}{C}}-(CH_2)_{12}CH_3 \end{array}$$

b.

$$\begin{array}{l} H_2C-O-\overset{O}{\overset{\|}{C}}-(CH_2)_{14}CH_3 \\ \;| \\ HC-O-\overset{O}{\overset{\|}{C}}-(CH_2)_7CH{=}CH(CH_2)_7CH_3 \\ \;| \\ H_2C-O-\overset{O}{\overset{\|}{C}}-(CH_2)_7CH{=}CHCH_2CH{=}CH(CH_2)_4CH_3 \end{array}$$

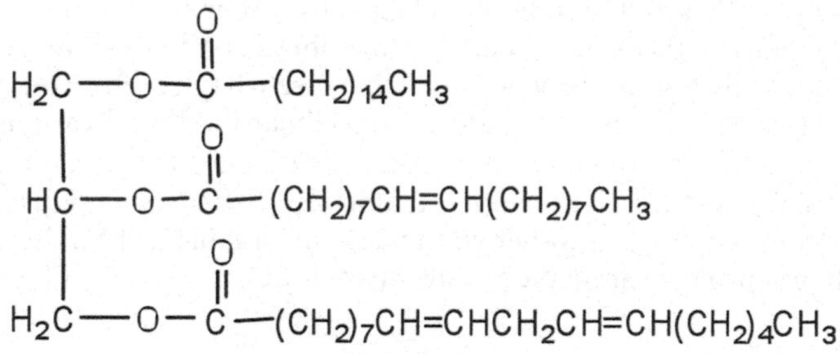

[other answers possible]

3.

$$\begin{array}{l} H_2C-O-C(=O)-(CH_2)_7CH{=}CH(CH_2)_5CH_3 \\ HC-O-C(=O)-(CH_2)_7CH{=}CH(CH_2)_5CH_3 \\ H_2C-O-C(=O)-(CH_2)_7CH{=}CH(CH_2)_5CH_3 \end{array} \xrightarrow[\text{Ni}]{\text{excess } H_2} \begin{array}{l} H_2C-O-C(=O)-(CH_2)_{14}CH_3 \\ HC-O-C(=O)-(CH_2)_{14}CH_3 \\ H_2C-O-C(=O)-(CH_2)_{14}CH_3 \end{array}$$

tripalmitin

5.

$$\begin{array}{l} H_2C-O-C(=O)-(CH_2)_{10}CH_3 \\ HC-O-C(=O)-(CH_2)_{10}CH_3 \\ H_2C-O-C(=O)-(CH_2)_{10}CH_3 \end{array} \xrightarrow[\text{H}_2\text{O, heat}]{\text{NaOH}} \begin{array}{l} H_2C-OH \\ HC-OH \\ H_2C-OH \end{array} + 3\ CH_3(CH_2)_{10}COO^-Na^+$$

7. a. smaller carboxylic acids, such as butyric, caprylic, and capric acids
   b. These compounds are formed by the hydrolysis of the triglycerides found in butter.
   c. Rancidity can be prevented by covering the butter (to keep out moisture) and storing it in a refrigerator. (Cold temperatures slow down hydrolysis reactions.)

3. MEMBRANES AND MEMBRANE LIPIDS

LEARNING OBJECTIVES

1. **Identify the distinguishing characteristics of membrane lipids.**
2. **Describe membrane components and how they are arranged.**

cytoplasm

Everything between the cell membrane and the nuclear membrane.

All living cells are surrounded by a cell membrane. Plant cells (Figure 17.3) and animal cells (Figure 17.4) contain a cell nucleus that is also surrounded by a membrane and holds the genetic information for the cell. (For more information about genetics and DNA, see Chapter 19.) Everything between the cell membrane and the nuclear membrane—including intracellular fluids and various subcellular components such as the mitochondria and ribosomes—is called the **cytoplasm**. The membranes of all cells have a fundamentally similar structure, but membrane function varies tremendously from one organism to another and even from one cell to another within a single organism. This diversity arises mainly from the presence of different proteins and lipids in the membrane.

FIGURE 17.3 An Idealized Plant Cell

Not all the structures shown here occur in every type of plant cell.

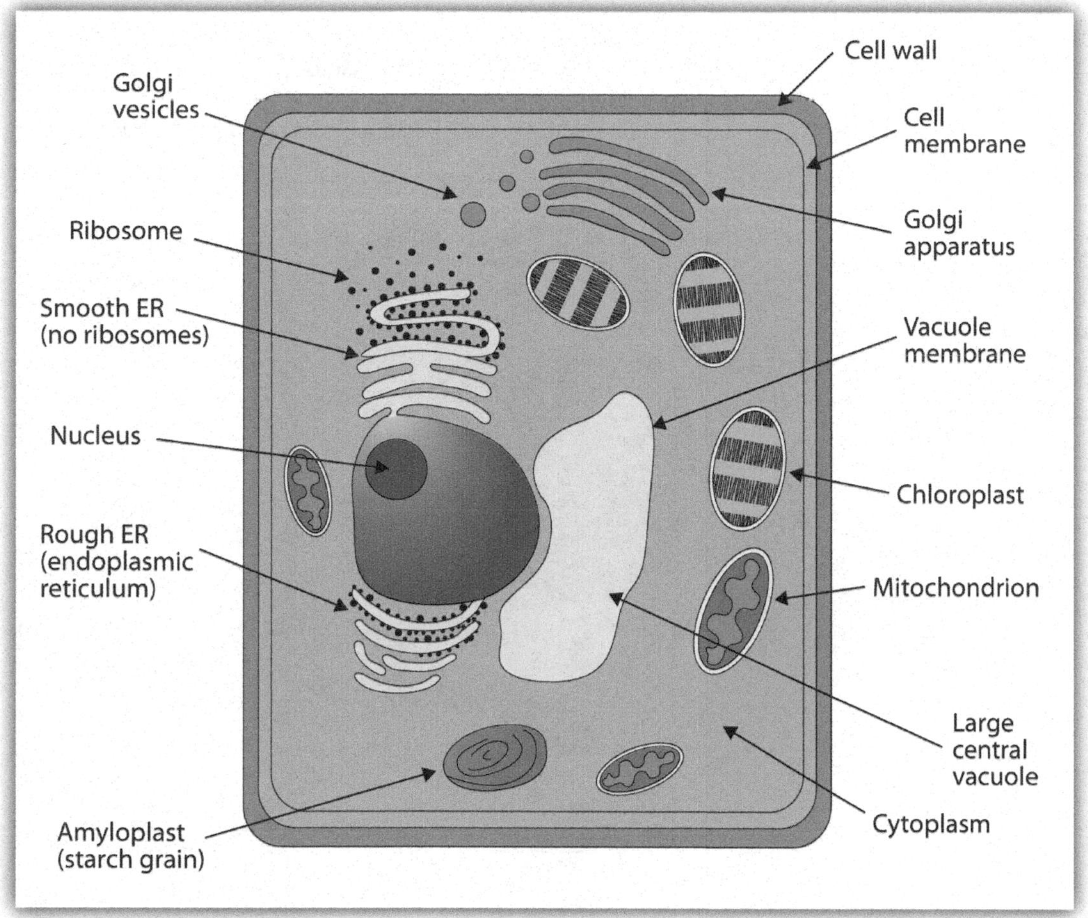

FIGURE 17.4 An Idealized Animal Cell

The structures shown here will seldom all be found in a single animal cell.

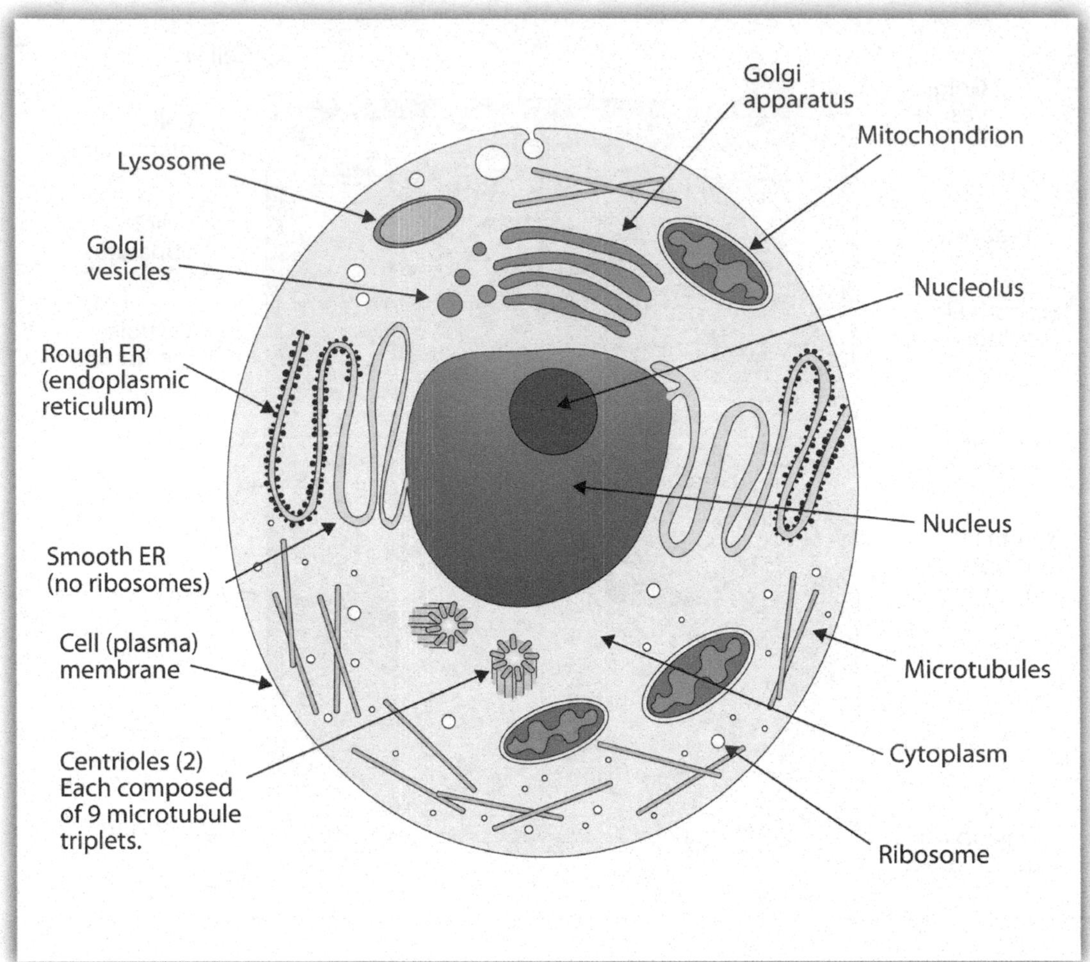

hydrophilic

Having an affinity for water; "water loving."

hydrophobic

Not having an affinity for water; "water fearing."

micelle

An aggregation in which a nonpolar tail is directed toward the center of the structure and the polar head is directed outward.

bilayer

A double layer of lipids arranged so that nonpolar tails are found between an inner surface and outer surface consisting of hydrophilic heads.

The lipids in cell membranes are highly polar but have dual characteristics: part of the lipid is ionic and therefore dissolves in water, whereas the rest has a hydrocarbon structure and therefore dissolves in nonpolar substances. Often, the ionic part is referred to as **hydrophilic**, meaning "water loving," and the nonpolar part as **hydrophobic**, meaning "water fearing" (repelled by water). When allowed to float freely in water, polar lipids spontaneously cluster together in any one of three arrangements: micelles, monolayers, and bilayers (Figure 17.5). **Micelles** are aggregations in which the lipids' hydrocarbon tails—being hydrophobic—are directed toward the center of the assemblage and away from the surrounding water while the hydrophilic heads are directed outward, in contact with the water. Each micelle may contain thousands of lipid molecules. Polar lipids may also form a monolayer, a layer one molecule thick on the surface of the water. The polar heads face into water, and the nonpolar tails stick up into the air. **Bilayers** are double layers of lipids arranged so that the hydrophobic tails are sandwiched between an inner surface and an outer surface consisting of hydrophilic heads. The hydrophilic heads are in contact with water on either side of the bilayer, whereas the tails, sequestered inside the bilayer, are prevented from having contact with the water. Bilayers like this make up every cell membrane (Figure 17.6).

FIGURE 17.5 Spontaneously Formed Polar Lipid Structures in Water: Monolayer, Micelle, and Bilayer

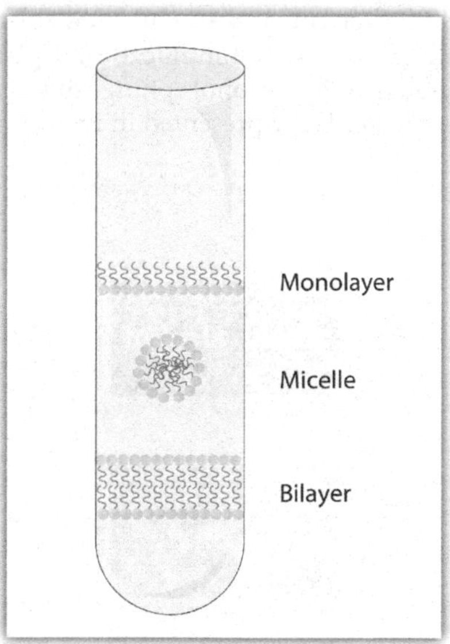

FIGURE 17.6 Schematic Diagram of a Cell Membrane

The membrane enclosing a typical animal cell is a phospholipid bilayer with embedded cholesterol and protein molecules. Short oligosaccharide chains are attached to the outer surface.

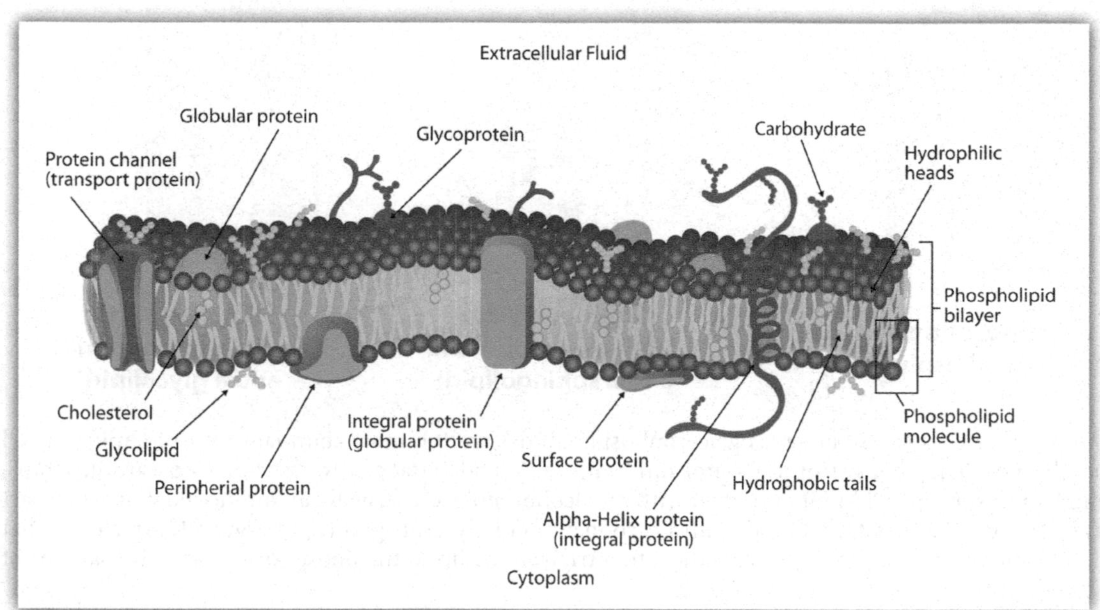

In the bilayer interior, the hydrophobic tails (that is, the fatty acid portions of lipid molecules) interact by means of dispersion forces. The interactions are weakened by the presence of unsaturated fatty acids. As a result, the membrane components are free to mill about to some extent, and the membrane is described as fluid.

phospholipid

A lipid containing phosphorus.

glycolipid

A sugar-containing lipid.

sphingolipid

A lipid that contains the unsaturated amino alcohol sphingosine.

The lipids found in cell membranes can be categorized in various ways. **Phospholipids** are lipids containing phosphorus. **Glycolipids** are sugar-containing lipids. The latter are found exclusively on the outer surface of the cell membrane, acting as distinguishing surface markers for the cell and thus serving in cellular recognition and cell-to-cell communication. **Sphingolipids** are phospholipids or glycolipids that contain the unsaturated amino alcohol sphingosine rather than glycerol. Diagrammatic structures of representative membrane lipids are presented in Figure 17.7.

FIGURE 17.7 Component Structures of Some Important Membrane Lipids

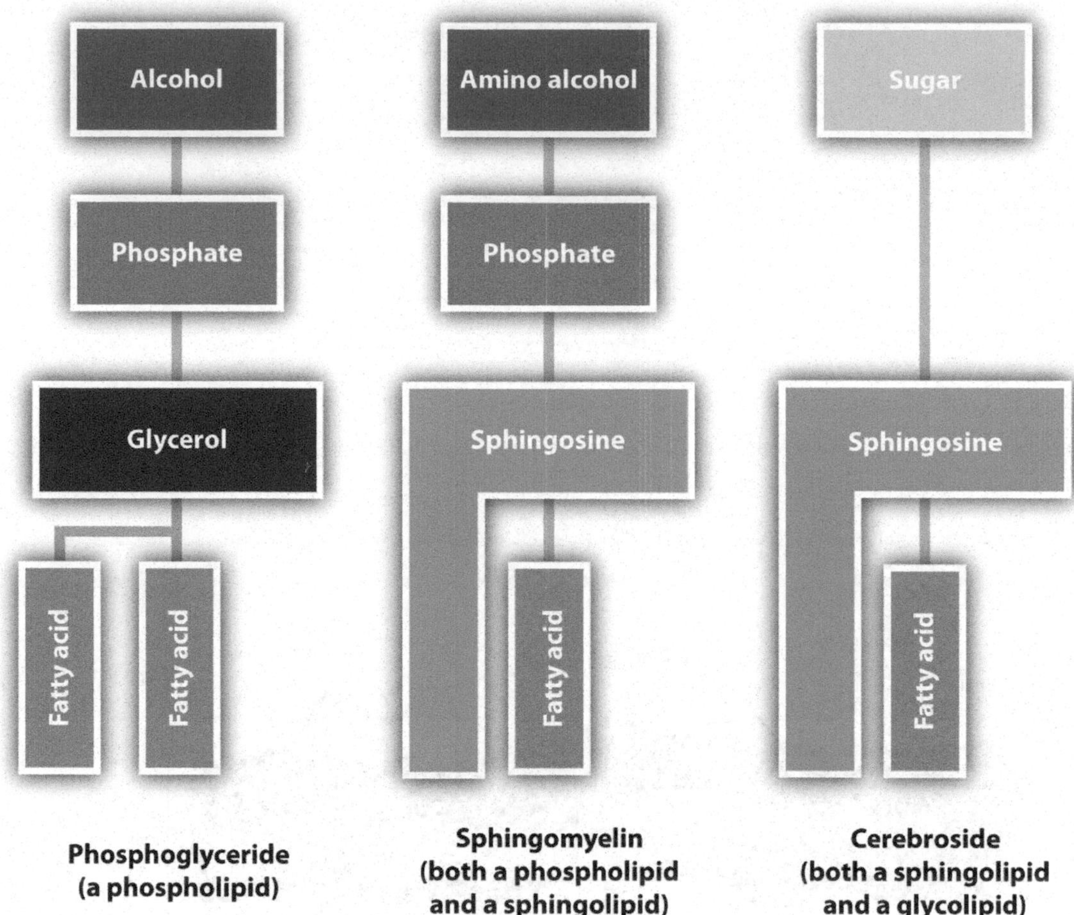

Phosphoglycerides (also known as glycerophospholipids) are the most abundant phospholipids in cell membranes. They consist of a glycerol unit with fatty acids attached to the first two carbon atoms, while a phosphoric acid unit, esterified with an alcohol molecule (usually an amino alcohol, as in part (a) of Figure 17.8) is attached to the third carbon atom of glycerol (part (b) of Figure 17.8). Notice that the phosphoglyceride molecule is identical to a triglyceride up to the phosphoric acid unit (part (b) of Figure 17.8).

FIGURE 17.8 Phosphoglycerides

(a) Amino alcohols are commonly found in phosphoglycerides, which are evident in its structural formula (b).

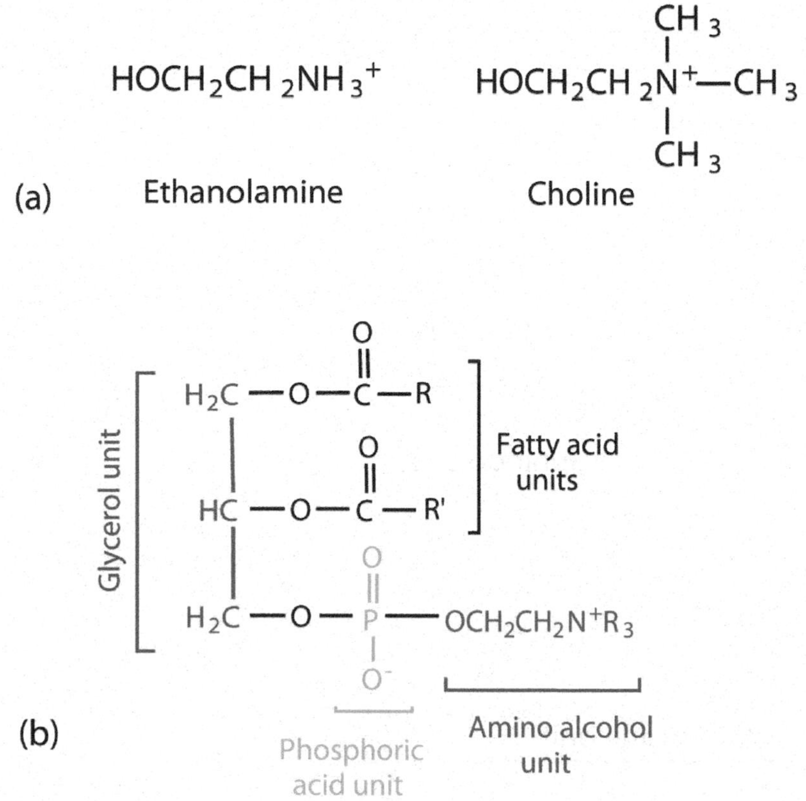

There are two common types of phosphoglycerides. Phosphoglycerides containing ethanolamine as the amino alcohol are called *phosphatidylethanolamines* or *cephalins.* Cephalins are found in brain tissue and nerves and also have a role in blood clotting. Phosphoglycerides containing choline as the amino alcohol unit are called *phosphatidylcholines* or *lecithins.* Lecithins occur in all living organisms. Like cephalins, they are important constituents of nerve and brain tissue. Egg yolks are especially rich in lecithins. Commercial-grade lecithins isolated from soybeans are widely used in foods as emulsifying agents. An emulsifying agent is used to stabilize an **emulsion**—a dispersion of two liquids that do not normally mix, such as oil and water. Many foods are emulsions. Milk is an emulsion of butterfat in water. The emulsifying agent in milk is a protein called *casein.* Mayonnaise is an emulsion of salad oil in water, stabilized by lecithins present in egg yolk.

emulsion

A dispersion of two liquids that do not normally mix.

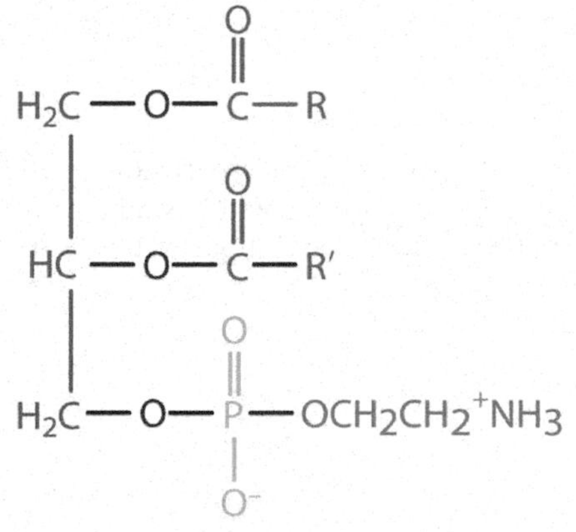

Phosphatidylethanolamine
(cephalin)

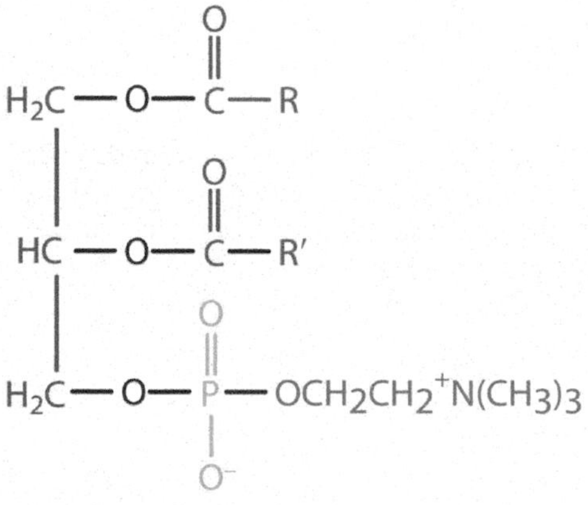

Phosphatidycholine
(lecithin)

sphingomyelin

A sphingolipid that contains a fatty acid unit, a phosphoric acid unit, a sphingosine unit, and a choline unit.

Sphingomyelins, the simplest sphingolipids, each contain a fatty acid, a phosphoric acid, sphingosine, and choline (Figure 17.9). Because they contain phosphoric acid, they are also classified as phospholipids. Sphingomyelins are important constituents of the myelin sheath surrounding the axon of a nerve cell. Multiple sclerosis is one of several diseases resulting from damage to the myelin sheath.

FIGURE 17.9 Sphingolipids

(a) Sphingosine, an amino alcohol, is found in all sphingolipids. (b) A sphingomyelin is also known as a phospholipid, as evidenced by the phosphoric acid unit in its structure.

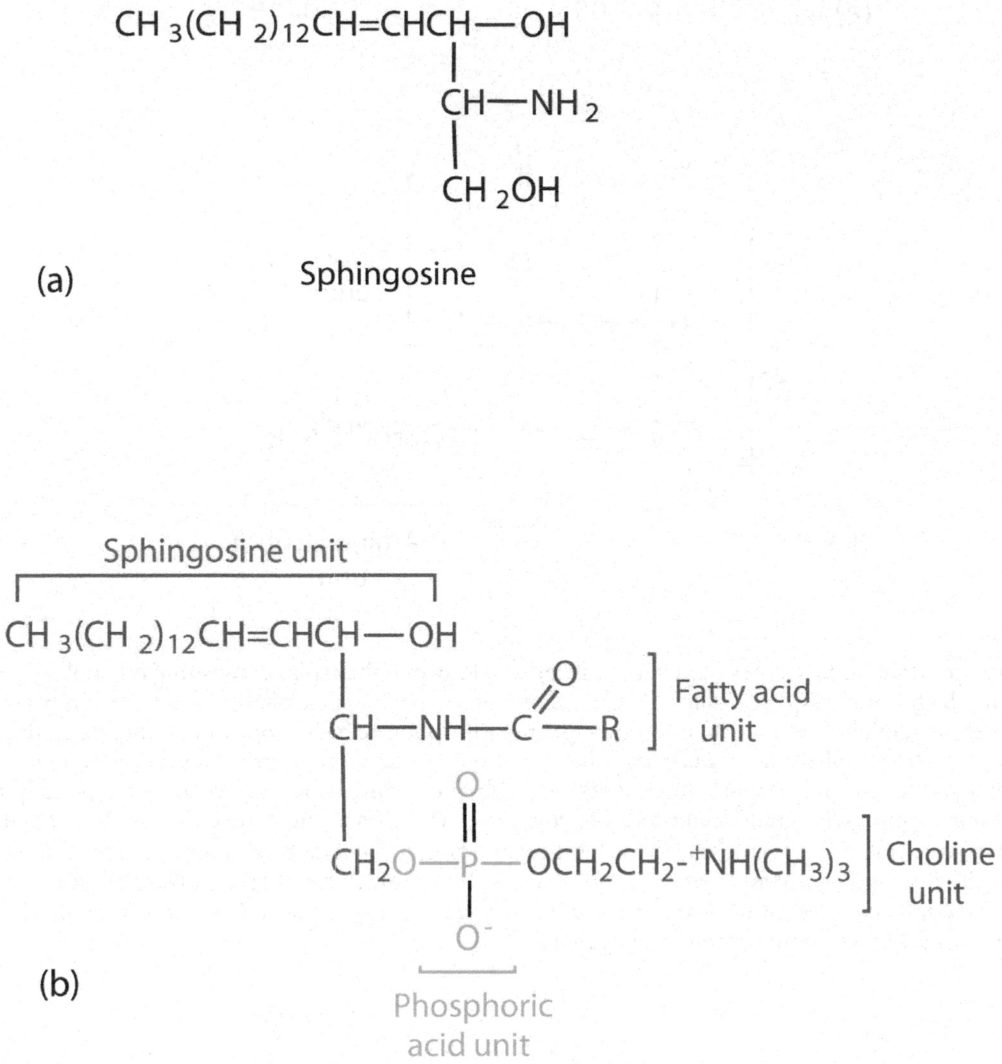

cerebroside

A sphingolipid that contains a fatty acid unit, a sphingosine unit, and galactose or glucose.

Most animal cells contain sphingolipids called **cerebrosides** (Figure 17.10). Cerebrosides are composed of sphingosine, a fatty acid, and galactose or glucose. They therefore resemble sphingomyelins but have a sugar unit in place of the choline phosphate group. Cerebrosides are important constituents of the membranes of nerve and brain cells.

FIGURE 17.10 Cerebrosides

Cerebrosides are sphingolipids that contain a sugar unit.

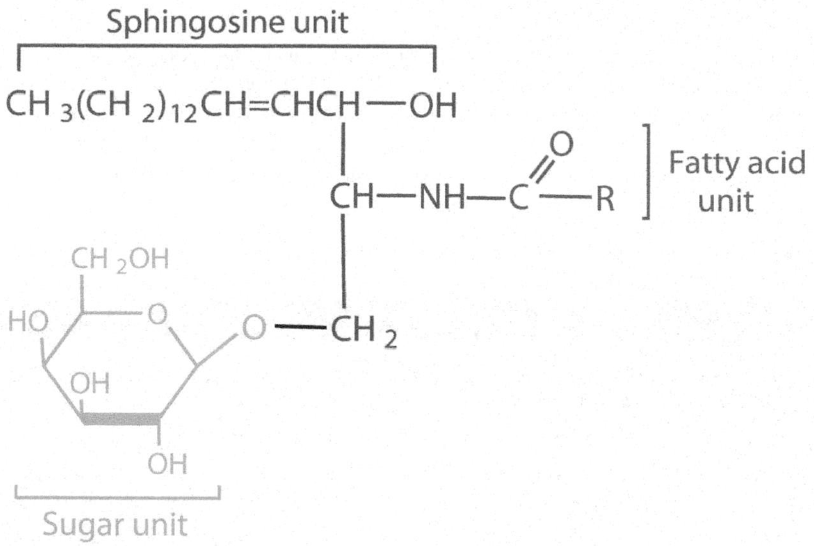

Sphingosine unit

$CH_3(CH_2)_{12}CH{=}CHCH{-}OH$

$CH{-}NH{-}C({=}O){-}R$ Fatty acid unit

CH_2OH, HO, O, OH, OH, $O{-}CH_2$

Sugar unit

The sphingolipids called **gangliosides** are more complex, usually containing a branched chain of three to eight monosaccharides and/or substituted sugars. Because of considerable variation in their sugar components, about 130 varieties of gangliosides have been identified. Most cell-to-cell recognition and communication processes (e.g., blood group antigens) depend on differences in the sequences of sugars in these compounds. Gangliosides are most prevalent in the outer membranes of nerve cells, although they also occur in smaller quantities in the outer membranes of most other cells. Because cerebrosides and gangliosides contain sugar groups, they are also classified as glycolipids.

ganglioside

A sphingolipid that contains a fatty acid unit, a sphingosine unit, and a complex oligosaccharide.

3.1 Membrane Proteins

If membranes were composed only of lipids, very few ions or polar molecules could pass through their hydrophobic "sandwich filling" to enter or leave any cell. However, certain charged and polar species do cross the membrane, aided by proteins that move about in the lipid bilayer. The two major classes of proteins in the cell membrane are **integral proteins**, which span the hydrophobic interior of the bilayer, and **peripheral proteins**, which are more loosely associated with the surface of the lipid bilayer (Figure 17.6). Peripheral proteins may be attached to integral proteins, to the polar head groups of phospholipids, or to both by hydrogen bonding and electrostatic forces.

Small ions and molecules soluble in water enter and leave the cell by way of channels through the integral proteins. Some proteins, called *carrier proteins*, facilitate the passage of certain molecules, such as hormones and neurotransmitters, by specific interactions between the protein and the molecule being transported.

integral protein

A protein that spans the lipids bilayer of membranes.

peripheral protein

A protein that is more loosely associated with the membrane surface.

CONCEPT REVIEW EXERCISES

1. Name the structural unit that must be present for a molecule to be classified as a
   a. phospholipid.
   b. glycolipid.
   c. sphingolipid.
2. Why is it important that membrane lipids have dual character—part of the molecule is hydrophilic and part of the molecule is hydrophobic?
3. Why do you suppose lecithins (phosphatidylcholines) are often added to processed foods such as hot cocoa mix?

ANSWERS

1. a. a phosphate group
   b. a saccharide unit (monosaccharide or more complex)
   c. sphingosine
2. The dual character is critical for the formation of the lipid bilayer. The hydrophilic portions of the molecule are in contact with the aqueous environment of the cell, while the hydrophobic portion of the lipids is in the interior of the bilayer and provides a barrier to the passive diffusion of most molecules.
3. Lecithin acts as an emulsifying agent that aids in the mixing of the hot cocoa mix with water and keeps the cocoa mix evenly distributed after stirring.

KEY TAKEAWAYS

- Lipids are important components of biological membranes. These lipids have dual characteristics: part of the molecule is hydrophilic, and part of the molecule is hydrophobic.
- Membrane lipids may be classified as phospholipids, glycolipids, and/or sphingolipids.
- Proteins are another important component of biological membranes. Integral proteins span the lipid bilayer, while peripheral proteins are more loosely associated with the surface of the membrane.

EXERCISES

1. Classify each as a phospholipid, a glycolipid, and/or a sphingolipid. (Some lipids can be given more than one classification.)

   a.

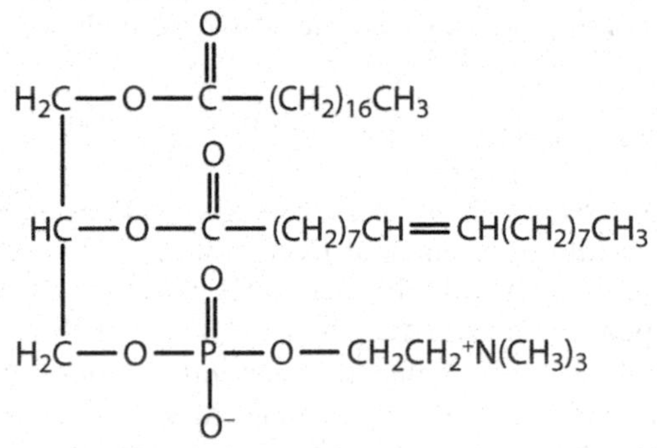

$$
\begin{array}{l}
H_2C-O-C(=O)-(CH_2)_{16}CH_3 \\
HC-O-C(=O)-(CH_2)_7CH=CH(CH_2)_7CH_3 \\
H_2C-O-P(=O)(O^-)-O-CH_2CH_2{}^+N(CH_3)_3
\end{array}
$$

   b.

$CH_3(CH_2)_{12}CH=CHCH-OH$

$CH-NH-C(=O)-(CH_2)_{14}CH_3$

$O-CH_2$ (linked to a sugar ring bearing CH_2OH, HO, OH, OH)

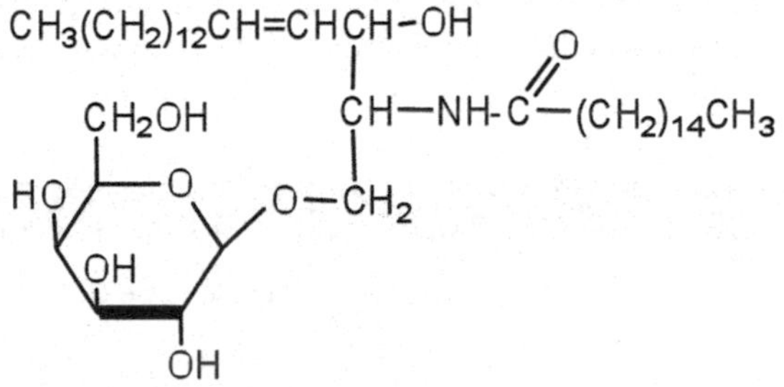

2. Classify each as a phospholipid, a glycolipid, and/or a sphingolipid. (Some lipids can be given more than one classification.)

   a.

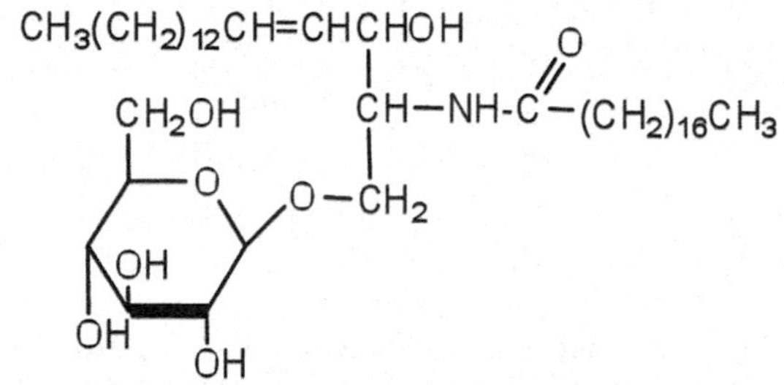

   $CH_3(CH_2)_{12}CH{=}CHCHOH$; $CH{-}NH{-}C(=O){-}(CH_2)_{16}CH_3$; $O{-}CH_2$; ring with CH_2OH, O, OH, OH, OH

   b.

   $H_2C{-}O{-}C(=O){-}(CH_2)_{14}CH_3$

   $HC{-}O{-}C(=O){-}(CH_2)_7CH{=}CH(CH_2)_7CH_3$

   $H_2C{-}O{-}P(=O)(O^-){-}O{-}$ ring with OH, OH, OH, OH, OH

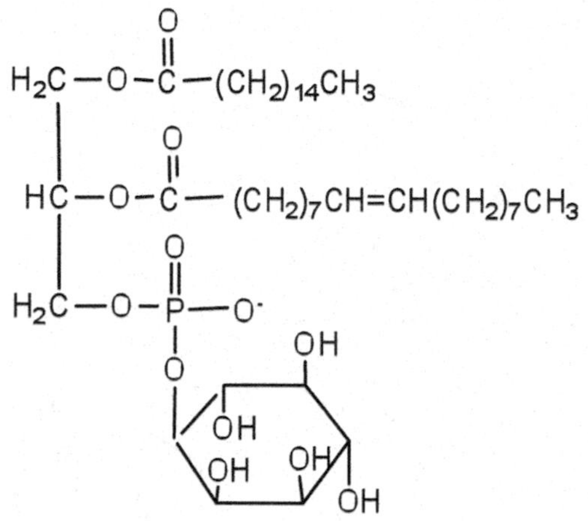

3. Draw the structure of the sphingomyelin that has lauric acid as its fatty acid and ethanolamine as its amino alcohol.
4. Draw the structure of the cerebroside that has myristic acid as its fatty acid and galactose as its sugar.
5.
   a. Distinguish between an integral protein and a peripheral protein.
   b. What is one key function of integral proteins?

ANSWERS

1. a. phospholipid
   b. sphingolipid and glycolipid
3.

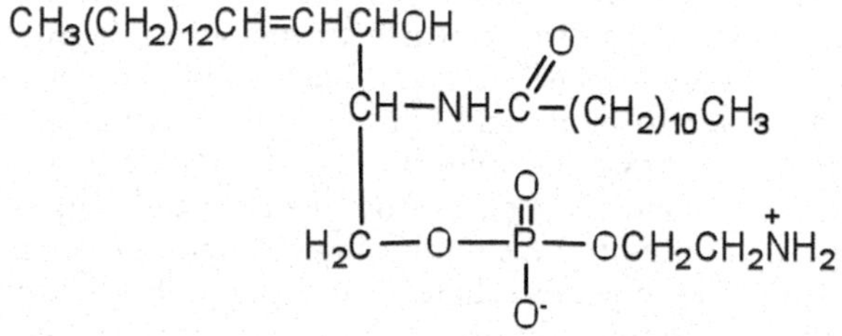

   $CH_3(CH_2)_{12}CH{=}CHCHOH$

   $CH{-}NH{-}C(=O){-}(CH_2)_{10}CH_3$

   $H_2C{-}O{-}P(=O)(O^-){-}OCH_2CH_2\overset{+}{N}H_2$

5. a. Integral proteins span the lipid bilayer, while peripheral proteins associate with the surfaces of the lipid bilayer.
   b. aid in the movement of charged and polar species across the membrane

4. STEROIDS

LEARNING OBJECTIVE

1. **Identify the functions of steroids produced in mammals.**

steroid

A lipid with a four-fused-ring structure.

All the lipids discussed so far are *saponifiable*, reacting with aqueous alkali to yield simpler components, such as glycerol, fatty acids, amino alcohols, and sugars. (For more information about saponification, see Section 2.) Lipid samples extracted from cellular material, however, also contain a small but important fraction that does not react with alkali. The most important nonsaponifiable lipids are the **steroids**. These compounds include the *bile salts*, *cholesterol* and related compounds, and certain *hormones* (such as cortisone and the sex hormones).

FIGURE 17.11 Steroids

(a) The four-fused-ring steroid skeleton uses letter designations for each ring and the numbering of the carbon atoms. (b) The cholesterol molecule follows this pattern.

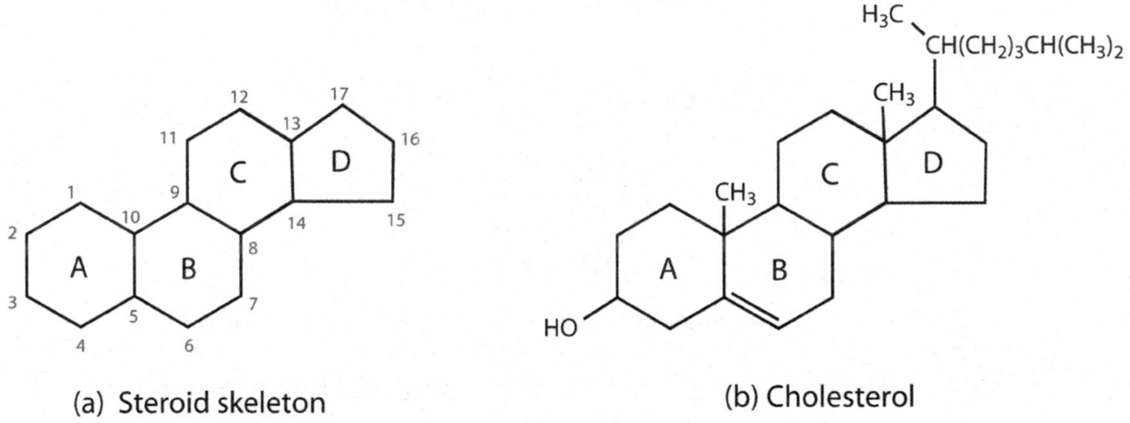

Steroids occur in plants, animals, yeasts, and molds but not in bacteria. They may exist in free form or combined with fatty acids or carbohydrates. All steroids have a characteristic structural component consisting of four fused rings. Chemists identify the rings by capital letters and number the carbon atoms as shown in part (a) of Figure 17.11. Slight variations in this structure or in the atoms or groups attached to it produce profound differences in biological activity.

4.1 Cholesterol

cholesterol

A steroid that is found in mammals.

Cholesterol (part (b) of Figure 17.11) does not occur in plants, but it is the most abundant steroid in the human body (240 g is a typical amount). Excess cholesterol is believed to be a primary factor in the development of atherosclerosis and heart disease, which are major health problems in the United States today. About half of the body's cholesterol is interspersed in the lipid bilayer of cell membranes (Figure 17.6). Much of the rest is converted to cholic acid, which is used in the formation of bile salts. Cholesterol is also a precursor in the synthesis of sex hormones, adrenal hormones, and vitamin D. Excess cholesterol not metabolized by the body is released from the liver and transported by the blood to the gallbladder. Normally, it stays in solution there until being secreted into the intestine (as a component of bile) to be eliminated. Sometimes, however, cholesterol in the gallbladder precipitates in the form of gallstones. Indeed, the name *cholesterol* is derived from the Greek *chole*, meaning "bile," and *stereos*, meaning "solid."

To Your Health: Cholesterol and Heart Disease

Heart disease is the leading cause of death in the United States for both men and women. The Centers for Disease Control and Prevention reported that heart disease claimed 631,636 lives in the United States (26% of all reported deaths) in 2006.

Scientists agree that elevated cholesterol levels in the blood, as well as high blood pressure, obesity, diabetes, and cigarette smoking, are associated with an increased risk of heart disease. A long-term investigation by the National Institutes of Health showed that among men ages 30 to 49, the incidence of heart disease was five times greater for those whose cholesterol levels were above 260 mg/100 mL of serum than for those with cholesterol levels of 200 mg/100 mL or less. The cholesterol content of blood varies considerably with age, diet, and sex. Young adults average about 170 mg of cholesterol per 100 mL of blood, whereas males at age 55 may have cholesterol levels at 250 mg/100 mL or higher because the rate of cholesterol breakdown decreases with age. Females tend to have lower blood cholesterol levels than males.

To understand the link between heart disease and cholesterol levels, it is important to understand how cholesterol and other lipids are transported in the body. Lipids, such as cholesterol, are not soluble in water and therefore cannot be transported in the blood (an aqueous medium) unless they are complexed with proteins that are soluble in water, forming assemblages called *lipoproteins*. Lipoproteins are classified according to their density, which is dependent on the relative amounts of protein and lipid they contain. Lipids are less dense than proteins, so lipoproteins containing a greater proportion of lipid are less dense than those containing a greater proportion of protein.

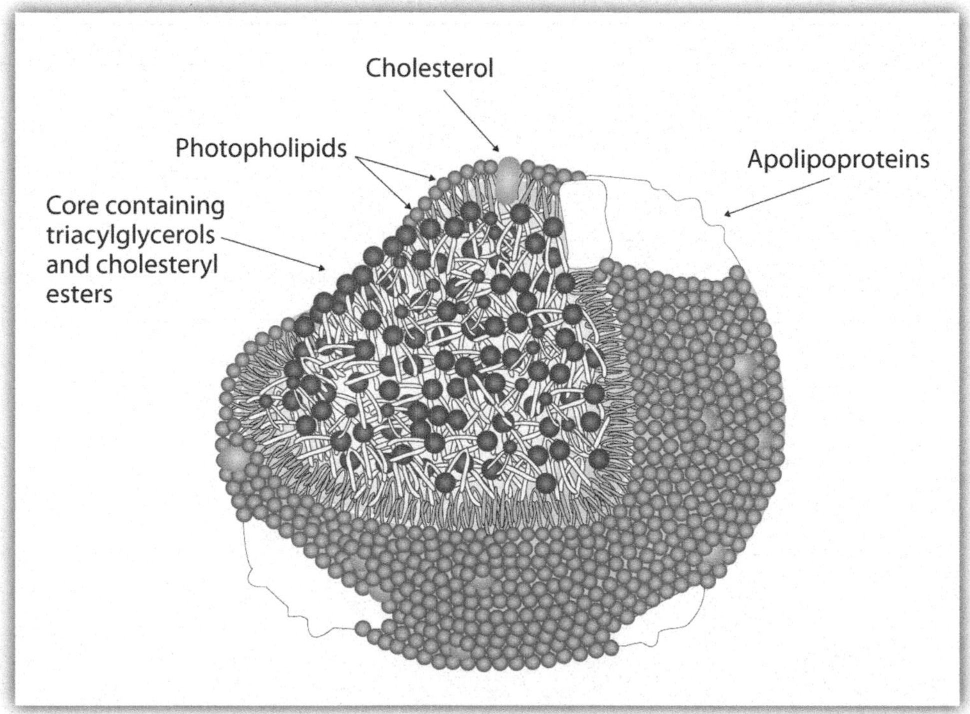

Research on cholesterol and its role in heart disease has focused on serum levels of low-density lipoproteins (LDLs) and high-density lipoproteins (HDLs). One of the most fascinating discoveries is that high levels of HDLs reduce a person's risk of developing heart disease, whereas high levels of LDLs increase that risk. Thus the serum LDL:HDL ratio is a better predictor of heart disease risk than the overall level of serum cholesterol. Persons who, because of hereditary or dietary factors, have high LDL:HDL ratios in their blood have a higher incidence of heart disease.

How do HDLs reduce the risk of developing heart disease? No one knows for sure, but one role of HDLs appears to be the transport of excess cholesterol to the liver, where it can be metabolized. Therefore, HDLs aid in removing cholesterol from blood and from the smooth muscle cells of the arterial wall.

Dietary modifications and increased physical activity can help lower total cholesterol and improve the LDL:HDL ratio. The average American consumes about 600 mg of cholesterol from animal products each day and also synthesizes approximately 1 g of cholesterol each day, mostly in the liver. The amount of cholesterol synthesized is controlled by the cholesterol level in the blood; when the blood cholesterol level exceeds 150 mg/100 mL, the rate of cholesterol biosynthesis is halved. Hence, if cholesterol is present in the diet, a feedback mechanism suppresses its synthesis in the liver. However, the ratio of suppression is not a 1:1 ratio; the reduction in biosynthesis does not equal the amount of cholesterol ingested. Thus, dietary substitutions of unsaturated fat for saturated fat, as well as a reduction in consumption of *trans* fatty acids, is recommended to help lower serum cholesterol and the risk of heart disease.

4.2 Steroid Hormones

Hormones are chemical messengers that are released in one tissue and transported through the circulatory system to one or more other tissues. One group of hormones is known as steroid hormones because these hormones are synthesized from cholesterol, which is also a steroid. There are two main groups of steroid hormones: adrenocortical hormones and sex hormones.

The adrenocortical hormones, such as aldosterone and cortisol (Table 17.3), are produced by the adrenal gland, which is located adjacent to each kidney. Aldosterone acts on most cells in the body, but it is particularly effective at enhancing the rate of reabsorption of sodium ions in the kidney tubules and increasing the secretion of potassium ions and/or hydrogen ions by the tubules. Because the concentration of sodium ions is the major factor influencing water retention in tissues, aldosterone promotes water retention and reduces urine output. Cortisol regulates several key metabolic reactions (for example, increasing glucose production and mobilizing fatty acids and amino acids). It also inhibits the inflammatory response of tissue to injury or stress. Cortisol and its analogs are therefore used pharmacologically as immunosuppressants after transplant operations and in the treatment of severe skin allergies and autoimmune diseases, such as rheumatoid arthritis.

TABLE 17.3 Representative Steroid Hormones and Their Physiological Effects

Hormone	Effect
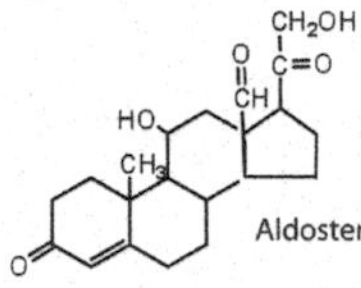 Aldosterone	regulates salt metabolism; stimulates kidneys to retain sodium and excrete potassium
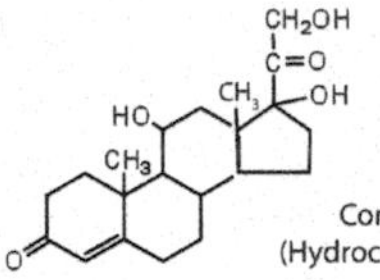 Cortisol (Hydrocortisone)	stimulates the conversion of proteins to carbohydrates
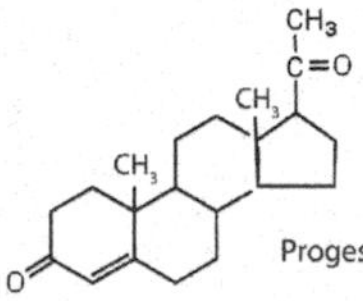 Progesterone	regulates the menstrual cycle; maintains pregnancy
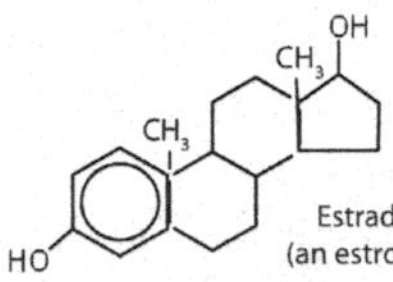 Estradiol (an estrogen)	stimulates female sex characteristics; regulates changes during the menstrual cycle
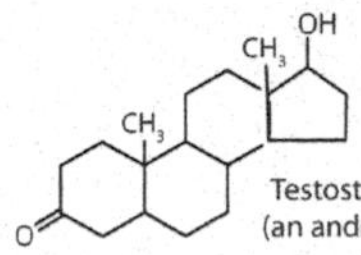 Testosterone (an androgen)	stimulates and maintains male sex characteristics

The sex hormones are a class of steroid hormones secreted by the gonads (ovaries or testes), the placenta, and the adrenal glands. Testosterone and androstenedione are the primary male sex hormones, or *androgens*, controlling the primary sexual characteristics of males, or the development of the male genital organs and the continuous production of sperm. Androgens are also responsible for the development of secondary male characteristics, such as facial hair, deep voice, and muscle strength. Two kinds of sex hormones are of particular importance in females: progesterone, which prepares the uterus for pregnancy and prevents the further release of eggs from the ovaries during pregnancy, and the estrogens, which are mainly responsible for the development of female secondary sexual characteristics, such as breast development and increased deposition of fat tissue in the breasts, the buttocks, and the thighs. Both males and females produce androgens and estrogens, differing in the amounts of secreted hormones rather than in the presence or absence of one or the other.

Sex hormones, both natural and synthetic, are sometimes used therapeutically. For example, a woman who has had her ovaries removed may be given female hormones to compensate. Some of the earliest chemical compounds employed in cancer chemotherapy were sex hormones. For example, estrogens are one treatment option for prostate cancer because they block the release and activity of testosterone. Testosterone enhances prostate cancer growth. Sex hormones are also administered in preparation for sex-change operations, to promote the development of the proper secondary sexual characteristics. Oral contraceptives are synthetic derivatives of the female sex hormones; they work by preventing ovulation.

4.3 Bile Salts

Bile is a yellowish green liquid (pH 7.8–8.6) produced in the liver. The most important constituents of bile are bile salts, which are sodium salts of amidelike combinations of bile acids, such as cholic acid (part (a) of Figure 17.12) and an amine such as the amino acid glycine (part (b) of Figure 17.12). They are synthesized from cholesterol in the liver, stored in the gallbladder, and then secreted in bile into the small intestine. In the gallbladder, the composition of bile gradually changes as water is absorbed and the other components become more concentrated.

bile

The yellowish green liquid produced in the liver.

FIGURE 17.12 Bile Acids

(a) Cholic acid is an example of a bile acid. (b) Sodium glycocholate is a bile salt synthesized from cholic acid and glycine.

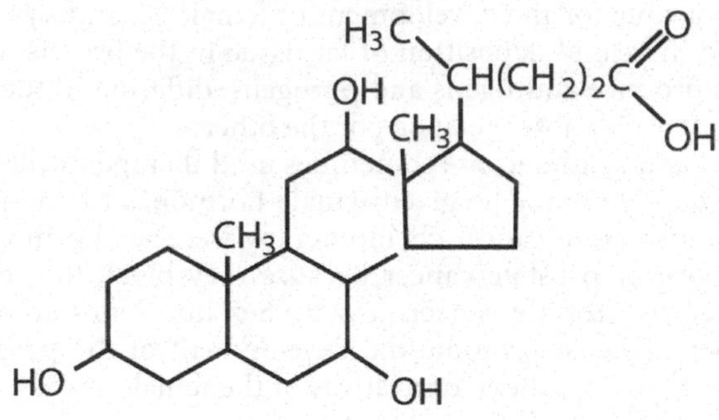

(a) Cholic acid (a bile acid)

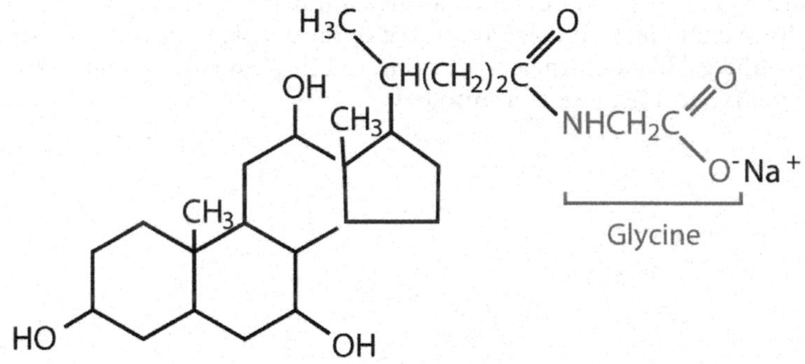

(b) Sodium glycocholate (a bile salt)

Because they contain both hydrophobic and hydrophilic groups, bile salts are highly effective detergents and emulsifying agents; they break down large fat globules into smaller ones and keep those smaller globules suspended in the aqueous digestive environment. Enzymes can then hydrolyze fat molecules more efficiently. Thus, the major function of bile salts is to aid in the digestion of dietary lipids.

Note

Surgical removal is often advised for a gallbladder that becomes infected, inflamed, or perforated. This surgery does not seriously affect digestion because bile is still produced by the liver, but the liver's bile is more dilute and its secretion into the small intestine is not as closely tied to the arrival of food.

CONCEPT REVIEW EXERCISES

1. Distinguish between a saponifiable lipid and a nonsaponifiable lipid.
2. Identify a key function for each steroid.
   a. bile salt
   b. cholesterol
   c. estradiol

ANSWERS

1. A saponifiable lipid reacts with aqueous alkali to yield simpler components, while a nonsaponifiable lipid does not react with alkali to yield simpler components.
2. a. acts as an emulsifying agent to break down large fat globules and keep these globules suspended in the aqueous digestive environment
   b. a key component of mammalian cell membranes (answers will vary)
   c. stimulates female sex characteristics and regulates changes during the menstrual cycle

KEY TAKEAWAYS

- Steroids have a four-fused-ring structure and have a variety of functions.
- Cholesterol is a steroid found in mammals that is needed for the formation of cell membranes, bile acids, and several hormones.
- Bile salts are secreted into the small intestine to aid in the digestion of fats.

EXERCISES

1. Which of these compounds are steroids—tripalmitin, cephalin, or cholesterol?
2. Which of these compounds are steroids—vitamin D, cholic acid, or lecithin?
3. Draw the basic steroid skeleton and label each ring with the appropriate letter designation.
4. Identify each compound as an adrenocortical hormone, a female sex hormone, or a male sex hormone.
   a. progesterone
   b. aldosterone
   c. testosterone
   d. cortisol

ANSWERS

1. cholesterol

3.

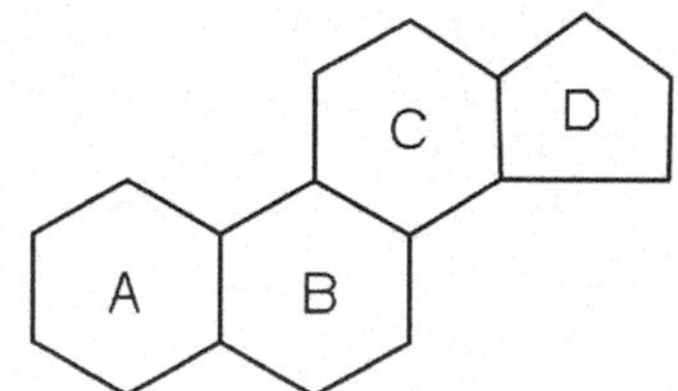

5. END-OF-CHAPTER MATERIAL

Chapter Summary

To ensure that you understand the material in this chapter, you should review the meanings of the bold terms in the following summary and ask yourself how they relate to the topics in the chapter.

Lipids, found in the body tissues of all organisms, are compounds that are more soluble in organic solvents than in water. Many of them contain **fatty acids**, which are carboxylic acids that generally contain an even number of 4–20 carbon atoms in an unbranched chain. **Saturated fatty acids** have no carbon-to-carbon double bonds. **Monounsaturated fatty acids** have a single carbon-to-carbon double bond, while **polyunsaturated fatty acids** have more than one carbon-to-carbon double bond. Linoleic and linolenic acid are known as **essential fatty acids** because the human body cannot synthesize these polyunsaturated fatty acids. The lipids known as **fats** and **oils** are triacylglycerols, more commonly called **triglycerides**—esters composed of three fatty acids joined to the trihydroxy alcohol glycerol. Fats are triglycerides that are solid at room temperature, and oils are triglycerides that are liquid at room temperature. Fats are found mainly in animals, and oils found mainly in plants. *Saturated triglycerides* are those containing a higher proportion of saturated fatty acid chains (fewer carbon-to-carbon double bonds); *unsaturated triglycerides* contain a higher proportion of unsaturated fatty acid chains.

Saponification is the hydrolysis of a triglyceride in a basic solution to form glycerol and three carboxylate anions or soap molecules. Other important reactions are the hydrogenation and oxidation of double bonds in unsaturated fats and oils.

Phospholipids are lipids containing phosphorus. In **phosphoglycerides**, the phosphorus is joined to an amino alcohol unit. Some phosphoglycerides, like lecithins, are used to stabilize an **emulsion**—a dispersion of two liquids that do not normally mix, such as oil and water. **Sphingolipids** are lipids for which the precursor is the amino alcohol sphingosine, rather than glycerol. A **glycolipid** has a sugar substituted at one of the OH groups of either glycerol or sphingosine. All are highly polar lipids found in cell membranes.

Polar lipids have dual characteristics: one part of the molecule is ionic and dissolves in water; the rest has a hydrocarbon structure and dissolves in nonpolar substances. Often, the ionic part is referred to as **hydrophilic** (literally, "water loving") and the nonpolar part as **hydrophobic** ("water fearing"). When placed in water, polar lipids disperse into any one of three arrangements: *micelles*, *monolayers*, and *bilayers*. **Micelles** are aggregations of molecules in which the hydrocarbon tails of the lipids, being hydrophobic, are directed inward (away from the surrounding water), and the hydrophilic heads that are directed outward into the water. **Bilayers** are double layers arranged so that the hydrophobic tails are sandwiched between the two layers of hydrophilic heads, which remain in contact with the water.

Every living cell is enclosed by a *cell membrane* composed of a lipid bilayer. In animal cells, the bilayer consists mainly of phospholipids, glycolipids, and the steroid cholesterol. Embedded in the bilayer are **integral proteins**, and **peripheral proteins** are loosely associated with the surface of the bilayer. Everything between the cell membrane and the membrane of the cell nucleus is called the **cytoplasm**.

Most lipids can be saponified, but some, such as **steroids**, cannot be saponified. The steroid **cholesterol** is found in animal cells but never in plant cells. It is a main component of all cell membranes and a precursor for hormones, vitamin D, and bile salts. Bile salts are the most important constituents of **bile**, which is a yellowish-green liquid secreted by the gallbladder into the small intestine and is needed for the proper digestion of lipids.

ADDITIONAL EXERCISES

1. The melting point of elaidic acid is 52°C.
   a. What trend is observed when comparing the melting points of elaidic acid, oleic acid, and stearic acid? Explain.
   b. Would you expect the melting point of palmitelaidic acid to be lower or higher than that of elaidic acid? Explain.

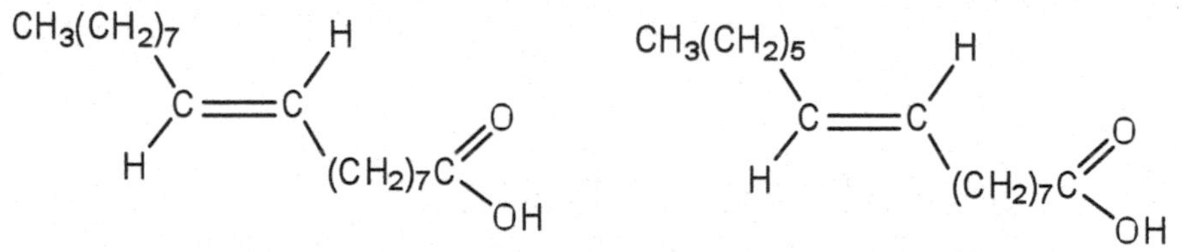

$CH_3(CH_2)_7$, H, C=C, H, $(CH_2)_7C(=O)OH$

Elaidic acid

$CH_3(CH_2)_5$, H, C=C, H, $(CH_2)_7C(=O)OH$

Palmitelaidic acid

2. Examine the labels on two brands of margarine and two brands of shortening and list the oils used in the various brands.
3. Draw a typical lecithin molecule that incorporates glycerol, palmitic acid, oleic acid, phosphoric acid, and choline. Circle all the ester bonds.
4. In cerebrosides, is the linkage between the fatty acid and sphingosine an amide bond or an ester bond? Justify your answer.

5. Serine is an amino acid that has the following structure. Draw the structure for a phosphatidylserine that contains a palmitic acid and a palmitoleic acid unit.

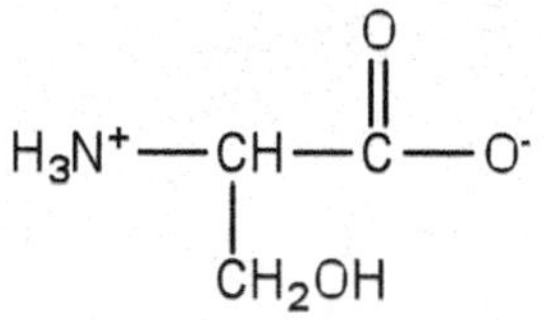

$$H_3N^+—CH(CH_2OH)—C(=O)—O^-$$

6. Explain whether each compound would be expected to diffuse through the lipid bilayer of a cell membrane.
   a. potassium chloride
   b. CH3CH2CH2CH2CH2CH3
   c. fructose
7. Identify the role of each steroid hormone in the body.
   a. progesterone
   b. aldosterone
   c. testosterone
   d. cortisol
8. How does the structure of cholic acid differ from that of cholesterol? Which compound would you expect to be more polar? Why?
9.
   a. What fatty acid is the precursor for the prostaglandins?
   b. Identify three biological effects of prostaglandins.
10. Why is it important to determine the ratio of LDLs to HDLs, rather than just the concentration of serum cholesterol?

ANSWERS

1. a. Stearic acid has the highest melting point, followed by elaidic acid, and then oleic acid with the lowest melting point. Elaidic acid is a *trans* fatty acid, and the carbon chains can pack together almost as tightly as those of the saturated stearic acid. Oleic acid is a *cis* fatty acid, and the bend in the hydrocarbon chain keeps these carbon chains from packing as closely together; fewer interactions lead to a much lower melting point.
   b. The melting point of palmitelaidic acid should be lower than that of elaidic acid because it has a shorter carbon chain (16, as compared to 18 for elaidic acid). The shorter the carbon chain, the lower the melting point due to a decrease in intermolecular interactions.
3.

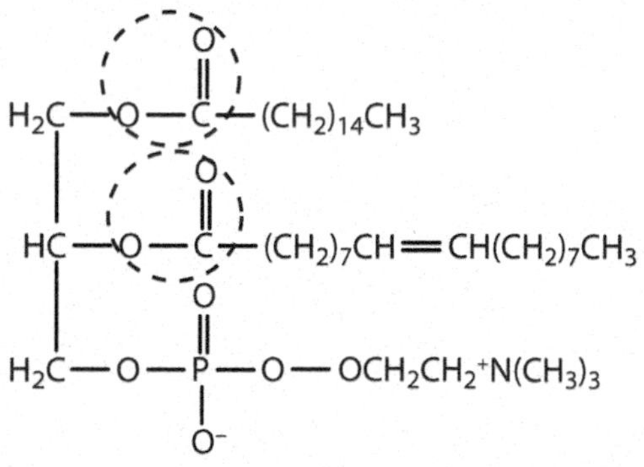

$$H_2C—O—C(=O)—(CH_2)_{14}CH_3$$
$$HC—O—C(=O)—(CH_2)_7CH{=}CH(CH_2)_7CH_3$$
$$H_2C—O—P(=O)(O^-)—O—OCH_2CH_2{}^+N(CH_3)_3$$

5.

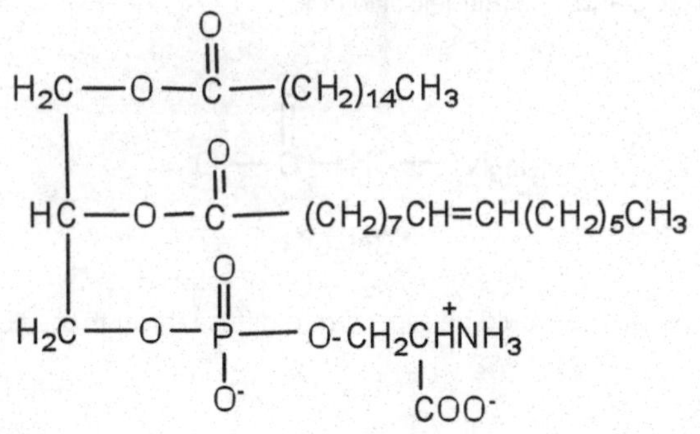

$$
\begin{array}{l}
H_2C-O-\overset{\overset{\displaystyle O}{\|}}{C}-(CH_2)_{14}CH_3 \\
\quad | \\
HC-O-\overset{\overset{\displaystyle O}{\|}}{C}-(CH_2)_7CH{=}CH(CH_2)_5CH_3 \\
\quad | \\
H_2C-O-\overset{\overset{\displaystyle O}{\|}}{\underset{\underset{\displaystyle O^-}{|}}{P}}-O\text{-}CH_2\underset{\underset{\displaystyle COO^-}{|}}{C}H\overset{+}{N}H_3
\end{array}
$$

7. a. regulates the menstrual cycle and maintains pregnancy
   b. regulates salt metabolism by stimulating the kidneys to retain sodium and excrete potassium
   c. stimulates and maintains male sex characteristics
   d. stimulates the conversion of proteins to carbohydrates
9. a. arachidonic acid
   b. induce smooth muscle contraction, lower blood pressure, and contribute to the inflammatory response

CHAPTER 18
Amino Acids, Proteins, and Enzymes

Opening Essay

The 1923 Nobel Prize in Medicine or Physiology was awarded to Frederick Grant Banting and John James Richard Macleod for their discovery of the protein *insulin*. In 1958, the Nobel Prize in Chemistry was awarded to Frederick Sanger for his discoveries concerning the structure of proteins and, in particular, the structure of insulin. What is so important about insulin that two Nobel Prizes have been awarded for work on this protein?

Insulin is a hormone that is synthesized in the pancreas. (For more information about hormones, see Chapter 17, [Unsupported Reference Type: chapter-section].) Insulin stimulates the transport of glucose into cells throughout the body and the storage of glucose as glycogen. People with diabetes do not produce insulin or use it properly. The isolation of insulin in 1921 led to the first effective treatment for these individuals.

An Insulin Pump

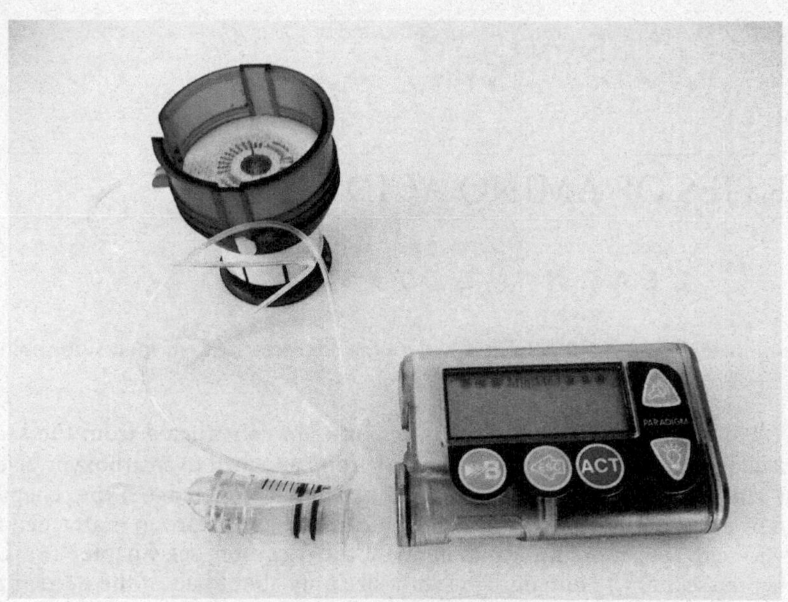

Proteins may be defined as compounds of high molar mass consisting largely or entirely of chains of amino acids. Their masses range from several thousand to several million daltons (Da). In addition to carbon, hydrogen, and oxygen atoms, all proteins contain nitrogen and sulfur atoms, and many also contain phosphorus atoms and traces of other elements. Proteins serve a variety of roles in living organisms and are often classified by these biological roles, which are summarized in Table 18.1. Muscle tissue is largely protein, as are skin and hair. Proteins are present in the blood, in the brain, and even in tooth enamel. Each type of cell in our bodies makes its own specialized proteins, as well as proteins common to all or most cells.

protein

A compound of high molar mass consisting largely or entirely of amino acids linked together.

Note

The *dalton* is a unit of mass used by biochemists and biologists. It is equivalent to the atomic mass unit. A 30,000 Da protein has a molar mass of 30,000 u.

TABLE 18.1 Classification of Proteins by Biological Function

Classification	Biological Function	Example
enzymes	accelerate biological reactions	α-Amylase catalyzes the hydrolysis of starch and glycogen.
structural	provide strength and structure	Keratin is the primary protein of hair and wool.
contractile	muscle contraction; cell division	Myosin is one protein needed for the contraction of muscles.
transport	transport substances from one place to another	Hemoglobin transports oxygen from the lungs throughout the body.
regulatory	regulate the functioning of other proteins	Insulin regulates the activity of specific enzymes in the body.
storage	provide storage of essential nutrients	Ovalbumin stores amino acids in the egg white that will be used by the developing bird.
protection	protect cells or the organism from foreign substances	Immunoglobulins recognize and breakdown foreign molecules.

We begin our study of proteins by looking at the properties and reactions of amino acids, which is followed by a discussion of how amino acids link covalently to form peptides and proteins. We end the chapter with a discussion of enzymes—the proteins that act as catalysts in the body.

1. PROPERTIES OF AMINO ACIDS

LEARNING OBJECTIVE

1. **Recognize amino acids and classify them based on the characteristics of their side chains.**

The proteins in all living species, from bacteria to humans, are constructed from the same set of 20 **amino acids**, so called because each contains an amino group attached to a carboxylic acid. (For more information about amino groups, see Chapter 15, [Unsupported Reference Type: chapter-section].) The amino acids in proteins are α-amino acids, which means the amino group is attached to the α-carbon of the carboxylic acid. (For more information about the α-carbon, see Chapter 15, [Unsupported Reference Type: chapter-section].) Humans can synthesize only about half of the needed amino acids; the remainder must be obtained from the diet and are known as **essential amino acids**.

amino acid

A molecule that contains an amino group and a carboxyl group.

essential amino acid

An amino acid that must be obtained from the diet because it cannot be synthesized in sufficient quantities by the body.

Note

Two more amino acids have been found in limited quantities in proteins. Selenocysteine was discovered in 1986, while pyrrolysine was discovered in 2002.

The amino acids are colorless, nonvolatile, crystalline solids, melting and decomposing at temperatures above 200°C. These melting temperatures are more like those of inorganic salts than those of amines or organic acids and indicate that the structures of the amino acids in the solid state and in neutral solution are best represented as having both a negatively charged group and a positively charged group. Such a species is known as a **zwitterion**.

zwitterion

An electrically neutral compound that contains both negatively and positively charged groups.

$$H_3N^+-\underset{\underset{R}{|}}{CH}-C\overset{\displaystyle O}{\swarrow}\!\!\searrow O^-$$

α-Amino acid drawn as a zwitterion

$$H_2N-\underset{\underset{R}{|}}{CH}-C\overset{\displaystyle O}{\swarrow}\!\!\searrow OH$$

α-Amino acid drawn as an uncharged molecule; not an accurate respresentation of amino acid structure

1.1 Classification

In addition to the amino and carboxyl groups, amino acids have a side chain or R group attached to the α-carbon. Each amino acid has unique characteristics arising from the size, shape, solubility, and ionization properties of its R group. As a result, the side chains of amino acids exert a profound effect on the structure and biological activity of proteins. Although amino acids can be classified in various ways, one common approach is to classify them according to whether the functional group on the side chain at neutral pH is nonpolar, polar but uncharged, negatively charged, or positively charged. The structures and names of the 20 amino acids, their one- and three-letter abbreviations, and some of their distinctive features are given in Table 18.2.

TABLE 18.2 Common Amino Acids Found in Proteins

Common Name	Abbreviation	Structural Formula (at pH 6)	Molar Mass	Distinctive Feature
Amino acids with a nonpolar R group				
glycine	gly (G)	$H_3N^+{-}CH(H){-}C(=O)O^-$	75	the only amino acid lacking a chiral carbon
alanine	ala (A)	$H_3N^+{-}CH(CH_3){-}C(=O)O^-$	89	—
valine	val (V)	$H_3N^+{-}CH(CH(H_3C)CH_3){-}C(=O)O^-$	117	a branched-chain amino acid
leucine	leu (L)	$H_3N^+{-}CH(CH_2CH(H_3C)CH_3){-}C(=O)O^-$	131	a branched-chain amino acid
isoleucine	ile (I)	$H_3N^+{-}CH(CH(H_3C)CH_2CH_3){-}C(=O)O^-$	131	an essential amino acid because most animals cannot synthesize branched-chain amino acids
phenylalanine	phe (F)	$H_3N^+{-}CH(H_2C{-}C_6H_5){-}C(=O)O^-$	165	also classified as an aromatic amino acid
tryptophan	trp (W)	$H_3N^+{-}CH(H_2C{-}\text{indolyl (NH)}){-}C(=O)O^-$	204	also classified as an aromatic amino acid

Common Name	Abbreviation	Structural Formula (at pH 6)	Molar Mass	Distinctive Feature
methionine	met (M)	$H_3N^+-CH(CH_2CH_2-S-CH_3)-COO^-$	149	side chain functions as a methyl group donor
proline	pro (P)	$^+NH_2$ (ring) $-COO^-$	115	contains a secondary amine group; referred to as an *α-imino acid*
Amino acids with a polar but neutral R group				
serine	ser (S)	$H_3N^+-CH(CH_2OH)-COO^-$	105	found at the active site of many enzymes
threonine	thr (T)	$H_3N^+-CH(HO-CH-CH_3)-COO^-$	119	named for its similarity to the sugar threose
cysteine	cys (C)	$H_3N^+-CH(CH_2SH)-COO^-$	121	oxidation of two cysteine molecules yields *cystine*
tyrosine	tyr (Y)	$H_3N^+-CH(H_2C-C_6H_4-OH)-COO^-$	181	also classified as an aromatic amino acid
asparagine	asn (N)	$H_3N^+-CH(CH_2-C(=O)-NH_2)-COO^-$	132	the amide of aspartic acid

Common Name	Abbreviation	Structural Formula (at pH 6)	Molar Mass	Distinctive Feature
glutamine	gln (Q)	$H_3N^+{-}CH{-}C({=}O){-}O^-$, R = $(CH_2)_2{-}C({=}O){-}NH_2$	146	the amide of glutamic acid
Amino acids with a negatively charged R group				
aspartic acid	asp (D)	$H_3N^+{-}CH{-}C({=}O){-}O^-$, R = $CH_2{-}C({=}O){-}O^-$	132	carboxyl groups are ionized at physiological pH; also known as aspartate
glutamic acid	glu (E)	$H_3N^+{-}CH{-}C({=}O){-}O^-$, R = $(CH_2)_2{-}C({=}O){-}O^-$	146	carboxyl groups are ionized at physiological pH; also known as glutamate
Amino acids with a positively charged R group				
histidine	his (H)	$H_3N^+{-}CH{-}C({=}O){-}O^-$, R = H_2C–imidazolium ring (NH, ^+NH)	155	the only amino acid whose R group has a pKa (6.0) near physiological pH
lysine	lys (K)	$H_3N^+{-}CH{-}C({=}O){-}O^-$, R = $(CH_2)_4{}^+NH_3$	147	—
arginine	arg (R)	$H_3N^+{-}CH{-}C({=}O){-}O^-$, R = $(CH_2)_3{-}HN{-}C({=}^+NH_2){-}NH_2$	175	almost as strong a base as sodium hydroxide

The first amino acid to be isolated was asparagine in 1806. It was obtained from protein found in asparagus juice (hence the name). Glycine, the major amino acid found in gelatin, was named for its sweet taste (Greek *glykys*, meaning "sweet"). In some cases an amino acid found in a protein is actually a derivative of one of the common 20 amino acids (one such derivative is hydroxyproline). The modification occurs *after* the amino acid has been assembled into a protein.

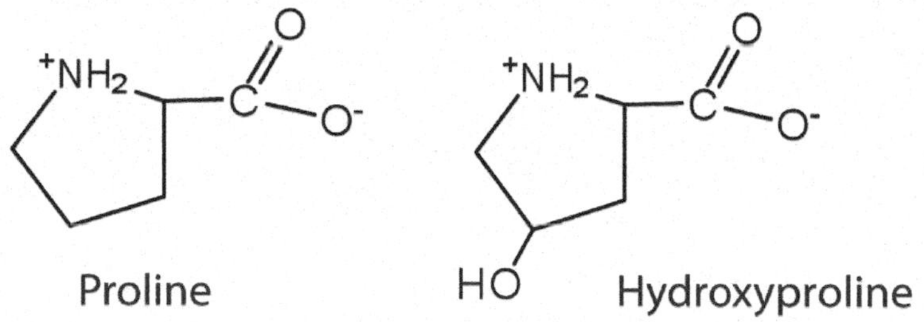

Proline Hydroxyproline

1.2 Configuration

Notice in Table 18.2 that glycine is the only amino acid whose α-carbon is *not* chiral. Therefore, with the exception of glycine, the amino acids could theoretically exist in either the D- or the L-enantiomeric form and rotate plane-polarized light. As with sugars, chemists use glyceraldehyde as the reference compound for the assignment of configuration to amino acids. (For more information about stereoisomers and configuration, see Chapter 16, [Unsupported Reference Type: chapter-section].) Its structure closely resembles an amino acid structure except that in the latter, an amino group takes the place of the OH group on the chiral carbon of the sugar.

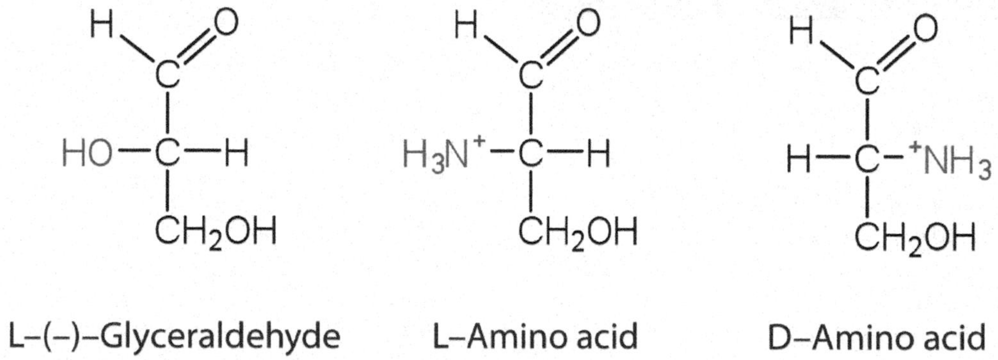

L-(−)-Glyceraldehyde L-Amino acid D-Amino acid

We learned in Chapter 16 that all naturally occurring sugars belong to the D series. It is interesting, therefore, that nearly all known plant and animal proteins are composed entirely of L-amino acids. However, certain bacteria contain D-amino acids in their cell walls, and several antibiotics (e.g., actinomycin D and the gramicidins) contain varying amounts of D-leucine, D-phenylalanine, and D-valine.

CONCEPT REVIEW EXERCISES

1. What is the general structure of an α-amino acid?
2. Identify the amino acid that fits each description.
    a. also known as aspartate
    b. almost as strong a base as sodium hydroxide
    c. does not have a chiral carbon

ANSWERS

1.

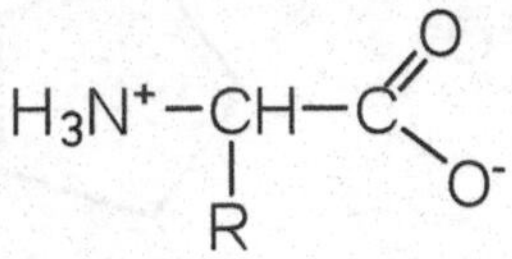

$$H_3N^+{-}\underset{\displaystyle R}{\underset{|}{CH}}{-}C(=O){-}O^-$$

2. a. aspartic acid
   b. arginine
   c. glycine

KEY TAKEAWAYS

- Amino acids can be classified based on the characteristics of their distinctive side chains as nonpolar, polar but uncharged, negatively charged, or positively charged.
- The amino acids found in proteins are L-amino acids.

EXERCISES

1. Write the side chain of each amino acid.
   a. serine
   b. arginine
   c. phenylalanine
2. Write the side chain of each amino acid.
   a. aspartic acid
   b. methionine
   c. valine
3. Draw the structure for each amino acid.
   a. alanine
   b. cysteine
   c. histidine
4. Draw the structure for each amino acid.
   a. threonine
   b. glutamic acid
   c. leucine
5. Identify an amino acid whose side chain contains a(n)
   a. amide functional group.
   b. aromatic ring.
   c. carboxyl group.
6. Identify an amino acid whose side chain contains a(n)
   a. OH group
   b. branched chain
   c. amino group

ANSWERS

1. a. $CH2OH^-$
   b. $-(CH_2)_3{-}NH{-}C(={}^+NH_2){-}NH_2$
   c. $-CH_2-C_6H_5$ (benzene ring)
3. a. $H_3N^+{-}CH(CH_3){-}C(=O){-}O^-$
   b. $H_3N^+{-}CH(CH_2SH){-}C(=O){-}O^-$
   c. $H_3N^+{-}CH(H_2C{-}\text{imidazolium ring: NH, }^+NH){-}C(=O){-}O^-$

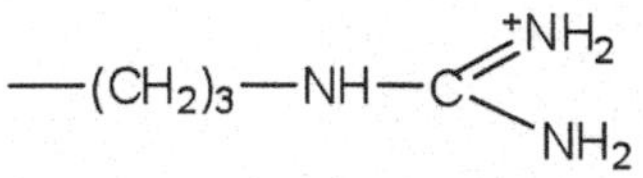

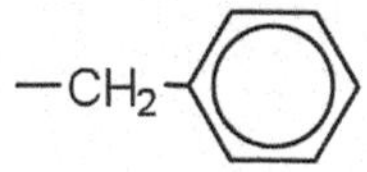

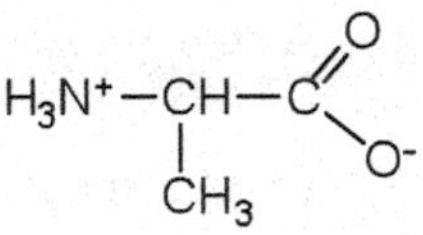

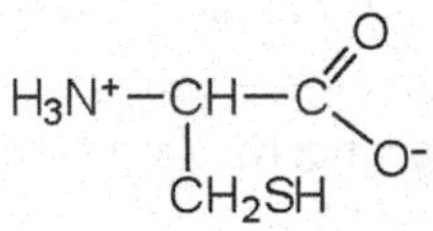

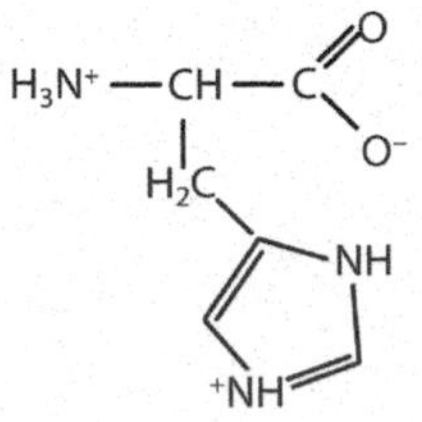

5. a. asparagine or glutamine
   b. phenylalanine, tyrosine, or tryptophan
   c. aspartic acid or glutamic acid

2. REACTIONS OF AMINO ACIDS

LEARNING OBJECTIVE

1. **Explain how an amino acid can act as both an acid and a base.**

The structure of an amino acid allows it to act as both an acid and a base. An amino acid has this ability because at a certain pH value (different for each amino acid) nearly all the amino acid molecules exist as zwitterions. If acid is added to a solution containing the zwitterion, the carboxylate group captures a hydrogen (H^+) ion, and the amino acid becomes positively charged. If base is added, ion removal of the H^+ ion from the amino group of the zwitterion produces a negatively charged amino acid. In both circumstances, the amino acid acts to maintain the pH of the system—that is, to remove the added acid (H^+) or base (OH^-) from solution.

Addition of an acid:

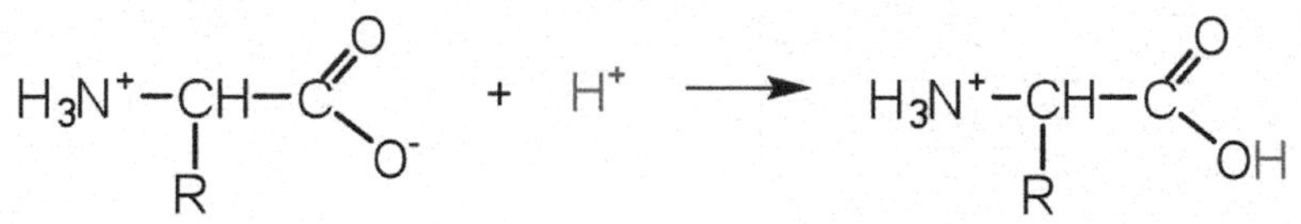

$$H_3N^+{-}CH(R){-}COO^- + H^+ \longrightarrow H_3N^+{-}CH(R){-}COOH$$

Addition of a base:

$$H_3N^+{-}CH(R){-}COO^- + OH^- \longrightarrow H_2N{-}CH(R){-}COO^- + H_2O$$

EXAMPLE 1

1. Draw the structure for the anion formed when glycine (at neutral pH) reacts with a base.
2. Draw the structure for the cation formed when glycine (at neutral pH) reacts with an acid.

Solution

1. The base removes H^+ from the protonated amine group.

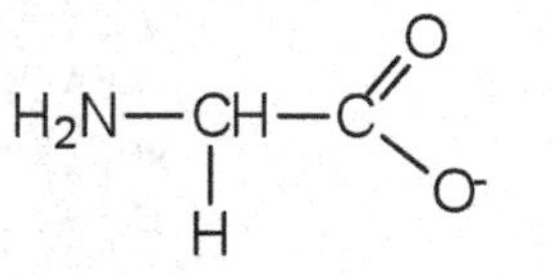

$$H_2N{-}CH(H){-}COO^-$$

2. The acid adds H^+ to the carboxylate group.

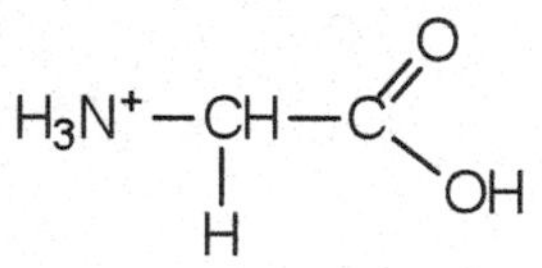

$$H_3N^+{-}CH(H){-}COOH$$

SKILL-BUILDING EXERCISE

1. Draw the structure for the cation formed when valine (at neutral pH) reacts with an acid.
2. Draw the structure for the anion formed when valine (at neutral pH) reacts with a base.

isoelectric point

The pH at which a given amino acid exists in solution as a zwitterion.

The particular pH at which a given amino acid exists in solution as a zwitterion is called the **isoelectric point** (pI). At its pI, the positive and negative charges on the amino acid balance, and the molecule as a whole is electrically neutral. The amino acids whose side chains are always neutral have isoelectric points ranging from 5.0 to 6.5. The basic amino acids (which have positively charged side chains at neutral pH) have relatively high pIs. Acidic amino acids (which have negatively charged side chains at neutral pH) have quite low pIs (Table 18.3).

TABLE 18.3 pIs of Some Representative Amino Acids

Amino Acid	Classification	pI
alanine	nonpolar	6.0
valine	nonpolar	6.0
serine	polar, uncharged	5.7
threonine	polar, uncharged	6.5
arginine	positively charged (basic)	10.8
histidine	positively charged (basic)	7.6
lysine	positively charged (basic)	9.8
aspartic acid	negatively charged (acidic)	3.0
glutamic acid	negatively charged (acidic)	3.2

Amino acids undergo reactions characteristic of carboxylic acids and amines. The reactivity of these functional groups is particularly important in linking amino acids together to form peptides and proteins, as you will see later in this chapter. Simple chemical tests that are used to detect amino acids take advantage of the reactivity of these functional groups. An example is the ninhydrin test in which the amine functional group of α-amino acids reacts with ninhydrin to form purple-colored compounds. Ninhydrin is used to detect fingerprints because it reacts with amino acids from the proteins in skin cells transferred to the surface by the individual leaving the fingerprint.

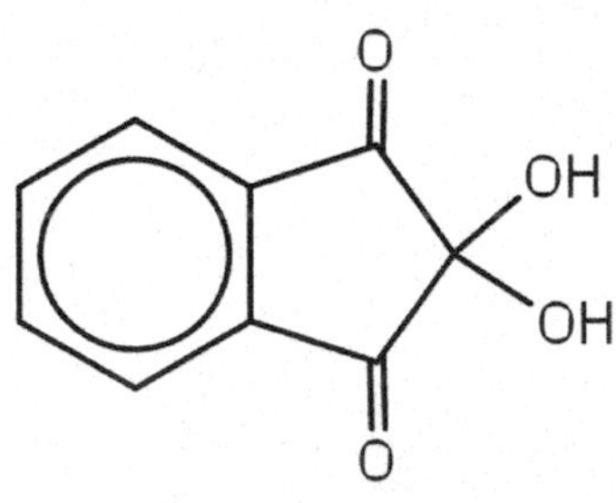

Ninhydrin

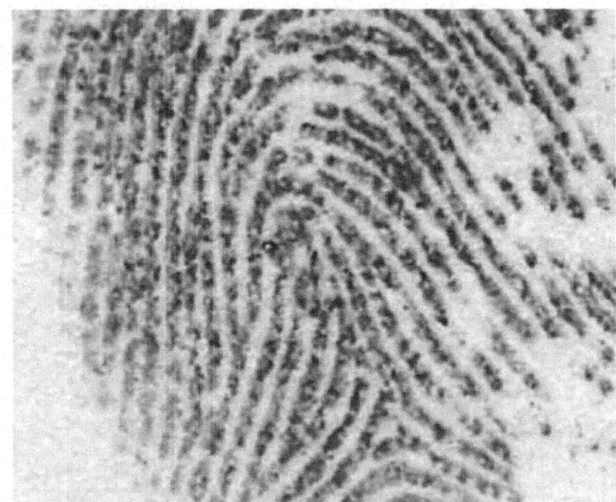

CONCEPT REVIEW EXERCISES

1. Define each term.
   a. zwitterion
   b. isoelectric point
2. Draw the structure for the anion formed when alanine (at neutral pH) reacts with a base.
3. Draw the structure for the cation formed when alanine (at neutral pH) reacts with an acid.

ANSWERS

1. a. an electrically neutral compound that contains both negatively and positively charged groups
   b. the pH at which a given amino acid exists in solution as a zwitterion
2.

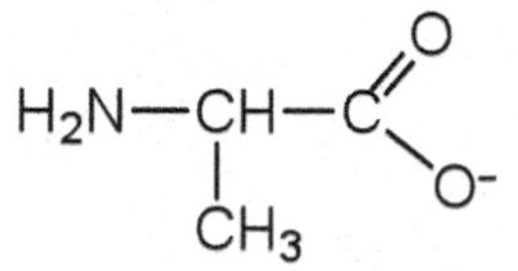

$$H_2N-\underset{\displaystyle CH_3}{\underset{|}{CH}}-C(=O)O^-$$

3.

$$H_3N^+-\underset{\displaystyle CH_3}{\underset{|}{CH}}-C(=O)OH$$

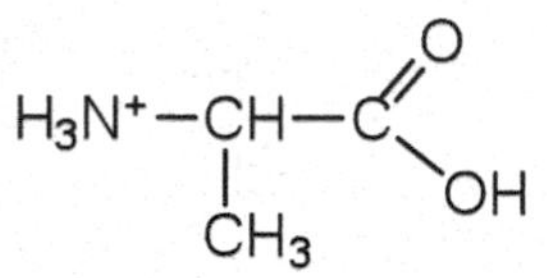

KEY TAKEAWAYS

- Amino acids can act as both an acid and a base due to the presence of the amino and carboxyl functional groups.
- The pH at which a given amino acid exists in solution as a zwitterion is called the *isoelectric point* (pI).

EXERCISES

1. Draw the structure of leucine and determine the charge on the molecule in a(n)
   a. acidic solution (pH = 1).
   b. neutral solution (pH = 7).
   c. a basic solution (pH = 11)
2. Draw the structure of isoleucine and determine the charge on the molecule in a(n)
   a. acidic solution (pH = 1).
   b. neutral solution (pH = 7).
   c. basic solution (pH = 11).

ANSWER

1. a.

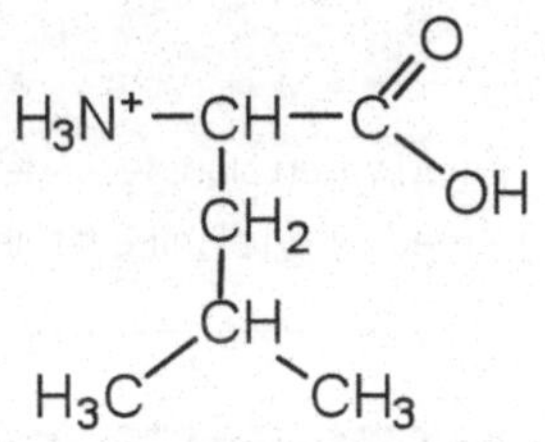

H_3N^+—CH—C(=O)OH
CH$_2$
CH
H_3C CH_3

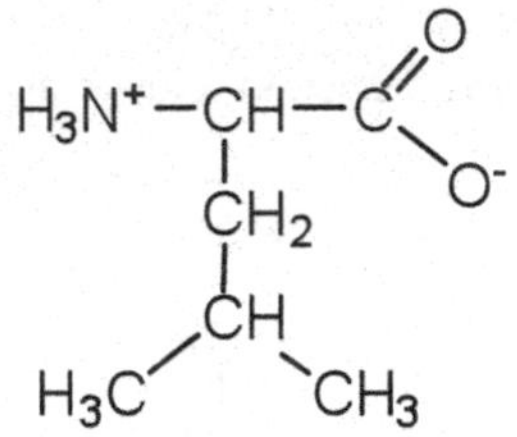

b.

H_3N^+—CH—C(=O)O$^-$
CH$_2$
CH
H_3C CH_3

c.

H_2N—CH—C(=O)O$^-$
CH$_2$
CH
H_3C CH_3

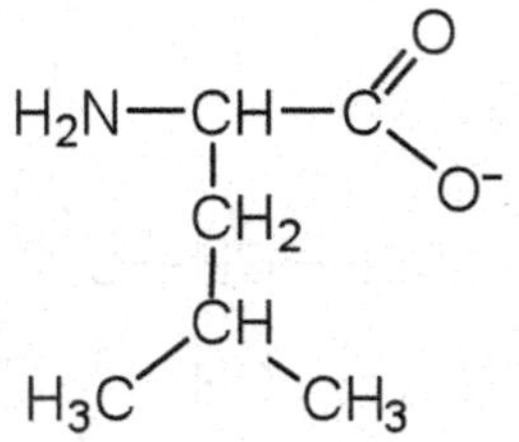

3. PEPTIDES

LEARNING OBJECTIVES

1. **Explain how a peptide is formed from individual amino acids.**
2. **Explain why the sequence of amino acids in a protein is important.**

Two or more amino acids can join together into chains called peptides. In Chapter 15, [Unsupported Reference Type: chapter-section], we discussed the reaction between ammonia and a carboxylic acid to form an amide. In a similar reaction, the amino group on one amino acid molecule reacts with the carboxyl group on another, releasing a molecule of water and forming an amide linkage:

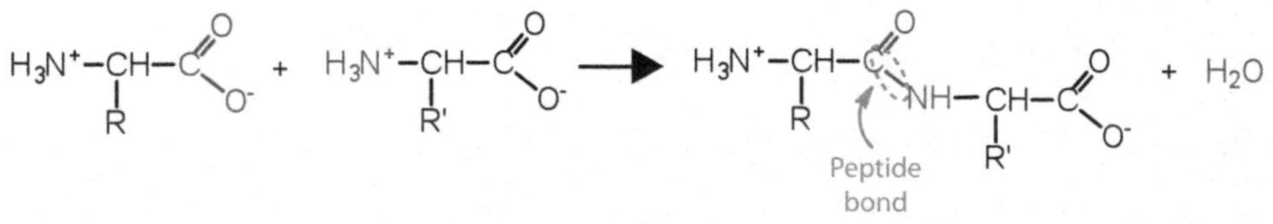

H_3N^+–CH(R)–C(=O)O$^-$ + H_3N^+–CH(R')–C(=O)O$^-$ → H_3N^+–CH(R)–C(=O)–NH–CH(R')–C(=O)O$^-$ + H_2O

Peptide bond

peptide bond

The amide bond joining two amino acid units in a peptide or protein.

An amide bond joining two amino acid units is called a **peptide bond**. Note that the product molecule still has a reactive amino group on the left and a reactive carboxyl group on the right. These can react with additional amino acids to lengthen the peptide. The process can continue until thousands of units have joined, resulting in large proteins.

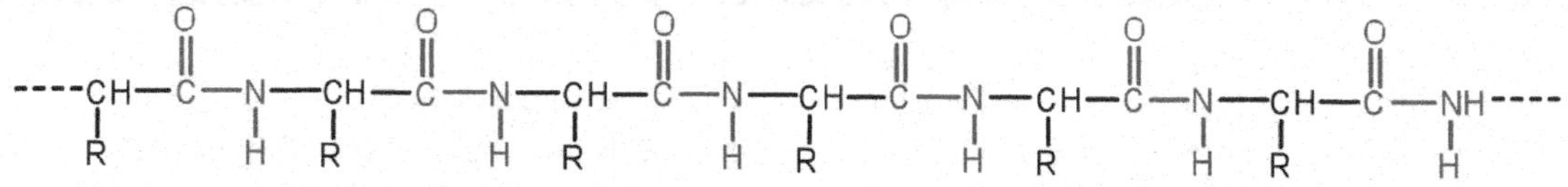

$$\cdots\text{CH}(\text{R})-\text{C}(=\text{O})-\text{N}(\text{H})-\text{CH}(\text{R})-\text{C}(=\text{O})-\text{N}(\text{H})-\text{CH}(\text{R})-\text{C}(=\text{O})-\text{N}(\text{H})-\text{CH}(\text{R})-\text{C}(=\text{O})-\text{N}(\text{H})-\text{CH}(\text{R})-\text{C}(=\text{O})-\text{N}(\text{H})-\text{CH}(\text{R})-\text{C}(=\text{O})-\text{NH}(\text{H})\cdots$$

A chain consisting of only two amino acid units is called a *dipeptide*; a chain consisting of three is a *tripeptide*. By convention, peptide and protein structures are depicted with the amino acid whose amino group is free (the N-terminal end) on the left and the amino acid with a free carboxyl group (the C-terminal end) to the right.

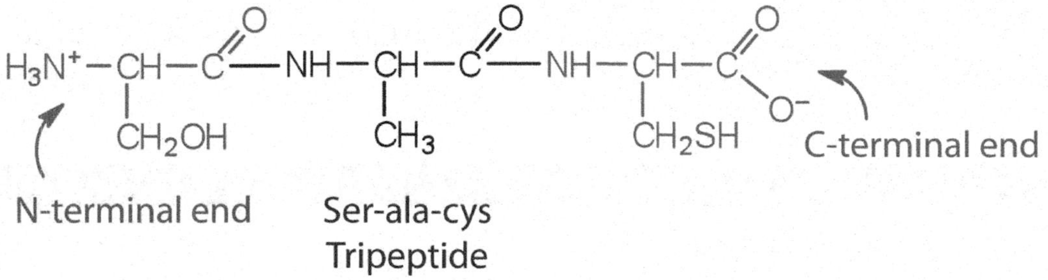

$$H_3N^+-\underset{CH_2OH}{CH}-\overset{O}{\overset{\|}{C}}-NH-\underset{CH_3}{CH}-\overset{O}{\overset{\|}{C}}-NH-\underset{CH_2SH}{CH}-\overset{O}{\overset{\|}{C}}-O^-$$

N-terminal end

C-terminal end

Ser-ala-cys
Tripeptide

The general term *peptide* refers to an amino acid chain of unspecified length. However, chains of about 50 amino acids or more are usually called proteins or **polypeptides**. In its physiologically active form, a protein may be composed of one or more polypeptide chains.

polypeptide
A chain of about 50 or more amino acids.

For peptides and proteins to be physiologically active, it is not enough that they incorporate certain amounts of specific amino acids. The order, or *sequence*, in which the amino acids are connected is also of critical importance. Bradykinin is a nine-amino acid peptide produced in the blood that has the following amino acid sequence:

arg-pro-pro-gly-phe-ser-pro-phe-arg

This peptide lowers blood pressure, stimulates smooth muscle tissue, increases capillary permeability, and causes pain. When the order of amino acids in bradykinin is reversed,

arg-phe-pro-ser-phe-gly-pro-pro-arg

the peptide resulting from this synthesis shows none of the activity of bradykinin.

Just as millions of different words are spelled with our 26-letter English alphabet, millions of different proteins are made with the 20 common amino acids. However, just as the English alphabet can be used to write gibberish, amino acids can be put together in the *wrong sequence* to produce nonfunctional proteins. Although the correct sequence is ordinarily of utmost importance, it is not always absolutely required. Just as you can sometimes make sense of incorrectly spelled English words, a protein with a small percentage of "incorrect" amino acids may continue to function. However, it rarely functions as well as a protein having the correct sequence. There are also instances in which seemingly minor errors of sequence have disastrous effects. For example, in some people, every molecule of hemoglobin (a protein in the blood that transports oxygen) has a single incorrect amino acid unit out of about 300 (a single valine replaces a glutamic acid). That "minor" error is responsible for sickle cell anemia, an inherited condition that usually is fatal.

CONCEPT REVIEW EXERCISES

1. Distinguish between the N-terminal amino acid and the C-terminal amino acid of a peptide or protein.
2. Describe the difference between an amino acid and a peptide.
3. Amino acid units in a protein are connected by peptide bonds. What is another name for the functional group linking the amino acids?

ANSWERS

1. The N-terminal end is the end of a peptide or protein whose amino group is free (not involved in the formation of a peptide bond), while the C-terminal end has a free carboxyl group.
2. A peptide is composed of two or more amino acids. Amino acids are the building blocks of peptides.
3. amide bond

KEY TAKEAWAYS

- The amino group of one amino acid can react with the carboxyl group on another amino acid to form a peptide bond that links the two amino acids together. Additional amino acids can be added on through the formation of addition peptide (amide) bonds.
- A sequence of amino acids in a peptide or protein is written with the N-terminal amino acid first and the C-terminal amino acid at the end (writing left to right).

EXERCISES

1. Draw the structure for each peptide.
   a. gly-val
   b. val-gly
2. Draw the structure for cys-val-ala.
3. Identify the C- and N-terminal amino acids for the peptide lys-val-phe-gly-arg-cys.
4. Identify the C- and N-terminal amino acids for the peptide asp-arg-val-tyr-ile-his-pro-phe.

ANSWERS

1. a.

$$H_3N^+{-}CH(H){-}C({=}O){-}NH{-}CH(CH(CH_3)_2){-}C({=}O)O^-$$

b.

$$H_3N^+{-}CH(CH(CH_3)_2){-}C({=}O){-}NH{-}CH(H){-}C({=}O)O^-$$

3. C-terminal amino acid: cys; N-terminal amino acid: lys

4. PROTEINS

LEARNING OBJECTIVES

1. Describe the four levels of protein structure.
2. Identify the types of attractive interactions that hold proteins in their most stable three-dimensional structure.
3. Explain what happens when proteins are denatured.
4. Identify how a protein can be denatured.

Each of the thousands of naturally occurring proteins has its own characteristic amino acid composition and sequence that result in a unique three-dimensional shape. Since the 1950s, scientists have determined the amino acid sequences and three-dimensional conformation of numerous proteins and thus obtained important clues on how each protein performs its specific function in the body.

Proteins are compounds of high molar mass consisting largely or entirely of chains of amino acids. Because of their great complexity, protein molecules cannot be classified on the basis of specific structural similarities, as carbohydrates and lipids are categorized. The two major structural classifications of proteins are based on far more general qualities: whether the protein is (1) fiberlike and insoluble or (2) globular and soluble. Some proteins, such as those that compose hair, skin, muscles, and connective tissue, are fiberlike. These **fibrous proteins** are insoluble in water and usually serve structural, connective, and protective functions. Examples of fibrous proteins are keratins, collagens, myosins, and elastins. Hair and the outer layer of skin are composed of keratin. Connective tissues contain collagen. Myosins are muscle proteins and are capable of contraction and extension. Elastins are found in ligaments and the elastic tissue of artery walls.

fibrous protein

A protein that is elongated or fiberlike and insoluble in water.

Globular proteins, the other major class, are soluble in aqueous media. In these proteins, the chains are folded so that the molecule as a whole is roughly spherical. Familiar examples include egg albumin from egg whites and serum albumin in blood. Serum albumin plays a major role in transporting fatty acids and maintaining a proper balance of osmotic pressures in the body. Hemoglobin and myoglobin, which are important for binding oxygen, are also globular proteins.

globular protein

A protein that is generally spherical in structure and soluble in water.

4.1 Levels of Protein Structure

The structure of proteins is generally described as having four organizational levels. The first of these is the **primary structure**, which is the number and sequence of amino acids in a protein's polypeptide chain or chains, beginning with the free amino group and maintained by the peptide bonds connecting each amino acid to the next. The primary structure of insulin, composed of 51 amino acids, is shown in Figure 18.2.

primary structure

The sequence of amino acids in a polypeptide chain or protein.

FIGURE 18.2 Primary Structure of Human Insulin

Human insulin, whose amino acid sequence is shown here, is a hormone that is required for the proper metabolism of glucose.

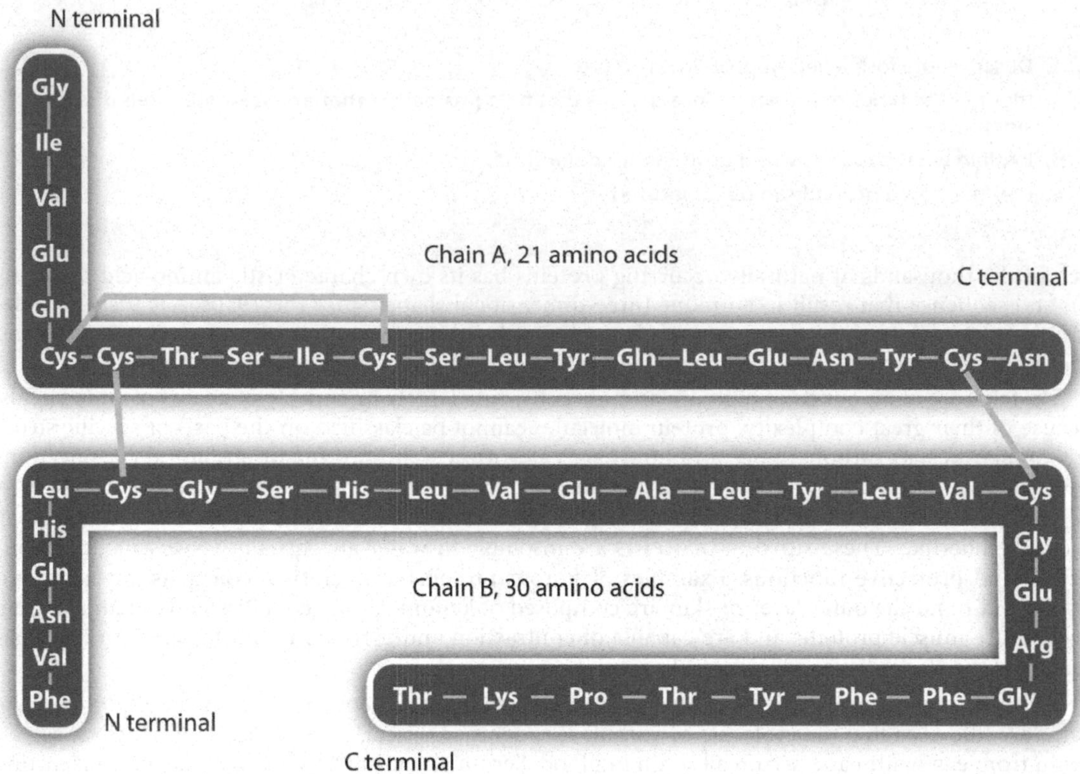

secondary structure

The fixed arrangement of the polypeptide backbone.

A protein molecule is not a random tangle of polypeptide chains. Instead, the chains are arranged in unique but specific conformations. The term **secondary structure** refers to the fixed arrangement of the polypeptide backbone. On the basis of X ray studies, Linus Pauling and Robert Corey postulated that certain proteins or portions of proteins twist into a spiral or a helix. This helix is stabilized by *intrachain* hydrogen bonding between the carbonyl oxygen atom of one amino acid and the amide hydrogen atom four amino acids up the chain (located on the next turn of the helix) and is known as a right-handed α-helix. X ray data indicate that this helix makes one turn for every 3.6 amino acids, and the side chains of these amino acids project outward from the coiled backbone (Figure 18.3). The α-keratins, found in hair and wool, are exclusively α-helical in conformation. Some proteins, such as gamma globulin, chymotrypsin, and cytochrome c, have little or no helical structure. Others, such as hemoglobin and myoglobin, are helical in certain regions but not in others.

FIGURE 18.3 A Ball-and-Stick Model of an α-Helix

This ball-and-stick model shows the intrachain hydrogen bonding between carbonyl oxygen atoms and amide hydrogen atoms. Each turn of the helix spans 3.6 amino acids. Note that the side chains (represented as green spheres) point out from the helix.

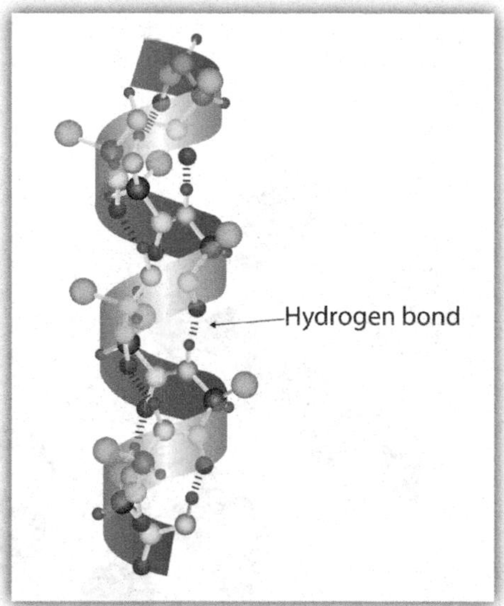

Another common type of secondary structure, called the *β-pleated sheet conformation*, is a sheetlike arrangement in which two or more extended polypeptide chains (or separate regions on the same chain) are aligned side by side. The aligned segments can run either parallel or antiparallel—that is, the N-terminals can face in the same direction on adjacent chains or in different directions—and are connected by *interchain* hydrogen bonding (Figure 18.4). The β-pleated sheet is particularly important in structural proteins, such as silk fibroin. It is also seen in portions of many enzymes, such as carboxypeptidase A and lysozyme.

FIGURE 18.4 A Ball-and-Stick Model of the β-Pleated Sheet Structure in Proteins

The side chains extend above or below the sheet and alternate along the chain. The protein chains are held together by interchain hydrogen bonding.

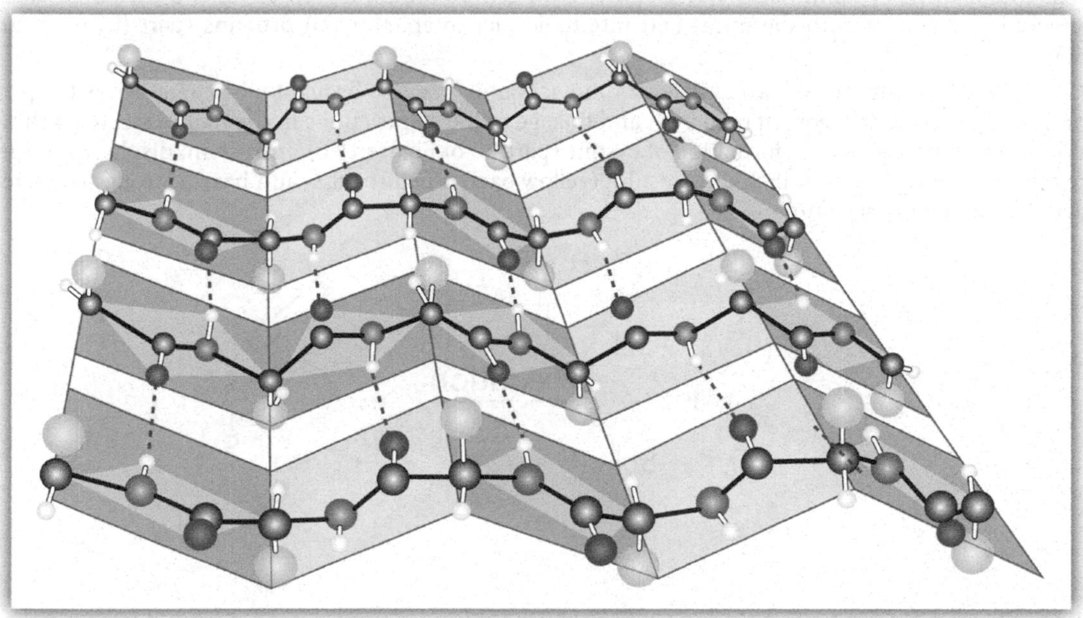

tertiary structure

The unique three-dimensional shape of a polypeptide chain as a whole.

Tertiary structure refers to the unique three-dimensional shape of the protein as a whole, which results from the folding and bending of the protein backbone. The tertiary structure is intimately tied to the proper biochemical functioning of the protein. Figure 18.5 shows a depiction of the three-dimensional structure of insulin.

FIGURE 18.5 A Ribbon Model of the Three-Dimensional Structure of Insulin

The spiral regions represent sections of the polypeptide chain that have an α-helical structure, while the broad arrows represent β-pleated sheet structures.

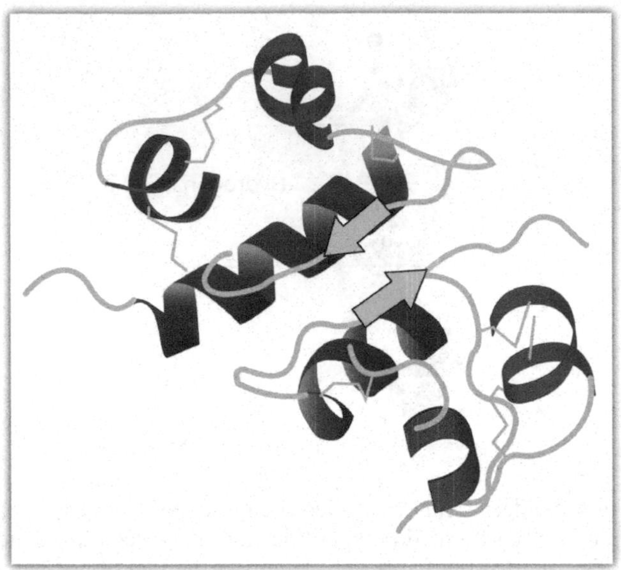

Four major types of attractive interactions determine the shape and stability of the tertiary structure of proteins. You studied several of these in Chapter 8, [Unsupported Reference Type: chapter-section].

ionic bonding

Bonding that results from electrostatic attractions between positively and negatively charged groups.

hydrogen bonding

Bonding between a highly electronegative oxygen atom or nitrogen atom and a hydrogen atom attached to another oxygen atom or nitrogen atom.

disulfide linkage

A covalent bond that forms by the oxidation and linkage of two sulfur atoms from the side chains of two cysteine residues.

1. **Ionic bonding**. Ionic bonds result from electrostatic attractions between positively and negatively charged side chains of amino acids. For example, the mutual attraction between an aspartic acid carboxylate ion and a lysine ammonium ion helps to maintain a particular folded area of a protein (part (a) of Figure 18.6).

2. **Hydrogen bonding**. Hydrogen bonding forms between a highly electronegative oxygen atom or a nitrogen atom and a hydrogen atom attached to another oxygen atom or a nitrogen atom, such as those found in polar amino acid side chains. Hydrogen bonding (as well as ionic attractions) is extremely important in both the intra- and intermolecular interactions of proteins (part (b) of Figure 18.6).

3. **Disulfide linkages**. Two cysteine amino acid units may be brought close together as the protein molecule folds. Subsequent oxidation and linkage of the sulfur atoms in the highly reactive sulfhydryl (SH) groups leads to the formation of cystine (part (c) of Figure 18.6). Intrachain disulfide linkages are found in many proteins, including insulin (yellow bars in Figure 18.2) and have a strong stabilizing effect on the tertiary structure.

Cys —SH
+
Cys —SH
Oxidation
Cys
S
|
S
Cys

4. **Dispersion forces.** Dispersion forces arise when a normally nonpolar atom becomes momentarily polar due to an uneven distribution of electrons, leading to an instantaneous dipole that induces a shift of electrons in a neighboring nonpolar atom. Dispersion forces are weak but can be important when other types of interactions are either missing or minimal (part (d) of Figure 18.6). This is the case with fibroin, the major protein in silk, in which a high proportion of amino acids in the protein have nonpolar side chains. The term *hydrophobic interaction* is often misused as a synonym for dispersion forces. Hydrophobic interactions arise because water molecules engage in hydrogen bonding with other water molecules (or groups in proteins capable of hydrogen bonding). Because nonpolar groups cannot engage in hydrogen bonding, the protein folds in such a way that these groups are buried in the interior part of the protein structure, minimizing their contact with water.

dispersion force

A force caused by the instantaneous imbalance of electrons about a molecule.

FIGURE 18.6 Tertiary Protein Structure Interactions

Four interactions stabilize the tertiary structure of a protein: (a) ionic bonding, (b) hydrogen bonding, (c) disulfide linkages, and (d) dispersion forces.

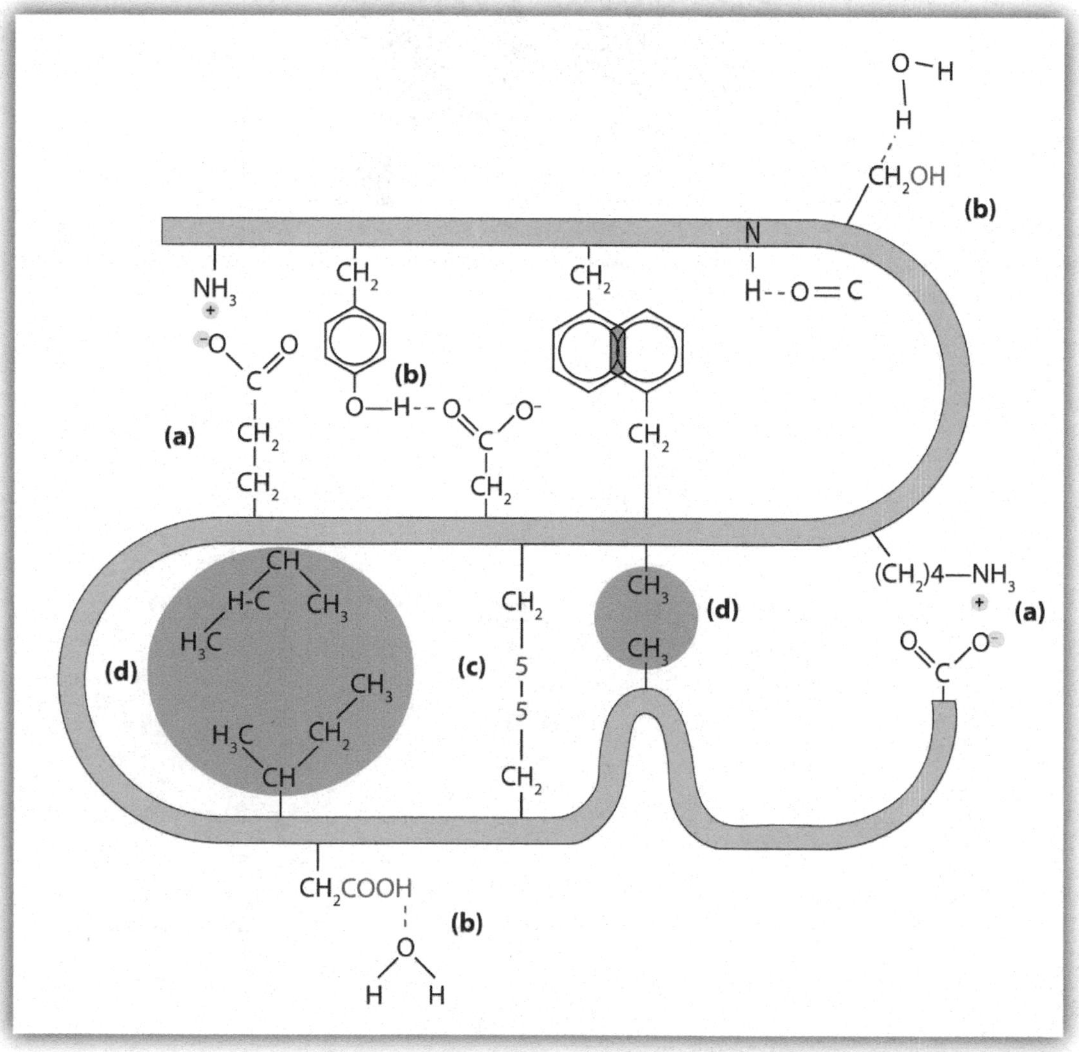

When a protein contains more than one polypeptide chain, each chain is called a *subunit*. The arrangement of multiple subunits represents a fourth level of structure, the **quaternary structure** of a protein. Hemoglobin, with four polypeptide chains or subunits, is the most frequently cited example of a protein having quaternary structure (Figure 18.7). The quaternary structure of a protein is produced and stabilized by the same kinds of interactions that produce and maintain the tertiary structure. A schematic representation of the four levels of protein structure is in Figure 18.8.

quaternary structure

The arrangement of multiple subunits in a protein.

FIGURE 18.7 The Quaternary Structure of Hemoglobin

Hemoglobin is a protein that transports oxygen throughout the body.

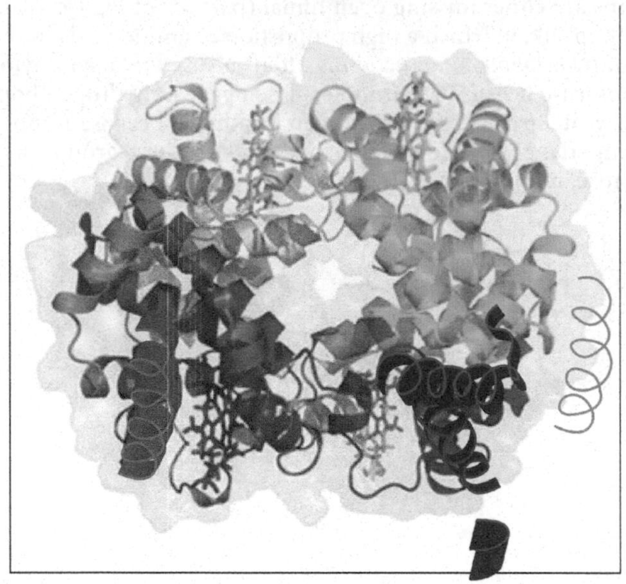

Source: Image from the RCSB PDB (www.pdb.org) of PDB ID 1I3D (R.D. Kidd, H.M. Baker, A.J. Mathews, T. Brittain, E.N. Baker (2001) Oligomerization and ligand binding in a homotetrameric hemoglobin: two high-resolution crystal structures of hemoglobin Bart's (gamma(4)), a marker for alpha-thalassemia. Protein Sci. 1739–1749).

FIGURE 18.8 Levels of Structure in Proteins

The *primary structure* consists of the specific amino acid sequence. The resulting peptide chain can twist into an α-helix, which is one type of *secondary structure*. This helical segment is incorporated into the *tertiary structure* of the folded polypeptide chain. The single polypeptide chain is a subunit that constitutes the *quaternary structure* of a protein, such as hemoglobin that has four polypeptide chains.

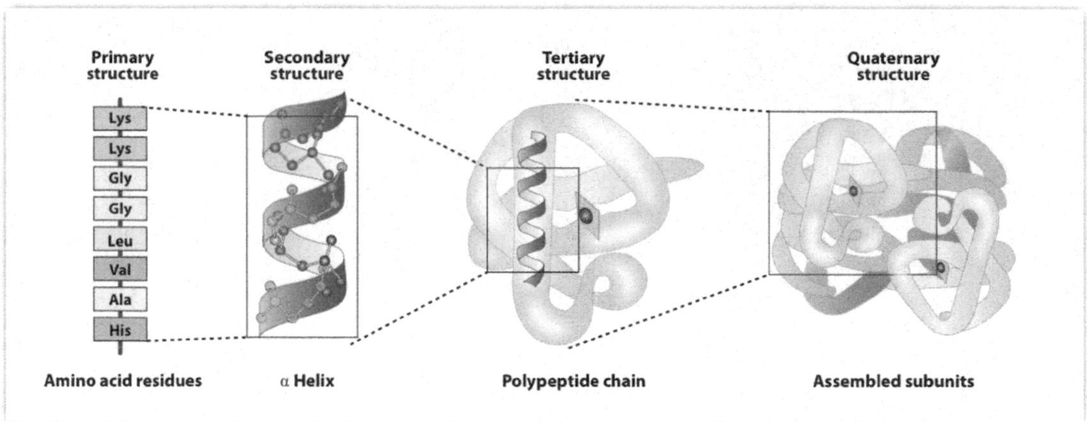

4.2 Denaturation of Proteins

denaturation

Any change in the three-dimensional structure of a macromolecule that renders it incapable of performing its assigned function.

The highly organized structures of proteins are truly masterworks of chemical architecture. But highly organized structures tend to have a certain delicacy, and this is true of proteins. **Denaturation** is the term used for any change in the three-dimensional structure of a protein that renders it incapable of performing its assigned function. A denatured protein cannot do its job. (Sometimes denaturation is equated with the precipitation or coagulation of a protein; our definition is a bit broader.) A wide variety of reagents and conditions, such as heat, organic compounds, pH changes, and heavy metal ions can cause protein denaturation (Table 18.4).

TABLE 18.4 Protein Denaturation Methods

Method	Effect on Protein Structure
Heat above 50°C or ultraviolet (UV) radiation	Heat or UV radiation supplies kinetic energy to protein molecules, causing their atoms to vibrate more rapidly and disrupting relatively weak hydrogen bonding and dispersion forces.
Use of organic compounds, such as ethyl alcohol	These compounds are capable of engaging in intermolecular hydrogen bonding with protein molecules, disrupting intramolecular hydrogen bonding within the protein.
Salts of heavy metal ions, such as mercury, silver, and lead	These ions form strong bonds with the carboxylate anions of the acidic amino acids or SH groups of cysteine, disrupting ionic bonds and disulfide linkages.
Alkaloid reagents, such as tannic acid (used in tanning leather)	These reagents combine with positively charged amino groups in proteins to disrupt ionic bonds.

Anyone who has fried an egg has observed denaturation. The clear egg white turns opaque as the albumin denatures and coagulates. No one has yet reversed that process. However, given the proper circumstances and enough time, a protein that has unfolded under sufficiently gentle conditions can refold and may again exhibit biological activity (Figure 18.9). Such evidence suggests that, at least for these proteins, the primary structure determines the secondary and tertiary structure. A given sequence of amino acids seems to adopt its particular three-dimensional arrangement naturally if conditions are right.

FIGURE 18.9 Denaturation and Renaturation of a Protein

The denaturation (unfolding) and renaturation (refolding) of a protein is depicted. The red boxes represent stabilizing interactions, such as disulfide linkages, hydrogen bonding, and/or ionic bonds.

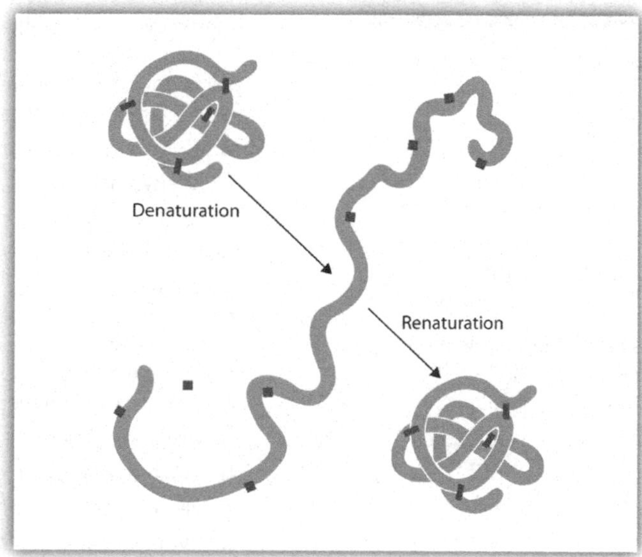

The primary structures of proteins are quite sturdy. In general, fairly vigorous conditions are needed to hydrolyze peptide bonds. At the secondary through quaternary levels, however, proteins are quite vulnerable to attack, though they vary in their vulnerability to denaturation. The delicately folded globular proteins are much easier to denature than are the tough, fibrous proteins of hair and skin.

CONCEPT REVIEW EXERCISES

1. What is the predominant attractive force that stabilizes the formation of secondary structure in proteins?
2. Distinguish between the tertiary and quaternary levels of protein structure.
3. Briefly describe four ways in which a protein could be denatured.

ANSWERS

1. hydrogen bonding
2. Tertiary structure refers to the unique three-dimensional shape of a single polypeptide chain, while quaternary structure describes the interaction between multiple polypeptide chains for proteins that have more than one polypeptide chain.
3. (1) heat a protein above 50°C or expose it to UV radiation; (2) add organic solvents, such as ethyl alcohol, to a protein solution; (3) add salts of heavy metal ions, such as mercury, silver, or lead; and (4) add alkaloid reagents such as tannic acid

KEY TAKEAWAYS

- Proteins can be divided into two categories: fibrous, which tend to be insoluble in water, and globular, which are more soluble in water.
- A protein may have up to four levels of structure. The primary structure consists of the specific amino acid sequence. The resulting peptide chain can form an α-helix or β-pleated sheet (or local structures not as easily categorized), which is known as secondary structure. These segments of secondary structure are incorporated into the tertiary structure of the folded polypeptide chain. The quaternary structure describes the arrangements of subunits in a protein that contains more than one subunit.
- Four major types of attractive interactions determine the shape and stability of the folded protein: ionic bonding, hydrogen bonding, disulfide linkages, and dispersion forces.
- A wide variety of reagents and conditions can cause a protein to unfold or denature.

EXERCISES

1. Classify each protein as fibrous or globular.
   a. albumin
   b. myosin
   c. fibroin
2. Classify each protein as fibrous or globular.
   a. hemoglobin
   b. keratin
   c. myoglobin
3. What name is given to the predominant secondary structure found in silk?
4. What name is given to the predominant secondary structure found in wool protein?
5. A protein has a tertiary structure formed by interactions between the side chains of the following pairs of amino acids. For each pair, identify the strongest type of interaction between these amino acids.
   a. aspartic acid and lysine
   b. phenylalanine and alanine
   c. serine and lysine
   d. two cysteines
6. A protein has a tertiary structure formed by interactions between the side chains of the following pairs of amino acids. For each pair, identify the strongest type of interaction between these amino acids.
   a. valine and isoleucine
   b. asparagine and serine
   c. glutamic acid and arginine
   d. tryptophan and methionine
7. What level(s) of protein structure is(are) ordinarily disrupted in denaturation? What level(s) is(are) not?
8. Which class of proteins is more easily denatured—fibrous or globular?

ANSWERS

1. a. globular
   b. fibrous
   c. fibrous
3. β-pleated sheet
5. a. ionic bonding
   b. dispersion forces
   c. dispersion forces
   d. disulfide linkage

7. Protein denaturation disrupts the secondary, tertiary, and quaternary levels of structure. Only primary structure is unaffected by denaturation.

5. ENZYMES

LEARNING OBJECTIVES

1. **Explain the functions of enzymes.**
2. **Explain how enzymes are classified and named.**

A **catalyst** is any substance that increases the *rate* or speed of a chemical reaction without being changed or consumed in the reaction. **Enzymes** are biological catalysts, and nearly all of them are proteins. The reaction rates attained by enzymes are truly amazing. In their presence, reactions occur at rates that are a million (10^6) or more times faster than would be attainable in their absence. What is even more amazing is that enzymes perform this function at body temperature (~37°C) and physiological pH (pH ~7), rather than at the conditions that are typically necessary to increase reaction rates (high temperature or pressure, the use of strong oxidizing or reducing agents or strong acids or bases, or a combination of any of these). In addition, enzymes are highly specific in their action; that is, each enzyme catalyzes only one type of reaction in only one compound or a group of structurally related compounds. The compound or compounds on which an enzyme acts are known as its **substrates**.

catalyst

Any substance that increases the rate or speed of a chemical reaction without being changed or consumed in the reaction.

enzyme

A biological catalyst.

substrate

A compound on which an enzyme acts.

Hundreds of enzymes have been purified and studied in an effort to understand how they work so effectively and with such specificity. The resulting knowledge has been used to design drugs that inhibit or activate particular enzymes. An example is the intensive research to improve the treatment of or find a cure for acquired immunodeficiency syndrome (AIDS). AIDS is caused by the human immunodeficiency virus (HIV). Researchers are studying the enzymes produced by this virus and are developing drugs intended to block the action of those enzymes without interfering with enzymes produced by the human body. Several of these drugs have now been approved for use by AIDS patients.

The first enzymes to be discovered were named according to their source or method of discovery. The enzyme *pepsin*, which aids in the hydrolysis of proteins, is found in the digestive juices of the stomach (Greek *pepsis*, meaning "digestion"). *Papain*, another enzyme that hydrolyzes protein (in fact, it is used in meat tenderizers), is isolated from papayas. As more enzymes were discovered, chemists recognized the need for a more systematic and chemically informative identification scheme.

In the current numbering and naming scheme, under the oversight of the Nomenclature Commission of the International Union of Biochemistry, enzymes are arranged into six groups according to the general type of reaction they catalyze (Table 18.5), with subgroups and secondary subgroups that specify the reaction more precisely. Each enzyme is assigned a four-digit number, preceded by the prefix EC—for enzyme classification—that indicates its group, subgroup, and so forth. This is demonstrated in Table 18.6 for alcohol dehydrogenase. Each enzyme is also given a name consisting of the root of the name of its substrate or substrates and the *-ase* suffix. Thus urease is the enzyme that catalyzes the hydrolysis of urea.

TABLE 18.5 Classes of Enzymes

Class	Type of Reaction Catalyzed	Examples
oxidoreductases	oxidation-reduction reactions	Dehydrogenases catalyze oxidation-reduction reactions involving hydrogen and reductases catalyze reactions in which a substrate is reduced.
transferases	transfer reactions of groups, such as methyl, amino, and acetyl	Transaminases catalyze the transfer of amino group, and kinases catalyze the transfer of a phosphate group.
hydrolases	hydrolysis reactions	Lipases catalyze the hydrolysis of lipids, and proteases catalyze the hydrolysis of proteins
lyases	reactions in which groups are removed without hydrolysis or addition of groups to a double bond	Decarboxylases catalyze the removal of carboxyl groups.
isomerases	reactions in which a compound is converted to its isomer	Isomerases may catalyze the conversion of an aldose to a ketose, and mutases catalyze reactions in which a functional group is transferred from one atom in a substrate to another.
ligases	reactions in which new bonds are formed between carbon and another atom; energy is required	Synthetases catalyze reactions in which two smaller molecules are linked to form a larger one.

TABLE 18.6 Assignment of an Enzyme Classification Number

Alcohol Dehydrogenase: EC 1.1.1.1	
The first digit indicates that this enzyme is an oxidoreductase; that is, an enzyme that catalyzes an oxidation-reduction reaction.	
The second digit indicates that this oxidoreductase catalyzes a reaction involving a primary or secondary alcohol.	
The third digit indicates that either the coenzyme NAD^+ or $NADP^+$ is required for this reaction.	
The fourth digit indicates that this was the first enzyme isolated, characterized, and named using this system of nomenclature.	
The systematic name for this enzyme is *alcohol:NAD$^+$ oxidoreductase*, while the recommended or common name is alcohol dehydrogenase.	
Reaction catalyzed:	$RCH_2{-}OH + NAD^+ \rightleftharpoons R{-}\overset{\overset{\large O}{\|}}{C}{-}H + NADH + H^+$

CONCEPT REVIEW EXERCISE

In the small intestine, sucrose is hydrolyzed to form glucose and fructose in a reaction catalyzed by sucrase.

1. Identify the substrate in this reaction.
2. Name the enzyme.

ANSWERS

1. sucrose
2. sucrase

KEY TAKEAWAYS

- An enzyme is a biological catalyst, a substance that increases the rate of a chemical reaction without being changed or consumed in the reaction.
- A systematic process is used to name and classify enzymes.

EXERCISES

1. Identify the substrate catalyzed by each enzyme.
   a. lactase
   b. cellulase
   c. peptidase
2. Identify the substrate catalyzed by each enzyme.
   a. lipase
   b. amylase
   c. maltase
3. Identify each type of enzyme.
   a. decarboxylase
   b. protease
   c. transaminase
4. Identify each type of enzyme.
   a. dehydrogenase
   b. isomerase
   c. lipase

ANSWERS

1. a. lactose
   b. cellulose
   c. peptides
3. a. lyase
   b. hydrolase
   c. transferase

6. ENZYME ACTION

LEARNING OBJECTIVE

1. **Describe the interaction between an enzyme and its substrate.**

Enzyme-catalyzed reactions occur in at least two steps. In the first step, an enzyme molecule (E) and the substrate molecule or molecules (S) collide and react to form an intermediate compound called the *enzyme-substrate* (E–S) *complex.* (This step is reversible because the complex can break apart into the original substrate or substrates and the free enzyme.) Once the E–S complex forms, the enzyme is able to catalyze the formation of product (P), which is then released from the enzyme surface:

$$S + E \rightarrow E\text{–}S$$

$$E\text{–}S \rightarrow P + E$$

Hydrogen bonding and other electrostatic interactions hold the enzyme and substrate together in the complex. The structural features or functional groups on the enzyme that participate in these interactions are located in a cleft or pocket on the enzyme surface. This pocket, where the enzyme combines with the substrate and transforms the substrate to product is called the **active site** of the enzyme (Figure 18.10). It possesses a unique conformation (including correctly positioned bonding groups) that is complementary to the structure of the substrate, so that the enzyme and substrate molecules fit together in much the same manner as a key fits into a tumbler lock. In fact, an early model describing the formation of the enzyme-substrate complex was called the **lock-and-key model** (Figure 18.11). This model portrayed the enzyme as conformationally rigid and able to bond only to substrates that exactly fit the active site.

active site

The location on an enzyme where a substrate binds and is transformed to product.

lock-and-key model

A model that portrays an enzyme as conformationally rigid and able to bond only to a substrate or substrates that exactly fit the active site.

FIGURE 18.10 Substrate Binding to the Active Site of an Enzyme

The enzyme dihydrofolate reductase is shown with one of its substrates: $NADP^+$ (a) unbound and (b) bound. The $NADP^+$ (shown in red) binds to a pocket that is complementary to it in shape and ionic properties.

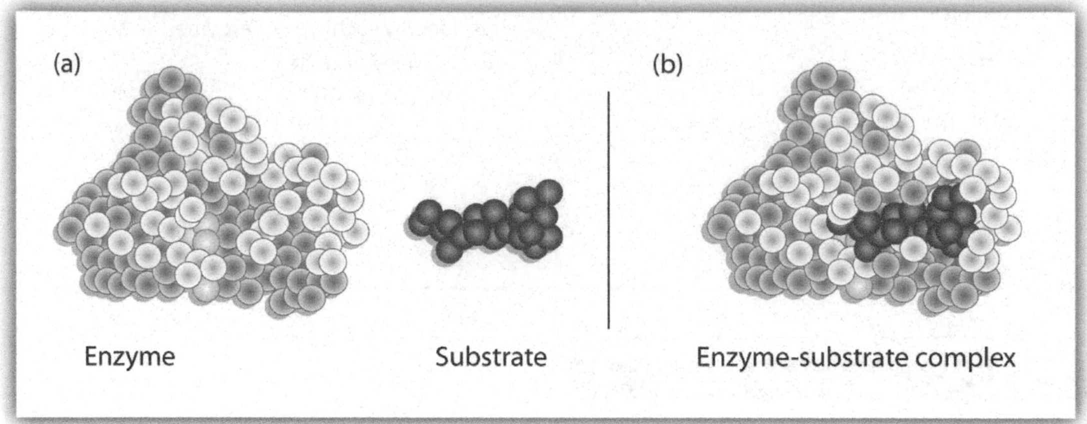

FIGURE 18.11 The Lock-and-Key Model of Enzyme Action

(a) Because the substrate and the active site of the enzyme have complementary structures and bonding groups, they fit together as a key fits a lock. (b) The catalytic reaction occurs while the two are bonded together in the enzyme-substrate complex.

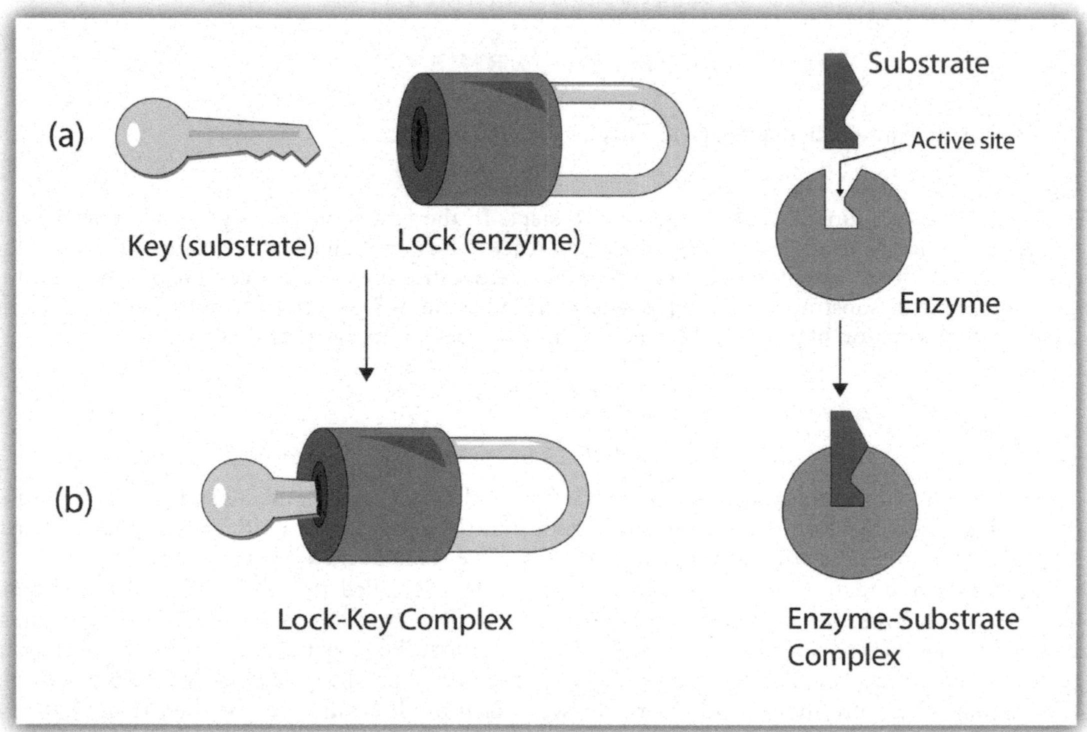

induced-fit model

A model that says an enzyme can undergo a conformational change when it binds substrate molecules.

Working out the precise three-dimensional structures of numerous enzymes has enabled chemists to refine the original lock-and-key model of enzyme actions. They discovered that the binding of a substrate often leads to a large conformational change in the enzyme, as well as to changes in the structure of the substrate or substrates. The current theory, known as the **induced-fit model**, says that enzymes can undergo a change in conformation when they bind substrate molecules, and the active site has a shape complementary to that of the substrate only *after* the substrate is bound, as shown for hexokinase in Figure 18.12. After catalysis, the enzyme resumes its original structure.

FIGURE 18.12 The Induced-Fit Model of Enzyme Action

(a) The enzyme hexokinase without its substrate (glucose, shown in red) is bound to the active site. (b) The enzyme conformation changes dramatically when the substrate binds to it, resulting in additional interactions between hexokinase and glucose.

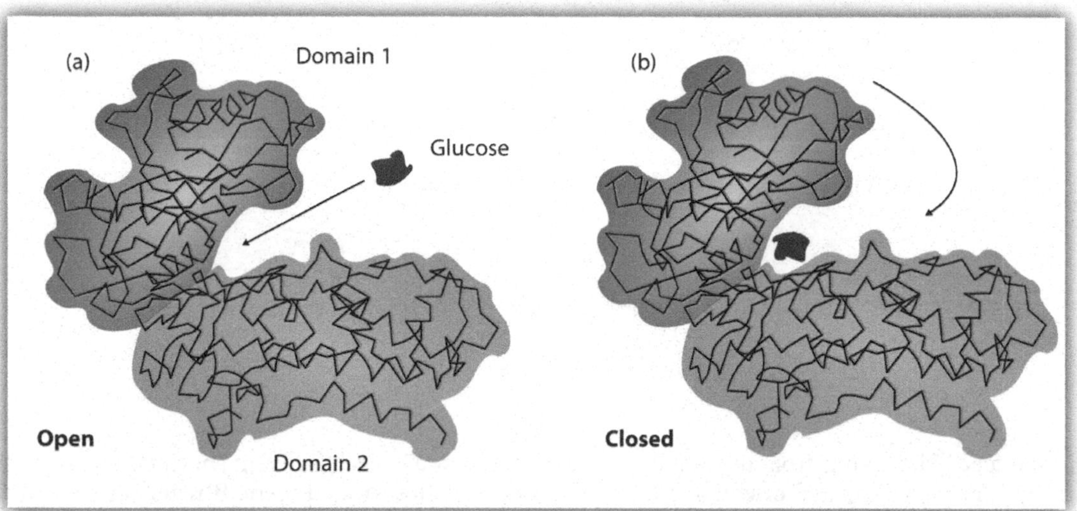

The structural changes that occur when an enzyme and a substrate join together bring specific parts of a substrate into alignment with specific parts of the enzyme's active site. Amino acid side chains in or near the binding site can then act as acid or base catalysts, provide binding sites for the transfer of functional groups from one substrate to another or aid in the rearrangement of a substrate. The participating amino acids, which are usually widely separated in the primary sequence of the protein, are brought close together in the active site as a result of the folding and bending of the polypeptide chain or chains when the protein acquires its tertiary and quaternary structure. Binding to enzymes brings reactants close to each other and aligns them properly, which has the same effect as increasing the concentration of the reacting compounds.

EXAMPLE 1

1. What type of interaction would occur between an OH group present on a substrate molecule and a functional group in the active site of an enzyme?
2. Suggest an amino acid whose side chain might be in the active site of an enzyme and form the type of interaction you just identified.

Solution

1. An OH group would most likely engage in hydrogen bonding with an appropriate functional group present in the active site of an enzyme.
2. Several amino acid side chains would be able to engage in hydrogen bonding with an OH group. One example would be asparagine, which has an amide functional group.

SKILL-BUILDING EXERCISE

1. What type of interaction would occur between an COO^- group present on a substrate molecule and a functional group in the active site of an enzyme?
2. Suggest an amino acid whose side chain might be in the active site of an enzyme and form the type of interaction you just identified.

One characteristic that distinguishes an enzyme from all other types of catalysts is its *substrate specificity*. An inorganic acid such as sulfuric acid can be used to increase the reaction rates of many different reactions, such as the hydrolysis of disaccharides, polysaccharides, lipids, and proteins, with complete impartiality. In contrast, enzymes are much more specific. Some enzymes act on a single substrate, while other enzymes act on any of a group of related molecules containing a similar functional group or chemical bond. Some enzymes even distinguish between D- and L-stereoisomers, binding one stereoisomer but not the other. Urease, for example, is an enzyme that catalyzes the hydrolysis of a single substrate—urea—but not the closely related compounds methyl urea, thiourea, or biuret. The enzyme carboxypeptidase, on the other hand, is far less specific. It catalyzes the removal of nearly any amino acid from the carboxyl end of any peptide or protein.

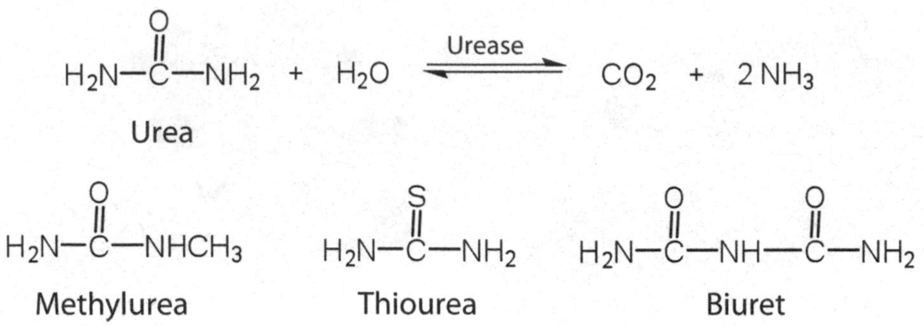

$$\underset{\text{Urea}}{H_2N{-}\overset{O}{\overset{\|}{C}}{-}NH_2} + H_2O \xrightleftharpoons{\text{Urease}} CO_2 + 2\,NH_3$$

$$\underset{\text{Methylurea}}{H_2N{-}\overset{O}{\overset{\|}{C}}{-}NHCH_3} \qquad \underset{\text{Thiourea}}{H_2N{-}\overset{S}{\overset{\|}{C}}{-}NH_2} \qquad \underset{\text{Biuret}}{H_2N{-}\overset{O}{\overset{\|}{C}}{-}NH{-}\overset{O}{\overset{\|}{C}}{-}NH_2}$$

Enzyme specificity results from the uniqueness of the active site in each different enzyme because of the identity, charge, and spatial orientation of the functional groups located there. It regulates cell chemistry so that the proper reactions occur in the proper place at the proper time. Clearly, it is crucial to the proper functioning of the living cell.

CONCEPT REVIEW EXERCISES

1. Distinguish between the lock-and-key model and induced-fit model of enzyme action.
2. Which enzyme has greater specificity—urease or carboxypeptidase? Explain.

ANSWERS

1. The lock-and-key model portrays an enzyme as conformationally rigid and able to bond only to substrates that exactly fit the active site. The induced fit model portrays the enzyme structure as more flexible and is complementary to the substrate only after the substrate is bound.
2. Urease has the greater specificity because it can bind only to a single substrate. Carboxypeptidase, on the other hand, can catalyze the removal of nearly any amino acid from the carboxyl end of a peptide or protein.

KEY TAKEAWAYS

- A substrate binds to a specific region on an enzyme known as the active site, where the substrate can be converted to product.
- The substrate binds to the enzyme primarily through hydrogen bonding and other electrostatic interactions.
- The induced-fit model says that an enzyme can undergo a conformational change when binding a substrate.
- Enzymes exhibit varying degrees of substrate specificity.

EXERCISES

1. What type of interaction would occur between each group present on a substrate molecule and a functional group of the active site in an enzyme?
   a. COOH
   b. NH_3^+
   c. OH
   d. $CH(CH_3)_2$
2. What type of interaction would occur between each group present on a substrate molecule and a functional group of the active site in an enzyme?
   a. SH
   b. NH_2
   c. C_6H_5
   d. COO^-
3. For each functional group in Exercise 1, suggest an amino acid whose side chain might be in the active site of an enzyme and form the type of interaction you identified.
4. For each functional group in Exercise 2, suggest an amino acid whose side chain might be in the active site of an enzyme and form the type of interaction you identified.

ANSWERS

1. a. hydrogen bonding
   b. ionic bonding
   c. hydrogen bonding
   d. dispersion forces
3. a. The amino acid has a polar side chain capable of engaging in hydrogen bonding; serine (answers will vary).
   b. The amino acid has a negatively charged side chain; aspartic acid (answers will vary).
   c. The amino acid has a polar side chain capable of engaging in hydrogen bonding; asparagine (answers will vary).
   d. The amino acid has a nonpolar side chain; isoleucine (answers will vary).

7. ENZYME ACTIVITY

LEARNING OBJECTIVE

1. **Describe how pH, temperature, and the concentration of an enzyme and its substrate influence enzyme activity.**

The single most important property of enzymes is the ability to increase the rates of reactions occurring in living organisms, a property known as *catalytic activity*. Because most enzymes are proteins, their activity is affected by factors that disrupt protein structure, as well as by factors that affect catalysts in general. Factors that disrupt protein structure, as we saw in Section 4, include temperature and pH; factors that affect catalysts in general include reactant or substrate concentration and catalyst or enzyme concentration. The activity of an enzyme can be measured by monitoring either the rate at which a substrate disappears or the rate at which a product forms.

7.1 Concentration of Substrate

In the presence of a given amount of enzyme, the rate of an enzymatic reaction increases as the substrate concentration increases until a limiting rate is reached, after which further increase in the substrate concentration produces no significant change in the reaction rate (part (a) of Figure 18.13). At this point, so much substrate is present that essentially all of the enzyme active sites have substrate bound to them. In other words, the enzyme molecules are saturated with substrate. The excess substrate molecules cannot react until the substrate already bound to the enzymes has reacted and been released (or been released without reacting).

FIGURE 18.13 Concentration versus Reaction Rate

(a) This graph shows the effect of substrate concentration on the rate of a reaction that is catalyzed by a fixed amount of enzyme. (b) This graph shows the effect of enzyme concentration on the reaction rate at a constant level of substrate.

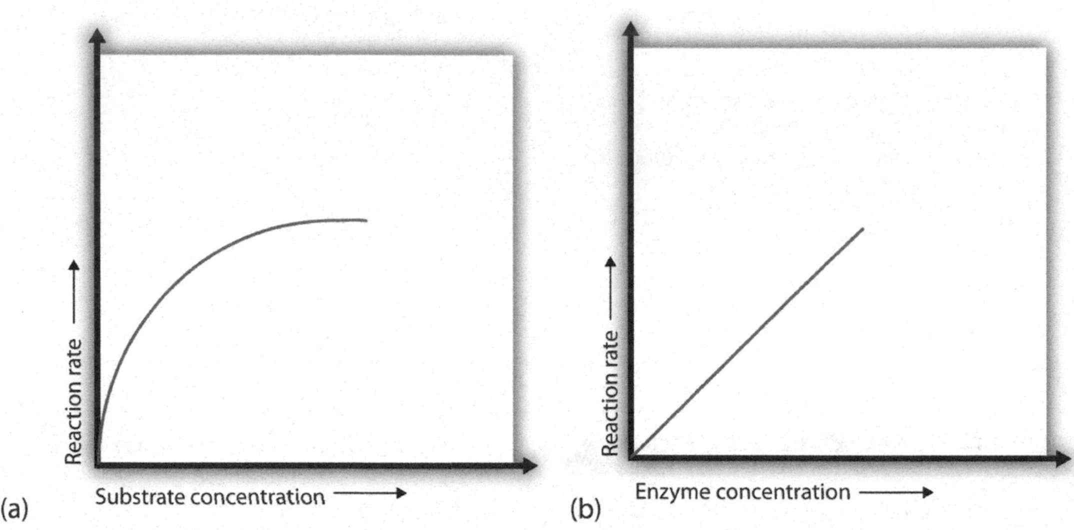

Let's consider an analogy. Ten taxis (enzyme molecules) are waiting at a taxi stand to take people (substrate) on a 10-minute trip to a concert hall, one passenger at a time. If only 5 people are present at the stand, the rate of their arrival at the concert hall is 5 people in 10 minutes. If the number of people at the stand is increased to 10, the rate increases to 10 arrivals in 10 minutes. With 20 people at the stand, the rate would still be 10 arrivals in 10 minutes. The taxis have been "saturated." If the taxis could carry 2 or 3 passengers each, the same principle would apply. The rate would simply be higher (20 or 30 people in 10 minutes) before it leveled off.

7.2 Concentration of Enzyme

When the concentration of the enzyme is significantly lower than the concentration of the substrate (as when the number of taxis is far lower than the number of waiting passengers), the rate of an enzyme-catalyzed reaction is directly dependent on the enzyme concentration (part (b) of Figure 18.13). This is true for any catalyst; the reaction rate increases as the concentration of the catalyst is increased.

7.3 Temperature

A general rule of thumb for most chemical reactions is that a temperature rise of 10°C approximately doubles the reaction rate. To some extent, this rule holds for all enzymatic reactions. After a certain point, however, an increase in temperature causes a decrease in the reaction rate, due to denaturation of the protein structure and disruption of the active site (part (a) of Figure 18.14). For many proteins, denaturation occurs between 45°C and 55°C. Furthermore, even though an enzyme may appear to have a maximum reaction rate between 40°C and 50°C, most biochemical reactions are carried out at lower temperatures because enzymes are not stable at these higher temperatures and will denature after a few minutes.

FIGURE 18.14 Temperature and pH versus Concentration

(a) This graph depicts the effect of temperature on the rate of a reaction that is catalyzed by a fixed amount of enzyme. (b) This graph depicts the effect of pH on the rate of a reaction that is catalyzed by a fixed amount of enzyme.

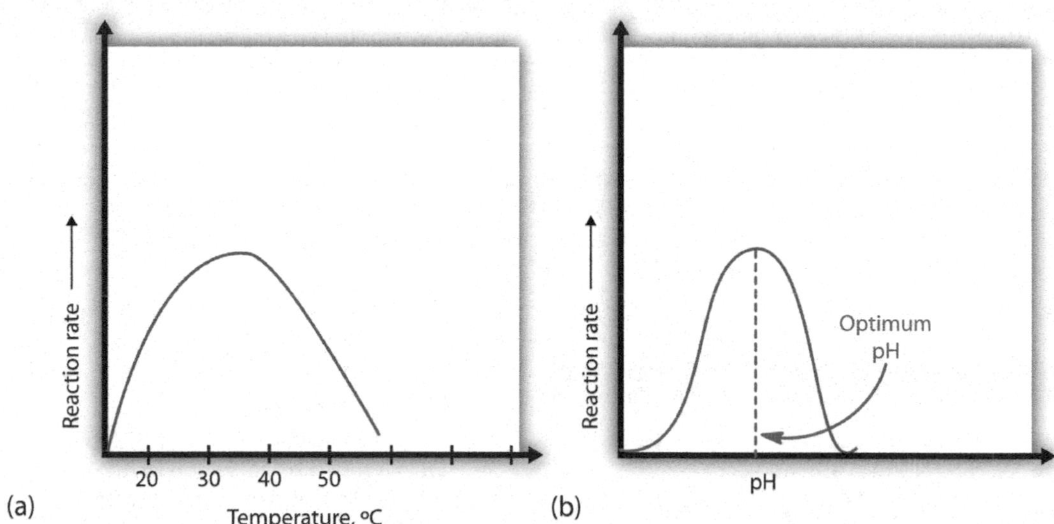

At 0°C and 100°C, the rate of enzyme-catalyzed reactions is nearly zero. This fact has several practical applications. We sterilize objects by placing them in boiling water, which denatures the enzymes of any bacteria that may be in or on them. We preserve our food by refrigerating or freezing it, which slows enzyme activity. When animals go into hibernation in winter, their body temperature drops, decreasing the rates of their metabolic processes to levels that can be maintained by the amount of energy stored in the fat reserves in the animals' tissues.

7.4 Hydrogen Ion Concentration (pH)

Because most enzymes are proteins, they are sensitive to changes in the hydrogen ion concentration or pH. Enzymes may be denatured by extreme levels of hydrogen ions (whether high or low); *any* change in pH, even a small one, alters the degree of ionization of an enzyme's acidic and basic side groups and the substrate components as well. Ionizable side groups located in the active site must have a certain charge for the enzyme to bind its substrate. Neutralization of even one of these charges alters an enzyme's catalytic activity.

An enzyme exhibits maximum activity over the narrow pH range in which a molecule exists in its properly charged form. The median value of this pH range is called the **optimum pH** of the enzyme (part (b) of Figure 18.14). With the notable exception of gastric juice (the fluids secreted in the stomach), most body fluids have pH values between 6 and 8. Not surprisingly, most enzymes exhibit optimal activity in this pH range. However, a few enzymes have optimum pH values outside this range. For example, the optimum pH for pepsin, an enzyme that is active in the stomach, is 2.0.

optimum pH

The pH at which a particular enzyme exhibits maximum activity.

CONCEPT REVIEW EXERCISES

1. The concentration of substrate X is low. What happens to the rate of the enzyme-catalyzed reaction if the concentration of X is doubled?
2. What effect does an increase in the enzyme concentration have on the rate of an enzyme-catalyzed reaction?

ANSWERS

1. If the concentration of the substrate is low, increasing its concentration will increase the rate of the reaction.

2. An increase in the amount of enzyme will increase the rate of the reaction (provided sufficient substrate is present).

KEY TAKEAWAYS

- Initially, an increase in substrate concentration leads to an increase in the rate of an enzyme-catalyzed reaction. As the enzyme molecules become saturated with substrate, this increase in reaction rate levels off.
- The rate of an enzyme-catalyzed reaction increases with an increase in the concentration of an enzyme.
- At low temperatures, an increase in temperature increases the rate of an enzyme-catalyzed reaction. At higher temperatures, the protein is denatured, and the rate of the reaction dramatically decreases.
- An enzyme has an optimum pH range in which it exhibits maximum activity.

EXERCISES

1. In non-enzyme-catalyzed reactions, the reaction rate increases as the concentration of reactant is increased. In an enzyme-catalyzed reaction, the reaction rate initially increases as the substrate concentration is increased but then begins to level off, so that the increase in reaction rate becomes less and less as the substrate concentration increases. Explain this difference.
2. Why do enzymes become inactive at very high temperatures?
3. An enzyme has an optimum pH of 7.4. What is most likely to happen to the activity of the enzyme if the pH drops to 6.3? Explain.
4. An enzyme has an optimum pH of 7.2. What is most likely to happen to the activity of the enzyme if the pH increases to 8.5? Explain.

ANSWERS

1. In an enzyme-catalyzed reaction, the substrate binds to the enzyme to form an enzyme-substrate complex. If more substrate is present than enzyme, all of the enzyme binding sites will have substrate bound, and further increases in substrate concentration cannot increase the rate.

3. The activity will decrease; a pH of 6.3 is more acidic than 7.4, and one or more key groups in the active site may bind a hydrogen ion, changing the charge on that group.

8. ENZYME INHIBITION

LEARNING OBJECTIVES

1. **Explain what an enzyme inhibitor is.**
2. **Distinguish between reversible and irreversible inhibitors.**
3. **Distinguish between competitive and noncompetitive inhibitors.**

In Section 7, we noted that enzymes are inactivated at high temperatures and by changes in pH. These are nonspecific factors that would inactivate any enzyme. The activity of enzymes can also be regulated by more specific inhibitors. Many compounds are poisons because they bind covalently to particular enzymes or kinds of enzymes and inactivate them (Table 18.7).

TABLE 18.7 Poisons as Enzyme Inhibitors

Poison	Formula	Example of Enzyme Inhibited	Action
arsenate	AsO_4^{3-}	glyceraldehyde 3-phosphate dehydrogenase	substitutes for phosphate
iodoacetate	ICH_2COO^-	triose phosphate dehydrogenase	binds to cysteine SH group
diisopropylfluorophosphate (DIFP; a nerve poison)	$F-P(=O)(OCH(CH_3)_2)-OCH(CH_3)_2$	acetylcholinesterase	binds to serine OH group

8.1 Irreversible Inhibition: Poisons

An **irreversible inhibitor** inactivates an enzyme by bonding covalently to a particular group at the active site. The inhibitor-enzyme bond is so strong that the inhibition cannot be reversed by the addition of excess substrate. The nerve gases, especially DIFP, irreversibly inhibit biological systems by forming an enzyme-inhibitor complex with a specific OH group of serine situated at the active sites of certain enzymes. The peptidases trypsin and chymotrypsin contain serine groups at the active site and are inhibited by DIFP.

irreversible inhibitor

A substance that inactivates an enzyme by bonding covalently to a specific group at the active site.

$$\text{—}CH_2OH + F-\overset{\overset{O}{\|}}{\underset{\underset{OCH(CH_3)_2}{|}}{P}}-OCH(CH_3)_2 \longrightarrow \text{—}CH_2O-\overset{\overset{O}{\|}}{\underset{\underset{OCH(CH_3)_2}{|}}{P}}-OCH(CH_3)_2 + HF$$

8.2 Reversible Inhibition

A **reversible inhibitor** inactivates an enzyme through noncovalent, more easily reversed, interactions. Unlike an irreversible inhibitor, a reversible inhibitor can dissociate from the enzyme. Reversible inhibitors include competitive inhibitors and noncompetitive inhibitors. (There are additional types of reversible inhibitors.) A **competitive inhibitor** is any compound that bears a structural resemblance to a particular substrate and thus competes with that substrate for binding at the active site of an enzyme. The inhibitor is not acted on by the enzyme but does prevent the substrate from approaching the active site.

reversible inhibitor

A substance that inactivates an enzyme by binding at the active site through noncovalent, reversible interactions.

competitive inhibitor

A compound that resembles a particular substrate and competes with the substrate for binding at the active site of an enzyme to slow the rate of the reaction.

The degree to which a competitive inhibitor interferes with an enzyme's activity depends on the relative concentrations of the substrate and the inhibitor. If the inhibitor is present in relatively large quantities, it will initially block most of the active sites. But because the binding is reversible, some substrate molecules will eventually bind to the active site and be converted to product. Increasing the substrate concentration promotes displacement of the inhibitor from the active site. Competitive inhibition can be completely reversed by adding substrate so that it reaches a much higher concentration than that of the inhibitor.

Studies of competitive inhibition have provided helpful information about certain enzyme-substrate complexes and the interactions of specific groups at the active sites. As a result, pharmaceutical companies have synthesized drugs that competitively inhibit metabolic processes in bacteria and certain cancer cells. Many drugs are competitive inhibitors of specific enzymes.

A classic example of competitive inhibition is the effect of malonate on the enzyme activity of succinate dehydrogenase (Figure 18.15). Malonate and succinate are the anions of dicarboxylic acids and contain three and four carbon atoms, respectively. The malonate molecule binds to the active site because the spacing of its carboxyl groups is not greatly different from that of succinate. However, no catalytic reaction occurs because malonate does not have a CH_2CH_2 group to convert to CH=CH. This reaction will also be discussed in connection with the Krebs cycle and energy production. (For more information about the Krebs cycle, see Chapter 20, [Unsupported Reference Type: chapter-section].)

FIGURE 18.15 Competitive Inhibition

(a) Succinate binds to the enzyme succinate dehydrogenase. A dehydrogenation reaction occurs, and the product—fumarate—is released from the enzyme. (b) Malonate also binds to the active site of succinate dehydrogenase. In this case, however, no subsequent reaction occurs while malonate remains bound to the enzyme.

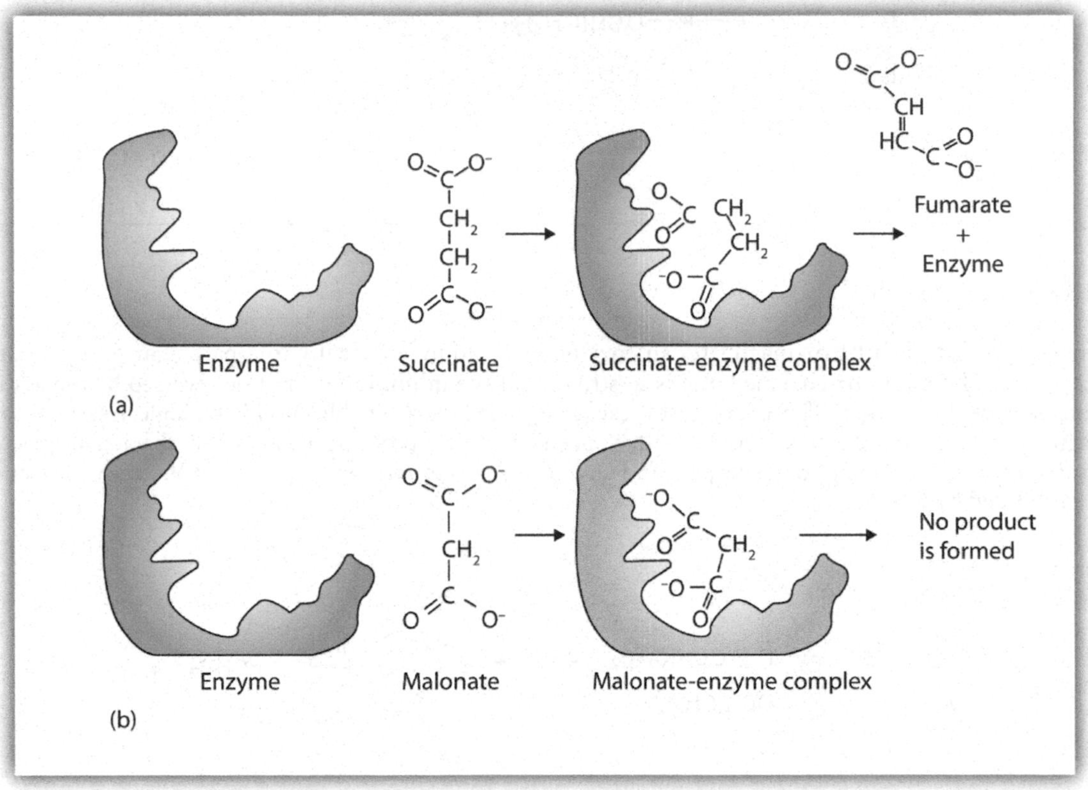

To Your Health: Penicillin

Chemotherapy is the strategic use of chemicals (that is, drugs) to destroy infectious microorganisms or cancer cells without causing excessive damage to the other, healthy cells of the host. From bacteria to humans, the metabolic pathways of all living organisms are quite similar, so the search for safe and effective chemotherapeutic agents is a formidable task. Many well-established chemotherapeutic drugs function by inhibiting a critical enzyme in the cells of the invading organism.

An *antibiotic* is a compound that kills bacteria; it may come from a natural source such as molds or be synthesized with a structure analogous to a naturally occurring antibacterial compound. Antibiotics constitute no well-defined class of chemically related substances, but many of them work by effectively inhibiting a variety of enzymes essential to bacterial growth.

Penicillin, one of the most widely used antibiotics in the world, was fortuitously discovered by Alexander Fleming in 1928, when he noticed antibacterial properties in a mold growing on a bacterial culture plate. In 1938, Ernst Chain and Howard Florey began an intensive effort to isolate penicillin from the mold and study its properties. The large quantities of penicillin needed for this research became available through development of a corn-based nutrient medium that the mold loved and through the discovery of a higher-yielding strain of mold at a United States Department of Agriculture research center near Peoria, Illinois. Even so, it was not until 1944 that large quantities of penicillin were being produced and made available for the treatment of bacterial infections.

Penicillin functions by interfering with the synthesis of cell walls of reproducing bacteria. It does so by inhibiting an enzyme—transpeptidase—that catalyzes the last step in bacterial cell-wall biosynthesis. The defective walls cause bacterial cells to burst. Human cells are not affected because they have cell membranes, not cell walls.

Several naturally occurring penicillins have been isolated. They are distinguished by different R groups connected to a common structure: a four-member cyclic amide (called a lactam ring) fused to a five-member ring. The addition of appropriate organic compounds to the culture medium leads to the production of the different kinds of penicillin.

The penicillins are effective against gram-positive bacteria (bacteria capable of being stained by Gram's stain) and a few gram-negative bacteria (including the intestinal bacterium *Escherichia coli*). They are effective in the treatment of diphtheria, gonorrhea, pneumonia, syphilis, many pus infections, and certain types of boils. Penicillin G was the earliest penicillin to be used on a wide scale. However, it cannot be administered orally because it is quite unstable; the acidic pH of the stomach converts it to an inactive derivative. The major oral penicillins—penicillin V, ampicillin, and amoxicillin—on the other hand, are acid stable.

Penicillin Structure	R Group	Drug Name
R—C(=O)—NH—CH—CH(S)—C(CH_3)$_2$—CH(COOH)—N (fused β-lactam, C=O); Lactam ring	$-CH_2-C_6H_5$	penicillin G
	$CH_2-O-C_6H_5$	penicillin V
	$-CH(NH_2)-C_6H_5$	ampicillin
	$-CH(NH_2)-C_6H_4-OH$	amoxicillin
	$-C_6H_3(OCH_3)_2$ (CH_3O, CH_3O)	methicillin

Some strains of bacteria become resistant to penicillin through a mutation that allows them to synthesize an enzyme—penicillinase—that breaks the antibiotic down (by cleavage of the amide linkage in the lactam ring). To combat these strains, scientists have synthesized penicillin analogs (such as methicillin) that are not inactivated by penicillinase.

Some people (perhaps 5% of the population) are allergic to penicillin and therefore must be treated with other antibiotics. Their allergic reaction can be so severe that a fatal coma may occur if penicillin is inadvertently administered to them. Fortunately, several other antibiotics have been discovered. Most, including aureomycin and streptomycin, are the products of microbial synthesis. Others, such as the semisynthetic penicillins and tetracyclines, are made by chemical modifications of antibiotics; and some, like chloramphenicol, are manufactured entirely by chemical synthesis. They are as effective as penicillin in destroying infectious microorganisms. Many of these antibiotics exert their effects by blocking protein synthesis in microorganisms.

Initially, antibiotics were considered miracle drugs, substantially reducing the number of deaths from blood poisoning, pneumonia, and other infectious diseases. Some seven decades ago, a person with a major infection almost always died. Today, such deaths are rare. Seven decades ago, pneumonia was a dreaded killer of people of all ages. Today, it kills only the very old or those ill from other causes. Antibiotics have indeed worked miracles in our time, but even miracle drugs have limitations. Not long after the drugs were first used, disease organisms began to develop strains resistant to them. In a race to stay ahead of resistant bacterial strains, scientists continue to seek new antibiotics. The penicillins have now been partially displaced by related compounds, such as the cephalosporins and vancomycin. Unfortunately, some strains of bacteria have already shown resistance to these antibiotics.

noncompetitive inhibitor

A compound that can combine with either the free enzyme or the enzyme-substrate complex at a site distinct from the active site to slow the rate of the reaction.

feedback inhibition

A normal biochemical process that makes use of noncompetitive inhibitors to control some enzymatic activity.

Some reversible inhibitors are noncompetitive. A **noncompetitive inhibitor** can combine with either the free enzyme or the enzyme-substrate complex because its binding site on the enzyme is distinct from the active site. Binding of this kind of inhibitor alters the three-dimensional conformation of the enzyme, changing the configuration of the active site with one of two results. Either the enzyme-substrate complex does not form at its normal rate, or, once formed, it does not yield products at the normal rate. Because the inhibitor does not structurally resemble the substrate, the addition of excess substrate does *not* reverse the inhibitory effect.

Feedback inhibition is a normal biochemical process that makes use of noncompetitive inhibitors to control some enzymatic activity. In this process, the final product inhibits the enzyme that catalyzes the first step in a series of reactions. Feedback inhibition is used to regulate the synthesis of many amino acids. For example, bacteria synthesize isoleucine from threonine in a series of five enzyme-catalyzed steps. As the concentration of isoleucine increases, some of it binds as a noncompetitive inhibitor to the first enzyme of the series (threonine deaminase), thus bringing about a decrease in the amount of isoleucine being formed (Figure 18.16).

FIGURE 18.16 Feedback Inhibition of Threonine Deaminase by Isoleucine

Threonine deaminase is the first enzyme in the conversion of threonine to isoleucine. Isoleucine inhibits threonine deaminase through feedback inhibition .

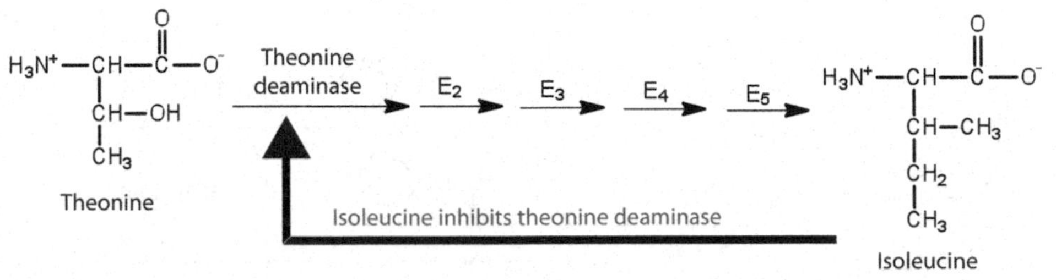

CONCEPT REVIEW EXERCISES

1. What are the characteristics of an irreversible inhibitor?
2. In what ways does a competitive inhibitor differ from a noncompetitive inhibitor?

ANSWERS

1. It inactivates an enzyme by bonding covalently to a particular group at the active site.
2. A competitive inhibitor structurally resembles the substrate for a given enzyme and competes with the substrate for binding at the active site of the enzyme. A noncompetitive inhibitor binds at a site distinct from the active site and can bind to either the free enzyme or the enzyme-substrate complex.

KEY TAKEAWAYS

- An irreversible inhibitor inactivates an enzyme by bonding covalently to a particular group at the active site.
- A reversible inhibitor inactivates an enzyme through noncovalent, reversible interactions.
- A competitive inhibitor competes with the substrate for binding at the active site of the enzyme.
- A noncompetitive inhibitor binds at a site distinct from the active site.

EXERCISES

1. What amino acid is present in the active site of all enzymes that are irreversibly inhibited by nerve gases such as DIFP?
2. Oxaloacetate (OOCCH2COCOO) inhibits succinate dehydrogenase. Would you expect oxaloacetate to be a competitive or noncompetitive inhibitor? Explain.

ANSWER

1. serine

9. ENZYME COFACTORS AND VITAMINS

LEARNING OBJECTIVE

1. **Explain why vitamins are necessary in the diet.**

Many enzymes are simple proteins consisting entirely of one or more amino acid chains. Other enzymes contain a nonprotein component called a **cofactor** that is necessary for the enzyme's proper functioning. There are two types of cofactors: inorganic ions [e.g., zinc or Cu(I) ions] and organic molecules known as **coenzymes**. Most coenzymes are vitamins or are derived from vitamins.

cofactor

A nonprotein component of an enzyme that is necessary for an enzyme's proper functioning.

coenzyme

A cofactor that is an organic molecule.

vitamin

An organic compound that is essential in very small amounts for the maintenance of normal metabolism.

Vitamins are organic compounds that are essential in very small (trace) amounts for the maintenance of normal metabolism. They generally cannot be synthesized at adequate levels by the body and must be obtained from the diet. The absence or shortage of a vitamin may result in a vitamin-deficiency disease. In the first half of the 20th century, a major focus of biochemistry was the identification, isolation, and characterization of vitamins.

Despite accumulating evidence that people needed more than just carbohydrates, fats, and proteins in their diets for normal growth and health, it was not until the early 1900s that research established the need for trace nutrients in the diet.

Because organisms differ in their synthetic abilities, a substance that is a vitamin for one species may not be so for another. Over the past 100 years, scientists have identified and isolated 13 vitamins required in the human diet and have divided them into two broad categories: the *fat-soluble vitamins*, which include vitamins A, D, E, and K, and the *water-soluble vitamins*, which are the B complex vitamins and vitamin C. All fat-soluble vitamins contain a high proportion of hydrocarbon structural components. There are one or two oxygen atoms present, but the compounds as a whole are nonpolar. In contrast, water-soluble vitamins contain large numbers of electronegative oxygen and nitrogen atoms, which can engage in hydrogen bonding with water. Most water-soluble vitamins act as coenzymes or are required for the synthesis of coenzymes. The fat-soluble vitamins are important for a variety of physiological functions. The key vitamins and their functions are found in Table 18.8 and Table 18.9.

TABLE 18.8 Fat-Soluble Vitamins and Physiological Functions

Vitamin	Physiological Function	Effect of Deficiency
vitamin A (retinol)	formation of vision pigments; differentiation of epithelial cells	night blindness; continued deficiency leads to total blindness
vitamin D (cholecalciferol)	increases the body's ability to absorb calcium and phosphorus	osteomalacia (softening of the bones); known as rickets in children
vitamin E (tocopherol)	fat-soluble antioxidant	damage to cell membranes
vitamin K (phylloquinone)	formation of prothrombin, a key enzyme in the blood-clotting process	increases the time required for blood to clot

TABLE 18.9 Water-Soluble Vitamins and Physiological Functions

Vitamin	Coenzyme	Coenzyme Function	Deficiency Disease
vitamin B1 (thiamine)	thiamine pyrophosphate	decarboxylation reactions	beri-beri
vitamin B2 (riboflavin)	flavin mononucleotide or flavin adenine dinucleotide	oxidation-reduction reactions involving two hydrogen atoms	—
vitamin B3 (niacin)	nicotinamide adenine dinucleotide or nicotinamide adenine dinucleotide phosphate	oxidation-reduction reactions involving the hydride ion (H^-)	pellagra
vitamin B6 (pyridoxine)	pyridoxal phosphate	variety of reactions including the transfer of amino groups	—
vitamin B12 (cyanocobalamin)	methylcobalamin or deoxyadenoxylcobalamin	intramolecular rearrangement reactions	pernicious anemia
biotin	biotin	carboxylation reactions	—
folic acid	tetrahydrofolate	carrier of one-carbon units such as the formyl group	anemia
pantothenic Acid	coenzyme A	carrier of acyl groups	—
vitamin C (ascorbic acid)	none	antioxidant; formation of collagen, a protein found in tendons, ligaments, and bone	scurvy

antioxidant

A substance that prevents oxidation.

Vitamins C and E, as well as the provitamin β-carotene can act as antioxidants in the body. **Antioxidants** prevent damage from free radicals, which are molecules that are highly reactive because they have unpaired electrons. Free radicals are formed not only through metabolic reactions involving oxygen but also by such environmental factors as radiation and pollution.

Note

β-carotene is known as a provitamin because it can be converted to vitamin A in the body.

Free radicals react most commonly react with lipoproteins and unsaturated fatty acids in cell membranes, removing an electron from those molecules and thus generating a new free radical. The process becomes a chain reaction that finally leads to the oxidative degradation of the affected compounds. Antioxidants react with free radicals to stop these chain reactions by forming a more stable molecule or, in the case of vitamin E, a free radical that is much less reactive. (Vitamin E is converted back to its original form through interaction with vitamin C.)

CONCEPT REVIEW EXERCISES

1. What is the difference between a cofactor and a coenzyme?
2. How are vitamins related to coenzymes?

ANSWERS

1. A coenzyme is one type of cofactor. Coenzymes are organic molecules required by some enzymes for activity. A cofactor can be either a coenzyme or an inorganic ion.
2. Coenzymes are synthesized from vitamins.

KEY TAKEAWAYS

- Vitamins are organic compounds that are essential in very small amounts for the maintenance of normal metabolism.
- Vitamins are divided into two broad categories: fat-soluble vitamins and water-soluble vitamins.
- Most water-soluble vitamins are needed for the formation of coenzymes, which are organic molecules needed by some enzymes for catalytic activity.

EXERCISES

1. Identify each vitamin as water soluble or fat soluble.
   a. vitamin D
   b. vitamin C
   c. vitamin B_{12}
2. Identify each vitamin as water soluble or fat soluble.
   a. niacin
   b. cholecalciferol
   c. biotin
3. What vitamin is needed to form each coenzyme?
   a. pyridoxal phosphate
   b. flavin adenine dinucleotide
   c. coenzyme A
   d. nicotinamide adenine dinucleotide
4. What coenzyme is formed from each vitamin?
   a. niacin
   b. thiamine
   c. cyanocobalamin
   d. pantothenic acid
5. What is the function of each vitamin or coenzyme?
   a. flavin adenine dinucleotide
   b. vitamin A
   c. biotin
6. What is the function of each vitamin or coenzyme?
   a. vitamin K
   b. pyridoxal phosphate
   c. tetrahydrofolate

ANSWERS

1. a. fat soluble
   b. water soluble
   c. water soluble
3. a. vitamin B_6 or pyridoxine
   b. vitamin B_2 or riboflavin
   c. pantothenic acid
   d. vitamin B_3 or niacin
5. a. needed by enzymes that catalyze oxidation-reduction reactions in which two hydrogen atoms are transferred
   b. needed for the formation of vision pigments
   c. needed by enzymes that catalyze carboxylation reactions

10. END-OF-CHAPTER MATERIAL

Chapter Summary

To ensure that you understand the material in this chapter, you should review the meanings of the bold terms in the following summary and ask yourself how they relate to the topics in the chapter.

A **protein** is a large biological polymer synthesized from **amino acids**, which are carboxylic acids containing an α-amino group. Proteins have a variety of important roles in living organisms, yet they are made from the same 20 L-amino acids. About half of these amino acids, the **essential amino acids**, cannot be synthesized by the human body and must be obtained from the diet. In the solid state and in neutral solutions, amino acids exist as **zwitterions**, species that are charged but electrically neutral. In this form, they behave much like inorganic salts. Each amino acid belongs to one of four classes depending on the characteristics of its R group or amino acid side chain: nonpolar, polar but neutral, positively charged, and negatively charged. Depending on the conditions, amino acids can act as either acids or bases, which means that proteins act as buffers. The pH at which an amino acid exists as the zwitterion is called the **isoelectric point (pI)**.

The amino acids in a protein are linked together by **peptide bonds**. Protein chains containing 10 or fewer amino acids are usually referred to as **peptides**, with a prefix such as di- or tri- indicating the number of amino acids. Chains containing more than 50 amino acid units are referred to as *proteins* or **polypeptides**. Proteins are classified globular or fibrous, depending on their structure and resulting solubility in water. **Globular proteins** are nearly spherical and are soluble in water; **fibrous proteins** have elongated or fibrous structures and are not soluble in water.

Protein molecules can have as many as four levels of structure. The **primary structure** is the sequence of amino acids in the chain. The **secondary structure** is the arrangement of adjacent atoms in the peptide chain; the most common arrangements are α-helices or β-pleated sheets. The **tertiary structure** is the overall three-dimensional shape of the molecule that results from the way the chain bends and folds in on itself. Proteins that consist of more than one chain have **quaternary structure**, which is the way the multiple chains are packed together.

Four types of intramolecular and intermolecular forces contribute to secondary, tertiary, and quaternary structure: (1) **hydrogen bonding** between an oxygen or a nitrogen atom and a hydrogen atom bound to an oxygen atom or a nitrogen atom, either on the same chain or on a neighboring chain; (2) **ionic bonding** between one positively charged side chain and one negatively charged side chain; (3) **disulfide linkages** between cysteine units; and (4) **dispersion forces** between nonpolar side chains.

Because of their complexity, protein molecules are delicate and easy to disrupt. A *denatured* protein is one whose conformation has been changed, in a process called **denaturation**, so that it can no longer do its physiological job. A variety of conditions, such as heat, ultraviolet radiation, the addition of organic compounds, or changes in pH can denature a protein.

An **enzyme** is an organic catalyst produced by a living cell. Enzymes are such powerful catalysts that the reactions they promote occur rapidly at body temperature. Without the help of enzymes, these reactions would require high temperatures and long reaction times.

The molecule or molecules on which an enzyme acts are called its **substrates**. An enzyme has an **active site** where its substrate or substrates bind to form an enzyme-substrate complex. The reaction occurs, and product is released:

$$E + S \rightarrow E\text{–}S \rightarrow E + P$$

The original **lock-and-key model** of enzyme and substrate binding pictured a rigid enzyme of unchanging configuration binding to the appropriate substrate. The newer **induced-fit model** describes the enzyme active site as changing its conformation after binding to the substrate.

Most enzymes have maximal activity in a narrow pH range centered on an **optimum pH**. In this pH range, the enzyme is correctly folded, and catalytic groups in the active site have the correct charge (positive, negative, or neutral). For most enzymes, the optimum pH is between 6 and 8.

Substances that interfere with enzyme function are called inhibitors. An **irreversible inhibitor** inactivates enzymes by forming covalent bonds to the enzyme, while a **reversible inhibitor** inactivates an enzyme by a weaker, noncovalent interaction that is easier to disrupt. A **competitive inhibitor** is a reversible inhibitor that is structurally similar to the substrate and binds to the active site. When the inhibitor is bound, the substrate is blocked from the active site and no reaction occurs. Because the binding of such an inhibitor is reversible, a high substrate concentration will overcome the inhibition because it increases the likelihood of the substrate binding. A **noncompetitive inhibitor** binds reversibly at a site distinct from the active site. Thus, it can bind to either the enzyme or the enzyme-substrate complex. The inhibitor changes the conformation of the active site so that the enzyme cannot function properly. Noncompetitive inhibitors are important in **feedback inhibition**, in which the amount of product produced by a series of reactions is carefully controlled. The final product in a series of reactions acts as a noncompetitive inhibitor of the initial enzyme.

Simple enzymes consist entirely of one or more amino acid chains. Complex enzymes are composed of one or more amino acid chains joined to **cofactors**—inorganic ions or organic **coenzymes**. **Vitamins** are organic compounds that are essential in very small amounts for the maintenance of normal metabolism and generally cannot be synthesized at adequate levels by the body. Vitamins are divided into two broad categories: *fat-soluble* vitamins and *water-soluble* vitamins. Many of the water-soluble vitamins are used for the synthesis of coenzymes.

ADDITIONAL EXERCISES

1. Draw the structure of the amino acid γ-aminobutyric acid (GABA). Would you expect to find GABA in the amino acid sequence of a protein? Explain.
2. Draw the structure of the amino acid homocysteine (R group = CH_2CH_2SH). Would you expect to find homocysteine in the amino acid sequence of a protein? Justify your answer.
3. Write equations to show how leucine can act as a buffer (that is, how it can neutralize added acid or base).
4. Write equations to show how isoleucine can act as a buffer (that is, how it can neutralize added acid or base).
5. Glutathione (γ-glutamylcysteinylglycine) is a tripeptide found in all cells of higher animals. It contains glutamic acid joined in an unusual peptide linkage involving the carboxyl group of the R group (known as γ-carboxyl group), rather than the usual carboxyl group (the α-carboxyl group). Draw the structure of glutathione.
6. Draw the structure of the pentapeptide whose sequence is arg-his-gly-leu-asp. Identify which of the amino acids have R groups that can donate or gain hydrogen ions.
7. Bradykinin is a peptide hormone composed of nine amino acids that lowers blood pressure. Its primary structure is arg-pro-pro-gly-phe-ser-pro-phe-arg. Would you expect bradykinin to be positively charged, negatively charged, or neutral at a pH of 6.0? Justify your answer.
8. One of the neurotransmitters involved in pain sensation is a peptide called substance P, which is composed of 11 amino acids and is released by nerve-cell terminals in response to pain. Its primary structure is arg-pro-lys-pro-gln-gln-phe-phe-gly-leu-met. Would you expect this peptide to be positively charged, negatively charged, or neutral at a pH of 6.0? Justify your answer.
9. Carbohydrates are incorporated into *glycoproteins*. Would you expect the incorporation of sugar units to increase or decrease the solubility of a protein? Justify your answer.
10. Some proteins have phosphate groups attached through an ester linkage to the OH groups of serine, threonine, or tyrosine residues to form *phosphoproteins*. Would you expect the incorporation of a phosphate group to increase or decrease the solubility of a protein? Justify your answer.
11. Refer to Table 18.5 and determine how each enzyme would be classified.
    a. the enzyme that catalyzes the conversion of ethanol to acetaldehyde
    b. the enzyme that catalyzes the breakdown of glucose 6-phosphate to glucose and inorganic phosphate ion (water is also a reactant in this reaction)
12. Refer to Table 18.5 and determine how each enzyme would be classified.
    a. the enzyme that catalyzes the removal of a carboxyl group from pyruvate to form acetate

$$^{-}O_2C-C(=O)-CH_3 \longrightarrow {}^{-}O_2C-CH_3 + CO_2$$

Pyruvate Acetate Carbon dioxide

    b. the enzyme that catalyzes the rearrangement of 3-phosphoglycerate to form 2-phosphoglycerate

$$^{-}O_2C-CH(OH)-CH_2OPO_3^{2-} \longrightarrow {}^{-}O_2C-CH(OPO_3^{2-})-CH_2OH$$

3–phosphoglycerate 2–phosphoglycerate

13. The enzyme lysozyme has an aspartic acid residue in the active site. In acidic solution, the enzyme is inactive, but activity increases as the pH rises to around 6. Explain why.

14. The enzyme lysozyme has a glutamic acid residue in the active site. At neutral pH (6–7), the enzyme is active, but activity decreases as the pH rises. Explain why.
15. The activity of a purified enzyme is measured at a substrate concentration of 1.0 μM and found to convert 49 μmol of substrate to product in 1 min. The activity is measured at 2.0 μM substrate and found to convert 98 μmol of substrate to product/minute.
    a. When the substrate concentration is 100 μM, how much substrate would you predict is converted to product in 1 min? What if the substrate concentration were increased to 1,000 μM (1.0 mM)?
    b. The activities actually measured are 676 μmol product formed/minute at a substrate concentration of 100 μM and 698 μmol product formed/minute at 1,000 μM (1.0 mM) substrate. Is there any discrepancy between these values and those you predicted in Exercise 15a? Explain.
16. A patient has a fever of 39°C. Would you expect the activity of enzymes in the body to increase or decrease relative to their activity at normal body temperature (37°C)?
17. Using your knowledge of factors that influence enzyme activity, describe what happens when milk is pasteurized.

ANSWERS

1.

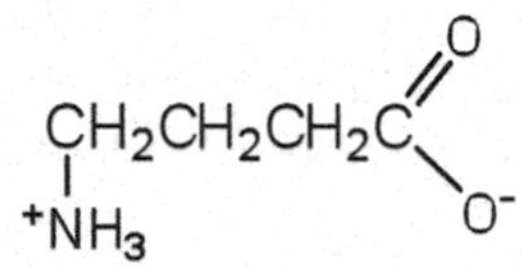

$CH_2CH_2CH_2C(=O)O^-$ with $^+NH_3$ on the first CH_2

This amino acid would not be found in proteins because it is not an α-amino acid.

3.

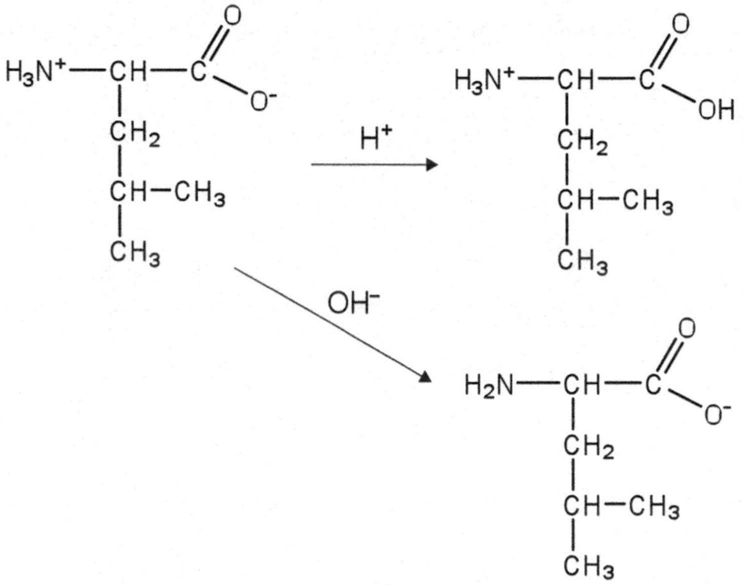

$H_3N^+—CH(CH_2CH(CH_3)CH_3)—C(=O)O^-$ $\xrightarrow{H^+}$ $H_3N^+—CH(CH_2CH(CH_3)CH_3)—C(=O)OH$

$H_3N^+—CH(CH_2CH(CH_3)CH_3)—C(=O)O^-$ $\xrightarrow{OH^-}$ $H_2N—CH(CH_2CH(CH_3)CH_3)—C(=O)O^-$

5.

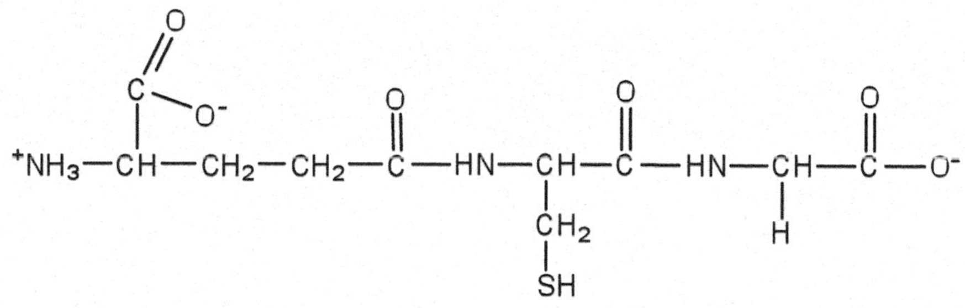

$$
\begin{array}{l}
\quad\quad\;\; \overset{O}{\overset{/\!/}{C}}\!\!\frown O^- \quad\quad\quad\quad\quad\; O \quad\quad\quad\quad\quad\; O \quad\quad\quad\quad\quad\; O \\
^+NH_3-CH-CH_2-CH_2-\overset{\|}{C}-HN-CH-\overset{\|}{C}-HN-CH-\overset{\|}{C}-O^- \\
\quad\quad\quad\quad\quad\quad\quad\quad\quad\quad\quad\quad\quad\quad\quad\;\; | \quad\quad\quad\quad\quad\quad\quad\;\; | \\
\quad\quad\quad\quad\quad\quad\quad\quad\quad\quad\quad\quad\quad\quad\; CH_2 \quad\quad\quad\quad\quad\quad\; H \\
\quad\quad\quad\quad\quad\quad\quad\quad\quad\quad\quad\quad\quad\quad\quad\;\; | \\
\quad\quad\quad\quad\quad\quad\quad\quad\quad\quad\quad\quad\quad\quad\;\; SH
\end{array}
$$

7. Bradykinin would be positively charged; all of the amino acids, except for arginine, have R groups that do not become either positively or negatively charged. The two arginines are R groups that are positively charged at neutral pH, so the peptide would have an overall positive charge.
9. Carbohydrates have many OH groups attached, which can engage in hydrogen bonding with water, which increases the solubility of the proteins.
11. a. oxidoreductase
    b. hydrolase
13. The enzyme is active when the carboxyl group in the R group of aspartic acid does not have the hydrogen attached (forming COO^-); the hydrogen is removed when the pH of the solution is around pH 6 or higher.
15. a. at 100 μM, you would predict that the rate would increase 100 times to 4,900 μmol of substrate to product in 1 min; at 1.0 mM, you would predict an increase to 49,000 μmol of substrate to product in 1 min.
    b. There is a great discrepancy between the predicted rates and actual rates; this occurs because the enzyme becomes saturated with substrate, preventing a further increase in the rate of the reaction (the reaction is no longer linear with respect to substrate concentration because it is at very low concentrations).
17. When milk is pasteurized, it is heated to high temperatures. These high temperatures denature the proteins in bacteria, so they cannot carry out needed functions to grow and multiply.

CHAPTER 19
Nucleic Acids

Opening Essay

Following the initial isolation of insulin in 1921, diabetic patients could be treated with insulin obtained from the pancreases of cattle and pigs. Unfortunately, some patients developed an allergic reaction to this insulin because its amino acid sequence was not identical to that of human insulin. In the 1970s, an intense research effort began that eventually led to the production of genetically engineered human insulin—the first genetically engineered product to be approved for medical use. To accomplish this feat, researchers first had to determine how insulin is made in the body and then find a way of causing the same process to occur in nonhuman organisms, such as bacteria or yeast cells. Many aspects of these discoveries are presented in this chapter on nucleic acids.

Human Insulin Products Now Being Used

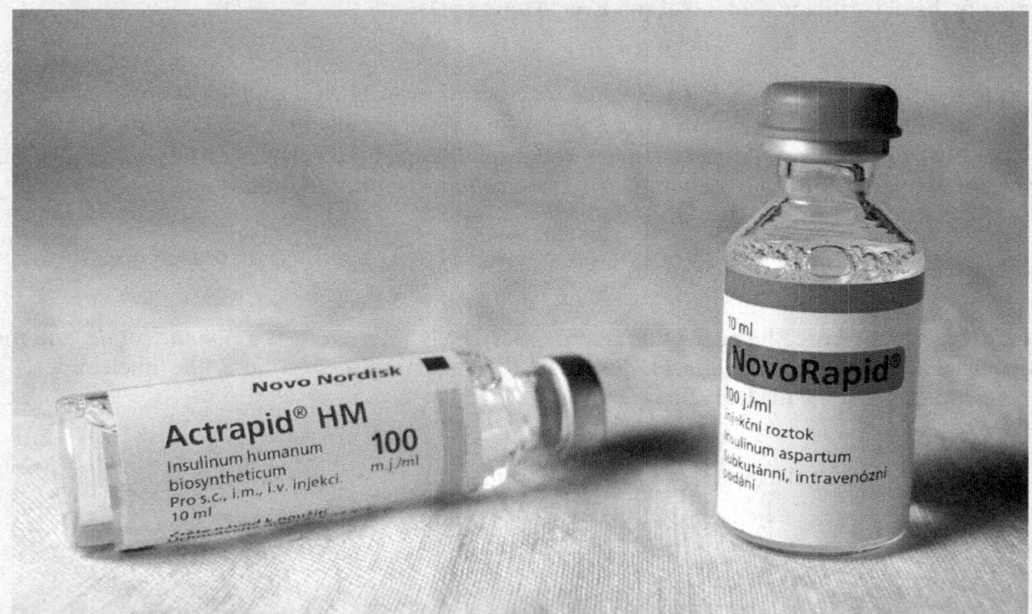

Source: Photo courtesy of Mr. Hyde, http://commons.wikimedia.org/wiki/File:Inzul%C3%ADn.jpg.

Dogs have puppies that grow up to be dogs. Foxes have kits that grow up to be foxes. From viruses to humans, each species reproduces after its own kind. Furthermore, within each multicellular organism, every tissue is composed of cells specific to that tissue. What accounts for this specificity at all levels of reproduction? How does a fertilized egg "know" that it should develop into a kangaroo and not a koala? What makes stomach cells produce gastric acid, whereas pancreatic cells produce insulin? The blueprint for the reproduction and the maintenance of each organism is found in the nuclei of its cells, concentrated in elongated, threadlike structures called **chromosomes**. These complex structures, consisting of DNA and proteins, contain the basic units of heredity, called **genes**. The number of chromosomes (and genes) varies with each species. Human body cells have 23 pairs of chromosomes having 20,000–40,000 different genes.

chromosome

An elongated, threadlike structure composed of protein and DNA that contains the genetic blueprint.

gene

The basic unit of heredity.

Sperm and egg cells contain only a single copy of each chromosome; that is, they contain only one member of each chromosome pair. Thus, in sexual reproduction, the entire complement of chromosomes is achieved only when an egg and sperm combine. A new individual receives half its hereditary material from each parent.

Calling the unit of heredity a "gene" merely gives it a name. But what really are genes and how is the information they contain expressed? One definition of a gene is that it is a segment of DNA that constitutes the code *for a specific polypeptide*. If genes are segments of DNA, we need to learn more about the structure and physiological function of DNA. We begin by looking at the small molecules needed to form DNA and RNA (ribonucleic acid)—the nucleotides.

1. NUCLEOTIDES

LEARNING OBJECTIVE

1. **Identify the different molecules that combine to form nucleotides.**

nucleotide

A monomer unit that is linked together to form nucleic acids.

The repeating, or monomer, units that are linked together to form nucleic acids are known as **nucleotides**. The deoxyribonucleic acid (DNA) of a typical mammalian cell contains about 3×10^9 nucleotides. Nucleotides can be further broken down to phosphoric acid (H_3PO_4), a pentose sugar (a sugar with five carbon atoms), and a nitrogenous base (a base containing nitrogen atoms).

$$\text{nucleic acids} \xrightarrow[\text{down into}]{\text{can be broken}} \text{nucleotides} \xrightarrow[\text{down into}]{\text{can be broken}} H_3PO_4 + \text{nitrogen base} + \text{pentose sugar}$$

If the pentose sugar is ribose, the nucleotide is more specifically referred to as a *ribonucleotide*, and the resulting nucleic acid is ribonucleic acid (RNA). If the sugar is 2-deoxyribose, the nucleotide is a *deoxyribonucleotide*, and the nucleic acid is DNA.

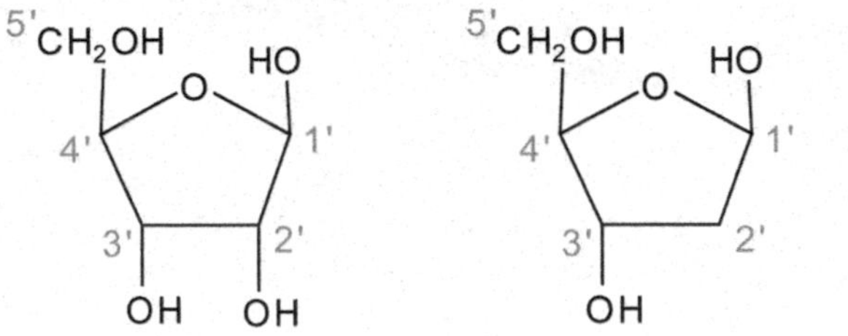

β-Ribose (found in RNA)

β-2-Deoxyribose (found in DNA)

pyrimidine

A heterocyclic amine with two nitrogen atoms in a six-member ring.

purine

A heterocyclic amine consisting of a pyrimidine ring fused to a five-member ring with two nitrogen atoms.

The nitrogenous bases found in nucleotides are classified as **pyrimidines** or **purines**. Pyrimidines are heterocyclic amines with two nitrogen atoms in a six-member ring and include uracil, thymine, and cytosine. (For more information about heterocyclic amines, see Chapter 15, [Unsupported Reference Type: chapter-section].) Purines are heterocyclic amines consisting of a pyrimidine ring fused to a five-member ring with two nitrogen atoms. Adenine and guanine are the major purines found in nucleic acids (Figure 19.2).

FIGURE 19.2 The Nitrogenous Bases Found in DNA and RNA

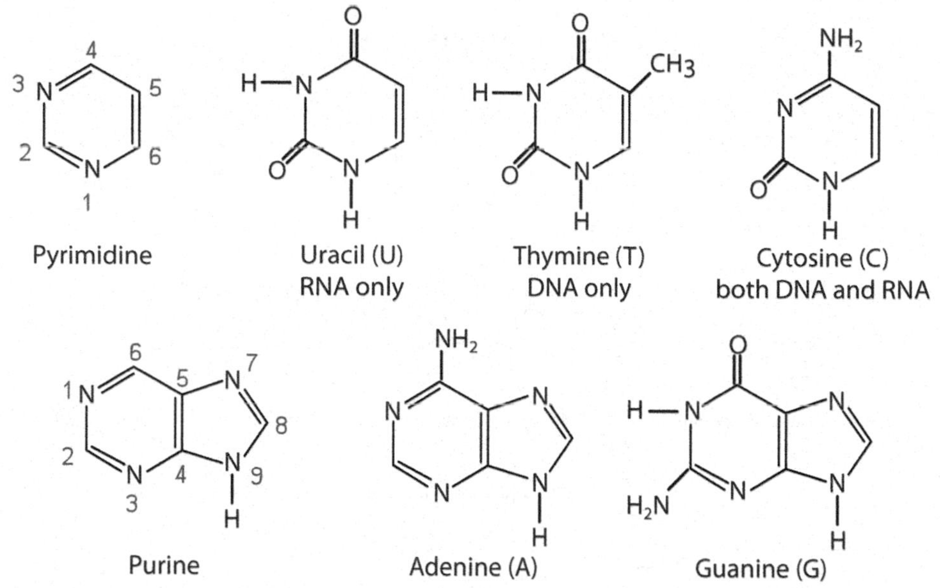

The formation of a bond between C1′ of the pentose sugar and N1 of the pyrimidine base or N9 of the purine base joins the pentose sugar to the nitrogenous base. In the formation of this bond, a molecule of water is removed. Table 19.1 summarizes the similarities and differences in the composition of nucleotides in DNA and RNA.

Note

The numbering convention is that primed numbers designate the atoms of the pentose ring, and unprimed numbers designate the atoms of the purine or pyrimidine ring.

TABLE 19.1 Composition of Nucleotides in DNA and RNA

Composition	DNA	RNA
purine bases	adenine and guanine	adenine and guanine
pyrimidine bases	cytosine and thymine	cytosine and uracil
pentose sugar	2-deoxyribose	ribose
inorganic acid	phosphoric acid (H_3PO_4)	H_3PO_4

The names and structures of the major ribonucleotides and one of the deoxyribonucleotides are given in Figure 19.3.

FIGURE 19.3 The Pyrimidine and Purine Nucleotides

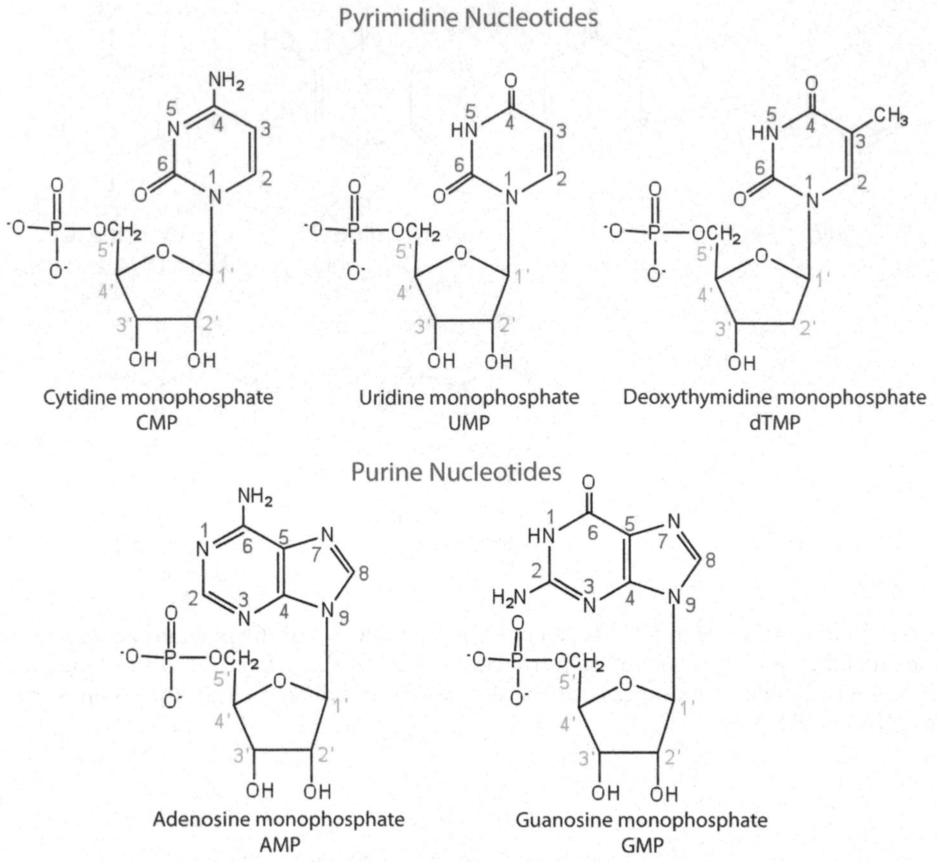

Pyrimidine Nucleotides

Cytidine monophosphate
CMP

Uridine monophosphate
UMP

Deoxythymidine monophosphate
dTMP

Purine Nucleotides

Adenosine monophosphate
AMP

Guanosine monophosphate
GMP

Apart from being the monomer units of DNA and RNA, the nucleotides and some of their derivatives have other functions as well. Adenosine diphosphate (ADP) and adenosine triphosphate (ATP), shown in Figure 19.4, have a role in cell metabolism that we will discuss in Chapter 20. Moreover, a number of coenzymes, including flavin adenine dinucleotide (FAD), nicotinamide adenine dinucleotide (NAD^+), and coenzyme A, contain adenine nucleotides as structural components. (For more information on coenzymes, see Chapter 18, [Unsupported Reference Type: chapter-section].)

FIGURE 19.4 Structures of Two Important Adenine-Containing Nucleotides

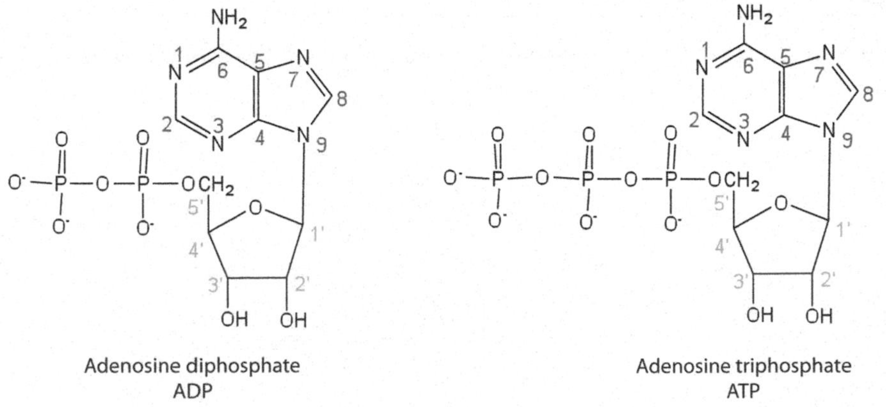

Adenosine diphosphate
ADP

Adenosine triphosphate
ATP

CONCEPT REVIEW EXERCISES

1. Identify the three molecules needed to form the nucleotides in each nucleic acid.
    a. DNA
    b. RNA
2. Classify each compound as a pentose sugar, a purine, or a pyrimidine.
    a. adenine
    b. guanine
    c. deoxyribose
    d. thymine
    e. ribose
    f. cytosine

ANSWERS

1. a. nitrogenous base (adenine, guanine, cytosine, and thymine), 2-deoxyribose, and H_3PO_4
    b. nitrogenous base (adenine, guanine, cytosine, and uracil), ribose, and H_3PO_4
2. a. purine
    b. purine
    c. pentose sugar
    d. pyrimidine
    e. pentose sugar
    f. pyrimidine

KEY TAKEAWAYS

- Nucleotides are composed of phosphoric acid, a pentose sugar (ribose or deoxyribose), and a nitrogen-containing base (adenine, cytosine, guanine, thymine, or uracil).
- Ribonucleotides contain ribose, while deoxyribonucleotides contain deoxyribose.

EXERCISES

1. What is the sugar unit in each nucleic acid?
    a. RNA
    b. DNA
2. Identify the major nitrogenous bases in each nucleic acid.
    a. DNA
    b. RNA

3. For each structure, circle the sugar unit and identify the nucleotide as a ribonucleotide or a deoxyribonucleotide.

   a.

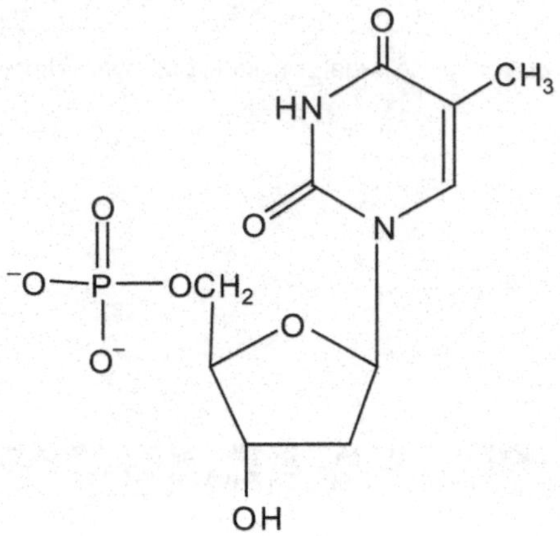

   b.

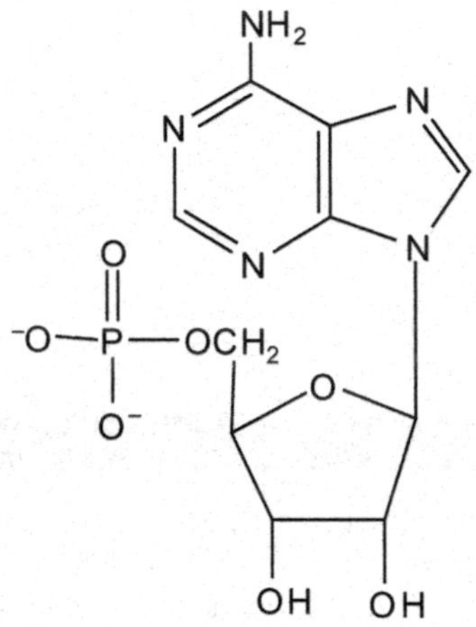

4. For each structure, circle the sugar unit and identify the nucleotide as a ribonucleotide or a deoxyribonucleotide.

a.

b.

5. For each structure, circle the nitrogenous base and identify it as a purine or pyrimidine.

   a.

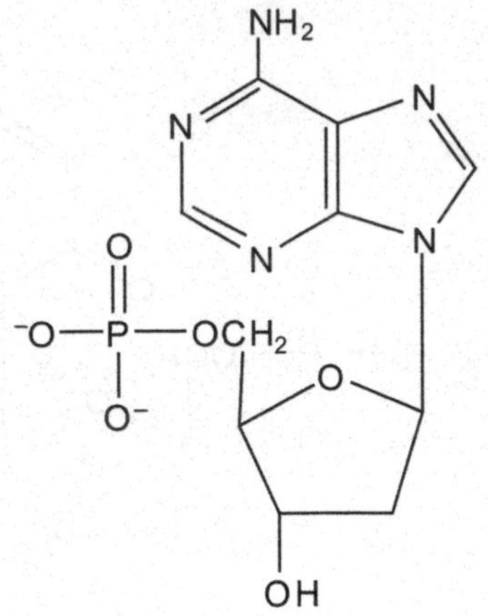

   b.

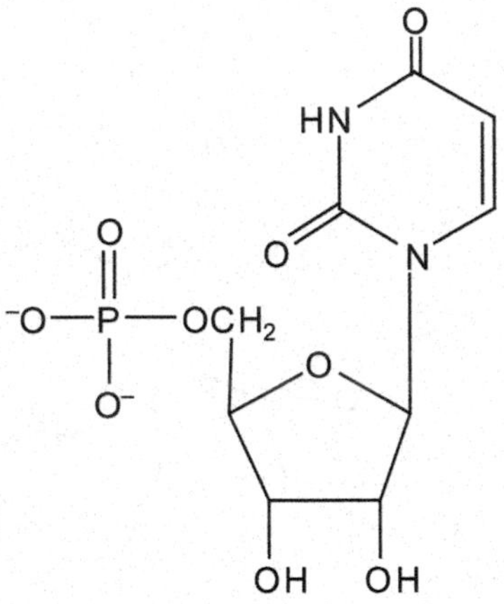

6. For each structure, circle the nitrogenous base and identify it as a purine or pyrimidine.

   a.

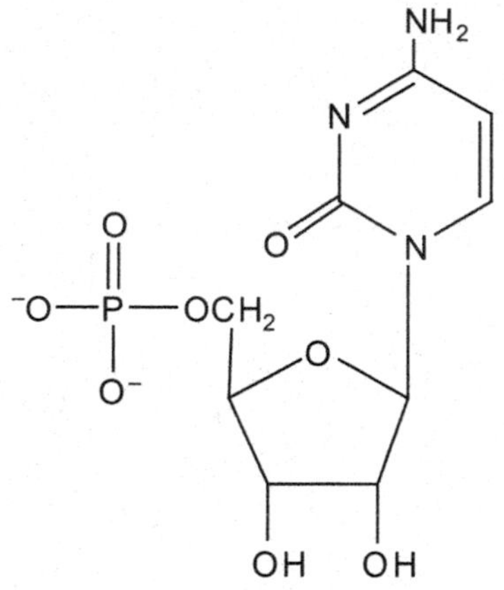

   b.

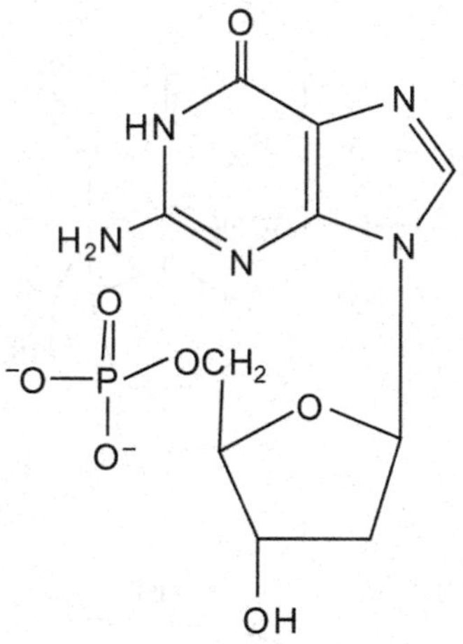

ANSWERS

1. a. ribose
   b. deoxyribose

3. a.

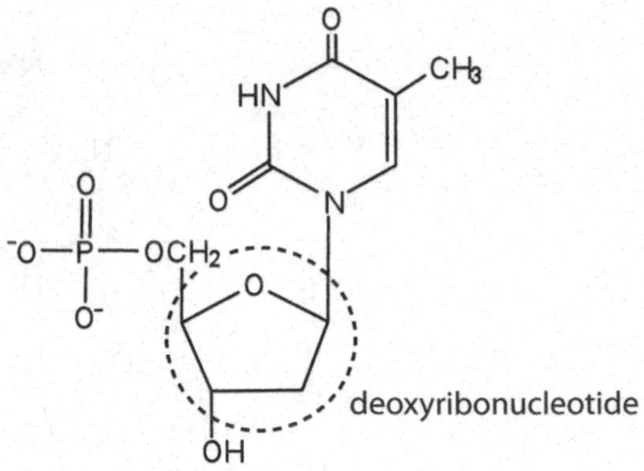

O
HN
CH3
O
N
O
-O
P
OCH2
O
O-
deoxyribonucleotide
OH

b.

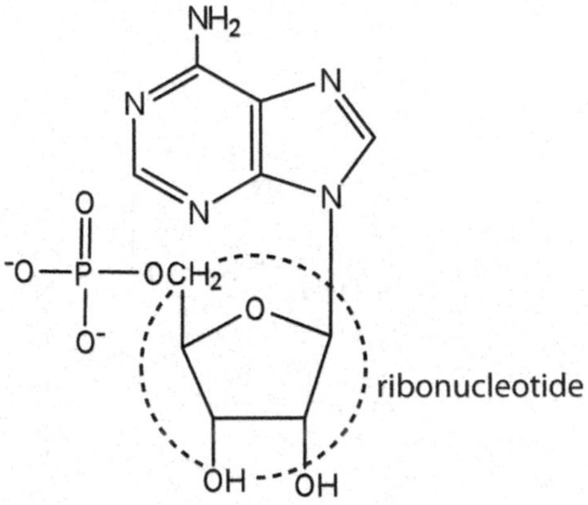

NH2
N
N
N
N
O
-O
P
OCH2
O
O-
ribonucleotide
OH
OH

5. a.

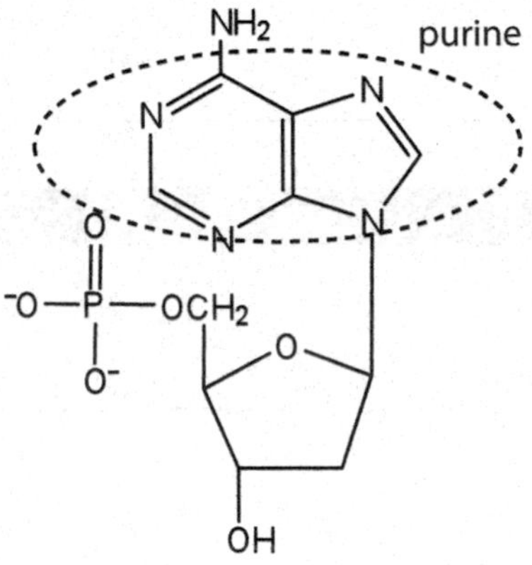

NH2
purine
N
N
N
N
O
-O
P
OCH2
O
O-
OH

b.

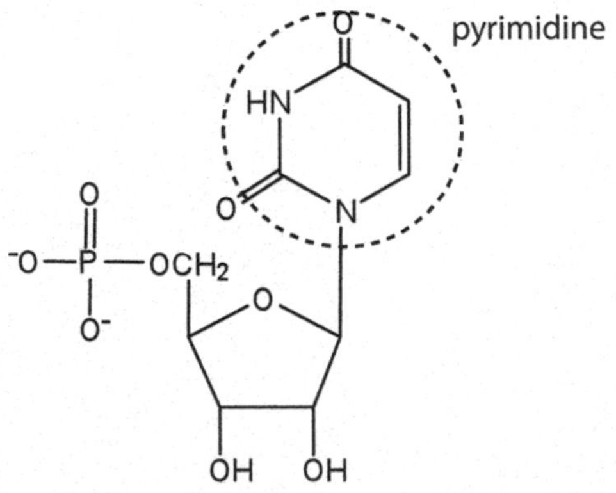

O
pyrimidine
HN
O
N
O
-O
P
OCH2
O
O-
OH
OH

2. NUCLEIC ACID STRUCTURE

LEARNING OBJECTIVES

1. Identify the two types of nucleic acids and the function of each type.
2. Describe how nucleotides are linked together to form nucleic acids.
3. Describe the secondary structure of DNA and the importance of complementary base pairing.

Nucleic acids are large polymers formed by linking nucleotides together and are found in every cell. **Deoxyribonucleic acid (DNA)** is the nucleic acid that stores genetic information. If all the DNA in a typical mammalian cell were stretched out end to end, it would extend more than 2 m. **Ribonucleic acid (RNA)** is the nucleic acid responsible for using the genetic information encoded in DNA to produce the thousands of proteins found in living organisms.

nucleic acid

A polymer formed by linking nucleotides together.

deoxyribonucleic acid (DNA)

The nucleic acid that stores genetic information.

ribonucleic acid (RNA)

The nucleic acid responsible for using the genetic information encoded in DNA.

2.1 Primary Structure of Nucleic Acids

Nucleotides are joined together through the phosphate group of one nucleotide connecting in an ester linkage to the OH group on the third carbon atom of the sugar unit of a second nucleotide. This unit joins to a third nucleotide, and the process is repeated to produce a long nucleic acid chain (Figure 19.5). The backbone of the chain consists of alternating phosphate and sugar units (2-deoxyribose in DNA and ribose in RNA). The purine and pyrimidine bases branch off this backbone.

Note

Each phosphate group has one acidic hydrogen atom that is ionized at physiological pH. This is why these compounds are known as nucleic *acids*.

FIGURE 19.5 Structure of a Segment of DNA

A similar segment of RNA would have OH groups on each C2′, and uracil would replace thymine.

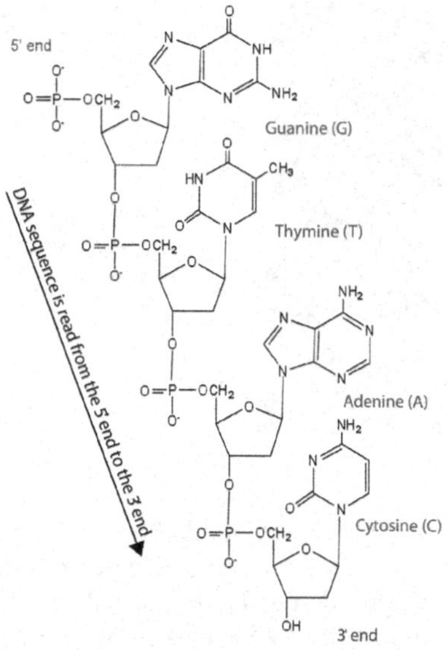

5′ end
Guanine (G)
Thymine (T)
Adenine (A)
Cytosine (C)
3′ end
DNA sequence is read from the 5′ end to the 3′ end

Like proteins, nucleic acids have a primary structure that is defined as the sequence of their nucleotides. Unlike proteins, which have 20 different kinds of amino acids, there are only 4 different kinds of nucleotides in nucleic acids. For amino acid sequences in proteins, the convention is to write the amino acids in order starting with the N-terminal amino acid. In writing nucleotide sequences for nucleic acids, the convention is to write the nucleotides (usually using the one-letter abbreviations for the bases, shown in Figure 19.5) starting with the nucleotide having a free phosphate group, which is known as the 5′ end, and indicate the nucleotides in order. For DNA, a lowercase *d* is often written in front of the sequence to indicate that the monomers are deoxyribonucleotides. The final nucleotide has a free OH group on the 3′ carbon atom and is called the *3′ end*. The sequence of nucleotides in the DNA segment shown in Figure 19.5 would be written 5′-dG-dT-dA-dC-3′, which is often further abbreviated to dGTAC or just GTAC.

2.2 Secondary Structure of DNA

The three-dimensional structure of DNA was the subject of an intensive research effort in the late 1940s to early 1950s. Initial work revealed that the polymer had a regular repeating structure. In 1950, Erwin Chargaff of Columbia University showed that the molar amount of adenine (A) in DNA was always equal to that of thymine (T). Similarly, he showed that the molar amount of guanine (G) was the same as that of cytosine (C). Chargaff drew no conclusions from his work, but others soon did.

double helix

The secondary structure of DNA.

complementary bases

Specific base pairings in the DNA double helix.

At Cambridge University in 1953, James D. Watson and Francis Crick announced that they had a model for the secondary structure of DNA. Using the information from Chargaff's experiments (as well as other experiments) and data from the X ray studies of Rosalind Franklin (which involved sophisticated chemistry, physics, and mathematics), Watson and Crick worked with models that were not unlike a child's construction set and finally concluded that DNA is composed of two nucleic acid chains running antiparallel to one another—that is, side-by-side with the 5′ end of one chain next to the 3′ end of the other. Moreover, as their model showed, the two chains are twisted to form a **double helix**—a structure that can be compared to a spiral staircase, with the phosphate and sugar groups (the backbone of the nucleic acid polymer) representing the outside edges of the staircase. The purine and pyrimidine bases face the inside of the helix, with guanine always opposite cytosine and adenine always opposite thymine. These specific base pairs, referred to as **complementary bases**, are the steps, or treads, in our staircase analogy (Figure 19.6).

FIGURE 19.6 DNA Double Helix

(a) This represents a computer-generated model of the DNA double helix. (b) This represents a schematic representation of the double helix, showing the complementary bases.

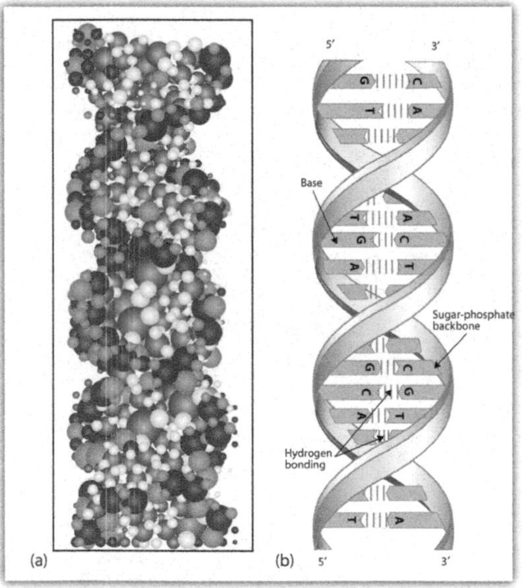

The structure proposed by Watson and Crick provided clues to the mechanisms by which cells are able to divide into two identical, functioning daughter cells; how genetic data are passed to new generations; and even how proteins are built to required specifications. All these abilities depend on the pairing of complementary bases. Figure 19.7 shows the two sets of base pairs and illustrates two things. First, a pyrimidine is paired with a purine in each case, so that the long dimensions of both pairs are identical (1.08 nm). If two pyrimidines were paired or two purines were paired, the two pyrimidines would take up less space than a purine and a pyrimidine, and the two purines would take up more space, as illustrated in Figure 19.8. If these pairings were ever to occur, the structure of DNA would be like a staircase made with stairs of different widths. For the two strands of the double helix to fit neatly, a pyrimidine must always be paired with a purine. The second thing you should notice in Figure 19.7 is that the correct pairing enables formation of three instances of hydrogen bonding between guanine and cytosine and two between adenine and thymine. The additive contribution of this hydrogen bonding imparts great stability to the DNA double helix.

FIGURE 19.7 Complementary Base Pairing

Complementary bases engage in hydrogen bonding with one another: (a) thymine and adenine; (b) cytosine and guanine.

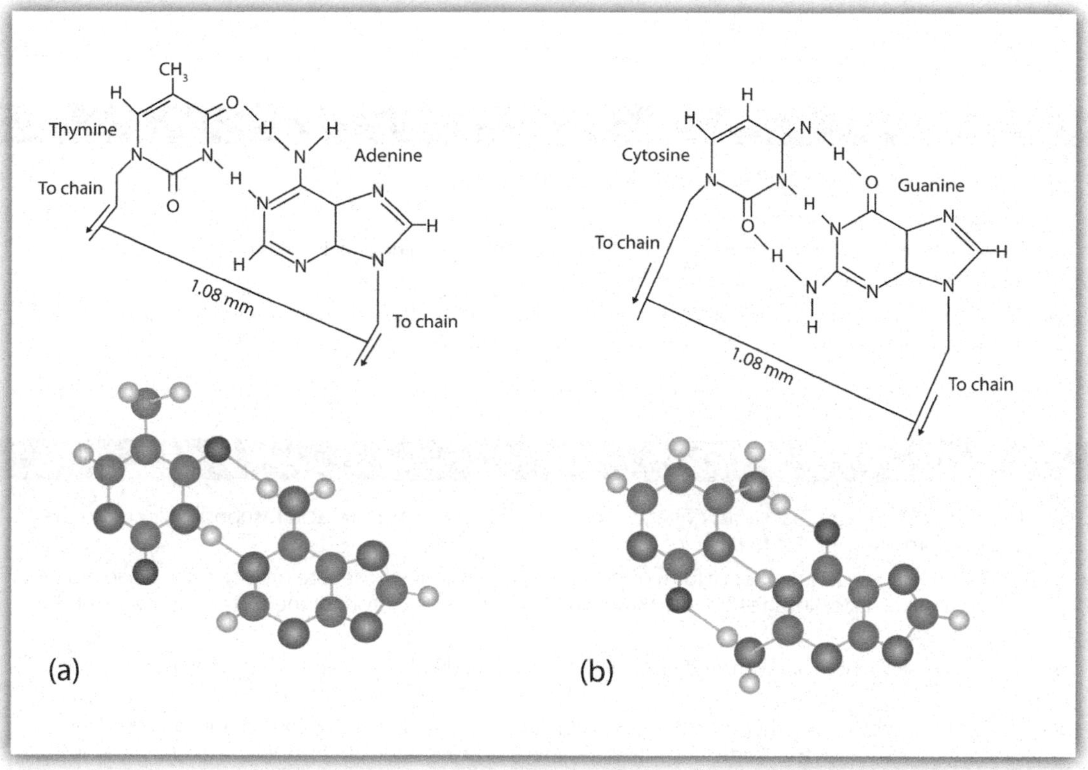

FIGURE 19.8 Difference in Widths of Possible Base Pairs

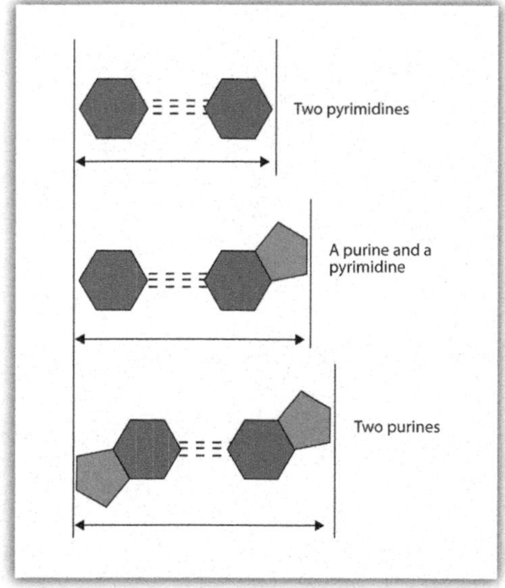

CONCEPT REVIEW EXERCISES

1.
   a. Name the two kinds of nucleic acids.
   b. Which type of nucleic acid stores genetic information in the cell?
2. What are complementary bases?
3. Why is it structurally important that a purine base always pair with a pyrimidine base in the DNA double helix?

ANSWERS

1. a. deoxyribonucleic acid (DNA) and ribonucleic acid (RNA)
   b. DNA
2. the specific base pairings in the DNA double helix in which guanine is paired with cytosine and adenine is paired with thymine
3. The width of the DNA double helix is kept at a constant width, rather than narrowing (if two pyrimidines were across from each other) or widening (if two purines were across from each other).

KEY TAKEAWAYS

- DNA is the nucleic acid that stores genetic information. RNA is the nucleic acid responsible for using the genetic information in DNA to produce proteins.
- Nucleotides are joined together to form nucleic acids through the phosphate group of one nucleotide connecting in an ester linkage to the OH group on the third carbon atom of the sugar unit of a second nucleotide.
- Nucleic acid sequences are written starting with the nucleotide having a free phosphate group (the 5′ end).
- Two DNA strands link together in an antiparallel direction and are twisted to form a double helix. The nitrogenous bases face the inside of the helix. Guanine is always opposite cytosine, and adenine is always opposite thymine.

EXERCISES

1. For this short RNA segment,
   a. identify the 5′ end and the 3′ end of the molecule.
   b. circle the atoms that comprise the backbone of the nucleic acid chain.
   c. write the nucleotide sequence of this RNA segment.

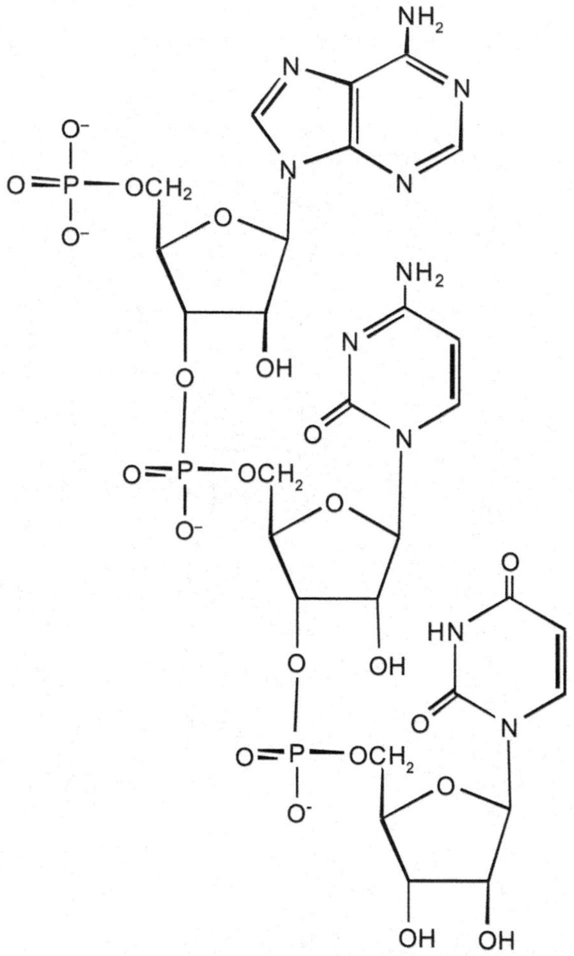

2. For this short DNA segment,
   a. identify the 5′ end and the 3′ end of the molecule.
   b. circle the atoms that comprise the backbone of the nucleic acid chain.
   c. write the nucleotide sequence of this DNA segment.

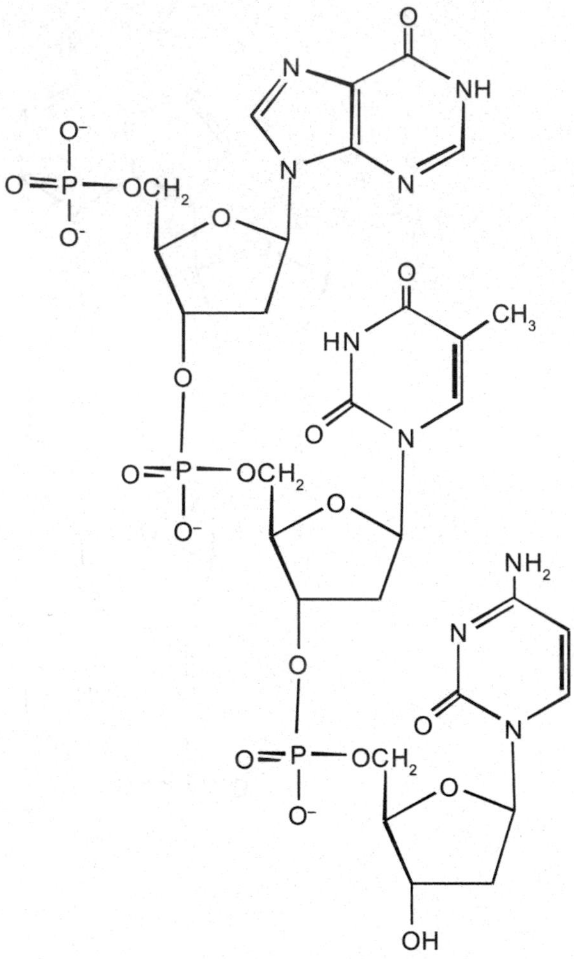

3. Which nitrogenous base in DNA pairs with each nitrogenous base?
   a. cytosine
   b. adenine
   c. guanine
   d. thymine
4. Which nitrogenous base in RNA pairs with each nitrogenous base?
   a. cytosine
   b. adenine
   c. guanine
   d. thymine
5. How many hydrogen bonds can form between the two strands in the short DNA segment shown below?

   5′ ATGCGACTA 3′

   3′ TACGCTGAT 5′

6. How many hydrogen bonds can form between the two strands in the short DNA segment shown below?

   5′ CGATGAGCC 3′

   3′ GCTACTCGG 5′

ANSWERS

1.

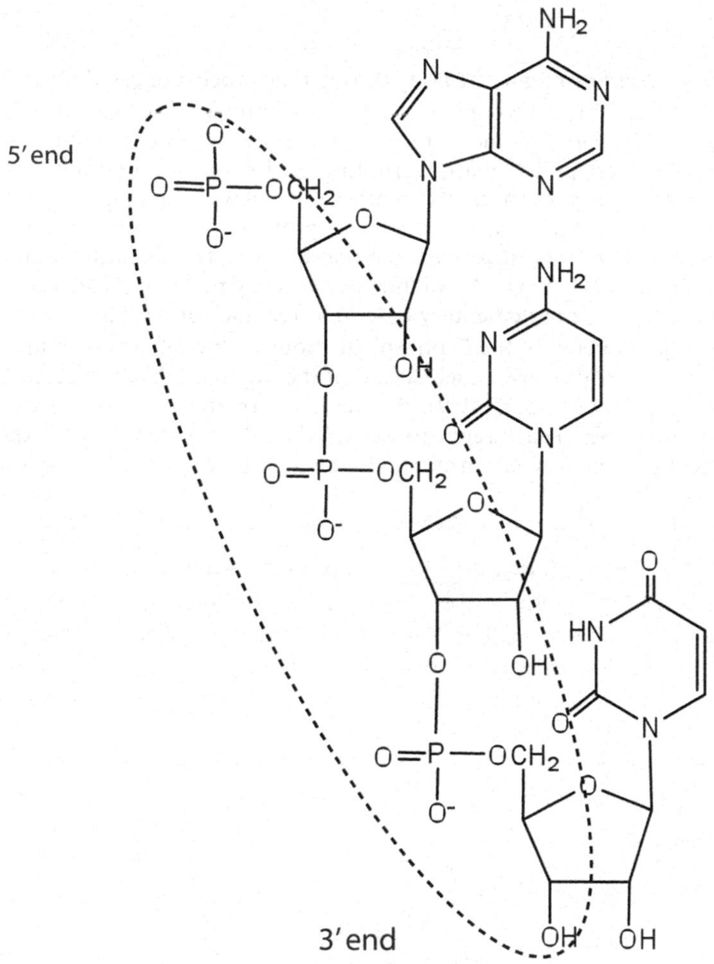

5′end

$O=P-OCH_2$

NH_2

3′end

c. ACU

3. a. guanine
   b. thymine
   c. cytosine
   d. adenine

5. 22 (2 between each AT base pair and 3 between each GC base pair)

3. REPLICATION AND EXPRESSION OF GENETIC INFORMATION

LEARNING OBJECTIVES

1. **Describe how a new copy of DNA is synthesized.**
2. **Describe how RNA is synthesized from DNA.**
3. **Identify the different types of RNA and the function of each type of RNA.**

We previously stated that deoxyribonucleic acid (DNA) stores genetic information, while ribonucleic acid (RNA) is responsible for transmitting or expressing genetic information by directing the synthesis of thousands of proteins found in living organisms. But how do the nucleic acids perform these functions? Three processes are required: (1) *replication*, in which new copies of DNA are made; (2) *transcription*, in which a segment of DNA is used to produce RNA; and (3) *translation*, in which the information in RNA is translated into a protein sequence. (For more information on protein sequences, see Section 4.)

3.1 Replication

replication

The process in which the DNA in a dividing cell is copied.

New cells are continuously forming in the body through the process of cell division. For this to happen, the DNA in a dividing cell must be copied in a process known as **replication**. The complementary base pairing of the double helix provides a ready model for how genetic replication occurs. If the two chains of the double helix are pulled apart, disrupting the hydrogen bonding between base pairs, each chain can act as a *template*, or pattern, for the synthesis of a new complementary DNA chain.

The nucleus contains all the necessary enzymes, proteins, and nucleotides required for this synthesis. A short segment of DNA is "unzipped," so that the two strands in the segment are separated to serve as templates for new DNA. DNA polymerase, an enzyme, recognizes each base in a template strand and matches it to the complementary base in a free nucleotide. The enzyme then catalyzes the formation of an ester bond between the 5′ phosphate group of the nucleotide and the 3′ OH end of the new, growing DNA chain. In this way, each strand of the original DNA molecule is used to produce a duplicate of its former partner (Figure 19.9). Whatever information was encoded in the original DNA double helix is now contained in each replicate helix. When the cell divides, each daughter cell gets one of these replicates and thus all of the information that was originally possessed by the parent cell.

FIGURE 19.9 A Schematic Diagram of DNA Replication

DNA replication occurs by the sequential unzipping of segments of the double helix. Each new nucleotide is brought into position by DNA polymerase and is added to the growing strand by the formation of a phosphate ester bond. Thus, two double helixes form from one, and each consists of one old strand and one new strand, an outcome called *semiconservative replications*. (This representation is simplified; many more proteins are involved in replication.)

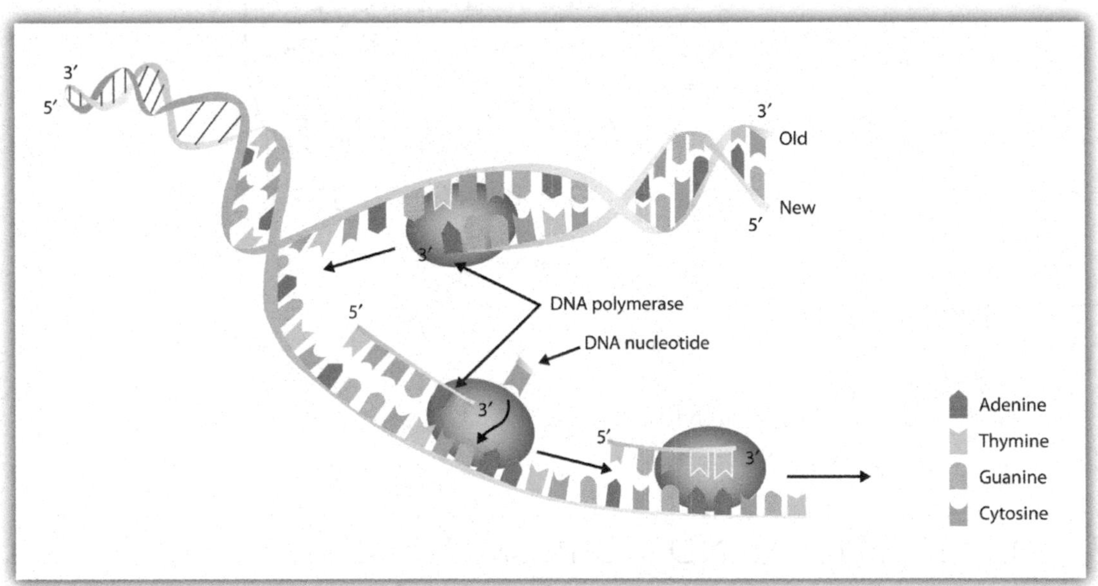

EXAMPLE 1

A segment of one strand from a DNA molecule has the sequence 5′-TCCATGAGTTGA-3′. What is the sequence of nucleotides in the opposite, or complementary, DNA chain?

Solution

Knowing that the two strands are antiparallel and that T base pairs with A, while C base pairs with G, the sequence of the complementary strand will be 3′-AGGTACTCAACT-5′ (can also be written as TCAACTCATGGA).

SKILL-BUILDING EXERCISE

1. A segment of one strand from a DNA molecule has the sequence 5′-CCAGTGAATTGCCTAT-3′. What is the sequence of nucleotides in the opposite, or complementary, DNA chain?

What do we mean when we say information is encoded in the DNA molecule? An organism's DNA can be compared to a book containing directions for assembling a model airplane or for knitting a sweater. Letters of the alphabet are arranged into words, and these words direct the individual to perform certain operations with specific materials. If all the directions are followed correctly, a model airplane or sweater is produced.

In DNA, the particular sequences of nucleotides along the chains encode the directions for building an organism. Just as *saw* means one thing in English and *was* means another, the sequence of bases CGT means one thing, and TGC means something different. Although there are only four letters—the four nucleotides—in the genetic code of DNA, their sequencing along the DNA strands can vary so widely that information storage is essentially unlimited.

3.2 Transcription

For the hereditary information in DNA to be useful, it must be "expressed," that is, used to direct the growth and functioning of an organism. The first step in the processes that constitute DNA expression is the synthesis of RNA, by a template mechanism that is in many ways analogous to DNA replication. Because the RNA that is synthesized is a complementary copy of information contained in DNA, RNA synthesis is referred to as **transcription**.

transcription

The process in which RNA is synthesized from a DNA template.

There are three key differences between replication and transcription: (1) RNA molecules are much shorter than DNA molecules; only a portion of one DNA strand is copied or transcribed to make an RNA molecule. (2) RNA is built from ribonucleotides rather than deoxyribonucleotides. (3) The newly synthesized RNA strand does not remain associated with the DNA sequence it was transcribed from.

The DNA sequence that is transcribed to make RNA is called the *template strand*, while the complementary sequence on the other DNA strand is called the *coding* or *informational strand*. To initiate RNA synthesis, the two DNA strands unwind at specific sites along the DNA molecule. Ribonucleotides are attracted to the uncoiling region of the DNA molecule, beginning at the 3′ end of the template strand, according to the rules of base pairing. Thymine in DNA calls for adenine in RNA, cytosine specifies guanine, guanine calls for cytosine, and adenine requires uracil. RNA polymerase—an enzyme—binds the complementary ribonucleotide and catalyzes the formation of the ester linkage between ribonucleotides, a reaction very similar to that catalyzed by DNA polymerase (Figure 19.10). Synthesis of the RNA strand takes place in the 5′ to 3′ direction, antiparallel to the template strand. Only a short segment of the RNA molecule is hydrogen-bonded to the template strand at any time during transcription. When transcription is completed, the RNA is released, and the DNA helix reforms. The nucleotide sequence of the RNA strand formed during transcription is identical to that of the corresponding coding strand of the DNA, except that U replaces T.

FIGURE 19.10 A Schematic Diagram of RNA Transcription from a DNA Template

The representation of RNA polymerase is proportionately much smaller than the actual molecule, which encompasses about 50 nucleotides at a time.

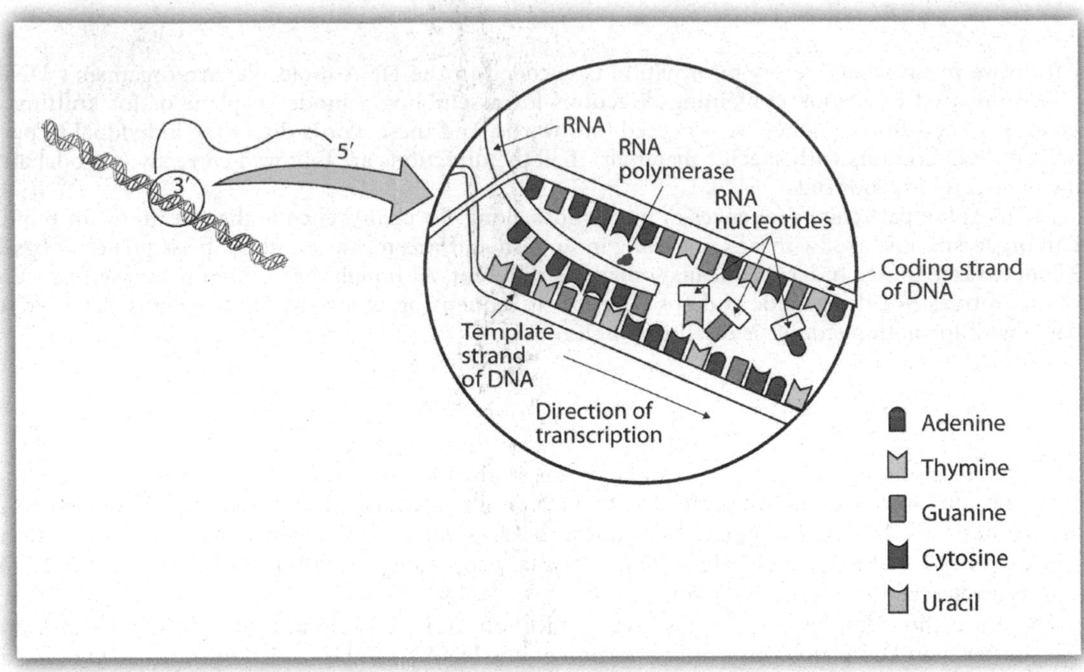

EXAMPLE 2

A portion of the template strand of a gene has the sequence 5′-TCCATGAGTTGA-3′. What is the sequence of nucleotides in the RNA that is formed from this template?

Solution

Four things must be remembered in answering this question: (1) the DNA strand and the RNA strand being synthesized are antiparallel; (2) RNA is synthesized in a 5′ to 3′ direction, so transcription begins at the 3′ end of the template strand; (3) ribonucleotides are used in place of deoxyribonucleotides; and (4) thymine (T) base pairs with adenine (A), A base pairs with uracil (U; in RNA), and cytosine (C) base pairs with guanine (G). The sequence is determined to be 3′-AGGUACUCAACU-5′ (can also be written as 5′-UCAACUCAUGGA-3′).

SKILL-BUILDING EXERCISE

1. A portion of the template strand of a gene has the sequence 5′-CCAGTGAATTGCCTAT-3′. What is the sequence of nucleotides in the RNA that is formed from this template?

Three types of RNA are formed during transcription: *messenger RNA* (mRNA), *ribosomal RNA* (rRNA), and *transfer RNA* (tRNA). These three types of RNA differ in function, size, and percentage of the total cell RNA (Table 19.2). mRNA makes up only a small percent of the total amount of RNA within the cell, primarily because each molecule of mRNA exists for a relatively short time; it is continuously being degraded and resynthesized. The molecular dimensions of the mRNA molecule vary according to the amount of genetic information a given molecule contains. After transcription, which takes place in the nucleus, the mRNA passes into the cytoplasm, carrying the genetic message from

DNA to the ribosomes, the sites of protein synthesis. In Section 5, we shall see how mRNA directly determines the sequence of amino acids during protein synthesis.

TABLE 19.2 Properties of Cellular RNA in *Escherichia coli*

Type	Function	Approximate Number of Nucleotides	Percentage of Total Cell RNA
mRNA	codes for proteins	100–6,000	~3
rRNA	component of ribosomes	120–2900	83
tRNA	adapter molecule that brings the amino acid to the ribosome	75–90	14

Ribosomes are cellular substructures where proteins are synthesized. They contain about 65% rRNA and 35% protein, held together by numerous noncovalent interactions, such as hydrogen bonding, in an overall structure consisting of two globular particles of unequal size.

Molecules of tRNA, which bring amino acids (one at a time) to the ribosomes for the construction of proteins, differ from one another in the kinds of amino acid each is specifically designed to carry. A set of three nucleotides, known as a **codon**, on the mRNA determines which kind of tRNA will add its amino acid to the growing chain. (For more information on sequences, see Section 4.) Each of the 20 amino acids found in proteins has at least one corresponding kind of tRNA, and most amino acids have more than one.

The two-dimensional structure of a tRNA molecule has three distinctive loops, reminiscent of a cloverleaf (Figure 19.11). On one loop is a sequence of three nucleotides that varies for each kind of tRNA. This triplet, called the **anticodon**, is complementary to and pairs with the codon on the mRNA. At the opposite end of the molecule is the acceptor stem, where the amino acid is attached.

ribosome

A cellular substructure where proteins are synthesized.

codon

A set of three nucleotides on the mRNA that specifies a particular amino acid.

anticodon

A set of three nucleotides on the tRNA that is complementary to, and pairs with, the codon on the mRNA.

FIGURE 19.11 Transfer RNA

(a) In the two-dimensional structure of a yeast tRNA molecule for phenylalanine, the amino acid binds to the acceptor stem located at the 3′ end of the tRNA primary sequence. (The nucleotides that are not specifically identified here are slightly altered analogs of the four common ribonucleotides A, U, C, and G.) (b) In the three-dimensional structure of yeast phenylalanine tRNA, note that the anticodon loop is at the bottom and the acceptor stem is at the top right. (c) This shows a space-filling model of the tRNA.

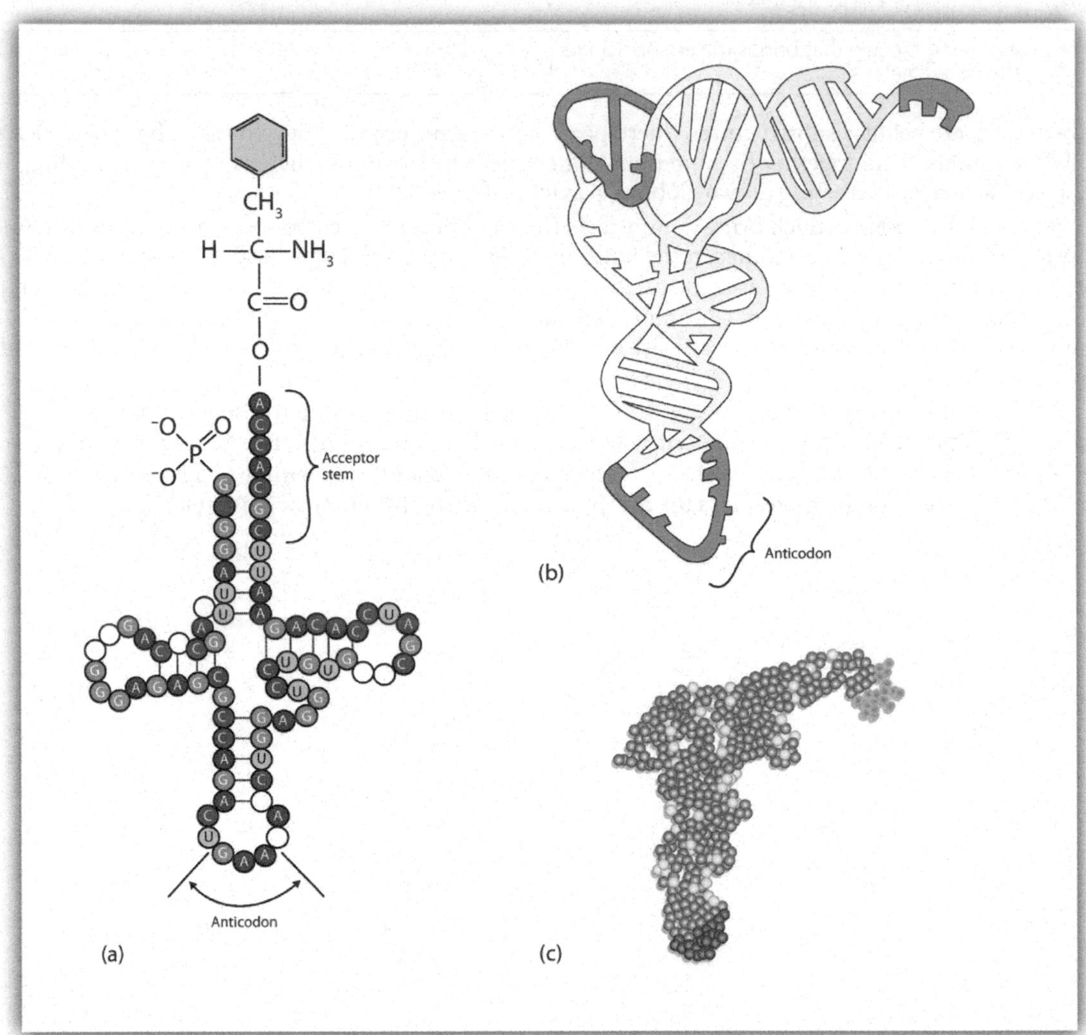

CONCEPT REVIEW EXERCISES

1. In DNA replication, a parent DNA molecule produces two daughter molecules. What is the fate of each strand of the parent DNA double helix?
2. What is the role of DNA in transcription? What is produced in transcription?
3. Which type of RNA contains the codon? Which type of RNA contains the anticodon?

ANSWERS

1. Each strand of the parent DNA double helix remains associated with the newly synthesized DNA strand.
2. DNA serves as a template for the synthesis of an RNA strand (the product of transcription).
3. codon: mRNA; anticodon: tRNA

KEY TAKEAWAYS

- In DNA replication, each strand of the original DNA serves as a template for the synthesis of a complementary strand.
- DNA polymerase is the primary enzyme needed for replication.
- In transcription, a segment of DNA serves as a template for the synthesis of an RNA sequence.
- RNA polymerase is the primary enzyme needed for transcription.
- Three types of RNA are formed during transcription: mRNA, rRNA, and tRNA.

EXERCISES

1. Describe how replication and transcription are similar.
2. Describe how replication and transcription differ.
3. A portion of the coding strand for a given gene has the sequence 5′-ATGAGCGACTTTGCGGGATTA-3′.
   a. What is the sequence of complementary template strand?
   b. What is the sequence of the mRNA that would be produced during transcription from this segment of DNA?
4. A portion of the coding strand for a given gene has the sequence 5′-ATGGCAATCCTCAAACGCTGT-3′.
   a. What is the sequence of complementary template strand?
   b. What is the sequence of the mRNA that would be produced during transcription from this segment of DNA?

ANSWERS

1. Both processes require a template from which a complementary strand is synthesized.
3. a. 3′-TACTCGCTGAAACGCCCTAAT-5′
   b. 5′-AUGAGCGACUUUGCGGGAUUA-3′

4. PROTEIN SYNTHESIS AND THE GENETIC CODE

LEARNING OBJECTIVES

1. **Describe the characteristics of the genetic code.**
2. **Describe how a protein is synthesized from mRNA.**

One of the definitions of a gene is as follows: a segment of deoxyribonucleic acid (DNA) carrying the code for a specific polypeptide. Each molecule of messenger RNA (mRNA) is a transcribed copy of a gene that is used by a cell for synthesizing a polypeptide chain. If a protein contains two or more different polypeptide chains, each chain is coded by a different gene. We turn now to the question of how the sequence of nucleotides in a molecule of ribonucleic acid (RNA) is translated into an amino acid sequence.

How can a molecule containing just 4 different nucleotides specify the sequence of the 20 amino acids that occur in proteins? If each nucleotide coded for 1 amino acid, then obviously the nucleic acids could code for only 4 amino acids. What if amino acids were coded for by groups of 2 nucleotides? There are 4^2, or 16, different combinations of 2 nucleotides (AA, AU, AC, AG, UU, and so on). Such a code is more extensive but still not adequate to code for 20 amino acids. However, if the nucleotides are arranged in groups of 3, the number of different possible combinations is 4^3, or 64. Here we have a code that is extensive enough to direct the synthesis of the primary structure of a protein molecule.

genetic code

The identification of each group of three nucleotides and its particular amino acid.

translation

The process in which the information encoded in mRNA is used to direct the sequencing of amino acids to synthesize a protein.

The **genetic code** can therefore be described as *the identification of each group of three nucleotides and its particular amino acid*. The sequence of these triplet groups in the mRNA dictates the sequence of the amino acids in the protein. Each individual three-nucleotide coding unit, as we have seen, is called a *codon*.

Protein synthesis is accomplished by orderly interactions between mRNA and the other ribonucleic acids (transfer RNA [tRNA] and ribosomal RNA [rRNA]), the ribosome, and more than 100 enzymes. The mRNA formed in the nucleus during transcription is transported across the nuclear membrane into the cytoplasm to the ribosomes—carrying with it the genetic instructions. The process in which the information encoded in the mRNA is used to direct the sequencing of amino acids and thus ultimately to synthesize a protein is referred to as **translation**.

Before an amino acid can be incorporated into a polypeptide chain, it must be attached to its unique tRNA. This crucial process requires an enzyme known as aminoacyl-tRNA synthetase (Figure 19.12). There is a specific aminoacyl-tRNA synthetase for each amino acid. This high degree of specificity is vital to the incorporation of the correct amino acid into a protein. After the amino acid molecule has been bound to its tRNA carrier, protein synthesis can take place. Figure 19.13 depicts a schematic stepwise representation of this all-important process.

FIGURE 19.12 Binding of an Amino Acid to Its tRNA

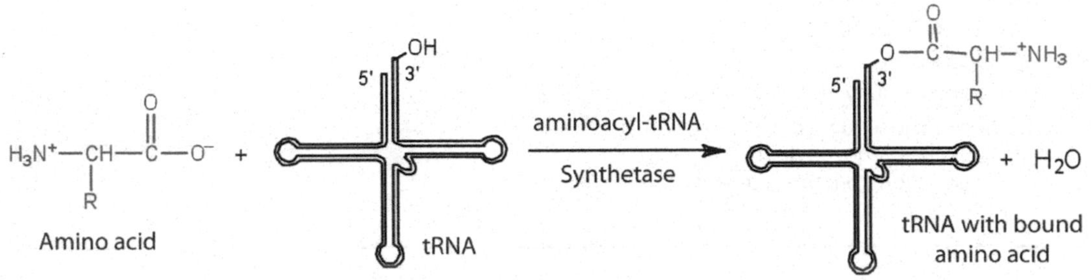

FIGURE 19.13 The Elongation Steps in Protein Synthesis

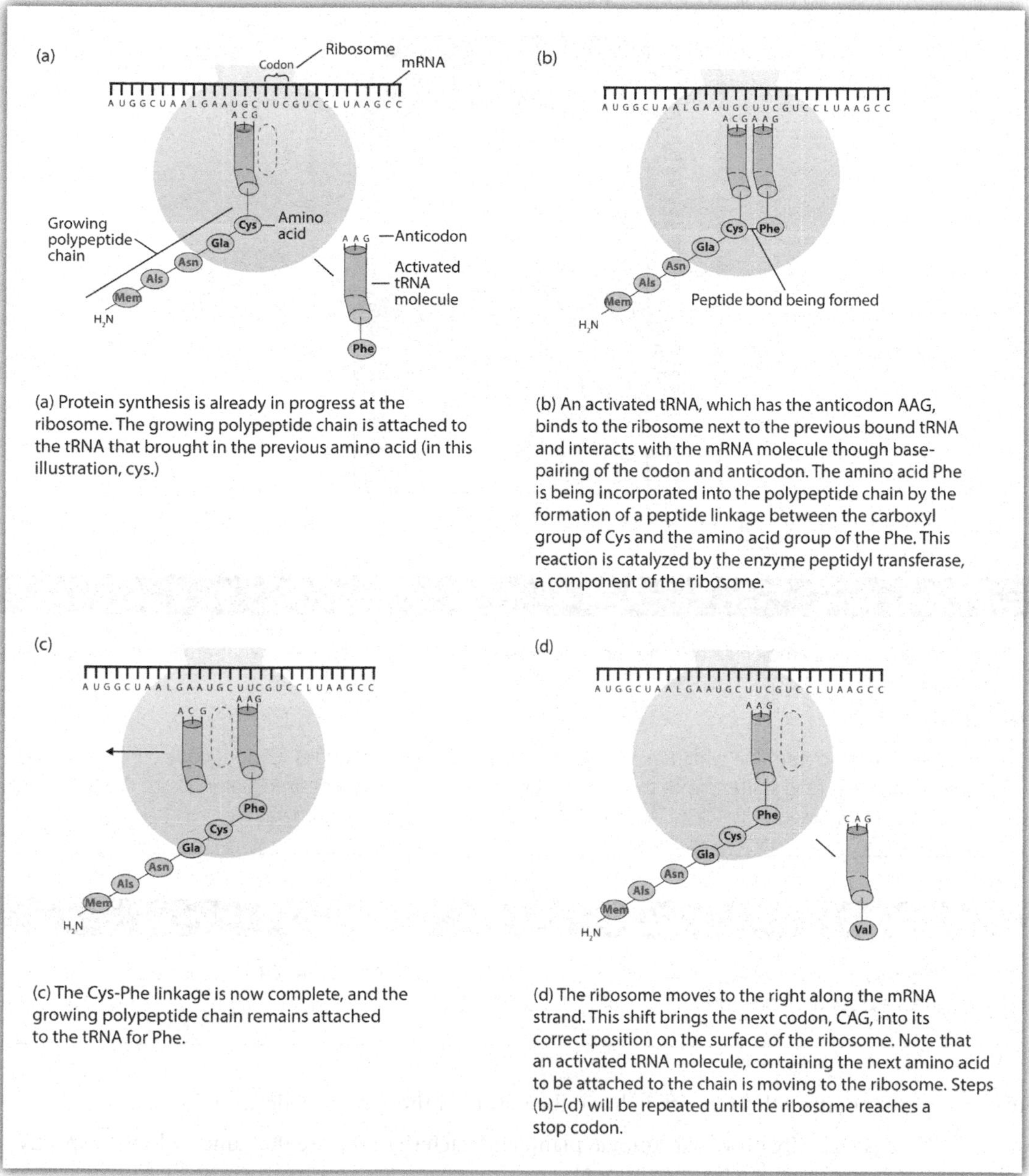

(a) Protein synthesis is already in progress at the ribosome. The growing polypeptide chain is attached to the tRNA that brought in the previous amino acid (in this illustration, cys.)

(b) An activated tRNA, which has the anticodon AAG, binds to the ribosome next to the previous bound tRNA and interacts with the mRNA molecule though base-pairing of the codon and anticodon. The amino acid Phe is being incorporated into the polypeptide chain by the formation of a peptide linkage between the carboxyl group of Cys and the amino acid group of the Phe. This reaction is catalyzed by the enzyme peptidyl transferase, a component of the ribosome.

(c) The Cys-Phe linkage is now complete, and the growing polypeptide chain remains attached to the tRNA for Phe.

(d) The ribosome moves to the right along the mRNA strand. This shift brings the next codon, CAG, into its correct position on the surface of the ribosome. Note that an activated tRNA molecule, containing the next amino acid to be attached to the chain is moving to the ribosome. Steps (b)–(d) will be repeated until the ribosome reaches a stop codon.

Early experimenters were faced with the task of determining which of the 64 possible codons stood for each of the 20 amino acids. The cracking of the genetic code was the joint accomplishment of several well-known geneticists—notably Har Khorana, Marshall Nirenberg, Philip Leder, and Severo Ochoa—from 1961 to 1964. The genetic dictionary they compiled, summarized in Figure 19.14, shows that 61 codons code for amino acids, and 3 codons serve as signals for the termination of polypeptide synthesis (much like the period at the end of a sentence). Notice that only methionine (AUG) and tryptophan (UGG) have single codons. All other amino acids have two or more codons.

FIGURE 19.14 The Genetic Code

First base	Second base: U	C	A	G	Third base
U	Phe	Ser	Tyr	Cys	U
U	Phe	Ser	Tyr	Cys	C
U	Leu	Ser	Stop	Stop	A
U	Leu	Ser	Stop	Trp	G
C	Leu	Pro	His	Arg	U
C	Leu	Pro	His	Arg	C
C	Leu	Pro	Gln	Arg	A
C	Leu	Pro	Gln	Arg	G
A	Ile	Thr	Asn	Ser	U
A	Ile	Thr	Asn	Ser	C
A	Ile	Thr	Lys	Arg	A
A	Met	Thr	Lys	Arg	G
G	Val	Ala	Asp	Gly	U
G	Val	Ala	Asp	Gly	C
G	Val	Ala	Glu	Gly	A
G	Val	Ala	Glu	Gly	G

EXAMPLE 3

A portion of an mRNA molecule has the sequence 5′-AUGCCACGAGUUGAC-3′. What amino acid sequence does this code for?

Solution

Use Figure 19.14 to determine what amino acid each set of three nucleotides (codon) codes for. Remember that the sequence is read starting from the 5′ end and that a protein is synthesized starting with the N-terminal amino acid. The sequence 5′-AUGCCACGAGUUGAC-3′ codes for met-pro-arg-val-asp.

SKILL-BUILDING EXERCISE

1. A portion of an RNA molecule has the sequence 5′-AUGCUGAAUUGCGUAGGA-3′. What amino acid sequence does this code for?

Further experimentation threw much light on the nature of the genetic code, as follows:

1. The code is virtually universal; animal, plant, and bacterial cells use the same codons to specify each amino acid (with a few exceptions).
2. The code is "degenerate"; in all but two cases (methionine and tryptophan), more than one triplet codes for a given amino acid.
3. The first two bases of each codon are most significant; the third base often varies. This suggests that a change in the third base by a mutation may still permit the correct incorporation of a given amino acid into a protein. (For more information on mutations, see Section 5.) The third base is sometimes called the "wobble" base.
4. The code is continuous and nonoverlapping; there are *no* nucleotides between codons, and adjacent codons do not overlap.
5. The three termination codons are read by special proteins called release factors, which signal the end of the translation process.
6. The codon AUG codes for methionine and is also the initiation codon. Thus methionine is the first amino acid in each newly synthesized polypeptide. This first amino acid is usually removed enzymatically before the polypeptide chain is completed; the vast majority of polypeptides do not begin with methionine.

CONCEPT REVIEW EXERCISES

1. What are the roles of mRNA and tRNA in protein synthesis?
2. What is the initiation codon?
3. What are the termination codons and how are they recognized?

ANSWERS

1. mRNA provides the code that determines the order of amino acids in the protein; tRNA transports the amino acids to the ribosome to incorporate into the growing protein chain.
2. AUG
3. UAA, UAG, and UGA; they are recognized by special proteins called release factors, which signal the end of the translation process.

KEY TAKEAWAYS

- In translation, the information in mRNA directs the order of amino acids in protein synthesis.
- A set of three nucleotides (codon) codes for a specific amino acid.

EXERCISES

1. Write the anticodon on tRNA that would pair with each mRNA codon.
   a. 5′-UUU-3′
   b. 5′-CAU-3′
   c. 5′-AGC-3′
   d. 5′-CCG-3′
2. Write the codon on mRNA that would pair with each tRNA anticodon.
   a. 5′-UUG-3′
   b. 5′-GAA-3′
   c. 5′-UCC-3′
   d. 5′-CAC-3′
3. The peptide hormone oxytocin contains 9 amino acid units. What is the minimum number of nucleotides needed to code for this peptide?
4. Myoglobin, a protein that stores oxygen in muscle cells, has been purified from a number of organisms. The protein from a sperm whale is composed of 153 amino acid units. What is the minimum number of nucleotides that must be present in the mRNA that codes for this protein?
5. Use Figure 19.14 to identify the amino acids carried by each tRNA molecule in Exercise 1.
6. Use Figure 19.14 to identify the amino acids carried by each tRNA molecule in Exercise 2.
7. Use Figure 19.14 to determine the amino acid sequence produced from this mRNA sequence:
   5′-AUGAGCGACUUUGCGGGAUUA-3′.
8. Use Figure 19.14 to determine the amino acid sequence produced from this mRNA sequence:
   5′-AUGGCAAUCCUCAAACGCUGU-3′

ANSWERS

1. a. 3′-AAA-5′
   b. 3′-GUA-5′
   c. 3′-UCG-5′
   d. 3′-GGC-5′

3. 27 nucleotides (3 nucleotides/codon)

5. 1a: phenylalanine; 1b: histidine; 1c: serine; 1d: proline

7. met-ser-asp-phe-ala-gly-leu

5. MUTATIONS AND GENETIC DISEASES

LEARNING OBJECTIVE

1. Describe the causes of genetic mutations and how they lead to genetic diseases.

mutation

Any chemical or physical change that alters the nucleotide sequence in DNA.

We have seen that the sequence of nucleotides in a cell's deoxyribonucleic acid (DNA) is what ultimately determines the sequence of amino acids in proteins made by the cell and thus is critical for the proper functioning of the cell. On rare occasions, however, the nucleotide sequence in DNA may be modified either spontaneously (by errors during replication, occurring approximately once for every 10 billion nucleotides) or from exposure to heat, radiation, or certain chemicals. Any chemical or physical change that alters the nucleotide sequence in DNA is called a **mutation**. When a mutation occurs in an egg or sperm cell that then produces a living organism, it will be inherited by all the offspring of that organism.

point mutation

A change in which one nucleotide is substituted, added, or deleted.

Common types of mutations include *substitution* (a different nucleotide is substituted), *insertion* (the addition of a new nucleotide), and *deletion* (the loss of a nucleotide). These changes within DNA are called **point mutations** because only one nucleotide is substituted, added, or deleted (Figure 19.15). Because an insertion or deletion results in a frame-shift that changes the reading of subsequent codons and, therefore, alters the entire amino acid sequence that follows the mutation, insertions and deletions are usually more harmful than a substitution in which only a single amino acid is altered.

FIGURE 19.15 Three Types of Point Mutations

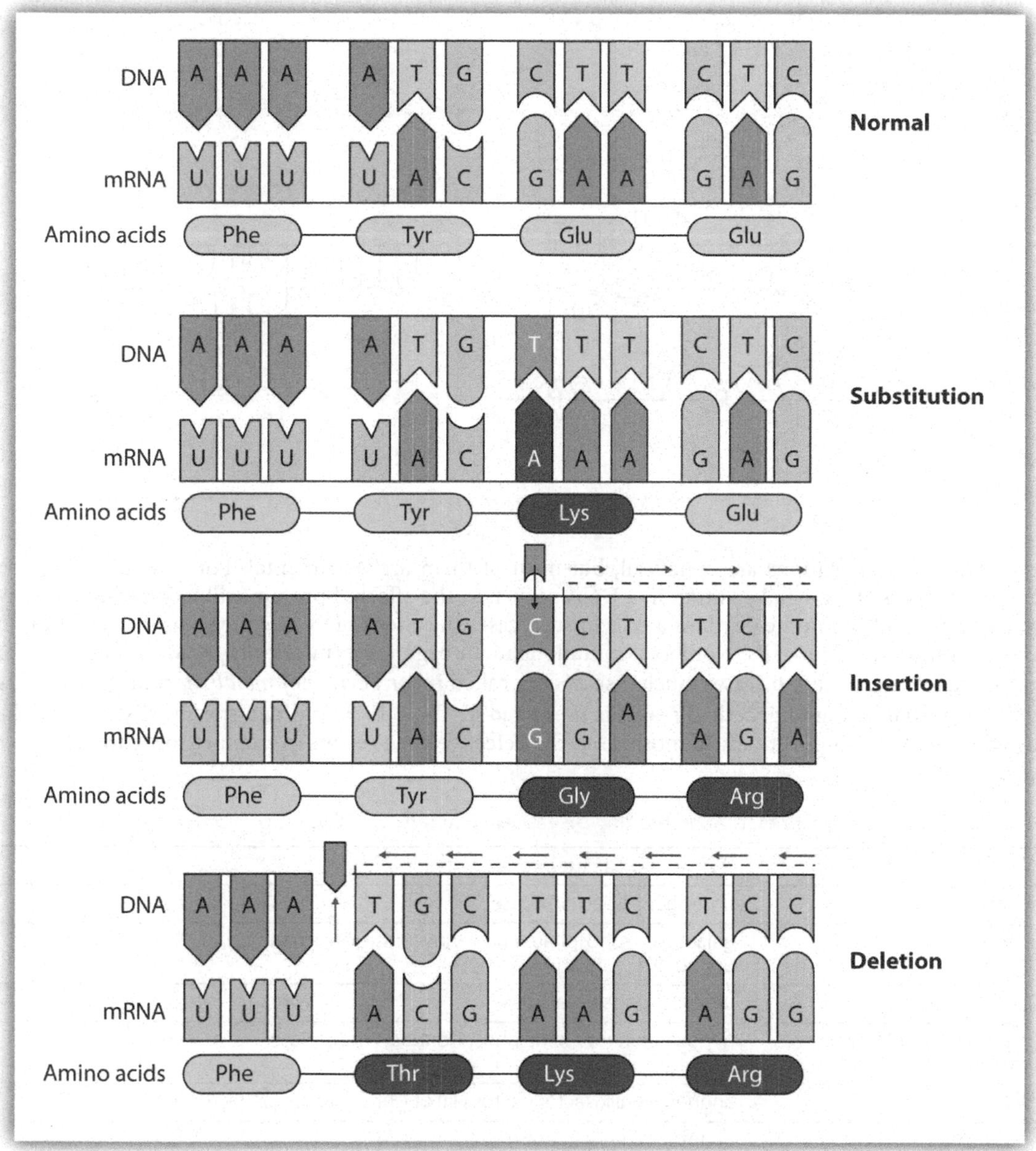

The chemical or physical agents that cause mutations are called **mutagens**. Examples of physical mutagens are ultraviolet (UV) and gamma radiation. Radiation exerts its mutagenic effect either directly or by creating free radicals that in turn have mutagenic effects. Radiation and free radicals can lead to the formation of bonds between nitrogenous bases in DNA. For example, exposure to UV light can result in the formation of a covalent bond between two adjacent thymines on a DNA strand, producing a thymine dimer (Figure 19.16). If not repaired, the dimer prevents the formation of the double helix at the point where it occurs. The genetic disease *xeroderma pigmentosum* is caused by a lack of the enzyme that cuts out the thymine dimers in damaged DNA. Individuals affected by this condition are abnormally sensitive to light and are more prone to skin cancer than normal individuals.

mutagen

A chemical or physical agent that cause mutations.

FIGURE 19.16 An Example of Radiation Damage to DNA

(a) The thymine dimer is formed by the action of UV light. (b) When a defect in the double strand is produced by the thymine dimer, this defect temporarily stops DNA replication, but the dimer can be removed, and the region can be repaired by an enzyme repair system.

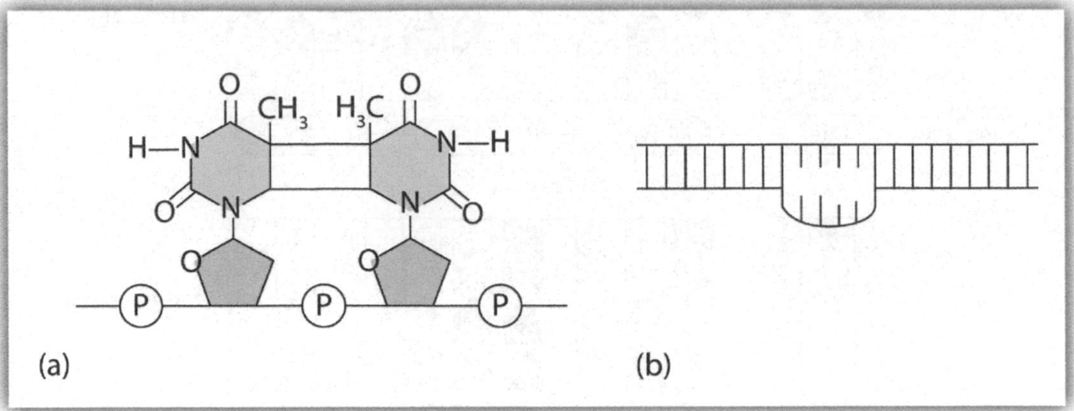

genetic disease

A hereditary condition caused by an altered DNA sequence.

Sometimes gene mutations are beneficial, but most of them are detrimental. For example, if a point mutation occurs at a crucial position in a DNA sequence, the affected protein will lack biological activity, perhaps resulting in the death of a cell. In such cases the altered DNA sequence is lost and will not be copied into daughter cells. Nonlethal mutations in an egg or sperm cell may lead to metabolic abnormalities or hereditary diseases. Such diseases are called *inborn errors of metabolism* or **genetic diseases**. A partial listing of genetic diseases is presented in Table 19.3, and two specific diseases are discussed in the following sections. In most cases, the defective gene results in a failure to synthesize a particular enzyme.

TABLE 19.3 Some Representative Genetic Diseases in Humans and the Protein or Enzyme Responsible

Disease	Responsible Protein or Enzyme
alkaptonuria	homogentisic acid oxidase
galactosemia	galactose 1-phosphate uridyl transferase, galactokinase, or UDP galactose epimerase
Gaucher disease	glucocerebrosidase
gout and Lesch-Nyhan syndrome	hypoxanthine-guanine phosphoribosyl transferase
hemophilia	antihemophilic factor (factor VIII) or Christmas factor (factor IX)
homocystinuria	cystathionine synthetase
maple syrup urine disease	branched chain α-keto acid dehydrogenase complex
McArdle syndrome	muscle phosphorylase
Niemann-Pick disease	sphingomyelinase
phenylketonuria (PKU)	phenylalanine hydroxylase
sickle cell anemia	hemoglobin
Tay-Sachs disease	hexosaminidase A
tyrosinemia	fumarylacetoacetate hydrolase or tyrosine aminotransferase
von Gierke disease	glucose 6-phosphatase
Wilson disease	Wilson disease protein

PKU results from the absence of the enzyme phenylalanine hydroxylase. Without this enzyme, a person cannot convert phenylalanine to tyrosine, which is the precursor of the neurotransmitters dopamine and norepinephrine as well as the skin pigment melanin.

Phenylalanine + 1/2 O_2 → (phenylalanine hydroxylase) → Tyrosine

When this reaction cannot occur, phenylalanine accumulates and is then converted to higher than normal quantities of phenylpyruvate. The disease acquired its name from the high levels of phenylpyruvate (a phenyl ketone) in urine. Excessive amounts of phenylpyruvate impair normal brain development, which causes severe mental retardation.

Phenylalanine → (transaminase) → Phenylpyruvate

PKU may be diagnosed by assaying a sample of blood or urine for phenylalanine or one of its metabolites. Medical authorities recommend testing every newborn's blood for phenylalanine within 24 h to 3 weeks after birth. If the condition is detected, mental retardation can be prevented by immediately placing the infant on a diet containing little or no phenylalanine. Because phenylalanine is plentiful in naturally produced proteins, the low-phenylalanine diet depends on a synthetic protein substitute plus very small measured amounts of naturally produced foods. Before dietary treatment was introduced in the early 1960s, severe mental retardation was a common outcome for children with PKU. Prior to the 1960s, 85% of patients with PKU had an intelligence quotient (IQ) less than 40, and 37% had IQ scores below 10. Since the introduction of dietary treatments, however, over 95% of children with PKU have developed normal or near-normal intelligence. The incidence of PKU in newborns is about 1 in 12,000 in North America.

Note

Every state has mandated that screening for PKU be provided to all newborns.

Several genetic diseases are collectively categorized as *lipid-storage diseases*. Lipids are constantly being synthesized and broken down in the body, so if the enzymes that catalyze lipid degradation are missing, the lipids tend to accumulate and cause a variety of medical problems. When a genetic mutation occurs in the gene for the enzyme hexosaminidase A, for example, gangliosides cannot be degraded but accumulate in brain tissue, causing the ganglion cells of the brain to become greatly enlarged and nonfunctional. (For more information on gangliosides, see Chapter 17, [Unsupported Reference Type: chapter-section].) This genetic disease, known as *Tay-Sachs disease*, leads to a regression in development, dementia, paralysis, and blindness, with death usually occurring before the age of three. There is currently no treatment, but Tay-Sachs disease can be diagnosed in a fetus by assaying the amniotic fluid (amniocentesis) for hexosaminidase A. A blood test can identify Tay-Sachs carriers—people who inherit a defective gene from only one rather than both parents—because they produce only half the normal amount of hexosaminidase A, although they do not exhibit symptoms of the disease.

Looking Closer: Recombinant DNA Technology

More than 3,000 human diseases have been shown to have a genetic component, caused or in some way modulated by the person's genetic composition. Moreover, in the last decade or so, researchers have succeeded in identifying many of the genes and even mutations that are responsible for specific genetic diseases. Now scientists have found ways of identifying and isolating genes that have specific biological functions and placing those genes in another organism, such as a bacterium, which can be easily grown in culture. With these techniques, known as *recombinant DNA technology*, the ability to cure many serious genetic diseases appears to be within our grasp.

Isolating the specific gene or genes that cause a particular genetic disease is a monumental task. One reason for the difficulty is the enormous amount of a cell's DNA, only a minute portion of which contains the gene sequence. Thus, the first task is to obtain smaller pieces of DNA that can be more easily handled. Fortunately, researchers are able to use *restriction enzymes* (also known as restriction endonucleases), discovered in 1970, which are enzymes that cut DNA at specific, known nucleotide sequences, yielding DNA fragments of shorter length. For example, the restriction enzyme *EcoRI* recognizes the nucleotide sequence shown here and cuts both DNA strands as indicated:

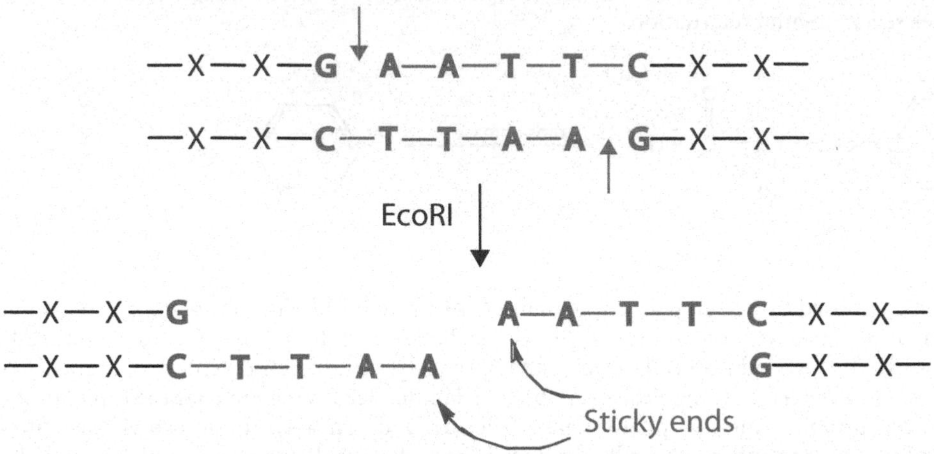

—X—X—G A—A—T—T—C—X—X—
—X—X—C—T—T—A—A G—X—X—

EcoRI

—X—X—G A—A—T—T—C—X—X—
—X—X—C—T—T—A—A G—X—X—

Sticky ends

Once a DNA strand has been fragmented, it must be cloned; that is, multiple identical copies of each DNA fragment are produced to make sure there are sufficient amounts of each to detect and manipulate in the laboratory. Cloning is accomplished by inserting the individual DNA fragments into phages (bacterial viruses) that can enter bacterial cells and be replicated. When a bacterial cell infected by the modified phage is placed in an appropriate culture medium, it forms a colony of cells, all containing copies of the original DNA fragment. This technique is used to produce many bacterial colonies, each containing a different DNA fragment. The result is a *DNA library*, a collection of bacterial colonies that together contain the entire genome of a particular organism.

The next task is to screen the DNA library to determine which bacterial colony (or colonies) has incorporated the DNA fragment containing the desired gene. A short piece of DNA, known as a *hybridization probe*, which has a nucleotide sequence complementary to a known sequence in the gene, is synthesized, and a radioactive phosphate group is added to it as a "tag." You might be wondering how researchers are able to prepare such a probe if the gene has not yet been isolated. One way is to use a segment of the desired gene isolated from another organism. An alternative method depends on knowing all or part of the amino acid sequence of the protein produced by the gene of interest: the amino acid sequence is used to produce an approximate genetic code for the gene, and this nucleotide sequence is then produced synthetically. (The amino acid sequence used is carefully chosen to include, if possible, many amino acids such as methionine and tryptophan, which have only a single codon each.)

After a probe identifies a colony containing the desired gene, the DNA fragment is clipped out, again using restriction enzymes, and spliced into another replicating entity, usually a plasmid. *Plasmids* are tiny mini-chromosomes found in many bacteria, such as *Escherichia coli* (*E. coli*). A recombined plasmid would then be inserted into the host organism (usually the bacterium *E. coli*), where it would go to work to produce the desired protein.

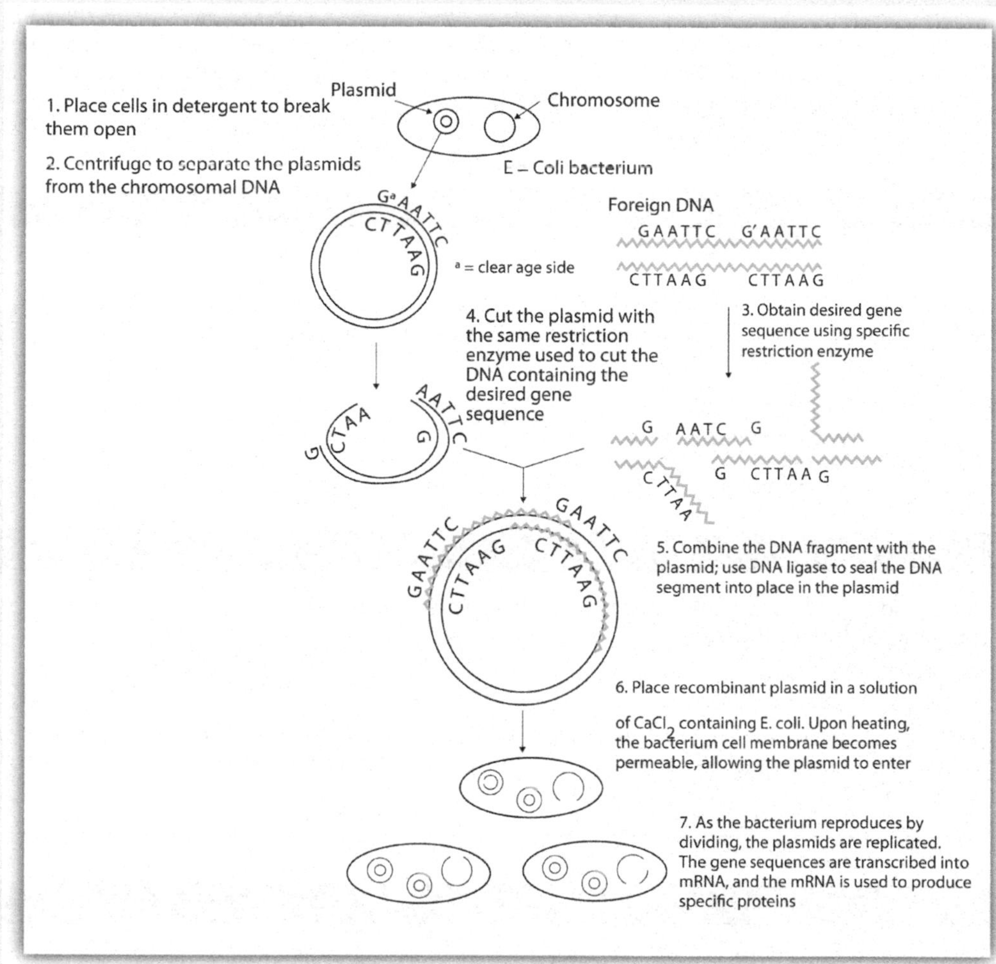

Proponents of recombinant DNA research are excited about its great potential benefits. An example is the production of human growth hormone, which is used to treat children who fail to grow properly. Formerly, human growth hormone was available only in tiny amounts obtained from cadavers. Now it is readily available through recombinant DNA technology. Another gene that has been cloned is the gene for epidermal growth factor, which stimulates the growth of skin cells and can be used to speed the healing of burns and other skin wounds. Recombinant techniques are also a powerful research tool, providing enormous aid to scientists as they map and sequence genes and determine the functions of different segments of an organism's DNA.

In addition to advancements in the ongoing treatment of genetic diseases, recombinant DNA technology may actually lead to cures. When appropriate genes are successfully inserted into *E. coli*, the bacteria can become miniature pharmaceutical factories, producing great quantities of insulin for people with diabetes, clotting factor for people with hemophilia, missing enzymes, hormones, vitamins, antibodies, vaccines, and so on. Recent accomplishments include the production in *E. coli* of recombinant DNA molecules containing synthetic genes for tissue plasminogen activator, a clot-dissolving enzyme that can rescue heart attack victims, as well as the production of vaccines against hepatitis B (humans) and hoof-and-mouth disease (cattle).

Scientists have used other bacteria besides *E. coli* in gene-splicing experiments and also yeast and fungi. Plant molecular biologists use a bacterial plasmid to introduce genes for several foreign proteins (including animal proteins) into plants. The bacterium is *Agrobacterium tumefaciens*, which can cause tumors in many plants but which can be treated so that its tumor-causing ability is eliminated. One practical application of its plasmids would be to enhance a plant's nutritional value by transferring into it the gene necessary for the synthesis of an amino acid in which the plant is normally deficient (for example, transferring the gene for methionine synthesis into pinto beans, which normally do not synthesize high levels of methionine).

Note

Restriction enzymes have been isolated from a number of bacteria and are named after the bacterium of origin. *EcoRI* is a restriction enzyme obtained from the R strain of *E. coli*. The roman numeral I indicates that it was the first restriction enzyme obtained from this strain of bacteria.

CONCEPT REVIEW EXERCISES

1.
   a. What effect can UV radiation have on DNA?
   b. Is UV radiation an example of a physical mutagen or a chemical mutagen?
2.
   a. What causes PKU?
   b. How is PKU detected and treated?

ANSWERS

1. a. It can lead to the formation of a covalent bond between two adjacent thymines on a DNA strand, producing a thymine dimer.
   b. physical mutagen
2. a. the absence of the enzyme phenylalanine hydroxylase
   b. PKU is diagnosed by assaying a sample of blood or urine for phenylalanine or one of its metabolites; treatment calls for an individual to be placed on a diet containing little or no phenylalanine.

KEY TAKEAWAYS

- The nucleotide sequence in DNA may be modified either spontaneously or from exposure to heat, radiation, or certain chemicals and can lead to mutations.
- Mutagens are the chemical or physical agents that cause mutations.
- Genetic diseases are hereditary diseases that occur because of a mutation in a critical gene.

EXERCISES

1. A portion of the coding strand of a gene was found to have the sequence 5′-ATGAGCGACTTTCGCCCATTA-3′. A mutation occurred in the gene, making the sequence 5′-ATGAGCGACCTTCGCCCATTA-3′.
   a. Identify the mutation as a substitution, an insertion, or a deletion.
   b. What effect would the mutation have on the amino acid sequence of the protein obtained from this mutated gene (use Figure 19.14)?
2. A portion of the coding strand of a gene was found to have the sequence 5′-ATGGCAATCCTCAAACGCTGT-3′. A mutation occurred in the gene, making the sequence 5′-ATGGCAATCCTCAACGCTGT-3′.
   a. Identify the mutation as a substitution, an insertion, or a deletion.
   b. What effect would the mutation have on the amino acid sequence of the protein obtained from this mutated gene (use Figure 19.14)?
3.
   a. What is a mutagen?
   b. Give two examples of mutagens.
4. For each genetic disease, indicate which enzyme is lacking or defective and the characteristic symptoms of the disease.
   a. PKU
   b. Tay-Sachs disease

ANSWERS

1. a. substitution
   b. Phenylalanine (UUU) would be replaced with leucine (CUU).

3. a. a chemical or physical agent that can cause a mutation
   b. UV radiation and gamma radiation (answers will vary)

6. VIRUSES

LEARNING OBJECTIVE

1. **Explain how viruses reproduce in cells.**

Infectious diseases caused by viruses include the common cold, influenza, and acquired immunodeficiency syndrome (AIDS) and are among the most significant health problems in our society. **Viruses** are infectious agents far smaller and simpler than bacteria that are composed of a tightly packed central core of nucleic acids enclosed in a protective shell. The shell consists of layers of one or more proteins and may also have lipid or carbohydrate molecules on the surface. Because of their simplicity, viruses must invade the cells of other organisms to be able to reproduce.

virus

An infectious agent that is much smaller and simpler than bacteria.

Viruses are visible only under an electron microscope. They come in a variety of shapes, ranging from spherical to rod shaped. The fact that they contain either deoxyribonucleic acid (DNA) or ribonucleic acid (RNA)—*but never both*—allows them to be divided into two major classes: DNA viruses and RNA viruses (Figure 19.17).

FIGURE 19.17 Viruses

Viruses come in a variety of shapes that are determined by their protein coats.

A *DNA virus* enters a host cell and induces the cell to replicate the viral DNA and produce viral proteins. These proteins and DNA assemble into new viruses that are released by the host cell, which may die in the process. The new viruses can then invade other cells and repeat the cycle. Cell death and the production of new viruses account for the symptoms of viral infections.

Most *RNA viruses* use their nucleic acids in much the same way as the DNA viruses, penetrating a host cell and inducing it to replicate the viral RNA and synthesize viral proteins. The new RNA strands and viral proteins are then assembled into new viruses. Some RNA viruses, however, called **retroviruses** (Figure 19.18), synthesize DNA in the host cell, in a process that is the reverse of the DNA-to-RNA transcription that normally occurs in cells. (See Figure 19.10 for the transcription process.) The synthesis of DNA from an RNA template is catalyzed by the enzyme reverse transcriptase.

retrovirus

An RNA virus that directs the synthesis of a DNA copy in the host cell.

FIGURE 19.18 Life Cycle of a Retrovirus

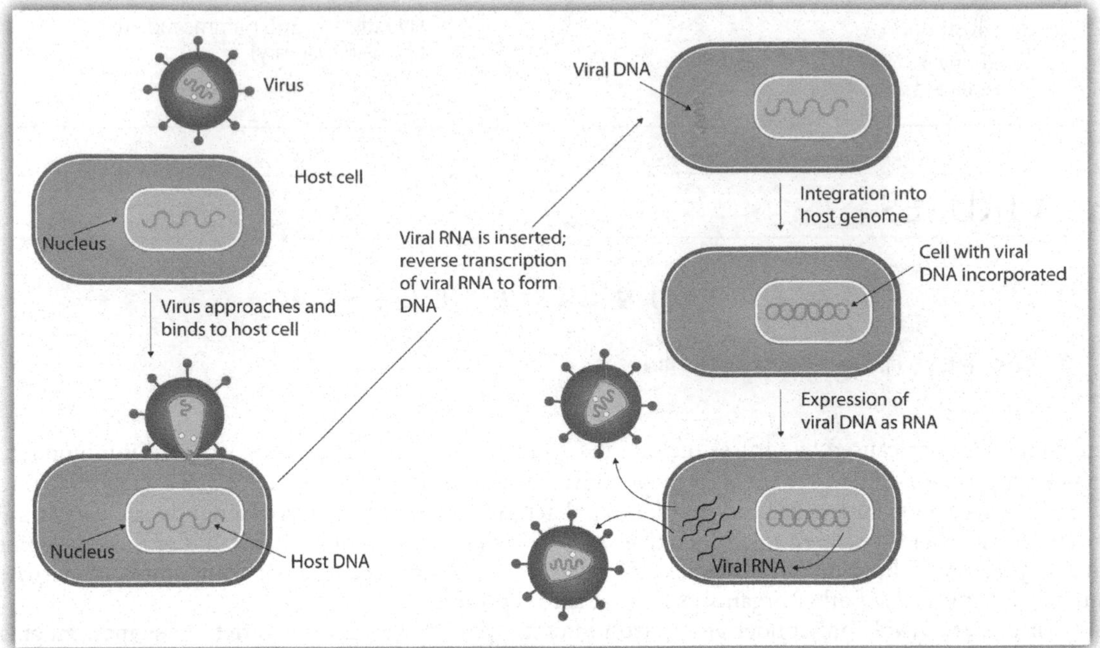

Perhaps the best-known retrovirus is the human immunodeficiency virus (HIV) that causes AIDS. It is estimated that there are about 33 million people worldwide testing positive for HIV infections, many of whom have developed AIDS as a result. In 2007 alone, 2.7 million people became infected with HIV, and in the same year, AIDS caused the deaths of approximately 2 million people. The virus uses glycoproteins on its outer surface to attach to receptors on the surface of T cells, a group of white blood cells that normally help protect the body from infections. The virus then enters the T cell, where it replicates and eventually destroys the cell. With his or her T cells destroyed, the AIDS victim is at increased risk of succumbing to pneumonia or other infectious diseases.

In 1987, azidothymidine (AZT, also known as zidovudine or the brand name Retrovir) became the first drug approved for the treatment of AIDS. It works by binding to reverse transcriptase in place of deoxythymidine triphosphate, after which, because AZT does not have a 3′OH group, further replication is blocked. In the past 10 years, several other drugs have been approved that also act by inhibiting the viral reverse transcriptase.

Deoxythymidine tiphosphate

Azidothymidine (AZT)

As part of HIV reproduction in an infected cell, newly synthesized viral proteins must be cut by a specific viral-induced HIV protease to form shorter proteins. An intensive research effort was made to design drugs that specifically inhibited this proteolytic enzyme, without affecting the proteolytic enzymes (like trypsin) that are needed by the host. In December 1995, saquinavir (brand names Invirase and Fortovase) was approved for the treatment of AIDS. This drug represented a new class of drugs known as protease inhibitors. Other protease inhibitors soon gained Food and Drug Administration (FDA) approval: ritonavir (Norvir), indinavir (Crixivan), and nelfinavir (Viracept).

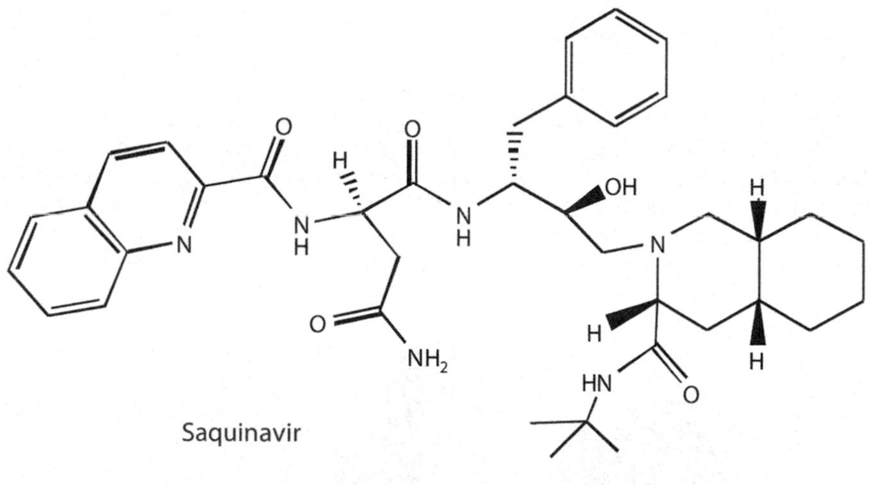

Saquinavir

Raltegravir (Isentress) is a newer anti-AIDS drug that was approved by the FDA in October 2007. This drug inhibits the integrase enzyme that is needed to integrate the HIV DNA into cellular DNA, an essential step in the production of more HIV particles.

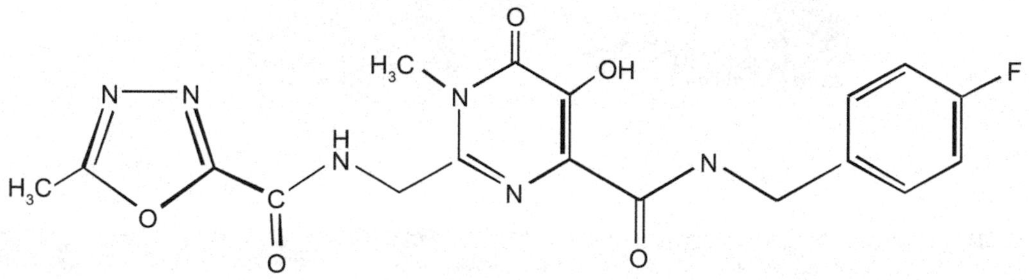

Raltegravir

A major problem in treating HIV infections is that the virus can become resistant to any of these drugs. One way to combat the problem has been to administer a "cocktail" of drugs, typically a combination of two reverse transcriptase inhibitors along with a protease inhibitor. These treatments can significantly reduce the amount of HIV in an infected person.

CONCEPT REVIEW EXERCISES

1. Describe the general structure of a virus.
2. How does a DNA virus differ from an RNA virus?
3. Why is HIV known as a retrovirus?

ANSWERS

1. A virus consists of a central core of nucleic acid enclosed in a protective shell of proteins. There may be lipid or carbohydrate molecules on the surface.
2. A DNA virus has DNA as its genetic material, while an RNA virus has RNA as its genetic material.
3. In a cell, a retrovirus synthesizes a DNA copy of its RNA genetic material.

Career Focus: Genetics Counselor

A genetics counselor works with individuals and families who have birth defects or genetic disorders or a family history of a disease, such as cancer, with a genetic link. A genetics counselor may work in a variety of health-care settings (such as a hospital) to obtain family medical and reproductive histories; explain how genetic conditions are inherited; explain the causes, diagnosis, and care of these conditions; interpret the results of genetic tests; and aid the individual or family in making decisions regarding genetic diseases or conditions. A certified genetics counselor must obtain a master's degree from an accredited program. Applicants to these graduate programs usually have an undergraduate degree in biology, psychology, or genetics.

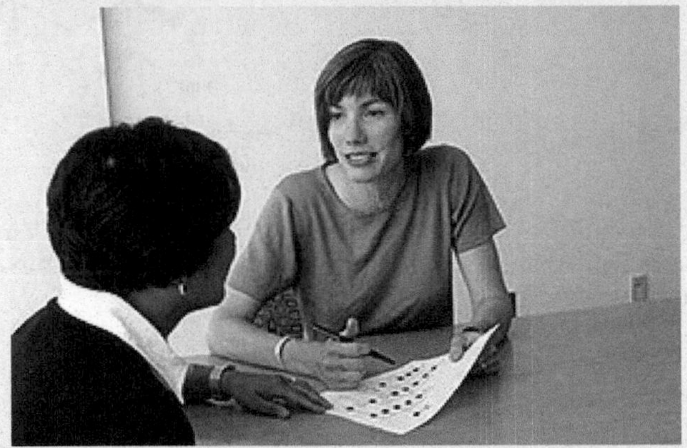

Source: Photo courtesy of the United States National Institutes for Health, http://commons.wikimedia.org/wiki/File:Geneticcounseling.jpg.

KEY TAKEAWAYS

- Viruses are very small infectious agents that contain either DNA or RNA as their genetic material.
- The human immunodeficiency virus (HIV) causes acquired immunodeficiency syndrome (AIDS).

EXERCISES

1. Describe how a DNA virus invades and destroys a cell.
2.
   a. Describe how an RNA virus invades and destroys a cell.
   b. How does this differ from a DNA virus?
3. What HIV enzyme does AZT inhibit?
4. What HIV enzyme does raltegravir inhibit?

ANSWERS

1. The DNA virus enters a host cell and induces the cell to replicate the viral DNA and produce viral proteins. These proteins and DNA assemble into new viruses that are released by the host cell, which may die in the process.

3. reverse transcriptase

7. END-OF-CHAPTER MATERIAL

Chapter Summary

To ensure that you understand the material in this chapter, you should review the meanings of the bold terms in the following summary and ask yourself how they relate to the topics in the chapter.

A cell's hereditary information is encoded in **chromosomes** in the cell's nucleus. Each chromosome is composed of proteins and **deoxyribonucleic acid (DNA)**. The chromosomes contain smaller hereditary units called **genes,** which are relatively short segments of DNA. The hereditary information is expressed or used through the synthesis of **ribonucleic acid (RNA)**. Both **nucleic acids**—DNA and RNA—are polymers composed of monomers known as **nucleotides**, which in turn consist of phosphoric acid (H_3PO_4), a nitrogenous base, and a pentose sugar.

The two types of *nitrogenous bases* most important in nucleic acids are **purines**—adenine (A) and guanine (G)—and **pyrimidines**—cytosine (C), thymine (T), and uracil (U). DNA contains the nitrogenous bases adenine, cytosine, guanine, and thymine, while the bases in RNA are adenine, cytosine, guanine, and uracil. The sugar in the nucleotides of RNA is ribose; the one in DNA is 2-deoxyribose. The sequence of nucleotides in a nucleic acid defines the primary structure of the molecule.

RNA is a single-chain nucleic acid, whereas DNA possesses two nucleic-acid chains intertwined in a secondary structure called a **double helix**. The sugar-phosphate backbone forms the outside the double helix, with the purine and pyrimidine bases tucked inside. Hydrogen bonding between **complementary bases** holds the two strands of the double helix together; A always pairs with T and C always pairs with G.

Cell growth requires **replication**, or reproduction of the cell's DNA. The double helix unwinds, and hydrogen bonding between complementary bases breaks so that there are two single strands of DNA, and each strand is a *template* for the synthesis of a new strand. For protein synthesis, three types of RNA are needed: *messenger RNA* (mRNA), *ribosomal RNA* (rRNA), and *transfer RNA* (tRNA). All are made from a DNA template by a process called **transcription**. The double helix uncoils, and ribonucleotides base-pair to the deoxyribonucleotides on one DNA strand; however, RNA is produced using *uracil* rather than thymine. Once the RNA is formed, it dissociates from the template and leaves the nucleus, and the DNA double helix reforms.

Translation is the process in which proteins are synthesized from the information in mRNA. It occurs at structures called **ribosomes**, which are located outside the nucleus and are composed of rRNA and protein. The 64 possible three-nucleotide combinations of the 4 nucleotides of DNA constitute the **genetic code** that dictates the sequence in which amino acids are joined to make proteins. Each three-nucleotide sequence on mRNA is a **codon**. Each kind of tRNA molecule binds a specific amino acid and has a site containing a three-nucleotide sequence called an **anticodon**.

The general term for any change in the genetic code in an organism's DNA is **mutation**. A change in which a single base is substituted, inserted, or deleted is a **point mutation**. The chemical and/or physical agents that cause mutations are called **mutagens**. Diseases that occur due to mutations in critical DNA sequences are referred to as **genetic diseases**.

Viruses are infectious agents composed of a tightly packed central core of nucleic acids enclosed by a protective shell of proteins. Viruses contain either DNA or RNA as their genetic material but not both. Some RNA viruses, called **retroviruses**, synthesize DNA in the host cell from their RNA genome. The human immunodeficiency virus (HIV) causes acquired immunodeficiency syndrome (AIDS).

ADDITIONAL EXERCISES

1. For this nucleic acid segment,

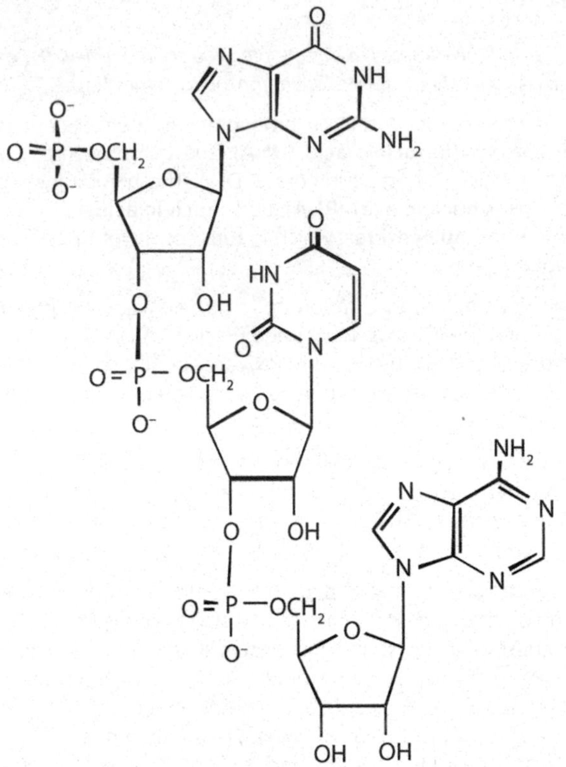

O⁻ O=P—OCH₂ O⁻ N NH N N NH₂ O O OH HN O N O O=P—OCH₂ O⁻ O O OH NH₂ N N N N O=P—OCH₂ O⁻ O OH OH

   a. classify this segment as RNA or DNA and justify your choice.
   b. determine the sequence of this segment, labeling the 5′ and 3′ ends.

2. For this nucleic acid segment,

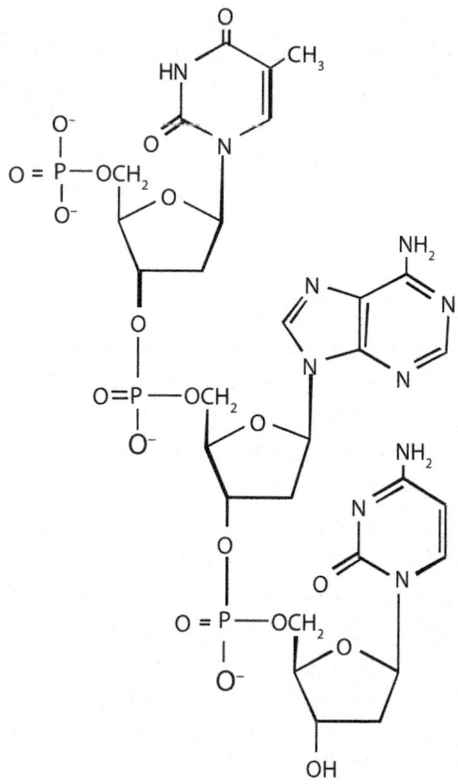

a. classify this segment as RNA or DNA and justify your choice.
b. determine the sequence of this segment, labeling the 5′ and 3′ ends.

3. One of the key pieces of information that Watson and Crick used in determining the secondary structure of DNA came from experiments done by E. Chargaff, in which he studied the nucleotide composition of DNA from many different species. Chargaff noted that the molar quantity of A was always approximately equal to the molar quantity of T, and the molar quantity of C was always approximately equal to the molar quantity of G. How were Chargaff's results explained by the structural model of DNA proposed by Watson and Crick?
4. Suppose Chargaff (see Exercise 3) had used RNA instead of DNA. Would his results have been the same; that is, would the molar quantity of A approximately equal the molar quantity of T? Explain.
5. In the DNA segment

5′-ATGAGGCATGAGACG-3′ (coding strand)

3′-TACTCCGTACTCTGC-5′ (template strand)

a. What products would be formed from the segment's replication?
b. Write the mRNA sequence that would be obtained from the segment's transcription.
c. What is the amino acid sequence of the peptide produced from the mRNA in Exercise 5b?

6. In the DNA segment

5′-ATGACGGTTTACTAAGCC-3′ (coding strand)

3′-TACTGCCAAATGATTCGG-5′ (template strand)

a. What products would be formed from the segment's replication?
b. Write the mRNA sequence that would be obtained from the segment's transcription.
c. What is the amino acid sequence of the peptide produced from the mRNA in Exercise 6b?

7. A hypothetical protein has a molar mass of 23,300 Da. Assume that the average molar mass of an amino acid is 120.
   a. How many amino acids are present in this hypothetical protein?
   b. What is the minimum number of codons present in the mRNA that codes for this protein?
   c. What is the minimum number of nucleotides needed to code for this protein?
8. Bradykinin is a potent peptide hormone composed of nine amino acids that lowers blood pressure.
   a. The amino acid sequence for bradykinin is arg-pro-pro-gly-phe-ser-pro-phe-arg. Postulate a base sequence in the mRNA that would direct the synthesis of this hormone. Include an initiation codon and a termination codon.
   b. What is the nucleotide sequence of the DNA that codes for this mRNA?
9. A particular DNA coding segment is ACGTTAGCCCCAGCT.
   a. Write the sequence of nucleotides in the corresponding mRNA.
   b. Determine the amino acid sequence formed from the mRNA in Exercise 9a during translation.
   c. What amino acid sequence results from each of the following mutations?
      i. replacement of the underlined guanine by adenine
      ii. insertion of thymine immediately after the underlined guanine
      iii. deletion of the underlined guanine
10. A particular DNA coding segment is TACGACGTAACAAGC.
   a. Write the sequence of nucleotides in the corresponding mRNA.
   b. Determine the amino acid sequence formed from the mRNA in Exercise 10a during translation.
   c. What amino acid sequence results from each of the following mutations?
      i. replacement of the underlined guanine by adenine
      ii. replacement of the underlined adenine by thymine
11. Two possible point mutations are the substitution of lysine for leucine *or* the substitution of serine for threonine. Which is likely to be more serious and why?
12. Two possible point mutations are the substitution of valine for leucine *or* the substitution of glutamic acid for histidine. Which is likely to be more serious and why?

ANSWERS

1. a. RNA; the sugar is ribose, rather than deoxyribose
   b. 5′-GUA-3′
3. In the DNA structure, because guanine (G) is always paired with cytosine (C) and adenine (A) is always paired with thymine (T), you would expect to have equal amounts of each.
5. a. Each strand would be replicated, resulting in two double-stranded segments.
   b. 5′-AUGAGGCAUGAGACG-3′
   c. met-arg-his-glu-thr
7. a. 194
   b. 194
   c. 582
9. a. 5′-ACGUUAGCCCCAGCU-3′
   b. thr-leu-ala-pro-ala
   c. i. thr-leu-thr-pro-ala
      ii. thr-leu-val-pro-ser
      iii. thr-leu-pro-gin
11. substitution of lysine for leucine because you are changing from an amino acid with a nonpolar side chain to one that has a positively charged side chain; both serine and threonine, on the other hand, have polar side chains containing the OH group.

CHAPTER 20

Energy Metabolism

Opening Essay

The discovery of the link between insulin and diabetes led to a period of intense research aimed at understanding exactly how insulin works in the body to regulate glucose levels. Hormones in general act by binding to some protein, known as the hormone's receptor, thus initiating a series of events that lead to a desired outcome. In the early 1970s, the insulin receptor was purified, and researchers began to study what happens after insulin binds to its receptor and how those events are linked to the uptake and metabolism of glucose in cells.

The insulin receptor is located in the cell membrane and consists of four polypeptide chains: two identical chains called α chains and two identical chains called β chains. The α chains, positioned on the outer surface of the membrane, consist of 735 amino acids each and contain the binding site for insulin. The β chains are integral membrane proteins, each composed of 620 amino acids. The binding of insulin to its receptor stimulates the β chains to catalyze the addition of phosphate groups to the specific side chains of tyrosine (referred to as phosphorylation) in the β chains and other cell proteins, leading to the activation of reactions that metabolize glucose. In this chapter we will look at the pathway that breaks down glucose—in response to activation by insulin—for the purpose of providing energy for the cell.

Model of the Structure of the Insulin Receptor

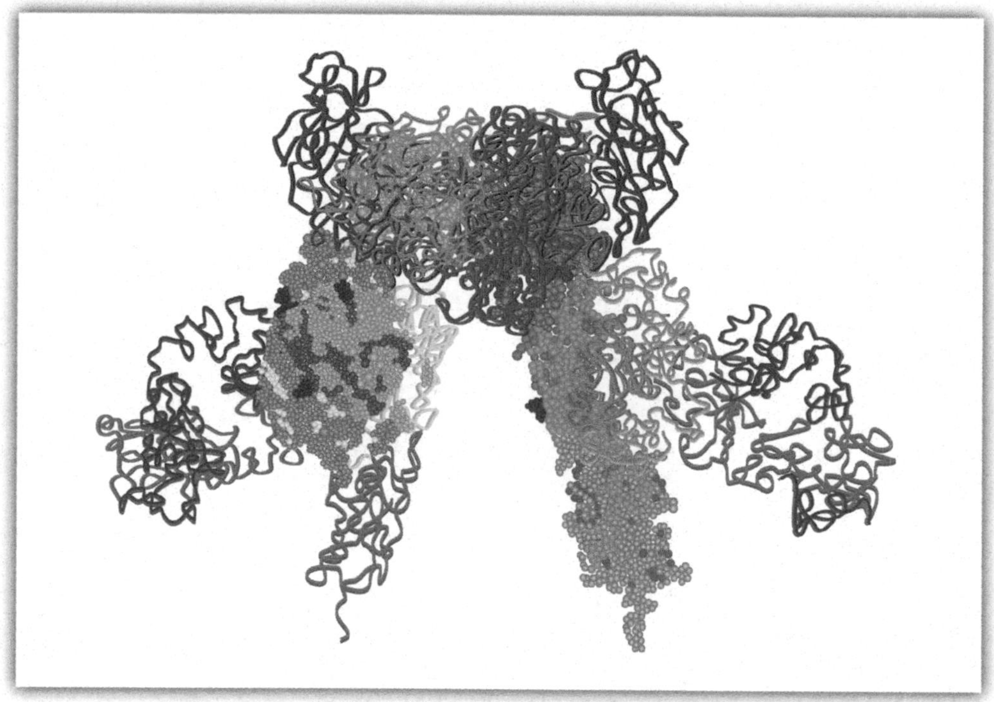

Life requires energy. Animals, for example, require heat energy to maintain body temperature, mechanical energy to move their limbs, and chemical energy to synthesize the compounds needed by their cells. Living cells remain organized and functioning properly only through a continual supply of energy. But only specific forms of energy can be used. Supplying a plant with energy by holding it in a flame will not prolong its life. On the other hand, a green plant is able to absorb radiant energy from the sun, the most abundant source of energy for life on the earth. Plants use this energy first to form glucose and then to make other carbohydrates, as well as lipids and proteins.

Unlike plants, animals cannot directly use the sun's energy to synthesize new compounds. They must eat plants or other animals to get carbohydrates, fats, and proteins and the chemical energy stored in them (Figure 20.2). Once digested and transported to the cells, the nutrient molecules can be used in either of two ways: as building blocks for making new cell parts or repairing old ones or "burned" for energy.

FIGURE 20.2 Some Energy Transformations in Living Systems
Plants and animals exist in a cycle; each requires products of the other.

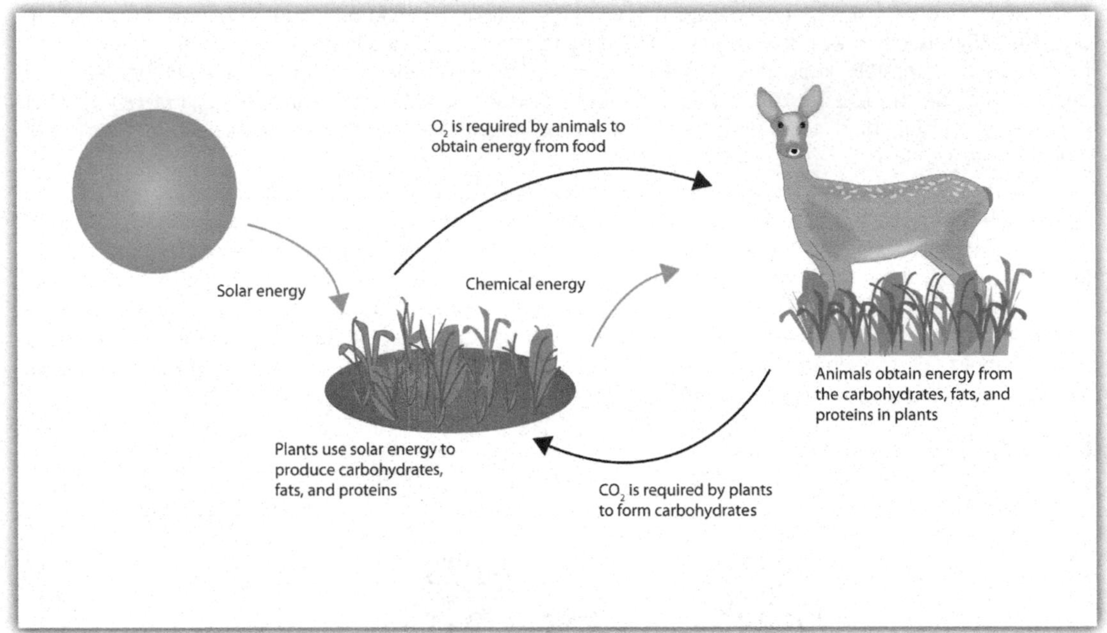

metabolism
The thousands of coordinated chemical reactions that keep cells alive.

catabolism
Metabolic reactions in which molecules are broken down to obtain energy.

anabolism
Metabolic reactions in which molecules are synthesized.

The thousands of coordinated chemical reactions that keep cells alive are referred to collectively as **metabolism**. In general, metabolic reactions are divided into two classes: the breaking down of molecules to obtain energy is **catabolism**, and the building of new molecules needed by living systems is **anabolism**.

Note

Any chemical compound that participates in a metabolic reaction is a *metabolite*.

Most of the energy required by animals is generated from lipids and carbohydrates. These fuels must be oxidized, or "burned," for the energy to be released. The oxidation process ultimately converts the lipid or carbohydrate to carbon dioxide (CO_2) and water (H_2O).

$$\textbf{Carbohydrate}: C_6H_{12}O_6 + 6O_2 \rightarrow 6CO_2 + 6H_2O + 670 \text{ kcal}$$

$$\textbf{Lipid}: C_{16}H_{32}O_2 + 23O_2 \rightarrow 16CO_2 + 16H_2O + 2{,}385 \text{ kcal}$$

respiration
The process by which cells oxidize organic molecules in the presence of gaseous oxygen to produce carbon dioxide, water, and energy in the form of ATP.

These two equations summarize the biological combustion of a carbohydrate and a lipid by the cell through respiration. **Respiration** is the collective name for all metabolic processes in which gaseous oxygen is used to oxidize organic matter to carbon dioxide, water, and energy.

Like the combustion of the common fuels we burn in our homes and cars (wood, coal, gasoline), respiration uses oxygen from the air to break down complex organic substances to carbon dioxide and water. But the energy released in the burning of wood is manifested entirely in the form of heat, and excess heat energy is not only useless but also injurious to the living cell. Living organisms instead conserve much of the energy respiration releases by channeling it into a series of stepwise reactions that produce adenosine triphosphate (ATP) or other compounds that ultimately lead to the synthesis of ATP. The remainder of the energy is released as heat and manifested as body temperature. Section 1 examines the structure of ATP and begins to explore its role as the chemical energy carrier of the body.

1. ATP—THE UNIVERSAL ENERGY CURRENCY

LEARNING OBJECTIVE

1. **Describe the importance of ATP as a source of energy in living organisms.**

Adenosine triphosphate (ATP), a nucleotide composed of adenine, ribose, and three phosphate groups, is perhaps the most important of the so-called energy-rich compounds in a cell. Its concentration in the cell varies from 0.5 to 2.5 mg/mL of cell fluid.

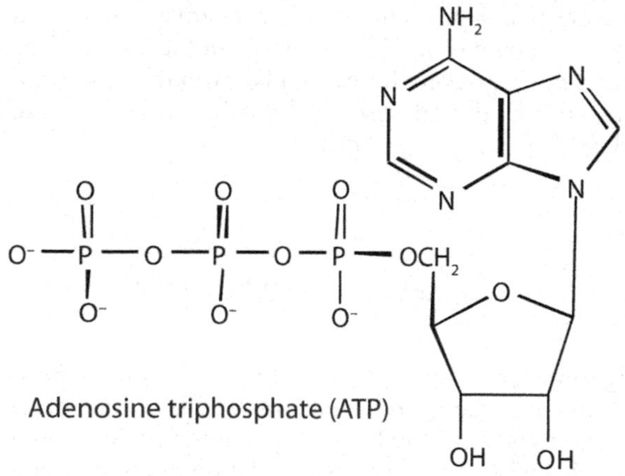

Adenosine triphosphate (ATP)

Energy-rich compounds are substances having particular structural features that lead to a release of energy after hydrolysis. As a result, these compounds are able to supply energy for biochemical processes that require energy. The structural feature important in ATP is the phosphoric acid anhydride, or pyrophosphate, linkage:

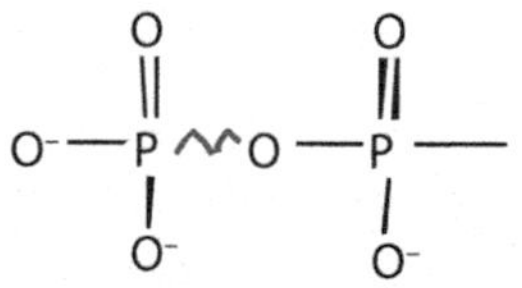

The pyrophosphate bond, symbolized by a squiggle (~), is hydrolyzed when ATP is converted to adenosine diphosphate (ADP). In this hydrolysis reaction, the products contain less energy than the reactants; there is a release of energy (> 7 kcal/mol). One reason for the amount of energy released is that hydrolysis relieves the electron-electron repulsions experienced by the negatively charged phosphate groups when they are bonded to each other (Figure 20.3).

FIGURE 20.3 Hydrolysis of ATP to Form ADP

Energy is released because the products (ADP and phosphate ion) have less energy than the reactants [ATP and water (H_2O)].

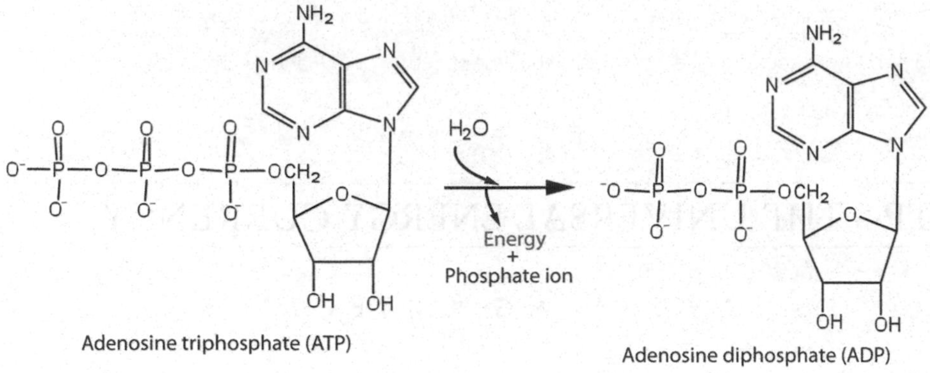

H_2O

Energy + Phosphate ion

Adenosine triphosphate (ATP)

Adenosine diphosphate (ADP)

The general equation for ATP hydrolysis is as follows:

$$ATP + H_2O \rightarrow ADP + P_i + 7.4 \text{ kcal/mol}$$

If the hydrolysis of ATP releases energy, its synthesis (from ADP) requires energy. In the cell, ATP is produced by those processes that supply energy to the organism (absorption of radiant energy from the sun in green plants and breakdown of food in animals), and it is hydrolyzed by those processes that require energy (the syntheses of carbohydrates, lipids, proteins; the transmission of nerve impulses; muscle contractions). In fact, ATP is the principal medium of energy exchange in biological systems. Many scientists call it the energy currency of cells.

Note

P_i is the symbol for the inorganic phosphate anions $H_2PO_4^-$ and HPO_4^{2-}.

ATP is not the only high-energy compound needed for metabolism. Several others are listed in Table 20.1. Notice, however, that the energy released when ATP is hydrolyzed is approximately midway between those of the high-energy and the low-energy phosphate compounds. This means that the hydrolysis of ATP can provide energy for the phosphorylation of the compounds below it in the table. For example, the hydrolysis of ATP provides sufficient energy for the phosphorylation of glucose to form glucose 1-phosphate. By the same token, the hydrolysis of compounds, such as creatine phosphate, that appear *above* ATP in the table can provide the energy needed to resynthesize ATP from ADP.

TABLE 20.1 Energy Released by Hydrolysis of Some Phosphate Compounds

Type	Example	Energy Released (kcal/mol)
acyl phosphate	1,3-bisphosphoglycerate (BPG)	−11.8
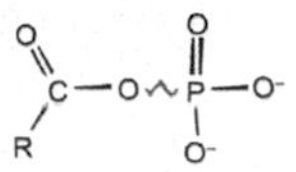	acetyl phosphate	−11.3
guanidine phosphates	creatine phosphate	−10.3
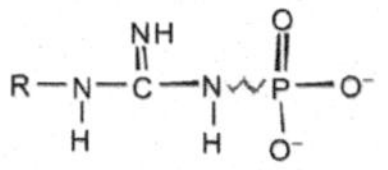	arginine phosphate	−9.1
pyrophosphates	PP_i* → $2P_i$	−7.8
	ATP → AMP + PP_i	−7.7
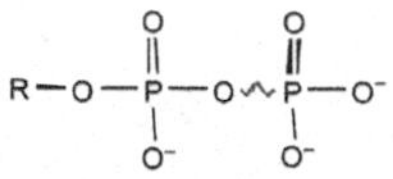	ATP → ADP + P_i	−7.5
	ADP → AMP + P_i	−7.5
sugar phosphates	glucose 1-phosphate	−5.0
	fructose 6-phosphate	−3.8
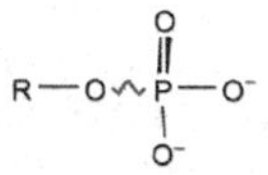	AMP → adenosine + P_i	−3.4
	glucose 6-phosphate	−3.3
	glycerol 3-phosphate	−2.2

***PPi is the pyrophosphate ion.**

CONCEPT REVIEW EXERCISE

1. Why is ATP referred to as the energy currency of the cell?

ANSWER

1. ATP is the principal molecule involved in energy exchange reactions in biological systems.

KEY TAKEAWAY

- The hydrolysis of ATP releases energy that can be used for cellular processes that require energy.

EXERCISES

1. How do ATP and ADP differ in structure?
2. Why does the hydrolysis of ATP to ADP involve the release of energy?
3. Identify whether each compound would be classified as a high-energy phosphate compound.
   a. ATP
   b. glucose 6-phosphate
   c. creatine phosphate

4. Identify whether each compound would be classified as a high-energy phosphate compound.
   a. ADP
   b. AMP
   c. glucose 1-phosphate

ANSWERS

1. ATP has a triphosphate group attached, while ADP has only a diphosphate group attached.

3. a. yes
   b. no
   c. yes

2. STAGE I OF CATABOLISM

LEARNING OBJECTIVE

1. **Describe how carbohydrates, fats, and proteins are broken down during digestion.**

digestion

The breakdown of food molecules by hydrolysis reactions into the individual monomer units in the mouth, stomach, and small intestine.

We have said that animals obtain chemical energy from the food—carbohydrates, fats, and proteins—they eat through reactions defined collectively as *catabolism*. We can think of catabolism as occurring in three stages (Figure 20.4). In stage I, carbohydrates, fats, and proteins are broken down into their individual monomer units: carbohydrates into simple sugars, fats into fatty acids and glycerol, and proteins into amino acids. One part of stage I of catabolism is the breakdown of food molecules by hydrolysis reactions into the individual monomer units—which occurs in the mouth, stomach, and small intestine—and is referred to as **digestion**.

In stage II, these monomer units (or building blocks) are further broken down through different reaction pathways, one of which produces ATP, to form a common end product that can then be used in stage III to produce even more ATP. In this chapter, we will look at each stage of catabolism—as an overview and in detail.

FIGURE 20.4 Energy Conversions

The conversion of food into cellular energy (as ATP) occurs in three stages.

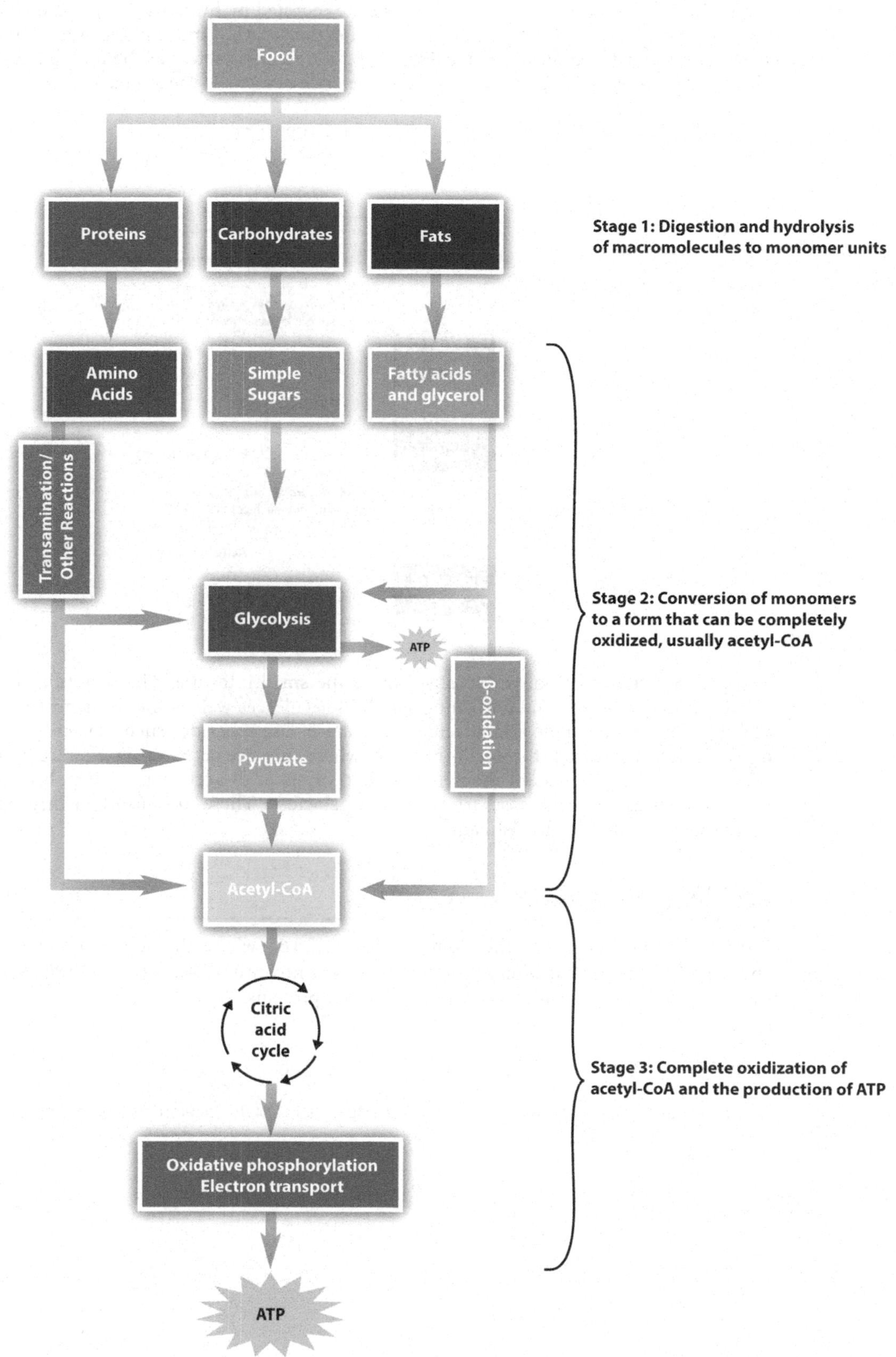

2.1 Digestion of Carbohydrates

Carbohydrate digestion begins in the mouth (Figure 20.5), where salivary α-amylase attacks the α-glycosidic linkages in starch, the main carbohydrate ingested by humans. Cleavage of the glycosidic linkages produces a mixture of dextrins, maltose, and glucose. (For more information about carbohydrates, see Chapter 16.) The α-amylase mixed into the food remains active as the food passes through the esophagus, but it is rapidly inactivated in the acidic environment of the stomach.

FIGURE 20.5 The Principal Events and Sites of Carbohydrate Digestion

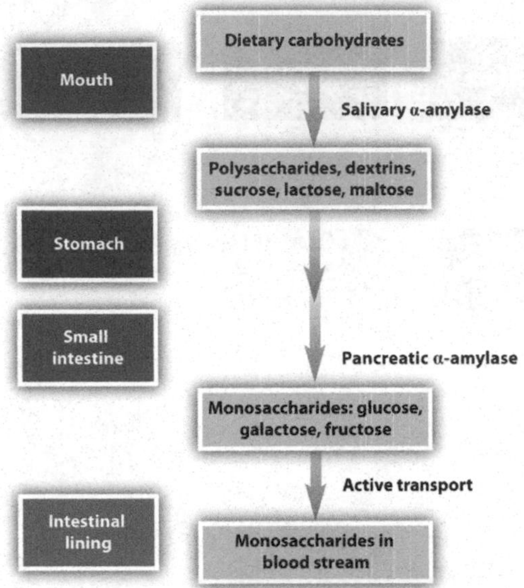

The primary site of carbohydrate digestion is the small intestine. The secretion of α-amylase in the small intestine converts any remaining starch molecules, as well as the dextrins, to maltose. Maltose is then cleaved into two glucose molecules by maltase. Disaccharides such as sucrose and lactose are not digested until they reach the small intestine, where they are acted on by sucrase and lactase, respectively. The major products of the complete hydrolysis of disaccharides and polysaccharides are three monosaccharide units: glucose, fructose, and galactose. These are absorbed through the wall of the small intestine into the bloodstream.

2.2 Digestion of Proteins

gastric juice

A mixture of water, inorganic ions, hydrochloric acid, and various enzymes and proteins found in the stomach.

Protein digestion begins in the stomach (Figure 20.6), where the action of gastric juice hydrolyzes about 10% of the peptide bonds. **Gastric juice** is a mixture of water (more than 99%), inorganic ions, hydrochloric acid, and various enzymes and other proteins.

Note

The pain of a gastric ulcer is at least partially due to irritation of the ulcerated tissue by acidic gastric juice.

FIGURE 20.6 The Principal Events and Sites of Protein Digestion

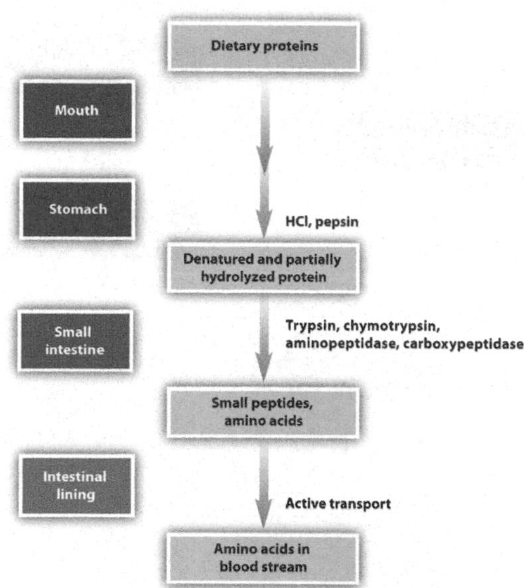

The hydrochloric acid (HCl) in gastric juice is secreted by glands in the stomach lining. The pH of freshly secreted gastric juice is about 1.0, but the contents of the stomach may raise the pH to between 1.5 and 2.5. HCl helps to denature food proteins; that is, it unfolds the protein molecules to expose their chains to more efficient enzyme action. The principal digestive component of gastric juice is pepsinogen, an inactive enzyme produced in cells located in the stomach wall. When food enters the stomach after a period of fasting, pepsinogen is converted to its active form—pepsin—in a series of steps initiated by the drop in pH. Pepsin catalyzes the hydrolysis of peptide linkages within protein molecules. It has a fairly broad specificity but acts preferentially on linkages involving the aromatic amino acids tryptophan, tyrosine, and phenylalanine, as well as methionine and leucine.

Protein digestion is completed in the small intestine. Pancreatic juice, carried from the pancreas via the pancreatic duct, contains inactive enzymes such as trypsinogen and chymotrypsinogen. They are activated in the small intestine as follows (Figure 20.7): The intestinal mucosal cells secrete the proteolytic enzyme enteropeptidase, which converts trypsinogen to trypsin; trypsin then activates chymotrypsinogen to chymotrypsin (and also completes the activation of trypsinogen). Both of these active enzymes catalyze the hydrolysis of peptide bonds in protein chains. Chymotrypsin preferentially attacks peptide bonds involving the carboxyl groups of the aromatic amino acids (phenylalanine, tryptophan, and tyrosine). Trypsin attacks peptide bonds involving the carboxyl groups of the basic amino acids (lysine and arginine). Pancreatic juice also contains procarboxypeptidase, which is cleaved by trypsin to carboxypeptidase. The latter is an enzyme that catalyzes the hydrolysis of peptide linkages at the free carboxyl end of the peptide chain, resulting in the stepwise liberation of free amino acids from the carboxyl end of the polypeptide.

FIGURE 20.7 Activation of Some Pancreatic Enzymes in the Small Intestine

Trypsinogen
Enteropeptidase
Trypsin
Chymotrypsinogen
Chymotrypsin

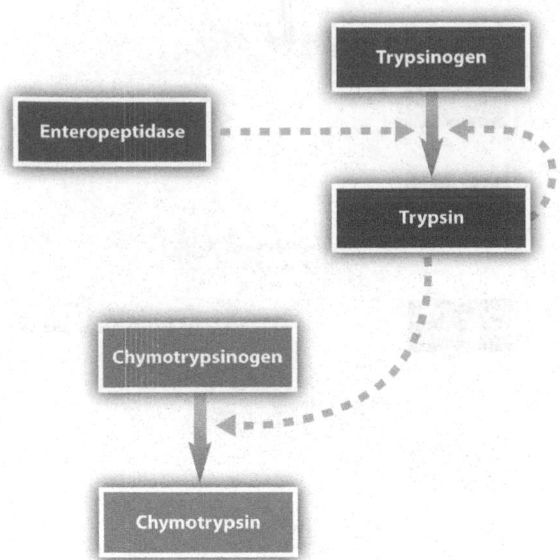

Aminopeptidases in the intestinal juice remove amino acids from the N-terminal end of peptides and proteins possessing a free amino group. Figure 20.8 illustrates the specificity of these protein-digesting enzymes. The amino acids that are released by protein digestion are absorbed across the intestinal wall into the circulatory system, where they can be used for protein synthesis.

FIGURE 20.8 Hydrolysis of a Peptide by Several Peptidases

This diagram illustrates where in a peptide the different peptidases we have discussed would catalyze hydrolysis the peptide bonds.

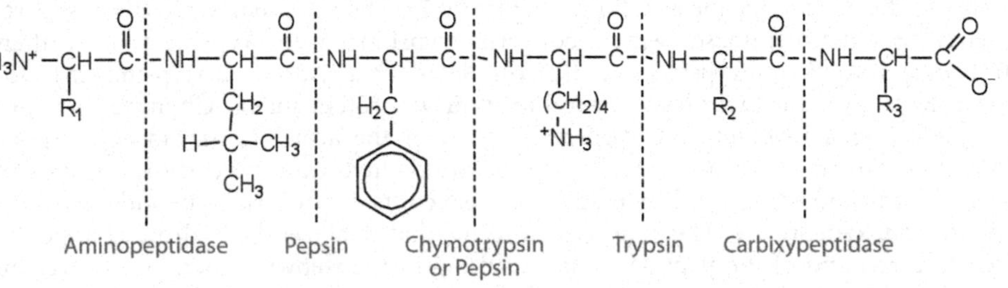

Aminopeptidase
Pepsin
Chymotrypsin or Pepsin
Trypsin
Carbixypeptidase

2.3 Digestion of Lipids

Lipid digestion begins in the upper portion of the small intestine (Figure 20.9). A hormone secreted in this region stimulates the gallbladder to discharge bile into the duodenum. The principal constituents of bile are the bile salts, which emulsify large, water-insoluble lipid droplets, disrupting some of the hydrophobic interactions holding the lipid molecules together and suspending the resulting smaller globules (micelles) in the aqueous digestive medium. (For more information on bile salts, see Chapter 17, [Unsupported Reference Type: chapter-section].) These changes greatly increase the surface area of the lipid particles, allowing for more intimate contact with the lipases and thus rapid digestion of the fats. Another hormone promotes the secretion of pancreatic juice, which contains these enzymes.

FIGURE 20.9 The Principal Events and Sites of Lipid (Primarily Triglyceride) Digestion

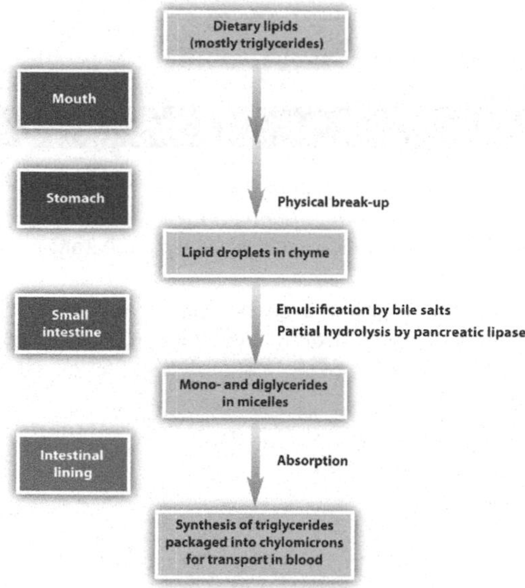

The lipases in pancreatic juice catalyze the digestion of triglycerides first to diglycerides and then to 2-monoglycerides and fatty acids:

$$\underset{\text{Triglyceride}}{\begin{array}{l} H_2C-O-\overset{O}{\overset{\|}{C}}-R \\ \quad | \\ HC-O-\overset{O}{\overset{\|}{C}}-R' \\ \quad | \\ H_2C-O-\overset{O}{\overset{\|}{C}}-R'' \end{array}} \xrightarrow[\text{lipase}]{H_2O} \underset{\text{Diglyceride}}{\begin{array}{l} H_2C-OH \\ \quad | \\ HC-O-\overset{O}{\overset{\|}{C}}-R' \\ \quad | \\ H_2C-O-\overset{O}{\overset{\|}{C}}-R'' \end{array}} + \underset{\text{Fatty acid}}{R-C(=O)OH} \xrightarrow[\text{lipase}]{H_2O} \underset{\text{Monoglyceride}}{\begin{array}{l} H_2C-OH \\ \quad | \\ HC-O-\overset{O}{\overset{\|}{C}}-R' \\ \quad | \\ H_2C-OH \end{array}} + \underset{\text{Fatty acid}}{R''-C(=O)OH}$$

The monoglycerides and fatty acids cross the intestinal lining into the bloodstream, where they are resynthesized into triglycerides and transported as lipoprotein complexes known as chylomicrons. Phospholipids and cholesteryl esters undergo similar hydrolysis in the small intestine, and their component molecules are also absorbed through the intestinal lining.

The further metabolism of monosaccharides, fatty acids, and amino acids released in stage I of catabolism occurs in stages II and III of catabolism.

CONCEPT REVIEW EXERCISES

1. Distinguish between each pair of compounds.
   a. pepsin and pepsinogen
   b. chymotrypsin and trypsin
   c. aminopeptidase and carboxypeptidase
2. What are the primary end products of each form of digestion?
   a. carbohydrate digestion
   b. lipid digestion
   c. protein digestion

3. In what section of the digestive tract does most of the carbohydrate, lipid, and protein digestion take place?

ANSWERS

1. a. Pepsinogen is an inactive form of pepsin; pepsin is the active form of the enzyme.
   b. Both enzymes catalyze the hydrolysis of peptide bonds. Chymotrypsin catalyzes the hydrolysis of peptide bonds following aromatic amino acids, while trypsin catalyzes the hydrolysis of peptide bonds following lysine and arginine.
   c. Aminopeptidase catalyzes the hydrolysis of amino acids from the N-terminal end of a protein, while carboxypeptidase catalyzes the hydrolysis of amino acids from the C-terminal end of a protein.
2. a. glucose, fructose, and galactose
   b. monoglycerides and fatty acids
   c. amino acids
3. the small intestine

KEY TAKEAWAYS

- During digestion, carbohydrates are broken down into monosaccharides, proteins are broken down into amino acids, and triglycerides are broken down into glycerol and fatty acids.
- Most of the digestion reactions occur in the small intestine.

EXERCISES

1. What are the products of digestion (or stage I of catabolism)?
2. What is the general type of reaction used in digestion?
3. Give the site of action and the function of each enzyme.
   a. chymotrypsin
   b. lactase
   c. pepsin
   d. maltase
4. Give the site of action and the function of each enzyme.
   a. α-amylase
   b. trypsin
   c. sucrase
   d. aminopeptidase
5.
   a. What is the meaning of the following statement? "Bile salts act to emulsify lipids in the small intestine."
   b. Why is emulsification important?
6. Using chemical equations, describe the chemical changes that triglycerides undergo during digestion.
7. What are the expected products from the enzymatic action of chymotrypsin on each amino acid segment?
   a. gly-ala-phe-thr-leu
   b. ala-ile-tyr-ser-arg
   c. val-trp-arg-leu-cys
8. What are the expected products from the enzymatic action of trypsin on each amino acid segment?
   a. leu-thr-glu-lys-ala
   b. phe-arg-ala-leu-val
   c. ala-arg-glu-trp-lys

ANSWERS

1. proteins: amino acids; carbohydrates: monosaccharides; fats: fatty acids and glycerol

3. a. Chymotrypsin is found in the small intestine and catalyzes the hydrolysis of peptide bonds following aromatic amino acids.
   b. Lactase is found in the small intestine and catalyzes the hydrolysis of lactose.
   c. Pepsin is found in the stomach and catalyzes the hydrolysis of peptide bonds, primarily those that occur after aromatic amino acids.
   d. Maltase is found in the small intestine and catalyzes the hydrolysis of maltose.
5. a. Bile salts aid in digestion by dispersing lipids throughout the aqueous solution in the small intestine.
   b. Emulsification is important because lipids are not soluble in water; it breaks lipids up into smaller particles that can be more readily hydrolyzed by lipases.
7. a. gly-ala-phe and thr-leu
   b. ala-ile-tyr and ser-arg
   c. val-trp and arg-leu-cys

3. OVERVIEW OF STAGE II OF CATABOLISM

LEARNING OBJECTIVE

1. **Describe the role of acetyl-CoA in metabolism.**

A **metabolic pathway** is a series of biochemical reactions by which an organism converts a given reactant to a specific end product. As you will learn in Section 5 through Section 7, there are specific metabolic pathways—which are different for carbohydrates, triglycerides, and proteins—that break down the products of stage I of catabolism (monosaccharides, fatty acids, and amino acids) to produce a common end product, acetyl-coenzyme A (acetyl-CoA) in stage II of catabolism.

metabolic pathway

A series of biochemical reactions by which an organism converts a given reactant to a specific end product.

Acetyl-CoA is shown in Figure 20.10. The acetyl unit, derived (as we will see) from the breakdown of carbohydrates, lipids, and proteins, is attached to coenzyme A, making the acetyl unit more reactive. Acetyl-CoA is used in a myriad of biochemical pathways. For example, it may be used as the starting material for the biosynthesis of lipids (such as triglycerides, phospholipids, or cholesterol and other steroids). Most importantly for energy generation, it may enter the citric acid cycle and be oxidized to produce energy, if energy is needed and oxygen is available. The various fates or uses of acetyl-CoA are summarized in Figure 20.11.

FIGURE 20.10 The Structure of Acetyl-Coenzyme A (Acetyl-CoA)

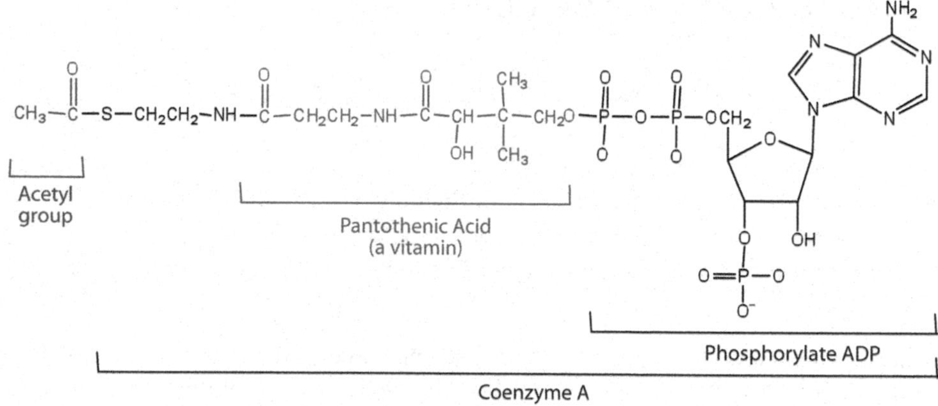

FIGURE 20.11 Cell Chemistry

Acetyl-CoA plays a variety of roles in cell chemistry.

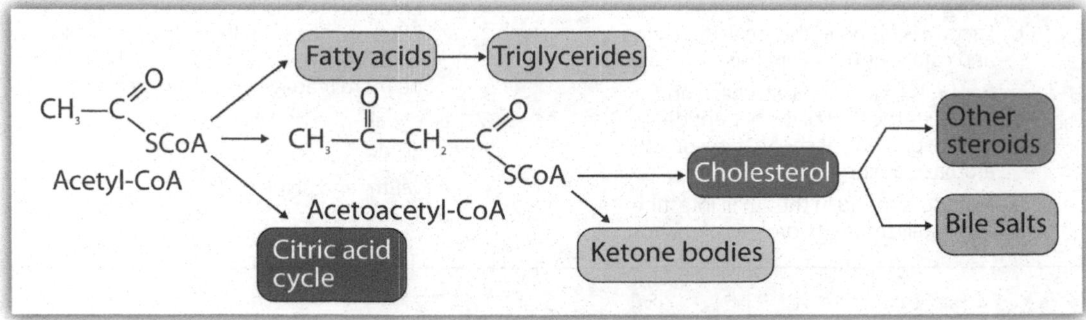

CONCEPT REVIEW EXERCISES

1. What is a metabolic pathway?
2. What vitamin is required to make coenzyme A?

ANSWERS

1. A metabolic pathway is a series of biochemical reactions by which an organism converts a given reactant to a specific end product.
2. pantothenic acid

KEY TAKEAWAY

- Acetyl-CoA is formed from the breakdown of carbohydrates, lipids, and proteins. It is used in many biochemical pathways.

4. STAGE III OF CATABOLISM

LEARNING OBJECTIVES

1. **Describe the reactions of the citric acid cycle.**
2. **Describe the function of the citric acid cycle and identify the products produced.**
3. **Describe the role of the electron transport chain in energy metabolism.**
4. **Describe the role of oxidative phosphorylation in energy metabolism.**

citric acid cycle (or Krebs cycle or tricarboxylic acid [TCA] cycle)

A cyclic sequence of reactions that brings about the oxidation of a two-C unit to carbon dioxide and water.

The acetyl group enters a cyclic sequence of reactions known collectively as the **citric acid cycle (or Krebs cycle or tricarboxylic acid [TCA] cycle)**. The cyclical design of this complex series of reactions, which bring about the oxidation of the acetyl group of acetyl-CoA to carbon dioxide and water, was first proposed by Hans Krebs in 1937. (He was awarded the 1953 Nobel Prize in Physiology or Medicine.) Acetyl-CoA's entrance into the citric acid cycle is the beginning of stage III of catabolism. The citric acid cycle produces adenosine triphosphate (ATP), reduced nicotinamide adenine dinucleotide (NADH), reduced flavin adenine dinucleotide ($FADH_2$), and metabolic intermediates for the synthesis of needed compounds.

4.1 Steps of the Citric Acid Cycle

At first glance, the citric acid cycle appears rather complex (Figure 20.12). All the reactions, however, are familiar types in organic chemistry: hydration, oxidation, decarboxylation, and hydrolysis. Each reaction of the citric acid cycle is numbered, and in Figure 20.12, the two acetyl carbon atoms are highlighted in red. Each intermediate in the cycle is a carboxylic acid, existing as an anion at physiological pH. All the reactions occur within the mitochondria, which are small organelles within the cells of plants and animals. We will look more closely at the structure of mitochondria in Section 5.

FIGURE 20.12 Reactions of the Citric Acid Cycle

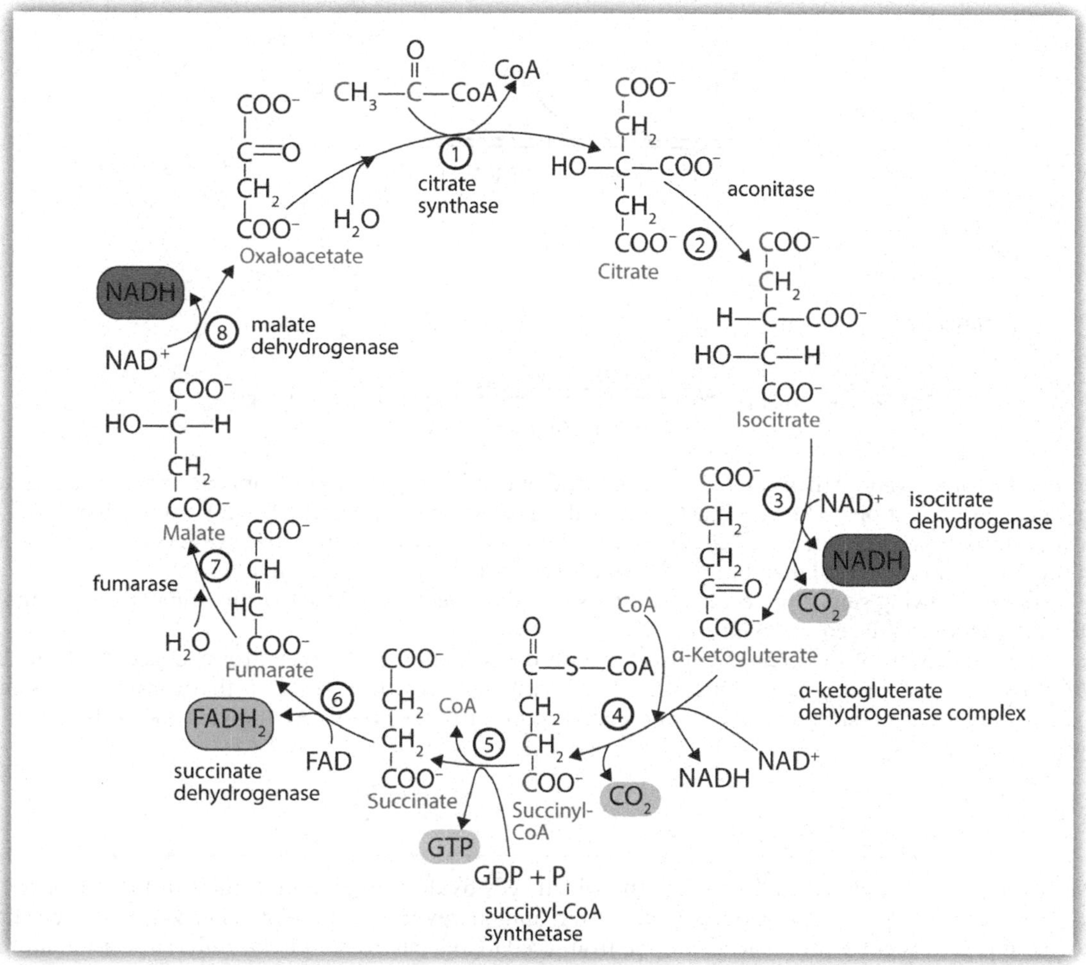

In the first reaction, acetyl-CoA enters the citric acid cycle, and the acetyl group is transferred onto oxaloacetate, yielding citrate. Note that this step releases coenzyme A. The reaction is catalyzed by *citrate synthase*.

In the next step, *aconitase* catalyzes the isomerization of citrate to isocitrate. In this reaction, a tertiary alcohol, which cannot be oxidized, is converted to a secondary alcohol, which can be oxidized in the next step.

Isocitrate then undergoes a reaction known as oxidative decarboxylation because the alcohol is oxidized and the molecule is shortened by one carbon atom with the release of carbon dioxide (decarboxylation). The reaction is catalyzed by *isocitrate dehydrogenase*, and the product of the reaction is α-ketoglutarate. An important reaction linked to this is the reduction of the coenzyme nicotinamide adenine dinucleotide (NAD^+) to NADH. The NADH is ultimately reoxidized, and the energy released is used in the synthesis of ATP, as we shall see.

The fourth step is another oxidative decarboxylation. This time α-ketoglutarate is converted to succinyl-CoA, and another molecule of NAD^+ is reduced to NADH. The *α-ketoglutarate dehydrogenase complex* catalyzes this reaction. This is the only irreversible reaction in the citric acid cycle. As such, it prevents the cycle from operating in the reverse direction, in which acetyl-CoA would be synthesized from carbon dioxide.

Comment: So far, in the first four steps, two carbon atoms have entered the cycle as an acetyl group, and two carbon atoms have been released as molecules of carbon dioxide. The remaining reactions of the citric acid cycle use the four carbon atoms of the succinyl group to resynthesize a molecule of oxaloacetate, which is the compound needed to combine with an incoming acetyl group and begin another round of the cycle.

In the fifth reaction, the energy released by the hydrolysis of the high-energy thioester bond of succinyl-CoA is used to form guanosine triphosphate (GTP) from guanosine diphosphate (GDP) and inorganic phosphate in a reaction catalyzed by *succinyl-CoA synthetase*. This step is the only reaction in the citric acid cycle that directly forms a high-energy phosphate compound. GTP can readily transfer its terminal phosphate group to adenosine diphosphate (ADP) to generate ATP in the presence of *nucleoside diphosphokinase*.

$$\text{Succinyl-CoA} \; (^-OOC{-}CH_2{-}CH_2{-}CO{-}SCoA) + H_2O \xrightarrow[\text{Succinyl-CoA synthetase}]{P_i + GDP \;\to\; GTP} \text{Succinate} \; (^-OOC{-}CH_2{-}CH_2{-}COO^-) + \text{Coenzyme A}$$

$$GTP + ADP \underset{\text{diphosphokinase}}{\overset{\text{nucleoside}}{\rightleftharpoons}} GDP + ATP$$

Succinate dehydrogenase then catalyzes the removal of two hydrogen atoms from succinate, forming fumarate. This oxidation-reduction reaction uses flavin adenine dinucleotide (FAD), rather than NAD^+, as the oxidizing agent. Succinate dehydrogenase is the only enzyme of the citric acid cycle located within the inner mitochondrial membrane. We will see soon the importance of this.

In the following step, a molecule of water is added to the double bond of fumarate to form L-malate in a reaction catalyzed by *fumarase*.

One revolution of the cycle is completed with the oxidation of L-malate to oxaloacetate, brought about by *malate dehydrogenase*. This is the third oxidation-reduction reaction that uses NAD^+ as the oxidizing agent. Oxaloacetate can accept an acetyl group from acetyl-CoA, allowing the cycle to begin again.

4.2 Cellular Respiration

Respiration can be defined as the process by which cells oxidize organic molecules in the presence of gaseous oxygen to produce carbon dioxide, water, and energy in the form of ATP. We have seen that two carbon atoms enter the citric acid cycle from acetyl-CoA (step 1), and two different carbon atoms exit the cycle as carbon dioxide (steps 3 and 4). Yet nowhere in our discussion of the citric acid cycle have we indicated how oxygen is used. Recall, however, that in the four oxidation-reduction steps occurring in the citric acid cycle, the coenzyme NAD^+ or FAD is reduced to NADH or $FADH_2$, respectively. *Oxygen is needed to reoxidize these coenzymes.* Recall, too, that very little ATP is obtained directly from the citric acid cycle. Instead, oxygen participation and significant ATP production occur subsequent to the citric acid cycle, in two pathways that are closely linked: electron transport and oxidative phosphorylation.

mitochondria

Small, oval organelles with double membranes; the "power plants" of a cell.

All the enzymes and coenzymes for the citric acid cycle, the reoxidation of NADH and $FADH_2$, and the production of ATP are located in the **mitochondria**, which are small, oval organelles with double membranes, often referred to as the "power plants" of the cell (Figure 20.13). A cell may contain 100–5,000 mitochondria, depending on its function, and the mitochondria can reproduce themselves if the energy requirements of the cell increase.

FIGURE 20.13 Respiration

Cellular respiration occurs in the mitochondria.

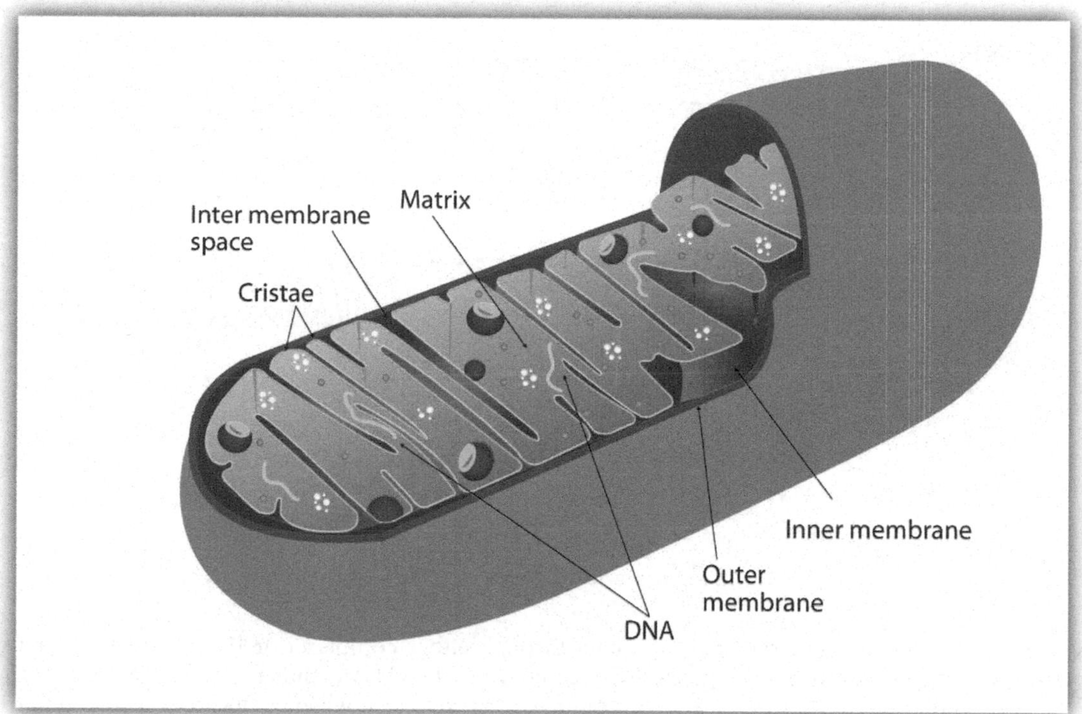

Figure 20.13 shows the mitochondrion's two membranes: *outer* and *inner*. The inner membrane is extensively folded into a series of internal ridges called *cristae*. Thus there are two compartments in mitochondria: the *intermembrane space*, which lies between the membranes, and the *matrix*, which lies inside the inner membrane. The outer membrane is permeable, whereas the inner membrane is impermeable to most molecules and ions, although water, oxygen, and carbon dioxide can freely penetrate both membranes. The matrix contains all the enzymes of the citric acid cycle with the exception of succinate dehydrogenase, which is embedded in the inner membrane. The enzymes that are needed for the reoxidation of NADH and $FADH_2$ and ATP production are also located in the inner membrane. They are arranged in specific positions so that they function in a manner analogous to a bucket brigade. This highly organized sequence of oxidation-reduction enzymes is known as the **electron transport chain (or respiratory chain)**.

electron transport chain (or respiratory chain)

An organized sequence of oxidation-reduction reactions that ultimately transports electrons to oxygen, reducing it to water.

4.3 Electron Transport

Figure 20.14 illustrates the organization of the electron transport chain. The components of the chain are organized into four complexes designated I, II, III, and IV. Each complex contains several enzymes, other proteins, and metal ions. The metal ions can be reduced and then oxidized repeatedly as electrons are passed from one component to the next. Recall from Chapter 5, [Unsupported Reference Type: chapter-section], that a compound is reduced when it gains electrons or hydrogen atoms and is oxidized when it loses electrons or hydrogen atoms.

FIGURE 20.14 The Mitochondrial Electron Transport Chain and ATP Synthase

The red line shows the path of electrons.

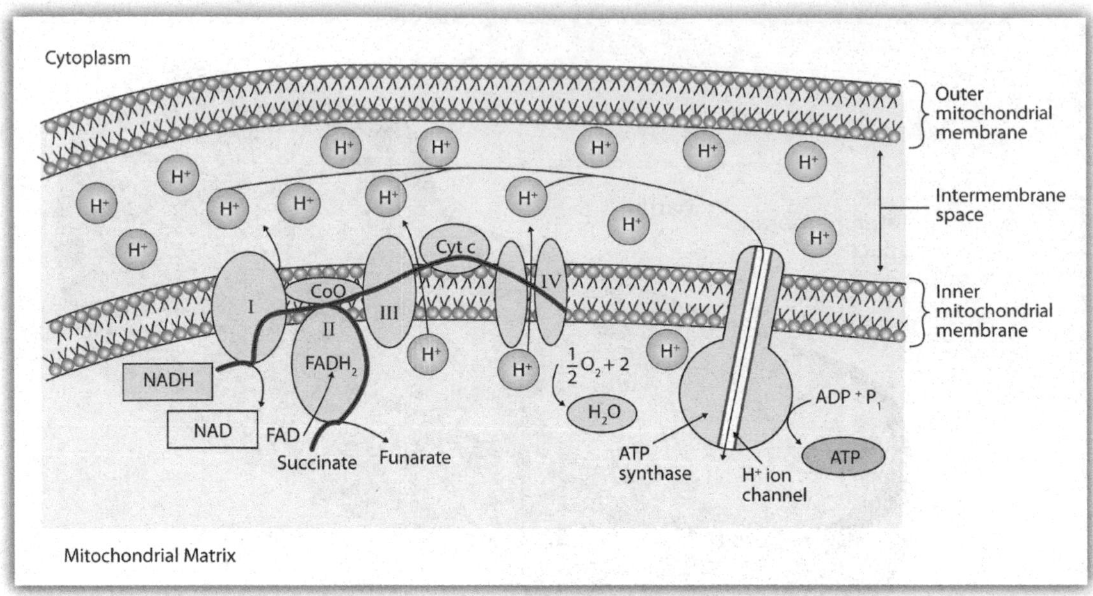

Electrons can enter the electron transport chain through either complex I or II. We will look first at electrons entering at complex I. These electrons come from NADH, which is formed in three reactions of the citric acid cycle. Let's use step 8 as an example, the reaction in which L-malate is oxidized to oxaloacetate and NAD^+ is reduced to NADH. This reaction can be divided into two half reactions:

Oxidation half-reaction:

$$^{-}OOC{-}CH_2{-}CH(OH){-}COO^{-} \longrightarrow {}^{-}OOC{-}CH_2{-}C(=O){-}COO^{-} + 2H^{+} + 2e^{-}$$

L-malate Oxaloacetate

Reduction half-reaction:

$$NAD^{+} + 2H^{+} + 2e^{-} \longrightarrow NADH + H^{+}$$

NAD^+ NADH

In the oxidation half-reaction, two hydrogen (H^+) ions and two electrons are removed from the substrate. In the reduction half-reaction, the NAD^+ molecule accepts both of those electrons and one of the H^+ ions. The other H^+ ion is transported from the matrix, across the inner mitochondrial membrane, and into the intermembrane space. The NADH diffuses through the matrix and is bound by complex I of the electron transport chain. In the complex, the coenzyme flavin mononucleotide (FMN) accepts both electrons from NADH. By passing the electrons along, NADH is oxidized back to NAD^+ and FMN is reduced to $FMNH_2$ (reduced form of flavin mononucleotide). Again, the reaction can be illustrated by dividing it into its respective half-reactions.

Oxidation half-reaction:

$$NADH + H^+ \longrightarrow NAD^+ + 2H^+ + 2e^-$$

Reduction half-reaction:

FMN + $2H^+$ + $2e^-$ ⟶ $FMNH_2$

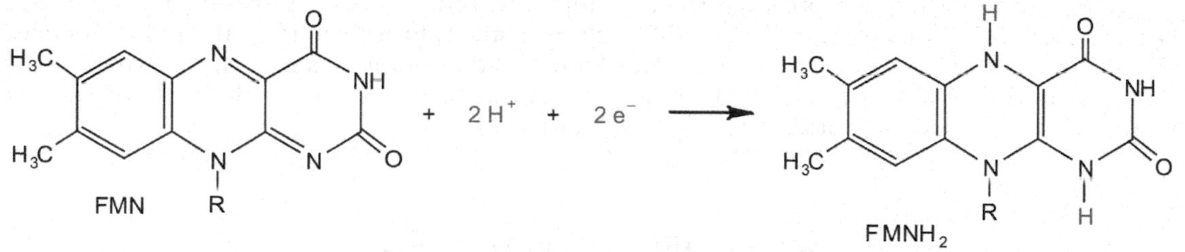

Complex I contains several proteins that have iron-sulfur (Fe·S) centers. The electrons that reduced FMN to $FMNH_2$ are now transferred to these proteins. The iron ions in the Fe·S centers are in the Fe(III) form at first, but by accepting an electron, each ion is reduced to the Fe(II) form. Because each Fe·S center can transfer only one electron, two centers are needed to accept the two electrons that will regenerate FMN.

Oxidation half-reaction:

$$FMNH_2 \rightarrow FMN + 2H^+ + 2e^-$$

Reduction half-reaction:

$$2Fe(III) \cdot S + 2e^- \rightarrow 2Fe(II) \cdot S$$

Electrons from $FADH_2$, formed in step 6 of the citric acid cycle, enter the electron transport chain through complex II. Succinate dehydrogenase, the enzyme in the citric acid cycle that catalyzes the formation of $FADH_2$ from FAD is part of complex II. The electrons from $FADH_2$ are then transferred to an Fe·S protein.

Oxidation half-reaction:

$$FADH_2 \rightarrow FAD + 2H^+ + 2e^-$$

Reduction half-reaction:

$$2Fe(III) \cdot S + 2e^- \rightarrow 2Fe(II) \cdot S$$

Electrons from complexes I and II are then transferred from the Fe·S protein to coenzyme Q (CoQ), a mobile electron carrier that acts as the electron shuttle between complexes I or II and complex III.

Note

Coenzyme Q is also called *ubiquinone* because it is ubiquitous in living systems.

Oxidation half-reaction:

$$2Fe(II) \cdot S \rightarrow 2Fe(III) \cdot S + 2e^-$$

Reduction half-reaction:

Coenzyme Q + $2H^+$ + $2e^-$ ⟶ Coenzyme QH_2

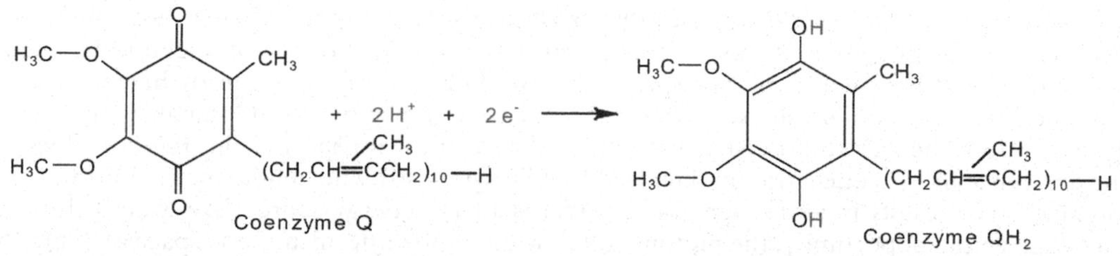

cytochrome

A protein that contains an iron porphyrin in which iron can alternate between Fe(II) and Fe(III).

Complexes III and IV include several iron-containing proteins known as **cytochromes**. The iron in these enzymes is located in substructures known as iron porphyrins (Figure 20.15). Like the Fe·S centers, the characteristic feature of the cytochromes is the ability of their iron atoms to exist as either Fe(II) or Fe(III). Thus, each cytochrome in its oxidized form—Fe(III)—can accept one electron and be reduced to the Fe(II) form. This change in oxidation state is reversible, so the reduced form can donate its electron to the next cytochrome, and so on. Complex III contains cytochromes b and c, as well as Fe·S proteins, with cytochrome c acting as the electron shuttle between complex III and IV. Complex IV contains cytochromes a and a3 in an enzyme known as *cytochrome oxidase*. This enzyme has the ability to transfer electrons to molecular oxygen, the last electron acceptor in the chain of electron transport reactions. In this final step, water (H_2O) is formed.

Oxidation half-reaction:

$$4\text{Cyt } a_3\text{–Fe(II)} \rightarrow 4\text{Cyt } a_3\text{–Fe(III)} + 4e^-$$

Reduction half-reaction:

$$O_2 + 4H^+ + 4e^- \rightarrow 2H_2O$$

FIGURE 20.15 An Iron Porphyrin

Iron porphyrins are present in cytochromes as well as in myoglobin and hemoglobin.

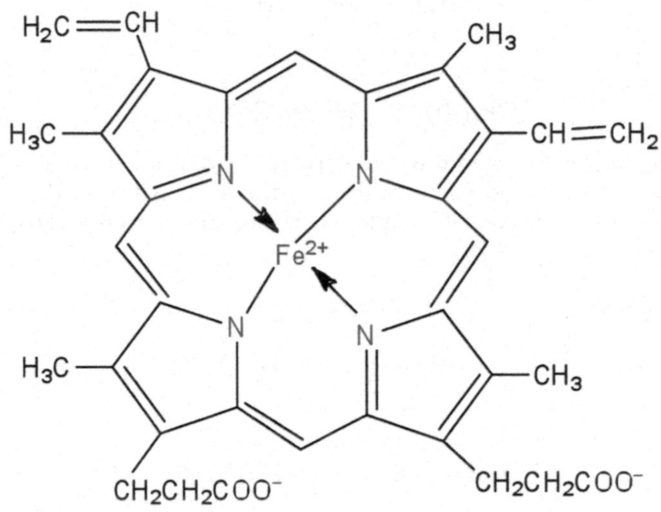

4.4 Oxidative Phosphorylation

oxidative phosphorylation

The process that links ATP synthesis to the operation of the electron transport chain.

Each intermediate compound in the electron transport chain is reduced by the addition of one or two electrons in one reaction and then subsequently restored to its original form by delivering the electron(s) to the next compound along the chain. The successive electron transfers result in energy production. But how is this energy used for the synthesis of ATP? The process that links ATP synthesis to the operation of the electron transport chain is referred to as **oxidative phosphorylation**.

Electron transport is tightly coupled to oxidative phosphorylation. The coenzymes NADH and $FADH_2$ are oxidized by the respiratory chain *only* if ADP is simultaneously phosphorylated to ATP. The currently accepted model explaining how these two processes are linked is known as the *chemiosmotic hypothesis*, which was proposed by Peter Mitchell, resulting in Mitchell being awarded the 1978 Nobel Prize in Chemistry.

Looking again at Figure 20.14, we see that as electrons are being transferred through the electron transport chain, hydrogen (H^+) ions are being transported across the inner mitochondrial membrane from the matrix to the intermembrane space. The concentration of H^+ is already higher in the intermembrane space than in the matrix, so energy is required to transport the additional H^+ there. This energy comes from the electron transfer reactions in the electron transport chain. But how does the extreme difference in H^+ concentration then lead to ATP synthesis? The buildup of H^+ ions in the intermembrane space results in an H^+ ion gradient that is a large energy source, like water behind a dam (because, given the opportunity, the protons will flow out of the intermembrane space and into the less concentrated matrix). Current research indicates that the flow of H^+ down this concentration gradient through a fifth enzyme complex, known as ATP synthase, leads to a change in the structure of the synthase, causing the synthesis and release of ATP.

In cells that are using energy, the turnover of ATP is very high, so these cells contain high levels of ADP. They must therefore consume large quantities of oxygen continuously, so as to have the energy necessary to phosphorylate ADP to form ATP. Consider, for example, that resting skeletal muscles use about 30% of a resting adult's oxygen consumption, but when the same muscles are working strenuously, they account for almost 90% of the total oxygen consumption of the organism.

Experiment has shown that 2.5–3 ATP molecules are formed for every molecule of NADH oxidized in the electron transport chain, and 1.5–2 ATP molecules are formed for every molecule of $FADH_2$ oxidized. Table 20.2 summarizes the theoretical maximum yield of ATP produced by the complete oxidation of 1 mol of acetyl-CoA through the sequential action of the citric acid cycle, the electron transport chain, and oxidative phosphorylation.

TABLE 20.2 Maximum Yield of ATP from the Complete Oxidation of 1 Mol of Acetyl-CoA

Reaction	Comments	Yield of ATP (moles)
Isocitrate → α-ketoglutarate + CO_2	produces 1 mol NADH	
α-ketoglutarate → succinyl-CoA + CO_2	produces 1 mol NADH	
Succinyl-CoA → succinate	produces 1 mol GTP	+1
Succinate → fumarate	produces 1 mol $FADH_2$	
Malate → oxaloacetate	produces 1 mol NADH	
1 $FADH_2$ from the citric acid cycle	yields 2 mol ATP	+2
3 NADH from the citric acid cycle	yields 3 mol ATP/NADH	+9
	Net yield of ATP:	+12

CONCEPT REVIEW EXERCISES

1. What is the main function of the citric acid cycle?
2. Two carbon atoms are fed into the citric acid cycle as acetyl-CoA. In what form are two carbon atoms removed from the cycle?
3. What are mitochondria and what is their function in the cell?

ANSWERS

1. the complete oxidation of carbon atoms to carbon dioxide and the formation of a high-energy phosphate compound, energy rich reduced coenzymes (NADH and $FADH_2$), and metabolic intermediates for the synthesis of other compounds
2. as carbon dioxide
3. Mitochondria are small organelles with a double membrane that contain the enzymes and other molecules needed for the production of most of the ATP needed by the body.

KEY TAKEAWAYS

- The acetyl group of acetyl-CoA enters the citric acid cycle. For each acetyl-CoA that enters the citric acid cycle, 2 molecules of carbon dioxide, 3 molecules of NADH, 1 molecule of ATP, and 1 molecule of $FADH_2$ are produced.
- The reduced coenzymes (NADH and $FADH_2$) produced by the citric acid cycle are reoxidized by the reactions of the electron transport chain. This series of reactions also produces a pH gradient across the inner mitochondrial membrane.
- The pH gradient produced by the electron transport chain drives the synthesis of ATP from ADP. For each NADH reoxidized, 2.5–3 molecules of ATP are produced; for each $FADH_2$ reoxidized, 1.5–2 molecules of ATP are produced.

EXERCISES

1. Replace each question mark with the correct compound.
   a. $? \xrightarrow{\text{aconitase}} \text{isocitrate}$
   b. $? + ? \xrightarrow{\text{citrate synthase}} \text{citrate} + \text{coenzyme A}$
   c. $\text{fumarate} \xrightarrow{\text{fumarase}} ?$
   d. $\text{isocitrate} + NAD^+ \xrightarrow{?} \alpha\text{-ketoglurate} + NADH + CO_2$
2. Replace each question mark with the correct compound.
   a. $\text{malate} + NAD^+ \xrightarrow{?} \text{oxaloacetate} + NADH$
   b. $? + ? \xrightarrow{\text{nucleoside diphosphokinase}} GDP + ATP$
   c. $\text{succinyl-CoA} \xrightarrow{\text{succinyl-CoA synthetase}} ? + ?$
   d. $\text{succinate} + FAD \xrightarrow{\text{succinate dehydrogenase}} ? + FADH_2$
3. From the reactions in Exercises 1 and 2, select the equation(s) by number and letter in which each type of reaction occurs.
   a. isomerization
   b. hydration
   c. synthesis
4. From the reactions in Exercises 1 and 2, select the equation(s) by number and letter in which each type of reaction occurs.
   a. oxidation
   b. decarboxylation
   c. phosphorylation
5. What similar role do coenzyme Q and cytochrome c serve in the electron transport chain?
6. What is the electron acceptor at the end of the electron transport chain? To what product is this compound reduced?
7. What is the function of the cytochromes in the electron transport chain?
8.
   a. What is meant by this statement? "Electron transport is tightly coupled to oxidative phosphorylation."
   b. How are electron transport and oxidative phosphorylation coupled or linked?

ANSWERS

1. a. citrate
   b. oxaloacetate + acetyl-CoA
   c. malate
   d. α-ketoglutarate hydrogenase complex
3. a. reaction in 1a
   b. reaction in 1c
   c. reaction in 1b
5. Both molecules serve as electron shuttles between the complexes of the electron transport chain.
7. Cytochromes are proteins in the electron transport chain and serve as one-electron carriers.

5. STAGE II OF CARBOHYDRATE CATABOLISM

LEARNING OBJECTIVES

1. **Describe the function of glycolysis and identify its major products.**
2. **Describe how the presence or absence of oxygen determines what happens to the pyruvate and the NADH that are produced in glycolysis.**
3. **Determine the amount of ATP produced by the oxidation of glucose in the presence and absence of oxygen.**

In stage II of catabolism, the metabolic pathway known as **glycolysis** converts glucose into two molecules of pyruvate (a three-carbon compound with three carbon atoms) with the corresponding production of adenosine triphosphate (ATP). The individual reactions in glycolysis were determined during the first part of the 20th century. It was the first metabolic pathway to be elucidated, in part because the participating enzymes are found in soluble form in the cell and are readily isolated and purified. The pathway is structured so that the product of one enzyme-catalyzed reaction becomes the substrate of the next. The transfer of intermediates from one enzyme to the next occurs by diffusion.

glycolysis

The metabolic pathway in which glucose is broken down to two molecules of pyruvate with the corresponding production of ATP.

5.1 Steps in Glycolysis

The 10 reactions of glycolysis, summarized in Figure 20.16, can be divided into two phases. In the first 5 reactions—phase I—glucose is broken down into two molecules of glyceraldehyde 3-phosphate. In the last five reactions—phase II—each glyceraldehyde 3-phosphate is converted into pyruvate, and ATP is generated. Notice that all the intermediates in glycolysis are phosphorylated and contain either six or three carbon atoms.

FIGURE 20.16 Glycolysis

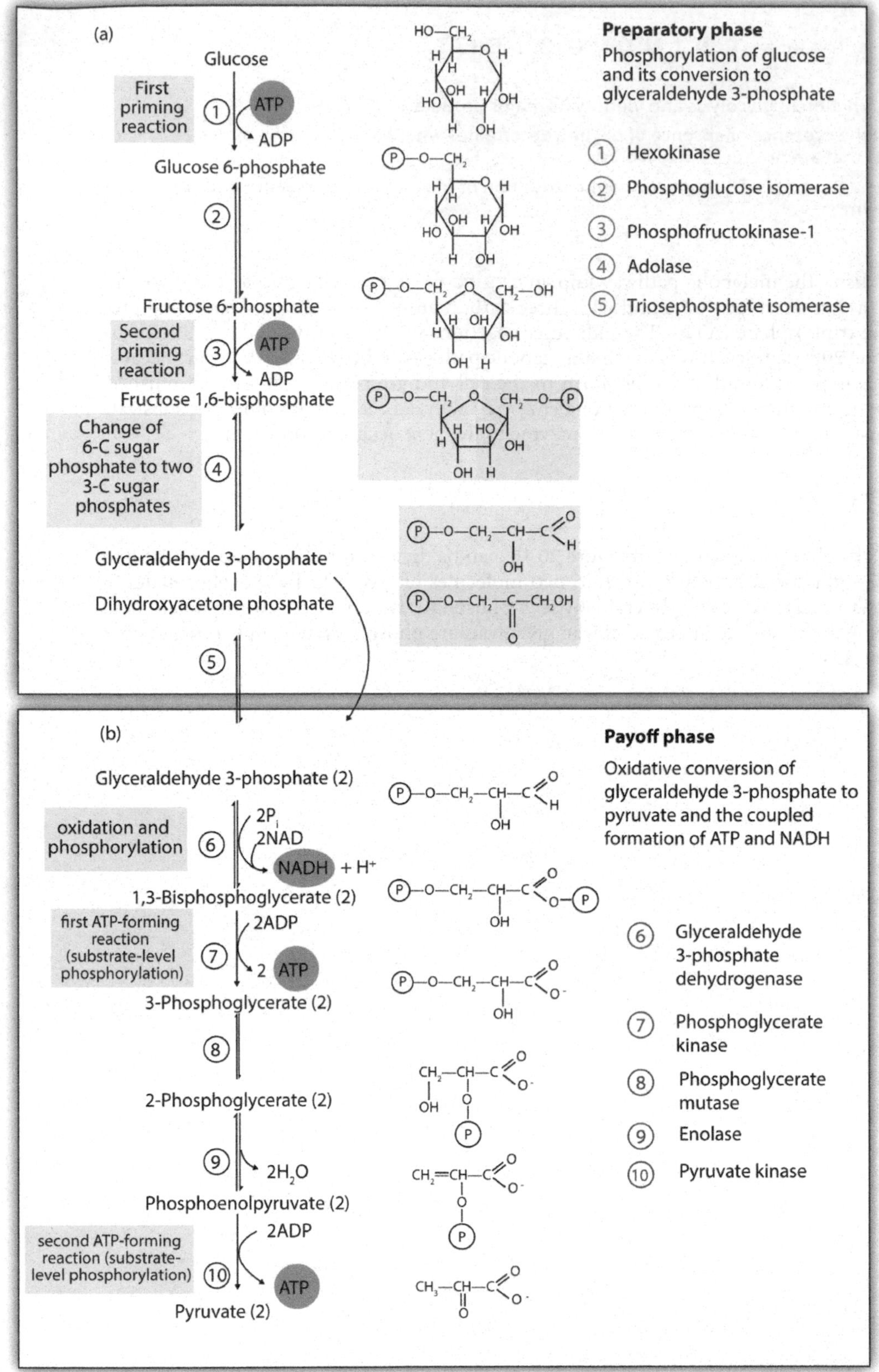

When glucose enters a cell, it is immediately phosphorylated to form glucose 6-phosphate, in the first reaction of phase I. The phosphate donor in this reaction is ATP, and the enzyme—which requires magnesium ions for its activity—is *hexokinase*. In this reaction, ATP is being used rather than being synthesized. The presence of such a reaction in a catabolic pathway that is supposed to *generate* energy may surprise you. However, in addition to activating the glucose molecule, this initial reaction is essentially irreversible, an added benefit that keeps the overall process moving in the right direction.

Furthermore, the addition of the negatively charged phosphate group prevents the intermediates formed in glycolysis from diffusing through the cell membrane, as neutral molecules such as glucose can do.

In the next reaction, *phosphoglucose isomerase* catalyzes the isomerization of glucose 6-phosphate to fructose 6-phosphate. This reaction is important because it creates a primary alcohol, which can be readily phosphorylated.

The subsequent phosphorylation of fructose 6-phosphate to form fructose 1,6-bisphosphate is catalyzed by *phosphofructokinase*, which requires magnesium ions for activity. ATP is again the phosphate donor.

Note

When a molecule contains two phosphate groups on different carbon atoms, the convention is to use the prefix *bis*. When the two phosphate groups are bonded to each other on the same carbon atom (for example, adenosine diphosphate [ADP]), the prefix is *di*.

Fructose 1,6-bisphosphate is enzymatically cleaved by *aldolase* to form two triose phosphates: dihydroxyacetone phosphate and glyceraldehyde 3-phosphate.

Isomerization of dihydroxyacetone phosphate into a second molecule of glyceraldehyde 3-phosphate is the final step in phase I. The enzyme catalyzing this reaction is *triose phosphate isomerase.*

Comment: In steps 4 and 5, aldolase and triose phosphate isomerase effectively convert one molecule of fructose 1,6-bisphosphate into *two* molecules of glyceraldehyde 3-phosphate. Thus, phase I of glycolysis requires energy in the form of two molecules of ATP and releases none of the energy stored in glucose.

In the initial step of phase II, glyceraldehyde 3-phosphate is both oxidized and phosphorylated in a reaction catalyzed by *glyceraldehyde-3-phosphate dehydrogenase*, an enzyme that requires nicotinamide adenine dinucleotide (NAD^+) as the oxidizing agent and inorganic phosphate as the phosphate donor. In the reaction, NAD^+ is reduced to reduced nicotinamide adenine dinucleotide (NADH), and 1,3-bisphosphoglycerate (BPG) is formed.

BPG has a high-energy phosphate bond (see Table 20.1) joining a phosphate group to C1. This phosphate group is now transferred directly to a molecule of ADP, thus forming ATP and 3-phosphoglycerate. The enzyme that catalyzes the reaction is *phosphoglycerate kinase*, which, like all other kinases, requires magnesium ions to function. This is the first reaction to produce ATP in the pathway. Because the ATP is formed by a direct transfer of a phosphate group from a metabolite to ADP—that is, from one substrate to another—the process is referred to as **substrate-level phosphorylation**, to distinguish it from the *oxidative phosphorylation* discussed in Section 4.

substrate-level phosphorylation

The synthesis of ATP by the direct transfer of a phosphate group from a metabolite to ADP.

In the next reaction, the phosphate group on 3-phosphoglycerate is transferred from the OH group of C3 to the OH group of C2, forming 2-phosphoglycerate in a reaction catalyzed by *phosphoglyceromutase*.

A dehydration reaction, catalyzed by *enolase*, forms phosphoenolpyruvate (PEP), another compound possessing a high-energy phosphate group.

The final step is irreversible and is the second reaction in which substrate-level phosphorylation occurs. The phosphate group of PEP is transferred to ADP, with one molecule of ATP being produced per molecule of PEP. The reaction is catalyzed by *pyruvate kinase*, which requires both magnesium and potassium ions to be active.

Comment: In phase II, two molecules of glyceraldehyde 3-phosphate are converted to two molecules of pyruvate, along with the production of four molecules of ATP and two molecules of NADH.

To Your Health: Diabetes

Most of the chapter-opening essays in Chapter 16 through Chapter 20 have touched on different aspects of diabetes and the role of insulin in its causation and treatment. Although medical science has made significant progress against this disease, it continues to be a major health threat. Some of the serious complications of diabetes are as follows:

- It is the leading cause of lower limb amputations in the United States.
- It is the leading cause of blindness in adults over age 20.
- It is the leading cause of kidney failure.
- It increases the risk of having a heart attack or stroke by two to four times.

Because a person with diabetes is unable to use glucose properly, excessive quantities accumulate in the blood and the urine. Other characteristic symptoms are constant hunger, weight loss, extreme thirst, and frequent urination because the kidneys excrete large amounts of water in an attempt to remove excess sugar from the blood.

There are two types of diabetes. In immune-mediated diabetes, insufficient amounts of insulin are produced. This type of diabetes develops early in life and is also known as *Type 1 diabetes*, as well as insulin-dependent or juvenile-onset diabetes. Symptoms are rapidly reversed by the administration of insulin, and Type 1 diabetics can lead active lives provided they receive insulin as needed. Because insulin is a protein that is readily digested in the small intestine, it cannot be taken orally and must be injected at least once a day.

In Type 1 diabetes, insulin-producing cells of the pancreas are destroyed by the body's immune system. Researchers are still trying to find out why. Meanwhile, they have developed a simple blood test capable of predicting who will develop Type 1 diabetes several years before the disease becomes apparent. The blood test reveals the presence of antibodies that destroy the body's insulin-producing cells.

Type 2 diabetes, also known as noninsulin-dependent or adult-onset diabetes, is by far the more common, representing about 95% of diagnosed diabetic cases. (This translates to about 16 million Americans.) Type 2 diabetics usually produce sufficient amounts of insulin, but either the insulin-producing cells in the pancreas do not release enough of it, or it is not used properly because of defective insulin receptors or a lack of insulin receptors on the target cells. In many of these people, the disease can be controlled with a combination of diet and exercise alone. For some people who are overweight, losing weight is sufficient to bring their blood sugar level into the normal range, after which medication is not required if they exercise regularly and eat wisely.

Those who require medication may use oral antidiabetic drugs that stimulate the islet cells to secrete insulin. First-generation antidiabetic drugs stimulated the release of insulin. Newer second-generation drugs, such as glyburide, do as well, but they also increase the sensitivity of cell receptors to insulin. Some individuals with Type 2 diabetes do not produce enough insulin and thus do not respond to these oral medications; they must use insulin. In both Type 1 and Type 2 diabetes, the blood sugar level must be carefully monitored and adjustments made in diet or medication to keep the level as normal as possible (70–120 mg/dL).

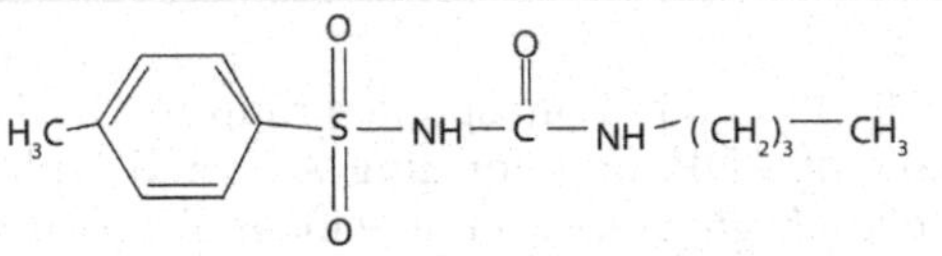

Tolbutamide (Orinase)

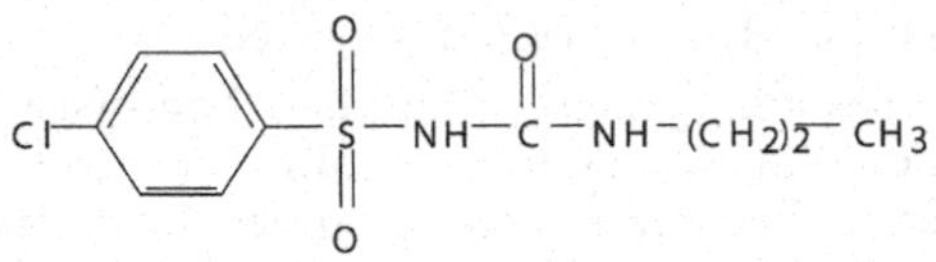

Chlorpropamide (Diabinese)

First-Generation Antidiabetic Drugs

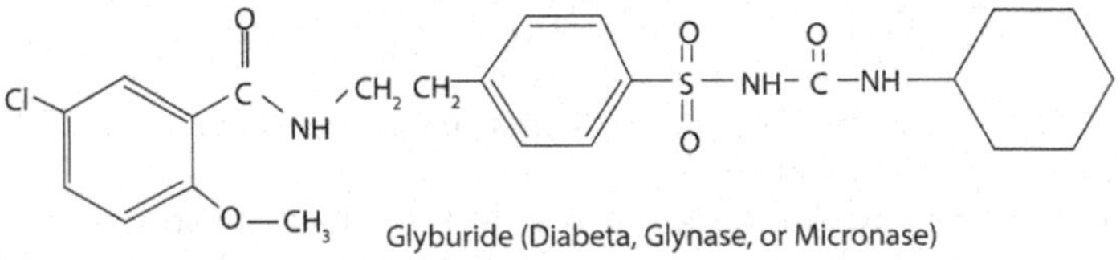

Glyburide (Diabeta, Glynase, or Micronase)

Second-Generation Antidiabetic Drugs

5.2 Metabolism of Pyruvate

The presence or absence of oxygen determines the fates of the pyruvate and the NADH produced in glycolysis. When plenty of oxygen is available, pyruvate is completely oxidized to carbon dioxide, with the release of much greater amounts of ATP through the combined actions of the citric acid cycle, the electron transport chain, and oxidative phosphorylation. (For more information about oxidative phosphorylation, see Section 4.) However, in the absence of oxygen (that is, under anaerobic conditions), the fate of pyruvate is different in different organisms. In vertebrates, pyruvate is converted to lactate, while other organisms, such as yeast, convert pyruvate to ethanol and carbon dioxide. These possible fates of pyruvate are summarized in Figure 20.17. The conversion to lactate or ethanol under anaerobic conditions allows for the reoxidation of NADH to NAD^+ in the absence of oxygen.

FIGURE 20.17 Metabolic Fates of Pyruvate

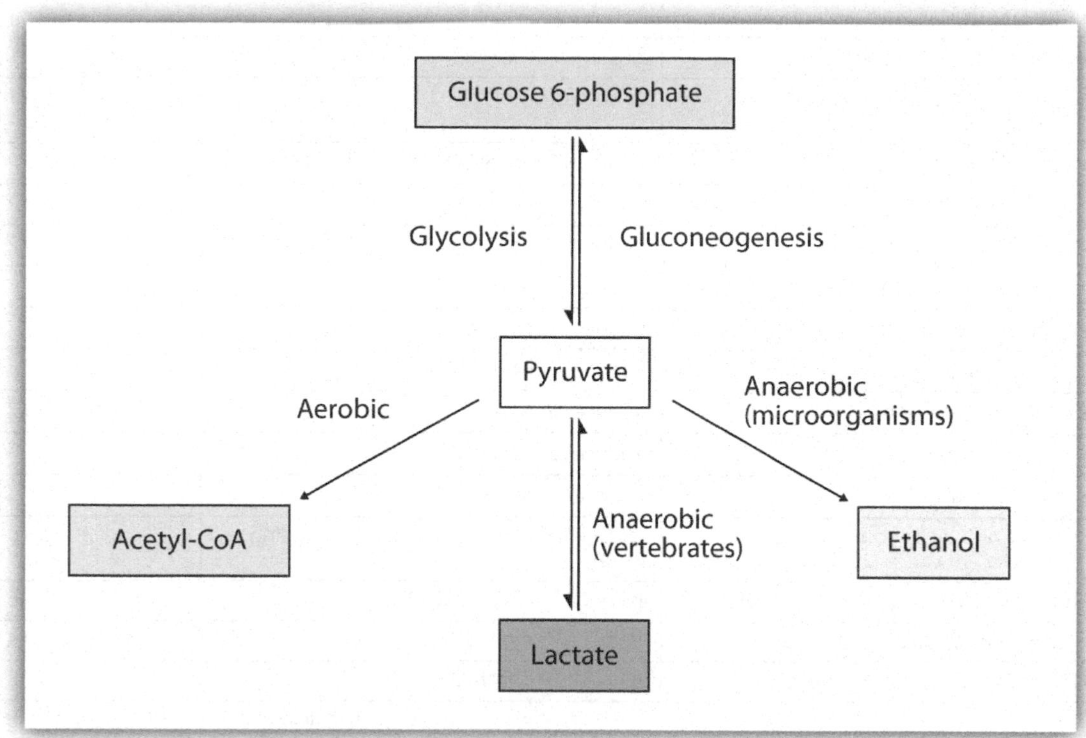

5.3 ATP Yield from Glycolysis

The net energy yield from anaerobic glucose metabolism can readily be calculated in moles of ATP. In the initial phosphorylation of glucose (step 1), 1 mol of ATP is expended, along with another in the phosphorylation of fructose 6-phosphate (step 3). In step 7, 2 mol of BPG (recall that 2 mol of 1,3-BPG are formed for each mole of glucose) are converted to 2 mol of 3-phosphoglycerate, and 2 mol of ATP are produced. In step 10, 2 mol of pyruvate and 2 mol of ATP are formed per mole of glucose.

For every mole of glucose degraded, 2 mol of ATP are initially consumed and 4 mol of ATP are ultimately produced. The net production of ATP is thus 2 mol for each mole of glucose converted to lactate or ethanol. If 7.4 kcal of energy is conserved per mole of ATP produced, and the total amount of energy that can theoretically be obtained from the complete oxidation of 1 mol of glucose is 670 kcal (as stated in the chapter introduction), the energy conserved in the anaerobic catabolism of glucose to two molecules of lactate (or ethanol) is as follows:

$$\frac{2 \times 7.4 \text{ kcal}}{670 \text{ kcal}} \times 100 = 2.2\%$$

Thus anaerobic cells extract only a very small fraction of the total energy of the glucose molecule.

Contrast this result with the amount of energy obtained when glucose is completely oxidized to carbon dioxide and water through glycolysis, the citric acid cycle, the electron transport chain, and oxidative phosphorylation as summarized in Table 20.3. Note the indication in the table that a variable amount of ATP is synthesized, depending on the tissue, from the NADH formed in the cytoplasm during glycolysis. This is because NADH is not transported into the inner mitochondrial membrane where the enzymes for the electron transport chain are located. Instead, brain and muscle cells use a transport mechanism that passes electrons from the cytoplasmic NADH through the membrane to flavin adenine dinucleotide (FAD) molecules inside the mitochondria, forming reduced flavin adenine dinucleotide ($FADH_2$), which then feeds the electrons into the electron transport chain. This route lowers the yield of ATP to 1.5–2 molecules of ATP, rather than the usual 2.5–3 molecules. A more efficient transport system is found in liver, heart, and kidney cells where the formation of one cytoplasmic NADH molecule results in the formation of one mitochondrial NADH molecule, which leads to the formation of 2.5–3 molecules of ATP.

TABLE 20.3 Maximum Yield of ATP from the Complete Oxidation of 1 Mol of Glucose

Reaction	Comments	Yield of ATP (moles)
glucose → glucose 6-phosphate	consumes 1 mol ATP	−1
fructose 6-phosphate → fructose 1,6-bisphosphate	consumes 1 mol ATP	−1
glyceraldehyde 3-phosphate → BPG	produces 2 mol of cytoplasmic NADH	
BPG → 3-phosphoglycerate	produces 2 mol ATP	+2
phosphoenolpyruvate → pyruvate	produces 2 mol ATP	+2
pyruvate → acetyl-CoA + CO_2	produces 2 mol NADH	
isocitrate → α-ketoglutarate + CO_2	produces 2 mol NADH	
α-ketoglutarate → succinyl-CoA + CO_2	produces 2 mol NADH	
succinyl-CoA → succinate	produces 2 mol GTP	+2
succinate → fumarate	produces 2 mol $FADH_2$	
malate → oxaloacetate	produces 2 mol NADH	
2 cytoplasmic NADH from glycolysis	yields 2–3 mol ATP per NADH (depending on tissue)	+4 to +6
2 NADH from the oxidation of pyruvate	yields 3 mol ATP per NADH	+6
2 $FADH_2$ from the citric acid cycle	yields 2 ATP per $FADH_2$	+4
3 NADH from the citric acid cycle	yields 3 ATP per NADH	+18
	Net yield of ATP:	+36 to +38

The total amount of energy conserved in the aerobic catabolism of glucose in the liver is as follows:

$$\frac{38 \times 7.4 \text{ kcal}}{670 \text{ kcal}} \times 100 = 42\%$$

Conservation of 42% of the total energy released compares favorably with the efficiency of any machine. In comparison, automobiles are only about 20%–25% efficient in using the energy released by the combustion of gasoline.

As indicated earlier, the 58% of released energy that is not conserved enters the surroundings (that is, the cell) as heat that helps to maintain body temperature. If we are exercising strenuously and our metabolism speeds up to provide the energy needed for muscle contraction, more heat is produced. We begin to perspire to dissipate some of that heat. As the perspiration evaporates, the excess heat is carried away from the body by the departing water vapor.

CONCEPT REVIEW EXERCISES

1. In glycolysis, how many molecules of pyruvate are produced from one molecule of glucose?
2. In vertebrates, what happens to pyruvate when
   a. plenty of oxygen is available?
   b. oxygen supplies are limited?
3. In anaerobic glycolysis, how many molecules of ATP are produced from one molecule of glucose?

ANSWERS

1. two
2. a. Pyruvate is completely oxidized to carbon dioxide.
   b. Pyruvate is reduced to lactate, allowing for the reoxidation of NADH to NAD^+.
3. There is a net production of two molecules of ATP.

KEY TAKEAWAYS

- The monosaccharide glucose is broken down through a series of enzyme-catalyzed reactions known as glycolysis.
- For each molecule of glucose that is broken down, two molecules of pyruvate, two molecules of ATP, and two molecules of NADH are produced.
- In the absence of oxygen, pyruvate is converted to lactate, and NADH is reoxidized to NAD^+. In the presence of oxygen, pyruvate is converted to acetyl-CoA and then enters the citric acid cycle.
- More ATP can be formed from the breakdown of glucose when oxygen is present.

EXERCISES

1. Replace each question mark with the correct compound.
   a. fructose 1,6-bisphosphate $\xrightarrow{\text{aldolase}}$? + ?
   b. ? + ADP $\xrightarrow{\text{pyruvate kinase}}$ pyruvate + ATP
   c. dihydroxyacetone phosphate $\xrightarrow{?}$ glyceraldehyde 3-phosphate
   d. glucose + ATP $\xrightarrow{\text{hexokinase}}$? + ADP
2. Replace each question mark with the correct compound.
   a. fructose 6-phosphate + ATP $\xrightarrow{?}$ fructose 1,6-bisphosphate + ADP
   b. ? $\xrightarrow{\text{phosphoglucose isomerase}}$ fructose 6-phosphate
   c. glyceraldehyde 3-phosphate + NAD^+ + P_i $\xrightarrow{?}$ 1,3-bisphosphoglycerate + NADH
   d. 3-phosphoglycerate $\xrightarrow{\text{phosphoglyceromutase}}$?
3. From the reactions in Exercises 1 and 2, select the equation(s) by number and letter in which each type of reaction occurs.
   a. hydrolysis of a high-energy phosphate compound
   b. synthesis of ATP
4. From the reactions in Exercises 1 and 2, select the equation(s) by number and letter in which each type of reaction occurs.
   a. isomerization
   b. oxidation
5. What coenzyme is needed as an oxidizing agent in glycolysis?
6. Calculate
   a. the *total* number of molecules of ATP produced for each molecule of glucose converted to pyruvate in glycolysis.
   b. the number of molecules of ATP hydrolyzed in phase I of glycolysis.
   c. the *net* ATP production from glycolysis alone.
7. How is the NADH produced in glycolysis reoxidized when oxygen supplies are limited in
   a. muscle cells?
   b. yeast?

8.

a. Calculate the number of moles of ATP produced by the aerobic oxidation of 1 mol of glucose in a liver cell.
b. Of the total calculated in Exercise 9a, determine the number of moles of ATP produced in each process.
   i. glycolysis alone
   ii. the citric acid cycle
   iii. the electron transport chain and oxidative phosphorylation

ANSWERS

1. a. glyceraldehyde 3-phosphate + dihydroxyacetone phosphate
   b. phosphoenolpyruvate
   c. triose phosphate isomerase
   d. glucose 6-phosphate
3. a. reactions 1b, 1d, and 2a
   b. reaction 1b
5. NAD^+
7. a. Pyruvate is reduced to lactate, and NADH is reoxidized to NAD^+.
   b. Pyruvate is converted to ethanol and carbon dioxide, and NADH is reoxidized to NAD^+.

6. STAGE II OF LIPID CATABOLISM

LEARNING OBJECTIVE

1. **Describe the reactions needed to completely oxidize a fatty acid to carbon dioxide and water.**

Like glucose, the fatty acids released in the digestion of triglycerides and other lipids are broken down in a series of sequential reactions accompanied by the gradual release of usable energy. Some of these reactions are oxidative and require nicotinamide adenine dinucleotide (NAD^+) and flavin adenine dinucleotide (FAD). The enzymes that participate in fatty acid catabolism are located in the mitochondria, along with the enzymes of the citric acid cycle, the electron transport chain, and oxidative phosphorylation. This localization of enzymes in the mitochondria is of the utmost importance because it facilitates efficient utilization of energy stored in fatty acids and other molecules.

Fatty acid oxidation is initiated on the outer mitochondrial membrane. There the fatty acids, which like carbohydrates are relatively inert, must first be activated by conversion to an energy-rich fatty acid derivative of coenzyme A called *fatty acyl-coenzyme A* (CoA). The activation is catalyzed by *acyl-CoA synthetase*. For each molecule of fatty acid activated, one molecule of coenzyme A and one molecule of adenosine triphosphate (ATP) are used, equaling a net utilization of the two high-energy bonds in one ATP molecule (which is therefore converted to adenosine monophosphate [AMP] rather than adenosine diphosphate [ADP]):

$$\underset{\text{Fatty acid}}{R{-}\overset{O}{\overset{\|}{C}}{-}OH} + \underset{\text{Coenzyme A}}{HS{-}CoA} \xrightarrow[\text{ATP} \;\rightarrow\; \text{AMP + PPi}]{\text{acyl-CoA synthetase}} \underset{\text{Fatty acyl-CoA}}{R{-}\overset{O}{\overset{\|}{C}}{-}S{-}CoA} + H_2O$$

The fatty acyl-CoA diffuses to the inner mitochondrial membrane, where it combines with a carrier molecule known as carnitine in a reaction catalyzed by *carnitine acyltransferase*. The acyl-carnitine derivative is transported into the mitochondrial matrix and converted back to the fatty acyl-CoA.

6.1 Steps in the β-Oxidation of Fatty Acids

Further oxidation of the fatty acyl-CoA occurs in the mitochondrial matrix via a sequence of four reactions known collectively as **β-oxidation** because the β-carbon undergoes successive oxidations in the progressive removal of two carbon atoms from the carboxyl end of the fatty acyl-CoA (Figure 20.18).

β-oxidation

A sequence of four reactions in which fatty acyl-CoA molecules are oxidized, leading to the removal of acetyl-CoA molecules.

FIGURE 20.18 Fatty Acid Oxidation

The fatty acyl-CoA formed in the final step becomes the substrate for the first step in the next round of β-oxidation. β-oxidation continues until two acetyl-CoA molecules are produced in the final step.

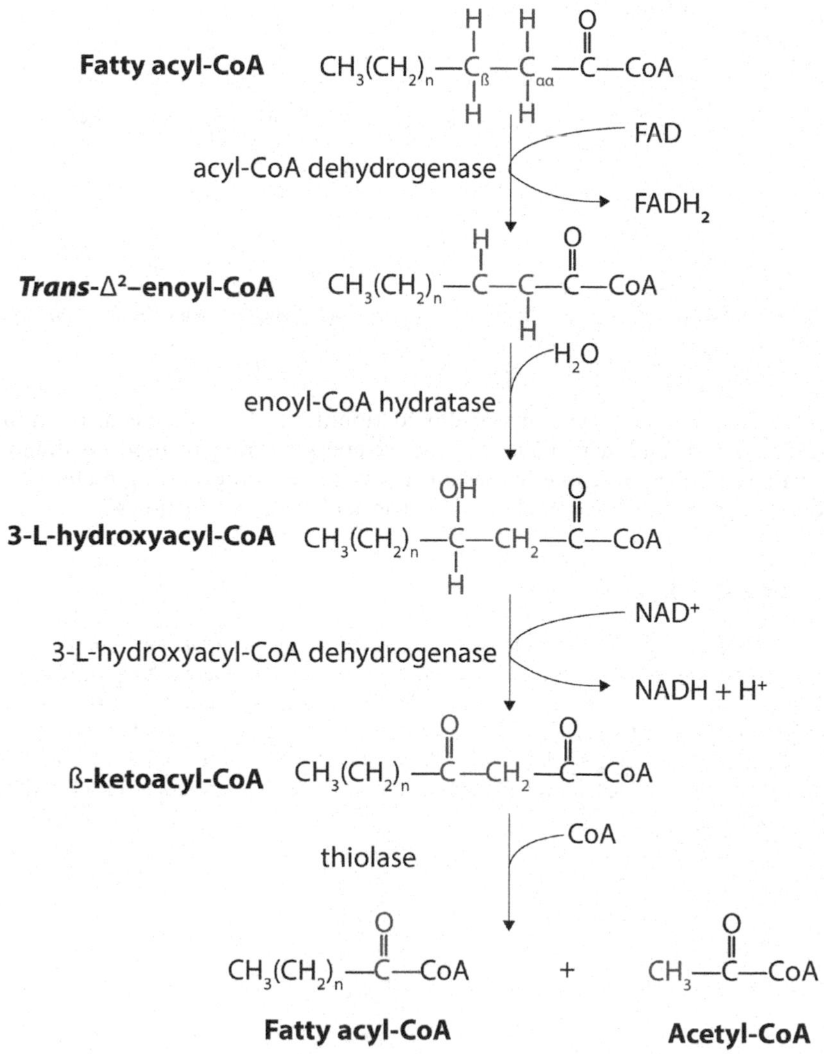

Fatty acyl-CoA $CH_3(CH_2)_n—CH_2(β)—CH_2(α)—C(=O)—CoA$

acyl-CoA dehydrogenase (FAD → $FADH_2$)

***Trans*-Δ²-enoyl-CoA** $CH_3(CH_2)_n—CH=CH—C(=O)—CoA$

enoyl-CoA hydratase (H_2O)

3-L-hydroxyacyl-CoA $CH_3(CH_2)_n—CH(OH)—CH_2—C(=O)—CoA$

3-L-hydroxyacyl-CoA dehydrogenase (NAD^+ → NADH + H^+)

ß-ketoacyl-CoA $CH_3(CH_2)_n—C(=O)—CH_2—C(=O)—CoA$

thiolase (CoA)

$CH_3(CH_2)_n—C(=O)—CoA$ + $CH_3—C(=O)—CoA$

Fatty acyl-CoA **Acetyl-CoA**

The first step in the catabolism of fatty acids is the formation of an alkene in an oxidation reaction catalyzed by *acyl-CoA dehydrogenase*. In this reaction, the coenzyme FAD accepts two hydrogen atoms from the acyl-CoA, one from the α-carbon and one from the β-carbon, forming reduced flavin adenine dinucleotide ($FADH_2$).

Note

The $FADH_2$ is reoxidized back to FAD via the electron transport chain. (For more information about the electron transport chain, see Section 4.) This supplies energy to form 1.5–2 molecules of ATP.

Next, the *trans*-alkene is hydrated to form a secondary alcohol in a reaction catalyzed by *enoyl-CoA hydratase*. The enzyme forms only the L-isomer.

The secondary alcohol is then oxidized to a ketone by *β-hydroxyacyl-CoA dehydrogenase*, with NAD^+ acting as the oxidizing agent. The reoxidation of each molecule of NADH to NAD^+ by the electron transport chain furnishes 2.5–3 molecules of ATP.

The final reaction is cleavage of the β-ketoacyl-CoA by a molecule of coenzyme A. The products are acetyl-CoA and a fatty acyl-CoA that has been shortened by two carbon atoms. The reaction is catalyzed by *thiolase*.

The shortened fatty acyl-CoA is then degraded by repetitions of these four steps, each time releasing a molecule of acetyl-CoA. The overall equation for the β-oxidation of palmitoyl-CoA (16 carbon atoms) is as follows:

$$CH_3(CH_2)_{14}C(=O)SCoA + 7\ FAD + 7\ NAD^+ + 7\ CoASH + 7\ H_2O \longrightarrow 8\ CH_3C(=O)SCoA + 7\ FADH_2 + 7\ NADH + 7\ H^+$$

Note

Because each shortened fatty acyl-CoA cycles back to the beginning of the pathway, β-oxidation is sometimes referred to as the *fatty acid spiral*.

The fate of the acetyl-CoA obtained from fatty acid oxidation depends on the needs of an organism. It may enter the citric acid cycle and be oxidized to produce energy, it may be used for the formation of water-soluble derivatives known as ketone bodies, or it may serve as the starting material for the synthesis of fatty acids. (For more information about the citric acid cycle, see Section 4.)

Looking Closer: Ketone Bodies

In the liver, most of the acetyl-CoA obtained from fatty acid oxidation is oxidized by the citric acid cycle. However, some of the acetyl-CoA is used to synthesize a group of compounds known as *ketone bodies*: acetoacetate, β-hydroxybutyrate, and acetone. Two acetyl-CoA molecules combine, in a reversal of the final step of β-oxidation, to produce acetoacetyl-CoA. The acetoacetyl-CoA reacts with another molecule of acetyl-CoA and water to form β-hydroxy-β-methylglutaryl-CoA, which is then cleaved to acetoacetate and acetyl-CoA. Most of the acetoacetate is reduced to β-hydroxybutyrate, while a small amount is decarboxylated to carbon dioxide and acetone.

$$CH_3COCoA + CH_3COCoA \rightleftharpoons CH_3COCH_2COCoA$$

2 molecules acetyl-CoA → Acetoacetyl-CoA

$$CH_3COCH_2COCoA + CH_3COCoA \rightleftharpoons HOOCCH_2C(OH)(CH_3)CH_2COCoA + CoA$$

β-hydroxy-β-methylglutaryl-CoA

$$HOOCCH_2C(OH)(CH_3)CH_2COCoA \rightarrow {}^-OOCCH_2COCH_3 + CH_3COCoA$$

$$^-OOCCH_2CH(OH)CH_3 \overset{NAD^+ \;\; NADH}{\rightleftharpoons} {}^-OOCCH_2COCH_3 \xrightarrow{-CO_2} CH_3COCH_3$$

β-hydroxybutyrate — Acetoacetate — Acetone

Ketone bodies

The acetoacetate and β-hydroxybutyrate synthesized by the liver are released into the blood for use as a metabolic fuel (to be converted back to acetyl-CoA) by other tissues, particularly the kidney and the heart. Thus, during prolonged starvation, ketone bodies provide about 70% of the energy requirements of the brain. Under normal conditions, the kidneys excrete about 20 mg of ketone bodies each day, and the blood levels are maintained at about 1 mg of ketone bodies per 100 mL of blood.

In starvation, diabetes mellitus, and certain other physiological conditions in which cells do not receive sufficient amounts of carbohydrate, the rate of fatty acid oxidation increases to provide energy. This leads to an increase in the concentration of acetyl-CoA. The increased acetyl-CoA cannot be oxidized by the citric acid cycle because of a decrease in the concentration of oxaloacetate, which is diverted to glucose synthesis. In response, the rate of ketone body formation in the liver increases further, to a level much higher than can be used by other tissues. The excess ketone bodies accumulate in the blood and the urine, a condition referred to as *ketosis*. When the acetone in the blood reaches the lungs, its volatility causes it to be expelled in the breath. The sweet smell of acetone, a characteristic of ketosis, is frequently noticed on the breath of severely diabetic patients.

Because two of the three kinds of ketone bodies are weak acids, their presence in the blood in excessive amounts overwhelms the blood buffers and causes a marked decrease in blood pH (to 6.9 from a normal value of 7.4). This decrease in pH leads to a serious condition known as *acidosis*. One of the effects of acidosis is a decrease in the ability of hemoglobin to transport oxygen in the blood. In moderate to severe acidosis, breathing becomes labored and very painful. The body also loses fluids and becomes dehydrated as the kidneys attempt to get rid of the acids by eliminating large quantities of water. The lowered oxygen supply and dehydration lead to depression; even mild acidosis leads to lethargy, loss of appetite, and a generally run-down feeling. Untreated patients may go into a coma. At that point, prompt treatment is necessary if the person's life is to be saved.

6.2 ATP Yield from Fatty Acid Oxidation

The amount of ATP obtained from fatty acid oxidation depends on the size of the fatty acid being oxidized. For our purposes here. we'll study palmitic acid, a saturated fatty acid with 16 carbon atoms, as a typical fatty acid in the human diet. Calculating its energy yield provides a model for determining the ATP yield of all other fatty acids.

The breakdown by an organism of 1 mol of palmitic acid requires 1 mol of ATP (for activation) and forms 8 mol of acetyl-CoA. Recall from Table 20.2 that each mole of acetyl-CoA metabolized by the citric acid cycle yields 10 mol of ATP. The complete degradation of 1 mol of palmitic acid requires the β-oxidation reactions to be repeated seven times. Thus, 7 mol of NADH and 7 mol of $FADH_2$ are produced. Reoxidation of these compounds through respiration yields 2.5–3 and 1.5–2 mol of ATP, respectively. The energy calculations can be summarized as follows:

1 mol of ATP is split to AMP and $2P_i$	−2 ATP
8 mol of acetyl-CoA formed (8 × 12)	96 ATP
7 mol of $FADH_2$ formed (7 × 2)	14 ATP
7 mol of NADH formed (7 × 3)	21 ATP
Total	129 ATP

Note

The number of times β-oxidation is repeated for a fatty acid containing *n* carbon atoms is *n*/2 – 1 because the final turn yields two acetyl-CoA molecules.

The combustion of 1 mol of palmitic acid releases a considerable amount of energy:

$$C_{16}H_{32}O_2 + 23O_2 \rightarrow 16CO_2 + 16H_2O + 2{,}340 \text{ kcal}$$

The percentage of this energy that is conserved by the cell in the form of ATP is as follows:

$$\frac{\text{energy conserved}}{\text{total energy available}} \times 100 = \frac{(129 \text{ ATP})(7.4 \text{ kcal/ATP})}{2{,}340 \text{ kcal}} \times 100 = 41\%$$

The efficiency of fatty acid metabolism is comparable to that of carbohydrate metabolism, which we calculated to be 42%. For more information about the efficiency of fatty acid metabolism, see Section 5.)

Note

The oxidation of fatty acids produces large quantities of water. This water, which sustains migratory birds and animals (such as the camel) for long periods of time.

CONCEPT REVIEW EXERCISES

1. How are fatty acids activated prior to being transported into the mitochondria and oxidized?
2. Draw the structure of hexanoic (caproic) acid and identify the α-carbon and the β-carbon.

ANSWERS

1. They react with CoA to form fatty acyl-CoA molecules.
2.

β-carbon α-carbon

$CH_3CH_2CH_2CH_2CH_2COOH$

KEY TAKEAWAYS

- Fatty acids, obtained from the breakdown of triglycerides and other lipids, are oxidized through a series of reactions known as β-oxidation.
- In each round of β-oxidation, 1 molecule of acetyl-CoA, 1 molecule of NADH, and 1 molecule of $FADH_2$ are produced.
- The acetyl-CoA, NADH, and $FADH_2$ are used in the citric acid cycle, the electron transport chain, and oxidative phosphorylation to produce ATP.

EXERCISES

1. For each reaction found in β-oxidation, identify the enzyme that catalyzes the reaction and classify the reaction as oxidation-reduction, hydration, or cleavage.

   a.

$$RCH_2CH_2CH{=}CHC(=O){-}SCoA + H_2O \xrightarrow{?} RCH_2CH_2CH(OH)CH_2C(=O){-}SCoA$$

   b.

$$RCH_2CH_2C(=O)CH_2C(=O){-}SCoA + CoASH \xrightarrow{?} RCH_2CH_2C(=O){-}SCoA + CH_3C(=O){-}SCoA$$

   c.

$$RCH_2CH_2C(=O){-}SCoA + FAD \xrightarrow{?} RCH{=}CHC(=O){-}SCoA + FADH_2$$

2. What are the products of β-oxidation?
3. How many rounds of β-oxidation are necessary to metabolize lauric acid (a saturated fatty acid with 12 carbon atoms)?
4. How many rounds of β-oxidation are necessary to metabolize arachidic acid (a saturated fatty acid with 20 carbon atoms)?
5. When myristic acid (a saturated fatty acid with 14 carbon atoms) is completely oxidized by β-oxidation, how many molecules of each are formed?
   a. acetyl-CoA
   b. $FADH_2$
   c. NADH
6. When stearic acid (a saturated fatty acid with 18 carbon atoms) is completely oxidized by β-oxidation, how many molecules of each are formed?
   a. acetyl-CoA
   b. $FADH_2$
   c. NADH
7. What is the net yield of ATP from the complete oxidation, in a liver cell, of one molecule of myristic acid?
8. What is the net yield of ATP from the complete oxidation, in a liver cell, of one molecule of stearic acid?

ANSWERS

1. a. enoyl-CoA hydratase; hydration
   b. thiolase; cleavage
   c. acyl-CoA dehydrogenase; oxidation-reduction
3. five rounds
5. a. 7 molecules
   b. 6 molecules
   c. 6 molecules
7. 112 molecules

7. STAGE II OF PROTEIN CATABOLISM

LEARNING OBJECTIVE

1. **Describe how excess amino acids are degraded.**

The liver is the principal site of amino acid metabolism, but other tissues, such as the kidney, the small intestine, muscles, and adipose tissue, take part. Generally, the first step in the breakdown of amino acids is the separation of the amino group from the carbon skeleton, usually by a transamination reaction. The carbon skeletons resulting from the deaminated amino acids are used to form either glucose or fats, or they are converted to a metabolic intermediate that can be oxidized by the citric acid cycle. The latter alternative, amino acid catabolism, is more likely to occur when glucose levels are low—for example, when a person is fasting or starving.

7.1 Transamination

transamination

An exchange of functional groups between any amino acid and an α-keto acid.

Transamination is an exchange of functional groups between any amino acid (except lysine, proline, and threonine) and an α-keto acid. The amino group is usually transferred to the keto carbon atom of pyruvate, oxaloacetate, or α-ketoglutarate, converting the α-keto acid to alanine, aspartate, or glutamate, respectively. Transamination reactions are catalyzed by specific transaminases (also called aminotransferases), which require pyridoxal phosphate as a coenzyme. (For more information about coenzymes, see Chapter 18, [Unsupported Reference Type: chapter-section].)

$$\underset{\text{Amino acid}}{R-CH(^{+}NH_3)-COO^-} + \underset{\alpha\text{-keto acid}}{R'-CO-COO^-} \underset{}{\overset{\text{transaminase}}{\rightleftharpoons}} \underset{\text{New }\alpha\text{-keto acid}}{R-CO-COO^-} + \underset{\text{New amino acid}}{R'-CH(^{+}NH_3)-COO^-}$$

Alanine and aspartate then undergo a second transamination reaction, transferring their amino groups to α-ketoglutarate and forming glutamate (Figure 20.19).

Note

In an α-keto acid, the carbonyl or keto group is located on the carbon atom adjacent to the carboxyl group of the acid. (For more information about acid carboxyl groups, see Chapter 15, [Unsupported Reference Type: chapter-section].)

FIGURE 20.19 Two Transamination Reactions

In both reactions, the final acceptor of the amino group is α-ketoglutarate, and the final product is glutamate.

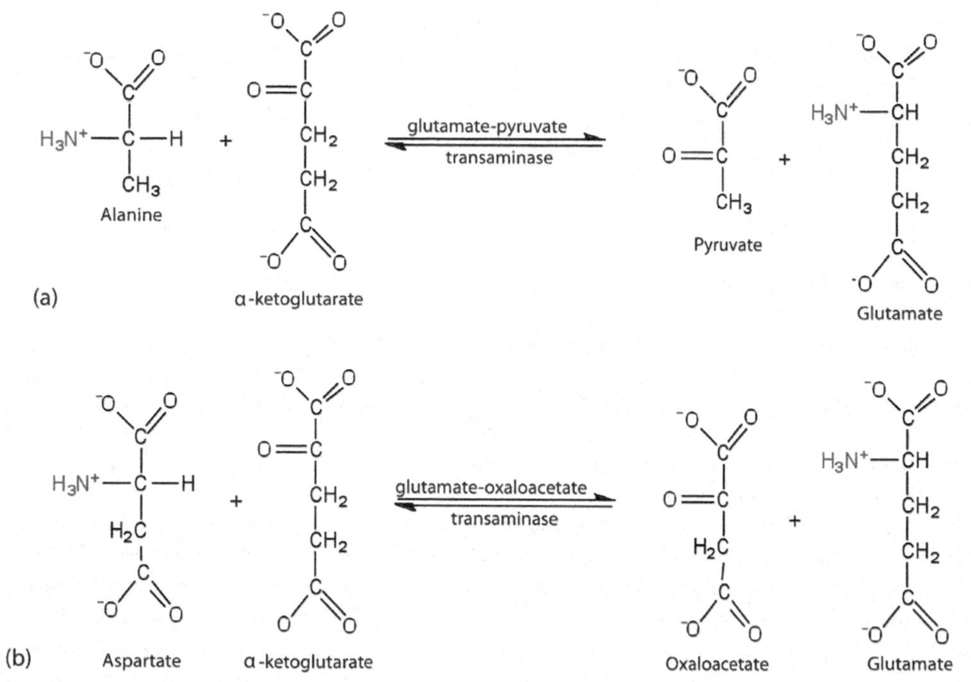

(a) Alanine + α-ketoglutarate ⇌ (glutamate-pyruvate transaminase) Pyruvate + Glutamate

(b) Aspartate + α-ketoglutarate ⇌ (glutamate-oxaloacetate transaminase) Oxaloacetate + Glutamate

7.2 Oxidative Deamination

In the breakdown of amino acids for energy, the final acceptor of the α-amino group is α-ketoglutarate, forming glutamate. Glutamate can then undergo **oxidative deamination**, in which it loses its amino group as an ammonium (NH_4^+) ion and is oxidized back to α-ketoglutarate (ready to accept another amino group):

oxidative deamination
A reaction in which glutamate loses its amino group as an ammonium ion and is oxidized back to α-ketoglutarate.

Glutamate + H_2O ⇌ (glutamate dehydrogenase; NAD^+ → NADH + H^+) α-ketoglutarate + NH_4^+

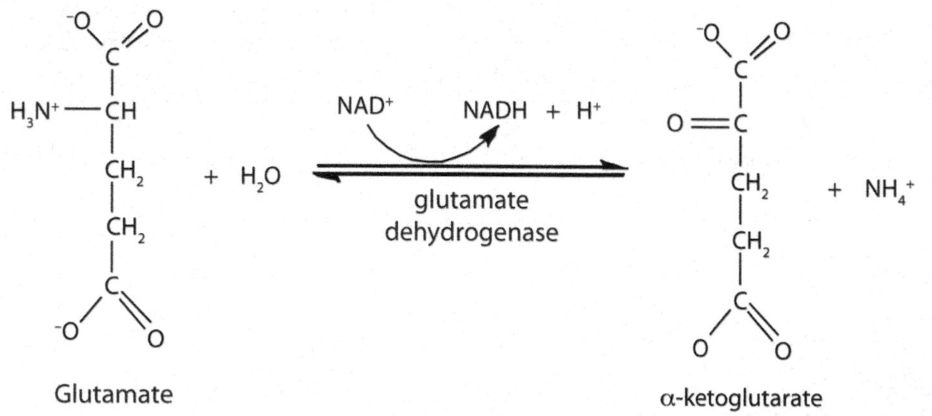

This reaction occurs primarily in liver mitochondria. Most of the NH_4^+ ion formed by oxidative deamination of glutamate is converted to urea and excreted in the urine in a series of reactions known as the urea cycle.

$$H_2N-\overset{\overset{\displaystyle O}{\|}}{C}-NH_2$$

urea

The synthesis of glutamate occurs in animal cells by reversing the reaction catalyzed by glutamate dehydrogenase. For this reaction nicotinamide adenine dinucleotide phosphate (NADPH) acts as the reducing agent. The synthesis of glutamate is significant because it is one of the few reactions in animals that can incorporate inorganic nitrogen (NH_4^+) into an α-keto acid to form an amino acid. The amino group can then be passed on through transamination reactions, to produce other amino acids from the appropriate α-keto acids.

7.3 The Fate of the Carbon Skeleton

Any amino acid can be converted into an intermediate of the citric acid cycle. Once the amino group is removed, usually by transamination, the α-keto acid that remains is catabolized by a pathway unique to that acid and consisting of one or more reactions. For example, phenylalanine undergoes a series of six reactions before it splits into fumarate and acetoacetate. Fumarate is an intermediate in the citric acid cycle, while acetoacetate must be converted to acetoacetyl-coenzyme A (CoA) and then to acetyl-CoA before it enters the citric acid cycle.

Those amino acids that can form any of the intermediates of carbohydrate metabolism can subsequently be converted to glucose via a metabolic pathway known as gluconeogenesis. These amino acids are called **glucogenic amino acids**. Amino acids that are converted to acetoacetyl-CoA or acetyl-CoA, which can be used for the synthesis of ketone bodies but not glucose, are called **ketogenic amino acids**. Some amino acids fall into both categories. Leucine and lysine are the only amino acids that are exclusively ketogenic. Figure 20.20 summarizes the ultimate fates of the carbon skeletons of the 20 amino acids.

glucogenic amino acid

An amino acid that can form any of the intermediates of carbohydrate metabolism and subsequently be converted to glucose.

ketogenic amino acid

An amino acid that is converted to acetoacetyl-CoA or acetyl-CoA, which can be used for the synthesis of ketone bodies but not glucose.

FIGURE 20.20 Fates of the Carbon Skeletons of Amino Acids

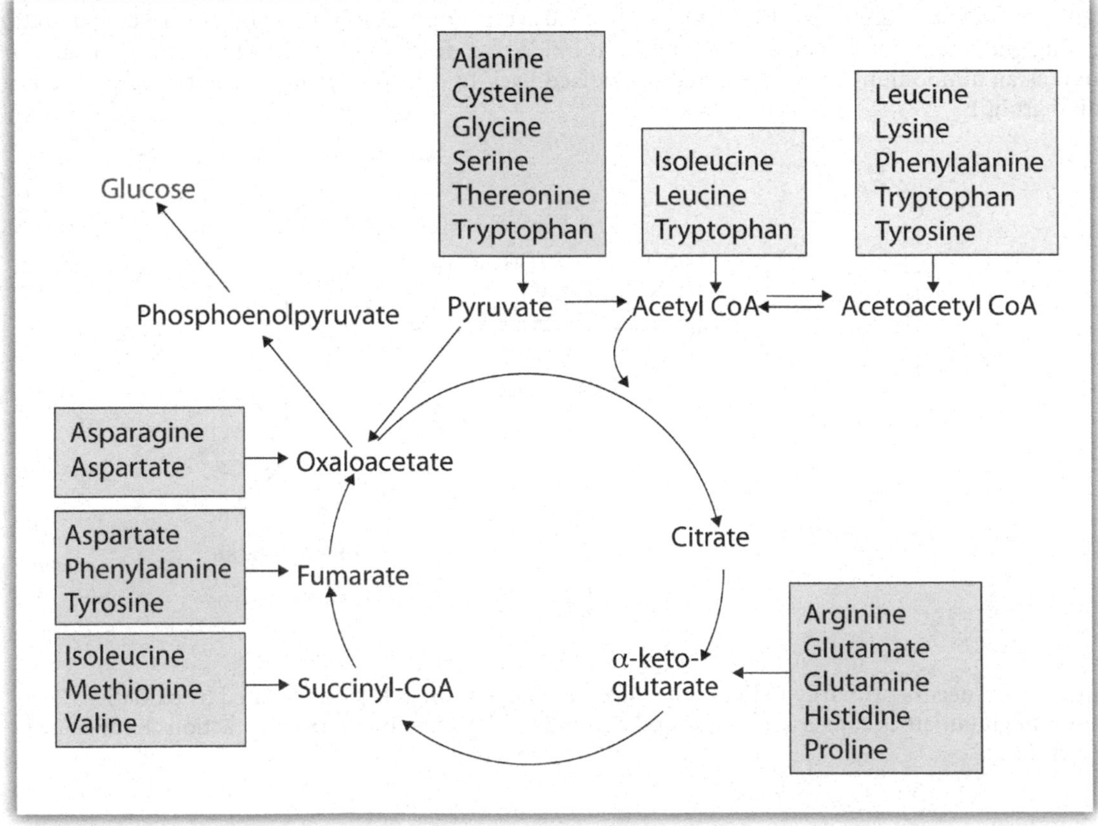

Career Focus: Exercise Physiologist

An exercise physiologist works with individuals who have or wish to prevent developing a wide variety of chronic diseases, such as diabetes, in which exercise has been shown to be beneficial. Each individual must be referred by a licensed physician. An exercise physiologist works in a variety of settings, such as a hospital or in a wellness program at a commercial business, to design and monitor individual exercise plans. A registered clinical exercise physiologist must have an undergraduate degree in exercise physiology or a related degree. Some job opportunities require a master's degree in exercise physiology or a related degree.

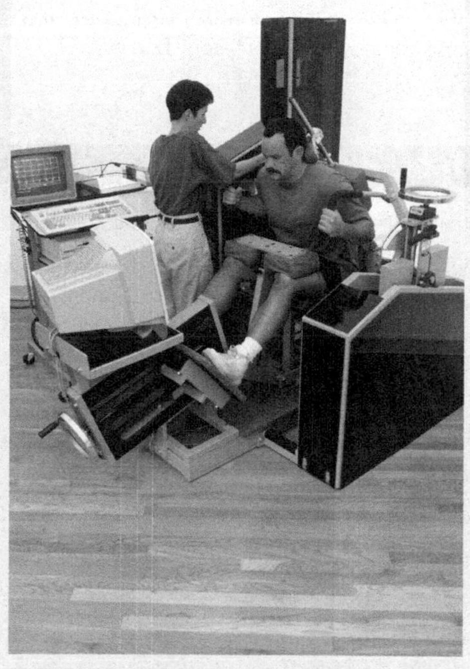

CONCEPT REVIEW EXERCISES

1.
    a. Write the equation for the transamination reaction between alanine and oxaloacetate.
    b. Name the two products that are formed.
2. What is the purpose of oxidative deamination?

ANSWERS

1. a.

$$H_3N^+{-}CH(CH_3){-}COO^- + {}^-OOC{-}C(=O){-}CH_2{-}COO^- \overset{\text{aminotransferase}}{\rightleftharpoons} \underset{\text{pyruvate}}{CH_3{-}C(=O){-}COO^-} + \underset{\text{aspartate}}{H_3N^+{-}CH(CH_2COO^-){-}COO^-}$$

   b. pyruvate and aspartate

2. Oxidative deamination provides a reaction in which the amino group [as the ammonium ($NH4^+$) ion] is removed from a molecule, not simply transferred from one molecule to another. Most of the $NH4^+$ ion is converted to urea and excreted from the body.

KEY TAKEAWAYS

- Generally the first step in the breakdown of amino acids is the removal of the amino group, usually through a reaction known as transamination.
- The carbon skeletons of the amino acids undergo further reactions to form compounds that can either be used for the synthesis of glucose or the synthesis of ketone bodies.

EXERCISES

1. Write the equation for the transamination reaction between valine and pyruvate.
2. Write the equation for the transamination reaction between phenylalanine and oxaloacetate.
3. What products are formed in the oxidative deamination of glutamate?
4. Determine if each amino acid is glucogenic, ketogenic, or both.
   a. phenylalanine
   b. leucine
   c. serine
5. Determine if each amino acid is glucogenic, ketogenic, or both.
   a. asparagine
   b. tyrosine
   c. valine

ANSWERS

1.

$$H_3N^+{-}CH(CH(CH_3){-}CH_3){-}C(=O){-}O^- + {}^-O{-}C(=O){-}C(=O){-}CH_3 \xrightleftharpoons{\text{transaminase}} O{=}C(CH(CH_3){-}CH_3){-}C(=O){-}O^- + H_3N^+{-}C(H)(CH_3){-}C(=O){-}O^-$$

3. α-ketoglutarate, NADH, and $NH4^+$
5. a. glucogenic
   b. both
   c. glucogenic

8. END-OF-CHAPTER MATERIAL

Chapter Summary

To ensure that you understand the material in this chapter, you should review the meanings of the bold terms in the following summary and ask yourself how they relate to the topics in the chapter.

Metabolism is the general term for all chemical reactions in living organisms. The two types of metabolism are **catabolism**—those reactions in which complex molecules (carbohydrates, lipids, and proteins) are broken down to simpler ones with the concomitant release of energy—and **anabolism**—those reactions that consume energy to build complex molecules. Metabolism is studied by looking at individual **metabolic pathways**, which are a series of biochemical reactions in which a given reactant is converted to a desired end product.

The oxidation of fuel molecules (primarily carbohydrates and lipids), a process called **respiration**, is the source of energy used by cells. Catabolic reactions release energy from food molecules and use some of that energy for the synthesis of *adenosine triphosphate* (ATP); anabolic reactions use the energy in ATP to create new compounds. Catabolism can be divided into three stages. In stage I, carbohydrates, lipids, and proteins are broken down into their individual monomer units—simple sugars, fatty acids, and amino acids, respectively. In stage II, these monomer units are broken down by specific metabolic pathways to form a common end product *acetyl-coenzyme A* (CoA). In stage III, acetyl-CoA is completely oxidized to form carbon dioxide and water, and ATP is produced.

The **digestion** of carbohydrates begins in the mouth as α-amylase breaks glycosidic linkages in carbohydrate molecules. Essentially no carbohydrate digestion occurs in the stomach, and food particles pass through to the small intestine, where α-amylase and intestinal enzymes convert complex carbohydrate molecules (starches) to monosaccharides. The monosaccharides then pass through the lining of the small intestine and into the bloodstream for transport to all body cells.

Protein digestion begins in the stomach as pepsinogen in **gastric juice** is converted to pepsin, the enzyme that hydrolyzes peptide bonds. The partially digested protein then passes to the small intestine, where the remainder of protein digestion takes place through the action of several enzymes. The resulting amino acids cross the intestinal wall into the blood and are carried to the liver.

Lipid digestion begins in the small intestine. Bile salts emulsify the lipid molecules, and then lipases hydrolyze them to fatty acids and monoglycerides. The hydrolysis products pass through the intestine and are repackaged for transport in the bloodstream.

In cells that are operating aerobically, acetyl-CoA produced in stage II of catabolism is oxidized to carbon dioxide. The **citric acid cycle** describes this oxidation, which takes place with the formation of the coenzymes reduced nicotinamide adenine dinucleotide (NADH) and reduced flavin adenine dinucleotide ($FADH_2$). The sequence of reactions needed to oxidize these coenzymes and transfer the resulting electrons to oxygen is called the **electron transport chain**, or the **respiratory chain**. The compounds responsible for this series of oxidation-reduction reactions include proteins known as **cytochromes**, Fe·S proteins, and other molecules that ultimately result in the reduction of molecular oxygen to water. Every time a compound with two carbon atoms is oxidized in the citric acid cycle, a respiratory chain compound accepts the electrons lost in the oxidation (and so is reduced) and then passes them on to the next metabolite in the chain. The energy released by the electron transport chain is used to transport hydrogen (H^+) ions from the mitochondrial matrix to the intermembrane space. The flow of H^+ back through ATP synthase leads to the synthesis and release of ATP from adenosine diphosphate (ADP) and inorganic phosphate ions (P_i) in a process known as **oxidative phosphorylation**. Electron transport and oxidative phosphorylation are tightly coupled to each other. The enzymes and intermediates of the citric acid cycle, the electron transport chain, and oxidative phosphorylation are located in organelles called **mitochondria**.

The oxidation of carbohydrates is the source of over 50% of the energy used by cells. Glucose is oxidized to two molecules of pyruvate through a series of reactions known as **glycolysis**. Some of the energy released in these reactions is conserved by the formation of ATP from ADP. Glycolysis can be divided into two phases: phase I consists of the first five reactions and requires energy to "prime" the glucose molecule for phase II, the last five reactions in which ATP is produced through **substrate-level phosphorylation**.

The pyruvate produced by glycolysis has several possible fates, depending on the organism and whether or not oxygen is present. In animal cells, pyruvate can be further oxidized to acetyl-CoA and then to carbon dioxide (through the citric acid cycle) if oxygen supplies are sufficient. When oxygen supplies are insufficient, pyruvate is reduced to lactate. In yeast and other microorganisms, pyruvate is not converted to lactate in the absence of oxygen but instead is converted to ethanol and carbon dioxide.

The amount of ATP formed by the oxidation of glucose depends on whether or not oxygen is present. If oxygen is present, glucose is oxidized to carbon dioxide, and 36–38 ATP molecules are produced for each glucose molecule oxidized, using the combined pathways of glycolysis, the citric acid cycle, the electron transport chain, and oxidative phosphorylation. Thus, approximately 42% of the energy released by the complete oxidation of glucose is conserved by the synthesis of ATP. In the absence of oxygen, only 2 molecules of ATP are formed for each molecule of glucose converted to lactate (2 molecules), and the amount of energy conserved is much less (2%).

Fatty acids, released by the degradation of triglycerides and other lipids, are converted to fatty acyl-CoA, transported into the mitochondria, and oxidized by repeated cycling through a sequence of four reactions known as **β-oxidation**. In each round of β-oxidation, the fatty acyl-CoA is shortened by two carbon atoms as one molecule of acetyl-CoA is formed. The final round of β-oxidation, once the chain has been shortened to four carbon atoms, forms two molecules of acetyl-CoA. β-oxidation also forms the reduced coenzymes $FADH_2$ and NADH, whose reoxidation through the electron transport chain and oxidative phosphorylation leads to the synthesis of ATP. The efficiency of fatty acid oxidation in the human body is approximately 41%.

Amino acids from the breakdown of proteins can be catabolized to provide energy. Amino acids whose carbon skeletons are converted to intermediates that can be converted to glucose through gluconeogenesis are known as **glucogenic amino acids**. Amino acids whose carbon skeletons are broken down to compounds used to form ketone bodies are known as **ketogenic amino acids**.

The first step in amino acid catabolism is separation of the amino group from the carbon skeleton. In a **transamination**, the amino acid gives its NH_2 to pyruvate, α-ketoglutarate, or oxaloacetate. The products of this reaction are a new amino acid and an α-keto acid containing the carbon skeleton of the original amino acid. Pyruvate is transaminated to alanine, α-ketoglutarate to glutamate, and oxaloacetate to aspartate. The amino groups used to form alanine and aspartate are ultimately transferred to α-ketoglutarate, forming glutamate. The glutamate then undergoes **oxidative deamination** to yield α-ketoglutarate and ammonia.

ADDITIONAL EXERCISES

1. Hydrolysis of which compound—arginine phosphate or glucose 6-phosphate—would provide enough energy for the phosphorylation of ATP? Why?
2. If a cracker, which is rich in starch, is chewed for a long time, it begins to develop a sweet, sugary taste. Why?
3. Indicate where each enzymes would cleave the short peptide ala-ser-met-val-phe-gly-cys-lys-asp-leu.
   a. aminopeptidase
   b. chymotrypsin
4. Indicate where each enzymes would cleave the short peptide ala-ser-met-val-phe-gly-cys-lys-asp-leu.
   a. trypsin
   b. carboxypeptidase
5. If the methyl carbon atom of acetyl-CoA is labeled, where does the label appear after the acetyl-CoA goes through one round of the citric acid cycle?
6. If the carbonyl carbon atom of acetyl-CoA is labeled, where does the label appear after the acetyl-CoA goes through one round of the citric acid cycle?
7. The average adult consumes about 65 g of fructose daily (either as the free sugar or from the breakdown of sucrose). In the liver, fructose is first phosphorylated to fructose 1-phosphate, which is then split into dihydroxyacetone phosphate and glyceraldehyde. Glyceraldehyde is then phosphorylated to glyceraldehyde 3-phosphate, with ATP as the phosphate group donor. Write the equations (using structural formulas) for these three steps. Indicate the type of enzyme that catalyzes each step.
8. What critical role is played by both BPG and PEP in glycolysis?
9. How is the NADH produced in glycolysis reoxidized when oxygen supplies are abundant?
10. When a triglyceride is hydrolyzed to form three fatty acids and glycerol, the glycerol can be converted to glycerol 3-phosphate and then oxidized to form dihydroxyacetone phosphate, an intermediate of glycolysis. (In this reaction, NAD^+ is reduced to NADH.) If you assume that there is sufficient oxygen to completely oxidize the pyruvate formed from dihydroxyacetone phosphate, what is the maximum amount of ATP formed from the complete oxidation of 1 mol of glycerol?
11. How is the $FADH_2$ from β-oxidation converted back to FAD?
12. If 1 mol of alanine is converted to pyruvate in a muscle cell (through transamination) and the pyruvate is then metabolized via the citric acid cycle, the electron transport chain, and oxidative phosphorylation, how many moles of ATP are produced?
13. If the essential amino acid leucine (2-amino-4-methylpentanoic acid) is lacking in the diet, an α-keto acid can substitute for it. Give the structure of the α-keto acid and the probable reaction used to form leucine from this α-keto acid.

ANSWERS

1. The hydrolysis of arginine phosphate releases more energy than is needed for the synthesis of ATP, while hydrolysis of glucose 6-phosphate does not.
3. a. The enzyme will cleave off amino acids one at a time beginning with alanine (the N-terminal end).
   b. following phenylalanine
5. Half of the label will be on the second carbon atom of oxaloacetate, while the other half will be on the third carbon atom.
7.

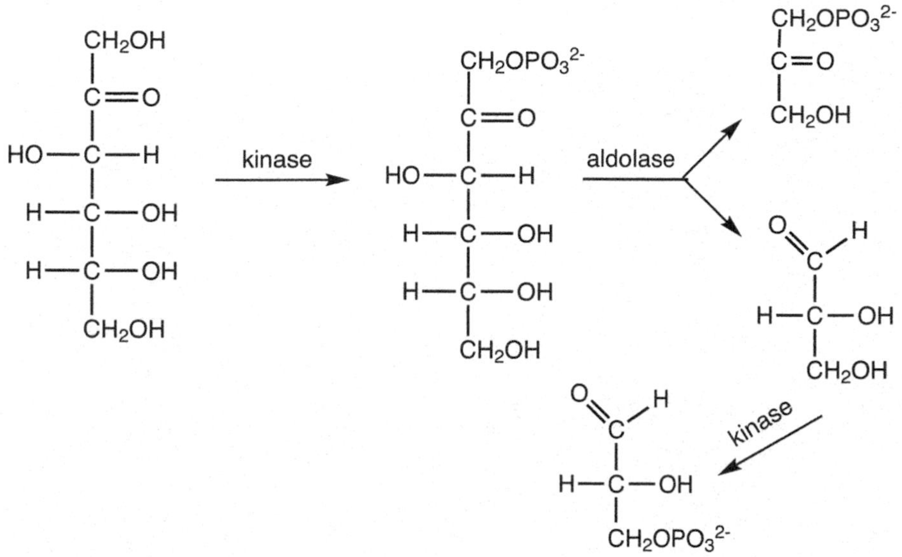

CH_2OH–C(=O)–C(HO)(H)–C(H)(OH)–C(H)(OH)–CH_2OH —kinase→ $CH_2OPO_3^{2-}$–C(=O)–C(HO)(H)–C(H)(OH)–C(H)(OH)–CH_2OH —aldolase→ $CH_2OPO_3^{2-}$–C=O–CH_2OH + O=C(H)–C(H)(OH)–CH_2OH

O=C(H)–C(H)(OH)–CH_2OH —kinase→ O=C(H)–C(H)(OH)–$CH_2OPO_3^{2-}$

9. When oxygen is abundant, NADH is reoxidized through the reactions of the electron transport chain.
11. FADH2 is reoxidized back to FAD via the electron transport chain.
13.

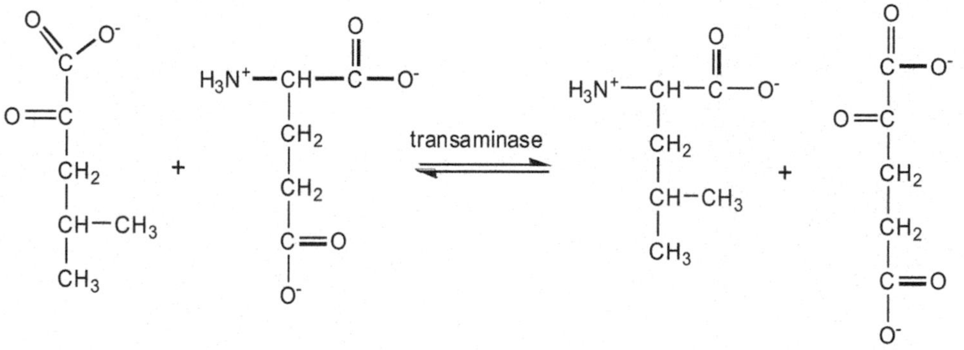

$^-$O–C(=O)–C(=O)–CH_2–CH–CH_3 (–CH_3) + H_3N^+–CH(–CH_2–CH_2–C(=O)–O$^-$)–C(=O)–O$^-$ $\underset{}{\overset{\text{transaminase}}{\rightleftharpoons}}$ H_3N^+–CH(–CH_2–CH–CH_3 (–CH_3))–C(=O)–O$^-$ + $^-$O–C(=O)–C(=O)–CH_2–CH_2–C(=O)–O$^-$

CHAPTER 21

Appendix: Periodic Table of the Elements

In this chapter, we present some data on the chemical elements. The periodic table lists all the known chemical elements, arranged by atomic number (that is, the number of protons in the nucleus). The periodic table is arguably the best tool in all of science; no other branch of science can summarize its fundamental constituents in such a concise and useful way. Many of the physical and chemical properties of the elements are either known or understood based on their positions on the periodic table. Periodic tables are available with a variety of chemical and physical properties listed in each element's box. What follows here is a relatively simple version. The Internet is a great place to find periodic tables that contain additional information.

One item on most periodic tables is the atomic mass of each element. For many applications, only one or two decimal places are necessary for the atomic mass. However, some applications (especially nuclear chemistry; see Chapter 11) require more decimal places. The atomic masses in Table 21.1 represent the number of decimal places recognized by the International Union of Pure and Applied Chemistry, the worldwide body that develops standards for chemistry. The atomic masses of some elements are known very precisely, to a large number of decimal places. The atomic masses of other elements, especially radioactive elements, are not known as precisely. Some elements, such as lithium, can have varying atomic masses depending on how their isotopes are isolated.

The web offers many interactive periodic table resources. For example, see http://www.ptable.com.

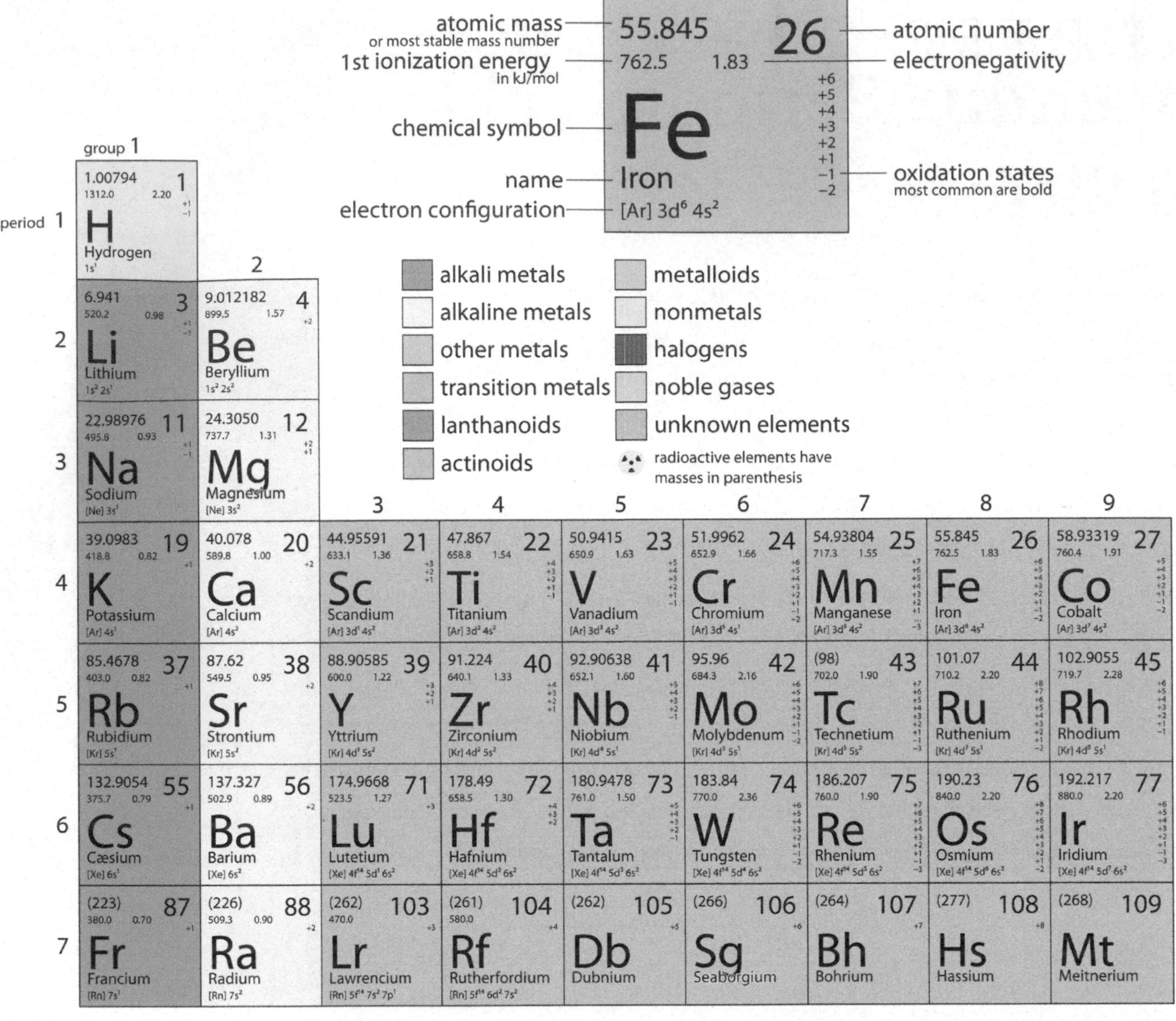

The properties listed in each box are introduced throughout the text. Atomic masses may vary by source.

by Robert Campion

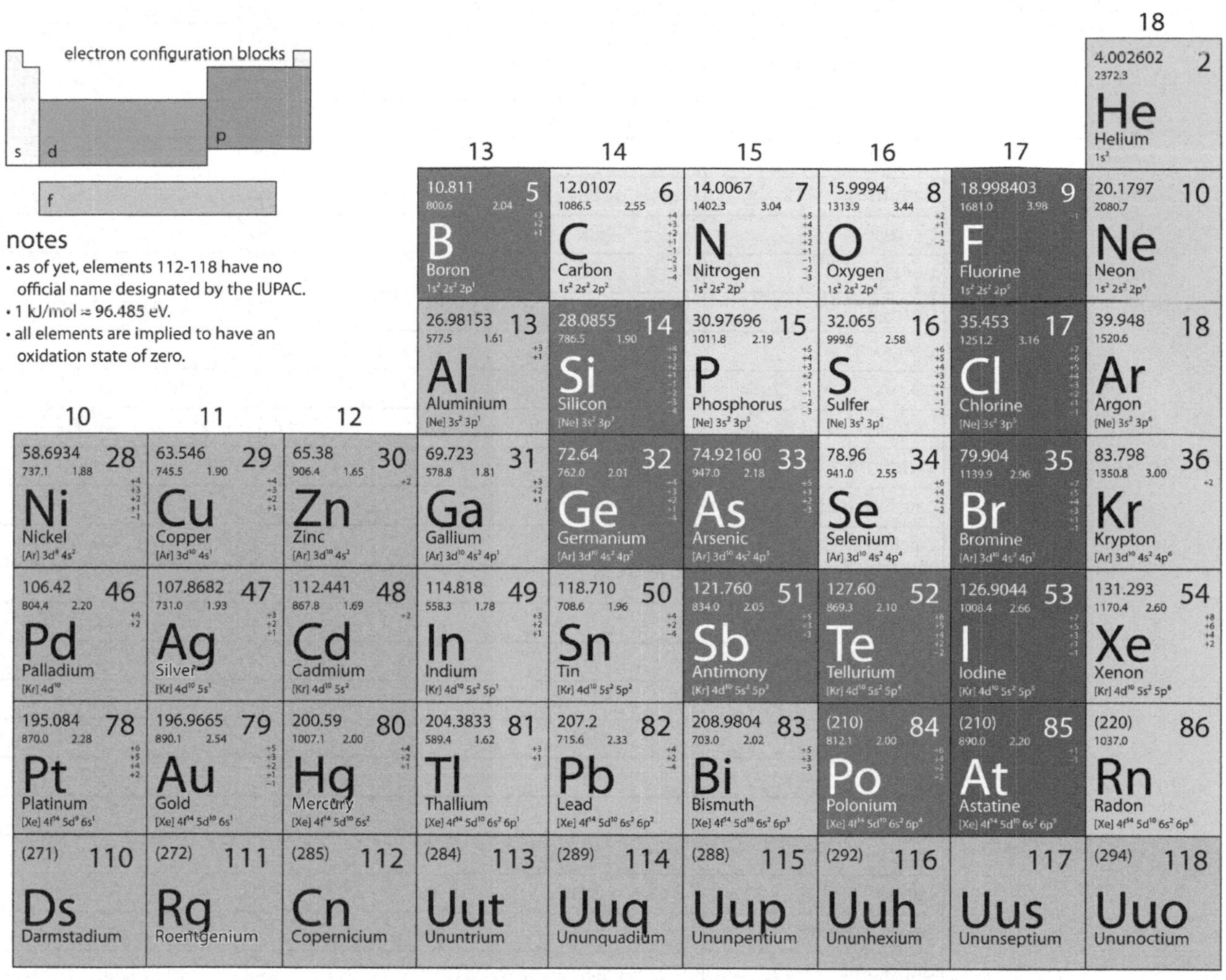

Atomic mass	Number	Ionization energy	Electronegativity	Symbol	Name	Configuration
157.25	64	593.4	1.20	Gd	Gadolinium	$[Xe] 4f^7 5d^1 6s^2$
158.9253	65	565.8		Tb	Terbium	$[Xe] 4f^9 6s^2$
162.500	66	573.0	1.22	Dy	Dysprosium	$[Xe] 4f^{10} 6s^2$
164.9303	67	581.0	1.23	Ho	Holmium	$[Xe] 4f^{11} 6s^2$
167.259	68	589.3	1.24	Er	Erbium	$[Xe] 4f^{12} 6s^2$
168.9342	69	596.7	1.25	Tm	Thulium	$[Xe] 4f^{13} 6s^2$
173.054	70	603.4		Yb	Ytterbium	$[Xe] 4f^{14} 6s^2$
(247)	96	581.0	1.30	Cm	Curium	$[Rn] 5f^7 6d^1 7s^2$
(247)	97	601.0	1.30	Bk	Berkelium	$[Rn] 5f^9 7s^2$
(251)	98	608.0	1.30	Cf	Californium	$[Rn] 5f^{10} 7s^2$
(252)	99	619.0	1.30	Es	Einsteinium	$[Rn] 5f^{11} 6s^2$
(257)	100	627.0	1.30	Fm	Fermium	$[Rn] 5f^{12} 7s^2$
(258)	101	635.0	1.30	Md	Mendelevium	$[Rn] 5f^{13} 7s^2$
(259)	102	642.0	1.30	No	Nobelium	$[Rn] 5f^{14} 7s^2$

TABLE 21.1 The Basics of the Elements of the Periodic Table

Name	Atomic Symbol	Atomic Number	Atomic Mass	Footnotes
actinium*	Ac	89		
aluminum	Al	13	26.9815386(8)	
americium*	Am	95		
antimony	Sb	51	121.760(1)	g
argon	Ar	18	39.948(1)	g, r
arsenic	As	33	74.92160(2)	
astatine*	At	85		
barium	Ba	56	137.327(7)	
berkelium*	Bk	97		
beryllium	Be	4	9.012182(3)	
bismuth	Bi	83	208.98040(1)	
bohrium*	Bh	107		
boron	B	5	10.811(7)	g, m, r
bromine	Br	35	79.904(1)	
cadmium	Cd	48	112.411(8)	g
caesium (cesium)	Cs	55	132.9054519(2)	
calcium	Ca	20	40.078(4)	g
californium*	Cf	98		
carbon	C	6	12.0107(8)	g, r
cerium	Ce	58	140.116(1)	g
chlorine	Cl	17	35.453(2)	g, m, r
chromium	Cr	24	51.9961(6)	
cobalt	Co	27	58.933195(5)	
copernicium*	Cn	112		
copper	Cu	29	63.546(3)	r
curium*	Cm	96		
darmstadtium*	Ds	110		
dubnium*	Db	105		
dysprosium	Dy	66	162.500(1)	g
einsteinium*	Es	99		
erbium	Er	68	167.259(3)	g
europium	Eu	63	151.964(1)	g
fermium*	Fm	100		
fluorine	F	9	18.9984032(5)	
francium*	Fr	87		
gadolinium	Gd	64	157.25(3)	g

***Element has no stable nuclides. However, three such elements (Th, Pa, and U) have a characteristic terrestrial isotopic composition, and for these an atomic mass is tabulated.**

†Commercially available Li materials have atomic weights that range between 6.939 and 6.996; if a more accurate value is required, it must be determined for the specific material.

g Geological specimens are known in which the element has an isotopic composition outside the limits for normal material. The difference between the atomic mass of the element in such specimens and that given in the table may exceed the stated uncertainty.

m Modified isotopic compositions may be found in commercially available material because it has been subjected to an undisclosed or inadvertent isotopic fractionation. Substantial deviations in the atomic mass of the element from that given in the table can occur.

r Range in isotopic composition of normal terrestrial material prevents a more precise *A*r(E) being given; the tabulated *A*r(E) value and uncertainty should be applicable to normal material.

Name	Atomic Symbol	Atomic Number	Atomic Mass	Footnotes
gallium	Ga	31	69.723(1)	
germanium	Ge	32	72.64(1)	
gold	Au	79	196.966569(4)	
hafnium	Hf	72	178.49(2)	
hassium*	Hs	108		
helium	He	2	4.002602(2)	g, r
holmium	Ho	67	164.93032(2)	
hydrogen	H	1	1.00794(7)	g, m, r
indium	In	49	114.818(3)	
iodine	I	53	126.90447(3)	
iridium	Ir	77	192.217(3)	
iron	Fe	26	55.845(2)	
krypton	Kr	36	83.798(2)	g, m
lanthanum	La	57	138.90547(7)	g
lawrencium*	Lr	103		
lead	Pb	82	207.2(1)	g, r
lithium	Li	3	[6.941(2)]†	g, m, r
lutetium	Lu	71	174.967(1)	g
magnesium	Mg	12	24.3050(6)	
manganese	Mn	25	54.938045(5)	
meitnerium*	Mt	109		
mendelevium*	Md	101		
mercury	Hg	80	200.59(2)	
molybdenum	Mo	42	95.94(2)	g
neodymium	Nd	60	144.242(3)	g
neon	Ne	10	20.1797(6)	g, m
neptunium*	Np	93		
nickel	Ni	28	58.6934(2)	
niobium	Nb	41	92.90638(2)	
nitrogen	N	7	14.0067(2)	g, r
nobelium*	No	102		
osmium	Os	76	190.23(3)	g
oxygen	O	8	15.9994(3)	g, r
palladium	Pd	46	106.42(1)	g
phosphorus	P	15	30.973762(2)	
platinum	Pt	78	195.084(9)	
plutonium*	Pu	94		

***Element has no stable nuclides. However, three such elements (Th, Pa, and U) have a characteristic terrestrial isotopic composition, and for these an atomic mass is tabulated.**

†Commercially available Li materials have atomic weights that range between 6.939 and 6.996; if a more accurate value is required, it must be determined for the specific material.

g Geological specimens are known in which the element has an isotopic composition outside the limits for normal material. The difference between the atomic mass of the element in such specimens and that given in the table may exceed the stated uncertainty.

m Modified isotopic compositions may be found in commercially available material because it has been subjected to an undisclosed or inadvertent isotopic fractionation. Substantial deviations in the atomic mass of the element from that given in the table can occur.

r Range in isotopic composition of normal terrestrial material prevents a more precise $Ar(E)$ being given; the tabulated $Ar(E)$ value and uncertainty should be applicable to normal material.

Name	Atomic Symbol	Atomic Number	Atomic Mass	Footnotes
polonium*	Po	84		
potassium	K	19	39.0983(1)	
praseodymium	Pr	59	140.90765(2)	
promethium*	Pm	61		
protactinium*	Pa	91	231.03588(2)	
radium*	Ra	88		
radon*	Rn	86		
roentgenium*	Rg	111		
rhenium	Re	75	186.207(1)	
rhodium	Rh	45	102.90550(2)	
rubidium	Rb	37	85.4678(3)	g
ruthenium	Ru	44	101.07(2)	g
rutherfordium*	Rf	104		
samarium	Sm	62	150.36(2)	g
scandium	Sc	21	44.955912(6)	
seaborgium*	Sg	106		
selenium	Se	34	78.96(3)	r
silicon	Si	14	28.0855(3)	r
silver	Ag	47	107.8682(2)	g
sodium	Na	11	22.98976928(2)	
strontium	Sr	38	87.62(1)	g, r
sulfur	S	16	32.065(5)	g, r
tantalum	Ta	73	180.94788(2)	
technetium*	Tc	43		
tellurium	Te	52	127.60(3)	g
terbium	Tb	65	158.92535(2)	
thallium	Tl	81	204.3833(2)	
thorium*	Th	90	232.03806(2)	g
thulium	Tm	69	168.93421(2)	
tin	Sn	50	118.710(7)	g
titanium	Ti	22	47.867(1)	
tungsten	W	74	183.84(1)	
ununhexium*	Uuh	116		
ununoctium*	Uuo	118		
ununpentium*	Uup	115		
ununquadium*	Uuq	114		
ununtrium*	Uut	113		

***Element has no stable nuclides. However, three such elements (Th, Pa, and U) have a characteristic terrestrial isotopic composition, and for these an atomic mass is tabulated.**

†Commercially available Li materials have atomic weights that range between 6.939 and 6.996; if a more accurate value is required, it must be determined for the specific material.

g Geological specimens are known in which the element has an isotopic composition outside the limits for normal material. The difference between the atomic mass of the element in such specimens and that given in the table may exceed the stated uncertainty.

m Modified isotopic compositions may be found in commercially available material because it has been subjected to an undisclosed or inadvertent isotopic fractionation. Substantial deviations in the atomic mass of the element from that given in the table can occur.

r Range in isotopic composition of normal terrestrial material prevents a more precise *Ar*(E) being given; the tabulated *Ar*(E) value and uncertainty should be applicable to normal material.

Name	Atomic Symbol	Atomic Number	Atomic Mass	Footnotes
uranium*	U	92	238.02891(3)	g, m
vanadium	V	23	50.9415(1)	
xenon	Xe	54	131.293(6)	g, m
ytterbium	Yb	70	173.04(3)	g
yttrium	Y	39	88.90585(2)	
zinc	Zn	30	65.409(4)	
zirconium	Zr	40	91.224(2)	g

***Element has no stable nuclides. However, three such elements (Th, Pa, and U) have a characteristic terrestrial isotopic composition, and for these an atomic mass is tabulated.**

†Commercially available Li materials have atomic weights that range between 6.939 and 6.996; if a more accurate value is required, it must be determined for the specific material.

g Geological specimens are known in which the element has an isotopic composition outside the limits for normal material. The difference between the atomic mass of the element in such specimens and that given in the table may exceed the stated uncertainty.

m Modified isotopic compositions may be found in commercially available material because it has been subjected to an undisclosed or inadvertent isotopic fractionation. Substantial deviations in the atomic mass of the element from that given in the table can occur.

r Range in isotopic composition of normal terrestrial material prevents a more precise *A*r(E) being given; the tabulated *A*r(E) value and uncertainty should be applicable to normal material.

Source: Pure and Applied Chemistry 78, no. 11 (2005): 2051–66. © IUPAC (International Union of Pure and Applied Chemistry).

Index

β-oxidation 655-659, 666

active site 543, 563-580

addition polymerization 345-347, 361

addition reaction 342-344, 348-351, 361

alcohol 16, 39, 126-135, 142, 155-157, 224, 235-238, 330, 342, 365-394, 400-414, 421-422, 430-440, 446-448, 462-463, 480, 487, 501, 507, 513-516, 524-529, 535-536, 559-562, 639, 649, 655-656

aldehyde 155, 342, 366, 378-383, 394-397, 401-402, 407-408, 420-422, 462, 468-474, 482-488, 501, 505

aldose 471, 475-477, 485, 562

alkaloid 450, 559-560

alkane (saturated hydrocarbon) 124, 298

alkene 123-126, 132-133, 329-351, 361-362, 366, 376-380, 384-385, 404-408, 517, 655

alkyl group 307-313, 317, 324, 367, 394-396, 427-429, 441, 462

alkyl halide (haloalkane) 317, 324

alkyne 123-125, 132-133, 329, 333, 348-349, 361, 366

alloy 13, 40, 222, 246

alpha particle 72, 274-278

amide 257-259, 413-415, 453-463, 536, 543-546, 550-555, 565, 573, 639

amine 413-415, 440-452, 459-462, 533, 543, 547-548, 584

amino acid 243, 357, 406, 410, 447, 458, 480, 532-533, 537-583, 593, 603-610, 614-616, 621-625, 630-637, 660-667

amino group 415, 440, 444, 540, 545-553, 562, 578, 634, 660-666

amorphous 204-206, 218

amphiprotic 259-260, 270

amylopectin 497-502

amylose 497-502

anabolism 626, 665

anaerobic metabolism 155-157

anion 75-82, 88-93, 97-98, 134, 219, 237, 250, 266-270, 293, 424-425, 449, 516, 547-549, 559, 572, 628, 639

anomeric carbon 483-495, 501, 505

anomers 481-484, 501

anticodon 603-604, 609, 621

antioxidant 155-157, 365, 517-518, 576

aromatic compound 351, 358, 362, 388

aromatic hydrocarbon 329-363, 389

Arrhenius acid 16, 86, 127-128, 134, 142-146, 150-159, 169-171, 175-177, 194, 221, 230-238, 249-271, 293, 339-342, 352, 357, 366, 376-393, 405-438, 449-463, 480, 486-492, 498-499, 504-519, 523-560, 565-567, 573-587, 593-599, 603-627, 632-646, 650-666

Arrhenius base 27-31, 36-37, 86, 221, 250-271, 308, 426, 435-436, 449-451, 459, 463, 515-518, 544-549, 565, 579, 584-602, 608, 621-624

aryl group 356, 362, 390, 394, 427-428, 440, 462

atmosphere 45, 72, 177, 194, 207-218, 283-285, 295, 319-320, 519

atom 13, 19, 39, 43, 49-63, 67-84, 93-98, 102-127, 132-134, 140-145, 150-165, 169, 176-178, 200-202, 218, 256-257, 271-274, 278-280, 289, 298-311, 317-326, 331-342, 349-356, 362-373, 379-383, 388-401, 405-409, 414, 418-420, 427-431, 435, 440-458, 462, 471-488, 501, 505, 524, 554-557, 562, 578, 593-596, 639, 649, 660, 666-667

atomic bomb 290-293

atomic mass 59-60, 64, 71-72, 93-98, 133, 163-167, 177, 540, 669-675

atomic mass unit 59-60, 71, 98, 133, 163-164, 540

atomic number 55-58, 64, 69-71, 274-280, 289, 669-675

atomic radius 68-72

autoionization of water 260, 264, 270

Avogadro's number 161-163, 177

balanced 83, 114, 126, 139-151, 157-159, 168-178, 194, 219, 231, 235, 252-257, 270, 289, 381

bar 180, 207, 218

base (basic) unit 28

becquerel (Bq) 281

beta particle 275-278, 287

bilayer 522-523, 527-530, 536-537

bile 164, 530-536, 634-637, 665

biochemistry 3-7, 154, 295, 416, 437-438, 462, 467, 561, 575

boiling point 16, 118, 185-187, 199, 219, 240-247, 270, 313-315, 321, 330, 341, 373-376, 386, 391-392, 401, 405, 423, 432, 446-448, 456-458, 462

boiling point elevation 240-241, 247

bond energy 188-194

bond length 103, 113-114, 118, 133

bonding pair of electrons 103, 133

Boyle's law 209-212, 217-218

Brønsted-Lowry acid 255-261, 270

Brønsted-Lowry base 255-261, 270

buffer 266-270, 579

calorie 30, 168, 180-183, 517

capacity 183-185, 195, 268-270, 507

carbohydrate 5, 156, 180, 192-195, 367, 382, 387, 394, 408, 467-507, 530-532, 538, 553, 575, 579-581, 617-619, 625-638, 647, 654-658, 662-665

carbonyl group
155, 394-401, 407, 413-415, 429-430, 462, 472-478, 483, 501

carboxyl group
127, 132, 414-422, 430-433, 462, 540, 546, 550-552, 579-581, 660

carboxylic acid
127, 155, 366, 383, 387, 407, 411-436, 453-462, 509, 540, 550, 639

catabolism
626, 630, 635-638, 647, 651-655, 660, 665-666

catalyst
342-343, 376-380, 409, 433-435, 488, 505, 561-562, 567-568, 578

cation
75-82, 88-93, 97-98, 134, 237, 245, 250-251, 259, 425, 449, 547-549

cerebroside
526-529, 536

chain reaction
290-293, 576

Charles's law
212-213, 217-218

chemical bond
73-74, 116, 189, 566

chemical equation
139-147, 157-158, 169-178, 219, 230-231, 235, 247, 252-265, 270, 274-277, 293

chemical equilibrium (equilibrium)
263

chemical formula
81-87, 93-98, 106-109, 140, 305

chemical property
12-16, 39, 51, 64-71, 88, 118, 143, 315, 329, 342, 348, 424, 459, 485, 669

chemical reaction
137-150, 157-159, 169-173, 177, 189-191, 261-265, 270, 285, 289, 316, 561-562

chemical symbol
43-48, 71, 78

chemistry
1-675

chiral carbon
473-475, 501, 542-545

cholesterol
101, 123-128, 365-367, 507-509, 515-517, 523, 530-537, 637

chromosome
583-584, 621

cis isomer
335-338, 361

cis-trans isomers (or geometric isomers)
335, 361

citric acid cycle (or Krebs cycle or tricarboxylic acid [TCA] cycle)
638

codon
603-609, 614, 621-624

coefficient
140-141, 170

coenzyme
562, 575-579, 586, 637-646, 653-656, 660-666

cofactor
575-577

colligative property
240-247

combination (composition) reaction
147

combined gas law
213-214, 218

combustion reaction
148-149, 155, 316

competitive inhibitor
571-578

complementary bases
594-596, 621

compound
12-17, 37-39, 45, 72-111, 115-127, 133-134, 147-148, 158, 164, 178, 188, 192, 223, 230, 238-240, 247-270, 274, 287, 293-326, 331-339, 349-372, 384-409, 414, 419-434, 438-463, 468, 472, 479-480, 492, 505-507, 511-519, 535-540, 545, 549, 561-563, 571-575, 587, 626-630, 640-647, 653, 665-666

concentration
85, 221-236, 240-255, 262-265, 270, 286, 404, 537, 565-574, 578-581, 627, 645, 657

condensed structural formula
299, 305-311, 320, 324-326, 330, 335, 347-348, 364, 371, 377-379, 394, 406-408, 420, 427-428, 452, 456-459, 463, 509-512

conversion factor
33-40, 144-145, 161-174, 207, 215-217, 226-228, 235

core electron
62-63, 71

covalent bond
74, 102-106, 113-119, 133, 199-202, 556, 611, 616

covalent network bonding
199, 218

crystal
82, 106, 120, 184, 203-206, 218, 239, 510, 558

curie (Ci)
281

cyclic hydrocarbon
321-324, 362, 450

cycloalkane
317, 321-324, 332, 337

cytochrome
554, 644-647, 665

cytoplasm
520, 536, 602, 606, 651

D sugar
471-478, 501

decomposition reaction
148-149

denaturation
558-561, 568, 578

density
16, 30-40, 206, 235, 247, 313-314, 325, 507, 531

deoxyribonucleic acid (DNA)
584, 593-599, 605, 610, 617, 621

derived unit
29-32, 40

diatomic molecule
50-51, 71, 142

digestion
249, 492, 534-536, 561, 630-637, 654, 665

dipole-dipole interaction
200-201, 218

disaccharide
470, 488, 493-495, 501-505

dispersion force
201-203, 218, 314, 373, 422, 510, 523, 557-560, 567, 578

dispersion force (London force)
201

dissociation
237-238, 246

disulfide linkage
406, 556-560, 578

double bond
111-113, 124-128, 132-134, 155, 330-337, 342-344, 361, 366, 382, 394, 400, 405-409, 414, 428, 509-512, 535, 562, 640

double helix
116, 594-596, 600, 604, 611, 621

electrolyte
238-239, 243-247

electron
51-55, 61-63, 67-80, 97-98, 102-106, 111-115, 120-122, 133, 150-151, 157, 200, 256, 270-271, 275-276, 287, 362, 400, 449, 499, 576, 617, 627, 638-655, 659, 665-667

electron configuration
61-63, 67-72, 76-80, 97-98, 104

electron transport chain (or respiratory chain)
641

electronegativity
114-119, 133-134

element
12-16, 39, 43-50, 55-60, 64-72, 76-77, 83-88, 93, 97, 103-109, 113, 119, 123, 130-133, 140-143, 159-164, 178, 201, 233, 250-254, 273-276, 280, 296, 357, 450, 669-675

emulsion
525, 536

enantiomers
472-475, 501

endothermic
188-194

energy
5, 30, 40, 61, 98-102, 148, 154-156, 179-205, 221-225, 241, 275-278, 282-293, 314-316, 373, 382, 438, 467-470, 478, 483, 496-502, 507, 513-514, 518, 559-562, 569-572, 625-667

enzyme
2, 69, 156, 249, 377-382, 386-387, 421, 458-462, 480, 484, 488-492, 498-502, 510, 515, 534, 539-581, 600, 605-606, 611-620, 632-636, 640-655, 659, 665-667

equivalent (Eq)
233

essential amino acid
357, 540-542, 578, 666

essential fatty acid
509, 535

ester
413-415, 427-438, 462-463, 513, 517, 536, 579, 593-596, 600-601

esterification
379, 385, 433-435, 462

ether
366, 380, 385, 390-393, 401, 405-414, 422, 440, 447

exact number
34-38

exothermic
188-194, 316

fat
30, 36, 125-126, 176, 180, 192-195, 314, 387, 493, 507, 513-518, 531-535, 569, 575-579

fatty acid
125, 176, 415, 428, 507-519, 523-537, 553, 576, 630, 635-637, 654-659, 665-666

feedback inhibition
574

fibrous protein
553, 559, 578

formula mass
93-98, 167, 293, 391, 432, 447

formula unit
82, 95-98, 105-106, 145, 162-164, 243-244

freezing point depression
241-242, 247

functional group
126-133, 155, 238, 312, 365-370, 379-381, 394-396, 401-416, 440, 445, 453-458, 462, 468-474, 501, 505, 541, 546-551, 562-567

fusion
14-17, 186-188, 194, 288-293

galactosemia
490-492, 501-504, 612

gamma ray
275-278, 282, 286-288

ganglioside
527, 613

gas law
6, 209-219

gastric juice
569, 632-633, 665

Geiger counter
284-285

gene
583-584, 602-605, 612-616, 621

genetic code
601, 605-608, 614, 621

genetic disease
490, 501, 610-616, 620-621

globular protein
553, 559

glucogenic amino acid
662, 666

glycol
230, 241, 386-387, 407, 433

glycolipid
479, 524-529, 536

glycolysis
647-654, 665-666

glycosidic linkage
487-496, 501

group (or family)
65

half reaction
150-157, 642

half-life
278-288, 292

halogenated hydrocarbon
295-327

halogenation
316, 342, 361

heat
65, 148-149, 179-195, 205, 225, 292, 316, 379, 480, 515, 558-560, 578, 610, 616, 625-627, 652

heat of fusion
186-188, 194

heat of vaporization
186-188, 194

heterocyclic compound
450-452

heterogeneous mixture
13-16

homogeneous mixture (solution)
13

homologous series
299-302, 324, 367, 401

hydration
236, 246, 342, 361, 376-380, 407-410, 639, 646, 659-660

hydrocarbon
5, 124-126, 130-133, 192, 201, 223, 289, 295-368, 373-375, 389-390, 394, 406, 414, 419-422, 445, 450, 462, 512-516, 522, 536-537, 575

hydrogen bonding
201-203, 218, 373-375, 382, 386, 391-393, 400-401, 405-407, 422-424, 431-433, 446-452, 456-458, 462-463, 486, 497-499, 527, 554-567, 575-581, 594-595, 600-603, 621

hydrogenation
126, 342, 361, 513, 517-519, 536

hydrolysis
386, 435-438, 459-462, 478, 485-502, 513-520, 536, 540, 561-566, 627-640, 653, 665-667

hydrophilic
522, 527-528, 534-536

hydrophobic
522-523, 527-528, 534-536, 557

hypothesis
10-12, 39, 645

ideal gas law
215-219

ideal gas law constant
215-218

immiscible
223, 246

induced-fit model
564-566, 578

inner transition metal
66, 72

inorganic chemistry
296-299, 324

insoluble
223, 246, 296-297, 313-315, 324, 340-341, 374, 402, 422, 426, 499, 553, 560, 634

integral protein
527-529

intermolecular interaction
198-207, 218-224, 537, 556

ion
73-98, 106-107, 119, 124, 134, 150-151, 155, 162-164, 177, 195-204, 218-221, 233-273, 284, 293, 315-316, 386-387, 402, 425, 444, 449-450, 463, 485-486, 527, 532, 536, 547, 556-560, 569-570, 575-579, 628-632, 641-649, 661-665

ionic bond
73-75, 106-107, 115, 189, 199, 296, 556-559

ionic bonding
73-101, 106, 130, 199-202, 219, 296, 556-560, 567, 578

ionic compound
73-102, 107-109, 117-120, 133-134, 161-164, 189, 194, 199-200, 222-223, 232, 238-240, 246-252, 315

ionic interaction
199-203, 218

irreversible inhibitor
571-578

isoelectric point
548-549, 578

isomers
299-307, 320, 324-326, 334-339, 361-362, 472, 489, 501

isothermal
186, 194

isotopes
55-60, 71-72, 276-281, 285-293, 669

IUPAC System of Nomenclature
307, 324

joule
30, 180-181, 293

ketogenic amino acid
662, 666

ketone
155, 342, 366, 381-383, 387, 394-404, 408, 468-474, 501, 613, 656-657, 662-666

ketose
471-477, 485, 562

kinetic theory of gases
206-208, 218

L sugar
471-477, 501

lactose intolerant
490, 501

lattice energy
189

law
6, 126, 138-142, 157-159, 171, 209-219, 274, 289

law of conservation of matter
138-142, 157-159, 274

Lewis diagram
75-80, 97-98, 103-106, 111-113, 122, 270

line-angle formula
305-306, 324, 350

lipid
314, 404, 467-469, 507-537, 553, 562-565, 613, 617-619, 625-628, 634-638, 654, 659, 665-666

lock-and-key model
563-566, 578

macroscopic
13, 50, 77, 82, 160-161

main group element
66, 70, 78-79

mass number
55-59, 71-72, 274-276, 280, 289

mass-mass calculation
173-178

mass/mass percent
225-226, 235, 246

mass/volume percent
226-227, 236, 246

matter
5-43, 48-50, 59, 63, 78, 82, 138-142, 157-160, 171, 185, 197-198, 202-210, 217-221, 274-277, 285, 626

melting point
185-188, 199, 203, 219, 297, 313, 330, 423, 432, 456, 501, 509-513, 518, 536-537

metabolic pathway
293, 637-638, 647, 662

metabolism
5, 154-158, 179, 193-195, 380-382, 387, 404, 438, 532, 538, 554, 575-579, 586, 612, 625-667

metal
13-16, 28, 50-55, 65-73, 79-85, 102, 107, 142, 146, 150-151, 169, 177, 183-184, 194, 222, 273, 347, 405, 558-560, 641

micelle
516, 522-523, 536, 634

microscopic
13

miscible
223, 246, 386, 403, 422-424, 447, 516

mitochondria
520, 639-641, 645, 651-654, 658-661, 665-666

mixture
12-16, 39, 57-60, 221-224, 246, 314-316, 483-484, 489-492, 497, 501, 516, 632

mmHg (millimeters of mercury)
207

modern atomic theory
49-50, 71

molar mass
164-168, 172-178, 192, 218, 228-231, 253, 288, 295, 314-315, 340-341, 373-375, 391-393, 401, 407, 422-424, 431-432, 446-449, 456-457, 462, 539-540, 553, 624

molarity
224, 228-235, 243-247, 253

mole
28, 159-178, 186-188, 193-194, 230-236, 240-242, 246, 289-292, 651, 658

mole-mass calculation
172-178

mole-mass conversion
166-168

molecular formula
107-109, 119-120, 133-134, 175, 238, 299-305, 320-326, 330, 343, 347-349, 362, 384, 391, 463, 468

molecular mass
119-123, 133

molecule
13, 39, 50-51, 67, 83, 103-113, 118-134, 142, 147-155, 159-164, 175-177, 189, 199-205, 238, 252-261, 270, 295-299, 305-308, 312-315, 334-339, 345-350, 361-368, 373, 380-381, 393, 401, 410, 423, 429, 436-437, 447, 468-473, 482-493, 497, 501, 507-514, 522-530, 536, 540, 548-557, 563-578, 585, 597-609, 621, 629, 639-659, 664-665

monomer
345-348, 361, 433, 458, 497, 584-586, 594, 621, 630, 665

monosaccharide
470-477, 481-496, 500-503, 527-528, 632-637, 653, 665

monounsaturated fatty acid
509-511, 535

mutagen
611, 616, 621

mutarotation
481-484, 492, 496, 501

mutation
573, 608-617, 621

neutralization
252-254, 270, 424-427, 462-463, 569

neutron
51-57, 71, 275-276, 289-290

nomenclature
88, 109-110, 307, 324, 351, 367, 371, 416-419, 428, 440, 561-562

nonbonding pair (or lone pair) of electrons
104, 133

noncompetitive inhibitor
574-578

nonelectrolyte
238-239, 246

nonmetal
65, 70, 82-85, 102, 106-109, 133, 177

nonpolar covalent bond
114-115, 133, 200-202

nuclear energy
283, 288-293

nuclear reactor
290-292

nucleic acid
394, 438, 450, 467-469, 583-623

nucleotide
584-589, 593-610, 614-616, 621-627, 654

nucleus
51-63, 68-75, 200, 273-278, 287-290, 520, 536, 600-602, 606, 621, 669

number
13, 17-27, 32-40, 55-78, 82-83, 93-97, 105-114, 123-126, 132-134, 138-142, 147-150, 157-164, 169-178, 184-186, 191, 201, 216-219, 226-231, 240-247, 251-253, 261, 273-284, 289, 299-302, 307-311, 317-323, 329-331, 340, 354-357, 364-372, 388, 397, 415, 440, 445, 462, 470-471, 475, 509-518, 530, 535, 553, 561-562, 568, 573, 578, 583-586, 603-605, 609, 616, 624, 646, 653-654, 658, 669-675

octet rule
73-76, 97, 102-106, 111-112, 121, 133

oil
39, 125, 222, 295-296, 313-315, 340, 352, 403-406, 509-518, 525, 536

optimum pH
569-570, 578

organic chemistry
5-6, 123-133, 154, 295-327, 342, 365, 406, 639

organic compound
109, 124-127, 258, 296, 314, 365-367, 390, 394, 414, 450, 492, 575

osmolarity
243-247

osmosis
242-247, 491

osmotic pressure
240-247, 270

oxidation
150-157, 175, 191-194, 365, 378-387, 395, 401-410, 421-422, 462-463, 485-487, 507, 513, 517-518, 536, 543, 556, 562, 576-577, 626, 638-647, 651-660, 665-666

oxidation-reduction reaction
150, 154-157, 562, 576-577, 640-641, 665

oxidative deamination
661-666

oxidative phosphorylation
638-640, 644-650, 654, 659, 665-666

oxidizing agent
150, 154-158, 381-383, 401, 421, 486, 640, 649, 653-656

parts per billion (ppb)
227, 246

parts per million (ppm)
227, 246

pascal
207, 218

peptide bond
458, 550-552

period
13, 65-71, 77-78, 282, 365, 607, 625, 633

periodic table
43-72, 77-80, 93, 97-99, 106-109, 120, 163, 177, 299, 405, 669-675

peripheral protein
527-529, 536

pH scale
261-265, 270

phase
12-16, 39, 140, 150, 185-187, 194-208, 218-222, 239-241, 246, 516, 647-649, 653, 665

phase change
14-16, 185-187, 194

phenol
352, 365, 388-389, 402, 407-411, 462

phospholipid
314, 438, 523-529, 536, 637

photosynthesis
156-157, 176, 285, 469-470

physical property
12-16, 39, 118, 198-203, 207, 217-218, 296, 313-314, 324, 329-330, 340-341, 361, 373, 386-387, 422-423, 431-432, 446-447, 451, 456, 462, 473, 515, 669

point mutation
610-611, 621-624

polar
114-118, 133, 200-203, 218, 222-224, 239, 313-314, 373, 400, 405, 431-432, 456, 462, 522-523, 527-529, 536-537, 541-548, 556-557, 567, 578, 624

polar covalent bond
114-115, 133, 200

polyamide
458

polyatomic ions
81-89, 93, 97, 106-107, 164

polycyclic aromatic hydrocarbon (PAH)
356, 362

polymer
152, 330, 345-347, 361, 433, 458, 496-502, 578, 593-594, 621

polypeptide
551-560, 565, 578, 584, 605-608, 625, 633

polysaccharide
468-470, 487, 496-502, 565, 632

polyunsaturated fatty acid
509-511, 517, 535

power
19-22, 152, 193, 273-276, 290-293, 640

pressure
5, 11-17, 73, 187, 197-198, 206-219, 240-247, 270, 290, 313, 510, 515, 531, 538, 551, 561, 579, 624

primary (1°) alcohol
370, 407

primary (1°) amine
440, 462

primary structure
553-554, 558-561, 578-579, 593, 605, 621

product
5, 36, 65, 101, 126, 138-151, 155-159, 169-170, 175-178, 184, 189-190, 194-197, 228-230, 244-255, 259-264, 270, 274-276, 283-291, 296, 314-319, 330, 342-350, 361-362, 377-378, 385-387, 393, 403-409, 416, 426, 435-436, 458-463, 479-480, 486-491, 499-507, 517-519, 531, 550, 563-567, 571-574, 578-583, 604, 623-639, 646-647, 656-666

protein
36, 45, 67-69, 116, 156, 180, 192-195, 232, 346, 378, 394, 402, 406, 413, 450-458, 467-469, 520-532, 536-583, 593-650, 660, 665-666

proteins
67-69, 156, 180, 192-194, 232, 346, 378, 394, 402, 406, 413, 456-458, 467-469, 520, 527-532, 536-583, 593-621, 625-647, 665-666

proton
51-57, 71, 200, 255-261, 270, 275, 449-452

purine
584-596, 621

pyrimidine
584-596, 621

quantity
7, 17-18, 24-40, 93, 150, 161-174, 180-186, 210, 218, 226, 230-232, 373, 623

quantized
61, 71

quantum mechanics
61, 71

quaternary structure
557-560, 565, 578

rad
282-284, 293

radioactivity
273-293

reactant
138-159, 169-172, 177-178, 189-190, 194-195, 228, 255-258, 285-292, 316, 361, 378, 387, 435, 565-570, 579, 628, 637-638, 665

reducing agent
150-151, 155-158, 402

reducing sugar
485-489, 493-495, 501-505

reduction
43, 150-157, 376, 491, 502, 531, 562, 576-577, 639-644, 659-660, 665

rem
282-286, 293

replication
599-605, 610-612, 621-623

respiration
67, 155-157, 626-627, 640-641, 658, 665

retrovirus
617-621

reversible inhibitor
571, 575-578

ribonucleic acid (RNA)
584, 593-599, 605, 621

ribosome
520, 603-609, 621

rounding
25-26, 40, 276, 640, 655, 659, 666

saponification
435-436, 462, 515-518, 536

saturated
124-126, 133, 225, 235, 246, 298, 324, 329-333, 342, 349, 362, 509-518, 531, 535-537, 567-570, 581, 658-659

saturated fatty acid
509-518, 535-536, 658-659

science
1, 5-12, 18-19, 27, 39, 50, 85, 138, 198, 212, 406, 460, 649, 669

scientific method
7-11, 39, 50

scientific notation
19-28, 37-40, 162

secondary (2°) alcohol
371, 407

secondary (2°) amine
440, 462

secondary structure
554-560, 578, 593-594, 621-623

semimetal (or metalloid)
65

shell
52, 61-63, 67-78, 83, 97-104, 111-112, 120, 133, 274-275, 617-621

significant figures
23-27, 31-41, 166, 172-174, 227

single bond
103, 133, 342, 400

solubility
222-225, 234-236, 246, 296, 313, 374-376, 391-393, 401, 422-424, 431, 447-450, 456, 507, 541, 578-581

soluble
98, 223-224, 236-238, 246, 257-258, 270, 296-297, 313-314, 340, 361, 373-375, 389-393, 401, 407-408, 422-426, 431-432, 447-451, 456-458, 462, 485-488, 507, 513-518, 527, 531, 535, 553, 560, 575-579, 637, 647, 656

solute
218, 222-247, 268-269

solution
9, 13-25, 30-31, 35-40, 47, 56-62, 68-69, 73-74, 78, 83-85, 89-94, 104-112, 117-122, 128, 140-141, 145-153, 157, 161-186, 190, 202-216, 221-271, 275 282, 289, 293 296, 309-311, 317-318, 322, 331-332, 337, 342-343, 352-355, 364, 369-370, 377-378, 383-386, 391, 396-398, 402-409, 417-420, 425-430, 435-436, 441-444, 449-450, 454, 459-463, 467-472, 479, 483-486, 491-492, 497, 504, 516-519, 530, 536, 547-549, 560, 565, 580-581, 600-602, 608, 637

solvation
236-239, 246

solvent
127, 155, 205, 222-224, 228, 233-247, 256-257, 296, 313-315, 319, 341, 350-352, 376, 387, 403-408, 432, 499

specific heat
182-184, 194

sphingolipid
524-529, 536

sphingomyelin
526-529

spontaneous fission
276-277, 292

standard temperature and pressure (STP)
218

stereoisomer
472-475, 483-484, 501, 566

steroid
169, 357, 404, 507-509, 530-537, 637

Stock system
88-90, 97

stoichiometry
5, 143-145, 157-159, 170-173, 178, 230-234, 252, 270

strong acid
262-271, 342

strong base
262-270, 426

strong electrolyte
238, 246

structural formula
299, 304-308, 320, 324-326, 330, 335, 347-350, 364, 371, 377-379, 406-408, 420, 427-428, 452, 456, 463, 472, 509-512, 525, 542-544

subshell
61-63, 67-72, 274

substance
8, 12-16, 29, 35, 39, 43, 48, 65, 69-71, 102, 137-178, 182-188, 194-206, 218, 225, 238-239, 251-252, 259, 265, 270, 278-281, 285, 293, 316, 324, 342-343, 362, 405, 435, 450, 475, 513, 561-562, 571, 575-579

substrate
561-581, 647-649, 655, 665

substrate-level phosphorylation
649, 665

tertiary (3°) alcohol
371, 407

tertiary (3°) amine
440, 462

tertiary structure
556-560, 578

theory
10-11, 49-51, 57, 61, 71, 120-123, 206-208, 218, 274, 288-290, 295-298, 564

thiol
366, 405-407

torr
207-218

tracer
285-288

trans isomer
335-338, 361

transamination
660-666

transcription
601-606, 617, 621-623

transition metal
66-72, 79

translation
599, 606-609, 621-624

triglyceride
513-520, 524, 535-536, 635-637, 654, 659, 666

triple bond
111-114, 123-128, 132-133, 295, 329, 333, 342, 348-349, 361, 366

unit
7, 13, 17-18, 28-40, 59-60, 71, 82, 94-98, 105-106, 119, 133, 145, 152, 159-172, 177-183, 207-215, 225-230, 234, 243-246, 281-282, 289, 293, 299-300, 307, 313, 324, 336, 345, 440, 488-489, 501-504, 517, 524-528, 536-540, 551, 583-589, 593-596, 606, 637-638

unsaturated
125-126, 225, 235, 246, 329-364, 509-519, 523-524, 536, 576

unsaturated hydrocarbon
329-333, 361

valence shell
62-63, 67-78, 83, 97-98, 102-104, 111, 120, 133

valence shell electron
62-63, 67-72, 78, 97, 104, 120, 133

valence shell electron pair repulsion (VSEPR)
120, 133

vapor pressure
240-241, 245-247

vapor pressure depression
240-241, 247

virus
295, 561, 583, 614-621

vitamin
39-40, 67, 116, 155-156, 193, 262, 340, 357, 394, 417, 507, 513, 517-518, 530, 535-536, 575-579, 615, 638

volume
14, 29-31, 35-40, 55, 191, 195, 203-221, 226-236, 240, 246-247, 253, 286, 350

volume/volume percent
226

weak acid
262-270, 417

weak base
262-270

weak electrolyte
238, 246

zwitterion
540, 547-549, 578

CPSIA information can be obtained
at www.ICGtesting.com
Printed in the USA
LVOW06s2226210917
549616LV00002B/4/P